ALGAE

OF THE

WESTERN GREAT LAKES AREA

ALGAE

OF THE
WESTERN GREAT LAKES AREA

With an Illustrated Key to the Genera of Desmids and Freshwater Diatoms

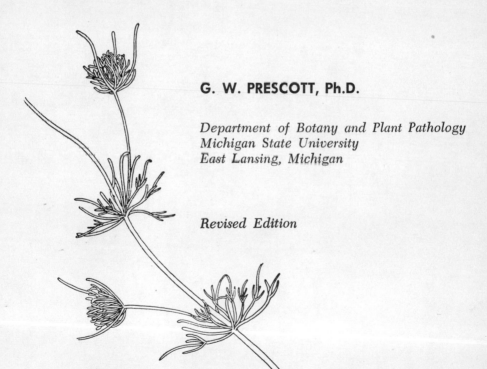

G. W. PRESCOTT, Ph.D.

Department of Botany and Plant Pathology
Michigan State University
East Lansing, Michigan

Revised Edition

WM. C. BROWN COMPANY PUBLISHERS
135 SOUTH LOCUST STREET • DUBUQUE, IOWA

Manufactured by WM. C. BROWN CO. INC., Dubuque, Iowa

Printed in U. S. A.

Investigations on the algal flora upon which this book is based were first made as part of the Wisconsin Geological and Natural History Survey. Circumstances necessitated the abandonment of plans to publish in the Wisconsin Survey Series. The Cranbrook Institute of Science then cooperated in bringing out the book after the material was expanded to include the algae of Michigan. Grateful acknowledgment is made to the University of Wisconsin and to the Trustees of the Cranbrook Institute of Science for the release of zinc cuts, and for the rights to revise and republish this volume.

G. W. Prescott   November, 1961
Department of Botany
Michigan State University

Preface

The Great Lakes region lies in a highly glaciated part of North America and therefore possesses a terrain which provides many hundreds of lakes, swamps, and marshes. Thus the area is highly suitable for an abundant algal flora, especially because of variation in water chemistry—a variation which is related primarily to the geological history and nature of the underlying rock in the different sections. Hence the list of algal species in the Great Lakes region is a long one. Approximately 1300 algae (exclusive of desmids and diatoms) have been reported from Wisconsin and Michigan, the latter region being represented principally in the papers of Ackley, Gustafson, Taft, and Transeau. To date, no major treatment of Michigan algae has appeared, but in 1920 and 1924 Gilbert M. Smith published the results of his extensive phytoplankton surveys of Wisconsin lakes. Probably for no other area of comparable size anywhere in the world has so much systematic field work been done, or so detailed and informative a presentation of algal distribution been issued. Smith's volumes, which are based upon collections made during the period 1913 to 1917, represent a survey of some 230 lakes, mostly in the northern counties of the state.

As indicated by Smith in his preface (1920, p. 2), he found it necessary to defer an originally planned study of filamentous and attached algae because of the magnitude of the survey, emphasis consequently being directed toward the plankton. It is well known, of course, that organisms which make up the phytoplankton represent a wide range of algal groups, inasmuch as almost all classes of algae have at least some free-floating or swimming members. Within the same genus there may be both drifting and normally attached species, whereas other, closely related, genera may contain only species which are sedentary, at least in the vegetative state. In the present study, special attention has been given the attached and tychoplanktonic forms, particularly the strictly aquatic filamentous algae. In order to make as complete a record as possible for this region, it has been considered advisable to describe here the species previously reported, as well as those new to the regional list. Species not collected by the author are included if they appear to be authentically reported or if the printed record is substantiated by preserved specimens. The reader is referred to the bibliography for a complete list of algal records for Michigan and Wisconsin. It is hoped that the usefulness of the present compilation and the desirability of having both planktonic and nonplanktonic algae arranged under one cover will justify what otherwise might be regarded as unnecessary duplication of previously published descriptions of many species.

Limnological investigations of the inland lakes have been carried on for more than three decades, especially by the exhaustive and tireless work of Dr. E. A. Birge, Professor Chancey Juday, and the staff of the Wisconsin Geological and Natural History Survey. Dr. P. S. Welch and associates have published on limnological features of Michigan lakes, particularly lakes in the northern part of the state. In addition, there are the detailed physiographic studies of Michigan lakes by Dr. I. D. Scott and the surveys by the Institute for Fisheries Research of Ann Arbor. The published volumes and papers of these men and of those working under their direction have presented us with a wealth of information on the physical, chemical, and biological features of several hundred bodies of water. Their data have permitted many correlations and generalizations to be made which are of great practical as well as of purely scientific value.

Since 1930 I have made collections of algae from Michigan, principally from the southern peninsula, although I made several excursions through large sections of the upper part of the state. Furthermore, as part of a plan to obtain as complete a picture as possible of the biology of Wisconsin lakes, I undertook a survey of the Wisconsin algae at the invitation of the late Professor Juday, then Director of the Trout Lake Limnological Laboratory. Using this station as headquarters I carried on field work during the summers of 1937–1939 in the northernmost counties of Wisconsin, and in the summer of 1939 on representative lakes in southeastern and central Wisconsin. In 1938 field collections were made in June and July; in 1937 and 1939 the work was done in August and early September. In all, I collected about 2400 vials of material from Michigan and Wisconsin habitats. Besides these, Professor Juday kindly contributed a few hundred vials of Wisconsin algae taken in his quantitative plankton studies of a large number of lakes in both northern and southern parts of the state. Also Mr. John Greenbank loaned 300 plankton catches which had been collected in an investigation of the Fox River, the East River, and Green Bay by the Wisconsin Committee on Water Pollution and the State Board of Health, in cooperation with the Green Bay Metropolitan Sewerage Commission, in 1938 and 1939 (Williamson *et al.*, 1939). I have been privileged also to examine numerous student collections, especially from northern Michigan. In selecting material for this survey, emphasis has been placed on collections from strictly aquatic habitats almost to the exclusion of shore and moist-soil floras. This was done intentionally because some line had to be drawn and because the major purpose of the survey was to study the distribution of algae in relation to known limnological conditions in the inland lakes of the region. I regret that the study could not include the algae of the soil and subaerial habitats, thereby making a more nearly complete contribution to knowledge of algae in the area. The exploration of these terrestrial habitats is an interesting project still awaiting the phycologist.

Although numerous tow samples were taken from Michigan lakes, only meager attention was given to such collections in Wisconsin, because Wisconsin phytoplankton had been studied by Smith (1920, 1924). The major portion of the collections that are the basis for the present list came from the margins of lakes, submerged substrates, and from weed beds in shallow bays and ponds. Many species were also obtained from marshes and bogs, especially the *Sphagnum* (acid) types, which abound in northern Michigan and Wisconsin.

As often as possible, identifications were made from living material. Many species in the preserved samples, especially flagellated forms and some Cyanophyta, were disregarded because their taxonomic characters had been lost. The preservative used was Transeau's Solution, known as Six-Three-One, made with six parts of water, three parts of 95 per cent alcohol, and one part formalin. When 5 cc. of glycerine per 100 cc. of preservative are added to this solution it proves to be especially valuable in preventing complete desiccation of bottled specimens in case of accidental drying. Furthermore this preservative is desirable because it produces the minimum amount of plasmolysis and preserves the sheath-characteristics of most blue-green algae. Formalin-aceto-alcohol was also used (formalin 5 cc., glacial acetic acid 5 cc., 50 per cent alcohol 90 cc.). Each sample was given several examinations, but inasmuch as many vials have a very rich mixture, the list of species for each collection may be incomplete. A number of herbarium specimens have been prepared directly from living material, and some mounts have been made from liquid-preserved collections when their abundance in the sample warranted. All preserved samples are filed at present in my collections. It is expected that the herbarium specimens, to be prepared as time and occasion permit, will be deposited, as are some already, in the Farlow Herbarium, the Chicago Museum of Natural History, the New York Botanical Garden, and in my own herbarium.

In summarizing the examination of samples collected in this survey, I have attempted to meet a request for a handbook which would be of use to students, conservationists, and investigators interested in the taxonomy, distribution, and ecological relationships of the algae. As indicated in the title, not all groups are represented here. The desmids,*too numerous to be given space in this volume, merit special treatment. The diatoms are being studied by Mr. Paul Conger, Research Associate of the Carnegie Institution, Washington, D. C.

The heterogeneity of algal groups encountered in a broad survey of the flora has resulted in such a long list of species that space is not available for a complete description of each one. Descriptive remarks, therefore, are confined to the important taxonomic characteristics. When reproductive structures and habits are essential for identification purposes, these are described briefly. Otherwise, only vegetative features and dimensions are given. I have tried to give a complete bibliography of the literature in which the species were originally described. Titles of treatises and of major papers recommended for the reader who wishes a more complete discussion of morphological features, reproduction, and taxonomy than is given here have been marked in the bibliography. These should prove of interest, especially to the less experienced student of the algae, for they give a better working foundation than the local floras and older handbooks can. A number of the latter are frequently used, and whereas they are of value after a student has acquired some judgement and discernment, they may be misleading if used to the exclusion of more critical and less abridged works. Papers and books which deal with or include reports on Michigan and Wisconsin algae have also been given a distinguishing mark in the bibliography.

In connection with the general descriptive remarks on the various groups of algae, as they are taken up in the taxonomic portion of the volume, references are made to those publications which either deal primarily with particular classes or families, or which should prove helpful in further systematic studies.

SECOND EDITION

For this new edition special attention has been directed toward corrections, and the removal of inconsistencies which appear in the first printing. A few keys to species have been rewritten to make them clearer and more useful. Although it has not been possible to include Desmids and Diatoms, an illustrated key to the genera in these groups is appended. Likewise it has not been possible to interpolate the many species of algae which have been reported from the Great Lakes area since the 1951 printing.

*See Appendix for key to Desmid and Diatom genera.

ACKNOWLEDGMENTS

I wish to express my appreciation to those who have given much valued assistance. Special acknowledgments are due the late Dr. Edward A. Birge, who generously gave much of the financial support necessary for the preparation of the manuscript and illustrations. I am grateful to him not only for material assistance but also for helpful advice and for the lively interest he showed during the entire project. Also I wish to express my indebtedness to the late Professor Chancey Juday for the help he contributed from his long experience and familiarity with limnological problems and also to Drs. C. E. Allen, Stanley Cain, Francis Drouet, Robert T. Hatt, C. M. Palmer, the late Gilbert M. Smith, Clarence E. Taft, Wm. Randolph Taylor, Lewis H. Tiffany, and the late Edgar N. Transeau, all of whom either made or confirmed identifications of some of the species listed herein, or gave helpful advice on certain portions of the work.

Dr. Hannah Croasdale, Dr. Ruth Patrick, and Miss Hilda Harris assisted in checking a number of bibliographic references. Mr. Thomas Cobbe helped in the preparation of some of the plates, and Mr. H. Ward Prescott did most of the photographic work involved. Dr. Croasdale helped to prepare Latin diagnoses which appear in preliminary reports (Prescott, 1944; Prescott, Silva, and Wade, 1949).

Further, I wish to express my appreciation of facilities provided by the following laboratories and libraries where various portions of this study have been carried on: Trout Lake Limnological Laboratory, Trout Lake, Wisconsin; University of Michigan Biological Station and the University of Michigan Library; Woods Hole Marine Biological Laboratory and Library; Farlow Herbarium and Reference Library; Albion College Biological Laboratory and Library; University of Minnesota Herbarium and Library; Chicago Natural History Museum Cryptogamic Herbarium; University of California Herbarium and Library; the library of the late Dr. Gilbert M. Smith; the University of Wisconsin Library; the John Crerar Library; the Lloyd Library; and the Library of the Academy of Natural Sciences of Philadelphia.

I wish to make grateful acknowledgment of grants in aid which directly or indirectly facilitated this study from the American Association for the Advancement of Science, the Wisconsin Geological and Natural History Survey, the Horace H. and Mary A. Rackham Fund, the Michigan State College Research Fund, the Muellhaupt Fellowship, and the Brittingham Trust Fund.

Finally, I wish to express my special thanks to Dr. Robert T. Hatt, Director and the Board of Trustees of the Cranbrook Institute of Science for the release of Copyright, thus permitting the publishing of a second edition of this volume.

G. W. PRESCOTT

Michigan State University

SYMBOLS AND ABBREVIATIONS USED

cc., cubic centimeter

μ, micron (0.001 mm.)

mg., milligram

mm., millimeter

pH, measure of free hydrogen ions in a solution. (Soft water or acid lakes have a pH below 7.0, the neutral point; hard water lakes give readings of pH 7.1 to pH 9.8.)

ppm, parts per million

*— Used in the keys, to indicate orders, families, genera, or species that are likely to be found in the central Great Lakes region but have not been reported there to date.

TABLE OF CONTENTS

Introduction

Although convenient, the term algae has been applied to such a great variety of plant groups and has been given so many interpretations that it has no very precise meaning. In the broadest sense it may refer to all chlorophyll-bearing thallophytes and protista, and their colorless close relatives. Life history studies have established genetic relationships between definitely plant-like and animal-like algae. Thus the incorporation of the Volvocales in the phylogeny of the Chlorophyta is necessary. Other protozoa-like, pigmented organisms, such as the Euglenophyta and the Cryptophyceae and other Pyrrhophyta, are examples of evolutionary lines which apparently have ended blindly in their present expressions. One might contend, therefore, that their inclusion among the other definitely plant-like algae cannot be justified because, unlike the Volvocales, they have no phylogenetic connections with the group. Notwithstanding the fact that the Euglenophyta and Pyrrhophyta include some colorless and definitely protozoa-like relatives, the groups merit a place in phycological study by virtue of their many plant-like attributes. Likewise, chlorophyll-bearing, bacteria-like organisms must be given a place in the broad definition of the Cyanophyta. Many of the organisms belonging to the Chrysophyta have only a few characteristics which entitle them to a place among the algae, but because the morphology and the habits of some members are fundamentally plant-like their inclusion is clearly justified.

Whatever limits of classification may be set up for the algae, all these groups of simple organisms are interesting to the phycologist, the aquatic biologist, the limnologist, and the oceanographer. In order to meet a number of these interests and to make the present work as useful as possible, the broader interpretation of the algae has been adopted and representatives from the eight divisions are treated here. (There are eight divisions, or phyla, if one recognizes the Chloromonadineae. This little-known class is represented by *Gonyostomum semen* Dies. in our collections.) Hardly any two phycologists are in complete agreement on the disposition of forms within the algal groups. The taxonomist will note, therefore, many inconsistencies if the details of the arrangement used here are compared with any one of the several schemes followed in handbooks, floras, and in some monographic works. I have chosen to use familiar names of long standing unless changes in such names have been adopted in generally used monographic studies which are easily obtainable for reference. For the most part I have followed the taxonomy and nomenclature suggested by Pascher (1931) and employed by Gilbert M. Smith (1938). The structure of the cell wall, the pigmentation, and the nature of food reserves have been used to unite the Heterokontae, the Chrysophyceae, and the Bacillariophyceae to form what seems to be a very natural division, the Chrysophyta. This rearrangement reduces the number of groups previously recognized among the algae. The colorless relatives of the motile algae are not included here. The taxonomic arrangement employed, then, takes the following plan:

Division I.   Chlorophyta (Green Algae)
    A. Chlorophyceae
    B. Charophyceae

Division II.   Chrysophyta (Yellow-green Algae)
    A. Xanthophyceae (Heterokontae)
    B. Chrysophyceae
    C. Bacillariophyceae (Diatoms)

Division III. Euglenophyta (Euglenoids)

Division IV.   Chloromonadophyta (Chloromonads)

Division V.   Pyrrhophyta (Yellow-brown Algae)
    A. Cryptophyceae
    B. Desmokontae
    C. Dinophyceae

Division VI.   Phaeophyta (Brown Algae, marine)

Division VII. Cyanophyta (Blue-green Algae)
    A. Myxophyceae
    B. Chlorobacteriaceae

Division VIII. Rhodophyta (Red Algae, mostly marine)

In the following pages certain terms will be used frequently when reference is made to the type of existence most characteristic of a species. The name *plankton,* of course, refers to organisms which have a drifting habit and includes all forms of both macro- and microscopic life which float free in the water or, if motile, are unable to swim against currents. Open-water plankters are called *euplankton* (true plankton). Many algal species existing as such have elongations of the cell, or bear long spines, whereas others may gain buoyancy through the possession of mucilage. There is evidence that pseudovacuoles in the cells of many blue-green plankters aid in this connection. Forms which are unattached but are caught among filamentous algae and other vegetation and reproduce in shallow water are called *tychoplankton*. The minute phytoplankters which pass through the meshes of a fine (No. 20) bolting-cloth collecting net are here termed *nannoplankton*. A special term, *periphyton*, may be applied to the organisms which form associations on the stems and leaves of aquatic plants. Benthic algae, *benthos*, are the organisms which live on the bottom especially in deep water, for example, *Chara, Nitella, Dichotomosiphon*, and some species of *Cladophora*.

Geological Features and Algal Distribution

Some species of aquatic plants may have a wider geographical distribution than terrestrial forms. This is true, for the most part, because of the more nearly universal similarity of aquatic habitats and the somewhat greater constancy of the factors which play a role in determining distribution. It need only be mentioned, by way of illustration, that in an aquatic habitat nutrients are more equally diffused and more readily obtained, temperature changes more gradual, and annual temperature range less, than in a terrestrial environment.

Ecologists, however, not infrequently assume a more universal distribution for aquatics than may actually exist; in a recent excellent volume on ecology one finds a complete disregard of plants in an aquatic environment. Facts bear out the reasonable assumption that habitats with similar floras have the necessary determining physical-chemical conditions in common. Where there are variations in the flora and when there is an absence of widely distributed species from certain habitats, correlated modifications in the environmental factors, sometimes obscure, must be sought for. As is well known, species are subject in their distribution, in water as on land, to limitations imposed by the presence or absence of certain ecological factors. Less than minimal requirements of salts, carbon dioxide, nitrogen, phosphorus or other nutrients, the degree of illumination, and temperature changes are a few of the factors involved in distribution and habitat selection.

The part ecological factors play in determining quantity and quality of algal floras is readily appreciated in a study of lakes in this area, famous for its great number of inland bodies of water, bogs, and forested swamps. In Michigan there are about 11,000 lakes, with a total area of 1137.6 sq. mi.; Antrim County has 10.1 per cent of its area in lakes, and several other counties have nearly as much (Brown, 1943). In Vilas County, Wisconsin, the area occupied by lakes is 15 per cent of the total, although this figure does not include the innumerable small ponds, permanent pools, and spring-like seeps where algae abound. It is estimated (Juday, 1914, p. xi) that

[4]

approximately 1620 sq. mi. of Wisconsin are water, as compared with 55,256 sq. mi. of land surface. The suitability for algae of this entire lake region is reflected in its rich and heterogeneous aquatic flora.

The great variety of aquatic habitats makes it possible to relate certain species or complexes of species to what may be called 'types' of lakes. In making such a correlation it is of course necessary to recognize that it is practically impossible to 'type' a lake, because each one, in final analysis, possesses a distinct individuality. It is possible, however, to classify lakes according to certain characteristics which are of known biological significance. Most lakes in the region are of glacial origin, but because geographical and geological features (and the geological history) are not uniform there are some general differences to be noted in the bodies of water occupying respective sections. For the surface features and geology of Michigan the reader is referred to Leverett (1911, 1917).

The pertinent geological features of Wisconsin have been adequately described by G. M. Smith (1920), and the reader is urged to refer to the highly informative introduction to his volume, "Phytoplankton of the Inland Lakes of Wisconsin, Part I." In this connection also see the remarks on p. 8 *et seq.*, of this volume.

SOIL TYPES AND ALGAL DISTRIBUTION

MICHIGAN

The physiography within the political boundaries of Michigan is extremely varied and is in part complicated by the differences in the geology of the Upper and Lower Peninsulas. The Upper Peninsula, lying between Lake Superior on the north and Lake Michigan on the south, is about 300 miles long, east and west, and averages about 50 miles in width. The Upper Peninsula itself has two definite areas the character of which is determined by the type of underlying rock formation. One, west of a north-south line passing through Marquette, is a highland region which continues on over into northern Wisconsin (to be discussed below), where it is referred to as the Highland Lake Region. This is underlain by ancient rock formations (Proterozoic) which are covered in most places by glacial drift; notable exceptions, of course, are the Porcupine Mountains in the far western part of the Upper Peninsula, and hard 'knobs' also project elsewhere. The basic rock is both sedimentary and igneous. These crystalline masses seem to have exerted an influence on water chemistry in certain sections of this western half of the Peninsula, especially in those sections where the rock is exposed or covered by only a thin mantle of glacial deposits. In general, the lakes of the region are characteristically soft or semi-hard and are poor producers of phytoplankton bulk. It is well known that waters associated with pre-Paleozoic rock are low in calcium, are usually but little mineralized, and support a predominantly desmid flora, especially in habitats that possess a low pH. (The symbol pH refers to the relative amount of free hydrogen ions in a solution. Soft water or acid lakes have a pH below the neutral point, pH 7.0, whereas hard water lakes give readings above neutral, pH 7.1–9.8.) Such algal collections as have been made in northwest Michigan, and in the same topography of northern Wisconsin, bear out this relationship. The moraines and drifts of sand left by the recession of the last glacial lobes are largely responsible for the numerous soft water lakes and acid swamps that are especially abundant north of Michigamme, in Michigan, and in upper Wisconsin.

The phytoplankton and the desmid flora are characteristic of soft water lakes in the western section, whereas in the second area, which forms the eastern part of the Upper Peninsula, the flora is, in general, that of semi-hard water habitats. This is in accord with the geology of the area, which is underlain by younger Paleozoic rock, all sedimentary and unmetamorphosed. The eastern section is known as the Lowlands because the greatest altitude (with possible exceptions) is only 250 feet above lake level. Shale and limestone predominate, the latter forming a tableland along the northern border of the present Lake Michigan. The Lowlands swing back westward both north and south of the western Highlands into Minnesota and Wisconsin. There are numerous outcroppings, and the effect on water chemistry is marked, finding expression in lakes with a pH generally higher than that of the western lakes. Like the western province, the eastern region has been covered by glacial drift that came in with the ice from northeast Canada, resulting in extensive swamps and sluggish streams. Whereas there are some habitats (such as an occasional acid swamp) that develop a rich algal flora, most of the waters in the eastern area are not good producers, and the flora is strangely poor in both bulk and number of species. Many of the slow-flowing streams of the area are practically barren, and such algal forms as are conspicuous are cyanophycean or hard water chlorophycean (*Phormidium, Oscillatoria, Spirogyra, Chara*). The darkly stained water of the Tahquamenon River, however, is characterized by a luxuriant growth of *Nitella*, a genus almost always confined to soft water or water rich in humic acids.

Big Spring, near Manistique, Michigan, is an interesting habitat with an algal flora that seems typical of the region. The spring has a tremendous flow of water that forms a deep pool and is the fount for a large stream. The pool is clear, the water hard, and there is a luxuriant growth of *Chara* over much of the bottom. There is also a scant development of *Spirogyra* spp. along the fringes of the pool, while *Oscillatoria* spp. and *Phormidium* spp. encrust submerged timbers and water-logged wood. The pool is bordered in part by the vestige of a tamarack swamp, bedded with *Sphagnum*. The water here is only slightly acid, and the algal flora in the swamp is not rich in desmids as might be expected but very meager and consists mostly of filamentous Zygnemataceae characteristic of hard or semi-hard water situations.

In the Lower Peninsula of Michigan, which is also underlain by Paleozoic rock, there are five physiographic regions. The most northern one, the Northern Upland, occupies roughly the upper quarter of the Peninsula and is bordered on the south by a diagonal line running northeast-southwest from Alpena toward Muskegon on the west coast. The line swings north, however, before reaching Muskegon and extends to the lake, passing up and around Manistee. The Northern Upland is characteristically a semi-hard and soft water lake region; although some bodies are basic (pH 7.8, for example) most of them are below pH 7.1 and some as low as pH 4.2. Except for a few limestone exposures the region is deeply covered with a sandy glacial drift which has formed innumerable lakes and swamps. The result is that the algal flora is richer and more varied than perhaps anywhere else in the state. There are both acid swamps favoring a luxuriant desmid and *Oedogonium* flora, and mineralized waters supporting a characteristic flora in which planktonic blue-green algae predominate. Meager water blooms develop in a few lakes of upper Michigan, which are alkaline, which have an ample supply of carbon dioxide, and which have been fertilized by nitrogenous matter from tilled soil or from human habitation. Such conditions are more common in the southern part of the state, where water is harder and where the lakes are frequently the eutrophic type.

Southwest from the Northern Upland is the Michigan Lowland, bordering Lake Michigan. To the southeast is first the Saginaw Lowland, extending southwest from Saginaw Bay of Lake Huron, then the Thumb Upland, including the 'Thumb' and the greater part of central southern Michigan. In the Thumb Upland, hard waters predominate and although there is an occasional kettlehole type of tamarack swamp, most of the water is rich in calcium, and the hard water (cyanophyte-diatom) flora prevails. Many lakes are bedded with *Chara*, and numerous marl deposits are found in old

[7]

lake bottoms of southern Michigan. The marl lakes are characteristically poor in both plankton and higher vegetations (*Potamogeton, Ceratophyllum, Myriophyllum*). In such hard water lakes, however, where nitrogenous substances and phosphorus are present, higher aquatic plants become so abundant as to cause serious problems.

The few collections that have been made from the Erie Lowlands (including the Detroit area and the extreme southeast of Michigan) show that here too the algal flora, like that of southern Wisconsin and Minnesota, is characteristically the hard water type.

WISCONSIN

The geological history of this state has determined six general soil areas which are shown in Figure 1. Except for the unglaciated limestone in the driftless area of the southwest corner of Wisconsin, the soils represent deposits from the various periods of glaciation. They overlie three chief types of basic rock formation shown in Figure 2: crystalline rock in the northern third of the state; limestone in the southern third and extending into the Green Bay region; a sandstone area in the middle portion of the state and the extreme northwestern corner. These soil types, in combination with their respective underlying rock formations, determine four great areas of the state, which, generally speaking, show corresponding differences in lake types and algal floras.

First, there is a glaciated limestone region, the northern boundary of which extends diagonally east to west, beginning just above Green Bay in Marinette and Oconto counties and ending with Green County in the south-central part of the state. This highly calcareous area occupies most of the southeastern third of Wisconsin. Second, there is an unglaciated limestone area made up of sixteen southwestern and western boundary counties. Because this is a driftless area there are few lakes in the region. As would be expected, the lakes in the entire lower portion of the state, both southeast and south-central, are rich in calcium, magnesium, carbonates, and bicarbonates. These qualities, together with such factors as relative shallowness and high summer temperatures, determine the character of the algal flora which, in general, is the cyanophyte-diatom, or hard water type.

In Lauderdale Lake, Walworth County, Wisconsin, for example, the number of species of Chlorophyta and Cyanophyta are about equal, but the abundance of the latter far exceeds the bulk of the green algal vegetation. This is in keeping with the general observation that where water is warm, rich in fixed and half-bound carbon

[8]

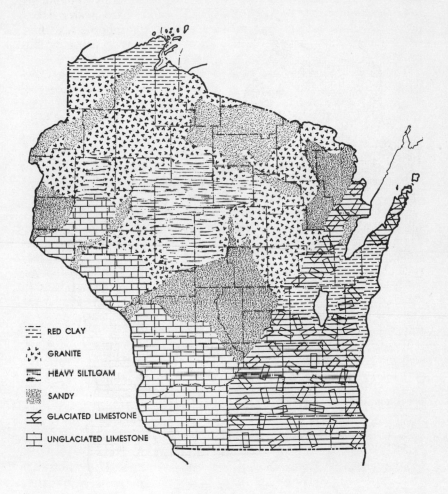

RED CLAY

GRANITE

HEAVY SILTLOAM

SANDY

GLACIATED LIMESTONE

UNGLACIATED LIMESTONE

Figure 1. Distribution of the chief soil types in Wisconsin. The unglaciated limestone region of the southwest is practically devoid of lakes. In the granite and sandy soils of the northern half of the state, the lakes are mostly soft water, and there are many acid bogs. In the central and southeast portion of the state, the lakes are basic (hard water). (Soil data from the Wisconsin Geological and Natural History Survey. Base map courtesy of A. J. Nystrom and Co.)

[9]

SANDSTONE

LIMESTONE

CRYSTALLINE ROCK

Figure 2. Distribution of three underlying rock formations in Wisconsin. (Data from the Wisconsin Geological and Natural History Survey. Base map courtesy of A. J. Nystrom and Co.)

dioxide, and high in nitrogen, cyanophycean and diatom species predominate, both in number of kinds (usually), and number of individuals. In the lakes which characterize this calcareous region, blue-green algal water blooms develop during summer periods. The water chemistry is reflected in the flora of the Green Bay and Fox River area, where the phytoplankton is made up almost entirely of *Microcystis aeruginosa, Aphanizomenon flos-aquae, Lyngbya Birgei, Stephanodiscus niagarae* Ehrenb., and *Melosira* spp., with infrequent specimens of *Pediastrum Boryanum, P. duplex,* and *Dinobryon sertularia.* The Fox and East rivers drain a calcareous and clay soil region, gathering considerable quantities of waste from agricultural lands and industrial plants. Williamson *et al.* (1939, p. 66) have expressed the opinion that a heavy bloom of blue-green algae in these waters is not related to the nitrogen content, but nitrogen in available form for plants is relatively abundant in these streams, especially as compared with that in inland lakes. Bound carbon dioxide is likewise relatively abundant. Such features are usually correlated with luxuriant cyanophyte–diatom floras (see Sawyer, Lackey, and Lenz, 1943). In lakes that have a chemistry similar to the Fox and East Rivers the number of blue-green algal individuals may reach several million per liter.

Lake Geneva, Walworth County, Wisconsin, is another hard water lake in the glaciated limestone soil area which is larger and deeper than Lauderdale Lake. It is high in carbonates (74 ppm), calcium (20.7 ppm), magnesium (26.9 ppm), sodium (4.4 ppm), and HCO (110.5 ppm). Analyses of Lake Geneva water samples made in August 1940 show a relatively high nitrogen content: organic nitrogen 0.55 ppm, ammonia 0.01 ppm, nitrate nitrogen 0.8 ppm, nitrites 0.0. As might be expected, the phytoplankton of this lake is predominantly blue-green, *Microcystis aeruginosa, Coelosphaerium Naegelianum,* and *Lyngbya Birgei* being the most conspicuous representatives. The green algae which occur here in June, for example, are *Cladophora fracta* and *C. glomerata,* species typical of hard water habitats. In contrast, the desmid and predominantly chlorophycean flora appears not to occur in the lakes of this limestone region. There is further discussion of hard water lakes below.

The third and fourth soil types, which are much less clearly defined, constitute, in general, the upper third of the state. This is basically a crystalline rock area, but within it are sandy soils and glaciated granite soils. The former predominate in the north-central counties: Vilas, Oneida, parts of Langlade, Lincoln, Forest, Iron, and Price. The same soil appears in the central part of the state in a sandstone region including Juneau, Adams, and Monroe counties, and there appear to be other sandy islands in the northwestern and northeastern corners of the state. The glaciated granite soils lie over crystalline rock areas both east and west of the north-central sandy soil region. Too few lakes have been sampled in northwestern Wisconsin to make it possible to generalize on the relative quality and quantity of the algal flora. Such limnological data as have been collected by Birge and Juday indicate that there are fewer soft water lakes in the northwest than in the north-central and eastern sections of Wisconsin. In Washburn County there is an extensive sand hill area in which the lakes are characteristically soft water. Here there was the expected paucity of algae, especially of phytoplankton.

An interesting situation exists in the Waupaca chain of lakes in Waupaca County, where there are glaciated granite soils, but also crystalline rock and sandstone, with small amounts of surface limestone in the extreme southeast (Whitson, Geib, and Tosterud, 1921). The glaciated granite soils extend up into the northeast section of the state, and there is a great area of similar soils in the northwest. Most lakes in this type of soil are soft water, with typical soft water algal floras. In many of the Waupaca lakes, however, the water is so exceedingly hard that lime incrustations form on stones and submerged objects of all kinds. Similar conditions occur in some south-central Michigan lakes. The floras are typical hard water types. *Chara* spp., heavily incrusted with lime, abound in many lakes. The explanation of these hard water lakes in the sandstone and granite soils of Waupaca County is found in the geological history of the area. Among the glacial soils brought into this part of the state from the east there was a considerable amount of dolomite, the outwash from which is highly calcareous. Hence, lakes in the Waupaca chain are characterized by hard water floras.

A greater part of the limnological work in Wisconsin has been done in the granite and sandy soil areas of the northeast and northwest sections. Accordingly more attention was given the highland lake areas when the present survey was made, in order to make correlations possible between types of floras and physical-chemical data. In the entire northern portion of the state the lakes are characteristically soft, poor in calcium, low in half-bound carbon dioxide and nitrogen, and give pH readings on the acid side of neutrality. A soft water lake might have 9.8 mg. or less of bound carbon dioxide per liter, whereas in a hard water lake there might be 43 mg. or more per liter.

It is in such soft water lakes of northern Michigan and Wisconsin that finely drawn differences can be noted in algal ecology.

For although most of the lakes are soft, those which do have a somewhat alkaline or basic character reflect their chemistry in a noticeably richer blue-green and diatom flora. In Arbor Vitae Lake, Wisconsin, for example, a lake somewhat harder than nearby Trout Lake, a relatively heavy bloom of *Gloeotrichia echinulata* is supported, and the flora as a whole is the cyanophyte–diatom type.

A comparison of the algal flora of the northern and northeastern sections with those of the south and southeastern sections of both Michigan and Wisconsin leads to the generalization that in the northern sections the bulk of the algal vegetation is low but the number of species is high. The larger number of species for the northern section is due to the luxuriant desmid flora which abounds in the soft (acid) water lakes and bogs. (See Fassett, 1930; Wilson, 1937, 1941, on the larger aquatic plants of lakes in northeastern Wisconsin.)

Approximately 200 collections were made from the sandy-crystalline rock area of northwest Wisconsin (Burnett, Washburn, and Sawyer counties). The lakes here, as has been pointed out, are mostly soft water, with a pH on the acid side. The bottoms and the shores are sandy, with little aquatic vegetation of any kind. Of course there are exceptions. Shell Lake in Washburn County, for example, is a habitat of relatively hard water, supporting a rich blue-green algal flora. This is the only lake in northern Wisconsin from which collections were made that had a bloom of *Aphanizomenon flos-aquae*. Although chemical analyses are not at hand for support, one can predict that this lake is relatively rich in nitrogen, as judged by the cyanophyte–diatom flora. This condition might be expected because the lake lies within the town of Shell Lake and is bordered, in part, by tilled soil, a situation which makes the accumulation of nitrogenous substances possible. In contrast is Round Lake, Sawyer County, a large lake with a considerable amount of shallow water which supports a very scant phytoplanktonic flora, with filamentous forms poorly represented. *Chara* spp., at least when collections were made in August, were found to be stunted. There were, however, luxuriant beds of *Nitella,* a genus which prefers soft water habitats.

LAKE TYPES AND ALGAL DISTRIBUTION

Inland lakes of the region fall naturally into four main types as determined by hydrographic features. In their Wisconsin lake surveys Birge and Juday noted and described significant limnological characteristics peculiar to these classes. Correspondingly, the production of plant and animal life, as might be expected, is found to vary when the biotas of the respective types of lakes are compared. The chief types are: 1) hard water drainage lakes, stream or spring-fed, with an outlet, at least during part of the year; 2) hard water seepage lakes (rare), high in calcium, magnesium, and half-bound carbon dioxide, landlocked; 3) soft water drainage lakes (uncommon in Wisconsin and Michigan), low in calcium and half-bound carbon dioxide, with inlet and outlet; 4) soft water seepage lakes (common, particularly in northern parts of the area, in the northern part of the Lower Peninsula, the Upper Peninsula of Michigan, and in upper Wisconsin), low in calcium, magnesium, and half-bound carbon dioxide, fed by seepage or drainage from bogs, without outlet.

To these four classes, two other types of lakes should be added: 5) acid bog lakes, mostly seepage, low in calcium; 6) alkaline bog lakes, mostly drainage, relatively high in calcium.

In general, the lake types are determined by differences in their geological history, differences principally related to glaciation. The most recent glaciation, Late Wisconsin, obviously had the greatest influence on the present physiography of the region. Although most lakes had their birth during and following the closing years of this period, it appears likely that a few of the deeper lakes, Lake Geneva and Green Lake in Wisconsin, for example, may antedate the Late Wisconsin. There are at least four types of lake formation in the Great Lakes region: 1) depressions formed by the melting away of great blocks of glacier fragments and the subsequent sloughing off of glacial drift so that mounds of debris were left about a kettle-hole, which is usually soft and is frequently the acid bog type; 2) lake basins formed by the damming of preglacial valleys; 3) basins created when terminal moraines were formed in parallel ridges and the intervening valleys dammed subsequently by deposits at either end; and 4) depressions formed in the ground moraine. (See Juday, 1914.)

The lakes which were left with an outlet became immediately a part of a drainage system Other drainage systems were evolved by subsequent wearing away of impounding glacial deposits and through variations in water level. Thus some lakes were included in a drainage system, but others were left perpetually land-locked and doomed consequently to extinction. Fundamental differences between the drainage and seepage types of lakes, which are so conspicuous today, are related, therefore, to the mode of the lakes' formation in the remote past.

Hard Water Drainage Lakes

These lakes are numerous and are to be found in such drainage systems as the Wisconsin River, the St. Croix River, the Fox River, and the Yahara River in Wisconsin, and in the Crooked River and Cheboygan River in Michigan. In general, they are high in calcium and half-bound carbon dioxide (see Table 1) and correspondingly have a high pH (pH 7.2–9.4). Reference has already been made to this type of lake and its characteristics. In southern Michigan and Wisconsin, most drainage lakes are naturally harder than in the northern parts of the states because of the difference in the chemistry of the soil. It is noteworthy that when the drainage type of lake in the highland region has a sandy bottom, and few flat beaches or shallow bays, it may be as poor a producer as some of the soft water lakes. In Table 1, 13 hard water drainage lakes are listed to show something of the quality of their algal floras in relation to critical limnological features. Compare Table 1 with Table 2, which summarizes collections made in Wisconsin from December through July.

These general quantitative and qualitative observations contribute to the evaluation of the hard water lake as an habitual producer of blue-green and diatom floras which are rich both in number of species and in number of individuals. Chlorophycean species, on the other hand, while not always fewer in number than the components of the cyanophyte–diatom flora, comprise but a small portion of the bulk of algal vegetation in hard water lakes. Except for the Volvocales, they seldom, if ever, form water blooms. Certain members of the Volvocales, *Volvox* and *Pandorina,* in some lakes may reach climaxes that form blooms, though of relatively short duration.

Drainage prevents hard water lakes from achieving a constantly high concentration of nutrients; yet the chemistry of the water, together with such eutrophic features as shallowness and high summer temperatures, make possible the characteristic luxuriant flora. This type of lake may also have a high productivity of larger aquatic vegetation—Sweeny Lake in Oneida County and Lake Mendota in Dane County, Wisconsin, and Ocqueoc Lake in Presque Isle County, Michigan, for example.

Although there is conflicting evidence regarding the role that phosphorus plays as a controlling factor in the development of aquatic floras, many critical studies indicate that it is a regulator. It is well known that soluble phosphorus in a lake decreases with the seasonal increment in plankton and increases as organisms die and disintegrate. Tressler and Domogalla (1931) have shown that in Lake Wingra (Wisconsin) soluble phosphorus declines and

Table 1
Wisconsin Hard Water Drainage Lakes

Lake	pH	Fixed CO_2 (ppm)	Ca (ppm)	N (ppm)	Soluble P (ppm)	Species Blue-green algae	Species Green algae	Larger vegetation
Alder	7.8–8.2	9.8–17.5	11.96		0.009	16 Abundant	9 Sparse	Abundant
Allequash	7.2–9.2	7.3–16.5	12.24	Nitrate 0.01	0.02–0.03	7 Abundant	3 Common	Abundant
Big Arbor Vitae	7.0–8.4	11.2–22.1	11.6		0.014–0.02	11 Abundant	8 Common	Sparse to abundant
Boulder	7.9–8.4	8–12	8.6–7.1	Nitrate 0.004		18 Abundant	14 Common	Moderately abundant
Carroll	7.6–9.0	20.3–23.5	12.3			4 Abundant	None	Abundant
Fishtrap	7.1–8.0	17.5 (max.)	11.0	Nitrate 0.003	0.025–0.02	18 Abundant	13 Abundant	Abundant
High	7.8	22.5	12.6	Total 0.393		12 Abundant	18 Abundant	Common
Little Crooked	7.4–7.8	21.8	14.7	Nitrate 0.03	0.027	7 Abundant	8 Abundant	Moderately abundant
Mendota	7.4–8.6	37.4	36.4	Total 13–19 Inorganic 0.08–0.36		4 Abundant	2 Common	Abundant
Minocqua	7.6	20.1	9.6	Total 0.37		23 Abundant	23 Abundant	Abundant
Sweeney	8.2	18.3	9.09			35 Abundant	31 Abundant	Abundant
Wild Cat	7.9	30.8	18.6	Total 0.459		7 Abundant	1 Scarce	Sparse
Wingra	7.8–8.7	70–120 3 M. 19–1200 M.	30–50	Total 0.3–0.4	0.5–1.4	4 Abundant	4 Common	Abundant

Note: The numbers of species indicated are based on samples obtained at one time only and do not represent exhaustive counts. ppm = parts per million. Readings of CO_2 for Lake Wingra are given at 3 meters depth and at the surface.

TABLE 2
OCCURRENCE OF ALGAE IN FOUR WISCONSIN HARD WATER LAKES
(From Sawyer, Lackey, and Lenz, 1943)

Number of species, with percentage of their occurrence in samples				
Lake and No. of Samples	Mendota (9)	Monona (30)	Kegonsa (25)	Wingra (10)
Cyanophyta	6 (20%)	12 (10%)	9 (8%)	13 (32%)
Diatoms	15 (28%)	19 (15%)	16 (30%)	21 (30%)
Dinoflagellates	0	1 (50%)	2 (50%)	3 (23%)
Cryptophyceae	4 (72%)	4 (50%)	5 (49%)	5 (56%)
Chrysophyceae	6 (18%)	8 (12%)	8 (15%)	10 (23%)
Euglenophyta	3 (11%)	8 (10%)	8 (7%)	8 (15%)
Volvocales	6 (27%)	11 (16%)	12 (15%)	6 (27%)
Chlorophyta (non-motile)	16 (23%)	35 (9%)	26 (14%)	41 (24%)

remains low during the spring and summer months but increases during the fall and winter periods when there is a reduction in the plankton. In general, where the total phosphate and nitrate content of drainage lakes is high, the algal flora is abundant. This relationship is clearly demonstrated by the higher productivity of plankton bulk in such lakes as Jordan in Michigan and Wingra in Wisconsin when compared with the productivity of lakes in the northern areas. It is noteworthy that in some of the Yahara River lakes near Madison there is a significant relationship between excessive growths and blooms of algae and the high phosphate-nitrate content resulting from sewage effluents and run-off water from populated areas. A similar condition is observable in Jordan Lake, Michigan, and in some of the eutrophic lakes in northwestern Iowa which have received a continuous flow of fertilizing elements during the past few decades.

Lake Mendota, Dane County, Wisconsin, in the Yahara River system, is a typical hard water drainage lake. The pH ranges from 7.4

TABLE 3

ABUNDANCE OF THREE CLASSES OF ALGAE, LAKE MENDOTA, WISCONSIN

Average number of individuals per liter of lake water			
	Chlorophyta (22 spp.)	Cyanophyta (6 spp.)	Diatoms (15 spp.)
January	7	612	1,668
February	0	1,912	754
March	31	879	414
April	130	504	1,661
May	7,985	4,044	2,695
June	2,019	1,426	13,059
July	11,494	6,483	3,904
September	119	11,931	10,413
October	398	1,969	28,751
November	155	4,666	5,016
December	114	782	17,780

NOTE: Readings for August were not available for the table.

in February to 8.6 (surface level) in August and October. In February, readings for carbonates at 21 meters have been as high as 43 ppm. Fixed carbon dioxide is relatively high, 36–37 ppm. Hardness is 163 mg. per liter (American Public Health Unit). Inorganic nitrogen is 0.08–0.36 ppm, whereas total nitrogen varies from 13.1 ppm at the surface to 15.2 ppm at 22 meters depth (June). Soluble phosphorus occurs in 0.01–0.02 ppm. Correlated with these physical-chemical characteristics, the algal flora is predominantly the cyanophyte–diatom type, although during summer months there may be a dense growth of *Staurastrum* (a desmid genus), which gives the Chlorophyta a larger representation as far as number of individuals is concerned. The over-all bulk of algal vegetation is not so great in Lake Mendota as in some of the other bodies of water in the

[18]

Yahara River system, but water blooms occasionally develop in it.

The average number of individuals per liter of lake water for the Chlorophyta, the Cyanophyta, and the diatoms are listed in Table 3. These figures were obtained by counts from centrifuged plankton samples from Lake Mendota, Wisconsin, a typical hard water drainage lake. It will be noted that it is only in the months of May, June, and July that the Chlorophyta exceed the Cyanophyta in numbers per liter. It is interesting also to note that the numbers represent 22 species of Chlorophyta, only 6 species of Cyanophyta, and 15 species of diatoms. This is a more nearly equal distribution of species among these three groups of algae than usually occurs in a hard water drainage lake when sedentary or attached species, as well as planktonic forms, are considered.

HARD WATER SEEPAGE LAKES

This type of lake is rarely found in our region, for seepage lakes are characteristically soft. Spider and Round Lakes, Vilas County, Wisconsin, are examples. Sloughs which have no outlet and some swampy ponds might be included in this class. Characteristics of hard water seepage lakes are shown in Table 4. These habitats, as might be expected, are not unlike the northern hard water drainage lakes except that the chlorophycean flora equals or exceeds the cyanophycean in abundance. Although the pH of the water in such lakes was found to be always above neutral, it is likely that great variations would be discovered if readings were made throughout the year. A much higher pH would be expected in late summer months because of increased photosynthetic activity which removes the half-bound carbon dioxide from the bicarbonates.

Euglenoid genera, such as *Phacus, Euglena,* and *Trachelomonas,* and some of the Chrysophyta, *Tribonema* spp. and *Synura uvella,* for example, are typical components of the algal flora in hard water seepage lakes.

SOFT WATER DRAINAGE LAKES

Soft water lakes are nearly always of the seepage type; a soft water lake with drainage, or a seepage lake with hard water, is seldom found. It will be noted in Table 5 that soft water drainage lakes have limnological and biological characteristics very similar to the soft water seepage type. The algal flora, in both quality and quantity, is predominantly chlorophycean. The phytoplankton is sparse, sometimes lacking except for an occasional diatom. It is noteworthy also that the available total-nitrogen readings for soft water drainage

TABLE 4
WISCONSIN HARD WATER SEEPAGE LAKES

Lake	pH	Fixed CO_2 (ppm)	Conductance	Ca (ppm)	Species Blue-green algae	Species Green algae	Larger vegetation
Arbor Vitae Slough	6.7–7.0	27	102		11 Abundant	14 Common	Abundant
Lost Canoe Slough	8.2	11	45		8 Abundant	22 Common	Abundant
Round Lake	7.8	17.5	67	9.4	25 Abundant	50 Abundant	Common
Spider Lake	7.5	21.5			11 Common	5 Abundant	Common

Table 5
Wisconsin Soft Water Drainage Lakes

Lake	pH	Fixed CO$_2$ (ppm)	Ca (ppm)	N (ppm)	Soluble P (ppm)	Species Blue-green algae	Species Green algae	Larger vegetation
Anna	6.4–7.5	1.8–3.5	1.2		0.026–0.003	6 Few	15 Abundant	Scarce
Big Portage	6.6–6.9	2.2–4.9		0.002	0.012–0.017	2 Scarce	8 Scarce	Scarce
Blue	6.4–7.1					2 Scarce	10 Scarce	Scarce
Deep						3 Common	22 Abundant	Common
Eagle	6.9	12.0	6.6			3 Common	6 Abundant	Common
Helen	6.1	3.2	1.4	0.566		1 Scarce	8 Abundant	Common
Lynx	5.5–6.1	1.0–1.6	1.15	0.02		11 Common	48 Abundant	Scarce
Mary	6.0	2.7	2.7	0.73		1 Common	23 Abundant	Scarce
Nebish	6.1–7.3	3.5–4.5	2.2–3.2	0.01	0.013	7 Scarce	25 Common	Few
Pine	5.2	13.0	7.1	0.318		5 Common	18 Common	Scarce
Trostel	5.5	1.8	1.64	0.324		None	17 Common	

TABLE 6
A COMPARISON OF WISCONSIN DRAINAGE (D) AND SEEPAGE (S) LAKES

Lake	pH	Fixed CO_2 (aver. mg./L)	Conductance	Total P (aver. mg./L)	Plankton (aver. mg./L)	Blue-green algal flora	Green algal flora
Allequash (D)	7.2–9.2	15.1	60	.026	1.26	++ Blue-greens and diatoms predominate	− Few species, not abundant
Adelaide (S)	5.9–7.1	3.17		.02	1.23	− Few blue-greens	+ Species dominant but not abundant
Arbor Vitae (D)	7.0–8.4	22.0	102	.024	1.86	+++ Blue-greens and diatoms predominate	+ Few species, but fairly abundant
Crystal (S)	6.0–6.4	1.4	9	.016	0.48	− Absent	− Few species, on bottom
Fishtrap (D)	7.1–8.0	17.5	52–70	.026		++ Common	++ Abundant in species and numbers
Clear (S)	6.1–6.8	3.6		.016	0.66	− Rare	+ Few

The relative degree of abundance of blue-green algae is indicated by the plus and minus signs.

lakes are higher than those for hard water drainage or soft water seepage types. This suggests that if other essential nutrients were present, the soft water drainage lake might be more productive. High nitrogen content is correlated seasonally with a low plankton count, for when the plankton is high, especially during summer months, the nitrogen content of the lake water is low, increasing, however, as the biota decreases in fall and winter. In many seepage, acid lakes (Lynx and Mary Lakes, Wisconsin, for example), the desmid flora has an abundance approaching that of bog lakes, which are highly productive.

Soft Water Seepage Lakes

In Table 6 three typical hard water drainage lakes are compared with three soft water seepage bodies. The latter type of lake usually has a sandy bottom, with few bays and shallows; the nutrients are low in concentration and the half-bound carbon dioxide content is much less than in the drainage lake. In soft water habitats the algal flora is almost entirely planktonic, and even this is relatively scant. Filamentous algae are practically non-existent. In many such lakes, only sterile *Mougeotia* and *Zygnema* can be found, entangled about the culms of rushes that form sparse beds. Zooplankton is scarce in the soft water lakes, which further explains their general low productivity of fish. The total plankton residue (dry weight analysis) in Crystal Lake, Wisconsin, is only 0.48 mg. per liter (Birge and Juday). When a soft water lake is found capable of supporting a substantial fish population, it is obvious that at least periodically there must be crops of phytoplankters of sufficient magnitude to support the intermediate zooplankton elements of the food chain. The proportionate production of fish in a soft water lake has been made very graphic in a paper by Juday (1942). One of his diagrams is shown in Figure 3. This illustrates the quantitative relationships of the several components of the biota as expressed in kilograms per hectare of lake surface (wet weight, ash-free computation). See also Table 7 for analyses of 27 soft water seepage lakes.

One of the many interesting problems involved in the differences in production of soft and hard water lakes is the role played by heterotrophic bacteria. The unanswered question is: Do the nature and abundance of the biota determine the kind and quantity of the bacterial flora, or does the bacterial flora function critically in releasing nutrients which, if sufficient, make possible an abundant and varied algal flora through the overturn of organic matter? This is doubtless a vicious circle, but Henrici and McCoy (1938) and Henrici (1939) have shown that soft water, oligotrophic lakes have fewer bacteria

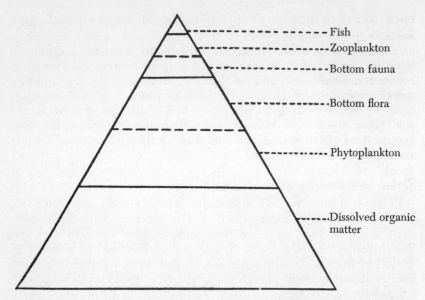

Figure 3. Relative weights of various components of the biota and dissolved organic matter in Weber Lake, Wisconsin, a soft water seepage type. Scale: 4.9 sq. mm. = 1 kilogram per hectare. (From Juday, 1943)

than hard water, eutrophic habitats. In their studies Henrici and McCoy (*l.c.*) show that the bacterial flora of the bottom is larger in numbers of individuals than that of open water and that, as might be expected, the difference between the bottom and upper level flora is greater in eutrophic than in oligotrophic lakes.

In oligotrophic Crystal Lake, Vilas County, Wisconsin, for example, the bacteria count per cc. of bottom mud sampled was 2,160; whereas in Alexander, a eutrophic lake in Minnesota, the count was 144,240 per cc. of bottom "*kalkgyttja*." In the former lake the total bacterial flora of the bottom (average bacteria per cc. × depth of the mud) was 38,880 as compared with 2,599,320 in Alexander Lake.

In the examination of the open water of the two lakes, an interesting bacterial count was secured. In Crystal Lake the average was 80 organisms per cc.; in Alexander, 675 per cc. When the ratio of the number of bottom bacteria to open water bacteria in the two lakes is compared, an even greater difference is noted. In Crystal Lake the total open water flora (average bacteria per cc. × depth of the lake) is 159,900, which, when compared with 38,880 on the bottom, gives a quotient of 0.2. A much higher ratio is found in the eutrophic type of lake. In Alexander there was a total of 538,300 organisms in the open water, or a quotient of 5.0 when this is compared with 2,599,320 in the total bottom count.

The activity of bacteria produces food substances for bottom organisms, as previously mentioned, and at the same time increases the concentration of nutrients available for plant and animal life in the upper levels. It is obvious that the quantity and quality of the bacteria in both bottom and open water floras can produce effects in the chemical nature of the water, and in the chemistry and physical condition of the bottom sediments. In a sense a closed cycle is involved here. In the first place a rich bacterial flora, through the rapid breakdown of organic matter, may produce (at least indirectly) a varied and rich phytoplankton and zooplankton. The quantity and quality of the microbiota, in turn, have far reaching effects on the productivity of other kinds of animal life, both on the bottom and in open water. And finally, the relative abundance and quality of the organisms (i. e., productivity) within a lake determine whether the bottom sediments will support a rich bacterial flora. The role of bacteria in this cycle has been clearly summarized by Waksman (1941).

The characteristic paucity of nutrients in a seepage lake is explainable, at least in some instances, by the source of the water, which percolates through sand and crystalline soils. Frequently there is seepage from bogs and marshes, with the result that the water is rich in humic acids. Birge and Juday found only 3–4 grams of organic matter per cubic meter in the soft water type of lake; of this amount, 15–18 per cent was accounted for by the plankton. Over a three-year period they found that the total nitrogen content of such a lake averaged 7.2 per cent of the dry weight of the plankton per cubic meter of water (as determined by ash-free analyses).

Table 7 lists 27 typical soft water seepage lakes with their biota and critical limnological features.

Acid Bog Lakes

The acid bog lake, usually found in *Sphagnum* bogs, is of the kettlehole type. The water is at times acid, although the marginal mat may be more acid than the open water. Here are found a great variety of desmids and a few Cyanophyta, such as *Scytonema ocellatum, Hapalosiphon pumilus,* and *Chroococcus Prescottii.* The plankton of these lakes is not abundant, usually, but the filamentous forms are luxuriantly developed, especially in the marginal waters and in the small seeps leading into the lake. Such bodies of water are aging rapidly, and there is a great accumulation of organic matter,

TABLE 7
WISCONSIN SOFT WATER SEEPAGE LAKES

Lake	pH	Fixed CO$_2$ (ppm)	Ca (ppm)	N (ppm)	Soluble P (ppm)	Species Blue-green algae	Species Green algae	Larger vegetation
Adelaide	5.9–7.1	2.2–6.7	2.4			3 Common	15 Common	Few
Big Carr	5.4–6.2	2.12–2.5	0.85	0.01		13 Common	56 Common	Few to common
Buffalo	6.2–6.6	3.7–4.1	1.32			2 Scarce	17 Common	Common
Bug	6.0–6.5	2.7–4.0	Cond. 17			5 Scarce	27 Common	Few
Carpenter	6.6–7.1	4.6	2.7			2 Scarce	26 Common	Few
Clear (Oneida Co.)	6.1–6.8	1.3–1.9	2.06	0.015–0.002	0.017–0.018	7 Scarce	22 Common	Few
Crane	5.6–6.1	1.1–2.5				3 Scarce	15 Common	Practically none
Crystal (Vilas Co.)	6.0–6.4	0.6–1.16				0 Plankton 2 bottom	2 Plankton 12 bottom	Common
Devils (Burnett Co.)						14 Common	45 Common	Few to scarce
Diamond	5.5–6.5	0.56–6.8	0.54–1.44	Trace	0.015	10 Common	26 Common Few plankt.	Few to scarce
Finger	6.5	6.7				None	4 Scarce	Scarce
Harmony	4.4	1.5	Cond. 25			4 Common	16 Common	Scarce

Helmet	4.7–6.0	1.5–1.8	2.4–2.6	0.3		7 Common	25 Common	Few
Ike Walton	5.9	1.3	1.28	0.332		10 Common	17 Common	Common
Jag	5.9	1.8	0.32			7 Common	32 Common	Common
Laura	7.2	5.3	4.48	0–0.004	0.02–0.019	12 Common	28 Common	Common
Little Bear	6.2–6.4	0.81–3.5	1.15	0.029–0.035	0.011–0.017	8 Scarce	7 Scarce	Scarce
Long (Vilas Co.)	5.5–5.8	1.5–1.7	2.5	0.01	0.012	8 Scarce	18 Common	?
Mud	6.2–6.4	2.5–6.0	Cond. 21	0.025	0.01	3 Common	42 Common	?
Oswego	6.4	2.3	1.35			3 Scarce	48 Common	Abundant
Palette	6.8	3.8	2.05	0.452		5 Common	56 Common	Common
Razorback	7.1	8.1	3.75	0.334		8 Scarce	18 Common	?
Starett	6.4	2.0	0.7	0.393		3 Common	42 Common	?
Summit	5.1	2.0				3 Scarce	48 Common	Abundant
Weber	6.1	1.1	1.43	0.058		5 Common	56 Common	Common
Wishow	6.0	2.5	0.35	0.218		3 Scarce	7 Common	?
Witches	5.8	3.4	0.22			8 Scarce	25 Common	Common

much of which eventually forms peat because it is only partially decayed by bacterial action. *Microspora* spp. are often the dominant filamentous forms, attached to *Chamaedaphne* stems at the margin of the open water. It has been observed that *Oedogonium,* often abundant in the vegetative condition, in the open water portion of acid bog lakes, rarely reproduces sexually there. In the pools and ditches of the marginal mat, however, where there is a concentration of organic acids and decaying matter, and where temperatures are higher, fruiting plants are abundant and numerous species may be identified in a single collection. *Batrachospermum* spp., in luxuriant tufts, are also characteristic of the acid bog lake. In general it may be stated that this type of lake, when shallow enough to permit optimal temperatures, is more productive than any of the other types in number of algal species.

ALKALINE BOG LAKES

The alkaline or basic bog lake usually involves a stream meandering through a kettlehole depression which has never been entirely closed. Mud Lake, Cheboygan County, Michigan, and a small lake near High Lake, Vilas County, Wisconsin, are clear examples. Although there is an acid type of terrestrial flora forming a marginal mat around such lakes, the water is fairly hard. The pH is 7.1–7.4, the bound carbon dioxide is 21.8 ppm and calcium is 11.25 ppm; the conductivity 85. They have, therefore, the chemistry of semihard lakes, but the algal flora is poor both quantitatively and qualitatively. There is a conspicuous growth of *Spirogyra crassa,* S. *decemina,* and *Chara* spp., all calcophiles (hard water organisms).

SUMMARY

Some of the correlations between types of algal floras and physical-chemical conditions in lakes are summarized in the charts in Figures 4, 5, and 6. The diagrams are based on analyses of 100 lakes in Vilas and Oneida counties, Wisconsin, selected at random from the list of habitats from which collections were made. The samples upon which counts of algal species are based were collected during July and August. The chemical data are from the records of E. A. Birge and C. Juday.

In Figure 4 the graph at the left shows the distribution of the lakes according to pH readings (expressed in number of lakes which fall within the pH range indicated). As will be noted, the majority of the lakes in the sample have a pH near 7.5. Only a few are as basic as 8.3; a somewhat larger number are as acid as 5.3. Correlated

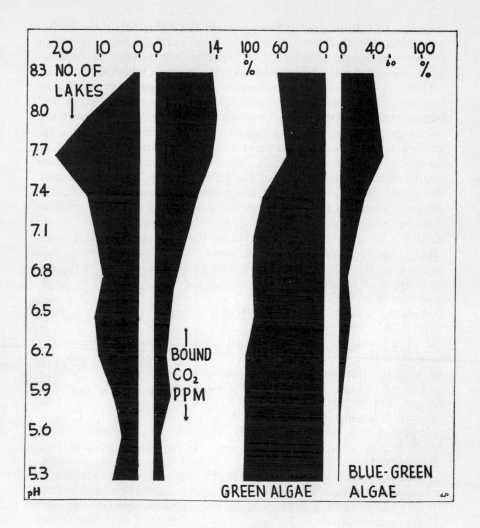

Figure 4. Diagram showing the number of Wisconsin lakes (in a random sample of 100) which lie within different pH readings; their bound carbon dioxide content (expressed in parts per million); and the percentages of green and blue-green algal species in their total algal flora. (See discussion in text.)

with this distribution is the first graph to the right, which shows the amount of bound carbon dioxide that occurs in the lakes (expressed in parts per million). As would be expected, since the majority have a pH above neutral, most of the lakes have a relatively high bound carbon dioxide content in the form of calcium and magnesium carbonates. In the particular group of lakes under consideration the bound carbon dioxide content was no higher than 14 ppm, however.

The graphs on the right of this diagram show the distribution of green and blue-green algal species (expressed in percentages of the lakes' total algal flora). It will be noted that where both the bound carbon dioxide and the pH are high the percentages of blue-green and green species are approximately equal. With a lowering of the pH and a corresponding decrease in the amount of bound carbon dioxide, however, there is an increase in the percentage of green algal species, reaching 100 per cent of the flora in the highly acid lakes. This increase is in almost exact inverse proportion to the decrease in the carbon dioxide content. In this connection it should be pointed out that there is no causal relationship between large numbers of individuals or numbers of species and high *bound* carbon dioxide content since in this form it is unavailable to most vegetation. Bound carbon dioxide content *is* significant, however, and is useful in providing an index of algal production, because almost invariably a lake with a high bound carbon dioxide content will also be high in bicarbonates. Half-bound carbon dioxide in $Ca(CO_3)_2$ and $MgCa(CO_3)_2$ is available to photosynthetic organisms, and it follows that such lakes are able to support an abundant algal flora, other factors being also favorable. Whereas the relationship between half-bound and bound carbon dioxide mentioned above usually holds, it is possible in senescent lakes to have a high bound carbon dioxide content with little or no half-bound or free carbon dioxide. In such cases one would expect to find a very scanty algal flora and a heavy deposition of marl or some similar carbonate. See Welch (1935) for an outline of the relationship between available carbon dioxide and bicarbonates.

In Figures 5 and 6, the lakes used in this analysis are divided into four groups: hard water drainage (HD), soft water drainage (SD), hard water seepage (HS), and soft water seepage (SS). In Figure 5 the distribution of the hard and soft water drainage lakes according to pH readings is shown in the graph on the left. With this distribution is compared bound carbon dioxide content, as in Figure 4. As was noted in Figure 4, the blue-green and green algae are present in almost equal percentages in the hard water lakes; the acid lakes have by far the larger percentage of green algae and almost no blue-green

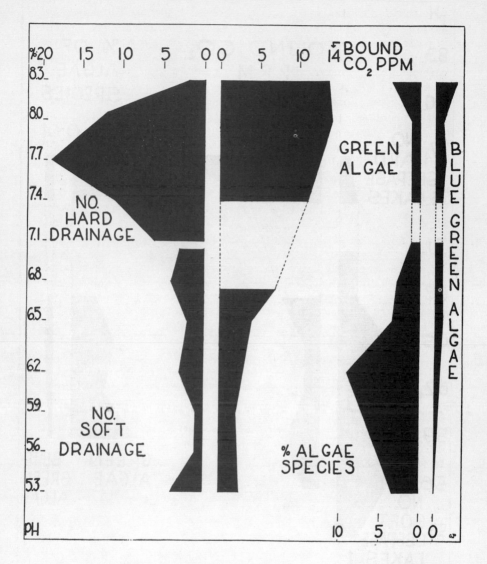

Figure 5. Diagram showing the percentages of hard and soft water drainage lakes in a random sample of 100 Wisconsin lakes; their bound carbon dioxide content (expressed in parts per million); and the percentages of green and blue-green algal species in their total algal flora. (See discussion in text.)

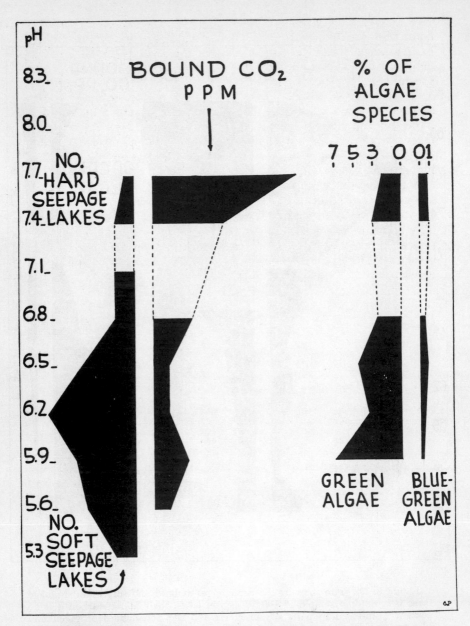

Figure 6. Diagram showing the relative number of hard and soft water seepage lakes in a random sample of 100 Wisconsin lakes; their bound carbon dioxide content (expressed in parts per million, the highest being 14); and the percentages of green and blue-green algal species in their total algal flora. (See discussion in text.)

flora. The decidedly larger number of algal species in the highly basic lakes is related to the richness of the phytoplankton in such habitats. It is in lakes with pH readings such as these that blue-green species often produce water blooms.

As was mentioned previously in another connection, hard water seepage lakes are rather rare. This is seen in Figure 6, which shows a few lakes having a pH between 7.2 and 7.7. In at least one of these lakes the bound carbon dioxide was as high as 14 ppm. In such lakes the green algal species are sometimes three times as numerous as the blue-green.

A considerable number of soft water seepage lakes were found among those used in this analysis; most of these had a pH between 6.0 and 6.8. As with the soft water drainage lakes, the seepage lakes have floras predominantly of the green algal type. It should be mentioned, however, that some of the soft water seepage lakes have a great bulk of certain blue-green algae, but the number of species is very small.

Relationships of Phytoplankton to Lake Productivity

One of the more interesting problems confronting the aquatic biologist, and one of great practical importance, is that of *productivity*. By this term is meant the quantity and quality of plant and animal life which a body of water is capable of supporting. Limnology comprises such a heterogeneity of fields of inquiry that limnological studies often seem to lack correlation. Nevertheless, the chief aim of the limnologist is to devise methods of evaluating productivity of aquatic habitats for both purely scientific and practical purposes. Many of the problems that arise in shellfish culture, fish management programs, and similar projects are problems of productivity. Considerable progress in both the Old and New Worlds has been made in determining index characters by which productivity of aquatic environments can be evaluated and predicted; that is, a set of characteristics or standards by which a lake may be measured in respect to the quantity and kinds of plants and animals it can produce. Physical-chemical factors, however, seem to defy analysis because they interlock and interact in bewildering complexities. Since they are never quite the same in any two lakes, they give each body of water a distinct individuality. Thus limnologists find great difficulty in determining a productivity index which can be generally applied. A brief consideration of a few biological and physical-chemical factors involved in the relationships of the algae to productivity in lakes is in order here.

No more graphic outline of the factors involved in production is at hand than a diagram prepared by D. S. Rawson (1940). Referring to this diagram (reproduced here, Fig. 7), it is of interest to check through the factors, noting which ones have a direct bearing upon the quantity and quality of the algae and other plant life, factors which also influence animal life, of course, either directly or indirectly. As complex as this chart may appear, it is, of necessity, a simplified presentation of the multitudinous factors involved and shows none of the ramifying and anastomosing interactivities of the components. If the contributing agents shown in this chart were to be analyzed further, the diagram would become very much in-

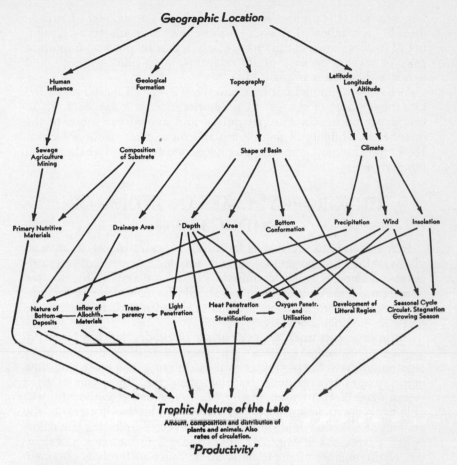

Figure 7. A diagram showing the contributions toward lake productivity by some interesting factors, both inside and outside of a body of water After a diagram by D. S. Rawson. (By courtesy of the American Association for the Advancement of Science.)

volved. For example, 'primary nutritive materials' depend on many specific factors which are interrelated with and are governed by 'topography,' 'drainage area,' and the 'inflow of allochthonous materials.' The availability to plants of the 'primary nutrient materials,' such as nitrogen, phosphorus, and various salts, would be, in part, determined by 'oxygen concentration and utilization,' as well as by the 'seasonal cycle of circulation and stagnation.' 'Depth' and 'wind' together, or wind alone, directly affect turbidity ('transparency'), which in turn determines 'light penetration. The amount of carbon dioxide (not indicated as such on the chart) is regulated by a number of factors shown in this chart. Carbon dioxide plays an important role, of course, because of its relationship to photosynthesis and hence to the amount of plant life.

As has been pointed out by Chandler (1944) all these factors fall into three groups or classes: edaphic, morphometric, and climatic. In this paper he relates seasonal pulses and annual variations in the quantity and quality of the phytoplankton to some of these factors. He found the most important to be turbidity, solar radiation, and temperature.

CHLOROPHYLL AS AN INDEX OF PRODUCTION

It is sufficient to say that chlorophyll in water plants, as in land plants, is the all-important agent and initiator in a series of physical-chemical changes which culminate in and are responsible for the fauna. In this connection, mention should be made here of the possible use of chlorophyll measurements as indirect, if not direct, indices of potential productivity.

An approach to such an evaluation of production has been described by Kozminski (1938). He secured acetone extractions of chlorophyll from the phytoplankton at different lake levels and then made quantitative readings by measuring the absorption of light waves 6200–6800 Å in length. By this photometric method he was able to secure an index of phytoplankton production in terms of the amount of chlorophyll at different lake levels. By plotting the chlorophyll (expressed in $Mg./M^3$) against depth in meters a useful index of the amount of phytoplankton at different levels is obtained. Then when the curves from various lakes are compared an evaluation of respective productivity potentials is established on the basis of the available chlorophyll. (See Fig. 8.)

It is interesting to correlate these readings (Fig. 8) with the quality of the phytoplankton and limnological characteristics. In Scaffold Lake, Wisconsin, for example, there is shown to be very great absorption of light in photometric tests, especially between 2 and 8 meters, and we find a very dense flora of nannoplankters. At the time observations were made, the lake had a peculiar bluish-tan color from a tremendous population of the chlorobacteriacean *Pelogloea bacillifera*. This is a colonial organism with minute cells rather loosely held in soft mucilage. In a plankton net, the aggregates usually break up and only individual cells or small clumps appear when the

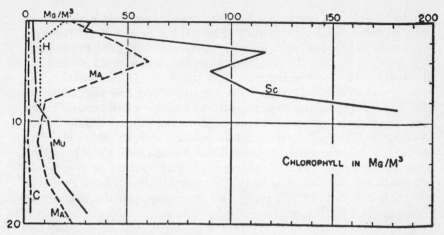

Figure 8. Graph showing vertical distribution of chlorophyll as determined by Kozminski's photometric studies of a number of Wisconsin lakes. C—Crystal; H—Helmet; Ma—Mary; Mu—Muskellunge; Sc—Scaffold. The ordinate represents depth in meters. The high chlorophyll-content of Scaffold Lake at eight meters is caused by an abundant growth of *Pelogloea bacillifera* Lauterbon. (From Kozminski, 1938.)

sample is examined microscopically. The organism is easily mistaken for a cluster of bacterial cells. In Scaffold Lake, *Pelogloea bacillifera* was apparently the only organism responsible for the heavy absorption in Kozminski's photometric analyses. *Phormidium mucicola* was the only other species found, and this was seen only after samples of the lake water had been cultured in the laboratory.

The rather curious flora of Scaffold Lake is accompanied by an equally interesting chemistry. The pH is high in the upper levels (pH 8.6–9.2) but drops to 6.3 at nine meters. Bound carbon dioxide is relatively low at the surface (5.0 ppm), but rises to 14.9 ppm at the bottom. Free carbon dioxide is likewise low at the surface (3.0 ppm) but is plentiful at or near the bottom (41.0 ppm). Calcium is present in 2.37–2.83 ppm. The color index is 26 (platinum cobalt scale). These data make it possible to classify Scaffold Lake as a medium hard water habitat, capable of supporting a luxuriant algal flora; hence it could be said to have a high production potentiality. An index to this is also to be found in Kozminski's chlorophyll analyses. (See also the remarks by Dutton, 1941, p. 397; Dutton and Manning, 1941, p. 516; Manning and Juday, 1941, p. 363.)

In such a transparent lake as Crystal (Wisconsin) the chlorophyll content is relatively low at all levels (Fig. 8), but shows a slight increase near the bottom. This is in keeping with the prediction one would be able to make on productivity of this lake from a consideration of other limnological features. The pH is low (6.0–6.4). The free carbon dioxide is 1.25 ppm near the surface, although at the bottom it is high, 10.5 ppm. The conductivity is low, the mineral content almost non-existent. It is reported that the water from Crystal Lake can be used safely in storage batteries. Repeated tow samples from this lake (July-August) yielded scarcely a single plankter, and there was a negligible amount of attached filamentous algae in the shallow water zone. On the bottom, at 10–15 meters, however, there is a carpet of the aquatic moss *Drepanocladus fluitans* and a meager algal flora of 15 species (including desmids). The stratum of vegetation accounts for the rise in chlorophyll content, shown by Kozminski (*l.c.*), in a layer where there is also an increase in the amount of available carbon dioxide.

PHYSICAL-CHEMICAL FACTORS

The quantity and quality of the algal flora is affected by many edaphic factors, and in turn these plants produce effects in the physical-chemical factors in the medium. These effects may directly or indirectly influence the biota of the environment, sometimes very drastically. Algae alter the oxygen and carbon dioxide content of the water, cause the pH to fluctuate, contribute to the nature of bottom sediments, and in other ways initiate series of cause-effect interactions. It is recognized that these changes are involved in what may be called algal ecology. This is an ill-defined term and broad in its application because it must cover such a complex of interacting factors and processes of nature. Since life itself is the product of these processes and the responses that protoplasm makes to them, it is not possible to regard any one ecological factor as more important than another. Carbon dioxide and oxygen might be selected arbitrarily for primary consideration.

Carbon Dioxide

Carbon dioxide and carbon dioxide tension (Burr, 1941) are critically important and only those bodies of water abundantly supplied with this gas, free or at least available, can support a luxuriant growth of algae. The quantity of carbon dioxide is regulated by a number of factors, many of which, in turn, are related to climatic conditions and geological events of the remote past. The temperature of the water at different times of the year and in different strata, the amount of carbon dioxide released by respiration, the chemical nature of the bottom and the overturn of organic matter by bacteria, the geographical and physiographic features of the terrain surrounding the water (or, in the case of a river, the land drained by it), all have their bearing on the carbon dioxide content.

Because of its crucial position in the lake's metabolism, a radical unbalancing of the amount of carbon dioxide in solution is felt throughout the entire biological cycle. A minimum amount will limit the quantity of phytoplankton a body of water can support, as indicated above in the remarks on Crystal Lake. A boundless supply, together with other favorable conditions, may influence the development of a superabundant water bloom, followed by a series of disturbed biological conditions. Examples of this are to be found in the prevalent water blooms in southern Michigan and Wisconsin, in Minnesota, and in some northern Iowa lakes. Only rarely have northern lakes been found with floras which approach the bloom condition. In southern parts of Wisconsin, the richness of the algal flora in the limestone region, as previously mentioned, is related to a high bound and half-bound carbon dioxide content. For example, Lake Geneva in Walworth County contains an average of 20.7 ppm of calcium and 3.7 ppm of carbonates. Trout Lake in Vilas County, a medium hard water lake, contains but 6.7 ppm of calcium and no carbonates. This great difference in the amount of available carbon dioxide is correlated with a great dissimilarity of the floras. Lake Geneva has at times a dense bloom of the eutrophic type, but in Trout Lake there is a relatively scant growth of algae in the main body of water. Birge and Juday (1911) have shown that there may be as many as 1000 phytoplankters per liter (mostly *Oscillatoria* sp.) at a depth of 15 meters in Lake Geneva At this level, free oxygen was 2.4 ppm and the temperature was 13.6° C. It may be of interest here to point out that the number of phytoplankters may be as high as 9 million (filaments, not cells) per liter in hard water lakes during periods when water blooms flourish (Prescott, 1932).

Although an adequate supply of carbon dioxide is essential, an increase in carbon dioxide tension, especially if rapid, may either kill fish or seriously upset their physiology. Death is brought about more or less directly through failure in elimination of carbon dioxide from the body on account of the high concentration of carbon dioxide in the water, or indirectly through ionization forming injurious carbonic acid (Powers, Shields, and Hickman, 1939).

Again, the basic chemistry of a lake varies greatly as carbon dioxide is removed from the bicarbonates. Some Iowa lakes that I surveyed developed a pH of 9.6–9.8 in the upper zones during the summer period of accelerated photosynthesis; an increase for the period of as much as 2.4. This is, of course, a logarithmic expression of increase and represents an enormous change in water chemistry with far-reaching biological effects.

OXYGEN

It is obvious that oxygen is one of the primary limiting and determining factors in phytoplankton ecology, as for all other forms of life. Because of their photosynthetic activities, plants in daylight are practically independent of free oxygen in solution. When carbon dioxide is present in sufficient quantities and other factors are favorable, chlorophyll-bearing organisms can automatically maintain the required amount of oxygen needed for their own respiration. But at night plants are required to draw upon free oxygen in the surrounding medium for this process. When there are excessive growths of algae, particularly in warm shallow water when the oxygen content is low, the available supply of oxygen may be reduced to a point below the amount normally required by the fauna. Thus, by increasing or decreasing the oxygen content, algae act as agents in determining the quantity and kinds of animal life which a body of water may support at different levels. Photosynthesis, however, is regulated by such factors as carbon dioxide, discussed above, and light.

LIGHT

Illumination as an ecological factor determines that most algae, particularly plankters, occupy what is termed the photosynthetic zone, the upper 2–5 meters of water. Turbidity, color, and amount of disturbance at the surface all help to determine the depth to which light favorable for photosynthesis will penetrate. Because of the great amount of light lost at the surface through reflection and because of further reductions by absorption and diffusion, photosynthetic plants are required to carry on their activities in the upper levels. This explains the (usually) greater quantity of dissolved oxygen in this stratum. The exhaustive studies of Birge and Juday (1911) describe the gas content and its fluctuations in 156 lakes. Their graphs clearly illustrate this relationship between oxygen and the photosynthetic zone. In their Figure 135 (p. 243), curves are shown for the oxygen content of Lake Mendota, Wisconsin, in July. At this time there was a heavy growth of phytoplankters (*Coelosphaerium* sp., *Aphanizomenon flos-aquae*) of more than 5000 organisms per liter. At the surface, the oxygen content was 6.6 ppm. From the surface flora the number of algae was irregularly reduced to about 1000 per liter at 20 meters, where the oxygen content was only 0.1 ppm. In May of the same year in which the above readings were made, the surface waters of Lake Mendota showed 28.5 ppm of calcium and 5.0 ppm of carbonates. This lake lies in the limestone region of the state and supports a eutrophic type of flora.

NITROGEN AND PHOSPHORUS

Special mention should be made of the significant roles of nitrogen in its various forms, and of phosphorus. The importance of these nutrients has been measured, although somewhat incompletely. That they are potential determiners of ultimate productivity is evidenced clearly by the many limnological studies which have related high nitrogen and phosphorus readings to luxuriant phytoplankton floras (Harvey, 1926; Wiebe, et al, 1929; Domogalla and Fred, 1926). The negative correlation of relatively high concentrations of these elements with periods of phytoplankton minima provides inferential evidence of their use by green plants. That is, when nitrates and phosphorus are low the phytoplankton population is high, the nutrients being consumed and stored in the organisms. When the phytoplankton decreases through an accelerated death rate and distintegration occurs, the elements are released and their percentages in the chemistry of the lake rises. Nitrogen enters directly into the phytoplankton cycle. Nitrogen content, in turn, is dependent upon several physical processes in and around the body of water (run-off from agricultural lands, for example). The nature of the bacterial flora, therefore, the chemistry of the drainage water, and the presence or absence of nitrogen-fixing bacteria and algae, are some of the more important factors determining nitrogen content. High oxygen content permits a rich plankton flora, but when nitrogen is low or absent, many kinds of algae are excluded from the flora. Some species of the Cyanophyta are especially rich in proteins and require, therefore, a highly nitrogenous medium. Thus a dense bloom of *Aphanizomenon flosaquae* or *Microcystis aeruginosa* would account for a great fluctuation in the free nitrogen and nitrate content of lake water at different periods of the year. Nitrogen fixation by some species of blue-green algae (see De, 1939; Fogg, 1942; Fritsch and De, 1938; Hutchinson, 1944) is also involved here. This specific relationship to nitrogen fixation is a reminder of the many reasons that limnological studies which involve analyses of the biota should include specific, not merely generic, determinations of the organisms concerned. Limnologists not infrequently list only algal genera in the published results of their studies, and this is not in keeping with the best scientific procedure.

Here it might be well to recall that although nitrogen content, carbon dioxide, phosphorus, and other elements are able to determine *abundance* of the algal flora, they also influence the variety, i.e., the kinds, of species present. As mentioned before, it does not follow that because water is a universal and standard medium selectivity is not being exercised rigorously. So clear-cut are some qualitative selections operating in algal ecology that the phycologist is able to use the presence of certain species or groups of species as indicators of physical-chemical conditions in a body of water. Without hydrogen ion determination equipment but just by observing the quantity and quality of the algal flora, especially the phytoplankters, the experienced worker can estimate the acidity or alkalinity (somewhat roughly to be sure) and the relative abundance of carbon dioxide; can predict whether there is a rich or poor supply of nitrates; and can tell something of other limnological features in a habitat.

Bottom Deposits

Another way in which modification of phytoplankton quantity and quality may come about is through the effects produced in bottom sediments when organic matter decomposes. The composition of the silt, or 'Gyttja', determines the quality of the bacterial flora, a group of organisms which is important in fixing the manner and speed with which nutrient elements are returned to solution. It is obvious, of course, that the kind and quantity of biota supported in the water above, as well as on, the floor influence the physical and chemical nature of the bottom sediments, which, in turn, acts in determining the number and, to a certain extent the kinds of bacteria in the sediments. Also, a lake bottom which supports dense populations of mollusks and midge larvae will be affected by the fauna.

In a lake where a luxuriant phytoplankton has become established, especially in a cyanophycean lake, a great accumulation of nitrogenous matter may result. As mentioned above, some of the blue-green algae are nitrogen fixers, and many of them are great accumulators of this element. Thus their physiology may result in an ever-increasing supply of organic nitrogen in a lake. With bacterial turnover, nitrogen appears first in one form and then another, and eventually alters the chemistry of the water above bottom sediments and so influences the biota.

Thus a closed cycle of interchanging and interacting phenomena is seen to be operating within a lake. The processes which make up the cycle are forever fluctuating. It is easy, therefore, to use the analogy so often made between organic metabolism and the flux, reflux, and pulsations within a body of water. The productivity of an aquatic habitat is achieved by its 'metabolism.'

[42]

QUALITY OF ALGAL FLORAS

The physical-chemical factors of the environment act not only in selecting the quality of a flora, but sometimes the very quality determines the quantity. A single example to illustrate this is the frequently encountered case of two lakes which support quite different qualities of phytoplankton, one predominantly chlorophycean, the other conspicuously cyanophycean. The factors which have acted selectively to determine the qualities of these floras are well known and include those mentioned above. The cyanophycean lake is high in nitrogen, there is a relatively large amount of phosphorus available, the water is alkaline, with a pH ranging from 7.2 to 9.5, and there is an abundance of free carbon dioxide or half-bound carbon dioxide. This is the eutrophic type of lake and because frequently it is relatively shallow the summer temperatures are high (25–30 C.). Thus, although the characteristics of the hard water lake are far from being detrimental to a chlorophycean flora, the combination of factors is such that an ultra-favorable habitat is provided for the blue-green algae and the diatoms. It is well known that the physiology of many species in these groups is such that they are able to carry on cell division and vegetative reproduction at an astoundingly high rate. In fact, certain species of blue-green algae are so much more successful in this respect than others even in the same group, that they completely take over at the expense of competing forms. Some pelagic *Anabaena* spp., *Aphanizomenon flos-aquae, Gloeotrichia echinulata, Coelosphaerium Naegelianum*, or *Microcystis aeruginosa*, for example, either singly or together, may constitute nearly 100 per cent of both the quantity and the variety of the phytoplankton because of their ability to reproduce rapidly. These organisms are often responsible for water blooms, the excessive growth being directly related to the quality of the flora.

In the chlorophycean lake, which frequently is the oligotrophic type, there is a minimum of nitrogen and phosphorus, the water is deeper than in the cyanophycean lake, there is proportionately less water in contact with the bottom, and the temperature is generally lower. Although the surface temperature may be the same in the two lakes at a given time in mid or late summer, the chlorophycean lake reaches its maximum temperature at a later date than the eutrophic or cyanophycean lake because of the greater amount of water in the hypolimnion and because of the greater time consumed in the spring-summer overturn. With little carbon dioxide available, there is no opportunity for a luxuriant growth of phytoplankters. The flora that does develop here may contain many blue-green and diatom species, but the greatest number of forms are chlorophycean. Even under ideal conditions, green algae and most diatoms seldom, if ever, form a bulky phytoplankton which can compare with the enormous and overwhelming blue-green algal blooms frequently encountered in hard water lakes, for their rate of reproduction is lower. Furthermore, green algae do not form sticky, floating mats of vegetation as do many of the cyanophycean species. Hence, the quantity of the algal vegetation is related to the kinds of plants that become established in a lake.

It is well known that some oligotrophic lakes are practically barren of a microflora, as well as being almost entirely devoid of higher aquatic plants. See Table 1, which shows a comparison of the nitrogen content and the quality of the plankton.

WATER BLOOMS

Serious economic problems and drastically unbalanced biological conditions frequently arise in sluggish streams and in lakes which are physico-chemically constituted to support a luxuriant water bloom. This is particularly true in southern Michigan and Wisconsin, as previously mentioned, where a body of water may become overgrown with cyanophycean species, many of which have the habit of floating high in the water. Their tremendous numbers cause floating crusts and scums to form, wherein plants die quickly and disintegrate in the intense sunlight. The living plants and the increased bacterial flora resulting from their decay after death deplete the oxygen below the point required for fish (2–3 ppm) and other animals. In my study of Iowa lakes I observed similar abundant blue-green floras. After a few hot days and nights in summer, when the oxygen was low in any case, a climax situation developed. The dissolved oxygen dropped to zero around midnight, with the result that within a few hours not a single living animal could be found in a lake with such a water bloom. Even bottom organisms, adapted to low oxygen supply, were killed, and there was a mass of dead *Chironomus* larvae and microcrustacea near the shore and in the shallows of bays. After such a climax, dead fish appeared within a few days, first floating at the surface and then collecting in heaps along the beaches. Thus enormous loss in game fish was sustained as a result of superabundant growth of blue-green algae.

I have some evidence that fish may be killed also by poisonous substances, such as hydroxylamine, produced from the decay of proteins with which blue-green algae are abundantly supplied. Fitch *et al.* (1934) have described the poisoning of domestic animals by toxic substances produced by certain species of these plants.

Excessive growths of phytoplankters may be costly in another way; they may interfere both chemically and physically with the operation of city water systems in which lakes, reservoirs, and filters are involved. Copper sulphate (Moore and Kellerman, 1905; Domogalla, 1941; Prescott, 1938), chlorine, sodium arsenite (Surber, 1929; Wiebe, 1930) and activated carbon are required to control algae or to eradicate objectionable tastes and odors produced by them. Sand filters are easily clogged by some species of algae such as *Melosira* spp. and *Aphanizomenon flos-aquae*, and must be cleaned frequently. Recreational sites are ruined and open bathing pools are rendered unusable when phytoplankters take advantage of optimal limnological conditions.

THE FOOD CHAIN

No single phase of the great cycle of events which occur within a water habitat is of greater importance to the main problem of productivity than the one which involves physiological activities carried on by the algal portion of the biota, especially the phytoplankton. This is particularly true because the phytoplankton is related to the food chain of aquatic animals, especially in lakes where larger aquatic vegetation is scarce. Chandler (1944) has pointed this out in connection with his studies of Lake Erie. No other group of organisms in a body of water, unless it be the bacteria, can produce such far-reaching effects by fluctuation in quality and quantity.

This leads to a consideration of the familiar position which phytoplankton and other forms of vegetation occupy in the food chain of animals. That algae deserve the often applied term, 'pasturage of the sea,' is seldom denied, and it is fairly well agreed that they hold a basic position in the food cycle of both fresh and salt water animals.

At the same time, many published studies, beginning with the work of Pütter published in 1909 (see also Petersen and Petersen, 1911), have raised a question concerning the degree to which aquatic animals are directly dependent upon phytoplankters. Hardly any of these papers which have pointed out aquatic animals' independence of phytoplankton made claims that *all* the microfauna subsists on nutrients of a non-particulate nature. Some students have shown, rather convincingly, that at least certain zooplankters are not directly supported by plants but are able, on the other hand, to take nourishment from colloidal matter, organic debris, and, to a minor degree, from substances in solution. In some such studies nannoplankters have been shown to be the source of food when larger phytoplankters have been excluded from the diet of experimental animals such as *Calanus* (Clarke and Gellis, 1935).

Furthermore, other researchers have indicated that the concentration of dissolved and colloidal matter used in the culturing of laboratory animals was greater than the normal concentration of these substances in nature which is supposedly not sufficient to maintain microfaunal populations. Thus the burden of direct support is thrown back on the phytoplankton.

It is noteworthy that although the idea that phytoplankters are important in the food chain is apparently sound and generally accepted, it is borne out by relatively few published scientific observations. It is evident that there is much to be learned in this connection, and the question certainly merits considerable attention both in the field and in the laboratory. This is especially true, since so many predictions and evaluations of productivity are based, in part, on the assumption that phytoplanktonic components in the biota *are* of basic importance in the food chain. A clear understanding of the exact nature of this problem must be reached before the quality and quantity of phytoplankton can be used as dependable indices of productivity.

There are many published studies bearing out the correlation between seasonal maxima in phytoplankton and peaks in microfaunal populations. The inference usually drawn from this correlation is that the increased phytoplankton makes possible a larger microfaunal foraging population, which in turn would support a more numerous macrofauna. But it is not known whether the microfauna achieves maxima after a peak in the phytoplanktonic population because it feeds directly on the plants, or because it is nourished by particulate matter resulting from the plants' disintegration.

Whatever the precise relationships are between the algae and the eventual productivity of fish and other animal life, it is well known that lakes with a luxuriant flora maintain a correspondingly dense population of animals. This relationship is illustrated many times over in lakes of the Michigan and Wisconsin area. Post Lake, Langlade County, Wisconsin, for example, and Ocqueoc Lake, Michigan, are highly productive and excellent for game fish, as many as eight species occurring in the former. These are medium hard water lakes and characteristically support a luxuriant vegetation of both algae and larger aquatic plants. *Chara* spp. abound, and the phytoplankton approaches the cyanophyte–diatom type. Near Post Lake is Elcho Lake, in which perch is the only game fish on record, and which has a poor phytoplanktonic flora and scarcely any larger vegetation, as compared with Post Lake.

In general, the lakes in the southern sections have the physical-chemical qualities which permit the production of a bulk of vegetation of all kinds greater than that of lakes in the central and northern regions. Hence the ultimate production of animal life is doubtless greater on the whole in the southern lakes, although there are few figures to support this. Crystal and Weber Lakes in Vilas County, and Clear Lake in Oneida County, Wisconsin, are notable examples of soft water lakes which are low in vegetation and are correspondingly poor producers of fish.

Experimental studies have been made, and others are still in progress, on the effect on ultimate faunal production of increasing the plankton by the addition of fertilizers. It has long been considered good practice in Europe to improve fish production in nursery ponds by this means, but few scientific evaluations have been made in this country. Wiebe, Radcliffe, and Ward (1929) report that in ponds to which fertilizers had been added, especially superphosphate, the microfauna and algae showed a great increase in numbers over control ponds. (See also Ball, 1949.)

Although the total quantity of plankton in a lake may be large, it is significant that the *kind* or *quality* of the plankters may be very important in regulating production of fish. There may be sufficient phytoplankton to support a rich microfauna on which fish feed. But if there is a paucity of intermediate feeders, such as minnows or other small predators, the food chain will thereby be interrupted,

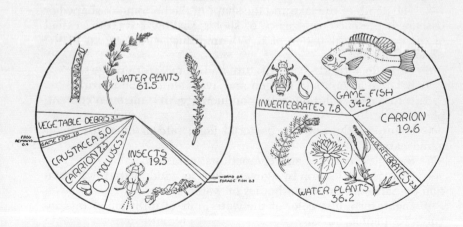

Figure 9. Diagrams illustrating the percentages of various types of food used by two species of turtles. Left: Percentages by volume of various foods consumed by western painted turtle (*Chrysemys picta marginata*). Right: Percentages by volume of various foods consumed by the snapping turtle (*Chelydra serpentina*). (Reproduced courtesy of Karl F. Lagler.)

[47]

for most of the larger fish cannot or do not feed directly upon the microfauna and flora. (See Fig. 3.)

In addition to serving as food for the microfauna, either directly or indirectly, phytoplankton makes up a large part of the food consumed by several species of fish such as the gizzard shad, young suckers, black bass fingerlings, and certain mollusks. Recently I examined the alimentary tracts of several dozen snapping turtles and found that in nearly every instance they were heavily packed with algae and other plant fragments, to the exclusion of almost all other types of food. *Spirogyra crassa*, *Cladophora* sp., and *Ceratophyllum demersum* L. were the principle plants eaten. Lagler (1940) has published on the food of the snapping turtle and points out that 36.2 per cent of the ingested material consisted of algae. He found that 70 per cent of all turtle specimens examined had consumed plant food. (See Fig. 9.) This is of interest because the snapping turtle had been considered almost entirely carnivorous. (See Lagler 1943.)

FACTORS THAT DETERMINE THE CHARACTER OF LAKE FLORAS

A SUMMARY

1. The geological history of the region and the nature of the soil over which the lake lies or which is drained by inlets.

2. The depth of the lake and the shape of the bottom—V-shaped or U-shaped; presence or absence of shoals, shallow bays, etc.; extent of the epilimnion, location of the thermocline; completeness of the seasonal overturn.

3. Latitude; altitude (temperature and temperature range).

4. Relative amounts of oxygen and available carbon dioxide.

5. Nutrients in solution; salts; conductivity; pH; nitrogen content; phosphorus.

6. Nature of the bottom; bacterial flora; rate of overturn of organic matter.

7. Biological enemies and competitors; parasites.

8. Chance distribution by agencies such as wind, waterfowl; isolation by barriers from other bodies of water.

9. Light; turbidity; color of the water; rate of diffusion of rays involved in photosynthesis.

Because of the interrelationships and the complete interdependence among some of the factors that determine the lake flora, it is obviously impossible to select any one as of paramount importance in a cause-effect analysis. Major interest here, however, is directed toward phytoplankters and other chlorophyll-bearing organisms. As is well known these, both directly and indirectly, contribute food to the microfauna, which in turn provides nourishment for the benthic, limnetic, and emergent faunas. ('Emergent' refers to the animal life which passes part of its life cycle in aquatic habitats, later emerging to join the land fauna.) In addition to their role in the food chain, chlorophyll-bearing organisms supply shelter and breeding places for many kinds of aquatic animals, and they also have important limnological bearings in that they alter the chemistry of the water, interfere with illumination, affect color, etc.

Some of the phytoplankton (members of the Cyanophyta) are able to fix nitrogen and so affect the supply of nitrates and the nitrogen cycle. Information on the nitrogen-fixing activities of the aquatic algae is meager, but evidence indicates that some forms play a more important role than is generally recognized in this connection.

The quantity of phytoplankton is determined, in part at least, by the abundance of available carbon dioxide contributed by the atmosphere, by half-bound carbon dioxide from bicarbonates, and from springs, etc. Carbon dioxide is, of course, continually being supplied also by respiration in all forms of life, including bacteria. At the same time all life draws upon dissolved oxygen, which diffuses from the atmosphere or is contributed as a result of photosynthesis.

Other elements necessary for plants, such as phosphorus and nitrogen, are supplied through drainage and by the continual overturn of organic matter by bacteria and other destructive organisms. Various edaphic, limnological, and geological factors which determine water chemistry, contour of the bottom, and the presence or absence of seasonal overturns of lake water. These, in turn, help to determine the nature of the bacterial flora, and hence the kinds and amounts of decomposition products and the completeness with which the organic matter is reconverted.

Lakes and streams may receive run-off water from agricultural lands and effluents of waste matter which are richly supplied with critical nutritive elements and compounds. These become incorporated in the food cycle.

To an unknown extent, substances produced by bacterial decomposition also furnish nutrients to the microfauna. Also unknown is the extent to which nitrates for the use of green plants are formed by nitrifying bacteria. Information is not at hand which will permit a definite statement concerning this portion of the nitrogen cycle, but there is ample justification for assuming that nitrification by bacteria occurs under favorable aquatic conditions as it does in terrestrial soils.

MORPHOLOGICAL TERMS
ILLUSTRATED

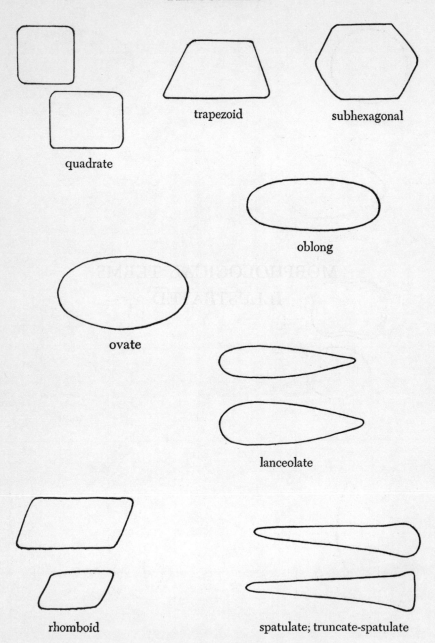

quadrate

trapezoid

subhexagonal

oblong

ovate

lanceolate

rhomboid

spatulate; truncate-spatulate

Regular Solid Forms

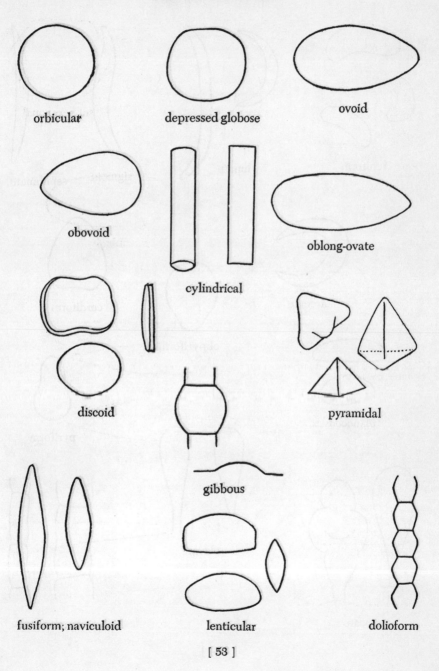

orbicular

depressed globose

ovoid

obovoid

cylindrical

oblong-ovate

discoid

pyramidal

gibbous

fusiform; naviculoid

lenticular

dolioform

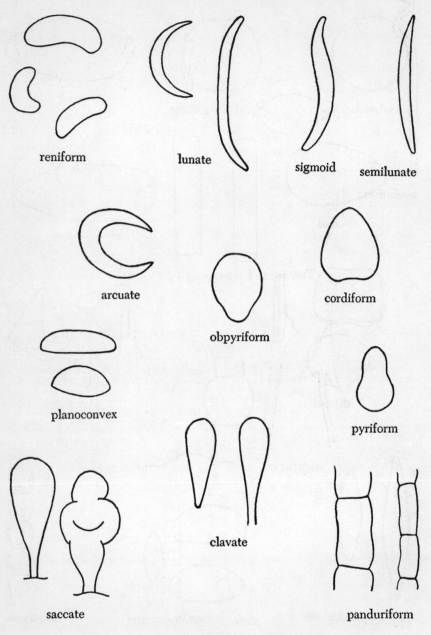

reniform

lunate

sigmoid

semilunate

arcuate

obpyriform

cordiform

planoconvex

pyriform

saccate

clavate

panduriform

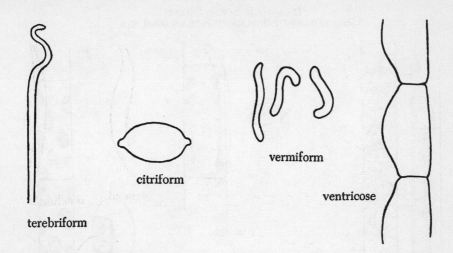

terebriform

citriform

vermiform

ventricose

TERMINAL FORMS AND STRUCTURES

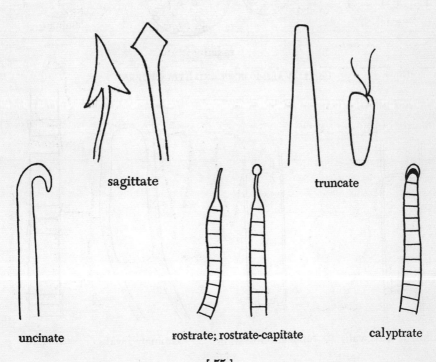

sagittate

truncate

uncinate

rostrate; rostrate-capitate

calyptrate

Chloroplast Forms and Arrangements

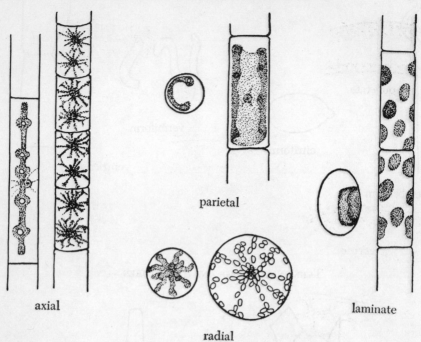

parietal

axial

radial

laminate

Cell Wall Forms and Structures

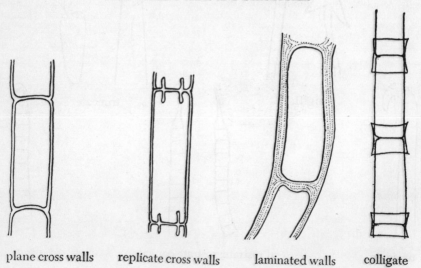

plane cross walls

replicate cross walls

laminated walls

colligate

SURFACE CHARACTERS

punctate

rugose

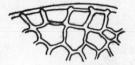

scrobiculate

verrucose

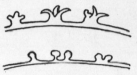

verrucae

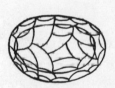

reticulate

areolate

plicate

costate

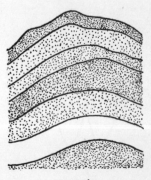

zonate

undulate

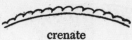

crenate

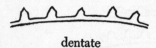

dentate

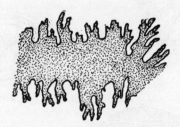

incised

laciniate

sinus

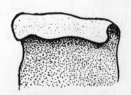

convolute

Sheaths

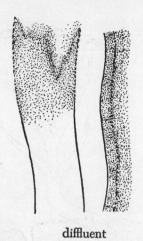 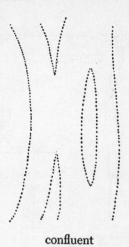

diffluent   confluent

Cellular Extensions

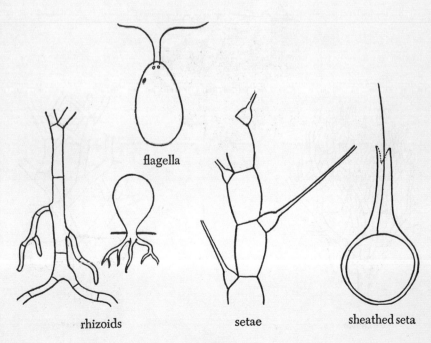

flagella

rhizoids   setae   sheathed seta

monaxial

multiaxial

penicillate

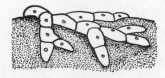

prostrate

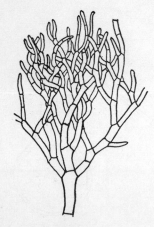

intricate

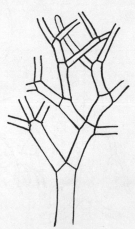

irregular

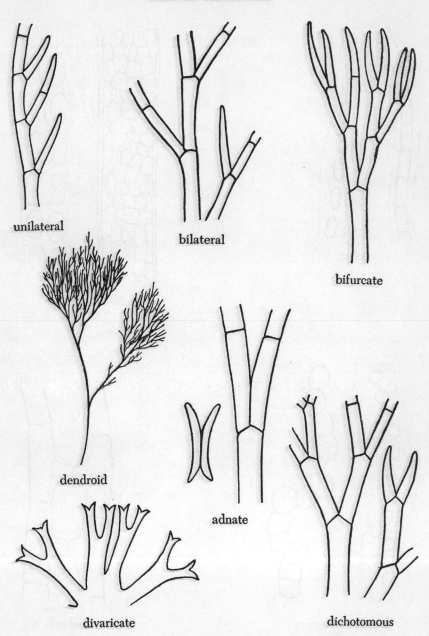

unilateral

bilateral

bifurcate

dendroid

adnate

divaricate

dichotomous

FILAMENTOUS COLONIES

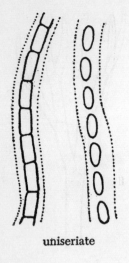

uniseriate

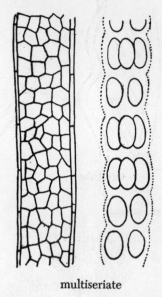

multiseriate

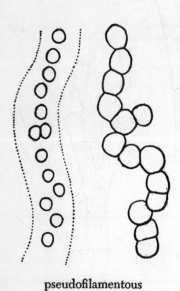

pseudofilamentous

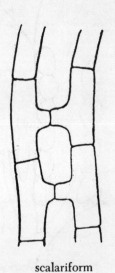

scalariform

circinate

filiform

flagelliform

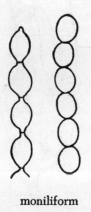

moniliform

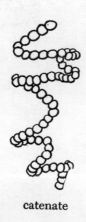

catenate

caespitose

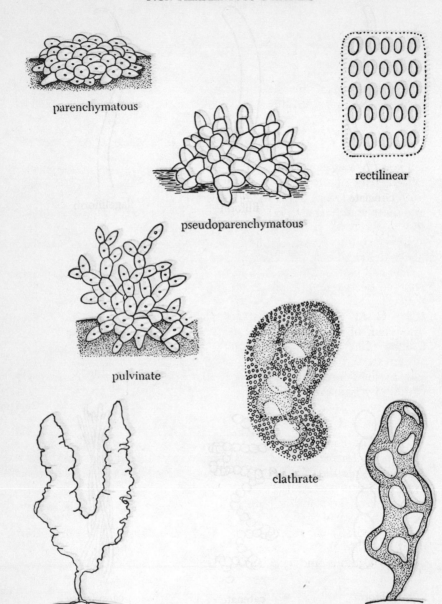

parenchymatous

pseudoparenchymatous

rectilinear

pulvinate

clathrate

foliose

lacunose

Systematic Account

Structural terms are illustrated in the preceding section and are defined, together with other technical terms, in the Glossary.

DIVISION CHLOROPHYTA

Plants belonging to this group are characterized by grass-green chloroplasts, one to many in each cell or protoplasmic unit. In most forms the chloroplast contains one or more pyrenoids, which accumulate starch as a food reserve. Even in plants which do not possess a pyrenoid, presence of starch makes possible the use of the iodine test for separating doubtful forms from those Chrysophyta which are similar in general appearance.

The cell wall, which is firm in most genera, is composed of cellulose and pectic compounds. There may be, also, a mucilaginous outer layer.

See G. M. Smith (1933, 1938) and F. E. Fritsch (1935) for a discussion of the reproduction and the taxonomy of this division; Collins (1909, 1918, 1918a) on the taxonomy; Blackman (1900), Blackman and Tansley (1902), and Fritsch (1916) on the phylogeny. The modern interpretation of this division recognizes two classes, Chlorophyceae and Charophyceae.

CLASS CHLOROPHYCEAE

This class, commonly known as the green algae, includes a great variety of forms: unicells (sometimes motile), simple or well-organized colonies, simple or branched filaments, partitioned coenocytes, and true coenocytes (filaments without cross walls). The chief evolutionary series in the Chlorophyceae begins with the motile unicells of the Volvocales.

The methods of reproduction, both asexual and sexual, vary greatly within the several orders. In some orders, the sexual reproductive methods and organs are unique and serve as a basis for classification. This is particularly true for the Zygnematales (Conjugales), the Oedogoniales, and the Siphonales.

See the authors mentioned above, as well as Oltmanns (1922), for an account of reproduction and life histories in the Chlorophyceae.

[65]

Key to the Orders

In the Keys, asterisks indicate orders, families, genera, or species that are likely to be found in the central Great Lakes region but have not been reported there to date.

1. Motile in the vegetative condition; flagella 2 or 4, rarely 8, equal in length; organism 1-celled or colonial ....VOLVOCALES
1. Not motile in the vegetative condition.. 2
2. Cells embedded in copious mucilage (which is either homogeneous or lamellated), united in colonies of indefinite shape (see *Apiocystis*, however), or in tubes forming gelatinous strands (pseudofilaments), or bullate masses (See mucilage-invested Chlorococcales also.); some forms unicellular or forming dendroid colonies which are epiphytic or epizoic; cells frequently possessing false flagella (pseudocilia), returning to a motile condition without resorting to reproductive cells ....TETRASPORALES
2. Plants not as above 3
3. Plants filamentous, composed of cells adjoined end to end in definite series, sometimes interrupted.. 4
3. Plants not composed of cells arranged to form filaments; unicellular or colonial or, if filamentous, occurring as coenocytes without cross walls.......15
4. Filaments unbranched; attached or free-floating................................ 5
4. Filaments with branches, the branches sometimes closely appressed, forming pseudoparenchymatous masses..13
5. Filaments composed of a single series of cells................................ 6
5. Filaments composed of more than 1 series of cells; cells adjoined; thallus a hollow tube or a ribbon-like or frond-like expansion 12
6. Chloroplasts 1 to several, large, in the form of spiral bands, stellate masses, or broad plates; pyrenoids conspicuous; reproduction by conjugation..ZYGNEMATALES
6. Chloroplasts parietal, plate-like, net-like, or small and ovate (in the latter case usually many in a cell); reproduction by iso- or heterogametes... 7
7. Cells with a single, parietal, plate-like or broadly discoid chloroplast; cells cylindrical; filaments uniseriate or multiseriate.................ULOTRICHALES
7. Cells with other types of chloroplasts................................ 8
8. Plants composed of long, cylindrical, coenocytic and thin-walled units, containing numerous disc-like chloroplasts arranged in narrow annular bands; cross partitions with knob-like thickenings; reproduction usually oogamous.. SPHAEROPLEALES
8. Plants not as above.. 9
9. Cells cylindrical, ovate or subspherical, each surrounded by lamellate mucilage; frequently losing their uniseriate arrangement and forming palmella stages; chloroplast massive, filling the cell, obscured by many starch grains; sexual reproduction oogamous.....................CYLINDROCAPSALES
9. Cells cylindrical, not surrounded by lamellate mucilage; chloroplast parietal...10
10. Cells with parietal, net-like or sheet-like chloroplasts, which usually cover both the end and lateral walls; wall composed of two sections which overlap in the midregion, forming H-shaped pieces upon fragmentation; pyrenoids lacking; sexual reproduction unknown.....................MICROSPORALES

10. Cells not showing H-shaped sections upon dissociation; pyrenoids present; sexual reproduction known_____11

11. Cells coenocytic, cylindrical, with thick walls; chloroplast a dense, parietal net with pyrenoids at the intersections of the meshwork, or with many ovoid parietal discs; walls without ring-like scars at the anterior end of the cells_____ CLADOPHORALES (in part)

11. Cells not coenocytic, cylindrical but usually perceptibly larger at the anterior end, which is ordinarily marked by one or more ring-like scars resulting from cell division; chloroplast a parietal net; reproduction oogamous, the female cells in the filament appearing swollen_____
_____OEDOGONIALES (in part)

12. Plant an expanded plate or tubular strand formed by several series of cells; chloroplast a parietal plate similar to that in the Ulotrichales....°ULVALES

12. Plant an expanded sheet, composed of several series of cells; chloroplast a stellate, axial body_____°SCHIZOGONIALES

13. Filaments composed of cylindrical or rectangular, uninucleate cells which have a single, plate-like and parietal chloroplast; branches terminating in setae, or with cell walls bearing hairs or bristles which usually are not distinctly bulbous at the base _____ CHAETOPHORALES

13. Filaments not as above_____14

14. Filaments composed of cylindrical, coenocytic cells which may become attenuated toward their apices; setae and bristles wanting_____
_____ CLADOPHORALES (in part)

14. Filaments composed of cells which are larger at the anterior end; bearing setae with much-enlarged, bulbous bases; reproduction oogamous, the female gametes produced in conspicuously swollen gametangia_____
_____ OEDOGONIALES (in part)

15. Plant composed of long, branched coenocytic strands without cross walls except where reproductive structures are cut off_____ SIPHONALES

15. Plant a single cell, or a colony of definite or indefinite form; cells various in shape, spherical, pyramidal, or polygonal, incapable of division in the vegetative state; reproduction by autospores, zoospores, or isogametes. (Compare with Tetrasporales, in which *Chlamydomonas*-like cells form colonies in mucilage that resemble some members of this order.)_____
_____ CHLOROCOCCALES

ORDER VOLVOCALES

In this order both vegetative and reproductive cells are motile. The prototype of the Chlorophyceae is to be found among the 1-celled members, from which colonial Volvocales, as well as other orders of green algae, are thought to have evolved. There may be 2, 4, or rarely 8 flagella. Usually there is a conspicuous pigment-spot. Although a few colorless forms are recognized, by far the majority of these organisms have a cup-shaped, parietal chloroplast (rarely stellate or axial) with one or more pyrenoids. Reproduction is by cell division, by zoospores (formed 2–8 in a cell), by isogametes, or by heterogametes, egg and antherozoids being formed in sexual reproduction among the more advanced colonial genera.

[67]

Key to the Families

1. Cells solitary, naked, i.e., inclosed only by a membrane; cell wall lacking..POLYBLEPHARIDACEAE
1. Cells possessing a definite wall and sometimes a mucilaginous sheath; solitary or united in colonies.. 2
2. Cells solitary 3
2. Cells united in colonies... 5
3. Wall bivalved, the cells compressed and the halves of the wall adjoined along their lateral margins..*PHACOTACEAE
3. Wall not bivalved; cells not flattened.. 4
4. Cells with protoplasts located at some distance within the cell wall and connected to it by radiating cytoplasmic strands ....HAEMATOCOCCACEAE (in part)
4. Cells without radiating cytoplasmic strands..............CHLAMYDOMONADACEAE
5. Cells with many radiating cytoplasmic processes connecting the protoplast with the cell wall..............................HAEMATOCOCCACEAE (in part)
5. Cells without such radiating protoplasmic processes.............................. 6
6. Cells united to form flat or globular colonies, evenly dispersed, although sometimes closely arranged within colonial mucilage..............VOLVOCACEAE
6. Cells compactly united in tiers of 4 with their anterior ends all directed the same way; gelatinous sheath lacking ......................SPONDYLOMORACEAE

FAMILY POLYBLEPHARIDACEAE

The chief characteristic of this family of unicellular individuals is the lack of a cellulose wall, the protoplast being inclosed by a membrane only. The cells have 2–4–8 anterior flagella of equal length, with contractile vacuoles sometimes present at their bases. A red pigment-spot is normally present. The chloroplast varies in form among the different members; usually it is a parietal cup containing a pyrenoid. Of the 7 genera reported from North America only 1 is known from this region at present.

PYRAMIMONAS Schmarda 1850, p. 9

Cells hemispherical or obpyriform, broadest at the anterior end, which is depressed and 4-lobed; 4 flagella attached in the apical depression, with 2 contractile vacuoles below their point of attachment. Chloroplast a parietal cup with a pyrenoid in the posterior portion.

Pyramimonas tetrarhynchus Schmarda 1850, p. 9
Pl. 1, Figs. 1, 2

Cells pyriform with the anterior end conspicuously 4-lobed; flagella attached close together in the apical depression. Chloroplast a parietal cup with 4 lobes. Cell 12–18μ in diameter, 20–28μ long. Wis.

FAMILY CHLAMYDOMONADACEAE

The unicellular organisms which compose this family have a smooth cellulose membrane in 1 piece. There are 2 or 4 flagella, equal in length, and 2–4 contractile vacuoles at the anterior end of the cell. In most forms the chloroplast is cup-shaped and contains 1 to several pyrenoids (posterior or scattered) and a red pigment-spot laterally placed, usually anterior.

Members of this family should be compared with those of the Phacotaceae in which the cell wall is in 2 valve-like pieces that adjoin along the lateral margins; and with the Haematococcaceae, in which there are radiating protoplasmic processes extending from the cytoplasm to the cell wall.

There are 10 genera of this family reported from the United States, but only 2 of these have appeared in our collections.

Key to the Genera

Cells with 4 flagella _____ *Carteria*
Cells with 2 flagella _____ *Chlamydomonas*

CHLAMYDOMONAS Ehrenberg 1835, p. 288

Cells ovoid, ellipsoid, or spherical, sometimes with 1 or 2 apical papillae, from which the 2 flagella arise; often with a narrow or wide mucilaginous sheath. Chloroplast a dense, padded body occupying the entire cell, or a thin parietal cup (in a few species H-shaped or stellate); pyrenoids 1 to many, basal or bilateral and scattered; pigment-spot lateral and anterior, rarely median; 2–4 apical contractile vacuoles usually discernible.

Species of this genus have the habit of coming to rest, losing their flagella, and entering upon a quiescent phase. Vegetative cell division continues, ordinarily accompanied by the secretion of mucilage, so that amorphous gelatinous masses are formed which contain many nonmotile cells. This is known as the palmella stage. Unicellular or colonial algae in which the cells are ovate or globose and which have cup-shaped chloroplasts (e.g., *Gloeocystis*) should be compared, in making identifications, with this palmelloid expression of *Chlamydomonas*.

Key to the Species

1. Cells inhabiting the empty loricas of *Dinobryon* _____ *C. Dinobryonii*
1. Cells not inhabiting the loricas of *Dinobryon* _____ 2
2. Cells with axial pyrenoids, basal or median _____ 3
2. Cells with 1 or more pyrenoids, lateral or scattered _____ 7
3. Cells without an apical papilla _____ *C. globosa*
3. Cells with 1 or more apical papillae _____ 4

4. Cells epiphytic, on the mucilage of *Microcystis* .... *C. epiphytica*
4. Cells not epiphytic on colonies of *Microcystis* 5
5. Cells globose, with 2 contractile vacuoles in
  the anterior end .... *C. pseudopertyi*
5. Cells ellipsoid or ovate 6
6. Papilla sharply pointed .... *C. Snowii*
6. Papilla broad and truncate; cell often truncate
  and angular at the anterior end .... *C. angulosa*
7. Cells with 2 apical papillae .... *C. sphagnicola*
7. Cells without papillae, or with only 1 8
8. Cells ellipsoid, with 1 pyrenoid .... *C. mucicola*
8. Cells ovate or cylindrical, with many pyrenoids 9
9. Cells ovoid, without a papilla; pyrenoids
  many (12–16), lateral .... *C. polypyrenoideum*
9. Cells cylindrical to subcylindrical, with a papilla;
  pyrenoids few .... *C. Cienkowskii*

Chlamydomonas angulosa Dill 1895, p. 337
Pl. 1, Fig. 3

Cells broadly ovoid to cylindric, often truncated anteriorly and with a prominent papilla. Contractile vacuoles 2, below the flagella, which are as long as or slightly longer than the cell body. Chloroplast a massive, parietal cup with a large angular pyrenoid in the base; pigment-spot anterior and lateral. Cells 11–13–(15)μ in diameter, 15–18–20μ long.

Tychoplankter. Wis.

Chlamydomonas Cienkowskii Schmidle 1903a, p. 349
Pl. 1, Fig. 4

Cells cylindric to subcylindric with a prominent apical papilla, below which are 2 contractile vacuoles. Flagella shorter than the cell in length. Chloroplast a thin, parietal, cylindrical cup with several. pyrenoids. Pigment-spot anterior and lateral. Cells 10–11μ in diameter, 20–25μ long.

Our specimens are shorter than usual for this species, but the shape of the cell, the form of the chloroplast, and the number of pyrenoids are in agreement.

Tychoplankter. Wis.

Chlamydomonas Dinobryonii G. M. Smith 1920, p. 91
Pl. 1, Fig. 5

Cells ovoid to pyriform, without an anterior papilla, inhabiting the empty loricas of *Dinobryon;* flagella 6–8μ long. Chloroplast disc-shaped to hemispherical, lying either at the base of the cell or along the lateral wall; pigment-spot lacking (?). Cells 2–3μ in diameter, 3–5μ long.

Rare to common in several lakes. Wis.

Chlamydomonas epiphytica G. M. Smith 1920, p. 91
Pl. 1, Figs. 6, 7

Cells spherical to nearly pyriform, anteriorly narrowed into a papilla-like beak. Cells becoming non-motile, adherent to the colonial mucilage of *Microcystis* without losing flagella. Chloroplast a thin parietal cup; pigment-spot lacking. Cells 7–8μ in diameter, 8–9μ long.

Common in several lakes. Wis.

Chlamydomonas globosa Snow 1903, p. 389
Pl. 1, Figs. 8, 9

Cells broadly ovoid to globose, inclosed in a hyaline, gelatinous sheath; anterior papilla absent. Chloroplast a dense parietal cup with a basal pyrenoid; 1 contractile vacuole in the anterior end of cell; pigment-spot lens-shaped, supramedian in position and lateral. Cells 5–7μ in diameter, 10–19μ long.

Tychoplankter; common. Mich., Wis.

Chlamydomonas mucicola Schmidle 1897a, p. 17
Pl. 46, Fig. 20

Cells narrowly elliptic or narrowly ovoid, attenuated to a blunt point anteriorly, broadly rounded posteriorly. Flagella 1½ times the body in length. Chloroplast a lateral plate with a single large pyrenoid; pigment spot and 4 contractile vacuoles in the anterior end. Cells 3–4μ in diameter, 6–10μ long.

Tychoplankter. Mich.

Chlamydomonas polypyrenoideum Prescott 1944, p. 348
Pl. 1, Figs. 10, 11

Cells ovoid to ellipsoid, without an apical papilla; gelatinous sheath lacking (?). Chloroplast a dense parietal cup with a deep median invagination; pyrenoids many (12–16), scattered; pigment-spot not observed. Cells 8–10μ in diameter, 9–12μ long.

Rare in euplankton. Wis.

[71]

Chlamydomonas pseudopertyi Pascher 1927, p. 214
Pl. 1, Fig. 12

Cells globose, with a prominent, hemispherical papilla. Chloroplast cup-shaped, dense in the basal portion; 2 anterior contractile vacuoles; pyrenoid posterior; pigment-spot lens-shaped, anterior and lateral. Cells 12–18–(27)μ in diameter.

Tychoplankter; rare. Wis.

Chlamydomonas Snowii Printz 1914, p. 18
Pl. 1, Figs. 13, 14

Cells narrowly ovoid to ellipsoid, with an anterior beak. Chloroplast a parietal cup, dense in the posterior portion; 1 pyrenoid, centrally located, palmella stages frequent. Cells 6.5–8μ in diameter, 10–15μ long.

Tychoplankter; rare. Mich., Wis.

Chlamydomonas sphagnicola Fritsch & Takeda 1916, p. 373
Pl. 1, Figs. 15, 16

Cells broadly ovoid to subglobose, broadly rounded both anteriorly and posteriorly, with 2 prominent papillae at the anterior end; the protoplast separated from the wall, also having pointed apical papillae. Chloroplast a parietal sheet, granular, covering most of the cell membrane (in our specimens more dense toward the basal part); pyrenoids several (4–6), scattered; pigment-spot prominent, anterior, nearly median. Cells 15–18μ in diameter, 21–29μ long.

This species commonly forms resting stages during which 2–4 cells are formed within the old mother cell.

Common in *Sphagnum* bogs; tychoplanktonic in lakes. Wis.

CARTERIA Diesing 1866, p. 356

Cells oval or round in cross section, elliptic, oval, or cordiform in front view, with a definite cell wall; furnished with 4 long flagella. Chloroplast parietal, cup-shaped, with or without a pyrenoid; pigment-spot usually present, at the anterior end of cell.

Species in this genus should be compared carefully with *Chlamydomonas* spp. *Carteria* in the past has been placed in a separate family (Carteriaceae), mostly on the basis of the number of flagella. Only 2 species have appeared in our collections.

Key to the Species

Cells cordiform, broadest at the anterior end,
   which is concave..*C. cordiformis*
Cells ellipsoid or ellipsoid-cylindric, narrower, and
   papillate at the anterior end................................*C. Klebsii*

Carteria cordiformis (Carter) Diesing 1866, p. 356

Pl. 1, Fig. 20

Cells cordiform, broadest at the anterior end, which is deeply depressed, the 4 flagella arising within the depression; somewhat smaller but broadly rounded posteriorly. Chloroplast a thin parietal cup, with 1 basal pyrenoid. Cells 16μ in diameter, 12–20μ long.

Rare in tychoplankton. Mich., Wis.

Carteria Klebsii (Dang.) Dill 1895, p. 353

Pl. 1, Figs. 17–19

Cells ellipsoid or ellipsoid-cylindric, narrower at the anterior end, which is sharply rounded with a papilla around which the flagella arise. Chloroplast a massive parietal cup, with 1 basal pyrenoid; pigment-spot lacking. Cells 5–10μ in diameter, 8–16μ long.

Rare in tychoplankton. Wis.

FAMILY PHACOTACEAE

The flattened, unicellular biflagellates of this family, with their two-valved walls, especially *Phacotus lenticularis* (Ehrenb.) Stein, and *Pteromonas angulosa* (Carter) Lemm., are to be expected in the central Great Lakes region, but no member of the family has appeared in our collections.

FAMILY VOLVOCACEAE

Members of this family are colonial. The cells are characteristically biflagellate and *Chlamydomonas*-like and are so arranged as to form globose or obovoid hollow colonies or flat plates. There may be as few as 4, or as many as 25,000, cells in a colony. Cell sheaths may be distinct or confluent with the colonial mucilage.

In most genera the cells of the colony are alike in size and function, but in the more advanced forms there is a certain amount of specialization. In *Pleodorina*, for example, a few of the cells are distinctly smaller than others and have no reproductive function. In *Volvox* some cells enlarge and become female gametes, whereas others undergo division to form plates of numerous, small antherozoids. Both kinds of gametes may be produced in the same colony (monoecious) or in separate colonies (dioecious) according to species. See Smith (1933, 1938, 1944), Fritsch (1935), and Pascher (1927) for the morphology, reproduction, and taxonomy of this family.

Key to the Genera

1. Colony spherical or ovoid.. 2
1. Colony a flat or twisted plate with cells in 1 layer.......................... 5
2. Colony spherical, ovoid, or obovoid, containing 256 or fewer cells.......... 3
2. Colony a hollow sphere, containing from 500 to several
   thousand cells.. *Volvox*
3. Colony containing from (32)–64 to 256 cells, which are of 2
   sizes ....*Pleodorina*
3. Colony containing less than 64 cells, all similar in size.................... 4
4. Colony ovoid or obovoid, composed of spherical or ellipsoid cells
   arranged at some distance from one another and often
   appearing in transverse tiers .... *Eudorina*
4. Colony ovate, composed of pyriform cells compactly arranged ...... *Pandorina*
5. Colony a flat, rectangular plate of from 4 to 32 cells .... *Gonium*
5. Colony horseshoe-shaped, slightly twisted on its
   axis, composed of 16 or 32 cells .... *Platydorina*

GONIUM Mueller 1773; *emend.* Prescott *in*
Prescott, Silva, & Wade 1949, p. 84

A free-swimming, plate-like, quadrangular colony of 4–32 ovate, ovoid, pyriform, or bilobed cells so arranged within a gelatinous envelope that a rectangle of 4–8 central cells is inclosed by a peripheral series of 12–24 individuals; the long axis of the central cells at right angles to the plane of the colony, but axis of peripheral cells radial to the center of the colony. Cells interconnected by fine protoplasmic processes; individual envelopes adjoined by stout processes with those of neighboring cells, so that oval or quadrangular interstices are formed in the colonial mucilage. Flagella 2, attached in the narrow anterior end just above 2 contractile vacuoles. Chloroplast a parietal cup with 1 or 2 pyrenoids; pigment-spot usually large and conspicuous, lying laterally in the anterior end. Sexual reproduction by the division of the vegetative cells into 4–16–(32?) isogametes which fuse in pairs, the quadriflagellate zygote becoming a thick-walled resting spore.

Key to the Species

1. Colony 4-celled, with anterior ends of cells all directed outward..... *G. sociale*
1. Colony 16–32-celled (rarely 4-celled); the outer cells with flagella directed
   in the transverse plane of the colony, the inner cells with flagella directed
   at right angles to the transverse plane.. 2
2. Cells ellipsoid or subspherical.. *G. pectorale*
2. Cells ovoid-pyriform, narrowed anteriorly.................................. *G. formosum*

Gonium formosum Pascher 1927, p. 418

Colony of 16 ovoid-pyriform cells inclosed in relatively wide individual sheaths which are joined to neighboring sheaths by narrow and relatively long arm-like extensions so that each of the inner 4 cells is connected with 6 other cells, leaving a large circular open space in the center of the plate. Chloroplast a parietal cup, thickened at the base, which incloses a pyrenoid; pigment-spot anterior and lateral. Cells about 10μ in diameter, $1–1\frac{1}{2}$ times as long as wide. Mich.

Gonium pectorale Mueller 1773, p. 60
Pl. 1, Fig. 21

Colony of (4)–8–16 ellipsoid, subspherical or sometimes ovoid cells closely arranged in a flat, quadrangular plate, usually with 4 inner cells bordered by a series of 12 marginal ones which have their anterior ends projected outward and parallel with the plane of the colony, the inner cells directed at right angles to the plane. Cells inclosed by individual sheaths, which are connected to neighboring sheaths by very short processes. Cells $5–15\mu$ in diameter.

Associated with other Volvocales in hard water rich in nitrogen. Mich., Wis.

Gonium sociale (Duj.) Warming 1876, p. 82
Pl. 1, Fig. 22

Colony of 4 ovoid cells, all directed outward, inclosed by colonial mucilage which has a central rectangular perforation. Cells $10–15\mu$ in diameter, $12–20\mu$ long.

This species, like G. pectorale, is often found in barnyard pools, watering troughs, and sloughs where nitrogen content is high.

Eu- and tychoplanktonic; in hard water lakes. Mich., Wis.

PANDORINA Bory 1824, p. 600

Colony ovate or obovoid, composed of 8–16–(32) globose or pyriform cells compactly arranged and inclosed by a common gelatinous envelope; cells with the broad anterior end directed outward. Chlorplast a parietal cup with 1 basal pyrenoid; pigment-spot anterior and lateral. Flagella 2, arising from the anterior end of the cell and diverging widely after emerging from the colonial envelope; the colony swimming in a rolling or tumbling fashion; vegetative reproduction by the simultaneous division of each cell in the colony to form as many colonies; sexual reproduction by isogametes formed in groups of 8 or 16 by the partition of some or all of the cells of the colony.

Pandorina morum (Muell.) Bory 1824, p. 600
Pl. 1, Fig. 23

Colony usually distinctly ovate, as much as 220μ in diameter. Cells pyriform, crowded, usually 16 in number, $10–15\mu$ in diameter, $12–17\mu$ long.

Common in the plankton of both hard and soft water lakes but more frequent among dense growths of algae in shallows, especially in water rich in nitrogenous matter. Mich., Wis.

EUDORINA Ehrenberg 1832b, p. 78

A free-swimming ovate, obovoid, or globose colony, in which 16–32–64 ovoid or ovate cells are inclosed within a gelatinous envelope. Cells sometimes arranged in transverse series, sometimes evenly disposed throughout the colonial mucilage; 2 long flagella present, which diverge widely beyond the periphery of the colonial envelope; cells often with 1 or 2 anterior beaks or papillae where the flagella arise; 2 minute contractile vacuoles at the base of the flagella. Chloroplast cup-shaped and parietal, with 1 to several pyrenoids. Red pigment-spot laterally placed at the anterior end of the cell. Cytoplasmic strands connecting the cells sometimes in evidence. Anisogamous sexual reproduction by small antherozoids and biflagellate female gametes similar in size to vegetative cells.

Eudorina elegans Ehrenberg 1832b, p. 78
Pl. 1, Figs. 24–26

Colony spherical or ovate with 16–32 ovoid cells evenly disposed within a gelatinous envelope, or arranged in transverse series, the cells usually lying near the periphery of the envelope but sometimes crowded toward the interior. Cells 10–20μ in diameter; colonies up to 200μ in diameter.

This species shows a great deal of variation in the size and shape of the colony. In liquid-preserved material the envelope shows the form of *E. unicocca* G. M. Smith, with posterior mammillate projections.

Common in euplankton of hard water lakes. Mich., Wis.

PLEODORINA Shaw 1894, p. 279

A free-swimming globose colony of 32–128 (rarely 256) spherical or ovoid cells arranged at the periphery of a gelatinous colonial investment. Cells differentiated and of 2 sizes, the purely vegetative (toward the posterior pole) being about half the size of the reproductive (anterior) cells. Chloroplast a parietal cup, with 1 or more basal pyrenoids. Pigment-spot lateral and anterior. Flagella, 2, attached at the anterior end of cell, just above 2 contractile vacuoles; the colony swimming in a rolling or tumbling fashion. Sexual reproduction anisogamous.

Key to the Species

Colony with 64–128 cells about half of which
are smaller and vegetative_____ *P. californica*
Colony with 32–64 cells, only 4 of which are
smaller and vegetative _____ *P. illinoisensis*

Pleodorina californica Shaw 1894, p. 282
Pl. 2, Fig. 1

Colony spherical, containing as many as 128 globose cells, about half of them vegetative and half reproductive in function, the latter distinctly larger than the former. Flagella subparallel within the mucilage, diverging widely outward. Vegetative cells 6–14μ in diameter; reproductive cells up to 34μ in diameter.

Rare in the plankton of several lakes; occasionally abundant in water rich in organic matter. Mich., Wis.

Pleodorina illinoisensis Kofoid 1898, p. 274
[*Eudorina illinoisensis* (Kofoid) Pascher]
Pl. 2, Fig. 3

Colony globose, containing 32–64 cells, 4 of which are small and vegetative, and located toward the posterior pole of the colony. Vegetative cells 8–10μ in diameter; reproductive cells 14–20μ in diameter.

Rare; found in a fish hatchery pond. Wis.

VOLVOX Linnaeus 1758, p. 820

Colony free-swimming, spherical or ovate, composed of from 500 to several thousand cells arranged at the periphery of a gelatinous sphere of homogeneous mucilage, in which, however, the individual cell sheaths may be distinct; the cells all directed outward and each having 2 flagella of equal length. In some species, the cells are interconnected by protoplasmic strands or 'canals'. Chloroplast a parietal incomplete cup covering most of the cell wall. Daughter colonies form within the interior of the sphere by repeated division of special gonidial cells which have withdrawn from peripheral layer. Sexual reproduction oogamous; female gametes large spherical cells within the sphere; male gametes spindle-shaped, formed in several to many rectangular plates or bundles in the interior of the colony, the antherozoids with their longitudinal axes at right angles to the surface plane of the plate. Zygote thick-walled, smooth, or bearing external decorations such as spines and warts.

[77]

Key to the Species

Volvox aureus Ehrenberg 1838, p. 71
Pl. 2, Fig. 4

Dioecious (rarely monoecious), spherical colonies of (500)–1300–3200 ellipsoidal cells, 4–6μ in diameter, with interconnections of fine protoplasmic strands; individual cell sheaths wanting. Strands of mucilage radiate from the center of the colony. Cells contain a circular, parietal plate-like chloroplast, with 2 contractile vacuoles at the anterior end, below the point of flagella attachment, and a pigment-spot, anterior and lateral. In mature coenobia, 2 or more daughter colonies are present. As many as 21 (usually about 9) eggs are formed in female colonies; half of the cells in male coenobia develop antherozoid bundles, 15–18μ in diameter, with as many as 32 antherozoids in each bundle. Zygote 38–62μ in diameter, with a smooth wall.

Common in the plankton of many lakes; sometimes abundant in shallow, backwater habitats; also found in inlets to lakes where water is slow-flowing or pooled. Mich., Wis.

Volvox globator Linnaeus 1758, p. 820
Pl. 2, Fig. 5

Large, monoecious, spherical or ovate, gelatinous colonies containing as many as 17,000 ovoid or pyriform cells. Cells 2.5–3.5μ in diameter, with conspicuous protoplasmic interconnections; with 1 parietal plate-like chloroplast and a pigment-spot in each cell, and with 2–6 small contractile vacuoles in the anterior region below the point of flagella attachment. Individual sheaths of the cells conspicuous and not confluent with the colonial mucilage, clearly visible in surface view of the colony, the sheaths 5–8-sided from mutual compression. Coenobium commonly containing 4–7 (or as many as 17) daughter colonies; sexual colony with 11–17, or up to 40, eggs, each inclosed by a wide gelatinous sheath; 3–7 rectangular plates of fusiform antherozoids in bundles of 64–256, 22–32μ in diameter. Zygotes 45–54μ in diameter, with thick walls exteriorly decorated with wart-like, blunt spines and verrucae.

Although not uncommon in the plankton of lakes, this species is most frequently found in the shallow water of bogs, ponds, and ditches especially where the nitrogen content is high; also in hard water habitats. Mich., Wis.

Volvox tertius A. Meyer 1896, p. 188
[*Volvox mononae* G. M. Smith]
Pl. 3, Fig. 12

Dioecious, relatively small colonies, 280–550μ wide, 302–590μ long, spherical to ellipsoidal, containing 500–2000 ovoid or ellipsoid cells without interconnecting protoplasmic strands, but with individual sheaths which sometimes are scarcely evident. Cells 5–8μ in diameter. Chloroplast parietal, cup- or bell-shaped; pigment-spot anterior and lateral; 2 (sometimes more) contractile vacuoles below the point of flagella attachment. Mature coenobium contains 3–10–(12) daughter colonies. Eggs, 3–8 large globose cells inclosed by a gelatinous sheath; antherozoid bundles 20–60 in number, consisting of 16–32 (sometimes as many as 64) fusiform antherozoids; zygotes 58–66μ in diameter, with a thick, smooth wall.

This species is reported from Lake Monona, Wisconsin (Smith, 1920). In Iowa (Prescott, 1931a) it was found in one of the semi-hard water lakes, forming a dense bloom, which endured for two or three days in late summer when the water temperature was high (28°C.).
Mich., Wis.

FAMILY SPONDYLOMORACEAE

In this family the cells are compactly arranged in small colonies of 8 or 16 individuals with their long axes parallel and all directed forward. There is no colonial mucilage. The chloroplast is a dense, parietal cup without a pyrenoid except in the genus *Pascheriella* Korshikov (not represented in our flora).

There are 2 or 4 flagella, 2 contractile vacuoles in the anterior region, and a pigment-spot, either anterior or posterior. See Fritsch (1934) and Smith (1933) for a discussion of reproduction in this family; also Korshikov (1923, 1924, 1928).

SPONDYLOMORUM Ehrenberg 1849, p. 236

Colony ovoid, of 8 or 16 pyriform cells compactly arranged in tiers without an evident gelatinous investment; the cells with their broad apices all directed anteriorly, and having 4 long flagella which arise from a conical protuberance, at the base of which are 2 contractile vacuoles. Chloroplast cup-shaped, without a pyrenoid; pigment-spot lateral and posterior.

Spondylomorum quaternarium Ehrenberg 1849, p. 236
Pl. 3, Figs. 1, 2

Cells narrowed and somewhat produced posteriorly to form bluntly rounded points, 5–15μ in diameter. Colony 36–75μ in diameter.

Reported by Stickney from a laboratory aquarium in Madison; to be expected in the plankton of lakes rich in nitrogenous substances. Wis.

FAMILY HAEMATOCOCCACEAE

In this family the cells are peculiar in that the protoplast lies some distance within the cell wall, to which it is connected by fine protoplasmic strands. Between the wall and the protoplast there is a wide layer of mucilage. There is a massive chloroplast, which in *Sphaerella* is usually masked by an abundance of haematochrome, a red pigment which develops when the cell is dormant. There are 2 flagella, several contractile vacuoles, and a lateral pigment-spot.

Key to the Genera

Cells solitary...*Haematococcus*
Cells in colonies, forming a circumferential band in a
    spheroidal gelatinous investment...*Stephanosphaera*

Haematococcus C. A. Agardh 1828, Icon. Algar., Pl. 22.

Cells ovoid to ellipsoid, having 2 widely diverging flagella from an anterior papilla; protoplast separated from the wall by a wide envelope of mucilage through which cytoplasmic strands radiate; pigment-spot lateral. Cells frequently appearing in a stationary (akinete) condition in which haematochrome pigment becomes predominant (assumed to be an adjustment to intense illumination, especially when the water is shallow). At least 1 species of the genus has been reported from red snow of alpine and subalpine regions.

Haematococcus lacustris (Girod.) Rostafinski, 1875, p. 139
Sphaerella lacustris (Girod.) Wittr.
Pl. 2, Fig. 2; Pl. 3, Figs. 3–5

Cells ellipsoid or ovoid; chloroplast apparently cup-shaped, sometimes appearing axial and usually masked by haematochrome; cells variable in diameter, 10–50μ in the encysted condition.

This species is usually found in small pools, crevices in rocks holding rain water, and in concrete basins of various kinds. A familiar habitat is the bird-bath in gardens. Because intermittent drying of the habitat keeps this plant in a dormant condition most of the time, it usually appears as a brick-red, slimy or granular encrustment on the substrate.

Mich., Wis.

STEPHANOSPHAERA Cohn 1852, p. 77

A colony of 4–8 ovoid cells with branched (both lateral and polar) protoplasmic extensions, arranged in a median circumferential band within an oblate-spheroid colonial mucilage. Cells free from, and some distance from, one another, not connected by protoplasmic extensions. Flagella 2; pigment-spot lateral, near the anterior end of cell; chloroplast parietal and usually dense, with 2 or more pyrenoids.

Stephanosphaera pluvialis Cohn 1852, p. 77

Pl. 46, Fig. 26

Characteristics as described for the genus. Cells $7–12.5\mu$ in diameter; colony up to 60μ in diameter. Reproduction by isogametes. Zygote up to 28μ in diameter.

Michigan.

ORDER TETRASPORALES[1]

Plants belonging to this order are essentially volvocaceous, but they are nonmotile in the vegetative condition. Some forms are free-floating, but many are sedentary. The volvocaceous characters are pseudocilia (non-functioning flagella), the pigment-spot, and the type of chloroplast. All of the features may not be exhibited by all members. Most forms are colonial, with the cells embedded in copious mucilage, but there are unicellular genera. It is easy to confuse some of the small free-floating colonies with certain plants belonging to the Chlorococcales. Differentiation must be made by considering a combination of characteristics and the type of reproduction used. The Tetrasporales are able to reproduce freely by cell division in the vegetative state, but the Chlorococcales are all incapable of this method of reproduction. In general, the chloroplast in the Tetrasporales (*Asterococcus* excepted), is a parietal cup (see *Elakatothrix,* however), with a single pyrenoid. In the Chlorococcales it is nearly always a parietal plate or sheet, not a *Chlamydomonas*-like cup.

[1]Some authors, Fritsch (1935), Pascher (1927), for example, treat the Tetrasporales as a suborder of the Volvocales.

Key to the Families

1. Cells solitary or in false dendroid colonies, attached by stalks or fine thread-like stipes to larger algae and microfauna........................CHLORANGIACEAE
1. Cells not as above; free-floating or adherent.. 2
2. Cells ellipsoidal or fusiform...COCCOMYXACEAE
2. Cells spherical.. 3
3. Cells bearing pseudocilia (frequently discerned only with difficulty); usually united in definitely shaped gelatinous colonies, macroscopic or microscopic; individual cell sheaths rarely present and if present may be scarcely visible...TETRASPORACEAE
3. Cells not bearing pseudocilia; solitary or united in amorphous gelatinous masses; individual cell sheaths usually clearly visible....PALMELLACEAE

FAMILY PALMELLACEAE

These plants have spherical or ovate cells united in amorphous or sometimes definitely shaped colonies. Individual cell sheaths (if present) are clearly evident and are usually lamellate. Although some colonies are spherical and free-floating, others are tubular or bullate and adherent, or entangled among other algae. In one genus (*Asterococcus*) the chloroplast is stellate, but in general it is parietal and cup-shaped. In 2 genera the sheaths are much lamellated and are deposited as mucilaginous secretions about the cell more on one side than on others so that the cell comes to lie excentrically in the investment. Sometimes this may result in the formation of branched, gelatinous strands.

Key to the Genera

1. Cells solitary.. 2
1. Cells arranged to form colonies or families which may be definite or indefinite in shape.. 3
2. Cells with a stellate chloroplast or with radiating strands from a common center..*Asterococcus* (in part)
2. Cells with a cup-shaped, parietal chloroplast...............*Gloeocystis* (in part)
       (see also *Urococcus*)
3. Cells grouped to form amorphous colonies.. 4
3. Cells grouped to form colonies of definite shape, spherical clusters, or tubular arrangements.. 5
4. Colonies of macroscopic size, amorphous masses, adherent; cells single or in pairs within a copious mucilage; cell sheaths confluent............*Palmella*
4. Colonies of microscopic size; cell sheaths definite, usually lamellate..*Gloeocystis* (in part)
5. Colonies spherical.. 6
5. Colonies elongate and tubular, forming false filaments................*Palmodictyon*
6. Chloroplasts stellate...*Asterococcus* (in part)
6. Chloroplasts parietal.. 7
7. Sheaths of cells definite, often lamellated; colonial mucilage lamellate..*Gloeocystis* (in part)
7. Cells without sheaths, colonial mucilage homogeneous................*Sphaerocystis*

[82]

PALMELLA Lyngbye 1819, p. 203

A shapeless, gelatinous mass, containing many spherical cells without any order of arrangement; individual cell sheaths usually distinct at first, becoming confluent with the colonial mucilage. Chloroplast cup-shaped or bell-shaped, with 1 pyrenoid. Plants aquatic or terrestrial.

Palmella mucosa Kuetzing 1843, p. 172

Pl. 3, Figs. 8, 9

Plant mass densely green, forming gelatinous expansions on the substrate; individual cell sheaths evident at first but becoming indistinct; chloroplast parietal, covering nearly the entire wall; cells 6–14μ in diameter.

On submerged logs, aquatic plants, and other substrates; frequently on wet rocks, on sides of aquaria, or on cement basins. Wis.

SPHAEROCYSTIS Chodat 1897, p. 119

A free-floating spherical colony of from 4 to 32 spherical cells, evenly spaced near the periphery of a non-lamellate gelatinous envelope, sometimes with a sheath about each group of 4 cells within the colony. Chloroplast cup-shaped and covering most of the wall, containing 1 pyrenoid.

Sphaerocystis Schroeteri Chodat 1897, p. 119

Pl. 3, Figs. 6, 7

Colony often including both undivided and recently divided cells which form small spherical clusters within the colonial envelope. Cells 6–20μ in diameter; colonies up to 500μ in diameter.

This plant should be compared with Planktosphaeria gelatinosa.

Widely distributed and common in a variety of lakes, both hard and soft water. Mich., Wis.

GLOEOCYSTIS Naegeli 1849, p. 65

Cells spherical, sometimes solitary, but usually grouped in colonies of 4, 8, or many individuals inclosed by a colorless gelatinous envelope, which may be globose or somewhat amorphous, lamellate or (rarely) homogeneous. Chloroplast parietal, cup-shaped, but often covering the entire wall, obscured by numerous starch grains or oil bodies; 1 pyrenoid. This genus should be compared with Sphaerocystis and Planktosphaeria.

Key to the Species

Gloeocystis ampla (Kuetz.) Lagerheim 1883, p. 63

Pl. 3, Fig. 17

Cells ovoid or oblong, arranged in amorphous or somewhat globular colonies and embedded in copious unlamellated gelatinous envelopes, the sheaths of each cell or group of cells not confluent but distinct and angular from mutual compression. Cells $9-11\mu$ in diameter, $10-14\mu$ long; colonies up to 150μ in diameter.

Common in the tychoplankton of many soft water lakes and acid swamps. Mich., Wis.

Gloeocystis gigas (Kuetz.) Lagerheim 1883, p. 63

Pl. 3, Fig. 16

One-celled or a colony of 8 spherical or slightly oblong individuals inclosed by a copious, gelatinous, lamellate envelope. Contents of the cell frequently brownish-green because of oil. Cells $9-12\mu$ in diameter. Forming gelatinous masses on submerged aquatics or entangled among other algae.

Common in the tychoplankton of many lakes and swamps. Mich., Wis.

Gloeocystis major Gerneck *ex* Lemmermann 1915, p. 35

Pl. 52, Figs. 9, 10

Cells ovoid, in colonies of 4–8, inclosed by a wide, lamellate sheath in which groups of individuals are surrounded by concentric layers; Chloroplast massive, completely covering the wall; cells $17-19\mu$ in diameter, $21-23\mu$ long.

Tychoplankter; in hard water lakes. Wis.

Gloeocystis planctonica (West & West) Lemmermann 1915, p. 34
Pl. 3, Figs. 10, 11

Cells spherical or ovoid, united in free-floating gelatinous colonies which are angular or pyramidal. Sheaths of each cell or group of cells distinct and lamellate. Cells 4–13μ in diameter; colonies up to 125μ wide.

Common in the littoral plankton of shallow lakes and ponds; intermingled with other algae. Mich., Wis.

Gloeocystis vesiculosa Naegeli 1849, p. 66
Pl. 3, Fig. 15

Cells spherical, arranged in large amorphous masses (usually attached), inclosed by copious lamellate mucilage. Cells 4.5–12μ in diameter.

Commonly intermingled with other algae in bogs and shallow lakes; on submerged aquatics. Mich., Wis.

PALMODICTYON Kuetzing 1845, p. 155

Thallus an anastomosing or irregularly branched gelatinous strand, inclosing families of globose cells with individual mucilaginous sheaths. Frequently several generations of cells are within a common investment. Chloroplast a parietal plate covering most of the cell wall, with 1 pyrenoid.

Key to the Species

Cells without evident individual sheaths... *P. varium*
Cells with distinct individual sheaths... *P. viride*

Palmodictyon varium (Naeg.) Lemmermann 1915, p. 37
Pl. 4, Figs. 3, 4

Thallus a simple or branched gelatinous strand, often many such tubular strands radiating from a common center, containing spherical cells without evident sheaths in linear series or irregularly crowded. Cells 4–8μ in diameter; thallus 20–50μ wide.

Entangled among dense growths of algae on submerged aquatics in soft water lakes. Mich., Wis.

Palmodictyon viride Kuetzing 1845, p. 155
Pl. 4, Figs. 5, 6

Thallus a branching and anastomosing gelatinous strand or cylinder in which families of globose cells are arranged in groups of 2–4 within a mucilaginous sheath. Cells arranged in 1 or 2 linear series,

[85]

with distinct, sometimes lamellate sheaths. Cells 5–10μ in diameter; thallus 15–17μ wide.

Not common in shallow water of acid lakes; among other algae in tychoplankton. Mich., Wis.

ASTEROCOCCUS Scherffel 1908, p. 762

Cells globose or subglobose, either solitary or in colonies of from 4 to 16, in colorless homogeneous envelopes of mucilage. Chloroplast a stellate mass with radiate arms from a central core, which contains a pyrenoid.

The shape of the chloroplast assists in differentiating this genus from similarly shaped and arranged species of *Gloeocystis*.

Key to the Species

1. Cell walls spiny_____ *A. spinosus*
1. Cell walls smooth_____ 2
2. Cells solitary or in colonies of 4, 36–43μ in diameter_____ *A. superbus*
2. Cells in colonies of 8 or 16, 10–25μ in diameter _____ *A. limneticus*

Asterococcus limneticus G. M. Smith 1918, p. 627
Pl. 4, Fig. 11

Cells spherical, arranged at some distance from one another in free-floating colonies of 4–16 within a colorless homogeneous investing mucilage. Chloroplast stellate with 4–16 lobes radiating from a central core, the lobes becoming flattened against the cell wall. Cells 10–25–(35)μ in diameter; colonies 50–125μ in diameter.

Common, usually in soft water. Mich., Wis.

Asterococcus spinosus Prescott *in* Prescott,
Silva, & Wade 1949, pp. 85, 93
Pl. 46, Figs. 17, 18

Cells spherical, solitary, or 2 within a gelatinous sheath, the cell wall thin and evenly beset with long, slender sharp spines. Chloroplast with numerous (more than in other species) narrow, radiating strands. Cells 12–16μ in diameter.

In shallow water of an acid lake. Mich.

Asterococcus superbus (Cienk.) Scherffel 1908, p. 762
Pl. 4, Fig. 10

Cells spherical, solitary, or in families of 4–8 inclosed by a lamellate gelatinous envelope. Chloroplast a stellate mass with several ridges or rays flattened against the cell wall. Cells 36–43μ in diameter; 8-celled colony 93μ in diameter.

Euplankter; tychoplankter among dense growths of miscellaneous algae in shallow, soft water lakes and ponds. Mich., Wis.

In this family colonies of spherical cells bearing long, fine hair-like pseudocilia are embedded in copious mucilage. The pseudocilia are extensions from the protoplast; because they are extremely fine, favorable optical conditions or special staining may be required in order to distinguish them. The cell contents are as described for the order, the chloroplast being a parietal cup or plate covering most of the cell wall.

The cells usually remain in groups of 4 after division of the parent cell and in most forms are disposed at the periphery of the colonial mucilage. The colony may be amorphous or somewhat definite in shape.

Key to the Genera

1. Plant mass mucilaginous, amorphous or intestiniform, macroscopic............ 2
1. Plant mass of definite shape, microscopic... 3
2. Plant an amorphous, usually floating, mass of mucilage in which
   fragments of old cell walls remain.. *Schizochlamys*
2. Plant an elongate, tubular, or intestiniform, gelatinous thallus,
   with cells arranged at the periphery of the mucilage;
   fragments of old cell walls lacking .... *Tetraspora* (in part)
3. An attached pyriform gelatinous thallus............................... *Apiocystis*
3. A free-floating, globular thallus of few cells,
   embedded in homogeneous gelatin.......................... *Tetraspora* (in part)

TETRASPORA Link 1809, p. 9

Thallus a gelatinous sac, or a tubular or membranous mass, containing spherical cells arranged in 2's and 4's. Chloroplast parietal, bell-shaped, covering almost the entire wall, with 1 pyrenoid. Cells often showing long, extremely fine pseudocilia which extend far beyond the limits of the colonial mucilage; thallus attached, at least when young, forming bulbous or vermiform masses, later becoming free-floating green skeins or sheets; rarely globular and euplanktonic.

Some species of *Tetraspora* occur in early spring and are among the first plants to develop in ditches and streams of cold water after the melting of ice. They may continue on in favorable habitats throughout early summer. *Draparnaldia* spp. are commonly found associated with *Tetraspora*.

Key to the Species

1. Thallus cylindrical at all ages, attached; narrowed and
   constricted below to form a short stipe........................ *T. cylindrica*
1. Thallus not cylindrical at all ages, becoming bullate or expanded........... 2
2. Cells with individual, thick gelatinous sheaths..................... *T. lamellosa*
2. Cells without individual sheaths, or with sheaths thin and diffluent........... 3
3. Thallus an attached gelatinous sac, becoming bullate and lobed.... *T. gelatinosa*
3. Thallus not an attached, bullate, or lobed sac 4

4. Thallus euplanktonic (or incidentally tychoplanktonic) spherical or
   elongate, composed of relatively few cells evenly distributed or
   arranged in groups of 4 within the colonial mucilage_____*T. lacustris*
4. Thallus not planktonic, although frequently becoming free-floating
   in age; at first tubular and sac-like, later expanded and laciniate,
   forming skeins_____*T. lubrica*

Tetraspora cylindrica (Wahl.) C. A. Agardh 1824, p. 188
Pl. 5, Figs. 1, 2

Thallus an attached, irregularly lobed cylinder of firm mucilage
which may be 1 meter long, narrowed at the point of anchorage.
Cells scattered, showing arrangement in 4's only when young,
14–17μ in diameter.

Forming long, green, intestiniform strands in streams of cold
water. Mich., Wis.

Tetraspora gelatinosa (Vauch.) Desvaux 1818, p. 18
Pl. 5, Figs. 3, 4

Thallus at first an attached cylindrical sac, later becoming bullate
and lobed but not perforate. Cells irregularly arranged in old plants
and differing in size, 2.5–13μ in diameter.

The globular and bullate form of the thallus, even when old, is
the chief differentiating character of this species. It is impossible to
separate this species clearly from young plants of *T. lubrica*.

In the quiet backwaters of lakes, among rushes. Mich., Wis.

Tetraspora lacustris Lemmermann 1898d, p. 152
Pl. 5, Fig. 11

Thallus a free-floating, spherical, or elongate and irregularly
shaped, microscopic gelatinous colony containing relatively few
spherical cells, the long pseudocilia usually clearly evident. Cells
arranged in groups of 2 or 4; 7–10μ in diameter.

This species is microscopic and apparently free-floating at all
stages. It should be compared with *Sphaerocystis Schroeteri*, from
which it may be differentiated by applying some simple stain to
determine the presence of pseudocilia. See Smith (1933, p. 352).

Common in the plankton of several lakes and inlets. Wis.

Tetraspora lamellosa Prescott 1944, p. 348
Pl. 5, Fig. 6

Thallus irregularly lobed and saccate, free-floating. Cells spherical,
in 2's, with thick walls and gelatinous, lamellate sheaths which are

distinct and not confluent with the colonial mucilage. Pseudocilia very fine and 20–30 times the diameter of the cell in length. Chloroplast a dense parietal plate covering almost the entire wall. Cells 9–10.5μ in diameter.

This species differs from others by the possession of distinct lamellate cell sheaths and the extraordinarily long pseudocilia.

Euplanktonic. Wis.

Tetraspora lubrica (Roth) C. A. Agardh 1824, p. 188
Pl. 5, Fig. 9

Thallus at first tubular or sac-like and attached, later becoming laciniate, irregularly expanded and floating, or forming streaming gelatinous strands or skeins when in flowing water. Cells in 4's or, when old, irregularly scattered through the rather firm mucilage; 7–10μ in diameter.

In ditches, in cold springs, and flowing water; and in the marginal flora of lakes. Mich., Wis.

APIOCYSTIS Naegeli *in* Kuetzing 1849, p. 208

Thallus a pyriform or irregularly bulbous, gelatinous vesicle, attached by a narrowed base to submerged aquatic plants and filamentous algae. Cells spherical, 64 to hundreds, evenly scattered or sometimes in pairs or in circular zonations within the colonial mucilage. Cells bearing a pair of very long pseudocilia. Chloroplast parietal, covering most of the wall; with 1 pyrenoid.

Underdeveloped stages of this plant can scarcely be differentiated from young or small colonies of *Tetraspora*.

Apiocystis Brauniana Naegeli 1849, p. 67
Pl. 5, Figs. 7, 8, 10

Thallus an attached, pear-shaped, gelatinous vesicle in which the cells are arranged at the periphery in 2's or 4's. Pseudocilia clearly evident. Cells 6–8μ in diameter.

Considerable variation in the shape of the vesicle occurs, young colonie being almost round, with a very short stipe, whereas old thalli are oboviform or pyriform.

This plant is attached to filamentous algae and submerged aquatics such as *Utricularia*. It is common in acid water habitats where temperatures are fairly high and where there is a great deal of organic material. Mich., Wis.

[89]

SCHIZOCHLAMYS Braun *in* Kuetzing 1849, p. 891

Thallus an amorphous gelatinous mass, either soft or firm, containing numerous spherical cells irregularly arranged; fragments of cell walls of previous generations lying about clusters of 2–4 cells. Chloroplast usually a single parietal cup, sometimes occurring as 2 parietal plates; in some plants more massive and completely filling the cell; with 1 pyrenoid. Pseudocilia sometimes discernible. Cells divide by a splitting of the mother cell wall into 2 or 4 fragments (sometimes old cell walls appearing as single pieces only), which persist within the colonial mucilage.

Key to the Species

Gelatinous investment firm; colony of definite shape;
old mother cell wall fragments 1 or 2 .... *S. compacta*
Gelatinous investment soft and amorphous;
wall fragments of old mother cell 2 or 4 .... *S. gelatinosa*

Schizochlamys compacta Prescott 1944, p. 348
Pl. 4, Figs. 12–14

Thallus microscopic, the mucilage firm and homogeneous and bounded by a definite tegument. Cells globose, with a conspicuous gelatinous cap-like concretion at one side. After division, 1 fragment (rarely 2) of the mother cell wall remains, the mucilage cap persisting on the old wall; daughter cells with apposed caps of mucilage. Cells 7.4–11 μ in diameter.

This plant should be compared with S. *delicatula* West, which forms but a single fragment of the mother cell wall upon division to liberate daughter cells. S. *compacta* differs in the definiteness of the shape of the colonial mucilage, in the larger size of the cells, and in the mucilage cap on the cell wall, the presence of which seems to be a constant character.

Rare; in a small pool within a *Sphagnum* bog. Wis.

Schizochlamys gelatinosa A. Braun *in* Kuetzing 1849, p. 891
Pl. 4, Fig. 15

Plant mass extensive, often macroscopic and free-floating; mucilage soft and amorphous. Cells spherical, 10–15μ in diameter, dividing by a splitting of the cell wall into 2 or 4 portions, these persisting and partially inclosing the daughter cells in pairs or in 4's. Cells have 1 or 2 chloroplasts; pseudocilia often evident.

Generally distributed in several types of lakes, but usually in shallow warm water. Mich., Wis.

Plants in this family are globose, ellipsoid, or oblong, attached by a stipe to other algae or to microfauna. They may be solitary or colonial, arranged in such a way as to form false filaments (i.e., series) that may be simple or arbuscular. The cells are attached, the anterior end downward, by a stalk-like extension of the sheath, in which the protoplasts are inclosed. There is 1 cup-shaped chloroplast or 2 elongate parietal bodies, sometimes with a pyrenoid. Usually there is an anterior pigment-spot.

Key to the Genera

Cells globose or ovoid; epiphytic in the mucilage
of colonial blue-green algae .... *Stylosphaeridium*
Cells elongate-ellipsoid or oblong-fusiform;
epizoic on microfauna .... *Chlorangium*

CHLORANGIUM Stein 1878, Pl. 19, Figs. 1–7

Cells ellipsoid or spindle-shaped, solitary or in arbuscular series, attached, anterior end downward, by mucilaginous (simple or branched) stalks. Chloroplasts 2 laminate parietal plates; without pyrenoids (?). Cells with 2 contractile vacuoles and a red pigment-spot at the anterior end. Reproduction by longitudinal cell division to form 2 or 4 daughter cells, which escape by the bursting of the mother cell membrane that elongates and forms branching stalks which result in arbuscular colonies. Biflagellate swarmers produced by resumption of motility of vegetative cells. Gametes have been reported.

Chlorangium stentorinum (Ehrenb.) Stein 1878, Pl. 19, Figs. 1–7
Pl. 46, Figs. 1, 2

Characteristics as described for the genus. Cells 12–14μ in diameter, 23–43 μ long.

Widely distributed in the region, on microfauna in several types of lakes. This species is not so common as *Colacium* spp. which also attach themselves to Cladocera and copepods. Mich., Wis.

STYLOSPHAERIDIUM Geitler & Gimesi *in* Geitler 1925, p. 608

Cells globose or ovoid, solitary, attached by a slender stipe in the mucilage of *Coelosphaerium* and *Anabaena*, and probably to other Cyanophyta. Chloroplast solitary, massive, covering the posterior (outer) portion of the cell wall, and containing a single pyrenoid.

This genus should be compared with *Peroniella*, a member of the

Chrysophyta which lacks a pyrenoid and has a parietal, plate-like chloroplast along the lateral walls. There are species in that genus which are similar in shape and habit to *Stylosphaeridium*, but they are usually much larger.

Stylosphaeridium stipitatum (Bachm.) Geitler & Gimesi
in Geitler 1925, p. 608
Pl. 4, Figs. 7–9

Characteristics as described for the genus. Cells 5–8μ in diameter, 8–10μ long; stipe 20μ long.

This species apparently is not widely distributed in lakes of our region, but in the habitats where it does occur it is common. The plants are gregarious, and the host colony is usually thickly beset with the epiphytes. Mich., Wis.

FAMILY COCCOMYXACEAE

Plants in this family are ovate, ellipsoidal, cylindrical or fusiform cells, either solitary or forming colonies inclosed by a copious mucilaginous investment. There is a single parietal chloroplast which may have a pyrenoid.

The genera of the Coccomyxaceae are not altogether typical of the Tetrasporales but are precluded from possible classification with the Chlorococcales by the fact that the cells can undergo cell division in the vegetative state.

Key to the Genera[2]

Cells fusiform or elongate-cylindric, arranged in a copious
  mucilage to form spindle-shaped colonies _____*Elakatothrix*
Cells ovate or oblong, arranged in a flat plate
  within a rectangular gelatinous sheath _____*Dispora*

DISPORA Printz 1914, p. 32

Cells ovate to oblong, sometimes nearly spherical; pairs or quartets of cells irregularly arranged within a wide gelatinous sheath, forming a flat, rectangular plate, the colony increasing in size by cell division in 2 directions in the same plane; chloroplast a parietal cup, without a pyrenoid (?).

Dispora has been placed by Printz in another family, the Pleurococcaceae, together with *Coccomyxa*, *Pseudotetraspora*, and *Elakatothrix*. Fritsch (1935) suggests that a suitable place for *Dispora* would be with the Palmellaceae.

---

[2]Since this key was written, *Coccomyxa dispar* Schmidle has been collected in a Michigan lake. This consists of ellipsoidal cells embedded in amorphous mucilage.

Dispora crucigenioides Printz 1914, p. 32

Pl. 46, Figs. 5, 6

Characteristics as described for the genus; cells broadly ovate to nearly spheroidal, 3–5μ in diameter, 4–6μ long; colonies 20–30μ in width.

Tychoplankter; in soft water, northern lakes. Mich.

ELAKATOTHRIX Wille 1898, p. 302

Gelatinous, fusiform or irregularly shaped colonies containing fusiform or ovate cells. Free-floating at least when mature. Cells with either 1 or both poles acutely pointed. Chloroplast a parietal plate containing 1 or 2 pyrenoids and covering almost all the wall along one side. Division transverse, the daughter cells lying in pairs with their longitudinal axes parallel with the axis of the colony.

Key to the Species

Cells small, narrow, spindle-shaped, 3–6μ in diameter,
  1 pole pointed, the other rounded_____*E. gelatinosa*
Cells broadly fusiform, larger, up to 15μ in diameter,
  tapering to a point at both poles_____*E. viridis*

Elakatothrix gelatinosa Wille 1898, p. 302

Pl. 3, Figs. 13, 14

A free-floating colony of 4–16 fusiform cells with longitudinal axes parallel, arranged end to end in pairs, broad at the adjoined poles, tapering to a blunt point at the opposite pole. Cells 3–6μ in diameter, 15–25μ long; colony 10–30μ in diameter, up to 160μ long.

Rare to common in various types of lakes; mostly euplanktonic. Mich., Wis.

Elakatothrix viridis (Snow) Printz 1914, p. 31

Pl. 4, Figs. 1, 2

A broadly ellipsoid colony, attached at first but later becoming free-floating. Cells ovate or fusiform and arranged in pairs; dividing transversely, but daughter cells with longitudinal axes at oblique angles to one another. Cells 6–15μ in diameter, 35μ long.

Rare. Mich., Wis.

ORDER ULOTRICHALES

As interpreted here, this order includes unbranched, simple filaments of mostly uniseriate cells, multiseriate in one suborder. With few exceptions, the cells are cylindrical and contain a single, band-like chloroplast which shows significant similarity to that possessed by the Volvocales and most Tetrasporales. Usually 1 or more pyrenoids are present. In some forms there is a basal-distal differentiation, with an attaching holdfast cell. Most species which are attached when young, however, become free-floating. Isogametes and zoospores are produced in unspecialized vegetative cells. There are two suborders.

Suborder Ulotrichineae

FAMILY ULOTRICHACEAE

Nearly all the members of this family have cylindrical, uniseriately arranged cells, either adjoined or separated from one another. In a few forms there is a gelatinous sheath. The chloroplast is a parietal plate or band which varies in the degree to which it encircles the cell wall. In a few species a special holdfast cell develops at the base of the filament, the only cell incapable of further division. Reproduction is by vegetative proliferation, by palmella stages, by zoospores, and by isogametes.

Key to the Genera

1. Filaments tapering at one end, and ending in a stout blunt point ..... *Uronema*
1. Filaments not tapering, the same diameter throughout 2
2. Filaments inclosed by a gelatinous sheath 3
2. Filaments not inclosed by a gelatinous sheath 7
3. Cells cylindrical, adjoined at the end walls to form continuous filaments 4
3. Cells oblong or spheroidal, sometimes not forming continuous threads 5
4. Chloroplast a parietal band, nearly encircling the cell .... *Ulothrix* (in part)
4. Chloroplast a parietal fold or plate, not encircling the cell,
    covering only a small portion of the wall .... *Geminella* (in part)
5. Cells spheroidal, adjoined in some species with the wall composed of
    2 helmet-shaped halves which adjoin
    in the midregion .... *Radiofilum*
5. Cells of different shapes from those above; wall
    not composed of two halves 6
6. Cells cylindrical, frequently in linear pairs, forming filaments
    of indefinite length .... *Geminella* (in part)
6. Cells transversely elliptic, in discontinuous series, often in groups of 4,
    each group inclosed by a sheath; filaments short .... *Hormidiopsis*
7. Filaments with cells in pairs, the protoplasts at some
    distance from the wall, the intervening space filled with
    lamellate gelatinous deposits .... *Binuclearia*
7. Filaments with cells not in pairs and without gelatinous
    deposits about the protoplasts 8
8. Filaments of indefinite length, composed of many cells,
    sometimes with basal differentiation 9

8. Filaments of definite length, short and frequently interrupted;
   basal differentiation lacking .... *Stichococcus* (in part)
9. Filaments often showing basal differentiation; chloroplast a complete
   or nearly complete parietal band .... *Ulothrix* (in part)
9. Filaments without basal differentiation; chloroplast a folded plate
   along one side of the cell and not nearly encircling it 10
10. Chloroplast as long as the cell or nearly so
    (See *Ulothrix cylindricum*, however) .... *Stichococcus* (in part)
10. Chloroplast half the length of the cell .... *Hormidium*

ULOTHRIX Kuetzing 1833, p. 517

Simple, unbranched filaments of cylindrical cells, often showing
basal differentiation and arising from a special holdfast cell; becoming free-floating in some species. Chloroplast a parietal band which
extends ⅔ to ¾ of the way around the cell (forming a complete ring
in 1 species), and sometimes extending the entire length of the cell.
Asexual reproduction by 4–8 quadriflagellate zoospores cut out from
the protoplast of unspecialized cells; sexual reproduction by isogametes formed 8–16–64 in a cell, smaller than the zoospores and
biflagellate. Palmella stages not uncommon.

This genus is distinguished from others in the family principally
by the approximate completeness with which the chloroplast covers
the wall, and also by the attached habit of growth, which involves a
basal holdfast cell in some species.

Key to the Species

1. Filaments (20)–25–45–(60)μ in diameter; wall thick;
   chloroplast a complete parietal band .... *U. zonata*
1. Filaments 20μ or less in diameter; wall thin 2
2. Filaments 11–20μ in diameter 3
2. Filaments smaller, 5–11μ in diameter 5
3. Filaments composed of long, cylindrical cells, 11–12.5μ in
   diameter, the length 2¼–3 times the width .... *U. cylindricum*
3. Filaments composed of shorter cells, 13–20μ in diameter 4
4. Cells up to 20μ in diameter, shorter than wide .... *U. tenuissima*
4. Cells 13–16μ in diameter, 1–2 times longer than wide .... *U. aequalis*
5. Cells 4–5μ in diameter; chloroplast extending nearly the entire
   length of the cell .... *U. subtilissima*
5. Cells wider; chloroplast extending ⅔ or less the length of the cell 6
6. Cells 5–6μ in diameter, short-cylindric; chloroplast covering
   ½ or less of the cell wall .... *U. variabilis*
6. Cells larger, 6–9μ in diameter 7
7. Filaments constricted at the cross walls, 5.7–9μ in diameter;
   cells 2–4 times diam. long .... *U. subconstricta*
7. Filaments not or slightly constricted at the cross walls; cells
   rectangular, 7.5–10μ in diameter, the length 2/3 to 1 1/3
   the width .... *U. tenerrima*

Ulothrix aequalis Kuetzing 1845, p. 197

Pl. 6, Fig. 1

Filaments very long, composed of cylindrical cells and without constrictions at the cross walls. Chloroplasts a parietal plate extending $\frac{4}{5}$ of the distance around the wall. Cells 13–15.5μ in diameter, 18–30μ long.

Common; forming pure, bright green masses in shallow water of several lakes and swamps; scattered among other algae. Mich., Wis.

Ulothrix cylindricum Prescott 1944, p. 349

Pl. 6, Fig. 2

Filaments long, curved, and lightly entangled. Cells elongate-cylindric, 11–12.5μ in diameter, 2$\frac{1}{4}$ to 3 times longer than wide; the wall thin and not constricted at the joints. Chloroplast a broad band, nearly equal to the cell in length and folded around $\frac{3}{4}$ of the circumference; pyrenoids 2–5.

This species should be compared with *Ulothrix aequalis* Kuetzing, which has thick walls, shorter cells, fewer pyrenoids, and a different form of chloroplast.

Tychoplankter. Wis.

Ulothrix subconstricta G. S. West 1915, p. 82

Pl. 6, Fig. 11

Filaments planktonic, composed of slightly inflated cells, which are moderately constricted at the cross walls and sometimes inclosed in a gelatinous sheath. Chloroplast a parietal plate extending through about $\frac{2}{3}$ of the median region of the cell, sometimes with a pyrenoid. Cells 5.7–9μ in diameter, 10–36μ long.

Euplankter. Wis.

Ulothrix subtilissima Rabenhorst 1868, Alg. Exsic. No. 655

Pl. 6, Fig. 3

Filaments long and slender, free-floating or attached. Cells very slightly inflated and constricted at the cross walls. Chloroplast extending the entire length of the cell, with 1 pyrenoid. Cells 4–5μ in diameter, 11–14.8μ long.

In shallow water of a swamp. Wis.

Ulothrix tenerrima Kuetzing 1843, p. 253

Pl. 6, Fig. 12

Filaments free-floating or attached; long, or in short sections; composed of cylindrical, relatively short cells with constrictions at the cross walls. Chloroplast an irregularly folded plate, about ½ the length of the cell, with 1 pyrenoid. Cells 7.5–10μ in diameter, 10–15μ long.

Common in many lakes and ponds, both the eutrophic and the soft water types. Mich., Wis.

Ulothrix tenuissima Kuetzing 1833, p. 518
Pl. 67, Figs. 11, 12

Filaments long, composed of cylindrical cells that are shorter than wide, 16–20μ in diameter, thin-walled and not constricted at the cross walls. Chloroplast a broad band encircling about ⅔ of the circumference of the cell, with 2 or several pyrenoids.

Mich.

Ulothrix variabilis Kuetzing 1849, p. 346
Pl. 6, Fig. 13

Filaments long, slender, and entangled, forming cottony masses. Cells cylindrical, without constrictions at the cross walls. Chloroplast a folded, parietal plate, ½ to ⅔ the length of the cell, with 1 pyrenoid (or 2 ?). Cells 4.5–6μ in diameter and up to 15μ long.

Common in a variety of lakes and in seeps along sandy shores; often forming bright green, slimy masses in trickles from springs. Mich., Wis.

Ulothrix zonata (Weber & Mohr) Kuetzing 1833, p. 517
Pl. 6, Fig. 14

Filaments attached, usually long and stout, variable in diameter in the same plant mass. Cells short , or elongate-cylindric, sometimes slightly swollen, with constrictions at the cross walls. Cell walls thick, especially near the base of the filament. Chloroplast a complete circular band in the midregion of the cell, with several pyrenoids. Cells 20–45μ in diameter, 21–60μ long.

Not uncommon in several lakes in early summer; frequently found in cold streams, artificial ponds, and in drinking troughs in which there is running water, especially in spring. Mich., Wis.

HORMIDIUM Kuetzing 1843, p. 244; *emend.* Klebs 1896, p. 326

Simple filaments of cylindrical, undifferentiated cells. Chloroplast a parietal plate extending around the cell for ½ or less of the circumference; 1 elongated or oval pyrenoid. Filament readily fragmenting to form *Stichococcus*-like sections.

Hormidium Klebsii G. M. Smith 1933, p. 385

Pl. 6, Fig. 4

Long unbranched filaments in which there is no basal-distal differentiation. Cells cylindrical, not constricted at the cross walls. Chloroplast a parietal plate covering only a small portion of the cell wall. Cells 5.8–6μ in diameter, 15.6–25μ long.

In *Sphagnum* bogs and roadside ditches. Wis.

URONEMA Lagerheim 1887, p. 517

Simple, unbranched filaments which are always attached. Cells cylindrical, the basal cell forming an organ of attachment, the terminal cell tapering unsymmetrically to a blunt boint. Chloroplast a parietal plate, ½ to ⅔ the length of the cell; with 1 or 2 pyrenoids.

Uronema elongatum Hodgetts 1918, p. 160

Pl. 5, Fig. 5

Cells cylindrical, as much as 13 times their diameter in length, and 5–10μ wide. Chloroplast a parietal folded plate extending for ⅔ of the circumference and ½ to ⅔ the length of the cell; with 2 pyrenoids. Terminal cell unsymmetrically tapering to a blunt point and often slightly curved.

This plant should be compared with germlings and young stages in the development of *Ulothrix* and such members of the Chaetophoraceae as *Stigeoclonium* and *Chaetophora*. The separation of *Uronema* from *Ulothrix* has been questioned; but the tapering apical cell persisting through maturity, the permanent attachment of the plants, and the type of basal holdfast of *Uronema* seem to be sufficient justification for the retention of the two names.

Attached to filamentous algae and other submerged aquatics in shallow backwaters. Mich., Wis.

STICHOCOCCUS Naegeli 1849, p. 77

Simple unbranched filaments of short, cylindrical, undifferentiated cells, which are often loosely connected, so that interrupted series are formed. Chloroplast a parietal folded plate, covering ½ or less of the cell wall, with 1 pyrenoid. Filament fragmenting easily to form short sections or solitary cells, which by vegetative division rebuild longer, curved (sometimes coiled) or straight filaments. Frequenting moist substrates in association with *Protococcus* [*Pleurococcus*]; also in algal mixtures encrusting submerged wood, or on aquatic plants.

Key to the Species

Stichococcus bacillaris Naegeli 1849, p. 77
Pl. 6, Fig. 5

Filaments composed of short cylindrical cells very slightly constricted, if at all, at the cross walls. Chloroplast a pale green parietal plate or folded disc covering a small portion of the wall. Cells 2–3.5µ in diameter, 3–8µ long.

On moist, aerial substrates, associated with other algae to form films on floating wood, etc. Mich., Wis.

Stichococcus scopulinus Hazen 1902, p. 161
Pl. 6, Fig. 6

Filaments of relatively long cylindrical cells without constrictions at the cross walls. Chloroplast a long, folded plate with an indistinct pyrenoid. Cells 3–4µ in diameter and up to 30µ long.

Our specimens are questionably assigned to this species. Hazen (l.c.) described the species as growing in dark green skeins on dripping rocks. It has not been possible to differentiate it clearly from S. bacillaris forma confervoidea Hazen (l.c., p. 60), except that the cells in S. scopulinus average slightly wider.

On stones and moist soil, forming small green patches. Mich., Wis.

Stichococcus subtilis (Kuetz.) Klercker 1896, p. 103
Pl. 6, Figs. 7, 8

Filaments very long, composed of rather stout, cylindrical cells without constrictions at the cross walls. Chloroplast an elliptical parietal plate with 1 pyrenoid. Cells 5–7–(8)µ in diameter, 7–20µ long.

In shallow water of beach pools and lake margins. Mich., Wis.

GEMINELLA Turpin 1828, p. 329

Filaments unbranched and uniseriate, composed of spheroidal, broadly ovoid, or short cylindrical cells inclosed by a wide gelatinous sheath and usually separated from each other; daughter cells approximated for some time after division to give a paired arrangement. Chloroplast a parietal folded plate, with 1 pyrenoid.

Key to the Species

Geminella crenulatocollis Prescott 1944, p. 349
Pl. 6, Figs. 9, 10

Uniseriate filaments of irregularly ovoid, subquadrate, or oblong cells, with emarginate, crenulate, or wavy lateral walls; truncate or broadly rounded at the poles, with folds and ridges sometimes present in the lateral walls. Cells inclosed by a broad gelatinous sheath and arranged in linear pairs, but often evenly spaced. Chloroplast an irregularly shaped, folded parietal plate, which makes an almost complete cylinder within the wall, often showing a ridge or wing-like flange extending radially toward the wall. Cells 12–15μ in diameter, 18–24μ long.

This species should be compared with _G. mutabilis,_ from which it differs in the irregularly creased cell wall and the shape of the chloroplast. Originally described from Wisconsin, this species has since been found in Michigan.

In soft water and acid swamps; tychoplanktonic in mixtures of algae in lake margins; in _Sphagnum_ bogs. Mich., Wis.

Geminella interrupta (Turp.) Lagerheim 1883, p. 68
Pl. 6, Fig. 15

Uniseriate filaments of broadly ovoid or subcylindric cells; pairs oı cells separated from the next pair in the series by at least a cell's length. Cells 5–8μ in diameter, 6–15μ long. Chloroplast a parietal plate covering ⅔ of the cell wall.

This species, even more than others in the genus, seems to be confined to soft water lakes. It appears in great profusion in desmid habitats. Mich., Wis.

Geminella minor (Naeg.) Heering 1914, p. 41
Pl. 6, Fig. 17

Uniseriate filaments of short, cylindrical cells adjoined without interruption within a wide gelatinous, homogeneous sheath. Chloroplast covering the entire lateral walls, but narrow, ring-like, and zonate immediately following cell division. Cells 4–8μ in diameter; filament (including sheath) 8–18μ in diameter.

This species often appears in the tychoplankton of acid lakes and in small pools of *Sphagnum* bogs. Mich., Wis.

Geminella mutabilis (de Bréb.) Wille 1911, p. 72
Pl. 6, Fig. 16

Uniseriate filaments of broadly ovate, spheroidal, or cylindrical cells, almost equally separated from one another, but with daughter cells remaining in approximation. Chloroplast completely covering the cell wall. Cells 9–13–(20)μ in diameter.

Intermingled with other algae in shallow water of small lakes and swamps. Wis.

Geminella ordinata (West & West) Heering 1914, p. 41
Pl. 24, Fig. 9

Uniseriate filaments of oblong-ellipsoid cells, arranged in an interrupted series, separated from each other by a distance of a cell's length or more. Chloroplast solitary, extending completely around the wall. Cells 5–5.8μ in diameter.

Intermingled with other algae in shallow water of lakes and ponds. Wis.

HORMIDIOPSIS Heering 1914, p. 50

Filaments short, composed of from 5 to 20 cells, arranged in continuous or interrupted linear series. Cells ovoid, cylindric, or transversely ellipsoid, inclosed by a gelatinous sheath. Chloroplast a parietal, incomplete band, without a pyrenoid (or with 1 ?). Oil formed as a food reserve. Reproduction by zoospores or gametes unknown.

Hormidiopsis ellipsoideum Prescott 1944, p. 350
Pl. 7, Figs. 1, 2

Cells transversely elliptic, arranged in linear series in groups of 4, each group inclosed by a wide, hyaline, and homogeneous gelatinous sheath. Chloroplast a parietal band as wide as the cell but not entirely encircling the wall; with 1 pyrenoid. Cells 8μ in diameter, 5.5μ long; filament 14.8μ wide.

Although this plant was found in only one collection it appeared distinctive enough to be worthy of description. *Hormidiopsis* is a little-understood genus, apparently containing but one other species, *H. crenulata* Heering. To this genus, Heering has also assigned ques-

[101]

tionably a plant previously described by Borge as *Ulothrix monili-formis.* Although our plant has the cell shape of the latter species and is approximately the same size, it differs in the arrangement of the cells. *Ulothrix moniliformis* Borge possesses cells in continuous filamentous arrangement inclosed by a sheath. All of the Wisconsin specimens had the cells arranged in crooked filaments in linear groups of 4, each group with an individual sheath. Occasionally the cells showed a tendency toward an irregular bilateral arrangement. The chief objection to placing the Wisconsin species in *Hormidiopsis* is the presence of a pyrenoid. The cell shape and arrangement would seem to preclude the assignment of this species to *Geminella.* Additional observations and life history studies are necessary before the plant can be satisfactorily identified.

Found in a *Sphagnum* bog lake intermingled with other algae. Wis.

BINUCLEARIA Wittrock 1886, p. 9

Filaments of long cylindrical cells. Protoplasts short-cylindric or oblong with rounded apices; not filling the cell, but surrounded by lamellated mucilage, which fills the space between the protoplasts and the end walls. Protoplasts in pairs (as a result of their remaining close together after cell division) separated by a thin cross wall. Chloroplast laminate, forming a band in the midregion of the cell; without pyrenoid.

Binuclearia tatrana Wittrock 1886, p. 9
Pl. 7, Figs. 7–9

Cells 7–10μ in diameter; the length sometimes as much as 6 times the width.

Common in acid bogs and soft water lakes; appearing quite frequently in small pools and ditches where the water is shallow and where there is an abundance of organic matter. Mich., Wis.

RADIOFILUM Schmidle 1894, p. 47

Filaments either unbranched or branched, the branches sometimes anastomosing to form a series of links. Cells lenticular, spherical, or oblate-spheroidal, dividing in 1 or 2 planes. The cell wall (at least in some species) composed of 2 cups or helmet-shaped halves, which adjoin in the midregion to form a transverse rim around the cell, at which point cell division occurs, new cell halves being interpolated between the older parts of the cell wall. Chloroplast a parietal plate, with 1 pyrenoid, lying along the transverse wall. Filament inclosed by a broad gelatinous sheath through which fibrillar concretions radiate to the periphery.

Key to the Species

1. Cells transversely ellipsoid or subquadrate, arranged to form a long continuous filament, inclosed in a relatively narrow sheath; cell wall halves not apparent _____ R. flavescens
1. Cells a different shape from above, not forming a continuous simple filament _____ 2
2. Cells transversely lenticular, pointed at the poles, separated from each other in a wide, gelatinous sheath, sometimes irregularly arranged, forming filaments with anastomosing branches; cell wall halves not apparent _____ R. irregulare
2. Cells spheroidal, evenly spaced and separate from each other; cell wall halves evident, forming a transverse rim around the cell _____ R. conjunctivum

Radiofilum conjunctivum Schmidle 1894, p. 48
[R. apiculatum West & West]
Pl. 7, Fig. 6

Filaments short, fragmenting readily, composed of spheroidal cells in a wide gelatinous sheath. Cell walls formed by 2 cup-shaped halves adjoined in the midregion and forming a rim which produces an apiculation at each side of the cell. Chloroplast a parietal plate lying along the end wall. Cells 6μ in diameter, $4-6\mu$ long.

Very common in a large number of lakes and swamps, especially in soft water and acid habitats, hence often associated with desmids. Mich., Wis.

Radiofilum flavescens G. S. West 1899, p. 57
Pl. 7, Fig. 10

Filaments long, composed of transversely ellipsoidal or subquadrate cells in a narrow gelatinous sheath in which radiating fibrils are apparent. Chloroplast a parietal plate. Cells $6.8-15\mu$ in diameter, $5-10\mu$ long; filament $9-25\mu$ wide, including sheath.

Some specimens in our collections are larger than the dimensions usually reported for R. flavescens, and have cells that are often definitely subquadrate. It is possible that such an expression justifies a separation to form a new species. The shape of the cell in this species is known to vary, however.

Scarce; in a few soft water lakes and in Sphagnum bogs. Mich., Wis.

[103]

Radiofilum irregulare (Wille) Brunnthaler 1913, p. 7
Pl. 7, Figs. 3–5

Filaments long, irregularly branched, branches often anastomosing to form a series of chain-like links. Cells transversely ellipsoid, dividing in 2 planes and appearing in more than 1 series within the wide gelatinous sheath. Cell wall in 2 saucer-shaped halves, adjoined in the midregion, the line of juncture not always evident. Cells 7–10μ in diameter, 3.5–5μ long.

Very common in desmid habitats and soft water lakes. Mich., Wis.

Published descriptions of this species do not mention the two-part structure of the cell wall, a character of *R. conjunctivum*. Also the shape of the cells in our specimens agrees closely with a plant which W. and G. S. West originally described as *R. apiculatum*. The arrangement of the cells and other features, the irregular form of the filament in particular, justify referring our specimens to *R. irregulare*. *Radiofilum apiculatum* West & West has been reduced to synonymy with *R. conjunctivum*. The characteristics of our specimens would apparently justify emending the description of *R. irregulare* if it were determined that the type specimens possess the wall structure of *R. conjunctivum*.

SUBORDER SCHIZOMERIDINEAE

FAMILY SCHIZOMERIDACEAE

In this family, which consists of the single genus *Schizomeris*, the unbranched filamentous habit takes on a multiseriate expression. The plant is uniseriate in the basal portion, where the cells are long and cylindrical, but becomes multiseriate through cell division in 3 planes in the distal region, where the cells are brick-like and quadrangular. The cross walls of the lower cells are thick plates. Chloroplasts are broad parietal bands which encircle about ⅔ of the cell wall in the lower cylindrical cells, but become massive and completely fill the cells in the distal portion of the filament.

The multiseriate habit and the method of zoospore escape (mentioned below) are characters which have influenced some phycologists to treat *Schizomeris* as a member of the Ulvaceae. It is an enigmatic plant, and its inclusion with either the Ulotrichales or the Ulvales seems justifiable.

SCHIZOMERIS Kuetzing 1843, p. 247

Characters as described for the family. Filaments uniseriate below, with cylindrical cells; multiseriate above, with brick-like cells. Chloroplast a parietal plate nearly encircling the lower cells, with several pyrenoids; distal cells have a dense chloroplast of indefinite shape.

See Smith (1933, p. 457) for a discussion of the various opinions concerning the taxonomic position of this genus.

Schizomeris Leibleinii Kuetzing 1843, p. 247
Pl. 7, Figs. 11–13

Filaments stout, macroscopic, 20–25μ in diameter below, and as much as 150μ wide in the multiseriate upper portion of the frond. Cells 15–30μ in diameter. Zoospores formed in the upper limits and escaping through an opening in the apex of the frond after interior cell walls have disintegrated.

Rather rare; in shallow water and marsh-like margins of both hard and soft water lakes; also in several swamps. Mich., Wis.

ORDER MICROSPORALES

In this order there is only one family, which is monogeneric. The plants are unbranched filaments, which are free-floating except when young. The most distinctive feature is found in the structure of the cell wall. The cells are cylindrical, with walls composed of two H-shaped sections which adjoin in the midregion. In the thin-walled species, however, this feature is scarcely discernible. When the filament dissociates, the cells fall apart into H-shaped sections because the cleavage occurs at the points of juncture in the midregion rather than at the cross walls. The end of a filament shows a half of the H adjoined to the terminating cell. A thin, internal cellulose membrane holds the wall sections together. Another characteristic which differentiates this order is the morphology of the chloroplast. Although it shows different specific expressions, its general form is that of a parietal reticulum or perforated sheet, which may be dense and padded or open and thin, covering almost all of the cell wall. Often the padded character gives the appearance of there being several chloroplasts. Starch accumulates as a food reserve, but there are no pyrenoids.

The absence of pyrenoids and the H-shaped wall sections are characteristics in common with *Tribonema* in the Chrysophyta. In that genus there are 2 to several disc-like, pale green chloroplasts, and starch is not formed.

Asexual reproduction is by biflagellate zoospores; gametes are unknown. Aplanospores are frequently formed, especially when water temperatures become high.

Microspora, the only genus, is sometimes included in the order Ulotrichales. The characteristics of *Microspora* species are so distinctive, however, that placing them in a separate order seems justifiable (Heering, 1914; *et al.*).

FAMILY MICROSPORACEAE
MICROSPORA Thuret 1850, p. 221

Plants unbranched, unattached filaments of uniseriately-arranged cylindrical, or slightly swollen, cells (attached filaments are not unknown, however). Cell walls thin in some species; in others thick and lamellate, composed of 2 sections overlapping in the midregion. Filaments fragmenting readily when mature by the separation of the walls at their point of juncture, so that H-shaped sections and fragments are formed. Chloroplast either a dense and irregularly padded parietal plate or net, or an open meshwork or "rosenkranz" form of reticulum; pyrenoids lacking. Cells frequently forming aplanospores or akinetes, the latter globose, with much-thickened walls.

Key to the Species

1. Walls thin, 1μ or less in thickness; juncture of the wall sections in the midregion of the cell not clearly evident except upon fragmentation of the filament _____ 2
1. Walls 1.5–2.5μ thick, often lamellate; juncture of the wall sections clearly evident _____ 6
2. Chloroplast an open meshwork, stringy, but sometimes thickened in places _____ 3
2. Chloroplast a parietal, perforated plate or close meshwork covering most of the cell wall _____ 4
3. Cells distinctly cylindrical, 14–17μ in diameter, 22–35μ long _____ *M. floccosa*
3. Cells quadrate or short-cylindric, 11–14μ in diameter and up to 22μ long _____ *M. Willeana*
4. Cells about 9μ in diameter, 1–3 times the diameter in length; chloroplast a granular plate _____ *M. stagnorum*
4. Cells narrower, and usually shorter; chloroplast dense _____ 5
5. Cells 6.7–9.5μ in diameter, quadrate (sometimes as much as twice the diameter in length); constricted at the cross walls _ *M. tumidula*
5. Cells 5.5–7.0μ in diameter, shorter than wide, or quadrate; not constricted at the cross walls _____ *M. quadrata*
6. Filaments 21.5–40μ in diameter _____ 7
6. Filaments 20μ or less in diameter _____ 8
7. Filaments 21.5–27μ in diameter, up to twice the diameter in length; slightly constricted at the cross walls _____ *M. amoena*
7. Filaments 26–33μ in diameter (rarely more), cells usually cylindrical, 1–$1\frac{1}{2}$ times the diameter in length _____ *M. crassior*
8. Cells cylindrical, 8–12μ in diameter, up to twice the diameter in length _____ *M. pachyderma*
8. Cells quadrate or cylindric, 13–20μ in diameter _____ 9

9. Cells elongate-cylindric, 13–15μ in diameter, up to 3 times
   the diameter in length.. *M. elegans*
9. Cells shorter, 15–20μ in diameter, ¾ to twice
   the diameter in length.. *M. Loefgrenii*

Microspora amoena (Kuetz.) Rabenhorst 1868, p. 321
Pl. 8, Fig. 8

Wall thick, lamellate, the 2 sections very evident in the midregion. Cells cylindrical, slightly constricted at the cross walls; (21.5)–25–27μ in diameter, 36–38μ long. Chloroplast sometimes completely covering the cell wall; in our specimens frequently perforate.

Intermingled with other algae in shallow water of bays and in swamps; quiet water. Mich., Wis.

Microspora crassior (Hansg.) Hazen 1902, p. 169
Pl. 8, Fig.1

Cell walls thick, the sections evident at the juncture in the midregion of the cell. Cells cylindrical or slightly swollen, very slightly constricted at the cross walls; 26–28–(33)μ in diameter, 28–34μ long. Chloroplast densely granular and covering the entire cell wall.

Very common in a number of soft water lakes, intermingled with other filamentous algae; often forming pure growths. Mich., Wis.

Microspora elegans Hansgirg 1891, p. 311

Walls thick, lamellate, the sections evident at the juncture in the midregion of the cells. Cells cylindrical or slightly constricted at the cross walls, 13–14–(15)μ in diameter, 15.6–20–(39)μ long. Chloroplast a parietal granular plate nearly covering the cell wall.

The thick walls and the proportions of the cell dimensions seem to warrant assigning our specimens to this species. They should be compared with *Microspora pachyderma*, which is smaller.

In a roadside swamp. Wis.

Microspora floccosa (Vauch.) Thuret 1850, p. 221
Pl. 8, Fig.4

Walls relatively thin, sections not always evident in the midregion of the cell. Cells cylindrical or slightly swollen; 14–17μ in diameter, 22–29–(35)μ long. Chloroplast usually reticulate.

In *Sphagnum* bogs and in swamps. Mich., Wis.

Microspora Loefgrenii (Nordst.) Lagerheim 1887a, p. 417
Pl. 8, Fig. 2

Walls thick, sections evident in the midregion of the cell. Cells short-cylindric, rectangular, as long as broad or a little longer;

[107]

15–20μ in diameter, 18–20μ long. Chloroplast a loose net, covering nearly all of the cell wall.

Entangled about the stems of *Chamaedaphne* in *Sphagnum* bogs. Mich., Wis.

Microspora pachyderma (Wille) Lagerheim 1887a, p. 415
Pl. 8, Fig. 3

Walls thick, sections evident in the midregion of the cell. Cells cylindrical; (8)–9–11–(12)μ in diameter, 14.8–16μ long. Chloroplast a folded plate, covering most of the cell wall.

Common in *Sphagnum* bogs and swamps. Mich., Wis.

Microspora quadrata Hazen 1902, p. 178

Walls thin, sections not evident. Cells short-cylindric, rectangular, about equal in length and diameter; 5.5–7μ in diameter, 5.5–7.5μ long. Chloroplast finely granular, covering the entire cell wall.

Found in a swamp near Sand Lake, Vilas County, Wisconsin; also in Michigan.

Microspora stagnorum (Kuetz.) Lagerheim 1887a, p. 417
Pl. 8, Figs. 6, 7

Walls thin, the two sections not evident. Cells cylindrical, or slightly constricted at the cross walls, as much as 3 times their diameter in length; 9μ wide, 10–25–(27)μ long. Chloroplast a granular sheet, incompletely covering the wall.

Common in the shallow water of many lakes, intermingled with other filamentous algae; also collected from a depth of 15 meters (in Crystal Lake, Vilas County, Wisconsin). Mich., Wis.

Microspora tumidula Hazen 1902, p. 177
Pl. 8, Fig. 9

Walls thin to relatively thick, lamellate, the sections of the wall very evident in the midregion of the cell. Cells cylindrical, slightly constricted at the cross walls; 7.4μ in diameter, 10–14.8μ long. Chloroplast densely granular.

Common in the shallow water of many lakes; in *Sphagnum* bogs and in swamps. Mich., Wis.

Microspora Willeana Lagerheim *in* De Toni 1889, p. 228
Pl. 8, Fig. 5

Walls thin, sections scarcely discernible. Cells cylindrical, slightly or not at all constricted at the cross walls; 11–14μ in diameter,

11–22μ long. Filaments very long. Chloroplast a perforated plate, sometimes densely padded. forate.

Common in swamps and in soft water lakes; intermingled with other algae and seldom found in pure growths. Mich., Wis.

ORDER CYLINDROCAPSALES

In this order there is a single family, Cylindrocapsaceae, with *Cylindrocapsa* as the only genus. The architecture is essentially filamentous with ovoid or oblong cells in uniseriate arrangement, but there is a frequent tendency toward palmelloid conditions with biseriate or irregular arrangement. The cells may be adjoined in pairs, or separate and evenly spaced within a lamellated gelatinous sheath, with concentric cellulose layers around each cell. The chloroplast is a massive, dense body without pattern and often obscured by starch grains. There is 1 pyrenoid. Sexual reproduction is oogamous. The oogonia are enlarged cells inclosed by much swollen walls, and usually occur in the same filament with the antheridia, which are smaller, somewhat quadrangular, cells arranged in double series, with two antherozoids being produced in each cell. These enter the oogonium through a pore in the thick wall of the female organ. Both sex organs are red and are in marked contrast to the dense green of the vegetative cells. Asexual reproduction is by biflagellate zoospores which in their germination form an attached filament. Upon ageing, the filaments become free-floating and are usually found entangled among masses of other algae.

The form of the chloroplast and the oogamous type of reproduction may be interpreted as characters so distinctive as to exclude *Cylindrocapsa* from the Ulotrichales, where it usually is classified.

FAMILY CYLINDROCAPSACEAE
CYLINDROCAPSA Reinsch 1867, p. 66

Plants short unbranched filaments of oblong, ovoid, or quadrate cells, uniseriate (rarely biseriate or palmelloid) in arrangement and inclosed by a wide, tough gelatinous sheath with distinct lamellations about the individual cells. Chloroplast (1 to each cell) a massive, dense body containing a central pyrenoid. Filaments attached when young by the adherence of the mucilaginous tube to the substrate. Enlarged oogonial cells occur in the same filament as the antheridia, or in separate filaments.

Key to the Species

Cells quadrate or quadrangular-ovate, 20–26μ wide_____*C. conferta*
Cells oblong or ovoid, up to twice their diameter
  in length, 12–18μ wide_____*C. geminella*

Cylindrocapsa conferta W. West 1892, p. 735

Pl. 9, Figs. 5, 6

Cells short, quadrate or quadrangular-ovate, enclosed by a wide sheath of lamellate mucilage. Cells 20–26μ in diameter, 14–29μ long; oogonia 41μ in diameter; fertilized egg 24μ in diameter (without envelope); male cells 18.5μ wide, biseriate (often uniseriate in our specimens).

Among other algae in shallows, especially in soft water lakes. Wis. (Previously reported from Iowa.)

Cylindrocapsa geminella Wolle 1887, p. 104

Pl. 9, Figs. 3, 4

Filaments long, composed of ovate or oblong cells that are up to twice their diameter in length; in copious, lamellate mucilage. Chloroplast massive and usually obscured by starch grains. Cells 12–18μ in diameter, 18–30μ long; oogonia globose or pyriform-globose, as much as 50μ in diameter (including the gelatinous sheath), usually in a series of 3–9.

This species is usually found entangled among other filamentous algae; especially abundant in desmid habitats, such as acid swamps. It is more common than other species of the genus in our collections. Mich., Wis.

Cylindrocapsa geminella var. *minor* Hansgirg 1888, p. 224

Pl. 9, Figs. 1, 2

A variety differing from the typical by its narrower cells and smaller oogonia. Cells ovate or ellipsoid, 12–15.6μ in diameter (including the sheath), 18.5μ long; oogonia 39μ in diameter; oospore 29.2μ in diameter, 31.2μ long. Filaments sometimes twisted and contorted.

Entangled among and attached to other filamentous algae in small ponds and swampy margins of lakes. Mich., Wis.

ORDER SPHAEROPLEALES

In this order there is but a single family, the Sphaeropleaceae, and one genus, *Sphaeroplea*. The plant body is a long unbranched filament of cylindrical 'cells,' without basal-distal differentiation. Each 'cell' contains several cytoplasmic units separated from one another by a large intervening vacuole. The cytoplasmic septae contain several nuclei and usually many ovoid, disc-like chloroplasts which are arranged to form zonate, annular bands. The chlorophyll-bearing body of the cell often takes the form of a close reticulum and shows, therefore, much variation. See Fritsch (1929).

Vegetative reproduction is by fragmentation. In sexual reproduction, unspecialized vegetative cells produce numerous globose eggs, which at first are multinucleate. In the cells of other filaments, or rarely in the same filament in which the eggs occur, numerous spindle-shaped, biflagellate antherozoids are formed. Entrance is effected by a small pore in the wall of the female gametangium. The resulting zygotes are thick-walled and have decorated membranes. They are capable of remaining dormant for several years, eventually germinating to produce 1–8 biflagellate zoospores, from which new filaments develop.

The unique organization of the coenocytic cells, the form and arrangement of the chloroplasts, and the method of sexual reproduction are characters which are here regarded as sufficiently dissimilar from the Ulotrichales to warrant separation of *Sphaeroplea* from that order. Although monogeneric orders make for an unwieldy taxonomic system and are, therefore, to be avoided, there seems to be no adequate justification for including *Sphaeroplea* in the Ulotrichales. Certainly it is consistent to regard the characteristics mentioned as criteria for segregation because they are fundamental and are used to define other groups.

FAMILY SPHAEROPLEACEAE

SPHAEROPLEA C. A. Agardh 1824, p. XXV

Free-floating filaments of long cylindrical multinucleate units with thickened cross walls. Chloroplasts numerous, ovate, and so grouped as to form up to 30 parietal bands or zones within each 'cell.' Sexual reproduction oogamous; non-motile eggs and antherozoids produced in unmodified vegetative 'cells' in the same or in separate filaments.

Sphaeroplea annulina (Roth) C. A. Agardh 1824, p. 76

Pl. 12, Figs 5–8

Characteristics as described for the genus. Cells 27–72μ in diameter, up to 20 times longer than wide. Spherical female gametes arranged in a double series within unspecialized vegetative cells; antherozoids numerous, fusiform, biflagellate bodies, usually produced in a separate filament.

University Farm, Madison, Wisconsin (Gilbert).

ORDER CHAETOPHORALES

This order includes branched filamentous plants which are either entirely prostrate or which have an erect system of branches that arise from a horizontal portion of the thallus. In many members there is a basal-distal differentiation. Exceptions are unicellular genera, *Protococcus* and *Chaetosphaeridium*. The cells are for the most part cylindrical, although in a few genera they are globose. A common, but not universal, character is the seta or hair, which has 2 expressions in the order; in some, the seta is a hair-like outgrowth of the cell wall, but in the second type it is either a lateral or terminal attenuated cell or series of cells. The cells forming the branches may be about the same size as those of the main axis, or they may be distinctly smaller.

The cell wall ordinarily is thin and sometimes mucilaginous, some forms being inclosed by a copious mucilage. The chloroplasts are ulotrichaceous parietal bands or plates which sometimes completely encircle the wall. There may be from 1 to several pyrenoids.

Variations from the usual form of the chloroplast are found in the Trentepohliaceae, a group which well might be interpreted as constituting a separate order because the species have features not shared by other members of the Chaetophorales.

Asexual reproduction is by zoospores produced in the upper or outer cells of the thallus, as well as in special sporangia. Isogamous sexual reproduction is the rule, but in *Chaetonema* and *Coleochaete* it is oogamous. Although these genera do not conform in their method of sexual reproduction, they have such vegetative characters as setae, habit of growth, and form of chloroplast in agreement with other members of this order. In *Aphanochaete* there is anisogamy. See Fritsch (1916, 1935) and West and Fritsch (1927) on the phylogenetic position and characteristics of the Chaetophorales.

Key to the Families

1. Plants unicellular or forming loose aggregates of cells without definite filamentous order_____ 2
1. Plants definitely filamentous or disc-like, or pseudoparenchymatous thalli (cushion-like expanses of densely compacted filaments)_____ 3
2. Cells solitary or in clumps, occasionally forming false filaments; setae lacking; plants mostly subaerial_____ PROTOCOCCACEAE
2. Cells solitary or gregarious, globose, each bearing a long seta which is sheathed at the base_____ COLEOCHAETACEAE (in part)
3. Filaments little branched, in our specimens without setae; walls thick; zoospores formed in swollen cell at the tips of the branches which arise from a prostrate portion of the thallus; plants growing on shells and wood, or aerial on tree trunks and rocks_____ TRENTEPOHLIACEAE

3. Filaments with setae or hairs, not forming zoospores in special sporangia 4
4. Filaments forming monostromatic expansions or cushions,
   bearing setae which are sheathed at the base; sexual
   reproduction oogamous _____ COLEOCHAETACEAE (in part)
4. Filaments forming prostrate or erect thalli, sometimes
   both types of thalli shown by the same plant; branches
   usually tapering (see *Microthamnion,* however) and
   setiferous; setae and hairs not sheathed _____ CHAETOPHORACEAE

FAMILY CHAETOPHORACEAE

In this family, as the name implies, most of the genera bear setae or hairs. These may develop as outgrowths of the cell wall or they may be formed by the attenuation of cells toward the apices of the branches, forming short or long hyaline bristles, one or more cells in length. The two chief expressions of these plants are the erect, branched filament, and the prostrate, cushion-like expansion. In some forms the thallus involves both a horizontal and an erect portion. In prostrate species the thallus may be a single layer of cells or it may be cushion-like and several cells in depth, especially in the center, becoming 1-celled in thickness at the margin. In such plants the true filamentous character may be lost because of the compactness of the cells and the irregular habit of branching.

Key to the Genera

1. Plant a prostrate or creeping filament, little or not at all branched............ 2
1. Plant a much-branched filament; filaments
   often adjoined and forming erect tufts, or
   pseudoparenchymatous expansions _____ 3
2. Filament creeping, little or not at all
   branched, if so, with branches not erect _____*Aphanochaete*
2. Filaments creeping, with infrequent, short branches_____*Chaetonema*
3. Plant consisting of an axial row of large, barrel-shaped or cylindrical
   cells giving rise to nodal whorls of branches, or oppositely arranged
   fascicles, of much smaller cells; thallus inclosed
   in a soft, copious mucilage_____*Draparnaldia*
3. Plants without an axial row of distinctly larger cells; branch cells
   about the same size as those of the main axis _____ 4
4. Plant a branched filament, the cells of the branches scarcely smaller
   than those of the main axis, gradually tapering to long or short setae
   or to pointed apical cells; horizontal or prostrate portion of the
   thallus often present; thallus inclosed in a thin mucilage which
   may not be evident_____ *Stigeoclonium*
4. Plant not as above _____ 5
5. Plant an erect, branched filament _____ 6
5. Plant a horizontal or pseudoparenchymatous expansion_____ 7
6. Plant a much-branched filament inclosed in firm, copious mucilage,
   forming macroscopic thalli of definite
   shape; branches attenuate _____*Chaetophora*
6. Plant microscopic; branches not at all or scarcely
   attenuate; investing mucilage wanting _____*Microthamnion*

7. Plant endophytic in the walls of large algae (sometimes epiphytic also), consisting of an irregularly branched filament or pseudoparenchymatous mass of cells which bear no setae .... *Entocladia*
7. Plant epiphytic or otherwise attached, not endophytic; pseudoparenchymatous or discoid 8
8. Thallus a compact disc of definite limitation, with colorless hairs arising from the outer sheath of the cells; filaments not evident .. *Chaetopeltis*
8. Thallus a flat, broad, epiphytic disc with filaments evident; cells without setae 9
9. Thallus a broad, epiphytic disc, several cells in thickness, with filaments radiating from a common center; margins of the frond definite; evanescent hairs sometimes present....................................*Pseudulvella*
9. Thallus an irregularly spreading epiphyte; filaments adjoined and compactly arranged, not radiating from a common center; one cell in thickness; setae lacking ....*Protoderma*

STIGEOCLONIUM Kuetzing 1843, p. 253

A branched filament arising from a prostrate portion of a thallus, which may be reduced to a pseudoparenchymatous mass of cells. In some species the major portion of the plant spreads in loosely branched, horizontal filaments; plant covered by a thin, scarcely evident, film of mucilage. Branches of first and second order either alternate or opposite, and composed of cells scarcely smaller than those of the main axis, ending in bluntly pointed or setiferous cells. Chloroplast a parietal plate covering most of the cell wall, especially in the cells of the branches; 1 to several pyrenoids. See Hazen (1902, p. 193) on the taxonomy of this genus in the United States.

Key to the Species

1. Plants mostly prostrate and creeping; filaments with a few short vertical branches ....*S. polymorphum*
1. Plants mostly erect, branched filaments; horizontal portion of the thallus reduced... 2
2. Branching mostly alternate... 3
2. Branching mostly opposite 7
3. Walls of main axial cells 1.5–2.5–(4)μ thick; branching very irregular, with long and tapering, as well as short, arbuscular or rhizoidal branches produced throughout the length of the main axis.... *S. pachydermum*
3. Walls of main axial cells thinner; branching regular, the branches gradually attenuated toward the apices 4
4. Plants short-tufted; apices of branches not tapering to setae but short-pointed..*S. nanum*
4. Plants not short-tufted; branches elongate, gradually attenuate, and ending in long setae 5
5. Plants slender, main axis less than 8μ in diameter....................*S. attenuatum*
5. Plants stouter, main axis 8–18μ in diameter............................... 6
6. Branches nearly always few-celled and thorn-like, 8–11μ in diameter in the main axis..*S. stagnatile*
6. Branches elongate, thorn-like branches rare; cells 12–18μ in diameter in the main axis.. *S. subsecundum*

7. Filaments slender and graceful, less than 10μ in diameter .... *S. tenue*
7. Filaments stouter, 14–18μ in diameter... 8
8. Main filaments 14–17μ in diameter; branches mostly short-pointed; cells of the main axis swollen, 1–2 times the diameter in length.....*S. lubricum*
8. Main filaments (12)–14–18μ in diameter; cells 4–8 times their diameter in length, cylindrical; branches attenuate and setiferous...*S. flagelliferum*

Stigeoclonium attenuatum (Hazen) Collins 1909, p. 301
Pl. 13, Fig. 1

Filaments elongate with upper branching mostly alternate, but dichotomously branched below; the branches either short and spinelike or long and tapering, terminating in a sharply pointed cell or series of cells forming a hyaline seta. Cells cylindrical, with little or no constriction at the cross walls; diameter of cells in the main axis 5–7μ, length 12–20μ. Prostrate portion of thallus little-developed.

In bogs, attached to submerged aquatics. Mich., Wis.

Stigeoclonium flagelliferum Kuetzing 1845, p. 198
Pl. 11, Figs. 1, 2

Filaments elongate; some branches dichotomous but mostly opposite, the branches arising from node-like zones, where a series of 2 or more swollen cells in the main axis develops pairs of branches; branches long and tapering to form slender, hyaline setae. Cells mostly cylindrical, but occasional cells barrel-shaped, 12–16–(18)μ in diameter, 30–48μ long. The basal portion of the thallus (in our specimens) only slightly developed.

Attached to wood in flowing water; in *Sphagnum* bogs. Mich., Wis.

Stigeoclonium lubricum (Dillw.) Kuetzing 1845, p. 198
Pl. 10, Figs. 1, 2

Filaments elongate and robust; the branches mostly opposite or whorled, developed from barrel-shaped axial cells; secondary branches often forming fascicles near the tips of the filaments, in which the cells are much smaller than in the main axis; branches ending in a blunt point or a hyaline seta. Cells in the main filament up to 17μ in diameter, 12–30μ long; branch cells 6–7μ in diameter. Prostrate portion of thallus well developed.

This is the most commonly observed species of *Stigeoclonium* in our region. It forms conspicuous tufts or extensive expansions on submerged wood, especially in running water. A favorite habitat is the sides of a wooden watering trough.

Forming bright green, thready tufts in several lakes; common. Mich., Wis.

Stigeoclonium nanum Kuetzing 1849, p. 354

Pl. 9, Figs. 7, 8

Thallus composed of short-tufted filaments, the branches arising alternately and tapering to blunt points. Cells of the branches scarcely smaller than those of the main axis, 6–8μ in diameter, 10–18μ long. Prostrate portion of the plant expansive, pseudoparenchymatous, becoming filamentous; the cells subglobose and giving rise to vertical branches.

This species forms green, fuzzy films on submerged aquatics, especially on the culms of rushes, and on wood. As pointed out by Collins (1909, p. 300), the morphology of this plant suggests that it is a juvenile or growth form of another species.

Attached to wood in flowing water. Mich., Wis.

Stigeoclonium pachydermum Prescott 1944, p. 350

Pl. 12, Figs. 1–4, 9, 10

Filaments much-branched, erect, with numerous basal, downward-projecting rhizoidal branches; branches in the upper portion irregularly disposed and extremely varied in form, mostly alternate, but with one branch arising immediately above another on the opposite side of the filament, or in a plane at right angles to it; branches often developing from short, barrel-shaped cells; many thorn-like and irregular, downward-projecting branches developing from the upper part of the main axis; branches tapering to a blunt point and frequently ending in somewhat enlarged quadrangular-globose sporangial cells, which may be intercalary near the ends of short branches also. Cells in the main axis 19.5–21μ in diameter, in the branches 15–16μ in diameter; cylindrical and several times longer than wide, short and barrel-shaped in the same filament. Walls of the cells in the main axis 3–4μ thick.

The chief characteristics of this species are the irregularly arranged crooked branches and the thick walls. In its coarse habit the plant resembles *S. lubricum*, which is, however, a species with opposite branching.

This plant has been found but once in the Great Lakes region, growing in the shallow water of High Lake, Vilas County, Wisconsin.

Stigeoclonium polymorphum (Franke) Heering 1914, p. 87

Pl. 9, Fig. 9

Filaments epiphytic or endophytic, short, and sparsely branched; arising from an extensive prostrate, pseudoparenchymatous, or monostromatic and radiating portion. Upright branches ending in long tapering setae. Cells quadrangular in the basal portion, cylindrical in the vertical branches; 4–10μ in diameter, 6–12μ long.

In lakes and ditches; on large filamentous algae and submerged vegetation. Wis.

Stigeoclonium stagnatile (Hazen) Collins 1909, p. 301
Pl. 11, Fig. 3

Thallus attached at first, later free-floating. Filaments long and sparingly branched; branches alternate but often opposite also in origin, short and ending in blunt points, or long and setiferous. Cells 8–11μ in diameter and up to 30μ long.

Floating in lakes and swamps. Mich., Wis.

Stigeoclonium subsecundum Kuetzing 1843, p. 253
Pl. 10, Figs. 3, 4

Filaments elongate and sparingly branched; the branches gradually and gracefully tapering to fine points, alternate in origin, sometimes short and composed of only 2 or 3 cells. Cells elongate and cylindrical but with slight constrictions at the cross walls; 12–18μ in diameter and up to 75μ long. Chloroplast a thin, parietal plate.

Generally distributed in a variety of lakes but always in quiet water protected from wave action; older plants free-floating. Mich., Wis.

Stigeoclonium tenue (C. A. Ag.) Kuetzing 1843, p. 253

Thallus an elongate tuft of very slender, gracefully tapering filaments, the branches mostly opposite, but occasionally alternate (solitary), tapering to setae. Cells long and cylindrical (sometimes nearly quadrate), or with walls slightly convex and constricted at the cross walls; 7–10μ in diameter below, 5–6μ in the branches. Mich.

CHAETOPHORA Schrank 1783, p. 124

Thallus consisting of highly branched filaments arising from a prostrate palmelloid mass of cells and inclosed by a mucilage of such firm consistency as to give the thallus a definite shape, globose, hemispherical, or arbuscular. Branches tapering to either a blunt point or a long, multicellular, hyaline hair. Chloroplast a parietal band which in the upper cells completely covers the lateral walls; with 1 or more pyrenoids. Zoospores and isogametes formed in the outer cells of the branches.

Key to the Species

1. An elongate, cartilaginous, branching thallus, sometimes short and
   arbuscular when young or when growing in warm water.......... *C. incrassata*
1. A globose or hemispherical, tuberculose thallus, 1–10 mm. in diameter........ 2
2. Colonial mucilage rather soft; filaments irregularly branched,
   spreading and entangled..*C. elegans*
2. Colonial mucilage firm; filaments erect and evidently radiating from
   a common center within the colonial mucilage 3
3. Branches fasciculate toward the outer limits of the thallus;
   cells 3–6 times the diameter in length................................*C. pisiformis*
3. Filaments radiating and subparallel; branches not fasciculate near
   the outer limits of the thallus; cells up to 10 times
   their diameter in length..*C. attenuata*

Chaetophora attenuata Hazen 1902, p. 213
Pl. 13, Figs. 4, 5

Forming attached, firm, gelatinous globules, 2–5 mm. in diameter, having radiating, nearly parallel, erect branches from numerous basal, rhizoidal processes. Filaments usually dichotomously (sometimes trichotomously) branched, ending in sharply pointed, setiferous cells; branches not fasciculate, but loose and evenly developed from the main axis and much elongated. Cells 5–6μ in diameter, 15–30μ long.

This is a fairly common species, often found in cold water, forming green globules on old leaves and submerged wood, gregarious but distinct from one another. Mich., Wis.

Chaetophora elegans (Roth) C. A. Agardh 1812, p. 42
Pl. 14, Figs. 3, 4

Thallus attached, globose or flattened green masses of soft mucilage; colonies often confluent with one another to form irregularly-shaped masses, in which dichotomous filaments spread out from a common center. Branches rather loose; branches of the second order somewhat more numerous near the upper part of the thallus, ending in abruptly pointed (rarely setiferous) cells. Cells 7–12μ in diameter in the main axis, 15–30μ long.

This is the most common species of the genus in our collections, appearing in many lakes and streams. Overhanging grass in shallow water may be a solid green gelatinous mass formed by numerous confluent colonies of the species. Mich., Wis.

Chaetophora incrassata (Huds.) Hazen 1902, p. 214
Pl. 14, Figs. 1, 2, 11

Thallus attached at first, free-floating when mature, forming tufted or arbuscular lobed and cartilaginous masses, varying from a few millimeters to 15 centimeters in height; composed of axial strands of long cells which give rise on all sides to dense fascicles of out-ward-directed branches, usually curved. Apical cells of branches sharp-pointed or setiferous. Cells of main axis 10–15μ in diameter; as much as 10 times the diameter in length in the axial filaments.

This is a variable species, occurring mostly in hard water habitats, although it is found in acid lakes and swamps. In swiftly flowing streams the plant may be very long luxuriantly-developed green strands. In lakes it is commonly found forming crinkly, tuberculose or short arbuscular growths on *Typha* and *Scirpus*, as well as on sub-merged wood. In very hard water the thalli are often lime-encrusted and pale green. Some expressions have been given varietal names, but the forms are so intergrading and seem to be so definitely related to environmental conditions that it is not possible to separate them. The rather firm mucilage of this species is one of the habitats of *Chaetonema irregulare* Nowak., which is easily overlooked among the dense branches of the host.

Common. Attached to stones and wood, mostly in flowing water, but frequently on the culms of rushes in shallow water of lakes. Mich., Wis.

Chaetophora pisiformis (Roth) C. A. Agardh 1812, p. 43
Pl. 13, Figs. 2, 3

Plants attached, in the form of either distinct or confluent globules of firm mucilage, in which dichotomously branched filaments radiate from a common center, ending anteriorly in fascicles of branches. Apical cells sharply pointed, rarely setiferous. Cells of the main axis about 7μ in diameter, 15–35μ long; cells of the branches only slightly narrower and shorter.

On submerged substrates, mostly in cold water streams and lakes; swamps. Mich., Wis.

DRAPARNALDIA Bory 1808a, p. 399

Thallus consisting of an axis of larger barrel-shaped or cylindrical cells attached to a substrate by rhizoidal branches and giving rise to alternate, opposite, or whorled fascicles of smaller-celled branches, which terminate in bluntly pointed or setiferous cells. Plants em-bedded in copious, soft mucilage. Chloroplast a parietal band in the cells of the main axis, a laminate plate covering the entire wall (or nearly so) in the smaller cells of the branches; pyrenoids 1 to several.

Because the species of this genus seem to prefer cold water hab-itats they frequently are collected during the spring months. In early summer, remnants are to be found in the bottoms of ditches of cold water, trickles from springs, or attached to stones in cold, swift streams.

Key to the Species

1. Lateral branches or the main filament forming a fascicle in
which there is an axis or rachis apparent throughout_____ 2
1. Lateral branches of the main filament forming a fascicle which is
glomerate and does not show a distinct rachis throughout_____ 3
2. Lateral branches forming a broad, spreading fascicle
which is acuminate; diameter of main filament as
much as 110μ (mostly 50–90μ)_____*D. acuta*
2. Lateral branches forming a narrow, elliptic, or plume-like fascicle,
the rachis apparent and much-extended; main filament averaging
smaller than above, 45–70μ in diameter_____*D. plumosa*
3. Fascicles of branches sparingly branched, the branches nearly
always ending in straight, rigid setae; chloroplast broad_____ 4
3. Fascicles of branches well-developed and densely tufted in
fully grown plants; chloroplast narrow_____*D. glomerata*
4. Fascicles of branches narrow in outline, opposite or whorled, arising
from near the midregion of the cell in the main filament_____*D. Judayi*
4. Fascicles arising from the joints of the cells
in the main filament and stalked_____*D. platyzonata*

Draparnaldia acuta (C. A. Ag.) Kuetzing 1845, p. 230
Pl. 15, Fig. 1

Main axis of the thallus bearing horizontal or ascending branches, from which opposite or whorled fascicles of branchlets arise; branchlets crowded, ovate to acuminate in outline, with an apparent rachis that extends beyond the other branches of the fascicle. Cells of the main axis and primary branches swollen, 50–100–(110)μ in diameter. Chloroplast about ½ the length of the cell. Diameter of branchlet cells 6–10μ.

Among grass in pooled stream, inlet to Buckatobon Lake, Wisconsin.

Draparnaldia glomerata (Vauch.) C. A. Agardh 1812, p. 41
Pl. 15, Fig. 5

Main axis composed of much-inflated cells, repeatedly branched; branches usually opposite and bearing opposite or whorled fascicles of small branches, which are tufted, orbicular or elliptic in outline, and spreading, without an evident rachis. Cells of the main axis 50–100μ in diameter and as much as twice their diameter in length. Chloroplast about ⅓ the length of the cell. Cells in fascicles 6–9μ in diameter.

Common in shallow water of lakes and pooled streams. Mich., Wis.

Draparnaldia Judayi Prescott 1944, p. 351

Pl. 16, Figs. 1–5

Plant invested by a very soft, watery mucilage. Main axis composed of slender, slightly inflated or cylindrical cells, with constrictions at the cross walls. Lateral secondary branches lacking, the axial filament giving rise only to rather simple fascicles of small branches, which are opposite or in whorls, arising at right angles from the midregion of the axial cells; rachis of the fascicles apparent only in the larger and well developed branches; the apices of most branchlets ending in stout, straight setae, which are often bulbous at the base; setae sometimes arising laterally or dichotomously. Chloroplast a narrow band in the main axial cells, covering most of the wall in the branches. Cells of the main axis 12–15.2μ in diameter, 30–40μ long.

One of the most distinctive characteristics of this species is the whorled arrangement of the very simple and much reduced fascicles of branches, arising from the midregion rather than from the joints of the main axial cells. The position of the branchlet origin suggests *Draparnaldiopsis alpinis* Smith and Klyver. In that species, however, the stalked fascicles arise from short, differentiated cells in the main filament. Another peculiarity is the form and location of the setae. These may be terminal, 1 or 2 arising from a non-tapered apical cell, or lateral, in which case they may take the place of a dichotomous branch. The setae are similar in morphology to those of *Chaetonema*.

Entangled in overhanging grass in a *Sphagnum* bog pool. Wis.

Draparnaldia platyzonata Hazen 1902, p. 222

Pl. 15, Figs. 2, 3

Axis of thallus with opposite, horizontal branches, composed of cylindrical cells with but slight constrictions at the cross walls; fascicles of branchlets opposite or in whorls, set at right angles to the main axis; sometimes with branches distinctly stipitate (the stipe composed of 2 or 3 cells) and without an apparent rachis. Main axis 50–90μ in diameter; cells in the branchlets 6–11μ in diameter.

In cold ponds and ditches of trickling water. Wis.

Draparnaldia plumosa (Vauch.) C. A. Agardh 1812, p. 42

Pl. 15, Fig. 4

Main axis composed of cylindrical cells 1½ to 2 times their diameter in length, slightly constricted at the cross walls. Lateral fascicles of branches alternate or opposite, at right angles to the main axis or somewhat ascending; fascicles with an apparent axis which extends through and beyond the other branches to give a tapering, plumed effect. Cells of the main axis 45–65μ in diameter; cells in the lateral branches 6–10μ in diameter. Chloroplast a narrow band about ¼ the length of the cell.

Found several times in cold water at the bottom of soft water lakes and in deep pools in *Sphagnum* bogs. Mich., Wis.

MICROTHAMNION Naegeli *in* Kuetzing 1849, p. 352

Attached, branched filaments, forming a minute arbuscular thallus on other algae, or on submerged aquatics such as mosses. Cells cylindrical. Branches opposite or alternate, often curved, not tapering to their apices but about the same diameter as the main axis throughout; the first cross wall of the branch often at some distance from the plane of origin. Chloroplast a parietal plate covering nearly the entire wall; pyrenoid lacking.

Key to the Species

Main axis of the filament apparent only at the base of
the thallus, soon lost in the ramifications _____ _____*M. Kuetzingianum*
Main axis of the filament distinct throughout the thallus _____ *M. strictissimum*

Microthamnion Kuetzingianum Naegeli *in* Kuetzing 1849, p. 352
Pl. 11, Fig. 4

Thallus highly branched and densely tufted, the main axis distinct only at the base, soon becoming lost in the ramifications, which are 1 to several cells in length, the branches attenuated but very little toward the apices. Cells cylindrical; apical cell of branches bluntly rounded. Diameter of axial cells about 4μ; length 10–15μ. Chloroplast bright blue-green, covering most of the cell wall.

This is a common species, apparently preferring soft water habitats where there is a high concentration of organic acids. It is frequently found in *Sphagnum* bogs. In Crystal Lake, Wisconsin, a habitat of very soft water, this species was not found growing in shallow water zones but was common on the moss (*Drepanocladus*) which carpets the bottom at a depth of 35 feet.

Attached to algae and submerged aquatics in many lakes and swamps. Mich., Wis.

Microthamnion strictissimum Rabenhorst 1859, No. 829
Pl. 11, Figs. 5, 6

Thallus minute, sparsely and alternately branched, the main axis evident throughout; branches all ascending, neither curved nor tapering, bluntly rounded at the apices. Cells cylindrical, with the initial cross wall of the branch slightly above the plane of origin. Cells 3–4μ in diameter, 14–25μ long.

On moss and other submerged aquatics and on large filamentous algae. Mich., Wis.

ENTOCLADIA Reinke 1879, p. 476

Thallus composed of irregularly-branched filaments which are spreading, or which form a thin cushion-like mass of ovoid or angular cells under and through the membrane of cladophoraceous cells. Chloroplast parietal, with a single pyrenoid.

Entocladia polymorpha (G. S. West) G. M. Smith 1933, p. 400
Pl. 14, Fig. 9

Filaments highly branched and irregularly spreading, composed of loosely arranged and irregularly shaped but more or less rectangular cells 9–12–(20)μ in diameter. Filamentous habit sometimes obscured by superimposed cells.

On *Cladophora* and *Rhizoclonium*. Wis.

PROTODERMA Kuetzing 1843, p. 295

Thallus an attached, monostromatic or pseudoparenchymatous disc of horizontally growing filaments, which are closely arranged and semi-radiate. Filaments irregularly branching, but the branches frequently indefinite and not clearly evident, becoming free and apparent at the margin of the thallus. Walls thin and without setae. Chloroplast a parietal disc with 1 pyrenoid.

Care must be used to separate this plant from the young stages of *Stigeoclonium* and other horizontally-growing members of the Chaetophoraceae.

Protoderma viride Kuetzing 1843, p. 295
Pl. 9, Fig. 10; Pl. 14, Fig. 10

Thallus an attached disc, irregular in outline, made up of branched filaments which are compact and parenchymatous internally but semi-radiate and spreading at the margin; terminal cells slightly narrowed. Cells quadrate or cylindrical, with thin walls; 3–6μ in diameter, 10–15μ in length.

Attached to *Cladophora* and other coarse filamentous algae. Wis.

PSEUDULVELLA Wille 1911, p. 90

Thallus an attached pseudoparenchymatous, cushion-like disc, several cells in thickness, inclosed by a mucilaginous envelope from the surface of which setae arise (often lacking). Cells loosely arranged in indefinite filaments, which radiate from a common center. Cell walls without setae. Chloroplasts several oval bodies, parietal or scattered through the cell; 1 pyrenoid in a cell.

Pseudulvella americana (Snow) Wille 1911, p. 90

Pl. 15, Fig. 6

(This species probably synonymous with *Chaetopeltis americana,* below)

Thallus pseudoparenchymatous, from 1 to 3 cells in thickness; cells in radiating linear series from a common center, 8–12μ in diameter.

Rare. Growing on culms of *Scirpus,* on submerged wood, etc. Wis.

CHAETOPELTIS Berthold 1878, p. 215

(Sometimes included in Tetrasporales)

Thallus a circular attached disc of rectangular or rounded cells, mono- or polystromatic, forming radiating filamentous series from a common center. Free walls occasionally with slender gelatinous bristles. Parietal plate-like chloroplast with a pyrenoid.

Members of this genus should be compared with species of *Coleochaete,* in which most monostromatic species form solid discs of radiating, laterally adjoined filaments composed of cells bearing an entirely different type of seta (with sheathed base).

Key to the Species

Cells 8–12μ in diameter... *C. americana*
Cells 15–20μ in diameter.. *C. orbicularis*

Chaetopeltis americana (Snow) Collins 1909, p. 289

Thallus an attached parenchymatous or polystromatic disc of rectangular cells, forming irregularly radiating series from a common center; outer and upper cells bearing fine hairs from their free walls. Chloroplast with irregular margins. Cells 8–12μ in diameter, 10–20μ long.

Epiphytic on filamentous algae; less common than the following species. Mich., Wis.

Chaetopeltis orbicularis Berthold 1878, p. 219

Pl. 16, Fig. 6

Thallus a monostromatic disc of rectangular cells forming filamentous series and radiating irregularly from a common center to form a circular plate, some cells bearing 1 or 2 fine setae. Chloroplast with smooth margins. Cells 15–20μ in diameter, 15–30μ long, with thick walls.

Epiphytic on large algae and on submerged aquatics; mostly in acid lakes. Mich., Wis.

[124]

APHANOCHAETE A. Braun 1851, p. 196
[Herposteiron Naegeli in Kuetzing 1849, p. 423]

Thallus composed of a creeping, irregularly branched (rarely unbranched) filament of cylindrical or inflated cells which bear 1 or more long setae with a bulbous base, the setae without a sheath and arising from the upper free walls.

Species in this genus are usually found on other filamentous algae, one in particular being confined to filamentous desmids. Differentiation of species cannot be made with certainty unless the plants are well developed.

Key to the Species

1. Filament arched; in contact with the host
   only at intervals .... A. vermiculoides
1. Filament creeping on the host; in contact
   throughout its length or nearly so 2
2. Cells bearing 2–6 setae (rarely 1), 9–15μ in diameter .... A. polychaete
2. Cells bearing but 1 seta (rarely 2), 8–10μ in diameter............A. repens

Aphanochaete polychaete (Hansg.) Fritsch 1902, p. 410
Pl. 17, Fig. 1

Sparsely branched, creeping on *Cladophora* filaments; composed of rounded or oblong-rectangular cells, 9–15μ in diameter, 1–2 times longer than wide, with 2–6 (rarely only 1) setae arising from the dorsal wall of each cell.

Rare. Wis.

Aphanochaete repens A. Braun 1851, p. 196
Pl. 17, Figs. 2, 3

Filaments creeping on or entwined about larger filamentous algae. Cells irregularly inflated or subcylindric, 8–10μ in diameter. Setae long and very slender, 3μ wide at the base.

This is the most common of the species of this genus which occur in North America. It is abundant in favorable habitats but seems to be restricted in its distribution, occurring most frequently in shallow warm water where there is a great mixture of algae.

On many kinds of filamentous algae in shallow water of lakes and swamps; intermingled with other algae. Common. Mich., Wis.

Aphanochaete vermiculoides Wolle 1887, p. 119
Pl. 17, Fig. 4

Filaments composed of short- or long-cylindric, or rounded cells, attached at 2 or 3 points only, on larger algae, highly arched and free between the points of contact. Setae sometimes absent, but frequently 2 or 3 arise from a single cell. Cells 4–6.5μ in diameter, 5–8μ long.

Rare; on filamentous algae. Mich., Wis.

CHAETONEMA Nowakowski 1877, p. 75

Thallus consisting of creeping, irregularly branched filaments of cylindrical cells; branches mostly vertical from a horizontal axis, ending in long, tapering, hair-forming cells; lateral walls of cells also bearing a long hair, arising near the distal end. Parietal zonate chloroplast, which covers about ½ the wall; with 1 or 2 pyrenoids.

This genus is confined to an epiphytic habit, occurring in the mucilage of such algae as *Chaetophora, Batrachospermum,* and *Tetraspora.*

Chaetonema irregulare Nowakowski 1877, pp. 73, 75
Pl. 13, Figs. 6, 7

Characters as described for the genus. Branch-bearing cells extended to form the base of the branch. Cells 8–12μ in diameter, 20–50μ long.

Creeping in the mucilage of *Tetraspora* sp., *Chaetophora incrassata,* and *Batrachospermum* sp.

Rare but widely distributed. Mich., Wis.

FAMILY PROTOCOCCACEAE

This family includes a few genera in which the thallus is a very much-reduced, branching filament. The plants are usually unicellular, but they may form clumps or expansions of considerable extent on moist aerial substrates. The cells are globular, or the walls may be flattened by intercellular compression. The ubiquitous genus *Protococcus* is placed here because of the interpretation that the clumps or strands of cells which are often formed in that genus are essentially simple filaments; the plants occur more commonly as single cells. The chloroplast is a parietal, lobed plate and ulotrichaceous in character. There may be a pyrenoid. Motile reproductive cells are not known, and cell division is the only method of multiplication. The family is here represented by a single genus, *Protococcus* Agardh. See Smith (1933, p. 407) for a discussion of the synonymy of *Protococcus* and *Pleurococcus* Meneghini.

PROTOCOCCUS C. A. Agardh 1824, p. 13
[Pleurococcus Meneghini 1837]

Unicellular or in indefinite clusters, the cells globose or angular from mutual compression and sometimes organized to form simple filaments. Occurring as green expansions on moist substrates; aerial (and aquatic ?). Branching of filaments vestigial, not evident. Chloroplast a dense, lobed parietal plate covering most of the cell wall, usually containing a single pyrenoid.

The true relationship of *Protococcus* is debatable, and opinions concerning its taxonomy are numerous. As mentioned by Smith (*l.c.*) the name *Protococcus* is preferable to *Pleurococcus* Meneghini. After discussing the synonymy of the genus, Pascher (1915, p. 223) retains it in the Protococcales (Chlorococcales) as of uncertain position.

Protococcus viridis C. A. Agardh 1824, p. 13
Pl. 10, Figs. 5–7

Characters as described for the genus; the cells 8–12–(25)μ in diameter.

Common and widely distributed on moist bark of trees, on old wood in subaerial habitats, and on floating (and submerged ?) logs. Mich., Wis.

FAMILY COLEOCHAETACEAE

This family is characterized by cells bearing sheathed setae, either simple or branched; the sheath a basal cylinder of firm mucilage. In one genus, branched filaments are formed, which may be entirely or only in part horizontal. In other forms the cells may be solitary, or if multicellular, not filamentous. The chloroplast is a parietal plate and usually contains a single pyrenoid. There are biflagellate zoospores in asexual reproduction, whereas sexual reproduction is carried on by either iso- or heterogametes (oogamy).

Key to the Genera

1. Plants globose or hemispherical unicells (sometimes 2-celled), solitary or gregarious and epiphytic, each cell bearing a long, sheathed seta............. 2
1. Plant a filamentous thallus, forming horizontal discs or cushions, or with erect, branched filaments ....*Coleochaete*
2. Plants globose, unicellular or 2-celled, each cell bearing a simple, sheathed seta .... *Chaetosphaeridium*
2. Plants hemispherical, unicellular, with a branched seta arising from the base of the cell .... *Dicranochaete*

COLEOCHAETE de Brébisson 1844, p. 29

Plant consisting of attached, branched filaments, either entirely prostrate and radiating, forming a monostromatic disc with the filaments laterally adjoined or loose and spreading, or in some species with erect branches. Cell wall frequently bearing a sheathed seta which develops through a special pore from a blepharoplast.

Chloroplast a parietal plate covering most of the cell wall, with 1 pyrenoid. Heterogamous in sexual reproduction, in which are formed enlarged oogonia, each containing a single egg, and box-like antheridial cells, each producing a single biflagellate antherozoid. Monoecious or dioecious. The oogonium becomes invested by a proliferation of neighboring vegetative cells after fertilization of the egg.

Key to the Species

1. Thallus composed of irregularly branched filaments of rectangular cells growing within the walls of *Nitella* and *Chara*............*C. Nitellarum*
1. Thallus not endophytic in the walls of *Nitella* and *Chara*.............. 2
2. Thallus a prostrate disc or horizontal expanse of regular or irregular outline.............. 3
2. Thallus a cushion of both prostrate and erect branching filaments.............. 6
3. Thallus a series of spreading, branched filaments which are not laterally adjoined.............. 4
3. Thallus a horizontal, continuous disc with the filaments laterally adjoined and sometimes scarcely evident.............. 5
4. Branches not adjoined laterally, radiating from a common center.............. *C. soluta*
4. Branches not adjoined, not radiating, but spreading and branching irregularly.............. *C. irregularis*
5. Cells large, up to 46μ in diameter; thallus a horizontal disc with irregular outline.............. *C. scutata*
5. Cells smaller, 12–15μ in diameter; thallus a horizontal disc with a regular outline.............. *C. orbicularis*
6. Thallus a cushion-like mass of irregularly branching filaments.............. *C. divergens*
6. Thallus a cushion-like mass of regularly branching filaments radiating from a common center.............. *C. pulvinata*

Coleochaete divergens Pringsheim 1860, p. 5
Pl. 17, Figs. 5–7

Thallus composed of irregularly branching filaments which do not radiate from a common center but spread irregularly, forming a cushion of upwardly directed fronds in which many of the cells are setae-bearing. Cells 25–30–(35)μ in diameter, 30–125μ long. Thalli monoecious. Oogonia (including cortex) 130–140μ in diameter.

This species should be compared with *C. pulvinata*, which also forms cushion-like thalli. *C. divergens* lacks the definite radiate arrangement of the branches that characterizes *C. pulvinata*. The vegetative cells of *C. pulvinata* average slightly larger than those of *C. divergens*.

Epiphytic on *Nitella* and other submerged aquatics, or on decaying fragments of vegetation, culms of rushes, etc. Mich., Wis.

Coleochaete irregularis Pringsheim 1860, p. 11
Pl. 17, Figs. 8, 9

Thallus discoidal and monostromatic, with horizontal, branched filaments spreading irregularly; usually free but sometimes adjoined laterally for a short distance; ending so that a circular disc with regular outline is formed. Cells quadrangular, 15–20μ in diameter. Oogonia (including cortex) 40–65μ in diameter.

Common on aquatic vegetation and large filamentous algae in several soft water lakes, acid swamps, and *Sphagnum* bogs. Mich., Wis.

Coleochaete Nitellarum Jost 1895, p. 433
Pl. 18, Figs. 1, 2

Thallus composed of irregularly branched filaments of rectangular or polygonal cells within the membranes of *Nitella* and *Chara* (sometimes epiphytic also). Filaments sometimes adjoined laterally to form a continuous expansion, but usually anastomosing and spreading. Setae few, projecting externally through the membrane of the host. Cells 11–20μ in diameter. Oogonia orbicular.

Common; nearly always found in collections of *Nitella;* especially evident and easy to study when the host plants are allowed to deteriorate slightly. Mich., Wis.

Coleochaete orbicularis Pringsheim 1860, p. 11
Pl. 18, Figs. 3–5

Thallus forming a regular, circular, monostromatic disc of branching filaments radiating from a common center and adjoined laterally. Cells quadrangular, 12–15μ in diameter, 12–20μ long. Oogonia ovoid or subglobose, 45–65μ in diameter and up to 85μ in the long dimension (including cortex).

For purposes of identification this species should be compared with the more irregular thallus of *C. scutata,* which has larger cells.

Common on submerged plant stems and leaves, and on shells. Mich., Wis.

Coleochaete pulvinata A. Braun *in* Kuetzing 1849, p. 425
Pl. 18, Figs. 7, 8

Thallus an epiphytic cushion of irregularly branched filaments radiating from a common center. Cells oblong or pyriform, larger at the anterior end; 25–40μ in diameter, 35–75μ long. Oogonia completely corticated, globose, 135–150μ in diameter (including cortex). Antheridia flask-like, attached just below the oogonia or nearby, on another branch.

To be compared with *C. divergens* Pringsh.

[129]

Common; epiphytic on larger algae and stems of submerged aquatics, in a variety of lakes. Mich., Wis.

Coleochaete scutata de Brébisson 1844, p. 29
Pl. 18, Fig. 9

Thallus discoid, circular or reniform in outline. Filaments compactly adjoined laterally, radiating from a common center. Cells quadrangular, 22–46μ in diameter, 30–65μ long. Dioecious. Oogonia subglobose with cortications above only; 145μ in diameter, 134μ long. Antheridial cells in groups of 4 as a result of segmentation of vegetative cells.

Common in a variety of lakes, on plant stems, shells, glass, etc. Mich., Wis.

Coleochaete soluta (de Bréb.) Pringsheim 1860, p. 6
Pl. 18, Figs. 6, 10, 11

Thallus consisting of loosely spreading, branched filaments, radiating from a common center and forming monostromatic expanses. Filaments tapering very slightly, with bluntly rounded apical cells; not adjoined laterally. Vegetative cells cylindric, 17–27μ in diameter, 50–75μ long. Mature oogonia globose, completely corticated, 100–150μ in diameter. Antheridia flask-shaped, up to 17μ in diameter.

Attached to the culms of reeds and other submerged aquatics in several lakes in northern counties; frequently found on bits of decaying vegetation in *Sphagnum* bogs. Mich., Wis.

CHAETOSPHAERIDIUM Klebahn 1892, p. 276

Plant consisting of a globose or flask-like attached cell from the base of which a lateral cell is cut off, this passing through a tubular elongation of the investing utricle to form another individual. Cell inclosed by a colorless sheath which forms a neck through which a long fine seta extends. Cells have 1 or 2 massive chloroplasts, each with 1 pyrenoid.

Key to the Species

1. Cells with 2 chloroplasts .... *C. ovalis*
1. Cells with 1 chloroplast 2
2. Cells solitary or clustered and inclosed by a common mucilaginous sheath; individual cells usually not interconnected by mucilaginous tubes from their bases .... *C. globosum*
2. Cells remote, or sometimes closely associated, but not inclosed by a common mucilaginous sheath; adjoined from the base by extensions of the utricle or cell sheath .... *C. Pringsheimii*

Chaetosphaeridium globosum (Nordst.) Klebahn 1893, p. 306
Pl. 14, Figs. 6, 7

Unicellular, solitary or gregarious, flask-like, the sheath tapering above to form a conical or cylindrical investment of the long fine seta which extends from the cell. Basal interconnecting tubes usually not apparent. Single chloroplast. Cells 12–20μ in diameter.

Common; attached to filamentous algae and small aquatic plants; frequently free-floating when old, appearing in the tychoplankton in shallow water of bays and swamps. Mich., Wis.

Chaetosphaeridium ovalis G. M. Smith 1916, p. 471
Pl. 14, Fig. 8

Unicellular; solitary or, more often, gregarious in groups of 5–20 ovoid individuals. Sheath indistinct about the cell but clearly evident around the base of the seta. Cell with 2 parietal chloroplasts, each with a pyrenoid. Cells 13–15μ in diameter, 20–22μ long; setae approximately 125μ long.

On submerged aquatics in shallow water. Wis.

Chaetosphaeridium Pringsheimii Klebahn 1892, p. 276
Pl. 14, Fig. 5

Unicellular; cells gregarious, but without a common mucilaginous investment. Sheaths present, often forming long basal tubes so that the cells appear in linear series and interconnected. Cells 9–12μ in diameter; setae up to 300μ long.
Mich.

Chaetosphaeridium Pringsheimii fa. *conferta*
Klebahn 1893, p. 307

A form in which the cells are more closely arranged than in the typical; utricles very short.

In several lakes and in Eagle River, Wis.

DICRANOCHAETE Hieronymus 1887, p. 293; 1892, p. 370

A unicellular epiphyte, hemispherical or flattened against the host, bearing a fine, branched seta which arises from the under side of the cell, the seta with a gelatinous sheath. Chloroplast an inverted, parietal cup with 2–3 pyrenoids. Plants solitary or gregarious. Reproduction by zoospores and isogametes.

The chaetophoraceous character of this genus and its similarity to *Chaetosphaeridium* necessitate its inclusion in the Chaetophorales. The fact that the plant does not reproduce vegetatively by cell division suggests, of course, strong affinities with the Chlorococcales.

[131]

Dicranochaete reniformis Hieronymus 1887, p. 293; 1892, p. 370

Pl. 19, Figs. 1, 2

Cells small, epiphytic, hemispherical in side view (reniform in vertical view), with a branched, vertical gelatinous bristle arising from the base of the cell. Chloroplast bell-shaped and nearly covering the cell wall. Cells 7–12–(32)μ in diameter; setae 40–80–(160)μ long.

Rare on algae in shallow water. Mich., Wis.

FAMILY TRENTEPOHLIACEAE

In this family, branched filaments form cushion-like or felt-like thalli in which there are horizontal portions giving rise to vertical branches. Most genera are without setae or hairs. Another differentiating character is the presence of swollen, somewhat specialized cells for zoospore or gamete production. These are usually borne at the ends of vertical branches. The family as a whole takes up rather unique habitats. Some perforate wood and shells or form encrusting growths over rocks in aerial situations. *Trentepohlia* forms yellow- or brick-red, felt-like encrustations on trees and stones, especially in humid climates. Other forms are endo- or epiphytic on higher plants—*Cephaleuros*, for example, which is capable of producing pathological conditions in the leaves of several southern and tropical angiosperms. Two genera only, *Gongrosira* on shells and *Trentepohlia* on moist, aerial substrates, are represented in our collections.

GONGROSIRA Kuetzing 1843, p. 281

An attached, branched thallus with pseudoparenchymatous, prostrate, and entangled branches giving rise to short, erect filaments terminating in enlarged cells. Growing on wood and old shells; sometimes with rhizoidal branches penetrating the substrate. Cells cylindrical or claviform, with thick, sometimes lamellated walls. Chloroplast 1, a parietal plate with 1 to several pyrenoids.

Key to the Species

Thallus flat; cells slender, 6–14μ in diameter, forming both
    horizontal and downward-growing filaments................................ *G. lacustris*
Thallus pseudoparenchymatous, stouter; cells 15–30μ in diameter,
    forming horizontal, but not downward-growing, filaments........ *G. Debaryana*

Gongrosira Debaryana Rabenhorst 1863, p. 223

Pl. 19, Fig. 3

Attached to and forming green patches on wood, or on shells of mollusks; possessing reduced horizontal branches, giving rise to densely packed, vertical filaments that terminate in enlarged cells, which may form akinetes or serve as sporangia. Cells cylindrical, or with convex lateral walls; 15–30µ in diameter, 35–60µ long. Cell walls becoming thick and lamellate.

On shells. Mich., Wis.

Gongrosira lacustris Brand 1907, p. 502

Growing on wood and stones, forming rather delicate fronds of horizontally growing and downward-projecting branches (which penetrate the substrate when on wood), as well as erect branches with cells about the same size as those in the prostrate filaments. Cells both short- and long-cylindric, 6–14µ in diameter.

Mich.

TRENTEPOHLIA Martius 1817, p. 351

An irregularly branched filament with a prostrate portion from which erect branches arise, forming velvety or cushion-like expansions on moist soil, rocks, logs, and tree trunks; brick- or rusty-red because of an abundance of haematochrome, which often completely masks the chlorophyll. Cells cylindrical or slightly swollen, the walls frequently thickened and roughened externally. Chloroplast a parietal band, usually breaking into irregularly shaped discs, without pyrenoids (the form of the chloroplast often masked by the density of the cell contents and by the red pigment). Branches but very little less in diameter than the main axis and slightly tapering toward the apical region. Terminal cell bluntly rounded at the apex, in some species having a cap of pectose material. Asexual reproduction by means of biflagellate swarmers, formed several to many within globose or ovate sporangia borne on lateral or terminal, hooked or recurved cells; sexual reproduction by isogametes produced in somewhat modified vegetative cells, terminal or intercalary.

Species of this genus frequently enter into association with fungi to form the lichen *Coenogonium*.

Key to the Species

Cells cylindrical, 11–20–(30)µ in diameter ....*T. aurea*
Cells slightly swollen, lateral walls convex,
    up to 35µ in diameter..*T. Iolithus*

Trentepohlia aurea (L.) Martius 1817, p. 351
Pl. 67, Figs. 6–9

Plants rusty-brown or golden-colored, sometimes yellow in shaded areas. Filaments branching variously according to habitat, sometimes sparingly, sometimes repeatedly branched. Cells somewhat inflated

[133]

below, but mostly cylindrical in the branches, which are but slightly reduced in diameter toward the apices. Walls either smooth or externally tubercular. Cells in the main axis 11–30μ in diameter. Gametangia globular, lateral on the branches, or terminal; 20–38μ in diameter. Sporangia usually terminal on curved cells; about the same size as the gametangia.

Forming extensive velvety growths on flat surfaces of moist rocks, cliffs, and tree trunks; in northern counties, especially along the Lake Superior shore. Mich.

Trentepohlia aurea var. polycarpa (Nees & Mont.) Hariot
1889–1890, p. 374

A variety with especially roughened tubercular cell walls; gametangia up to 45μ in diameter, occurring in series.

Mich.

Trentepohlia Iolithus (L.) Wallroth 1833, p. 151
Pl. 19, Figs. 4–8

Plants golden-red, forming a compact felt on moist rocks. Basal filaments composed of fusiform or slightly swollen cells. Branches possessing cylindrical cells and ending in bluntly rounded apices. Cell walls roughened, often clearly lamellated. Sporangia globose; terminal, or lateral on much curved or hooked stalks. Cells 14–35μ in diameter, 24–50μ long; sporangia 20–48μ in diameter.

Rare; forming orange or golden-red, felt-like expansions on rocks and logs in forested ravines. Mich., Wis.

ORDER CLADOPHORALES

In this order the plants are filamentous, usually branched, with multinucleate cells. Some forms are permanently attached, but others become free-floating and occur as tangled mats. In two genera especially, *Cladophora* and *Basicladia*, there is a basal-distal differentiation with the branches gradually attenuated to bluntly rounded apical cells. There are no setae or hair-like extensions of the branches. The chloroplast form has two primary expressions. In some it is a parietal network or reticulum covering most of the cell wall, or there may be many disc-like chloroplasts, also parietal. Each cell contains many pyrenoids. Starch grains frequently are so abundant as to obscure the form of the chloroplasts. In many forms the walls are thick, sometimes lamellate, always without an external mucilaginous layer. This accounts for the fact that members of this order are often heavily epiphytized by diatoms and other algae. Most species are macroscopic, attaining a length of 10 cm. or more, and are coarse and wiry.

[134]

Vegetative reproduction is carried on by fragmentation and in one genus, *Pithophora,* by large akinetes. Sexual reproduction is by biflagellate isogametes, usually produced in large numbers in the terminal or subterminal cells of the branches. Biflagellate zoospores are common, especially in *Cladophora.* There is one family.

FAMILY CLADOPHORACEAE

Characteristics as described for the order. Plants branched, either regularly or irregularly, although in a few species branches are rare or wanting. Attached feathery tufts in either flowing or quiet water, or occurring as free-floating mats.

Key to the Genera

1. Filaments growing on the backs of turtles; branching only from the base ....*Basicladia*
1. Filaments not growing on the backs of turtles; branching or not branching 2
2. Filaments not branching .... *Rhizoclonium* (in part)
2. Filaments branching 3
3. Filaments repeatedly branched and showing distinct basal-distal differentiation in the habit of branching; branches gradually attenuated toward the apices; akinetes lacking ....*Cladophora*
3. Filaments not repeatedly branched, not clearly showing basal-distal differentiation, akinetes sometimes present 4
4. Filaments branching irregularly; enlarged akinete cells frequent .... *Pithophora*
4. Filaments branching irregularly; akinetes wanting 5
5. Branches short and rhizoidal, mostly 1- or few-celled .... *Rhizoclonium* (in part)
5. Branches long, multicellular 6
6. Branching sparse but rather regular, the branches mostly diverging dichotomously, or oppositely .... Old, floating thalli of *Cladophora*
6. Branching frequent, irregular, the branches mostly at right angles to the main axis, scarcely attenuated toward the apices ..... *Rhizoclonium* (in part)

CLADOPHORA Kuetzing 1843, p. 262

A repeatedly-branched filamentous thallus with basal-distal differentiation; attached when young but in some species becoming free-floating; forming feathery tufts on substrates, especially in flowing water; branching alternate, opposite, or sometimes di- or trichotomous, the branches smaller than the main axis, or at least tapering slightly toward the apices; cells cylindrical or swollen; walls thick and lamellate in most species, sometimes thin and firm; chloroplast a parietal reticulum which sometimes becomes fragmented and appears as numerous discs; pyrenoids present; asexual reproduction by zoospores; sexual reproduction by isogametes produced in apical or subapical, unspecialized cells.

Species of this genus are almost invariably confined to hard or semi-hard water and in general are index organisms for high pH.

Cladophora is a fairly large genus composed of many marine and fresh-water species. There is a great deal of variation within a species with respect to cell shape and manner of branching, apparently related to environmental conditions. The interpretations of these variations by taxonomists, and the limitations which have been set up to define species in the genus are conflicting. A great deal of confusion has arisen in the literature because these variables and intergrading forms have been separately described. An examination of supposedly authentically named herbarium material is of little help to the student, because the specimens frequently are not in agreement with the original descriptions. There is a great need, therefore, for a monographic review of the genus and a clarification of the synonymy which exists among the names attached to herbarium specimens and in the literature.

Most of the species found in our region are free-floating, lacustrine forms. Several of these show considerable variation according to whether they are in quiet backwaters or are subjected to wave action. Those which seem to have clear-cut characters are listed, together with some of their varieties, and an attempt has been made to describe those expressions which are most likely to be found in this area. Many collections have been set aside for further study. Although the following key is of limited value, it may serve to separate the species which I consider recognizable in our collections.

Key to the Species

1. Plants growing at great depths (10–50 meters); permanently attached; branching very irregular and interlacing, the branches arising from below the apex of the cell............*C. profunda* var. *Nordstedtiana*
1. Plants not growing at great depths; branches less irregular, arising from the apices of the cells of the main axis 2
2. Plants permanently attached, mostly in flowing water, forming feathery tufts of repeatedly branched filaments 3
2. Plants free-floating, at least when mature; when attached, coarser and less regularly branched than above.. 4
3. Branching increasing toward the upper portions of the frond to form dense terminal tufts ....*C. glomerata*
3. Branching decreasing toward the upper portions of the frond to form penicillate tufts..*C. callicoma*
4. Filaments very crooked and bent; cells ovate or pyriform, or irregularly swollen..*C. fracta*
   (See also the varieties of *C. fracta,* some of which have cylindrical cells, although the filament is still rather crooked and does not show the definite arbuscular habit of the species mentioned below.)
4. Filaments straight; cells cylindrical or very slightly swollen 5

5. Branching irregular and sparse, often unilateral; short,
   1-celled curved branches frequent_____ *C. oligoclona*
5. Branches pluricellular; filaments straight_____ 6
6. Branches infrequent, often arising at right angles to the main filament;
   seldom bearing branches of the second order_____ *C. insignis*
6. Branches frequent, repeatedly branched, the branches long and tapering,
   up to 20 times their diameter in length_____ *C. crispata*

Cladophora callicoma Kuetzing 1843, p. 267

Attached, densely branched tufts in flowing water. Filaments stout, 75–125μ in diameter at the base, with the cells mostly cylindrical, narrowing to cells which are 35–50μ in diameter and inflated in the upper branches. Cells 6–8 diameters long below, shorter above (2–4 diameters long). Branching both dichotomous and, especially in the secondary branchings, alternate. Ends of the branches bluntly rounded.

Mich.

Cladophora crispata (Roth) Kuetzing 1843, p. 264
Pl. 19, Figs. 9–11

Free floating except when young, forming rather delicate thalli of successively branched filaments with long, cylindrical cells, gradually attenuated in the branches to slightly narrowed but rounded apices. Main axis 40–75μ in diameter; branches 20–35μ in diameter. Cells up to 20 times their diameter in length. Cell walls relatively thin.

This species should be compared with the attached *C. glomerata*, which occasionally is found free-floating.

Floating in shallow water of lakes. Mich., Wis.

Cladophora fracta (Dillw.) Kuetzing 1843, p. 263
Pl. 20, Figs. 1–6

Floating; forming coarse, light-green masses of irregularly branched filaments, the branches often curving. Cells irregularly swollen or clavate (cylindrical in some of the varieties, however); 60–120μ in diameter in the main axis, 1–3 times their diameter in length; 20–40μ in diameter in the ultimate branches, 3–6 times their diameter in length.

This is an extremely variable species, and there are many described forms and expressions. Although the typical plant is considerably branched, some of the forms have few branches and are confusingly similar to *Rhizoclonium* spp.

Mich., Wis.

Cladophora fracta var. *normalis* Rabenhorst *ex* Heering 1921, p. 44

Filament 80–120μ in diameter, very slightly branched, the branches about the same diameter as the main axis, becoming attenuated to about 25μ. Cells cylindrical, with thick, lamellate walls.

In our collections a number of forms or expressions appear which agree with descriptions and designations given by Heering (*l.c.*, pp. 44–46).

Floating in lakes. Mich., Wis.

Cladophora fracta var. *lacustris* (Kuetz.)
Brand *ex* Heering 1921, p. 46
[*C. fracta* fa. *subsimplex* Kuetzing 1845]
Pl. 20, Fig. 7

A coarse, rigid form with very little branching, the branches arising irregularly, often at right angles to the main axis. Cells long and cylindrical, 25–60μ in diameter.

This variety greatly resembles a form of *Rhizoclonium* because of the almost total lack of branching.

Floating. Mich., Wis.

Cladophora glomerata (L.) Kuetzing 1845, p. 212
Pl. 20, Figs. 8, 9; Pl. 21, Figs. 1, 2

Attached, forming dark green, fluffy or streaming arbuscular thalli, usually in flowing water. Filaments successively and regularly branched, the branches usually crowded in the upper limits. Cells very slightly attenuated toward the apices of the branches, which are bluntly pointed. Main axis 75–100μ in diameter, 6–7 times the diameter in length; cells in the branches 35–50μ in diameter, 3–6 times the diameter in length.

This species is variable, and many forms are recognized. Few of them seem to be sharply defined, and some authors regard the names assigned to them as synonymous with other species.

Attached to rocks and cement walls, especially in waterfalls and rapids. Mich., Wis.

Cladophora glomerata fa. *Kuetzingiana*
(Grunow) Heering 1921, p. 39
Pl. 21, Fig. 3

A form which is much more elongate and more loosely branched than the typical. Main axis up to 74μ in diameter; branches 39–42μ in diameter; ultimate branches 19–21μ in diameter.

On stones along lake shores. Wis.

Cladophora insignis (C. A. Ag.) Kuetzing 1845, p. 217

Pl. 21, Figs. 4, 5

Floating; the thallus composed of straight, coarse, and sparsely branched filaments, the branches often arising at right angles to the main axis and very slightly smaller. Main filament 75–120μ in diameter, the cells cylindrical or swollen; branches 40–70μ in diameter, 4–6 times the diameter in length.

In hard water lakes. Mich., Wis.

Cladophora oligoclona Kuetzing 1845, p. 218

Pl. 21, Figs. 6–8

Floating or attached; thallus little branched, the branches opposite or dichotomous, the secondary branches bearing many alternate or unilaterally disposed, clavate or thorn-like 1-celled branches. Cells in the main axis cylindrical, 45–55μ in diameter, 2–6 times the diameter in length; branches of the first order 30–40μ in diameter, the cells cylindrical, up to 10 times the diameter in length.

In lakes. Wis.

Cladophora profunda var. *Nordstedtiana* Brand 1902a, p. 34

Pl. 22, Figs. 1–4

Thallus composed of attached, irregularly and much branched filaments growing from a prostrate, colorless, rhizoidal portion. Basal branches directed downward and ending in colorless rhizoid-like cells; upper branches irregular in arrangement, often entangled and interlocked to form snarled tufts. Cells irregularly inflated or sub-cylindric, 25–50μ in diameter, 36–250μ long in the main axis. Walls of cells encrusted or merely roughened with lime and sometimes with iron deposits, giving a rust-colored appearance to older plants.

This species has been found growing on rocks at 10–15 meters in Trout Lake, Wisconsin. Well developed plants were found on large stones obtained by dredging, which had rims or ridges of iron deposits at the level where the stone emerged from the bottom sediment. The iron deposit apparently is the same as that noted on the walls of the plant and suggests the possibility of having been laid down by physiological action.

PITHOPHORA Wittrock 1877, p. 48

Free-floating, branched, coenocytic filaments of very long, cylindrical or slightly swollen cells; branches arising at right angles to the main axis. Swollen, cask-like or cylindrical akinetes frequent, sometimes giving rise to branches (akinetes wanting in young plants). Chloroplast a parietal net, sometimes close and dense, covering the entire wall, containing many pyrenoids.

Under some environmental conditions (particularly in aquaria) plants develop luxuriantly without forming akinetes, but akinetes are so generally present that they constitute an identifying character. The akinetes may be intercalary or both intercalary and terminal. Branching is frequent, but there is no definite order or basal-distal differentiation in the thallus.

Key to the Species

1. Filaments slender, up to 70μ in diameter;
   akinetes all cask-shaped _____*P. oedogonia*
1. Filaments stouter; akinetes cylindrical, ovoid, or irregular_____ 2
2. Akinetes all the same shape in the filament, alternating with the
   vegetative cells throughout much of the plant; filaments
   95–140μ in diameter_____ _____*P. Mooreana*
2. Akinetes variously shaped within the same filament, 1–3 in a
   series; filaments 75–100μ in diameter _____*P. varia*

Pithophora Mooreana Collins 1912, p. 97
Pl. 22, Figs. 5, 6

Filaments highly branched to the third order, (65)–95–140μ in diameter; tertiary branches about 50μ in diameter. Both terminal and intercalary akinetes cylindrical, those terminating the branches becoming acuminate, the tips broadly rounded, 95μ in diameter, up to 215μ long.

Floating mats in shallow pond. Wis.

Pithophora oedogonia (Mont.) Wittrock 1877, p. 55
Pl. 22, Figs. 7–10

Filaments slender, 45–70μ in diameter; branching mostly solitary, rarely opposite. Cells long and cylindrical, as much as 20 times their diameter in length. Akinetes cylindrical or slightly swollen to cask-shaped, conical, or more often acuminate, when terminal, 57–144μ in diameter, 95–380μ long.

Forming tangled mats in quiet water, Yellow River, Wisconsin.

Pithophora varia Wille 1902, Phyc. Bor.-Amer. No. 983
Pl. 24, Figs. 5, 6

Filaments with branches about the same diameter as the main axis, 75–105μ wide, narrowing to 43–70μ at the apices. Akinetes variable within the same filament; ovate, cylindrical or irregularly ovate; 1–3 in a series; 60–112μ in diameter, 70–240μ long.

Mich.

RHIZOCLONIUM Kuetzing 1843, p. 261
emend. Brand 1908, p. 69

Filamentous, coarse and wiry, forming tangled floating mats or caught about submerged aquatics; either unbranched or with short rhizoidal branches, occasionally with long, multicellular branches but without distinct basal-distal differentiation in the plan of branching. Cells stout, either short- or long-cylindric; rarely with slightly inflated lateral walls, which in most species are thick and lamellate, and often completely overgrown with epiphytic diatoms and blue-green algae. Chloroplast a parietal reticulum, often dense and difficult of interpretation, sometimes loose and appearing as if composed of many irregularly shaped ovate chloroplasts, each with a pyrenoid.

Some species of *Rhizoclonium* should be compared with certain expressions of *Cladophora* which sometimes form floating tangled mats of slightly branched filaments with thick-walled cells.

Key to the Species

1. Filaments frequently branched, usually very irregularly; branches many-celled_____ 3
1. Filaments seldom branched, or if so, 1-celled_____ 2
2. Filaments up to 80µ in diameter; walls as much as 13µ thick_____*R. crassipellitum*
2. Filaments (10)–25–35–(52)µ in diameter; wall up to 2µ thick_____*R. hieroglyphicum*
3. Filaments 12–22µ in diameter; branches simple_____*R. fontanum*
3. Filaments 60–64–(108)µ in diameter; branches of a second order frequently present_____*R. Hookeri*

Rhizoclonium crassipellitum West & West 1897, p. 35. fa.
Pl. 23, Fig. 1

Filaments very coarse and wiry; unbranched; twisted and entangled into a floating mat. Cells cylindrical or sometimes slightly inflated, with thick lamellate walls; 50–70–(80)µ in diameter,100–342µ long.

The specimens are tentatively assigned to *R. crassipellitum*. Plants were not uncommonly found forming tangled clots about submerged vegetation in hard water lakes. They are much too stout and the wall too thick to agree with the larger forms of *R. hieroglyphicum* (C. A. Ag.) Kuetz *R. crassipellitum* is an African species, although a variety (var. *robustum* G. S. West) has been reported from the West Indies. Transeau (1917) reports a form from Holland, Michigan, which he questionably refers to *R. crassipellitum*. The African and West Indies plants were collected on moist soil.

[141]

Herbarium specimens of *R. crassipellitum* show the filaments to be stout, but the cells are short-cylindric and more irregular than in our specimens. Also in the tropical specimens there are rhizoidal branches which arise from an inflated cell in the main axis. It is thought that our specimens may be an aquatic form of the subaerial typical expression of *R. crassipellitum*.

Floating in sloughs and lakes. Mich., Wis.

Rhizoclonium fontanum Kuetzing 1843, p. 261
Pl. 23, Fig. 2

Filaments coarse, crooked or straight. Cells cylindrical but with uneven lateral walls that are $1.5–2\mu$ thick; $12–22\mu$ in diameter and up to 80μ long. Branches multicellular, very slightly smaller than the main axis.

Tychoplanktonic mats in shallow water of lakes. Mich., Wis.

Rhizoclonium hieroglyphicum (C. A. Ag.) Kuetzing 1845, p. 206
Pl. 23, Fig. 3

Filaments long, wiry, unbranched. Cells with walls of variable thickness, usually thin in the typical form; $10–52\mu$ in diameter, 2½ to 10 times their diameter in length. Chloroplast varying with the age of the plant, sometimes a close net and very dense, or an open reticulum.

Common in standing water, especially in hard water lakes. Mich., Wis.

Rhizoclonium hieroglyphicum var. *Hosfordii* (Wolle) Collins
1909, p. 169

A variety with short, lateral branches. Filaments $36–40\mu$ in diameter. Cells up to 6 times the diameter in length; with thicker walls.

Rhizoclonium hieroglyphicum and its various expressions are more widely distributed and more common than any other species of the genus in our collections. The diameter of the cell and the thickness of the wall vary greatly. Some specimens agree with var. *macromeres* Wittrock, a stout plant $20–30–(53)\mu$ in diameter, with cells 6–12 times their diameter in length. Inasmuch as confusion exists within the nomenclature of the various forms of this species no attempt is made to assign names to the several expressions found in our region other than the var. *Hosfordii*. At present it seems best to refer all unbranched, long-jointed plants to *R. hieroglyphicum*.

Mich.

Rhizoclonium Hookeri Kuetzing 1849, p. 383
Pl. 23, Figs. 4–7

Filaments crisp, freely-branching, composed of long, cylindrical or irregularly inflated cells, 60–64μ in diameter (rarely up to 103μ) and 6–7 times their diameter in length. Cells of the branches about the same diameter as those of the main filament. Secondary branching not uncommon.

In hard water lakes and ponds; entangled about submerged aquatics. Mich., Wis.

BASICLADIA Hoffman & Tilden 1930, p. 380

Thallus a coarse, erect, and attached filament with prostrate, rhizoidal portions serving as anchoring organs, giving rise to the erect filaments which branch near the base, but sparsely. Basal cells cylindrical, very long, becoming shorter and wider above. Walls thick and lamellate. Chloroplast a thin, sometimes dense, parietal reticulum. Sexual reproduction by isogametes produced in unmodified cells in the distal region of the filament (Hamilton, 1948); asexual reproduction by zoospores possible also.

This genus contains only 2 known species at present, both of which are specifically epizoic on the backs of turtles although they may occur on other hard surfaces also. The filaments are often tightly compacted and entangled, making it difficult to observe the origin of branches and the exact relation of the rhizoidal basal portions of the thallus to the erect filaments.

Key to the Species

Cells 12–20μ in diameter below, 35μ in diameter
in the distal region _____ *B. chelonum*
Cells 50μ in diameter below, 120μ in diameter
in the distal region _____ _____ _____ *B. crassa*

Basicladia chelonum (Collins) Hoffmann & Tilden 1930, p. 382
Pl. 23, Figs. 8–12

Frond a coarse, attached, erect filament; branching only at the base, just above the attaching organs, which anchor the plant to the backs of turtles (especially the snapping turtle, *Chelydra serpentina*). Main filament 12–20μ in diameter below and up to 35μ in diameter in the distal region. Cells cylindrical, especially the basal cells, which may be as much as 50 times their diameter in length. Walls thick and lamellate.

On backs of snapping turtles; widely distributed. Mich., Wis.

[143]

Basicladia crassa Hoffmann & Tilden 1930, p. 382

Pl. 77, Figs. 11–13

Thallus composed of tangled prostrate filaments giving rise to upright filaments as much as 2 cm. long; upright branches rigid, 50–120μ in diameter in the distal portions, composed of thick-walled coenocytic units up to 3175μ in length, the vertical filaments sometimes dichotomously branched, sometimes to the second order, but straight and rigid, gradually tapering toward the anterior end.

On backs of snapping turtles in northern lakes; producing zoospores in August. Mich., Wis.

ORDER OEDOGONIALES

In this order the plants are filamentous, either simple or branched, and always attached, at least when young. The cells are sometimes cylindrical, but usually they show a slight inflation or increase in size toward the anterior end. In *Oedogonium*, cell division occurs by the interpolation of a new section or cylindrical piece that develops by the stretching of a thick inner ring of material which forms near the anterior end of a cell. The rupturing of the wall as the elongation occurs leaves an external ring-like scar at the anterior end of the cell. The chloroplast is a parietal reticulum containing several pyrenoids. The cells are uninucleate. Asexual reproduction occurs by large multiflagellate zoospores formed singly in undifferentiated vegetative cells. Sexual reproduction is heterogamous. The female organ (oogonium containing a single egg) is much enlarged and opens by a pore or lid to permit the entrance of the antherozoid, which is a small motile gamete produced either in box-like antheridial cells in filaments the same size as those which bear the oogonia, or in dwarf male plants epiphytic on the female.

There is one family, the Oedogoniaceae. Two of the three genera which compose this family are well represented in the region, but *Oedocladium* has not yet been reported. *Oedocladium* is a genus small in number of known species. Some of them undoubtedly occur here and are to be sought for in terrestrial rather than aquatic habitats.

FAMILY OEDOGONIACEAE

Characters as described for the order.

Special terms used in describing taxonomic features of the Oedogoniaceae will be found in the Glossary. For complete descriptions of the reproductive and morphological characteristics of this family, see Tiffany (1930 and 1937).

Key to the Genera

BULBOCHAETE C. A. Agardh 1817, p. XXIX

Thallus a unilaterally branched filament arising from a basal cell which has a holdfast organ (adhesive disc or rhizoidal processes). Cells cylindrical, ovoid, or rarely repand; usually distinctly larger at the anterior end where, by oblique cell division, a branch may arise; vertical elongation of the plant is accomplished by successive divisions of the basal cell only. Approximately all cells bearing a long seta with a bulbous base, arising obliquely from the anterior end of the cell. Chloroplast a parietal net-work, either dense or loose, covering almost the entire lateral walls. Female reproductive organs (oogonia) swollen ovoid, oblong, or globose, formed by two divisions of a vegetative cell to produce an outer gametangium and usually supporting suffultory cells, patent or erect; the oogonium surmounted only by a seta, or by a vegetative cell, or an androsporangium; in some species the oogonia sessile and lateral, in all cases, with transverse band-like scars of cell division localized in the median part of the oogonium. Division of the supporting suffultory cell either basal, median, or superior. Male cells either small rectangular cells transformed from the vegetative cells of the female filament, or in dwarf male filaments growing epiphytically on the female plant, having developed from special spores (androspores) produced in androsporangia which may be either idio- or gynandrosporous. Oospore usually filling the oogonium, the wall of the oospore thick, and usually decorated with pits, areolae, ribs, or reticulations, but smooth in some species.

The habit of branching and the characteristic bulbous setae make this genus easy of identification. It is desirable to examine many individuals, however, to obtain a complete analysis of the combination of characteristics which define each species. Besides the wall markings of the oospore and the location of the division of the suffultory cell, the range in size of the sex organs, as well as of the oospore and the vegetative cells must be considered. A key to the known species of the region is given below. Attention of the reader is called to the fact that these include only about half of the total species. Reference should be made to the keys in Tiffany (1930, 1937) if plants in question do not readily key out in the scheme used below.

Key to the Species

Bulbochaete alabamensis Transeau & Brown *in* Tiffany 1928, p. 142
Pl. 25, Figs. 1–2

Nannandrous; gynandrosporous. Vegetative cells elongate, (22)–25.9–(40)μ in diameter, (62)–92.5–(111)μ long. Oogonia globose or depressed-globose, (74)–77–92μ in diameter, (68)–78.4–(88)μ long. Oospores depressed-globose, outer spore wall areolate, (70)–75–90μ in diameter, (62.9)–68–86μ long. Male filaments scattered on vegetative cells; 14.8μ in diameter, 29.6μ long. Antheridium 14.8μ in diameter, 14.8μ long. Division of suffultory cell superior.

Attached to grass in a ditch running through a *Sphagnum* bog. Wis.

Bulbochaete angulosa Wittrock & Lundell *in* Wittrock 1875, p. 45
Pl. 25, Fig. 4

Nannandrous; gynandrosporous. Vegetative cells (13)–14–16–(18)μ in diameter, (20)–25–40–(45)μ long. The oogonia angularly globose (in our specimens), 38.6–42μ in diameter, (33)–38.6–39μ long. Oospores the same shape as the oogonium; outer spore wall smooth; (34)–36–40μ in diameter. Dwarf males on the oogonia, 7–8μ wide, 19μ long. Androsporangium 11μ in diameter, 8μ long. Division of the suffultory cell supramedian (sometimes nearly superior).

Our specimens agree throughout with descriptions of this species except that the division of the suffultory cell is more nearly superior than median.

On grass in a roadside fosse. Wis.

Bulbochaete borealis Wittrock 1871, p. 138
Pl. 25, Fig. 3

Nannandrous; gynandrosporous. Vegetative cells (14.8)–16–(21)μ in diameter, (20)–21–26–(42)μ long. Oogonia depressed-globose (40)–44.4–46–(48)μ in diameter, 36–37–(38)μ long. Oospores depressed-globose; outer spore wall finely scrobiculate; 38–(46)μ in diameter, 32–33–(38)μ in length. Male filaments on the suffultory cell (in our specimens) 10μ in diameter, 22μ long. Division of the suffultory cell superior.

Attached to grass in a small acid lake. Wis.

Bulbochaete Brebissonii Kuetzing 1854, Tab. Phyc. 4, p. 19

Nannandrous; gynandrosporous. Vegetative cells 17–20μ in diameter, 50–90μ long. Oogonia depressed-subquadrangular-globose, 42–50μ in diameter, 37–45μ long. Oospores depressed-globose, outer spore wall coarsely scrobiculate; 40–80μ in diameter, 35–43μ long. Dwarf males 10–12μ in diameter, 28–33μ long. Division of suffultory cell basal.

Mich.

Bulbochaete congener Hirn 1900, p. 346
Pl. 25, Fig. 5

Nannandrous; idioandrosporous. Vegetative cells elongate, (19)–21–27μ in diameter, (40)–46–50–(75)μ long. Oogonia depressed-globose, 44.8–54μ in diameter, 37–43.9–(48)μ long. Oospores globose; wall scrobiculate; (42)–44.8–(52)μ in diameter, (35)–38–46μ long. Male plants on the oogonium, 9–15μ in diameter, 29–34μ long. Antheridial cell 10–11μ wide, (14)–15.6–17μ long. Division of suffultory cell inframedian.

On grass in a marginal ditch of a *Sphagnum* bog. Wis.

Bulbochaete crassa Pringsheim 1858, p. 72

Pl. 25, Fig. 8

Nannandrous; gynandrosporous. Vegetative cells 22–26μ wide, 44–(60)–70μ long. Oogonia subdepressed-globose, (52)–56–60μ in diameter, 42.5–47–(51)μ long. Oospores depressed-globose with scrobiculate outer wall, 51–58μ in diameter, 41–48μ long. Male filaments on the oogonia; stipe 9–11μ wide, 32–33–(41)μ long. Division of the suffultory cell median or supramedian.

On grass in the marshy end of a lake. Wis.

Bulbochaete crassiuscula Nordstedt 1877, p. 30

Nannandrous; idioandrosporous. Vegetative cells 22–27μ in diameter, 55–148μ long. Oogonia subquadrangularly depressed-globose; patent; 60–78μ in diameter, 50–62μ long. Oospores depressed-globose; outer spore wall coarsely scrobiculate; 58–76μ in diameter, 48–60μ long. Male filaments 12–14μ in diameter, 30–34μ long. Division of suffultory cell superior (or supramedian).

Mich.

Bulbochaete crenulata Pringsheim 1858, p. 72

Nannandrous; gynandrosporous. Vegetative cells 16–20μ in diameter, 32–70μ long. Oogonia subdepressed-globose; patent; 43–48μ in diameter, 35–43μ long. Oospores depressed-globose; outer spore wall coarsely crenulate or scrobiculate; 40–46μ in diameter, 33–40μ long. Male filaments 9–10μ in diameter, 24–26μ long. Division of suffultory cell median or inframedian.

Mich.

Bulbochaete dispar Wittrock *in* Wittrock & Nordstedt 1882, No. 401

Pl. 25, Figs. 6, 7

Nannandrous; gynandrosporous. Vegetative cells (16)–25–30μ in diameter, (32)–38–70–(65)μ long. Oogonia depressed-globose, 44–56–(58)μ in diameter, (42)–50–51μ long. Oospores depressed-globose; the outer spore wall scrobiculate; 40–58μ in diameter, 38–48–(50)μ long. Male filaments 11–12μ in diameter, (23)–37–38μ long. Division of the suffultory cell supramedian to superior.

On grass in small lakes. Mich., Wis.

Bulbochaete elatior Pringsheim 1858, p. 73

Pl. 26, Fig. 3

Nannandrous; gynandrosporous. Vegetative cells (13)–15–17–(18)μ in diameter, (20)–36–56–(63)μ long. Oogonia depressed-globose, (34)–45–48μ in diameter, (31)–38–39μ long. Oospores depressed-globose; outer spore wall smooth (middle wall wrinkled?); (32)–43μ in diameter, (29)–36μ long. Male filaments on the suffultory cell, 11μ in diameter, 19–32μ long. Division of the suffultory cell basal.

On *Chamaedaphne* stems and grass in a small pond. Wis.

Bulbochaete Furberae Collins 1918, p. 142
Pl. 26, Fig. 2

Nannandrous; gynandrosporous. Vegetative cells (10)–16–19μ in diameter, (30)–32–67–(75)μ long. Oogonia depressed-globose, (36)–43.7–(45.6)μ in diameter, (27)–30.4–33–(34)μ long. Oospores depressed-globose; outer spore wall deeply scrobiculate; (34)–39–40μ in diameter, (25)–28–30–(32)μ long. Male filaments on the oogonia, 8μ in diameter, 22μ long. Division of the suffultory cell inferior.

On *Drepanocladus* at bottom of a soft water lake, depth 35 feet. Wis.

Bulbochaete gigantea Pringsheim 1858, p. 71
Pl. 26, Fig. 1

Nannandrous; gynandrosporous. Vegetative cells (15)–20–32μ in diameter, 45–100–(112)μ long. Oogonia subdepressed-globose, 60–70μ in diameter, 50–58μ long. Oospores depressed-globose; the outer spore wall reticulate-scrobiculate; 58–68μ in diameter, 48–56μ long. Male filaments on the oogonia; antheridia 13–14μ in diameter, 20–30μ long. Division of the suffultory cell submedian.

In several small lakes and ponds. Mich., Wis.

Bulbochaete hiloensis (Nordst.) Tiffany 1937, p. 13
Pl. 24, Fig. 1

Nannandrous; gynandrosporous. Vegetative cells 14–20μ in diameter, 24–48μ long. Oogonia ellipsoid, patent, 28–33μ in diameter, 43–51μ long. Oospores ellipsoid; outer spore wall with longitudinal crenulate costae; 26–30μ in diameter, 38–45μ long. Male filament 13–17μ in diameter, 30–34μ long. Division of suffultory cell superior. Mich.

Bulbochaete insignis Pringsheim 1858, p. 73
Pl. 26, Figs. 4–6

Nannandrous; gynandrosporous. Vegetative cells (19)–20–22–(25)μ in diameter, (48)–55–62–(88)μ long. Oogonia oblong-ellipsoid, (46)–48–56μ in diameter, (70)–74–90μ long. Oospores oblong-ellipsoid; outer spore wall with high thick denticulate costae (that in our specimens show evidence of being also coarsely punctate); (44)–46μ in diameter, (70)–72–92μ long. Male filaments on the oogonia, 14–18μ in diameter, 26–30μ long. Division of the suffultory cell supreme.

Attached to submerged aquatics in many lakes. Mich., Wis.

Bulbochaete intermedia DeBary 1854, p. 72
Pl. 26, Fig. 9

Nannandrous; gynandrosporous. Vegetative cells 17–19.5μ in diameter, 31–45–(70)μ long. Oogonia globose or depressed-globose, (40)–43–44–(48)μ in diameter, (37)–40–41μ long. Oospores globose or subglobose; outer spore wall deeply scrobiculate; (38)–49μ in diameter, (30)–33–38μ long. Male filaments on the oogonia, (7.9)–9–10μ in diameter, 31–35μ long. Division of the suffultory cell median.

On *Drepanocladus* and reeds in soft water lakes. Mich., Wis.

Bulbochaete intermedia var. depressa Wittrock 1875, p. 44
Pl. 26, Fig. 8

A variety in which the vegetative cells are longer than in the typical, 14–19μ in diameter 30–80–(88)μ long. Oogonia depressed-globose 42–46μ in diameter, 30–40μ long. Oospores depressed-globose, outer spore wall scrobiculate; 40–44μ in diameter, 28–38μ long.

In a swampy lake. Wis.

Bulbochaete minor A. Braun in Kuetzing 1849, p. 422
Pl. 26, Fig. 7

Nannandrous; gynandrosporous. Vegetative cells (18)–19–22–(25)μ in diameter, 26–48–(50)μ long. Oogonia ovoid, 30–40μ in diameter, (58)–59–62–(69)μ long. Oospores ovoid; the outer spore wall with longitudinal costae; 29–36–(40)μ in diameter, 54–60–(67)μ long. Male filaments on the oogonia or the suffultory cell. Division of the suffultory cell supreme.

In a roadside fosse. Mich., Wis.

Bulbochaete minuta West & West 1902a, p. 126

Nannandrous; gynandrosporous. Vegetative cells 9–12μ in diameter, 18–35μ long. Oogonia depressed-globose; patent or erect; 29–35μ in diameter, 24–27μ long. Oospores depressed-globose; wall smooth; 27–33μ in diameter, 22–25μ long. Male filaments 6–7μ in diameter, 18–20μ long. Suffultory cell not divided.

Mich.

Bulbochaete mirabilis Wittrock 1871, p. 137
Pl. 27, Figs. 1, 2

Monoecious. Vegetative cells 15.6–20–(25)μ in diameter, (20)–25–40–(56)μ long. Basal cell 15.6μ in diameter, 23.4μ long. Oogonia oblong-ellipsoid, 26–33μ in diameter, 44–58μ long. Oospores oblong to subcylindric; outer spore wall longitudinally ribbed with costae; 25–31–(37)μ in diameter, 43–56μ long. Antheridial cells 7–10μ in diameter, 8μ long. Division of the suffultory cell superior.

On submerged aquatics in lakes and in a roadside fosse. Mich., Wis.

Bulbochaete mirabilis fa. immersa (Wittr.) Hirn 1900, p. 352

Vegetative cells 13–17μ in diameter, 16–30μ long. Oogonia 25–33μ in diameter, 40–48μ long. Oospores 23–30μ in diameter, 38–46μ long. Antheridia 7–11μ in diameter, 6–8μ long.
Mich.

Bulbochaete Nordstedtii Wittrock 1875, p. 44
Pl. 27, Fig. 3

Nannandrous; gynandrosporous. Vegetative cells 14.8–(18)μ in diameter, (28)–30–45–(85)μ long. Oogonia depressed-globose; below androsporangium (usually); 33–38–(43)μ in diameter, 29–36μ long. Oospores depressed-globose; outer spore wall finely scrobiculate; 32–34–(41)μ in diameter, 27–34μ long. Male filaments on the oogonia, 12μ in diameter, 23μ long. Division of the suffultory cell superior.

Attached to grass in a ditch through a Sphagnum bog. Wis.

Bulbochaete obliqua Lundell in Hirn 1900, p. 344
Pl. 24, Fig. 7

Nannandrous; gynandrosporous or idioandrosporous. Vegetative cells 21–27μ in diameter, 42–108μ long. Oogonia depressed-globose; patent; 55–64μ in diameter, 43–51μ long. Oospores depressed-globose; wall smooth; 53–62μ in diameter, 40–49μ long. Male filaments 9–10μ in diameter, 40–57μ long. Division of suffultory cell median.
Mich.

Bulbochaete polyandria Cleve in Wittrock 1871, p. 140
Pl. 27, Figs. 4, 5

Nannandrous; idioandrosporous. Vegetative cells elongate, 14.8–20μ in diameter, (45)–74–100μ long. Oogonia depressed-globose, 46.2μ in diameter, (32)–33.3–(42)μ long. Oospores the same shape as the oogonia; outer membrane pitted with scrobiculations; (37)–44μ in diameter, (30)–33–40μ long. Dwarf male filaments on the oogonia, 8–9μ in diameter, 23–26μ long. Division of suffultory cell superior, sometimes nearly median.

On Drepanocladus on bottom of a soft water lake, depth 35 feet. Wis.

Bulbochaete praereticulata Jao 1936, p. 71
Pl. 27, Fig. 6

Nannandrous; idioandrosporous. Vegetative cells $(16)-22-25\mu$ in diameter, $(39)-40-93\mu$ long. Walls of vegetative cells and oogonia with spiral punctations. Oogonia globose or depressed-globose, $54-58-(62.4)\mu$ in diameter, $(41)-50-54-(58)\mu$ long. Oospores globose; the outer spore wall reticulate-scrobiculate; $52-58\mu$ in diameter, $(41)-48.7-56\mu$ long. Male filaments numerous (in our specimens), on the suffultory cell or oogonium; stipe 9.7μ in diameter, 44.8μ long. Antheridial cell 11.7μ in diameter, 13.6μ long. Division of suffultory cell median.

On culms of rushes. Wis.

Bulbochaete pygmaea Pringsheim 1858, p. 74
Pl. 27, Figs. 7, 8

Nannandrous; gynandrosporous. Vegetative cells $(11)-14.8\mu$ in diameter, $(10)-15-18\mu$ long. Oogonia ellipsoid, $(22)-23-27\mu$ in diameter, $29-37-(40)\mu$ long. Oospores ellipsoid; the outer spore wall ribbed with longitudinal costae which are punctate; $20-22-(23)\mu$ in diameter, $(30)-33-34-(38)\mu$ long. Dwarf male filaments on suffultory cell, $11-12\mu$ in diameter, $22-23\mu$ long; stipe 14.8μ long. Suffultory cell undivided.

Attached to grass in a ditch through a *Sphagnum* bog. Wis.

Bulbochaete rectangularis Wittrock 1871, p. 142
Pl. 27, Figs. 9, 10

Nannandrous; gynandrosporous. Vegetative cells $15-23\mu$ in diameter, $(20)-40-46\mu$ long. Oogonia oblong-ellipsoid, $32-39\mu$ in diameter, $45-56-(65)\mu$ long. Oospores ellipsoid; outer spore wall costate; $29-37\mu$ in diameter, $(47)-49-55\mu$ long. Dwarf male filaments usually on the oogonia; stipe $14-18\mu$ in diameter, $22-27\mu$ long. Antheridial cell $8-10\mu$ wide, $5-7\mu$ long. Division of the suffultory cell supreme.

On culms of *Scirpus*. Mich., Wis.

Bulbochaete regalis (Wittr.) Tiffany 1934, p. 323
Pl. 28, Figs. 1, 2

Nannandrous; gynandrosporous. Vegetative cells $18-21-(26)\mu$ in diameter, $54-117\mu$ long. Oogonia ellipsoid or ovoid-ellipsoid; erect; $(58)-68-70\mu$ in diameter, $90-108\mu$ long. Oospores broadly ellipsoid; outer spore wall with anastomosing, crenulate costae; $54-61\mu$ in diameter, $90-98\mu$ long. Dwarf male filaments on the oogonia; stipe 12.5μ in diameter. Antheridial cell 10.8μ in diameter. Division of suffultory cell supreme.

Attached to grass in soft water lakes. Wis.

Bulbochaete repanda Wittrock 1875, p. 55
Pl. 28, Figs. 3, 4

Nannandrous; gynandrosporous. Vegetative cells frequently repand, (12)–15.6–17μ in diameter, (24)–39–60μ long. Oogonia oblong-ellipsoid, (26)–31.2–36μ in diameter, (43)–48–50–(58)μ long. Oospores oblong-ellipsoid; the outer spore wall showing about 6 costae with serrate margins; (20)–27.3–(33)μ in diameter, (40)–46.8–50μ long. Dwarf male filaments 13.6μ in diameter, 35μ long, attached to the oogonia. Division of suffultory cell superior.

On culms of rushes. Mich., Wis.

Bulbochaete reticulata Nordstedt 1877, p. 32
Pl. 28, Fig. 5

Nannandrous; gynandrosporous. Vegetative cells (20)–22–26μ in diameter, (42)–65–87μ long. Oogonia broadly ellipsoid, 42–50–(52)μ in diameter, 63–80–(85)μ long. Oospores ovoid; outer spore wall with anastomosing costae which are denticulate and transversely adjoined by ridges to teeth in other costae; 42–50μ in diameter, 64–70–(83)μ long. Dwarf male filaments on the oogonia; stipe 17–20μ in diameter, 30–33μ long. Antheridial cell 10–13μ in diameter, 6–10μ long. Division of suffultory cell superior.

In a ditch through a *Sphagnum* bog. Wis.

Bulbochaete scrobiculata (Tiff.) Tiffany 1934, p. 323
Pl. 28, Fig. 6

Nannandrous; gynandrosporous. Vegetative cells 8–13–(16)μ in diameter, 28–42μ long. Oogonia depressed-globose (rarely almost globose), 28–38–(44)μ in diameter, 28–36μ long. Oospores depressed-globose, 26–35–(42)μ in diameter, 26–34μ long. Dwarf male filaments on the suffultory cell, 8μ in diameter, 17.5μ long. Division of suffultory cell basal.

On grass in a roadside swamp. Wis.

Bulbochaete sessilis Wittrock 1872, p. 18
Pl. 28, Fig. 12

Nannandrous; gynandrosporous. Vegetative cells (19)–20–22–(26)μ in diameter, 40–90–(108)μ long. Oogonia depressed-globose, 50–60–(64)μ in diameter, (42)–44–50μ long. Oospores depressed-globose; with smooth walls; (48)–50–54–(60)μ in diameter, 42–48–(50)μ long. Dwarf male filaments on the oogonia; stipe 9–10μ in diameter, 25–30μ long. Antheridial cell 10–12μ in diameter, 15–21μ long. Division of suffultory cell superior.

In a kettlehole pond. Wis.

Bulbochaete setigera (Roth) C. A. Agardh 1817, p. 71

Pl. 28, Figs. 10, 11

Nannandrous; gynandrosporous. Vegetative cells elongate, 20–28μ in diameter, (62)–121–140μ long. Oogonia depressed-globose, 70–80μ in diameter, (40)–56–65μ long. Oospores depressed-globose; outer spore wall finely scrobiculate; (64)–67–77μ in diameter, (53)–57–62μ long. Dwarf male filaments on or near the oogonia, 4–5μ in diameter, 26.6μ long. Division of suffultory cell median or supramedian.

Attached to grass in a ditch through a *Sphagnum* bog; on submerged aquatics in lakes and ponds. Mich., Wis.

Bulbochaete tenuis (Wittr.) Hirn 1900, p. 368

Nannandrous; gynandrosporous. Vegetative cells 13–16μ in diameter, 20–40μ long. Oogonia suboblong-ellipsoid; erect or patent; 22–26μ in diameter, 42–48μ long. Oospores ellipsoid or oblong-ellipsoid; outer spore wall with longitudinal costae; 20–24μ in diameter, 40–46μ long. Male filaments 12–14μ in diameter, 24–31μ long. Division of suffultory cell superior.

Mich.

Bulbochaete valida Wittrock 1872, p. 17

Pl. 24, Fig. 8

Nannandrous; gynandrosporous. Vegetative cells 23–27μ in diameter, 46–95μ long. Oogonia depressed-globose; patent; 59–70μ in diameter, 48–56μ long. Oospores depressed-globose; outer spore wall coarsely scrobiculate; 57–68μ in diameter, 46–54μ long. Male filaments 9–10μ in diameter, 43–51μ long. Division of suffultory cell median.

Mich.

Bulbochaete varians Wittrock 1871, p. 143

Pl. 28, Figs. 7–9

Nannandrous; gynandrosporous. Vegetative cells 17–19.5–(22)μ in diameter, 22–33–(54.6)μ long. Oogonia oblong-ellipsoid to subcylindrical, (30)–31.2–(36)μ in diameter, (44)–48–50.7–(54)μ long. Oospores oblong-ellipsoid; outer spore wall ribbed with serrate costae; (27.3)–28–34μ in diameter, (47)–46.8–(52)μ long. Dwarf male filaments on the oogonia or suffultory cell; 12.6μ in diameter; 27.3μ long. Antheridial cell 8μ in diameter, 12μ long. Division of suffultory cell supreme.

Attached to submerged grass. Mich., Wis.

Bulbochaete varians var. *subsimplex* (Wittr.) Hirn 1900, p. 357

Vegetative cells 13–18μ in diameter, 16–34μ long. Oogonia 26–30μ in diameter, 39–46μ long. Oospores with either smooth or serrate margins, 24–28μ in diameter, 37–44μ long. Male filaments 11–14μ in diameter, 20–31μ long.

Mich.

OEDOGONIUM Link 1820, p. 5

Attached, unbranched filaments (sometimes becoming free-floating in age). Cells cylindrical or enlarged toward the anterior end, where one or more ring-like scars resulting from cell division are usually apparent. Chloroplast a parietal reticulum with many pyrenoids. Nucleus at the periphery of the protoplast. Swollen female cells (oogonia) present at maturity, one to several in each filament. Male cells (antheridia) either short, compartment-like cells, each bearing one or two antherozoids, occurring in filaments the same size as those which bear the oogonia, or minute male filaments growing epiphytically on the female plants. Fertilization by the entrance of an antherozoid through a pore or lid of the oogonium wall; resulting oospore of various shapes, surrounded by a wall of two or three layers, which may be smooth or variously decorated.

In the identification of *Oedogonium* species, the size of the vegetative cells, the shape and size of the oogonia, the form and decoration of the oospore wall, and the location of the antheridial cells are the more important differentiating and specific characters. There is no single specific feature which may be used for identification purposes but rather a combination of the above-mentioned features. Some of these (such as size, for example) vary considerably within a given species, and the student should bear this in mind, especially when using keys. Less than half the known species of *Oedogonium* are listed here; consequently the key is incomplete. The reader is referred to Tiffany (1930, 1937) when plants in question cannot be identified by the scheme used below.

The genus *Oedogonium* is a large one and is easily divided into 10 sections on the basis of the location of the male sex organs and the character of the oogonium. Following are keys, one to the sections and one to the species. (The species are alphabetically arranged within each section.)

Key to the Sections of the Genus *Oedogonium*

1. Plants dioecious, the male plants dwarfed and epiphytic
   on the female (nannandrous)_____ 2
1. Plants dioecious or monoecious, the male plants approximately the same
   size as the female plants, or with the antheridia in
   the same filament as the oogonia_____ 7
2. Plants idioandrosporous_____ 3
2. Plants gynandrosporous, or both gynandrosporous and
   idioandrosporous in the same species_____ 4

Key to the Species

[157]

15. Oospores with one spiral ridge; vegetative cells 30–33µ in
diameter; oogonia 63–67µ in diameter _____ *Oe. Sawyerii*
15. Oospores with 4–7 spiral ribs; vegetative cells 15–35µ in
diameter; oogonia 51–64µ in diameter _____ *Oe. stellatum*
16. Oogonia with longitudinal ribs on the inner surface; outer spore
wall with 35–40 longitudinal ribs _____ *Oe. striatum*
16. Oogonia wall smooth; oospores with fewer longitudinal ribs _____ 17
17. Ribs of oospore wall 16–24, anastomosing _____ 18
17. Ribs of oospore wall 25–35, not anastomosing _____ *Oe. Wolleanum*
18. Oogonia 65–85µ in diameter; oospores
61–80µ in diameter _____ *Oe. perfectum*
18. Oogonia smaller, 57–66µ in diameter;
oospores 51–62µ in diameter _____*Oe. cyathigerum*
19. Oospore wall layers smooth ____ _____ 20
19. Oospore wall decorated ____ _____ 25
20. Oogonia sexangular-ellipsoid_____ 21
20. Oogonia globose or subglobose _____ 22
21. Oogonia 36–48µ in diameter; oospores 34–40µ
in diameter _____ __ _____ *Oe. subsexangulare*
21. Oogonia 29–33µ in diameter; oospores 27–31µ
in diameter _____ *Oe. sexangulare*
22. Vegetative cells 8–9µ in diameter _____ *Oe. depressum*
22. Vegetative cells larger _____ 23
23. Oospores 27–33µ in diameter_____ *Oe. Braunii*
23. Oospores larger _____ 24
24. Pore supramedian (sometimes median), vegetative
cells 14–18µ in diameter _____ *Oe. magnum*
24. Pore median; vegetative cells averaging larger,
17–22µ in diameter _____*Oe. gallicum*
25. Oospore wall spiny _____ 26
25. Oospore wall with 4–7 spiral ridges_____ *Oe. spiralidens*
26. Vegetative cells 18–30µ in diameter_____*Oe. echinospermum*
26. Vegetative cells smaller _____ 27
27. Oogonia terminal, subellipsoid_____ *Oe. hispidum*
27. Oogonia intercalary, globose or obovoid _____ *Oe. hystricinum*
28. Opening of oogonium inferior or inframedian_____ 29
28. Opening of oogonium median, supramedian, or superior_____ 31
29. Walls of vegetative cells undulate _____ 30
29. Walls of vegetative cells not undulate, but capitellate_____*Oe. ambiceps*
30. Oogonia 56–68µ in diameter_____ *Oe. sinuatum*
30. Oogonia 48–55µ in diameter_____ *Oe. undulatum*
31. Opening median or supramedian_____ 32
31. Opening clearly superior or supreme_____ 40
32. Oogonia (46)–48–63µ in diameter_____ 33
32. Oogonia smaller _____ 34
33. Vegetative cells 14–16µ in diameter; oogonia 46–52µ
in diameter, opening supramedian_____ *Oe. Kozminskii*
33. Vegetative cells 16–22µ in diameter; oogonia
53–63µ in diameter _____ *Oe. brasiliense*
34. Opening supramedian _____ 35
34. Opening median____ _____ 36
35. Oogonia depressed-globose, 25–32µ long, with
12–16 longitudinal ridges_____ *Oe. oelandicum*

56. Oogonia 32–38μ in diameter _____ _Oe. laeve_
56. Oogonia smaller _____ 57
57. Oogonia solitary, 23–29μ in diameter _____ _Oe. cryptoporum_
57. Oogonia nearly always in a series up to 5;
    averaging smaller, 18–25μ in diameter _____ _Oe. vulgare_
58. Pore supramedian _____ 59
58. Pore superior (species in the following group are separable
    by a combination of characteristics) _____ 61
59. Oospores 40–48μ in diameter _____ _Oe. tyrolicum_
59. Oospores smaller _____ 60
60. Oospores 31–41μ in diameter; vegetative cells
    31–144μ long; pore nearly superior _____ _Oe. varians_
60. Oospores 34–45μ in diameter; vegetative cells
    24–77μ long, pore nearly median _____ _Oe. plusiosporum_
61. Oospore wall with longitudinal ribs or costae _____ 62
61. Oospore wall smooth _____ 63
62. Oogonia 39–48μ in diameter _____ _Oe. paludosum_
62. Oogonia 54–63μ in diameter _____ _Oe. carolinianum_
63. Vegetative cells capitellate _____ 64
63. Vegetative cells not capitellate _____ 65
64. Vegetative cells 8–13μ in diameter; oogonia 32–37μ in
    diameter (cells sometimes somewhat capitellate) _____ _Oe. Hirnii_
64. Vegetative cells 13–15μ in diameter; oogonia
    38–40μ in diameter _____ _Oe. patulum_
65. Oospores ellipsoid or subellipsoid _____ 66
65. Oospores globose, subglobose, ovoid, or subovoid _____ 69
66. Vegetative cells 20–24μ in diameter _____ _Oe. Sodiroanum_
66. Vegetative cells smaller _____ 67
67. Vegetative cells 8–14μ in diameter;
    oogonia 75–105μ long _____ _Oe. pseudo-Boscii_
67. Vegetative cells larger _____ 68
68. Vegetative cells 12–21μ in diameter; oospores
    subellipsoid, 48–74μ long _____ _Oe. Richterianum_
68. Vegetative cells 44–52μ in diameter; oospores
    subglobose, 80–93–(98)μ long _____ _Oe. Kurzii_
69. Vegetative cells spirally punctate _____ _Oe. curtum_
69. Vegetative cells with smooth walls _____ 70
70. Filaments (mature) relatively short, not more than 20 cells long;
    oogonia usually in a series up to 4 _____ _Oe. curtum_
70. Filaments longer; oogonia solitary (rarely 2) _____ 71
71. Oogonia 32–36μ in diameter _____ 72
71. Oogonia larger _____ 74
72. Vegetative cells 15–18μ in diameter _____ _Oe. intermedium_
72. Vegetative cells narrower _____ 73
73. Oospores 28–31μ in diameter, 32–39μ long _____ _Oe. Hirnii_
73. Oospores 30–37μ in diameter, 32–46μ long _____ _Oe. globosum_
74. Oospores globose or subglobose _____ 75
74. Oospores obovoid or ovoid _____ 76
75. Vegetative cells 20–30μ in diameter _____ _Oe. Vaucherii_
75. Vegetative cells 17–19μ in diameter _____ _Oe. fennicum_
76. Oogonia oblong or elongate-obovoid; oospores
    42–47μ in diameter _____ _Oe. upsaliense_
76. Oogonia obovoid to ovoid _____ 77

[160]

[164]

SECTION 1

Macrandrous—Dioecious—Poriferous

Oedogonium americanum Transeau 1917, p. 231

Pl. 43, Figs. 18, 19

Macrandrous; dioecious. Vegetative cells cylindrical, 28–48μ in diameter, 40–100μ long. Oogonia solitary; globose to depressed-globose, or somewhat ellipsoid; opening by a superior pore; 40–76μ in diameter, 48–70μ long. Oospores globose to ellipsoid-globose (or depressed-globose); median wall scrobiculate; 38–74μ in diameter, 46–56μ long. Antheridia 20–28μ in diameter, 4–12μ long,

Mich.

Oedogonium amplum Magnus & Wille _in_ Wille 1884, p. 40

Macrandrous; dioecious. Vegetative cells (female) cylindrical, 46–54μ in diameter, 70–160μ long. Oogonia ovoid or ovoid-ellipsoid; opening by a superior pore; 75–90μ in diameter, 83–115μ long. Oospores broadly ellipsoid to globose; wall smooth; 72–85μ in diameter, 77–100μ long. Antheridia 40–50μ in diameter, 8–20μ long.

Mich.

Oedogonium angustum (Hirn) Tiffany 1934, p. 324

Pl. 29, Figs. 1, 2

Macrandrous; dioecious. Vegetative cells elongate-cylindric, (14)–19–30–(36)μ in diameter, (57)–70–75–(330)μ long. Oogonia usually solitary (sometimes as many as 4 in a series); subovoid; opening by a superior pore; (40)–42–53μ in diameter, (62)–83–110μ long.

Oospores oblong-ovoid; wall smooth; (40)–45–48–(53)μ in diameter, (40)–57–70–(89)μ long. Antheridia 18–22μ in diameter, 7–10–(15)μ long.

Attached to submerged aquatics. Mich., Wis.

Oedogonium anomalum Hirn 1900, p. 112
Pl. 29, Figs. 3, 4

Macrandrous; dioecious. Vegetative cells stout, cylindric; (37)–40–50μ in diameter, 80–85–(300)μ long. Oogonia solitary; subovoid or cylindric-ovoid; opening by a superior pore; (54)–56.3–64μ in diameter, (68)–75–85μ long. Oospores globose or subglobose; not filling the oogonia; wall of oospore smooth, thick; (48)–54–56–(60)μ in diameter, (52)–54–58–(61)μ long; antheridia (not observed in our specimens) 30–40μ in diameter, 6–18μ long.

This plant should be compared with *Oe. crassum*, in which the oogonium is ovoid or ellipsoid and in which the oospore more nearly fills the oogonium.

Mich., Wis.

Oedogonium areolatum Lagerheim 1890, p. 80
Pl. 31, Figs. 8, 9

Macrandrous; dioecious. Vegetative cells cylindric, (16)–17–19–(21)μ in diameter, (59)–65–151–(165)μ long. Oogonia 1–4; obovoid or somewhat globose; opening by a superior pore; 48–56–(60)μ in diameter, 60–70–(75)μ long. Oospores subellipsoid; nearly or quite filling the oogonia; middle spore membrane coarsely areolate; (45)–46–52–(57)μ in diameter, 48–56–(60)μ long. Antheridia 14–15μ in diameter, 8–9–(10)μ long.

Attached to reeds and grasses. Mich., Wis.

Oedogonium argenteum Hirn 1900, p. 289
Pl. 31, Figs. 10, 11

Macrandrous; dioecious. Vegetative cells cylindric, 14.2–23–(28)μ in diameter, (80)–107–133–(160)μ long. Oogonia solitary; globose or obovoid-globose; opening by a superior pore; 44–46–(52)μ in diameter, (48)–62.9–(66.6)μ long. Oospores globose or ovoid; not filling the oogonia; outer spore wall deeply scrobiculate; (42.5)–43–48μ in diameter, (44)–48–50μ long. Antheridia 14–18–(22)μ in diameter, 8–10μ long.

Attached to reeds in a gravel pit, and in a small pond. Mich., Wis.

Oedogonium argenteum fa. *michiganense* Tiffany 1930, p. 97
Pl. 43, Figs. 4, 5

Similar to the typical form except that the median spore wall is scrobiculate; the pore supramedian.

Oedogonium australe (G.S. West) Tiffany 1934, p. 324
Pl. 30, Figs. 1, 2

Macrandrous; dioecious. Vegetative cells cylindrical, (12)–14–16μ in diameter, (46)–56–78–(80)μ long. Oogonia solitary; globose or subglobose; (39)–40–41–(43)μ in diameter, (40)–42–43μ long; opening by a median pore. Oospores globose; nearly filling the oogonia; wall thick, the outer layer echinate; (31)–32–34μ in diameter, 31–34–(35)μ long. Antheridia 12–15μ in diameter, 15–16μ long.

This species should be compared with *Oe. suecicum,* which is smaller throughout but has some morphological similarities.

In a roadside fosse, and in a ditch through a *Sphagnum* bog. Mich., Wis.

Oedogonium Boscii (Le Cl.) Wittrock 1874, p. 34
Pl. 30, Figs. 5, 6

Macrandrous; dioecious. Vegetative cells cylindric, (14)–16–17–(23)μ in diameter, (45)–129–148μ long. Oogonia solitary; ellipsoid or subcylindrical-ellipsoid; opening by a superior pore; (39)–51–52μ in diameter, (75)–93–96–(110)μ long. Oospores ellipsoid; not filling the oogonia; the outer and middle layers of the spore wall with 22–28–(35) longitudinal ribs (not anastomosing in our specimens); (36)–43–46μ in diameter, (56)–59–70μ long. Antheridia (not observed in our collections) 13–14μ in diameter, 6–16μ long.

In a small pond. Wis.

Oedogonium capillare (L.) Kuetzing 1843, p. 255
Pl. 43, Figs. 13, 14

Macrandrous; dioecious. Vegetative cells cylindric, 35–56μ in diameter, 36–120μ long. Oogonia solitary; cylindric; not much greater in diameter than the vegetative cells; opening by a superior pore; 40–60μ in diameter, 45–75μ long. Oospores globose to ovoid, or cylindric-globose; wall smooth; 30–52μ in diameter, 35–65μ long. Antheridia 30–48μ in diameter, 5–10μ long.

Mich.

Oedogonium capilliforme Kuetzing 1853, Tab. Phyc., p. 12;
Wittrock 1872, p. 21
Pl. 44, Figs. 7, 8

Macrandrous; dioecious. Vegetative cells cylindric, usually elongate; 28–32–(38)μ in diameter, (42)–45–96–(120)μ long. Oogonia solitary; obovoid; opening by a superior pore; (42)–43–48–(50)μ in diameter, (51)–52–58–(62)μ long. Oospores subglobose; not filling the oogonia; wall smooth; (37)–38–42–(45)μ in diameter, 38–48–(50)μ long. Antheridia 20–25μ in diameter, 8–10μ long.

Attached to submerged grass in a pooled seep on bank of a lake. Mich., Wis.

Oedogonium capilliforme var. *australe* Wittrock *in* Wittrock & Nordstedt 1886, Algae Exsic. No. 704
Pl. 29, Figs. 5, 6

Macrandrous; dioecious. Vegetative cells cylindric, 24–31.4–(36)μ in diameter, (26)–65–103μ long. Oogonia solitary; obovoid-globose; opening by a superior pore; (37)–38–55.5μ in diameter, 53–55.5μ long. Oospores subglobose; not filling the oogonia; wall thick, smooth; 35–50μ in diameter, 36–55μ long. Antheridial cells 21–26μ in diameter, 4–9μ long.

In a roadside fosse. Wis.

Oedogonium cardiacum (Hass.) Wittrock 1871, p. 135
Pl. 29, Figs. 7, 8

Macrandrous; dioecious. Vegetative cells cylindric, rather stout; 18.5–25–(30)μ in diameter, (50)–60–85–(200)μ long. Oogonia solitary; globose or subcordiform-globose; opening by a supramedian pore; 48–70μ in diameter, (48)–52–78μ long. Oospores globose; not filling the oogonia; wall thick, smooth; 39–42–(60)μ in diameter. Antheridia (not observed in our collections) 15–21μ in diameter, 10–14μ long. Cell below the oogonium sometimes enlarged in our specimens, 25.9μ in diameter, 48μ long.

In an acid pond and attached to grass in a swampy pond. Mich., Wis.

Oedogonium crassum (Hass.) Wittrock 1872, p. 20
Pl. 44, Figs. 9, 10

Macrandrous; dioecious. Vegetative cells cylindric, 30–42–(50)μ in diameter, (69)–72–340μ long. Oogonia 1–2; ovate; opening by a superior pore; (60)–65–80μ in diameter, 75–115–(120)μ long. Oospores ellipsoid or ellipsoid-globose; not filling the oogonia; wall smooth; 56–68–(76)μ in diameter, 60–86–(96)μ long. Antheridia (not observed in our collections) 28–33μ in diameter, 8–20μ long.

Attached to grass in flowing water; in several lakes and ponds. Mich., Wis.

Oedogonium crenulatocostatum Wittrock 1878, p. 139
Pl. 30, Fig. 7

Macrandrous; dioecious. Vegetative cells cylindric, 11.5–13–(18)μ in diameter, 25–51–(125)μ long. Oogonia 1–6; obovoid or ellipsoid;

opening by a superior pore; $30-36\mu$ in diameter, $40-61-(65)\mu$ long. Oospores ellipsoid; not filling the oogonia; median spore wall with about 20 longitudinal ribs with crenulate edges; $27-35\mu$ in diameter, $40-65\mu$ long. Antheridia $10-12\mu$ in diameter, $13-14\mu$ long.

Rather common, mostly in small ponds and roadside swamps. Mich., Wis.

Oedogonium crenulatocostatum var. cylindricum
(Hirn) Tiffany 1937, p. 42
Pl. 30, Figs. 13–15

Similar to the typical plant, but with oogonia and oospores distinctly cylindric-oblong, and with the costae of the oospore wall nearly entire or smooth. Oogonia $30-35\mu$ in diameter, $42-78-(81)\mu$ long; oospores $27-30-(34)\mu$ in diameter, $(42)-52-62\mu$ long.

Attached to submerged aquatics with several other species of *Oedogonium*. Wis.

Oedogonium crenulatocostatum var. cylindricum fa. major
Prescott 1944, p. 352

A form larger than the typical. Vegetative cells 25.9μ in diameter, 88.8μ long. Oogonia 1–3; obovoid-ellipsoid or cylindric-oblong; opening by a superior pore; $42.5-44\mu$ in diameter, $63-74\mu$ long. Oospores ovoid-ellipsoid; wall thick; middle layer with about 16 longitudinal ribs which are quite smooth (not crenulate); $37-39\mu$ in diameter, $55.5-57\mu$ long.

Floating in backwater of small lakes. Wis.

Oedogonium diversum (Hirn) Tiffany 1934, p. 324
Pl. 29, Figs. 9–11

Macrandrous; dioecious. Vegetative cells stout, cylindric; $40-(43)-44.4-(46)\mu$ in diameter, $(45)-56-92-(130)\mu$ long. Oogonia solitary; obovoid; opening by a superior pore; $(43)-55-56-(62)\mu$ in diameter, $(46)-66-70\mu$ long. Oospores globose or subglobose; not filling the oogonia; wall thick, smooth; $(43)-45-55.5\mu$ in diameter, $(40)-55.5-(58)\mu$ long. Cells of male filament $33.3-37-(40)\mu$ in diameter, $(50)-56-92-(120)\mu$ long. Antheridia 2–5, $33-37\mu$ in diameter, 6μ long.

Pooled seeps. Wis.

Oedogonium exocostatum Tiffany 1921, p. 272
Pl. 30, Figs. 11, 12

Macrandrous; dioecious. Vegetative cells cylindric, $12.9-22.2-(25)\mu$ in diameter, $(72)-85-92-(140)\mu$ long. Oogonia 1-2-(3); ellipsoid or ellipsoid-globose; opening by a superior pore; $40-50-(52)\mu$ in diameter, (60)–80–96μ long. Oospores ellipsoid; nearly filling the oogonia; wall of two layers, the outer with 13–15 longitudinal ribs with smooth edges; 44.5μ in diameter, 66.6μ long. Antheridia 14.8μ in diameter, 7.5μ long. Suffultory cell 27.7μ in diameter, 65–85μ long.

Attached to submerged aquatics in shallow water. Wis.

Oedogonium giganteum Kuetzing 1845, p. 200
Pl. 30, Figs. 3, 4

Macrandrous; dioecious (male plants not observed in our collections). Vegetative cells cylindrical, (30)–46–48–(50)μ in diameter, 65–200–(225)μ long. Oogonia solitary; cylindric-obovoid or ellipsoid; opening by a superior pore; (53)–55–60–(69)μ in diameter, 65–95–(106)μ long. Oospores ellipsoid; nearly filling the oogonium; wall of three layers, the middle layer with longitudinal rows of deep pits; (51)–55–65μ in diameter, 90–93–(103)μ long.

In shallow swamp. Wis.

Oedogonium gracilius (Wittr.) Tiffany 1934, p. 324
Pl. 29, Figs. 12–14

Macrandrous; dioecious. Vegetative cells cylindric, 20–25μ in diameter, (40)–51–100μ long. Oogonia solitary; obovoid-globose; opening by a superior pore; 36–42μ in diameter, 44.4–46–(57)μ long. Oospores globose; nearly filling the oogonia; wall smooth; 33–35–(39)μ in diameter, 33–35–(44)μ long. Antheridia (not observed in our collections) 19–22μ in diameter, 7–10μ long.

Attached to grass in several shallow water habitats. Mich., Wis.

Oedogonium grande Kuetzing 1845, p. 200
Pl. 29, Figs. 15–17

Macrandrous; dioecious. Vegetative cells cylindric, (28)–33–37–(40)μ in diameter, (70)–122–159–(210)μ long. Holdfast cell elongate. Oogonia 1–5; ellipsoid or subovoid; opening by a superior pore; (49)–59.2–60μ in diameter, (74)–86–110μ long. Oospores the same shape as the oogonia, which they completely fill; wall smooth; (47)–52–58μ in diameter, (60)–70–80–(94)μ long. Antheridia (not observed in our collections) 25–33μ in diameter, 11–18μ long.

Attached to submerged grass and leaves in swampy end of a lake, Wis.; also Mich.

Oedogonium grande var. aequatoriale Wittrock in Wittrock & Nordstedt 1893, Algae Exsic. No. 1016
Pl. 29, Fig. 18

Macrandrous; dioecious. Vegetative cells cylindric, (22)–24–26–(33)μ in diameter, (70)–88–90–(165)μ long. Oogonia 1–5; ob-

[170]

long or subovoid; opening by a superior pore; (44)–51.8–52μ in diameter, (75)–88–90–(44)μ long. Oospores the same shape as the oogonia, which they nearly fill; wall smooth; (42)–48–49μ in diameter; (50)–77.7–81μ long. Antheridia not observed.

On submerged grass in a small pond. Wis.

Oedogonium Kjellmanii Wittrock in Hirn 1900, p. 127

Macrandrous; dioecious. Vegetative cells cylindric; female 15–22μ in diameter, 45–120μ long; male 14–18μ in diameter, 56–120μ long. Oogonia solitary; obovoid or subellipsoid; opening by a superior pore; (39)–41–47–(50)μ in diameter, 60–75μ long. Oospores ellipsoid or subellipsoid; the outer layer of the wall ribbed on the inner surface, and the middle layer also, with 35–45 crenulate, anastomosing ribs; inner layer smooth; 39–47μ in diameter, 48–57μ long. Antheridia 12–15μ in diameter, 4–12μ long, occurring in series up to 30.

Typical plant not observed in our collections.

Oedogonium Kjellmanii var. granulosa Prescott 1944, p. 352
Pl. 30, Figs. 8–10

Macrandrous; dioecious. Vegetative cells cylindric, 19.5–23.4μ in diameter, 109–117μ long. Oogonia solitary; ellipsoid; opening by a superior pore; 53–55μ in diameter, 97–102μ long. Oospores ellipsoid; not filling the oogonia; wall of 3 layers, the outer smooth, the middle layer with about 22 longitudinal ribs, which are crenulate and granular, frequently interrupted, but not anastomosing; 50.7–53μ in diameter, 74–76μ long. Antheridia not observed.

This plant should be compared with Oe. margaritiferum Nordst. & Hirn, which has similarly marked oospore walls in both the outer and middle layers. The variety differs from the typical form of Oe. Kjellmanii by its larger size and in the markings of the spore wall.

On old wood in a roadside tarn. Wis.

Oedogonium Landsboroughii (Hass.) Wittrock 1875, p. 35
Pl. 32, Figs. 1, 2

Macrandrous; dioecious. Vegetative cells cylindric, stout; (31)–35–40μ in diameter, (74)–85–90–(240)μ long. Oogonia solitary; obovoid or ovate; opening by a superior pore; (62)–63–78μ in diameter, (78)–85–115μ long. Oospores ovoid or broadly ellipsoid-ovoid; wall smooth; (55)–59–70μ in diameter, (68)–73–102μ long. Antheridia (not observed in our collections) 27–35μ in diameter, 9–20μ long.

This plant should be compared with *Oe. crassum* and *Oe. martinicense* Hirn. From the latter, which is monoecious, it is easily distinguishable if favorable material is at hand.

In kettlehole pond. Mich., Wis.

Oedogonium lautumniarum Wittrock *in* Wittrock & Nordstedt 1877, Algae Exsic. No. 7, p. 22

Macrandrous; dioecious. Vegetative cells cylindric, 16–22μ in diameter, 40–110μ long. Oogonia solitary (sometimes 2); subovoid-globose; opening by a supramedian or sometimes nearly superior pore; 40–49μ in diameter, 45–51μ long. Oospores subglobose (subangular-globose); filling the oogonia; wall smooth; 36–46μ in diameter, 35–47μ long. Antheridia 14–17μ in diameter, 7–10μ long.
Mich.

Oedogonium longiarticulatum (Hansg.) Tiffany 1934, p. 325

Macrandrous; dioecious. Vegetative cells cylindric, 12–15μ in diameter, 60–90μ long. Oogonia solitary; obovoid to subellipsoid; opening by a superior pore; 27–32μ in diameter, 58–60μ long. Oospores obovoid to ellipsoid; outer wall smooth; median wall with 12–18 longitudinal, crenate costae; 24–30μ in diameter, 44–52μ long. Antheridia 8–11μ in diameter, 10–15μ long.
Mich.

Oedogonium Magnusii Wittrock 1875, p. 38

Macrandrous; dioecious. Vegetative cells cylindric, elongate; 7–10μ in diameter, 12–40μ long. Oogonia 1–3; depressed-globose; opening by a median pore; 24–27μ in diameter, 21–26μ long. Oospores depressed-globose and filling the oogonia; the outer wall smooth, the median wall coarsely scrobiculate; 22–25μ in diameter, 18–23μ long. Antheridia 8–10μ in diameter, 5–11μ long.
Mich.

Oedogonium majus (Hansg.) Tiffany 1934, p. 324

Macrandrous; dioecious. Vegetative cells cylindric, 36–46μ in diameter, 80–200μ long. Oogonia 1–3; subobovoid to nearly ellipsoid; opening by a superior pore; 52–58μ in diameter, 75–90μ long. Oospores subobovoid, filling the oogonia; wall smooth; 50–64μ in diameter, 68–88μ long. Antheridia 30–36μ in diameter, 10–16μ long.
Mich.

Oedogonium mexicanum Wittrock 1878, p. 138

Macrandrous; dioecious. Vegetative cells cylindric, 34–41μ in diameter, 60–140μ long. Oogonia cylindric-ovoid; opening by a superior pore; 53–63μ in diameter, 76–110μ long. Oospores cylindric-

ovoid; filling the oogonia; wall smooth; 51–60μ in diameter, 63–80μ long. Antheridia 28–35μ in diameter, 7–17μ long.
Mich.

Oedogonium moniliforme Wittrock 1875, p. 40

Macrandrous; dioecious. Vegetative cells cylindric, 9–13μ in diameter, 30–72μ long. Oogonia 1–5; pyriform or somewhat ovoid-globose; opening by a supramedian to nearly superior pore; 23–33μ in diameter, 28–42μ long. Oospores globose or depressed-globose; not filling the oogonia; outer wall smooth, median wall scrobiculate; 22–32μ in diameter, 22–32μ long. Antheridia 10–12μ in diameter, 8–13μ long.
Mich.

Oedogonium orientale Jao 1934, p. 85
Pl. 41, Figs. 8, 9

Macrandrous; dioecious. Vegetative cells cylindric, 12–15μ in diameter, 55–66μ long. Oogonia solitary; oblong-ellipsoid; opening by a superior pore; 38–42μ in diameter, 79–82μ long. Oospores ellipsoid to oblong; filling the oogonia laterally but not longitudinally; outer spore wall smooth, middle wall layer with about 18 longitudinal ribs which are entire and continuous; 32–34μ in diameter, 54–56μ long. Antheridia (not observed in our collections) 11–14μ in diameter, 8–17μ long.

Our specimens lack the terminal, hyaline seta described for *Oe. orientale.* They are tentatively assigned to this species, however, on the basis of oospore characters and size. The discovery of the male filaments might make it necessary to describe our specimens as a new species.

Attached to submerged grass. Wis.

Oedogonium plagiostomum Wittrock 1875, p. 41
Pl. 32, Figs. 3, 4

Macrandrous; dioecious. Vegetative cells cylindric, rather stout, (18.5)–22–25–(27)μ in diameter. Oogonia solitary; ovate-globose; opening by a superior pore; (38)–42–49μ in diameter, (44.4)–60–65μ long. Oospores globose; wall thick, smooth; (35)–41–47μ in diameter. Antheridia 20–24μ in diameter, 8–12μ long.

Attached to overhanging grass in small lake. Wis.

Oedogonium princeps (Hass.) Wittrock 1875, p. 42
Pl. 43, Figs. 16, 17

Macrandrous; dioecious. Vegetative cells cylindric, 33–43μ in diameter, 40–155μ long. Oogonia solitary; subobovoid; little wider than the vegetative cells; opening by a superior pore; 57–63μ in diameter, 54–80μ long. Oospores globose or subglobose; not filling the oogonia; wall smooth; 47–58μ in diameter, 47–65μ long. Antheridia 32–38μ in diameter, 5–20μ long.

Mich.

Oedogonium rivulare (Le Cl.) A. Braun 1856, p. 23
Pl. 32, Figs. 5, 6

Macrandrous; dioecious. Vegetative cells cylindric, (35)–40–45μ in diameter, (110)–160–185–(350)μ long. Oogonia solitary or 3–7 in a series; obovoid-ellipsoid; opening by a superior pore; (70)–85μ in diameter, (84)–118.4–160μ long. Oospores ellipsoid or subglobose; much smaller than oogonia; wall thick, smooth; (55)–66.6–70μ in diameter, (65)–83.5–100μ long. Male filaments with cells 30–36μ in diameter, 120–280μ long. Antheridia 21–28μ in diameter, 14–26μ long.

Attached to submerged aquatics. Wis.

Oedogonium rufescens Wittrock 1871, p. 134

Macrandrous; dioecious. Vegetative cells cylindric, slender; 8–10μ in diameter, 34–70μ long. Oogonia 1–3; obovoid or depressed-obovoid-globose; opening by a median pore; 22–24μ in diameter, 22–30μ long. Oospores globose or depressed-globose; filling the oogonia; wall smooth; 21–23μ in diameter, 17–22μ long. Antheridia 6–8μ in diameter, 8–12μ long.

Mich.

Oedogonium sociale Wittrock in Wittrock & Nordstedt
1882, Algae Exsic. No. 401
Pl. 32, Figs. 7–9

Macrandrous; dioecious. Vegetative cells cylindric, (9)–15.5–16μ in diameter, (30)–74–130μ long. Oogonia solitary; subglobose or ellipsoid-globose, opening by a median pore; (30)–37–38–(40)μ in diameter, (33)–41–43μ long. Oospores globose or broadly ellipsoid-globose; nearly filling the oogonia; wall smooth; (26)–30–32–(35)μ in diameter, (26)–32–36μ long. Antheridia 12–14μ in diameter, 10μ long.

Attached to grass in small lake. Wis.

Oedogonium suecicum Wittrock 1872a, p. 6
Pl. 33, Figs. 4, 5

Macrandrous; dioecious. Vegetative cells cylindric, 9–12.9–(14)μ in diameter, (30)–37–44–(90)μ long. Oogonia solitary; subglobose; opening by a median pore; (32)–33.3–37–(38)μ in diameter, (34)–40.7–41–(44)μ long. Oospore globose; not quite filling the oogonia; outer spore wall echinate; $31.5-32-(33)\mu$ in diameter. Antheridia $10-12-(13)\mu$ in diameter, $13-17\mu$ long.

This species should be compared with the larger *Oe. australe* (G. S. West) Tiffany.

Attached to submerged logs; widely distributed. Mich., Wis.

Oedogonium taphrosporum Nordstedt & Hirn *in* Hirn 1900, p. 133

Macrandrous; dioecious. Vegetative cells cylindric, $25-38\mu$ in diameter, $100-375\mu$ long. Oogonia 1–6; obovoid or obovoid-ellipsoid; opening by a superior pore; $70-83\mu$ in diameter, $81-113\mu$ long. Oospores globose or ellipsoid-globose; outer spore wall scrobiculate; $58-65\mu$ in diameter, $62-70\mu$ long. Antheridia $24-32\mu$ in diameter, $8-12\mu$ long.

Mich.

Oedogonium Tiffanyi Ackley 1929, p. 304

Pl. 43, Figs. 6, 7

Macrandrous; dioecious. Vegetative cells cylindric, $(15)-21-24\mu$ in diameter, $100-240\mu$ long. Oogonia solitary (sometimes 2); subdepressed-globose; opening by a superior pore; $64-76\mu$ in diameter, $65-69\mu$ long. Oospores globose; nearly filling the oogonia; outer wall smooth; median wall scrobiculate; $54-65\mu$ in diameter, $55-66\mu$ long. Antheridia $19-21\mu$ in diameter, $14-20\mu$ long.

Mich.

Oedogonium urceolatum Nordstedt & Hirn *in* Hirn 1900, p. 293

Pl. 33, Figs. 9, 10

Macrandrous; dioecious (?). Vegetative cells cylindric, $(24)-25-(30)\mu$ in diameter, $80-200-(210)\mu$ long. Oogonia solitary; oblong-ellipsoid, in some obpyriform; opening by a superior pore; $(53)-57-(70)\mu$ in diameter, $79-82-(125)\mu$ long. Oospores ellipsoid; filling the lower part of the oogonia; middle layer of spore wall with about 20 longitudinal ribs, interrupted and anastomosing in our specimens; $(48)-54-60\mu$ in diameter, $57-60-(70)\mu$ long; male filaments not observed.

This plant should be compared with *Oe. margaritiferum* Nordst. & Hirn. The irregularly inflated oogonium and the shape of the oospore, together with the dimensions, are characters which agree with *Oe. urceolatum* and which separate it from *Oe. margaritiferum*. It is larger than *Oe. Boscii*, also a dioecious species.

Attached to grass in small ponds. Wis.

Oedogonium verrucosum Hallas 1905, p. 408

Pl. 24, Figs. 2, 3

Macrandrous; dioecious. Vegetative cells cylindric, 11–26μ in diameter, 45–200μ long, the suffultory cell enlarged. Oogonia solitary (sometimes 2); broadly ellipsoid or ovoid-globose; opening by a superior pore; 56–68μ in diameter, 56–94μ long. Oospores globose to ellipsoid-globose; not filling the oogonia; outer wall smooth; median wall scrobiculate; 52–64μ in diameter, 44–68μ long. Antheridia 16μ wide, the same in length.

Mich.

Oedogonium Wyliei Tiffany 1926, p. 90

Pl. 37, Figs. 13, 14

Macrandrous; dioecious. Vegetative cells cylindric, (16)–22.2–(24)μ in diameter, (80)–148–(170)μ long. Oogonia 1–4; globose or ovoid-globose; opening by a superior pore; (52)–55–56–(64)μ in diameter, (56)–64–68–(112)μ long. Oospores globose; nearly filling the oogonium; outer layer of spore wall with deep scrobiculations; 48–50–(60)μ in diameter. Antheridia 18μ in diameter, 12–16μ long.

Attached to submerged aquatics. Mich., Wis.

SECTION 2

Macrandrous—Monoecious—Poriferous

Oedogonium angustissimum West & West 1897, p. 6

Pl. 44, Fig. 6

Macrandrous; monoecious. Vegetative cells cylindric, 1.8–2μ in diameter, 13–25–(28)μ long. Oogonia 2; inflated; 9μ in diameter, 10–13.5–(14.5)μ long; opening by a median pore (?). Oospores elliptical; filling the oogonia laterally; wall smooth; 9–9.5μ in diameter, 6μ long.

Rare; attached to filamentous algae (usually larger species of *Oedogonium*). Wis.

Oedogonium areoliferum (Jao) Tiffany 1937, p. 29

Macrandrous; monoecious. Vegetative cells cylindric, 6–10μ in diameter, 25–64μ long. Oogonia solitary; depressed-globose; opening by a median pore; 28–32μ in diameter, 25–41μ long. Oospores depressed-globose; filling the oogonia; outer wall layer smooth, median wall layer areolate; 25–29μ in diameter, 19–27μ long. Antheridia rectangular, 6–10μ in diameter.

Mich.

Oedogonium carolinianum Tiffany 1934, p. 324

Pl. 33, Figs. 11, 12

Macrandrous; monoecious. Vegetative cells cylindric, elongate; (14)–17.5–19–(23)μ in diameter, (45)–117–(156)μ long. Oogonia solitary; ellipsoid; opening by a superior pore; (54)–58–(63)μ in diameter, (70)–78–(86)μ long. Oospores broadly ellipsoid; the outer layer of the spore wall striated with longitudinal ribs, 22–28 in number, sometimes spiral in our specimens; not filling the oogonia; 48.7–57μ in diameter, 58.5–69–(75)μ long. Antheridia 12–16–(18)μ in diameter, (7)–8–11–(12)μ long.

Our plants agree closely with *Oe. carolinianum,* but the oospores do not fill the oogonia as described for that species.

In a *Sphagnum* bog pond. Wis.

Oedogonium cryptoporum Wittrock 1871, p. 119

Macrandrous; monoecious. Vegetative cells cylindric, 7–10μ in diameter, 28–60μ long. Oogonia solitary; subdepressed-ovoid-globose or subdepressed-globose; opening by a median pore; 23–29μ in diameter, 25–31μ long. Oospores subdepressed-globose; filling the oogonia; wall smooth; 20–27μ in diameter, 19–22μ long. Antheridia 6–8μ in diameter, 7–11μ long.

Mich.

Oedogonium curtum Wittrock 1871, p. 121

Macrandrous; monoecious. Vegetative cells cylindric, with spirally arranged punctations; 12–22μ in diameter, 25–110μ long. Suffultory cell sometimes enlarged. Oogonia 1–4; obovoid-globose; opening by a superior pore; 38–55μ in diameter, 37–54μ long. Oospores obovoid-globose; nearly filling the oogonia; wall smooth; 36–52μ in diameter, 35–51μ long. Antheridia 10–17μ in diameter, 8–13μ long.

Mich.

Oedogonium fennicum (Tiff.) Tiffany 1934, p. 324

Pl. 32, Fig. 12

Macrandrous; monoecious. Vegetative cells cylindric, (14.8)–17–18–(19)μ in diameter, (44)–50–70–(120)μ long. Oogonia solitary; obovate-globose; opening by a superior pore; 38.8–42–(46)μ in diameter, (40.7)–42–48–(60)μ long. Oospores subglobose; not quite filling the oogonia; wall smooth; 33–35–(40)μ in diameter, 35–37–(40)μ long. Antheridia of 1–4 cells, 12–18μ in diameter, 6–7–(8)μ long.

Attached to grass in a roadside fosse. Wis.

Oedogonium fragile Wittrock 1871, p. 120
Pl. 32, Fig. 13

Macrandrous; monoecious. Vegetative cells cylindric, (12)–15–18.5μ in diameter, 51.8–120μ long. Oogonia solitary; globose; opening by a superior pore; (42)–44–50μ in diameter, 44–50–(55)μ long. Oospores globose; nearly filling the oogonia; wall smooth; 39–40–(46)μ in diameter, (38)–39–40–(46)μ long. Antheridia 15–18μ in diameter, 4–9.6μ long.

This species should be compared with *Oe. fennicum,* from which it differs but slightly. In the latter the vegetative cells are a little larger and the oogonia smaller than in *Oe. fragile.* No specimens of *Oe. fragile* were found with epigynous and hypogynous antheridia, a condition common in *Oe. fennicum.*

Common in shallow water of several lakes and ponds. Mich., Wis.

Oedogonium globosum Nordstedt 1878, p. 20
Pl. 31, Figs. 1–3

Macrandrous; monoecious. Vegetative cells cylindric, 10.8–14μ in diameter, (40)–75–(95)μ long. Oogonia solitary; globose; opening by a superior pore; (32)–40μ in diameter, (32)–40–46μ long. Oospores globose; wall thick, smooth; nearly filling the oogonia; (30)–38μ in diameter. Antheridial cells (9)–10–12μ in diameter, (4)–6–8μ long.

Growing on submerged grass. Mich., Wis.

Oedogonium Hirnii Gutwiński 1896, p. 34
Pl. 31, Fig. 4

Macrandrous; monoecious. Vegetative cells cylindric or slightly capitellate, 8–11–(13)μ in diameter, (28)–61–72–(80)μ long. Oogonia solitary; subglobose or subovate; opening by a superior pore; 32–37μ in diameter, 32–39μ long. Oospores globose; wall thick, smooth; (27)–28–(31)μ in diameter. Antheridial cells (8)–10.8–(11)μ in diameter, 5–7.2μ long.

On submerged sticks and leaves. Wis.

Oedogonium intermedium Wittrock *in* Wittrock & Nordstedt 1886, Algae Exsic. No. 708
Pl. 31, Figs. 5, 6

Macrandrous; monoecious; Vegetative cells cylindric, (15)–16.6–17–(18)μ in diameter, (45)–59–66–(80)μ long. Oogonia solitary; obovoid or obovoid-globose; opening by a superior pore; (31)–37–38μ in diameter, (34)–40–42–(45)μ long. Oospores globose; nearly filling the oogonia; wall smooth; (30)–33–36μ in diameter, 33–36–(41)μ long; antheridia 14.8–16μ in diameter, 4–10μ long.

Pool in a gravel pit; in a roadside fosse. Wis.

Oedogonium Kurzii Zeller 1873, p. 189
Pl. 34, Fig. 10

Macrandrous; monoecious. Vegetative cells long, cylindric; (44)–48.5–50–(52)μ in diameter and up to 260μ long. Oogonia solitary; oblong or subellipsoid; opening by a superior pore; (76)–88–90–(95)μ in diameter, (111)–118.4–120–(130)μ long. Oospores subglobose or ellipsoid; not filling the oogonia; wall smooth, thick; (67)–82–84–(86)μ in diameter, (80)–96.2–98μ long. Antheridia 2–15 in series, frequently immediately below the oogonia; 40.7μ in diameter, 11μ long.

Attached to submerged aquatics in a slough. Wis.

Oedogonium laeve Wittrock 1875, p. 8

Macrandrous; monoecious. Vegetative cells cylindric, 10–14μ in diameter, 20–70μ long. Oogonia solitary; depressed-globose; opening by a median pore; 32–38μ in diameter, 24–30μ long. Oospores depressed globose; filling the oogonia; wall smooth; 30–35μ in diameter, 23–26μ long. Antheridia 9–10μ in diameter, 9–13μ long. Mich.

Oedogonium oviforme (Lewin) Hirn 1900, p. 116
Pl. 31, Figs. 7, 7a

Macrandrous; monoecious. Vegetative cells cylindric, elongate; (9.2)–15–23μ in diameter, (40)–96–135μ long. Oogonia solitary; obovoid or ellipsoid-ovoid; opening by a superior pore; (40)–48–55μ in diameter, (51)–57–80μ long. Oospores ovoid; nearly filling the oogonia; wall smooth; (42)–46–53μ in diameter, (48)–52–63μ long. Antheridia 12–19μ in diameter, (7)–10–12μ long.

Attached to aquatic moss. Wis.

Oedogonium oviforme fa. gracile Prescott 1944, p. 352
Pl. 33, Figs. 6, 7

A form with more slender vegetative cells and smaller oogonia than the typical plant. Vegetative cells 7.6–9.2μ in diameter, 103.6–125μ long. Oogonia solitary; ellipsoid-ovoid; 44.4–46μ in diameter, 51.8–53μ long. Oospores ellipsoid; nearly filling the oogonia; wall smooth; 40.7μ in diameter, 49.9μ long. Antheridia 9.2μ in diameter, 11.1μ long; antherozoids 2, division horizontal.

Attached to submerged aquatics. Wis

Oedogonium paludosum (Hass.) Wittrock 1871, p. 124

Macrandrous; monoecious. Vegetative cells cylindric, 15–20μ in diameter, 50–140μ long. Oogonia solitary; ellipsoid; opening by a superior pore; 39–48μ in diameter, 60–84μ long. Oospores ellipsoid; filling the oogonia; outer and median wall layers with 27–35 longitudinal ribs; 36–45μ in diameter, 54–63μ long. Antheridia 14–16μ in diameter, 6–13μ long.

Mich.

Oedogonium patulum Tiffany 1934, p. 324
Pl. 33, Fig. 8

Macrandrous; monoecious. Vegetative cells capitellate, (13)–14–15–(16)μ in diameter, (35)–37–50–(60)μ long. Oogonia solitary; globose or subglobose; opening by a superior pore; 38–40μ in diameter, 38–40μ long. Oospores globose; nearly filling the oogonia; wall smooth; (33)–35–36–(38)μ in diameter, (33)–35–36–(38)μ long. Antheridia 12–14μ in diameter, 5–6μ long.

In a roadside fosse. Wis.

Oedogonium plusiosporum Wittrock 1875, p. 11
Pl. 33, Figs. 1–3

Macrandrous; monoecious. Vegetative cells cylindric, (12)–15.6–18–(19)μ in diameter, (24)–50–58–(77)μ long. Oogonia solitary; globose or subellipsoid-globose; opening by a superior or supramedian pore; (28)–41–42–(45)μ in diameter, (35)–46–48–(50)μ long. Oospores globose; filling the oogonia; wall smooth; (25)–35–39–(45)μ in diameter, 30–39μ long. Antheridia 12μ in diameter, (8)–10–12μ long.

Attached to aquatic moss and other vegetation. Wis.

Oedogonium pseudo-Boscii Hirn 1895, p. 21
Pl. 35, Fig. 4

Macrandrous; monoecious. Vegetative cells slender and cylindric, 8–14μ in diameter, 64–275μ long. Oogonia solitary; subovoid or pyriform, unsymmetrically bulged in the lower portion; opening by a superior pore; 41–50μ in diameter, 75–105μ long. Oospores ovoid or oval to ellipsoid-ovoid; filling and extending the oogonia in the basal part; 38–45μ in diameter, 48–60μ long. Antheridia quadrate, 11–12μ in diameter, 10–11μ long.

Attached to submerged aquatics. Wis.

Oedogonium Richterianum Lemmermann 1895, p. 26
Pl. 43, Fig. 8

Macrandrous; monoecious. Vegetative cells cylindric, 12–21μ in diameter, 36–126μ long. Oogonia 1–2, obovoid or subellipsoid;

opening by a superior pore; 36–48µ in diameter, 48–74µ long. Oospores subobovoid or subellipsoid; sometimes filling the oogonia; wall smooth; 35–43µ in diameter, 43–59µ long. Antheridia 12–15µ in diameter, 6–10µ long.

Mich.

Oedogonium Sodiroanum Lagerheim 1890, p. 81
Pl. 43, Fig. 12

Macrandrous; monoecious. Vegetative cells cylindric, 20–24µ in diameter, 44–84µ long. Oogonia solitary; ellipsoid-ovoid; opening by a superior pore; 40–45µ in diameter, 70–90µ long. Oospores ellipsoid; filling the oogonia in diameter only; wall smooth; 38–42µ in diameter, 56–64µ long. Antheridia 20–22µ in diameter, 6–8µ long.

Mich.

Oedogonium tyrolicum Wittrock 1875, p. 12
Pl. 32, Fig. 11

Macrandrous; monoecious. Vegetative cells cylindric, 16–18.5–(24)µ in diameter, (45)–51.8–74–(120)µ long. Oogonia solitary; ellipsoid-globose or depressed-globose; opening by a superior pore; 44.4–45.8–(53)µ in diameter, (51.8)–53–57–(70)µ long. Oospores globose; not filling the oogonia; wall smooth; 40–42.5–(48)µ in diameter, 40–42.5µ long. Antheridia 1–4 in series; 11–18–(21)µ in diameter, (5.5)–9–11µ long.

Attached to grass in a roadside fosse. Wis.

Oedogonium upsaliense Wittrock 1871, p. 125
Pl. 43, Fig. 15

Macrandrous; monoecious. Vegetative cells cylindric, 13–20µ in diameter, 55–160µ long; suffultory cell somewhat enlarged. Oogonia solitary; obovoid; or suboblong-ellipsoid; opening by a superior pore; 45–50µ in diameter, 66–100µ long. Oospores obovoid or suboblong-ellipsoid; filling the oogonia; wall smooth; 42–47µ in diameter, 60–75µ long. Antheridia 15–18µ in diameter, 7–10µ long.

Mich.

Oedogonium varians Wittrock & Lundell in Wittrock 1875, p. 11
Pl. 32, Fig. 10

Macrandrous; monoecious or dioecious. Vegetative cells cylindric, 12–14–(16)µ in diameter, 33–66–(144)µ long. Oogonia solitary or 2 together; globose or depressed-globose; opening by a superior pore; (33)–35–(50)µ in diameter, 34–37–(55)µ long. Oospores globose or depressed-globose; nearly or quite filling the oogonia;

wall smooth; 31.4–41μ in diameter, 30–32–(41)μ long. Antheridia 10–11–(15)μ in diameter, 5–6–(7)μ long.

In small ponds. Mich., Wis.

Oedogonium Vaucherii (Le Cl.) A. Braun 1855, p. 40
Pl. 43, Fig. 20

Macrandrous; monoecious. Vegetative cells cylindric, 20–30μ in diameter, 32–118μ long. Oogonia solitary; ovoid; opening by a superior pore; 40–58μ in diameter, 45–65μ long. Oospores globose or subglobose; not filling the oogonia; wall thick and smooth; 35–45μ in diameter, 35–55μ long. Antheridia 17–30μ in diameter, 6–15μ long. Mich.

Oedogonium vulgare (Wittr.) Tiffany 1934, p. 324

Macrandrous; monoecious. Vegetative cells cylindric, 5–8μ in diameter, 15–48μ long. Oogonia 1–5; subdepressed-ovoid-globose or subdepressed-globose; opening by a median pore; 18–25μ in diameter, 18–26μ long. Oospores subdepressed-globose; filling the oogonia; wall smooth; 16–23μ in diameter, 15–19μ long. Antheridia 5–7μ in diameter, 9–12μ long.

Mich.

SECTION 3
Macrandrous—Dioecious—Operculate

Oedogonium abbreviatum (Hirn) Tiffany 1934, p. 325
Pl. 36, Figs. 15, 16

Macrandrous; dioecious. Vegetative cells short-cylindric, forming rather stout plants; (10)–18–22μ in diameter, (15)–37–50μ long. Oogonia solitary, sometimes 2 together; ovoid-globose or subglobose; operculate; division superior; (28)–37–40μ in diameter, (30)–38–48μ long. Oospores subglobose; wall smooth; (26)–27–33–(34)μ in diameter, (26)–27–34–(37)μ long. Antheridia (not observed in our collections) 9–16μ in diameter, 5–10μ long.

In backwash pools on beach; attached to moss in shallow water. Wis.

Oedogonium calvum Wittrock 1875, p. 37
Pl. 37, Figs. 15, 16

Macrandrous; dioecious. Vegetative cells capitellate; 7.4–8.5μ in diameter, 26–28–(40)μ long; basal cell much elongated. Oogonia solitary or as many as 4 in a series; globose or depressed-globose; operculate; division median; (25.9)–27–(30)μ in diameter, (22.2)–25–30–(40)μ long. Oospores globose or depressed-globose; filling the oogonia or nearly so; wall smooth; 22.2μ in diameter, 19–22μ long. Antheridia not observed.

This species should be compared with *Oe. Howardii,* which also has capitellate cells. In that form, however, the oogonia average larger and the basal cell is subhemispherical or nearly spherical. Our specimens of *Oe. calvum* usually showed oogonia in series of 4. Entangled about grass in a roadside pool. Wis.

Oedogonium epiphyticum Transeau & Tiffany *in* Tiffany 1934, p. 325
Pl. 36, Figs. 20, 21

Macrandrous; dioecious. Vegetative cells cylindric, (6)–7.4–8–$(9)\mu$ in diameter, 15–25–$(45)\mu$ long; basal cell elongate. Oogonia solitary or (rarely) as many as 3 in a series; ellipsoid or ellipsoid-ovate; operculate; division superior; (16)–17–18–$(20)\mu$ in diameter, (20)–26–$(30)\mu$ long. Oospores elliptical; nearly filling the oogonia; wall smooth; 14.8–16–$(18)\mu$ in diameter, 16–19–$(28)\mu$ long. Antheridia 5–6μ in diameter, (5)–8–10μ long.
Entangled about grass in a roadside pond. Wis.

Oedogonium Howardii G. S. West 1904a, p. 281

Macrandrous; dioecious. Vegetative cells capitellate; elongate, 8–10–$(12)\mu$ in diameter, (18)–20–40–$(42)\mu$ long. Oogonia solitary or 2 together; globose; operculate; division median; (25)–28–29–$(33)\mu$ in diameter, (26)–30–34μ long. Oospores globose; wall smooth; 22–26–$(30)\mu$ in diameter. Antheridia (7)–10–12.5μ in diameter, (10)–12–14μ long.
Floating clots of filaments. Wis.

Oedogonium inclusum Hirn 1895, p. 2
Pl. 35, Figs. 5–7

Macrandrous; dioecious (?). Vegetative cells cylindric or somewhat capitellate, (8)–12.9μ in diameter, (33)–62.9–150μ long. Oogonia solitary; oblong-ellipsoid or fusiform, with lateral walls much thickened; operculate (?), opening superior; 24–30μ in diameter, 48–55–$(62)\mu$ long. Oospores ellipsoid; filling the oogonia laterally; wall smooth; (18)–24–$(30)\mu$ in diameter, 38–45–$(48)\mu$ long. Antheridia not observed.
Attached to overhanging grass in *Sphagnum* bog ditches. Wis.

Oedogonium inconspicuum Hirn 1895, p. 23
Pl. 37, Figs. 1, 2

Macrandrous; dioecious. Vegetative cells cylindric; sometimes twisted and swollen irregularly; 3.7–5μ in diameter, 17.8–25–$(35)\mu$ long. Oogonia solitary; globose or pyriform-globose; operculate;

division median (to supramedian in our specimens); 12.5–13–(18)μ in diameter, 11–12.5–(23)μ long. Oospores depressed-globose; nearly filling the oogonia; wall smooth; (12)–14–17μ in diameter, (8)–11–12μ long. Antheridia (?).

This species is one of the smallest in the genus. It frequently is found growing on filamentous algae, especially on other species of *Oedogonium*, on *Nitella*, and on *Chara*. Our collections show a great deal of variation in the plant in respect to form of vegetative cells, the length of filaments, and the shape of oogonia. Some of the smaller expressions of *Oe. tapeinosporum* are scarcely differentiated from *Oe. inconspicuum*. Both of the species are imperfectly known.

Common in many soft water lakes and bogs. Wis.

Oedogonium iowense Tiffany 1924, p. 181
Pl. 35, Figs. 1–3

Macrandrous; dioecious. Vegetative cells cylindric, 10–16–(18.5)μ in diameter, (44)–74–99–(100)μ long. Oogonia solitary (sometimes 2 together); ellipsoid; operculate; division superior; 52–60μ in diameter, 60–80μ long. Oospores ellipsoid; usually not filling the oogonia; wall smooth; 45–52–(56)μ in diameter, 50–64–(68.4)μ long. Antheridia 1–4, 10–12–(14.8)μ in diameter, 8–10–(20)μ long; antherzoids 2; division horizontal.

Attached to submerged vegetation. Wis.

Oedogonium latiusculum (Tiff.) Tiffany 1924, p. 182
Pl. 44, Fig. 3

Macrandrous; dioecious. Vegetative cells capitellate, (10)–12–16–(18)μ in diameter, (16)–20–38–(40)μ long. Oogonia solitary (or 2 together); subglobose to pyriform-globose; 32–36μ in diameter, 31.5–32–(40)μ long; operculate; division median. Oospores globose; not filling the oogonia; wall smooth; 28–30–(32)μ in diameter, (28)–30–34μ long. Antheridia (14)–16–18μ in diameter, 14–18μ long.

In a ditch through a *Sphagnum* bog. Wis.

Oedogonium microgonium Prescott 1944, p. 353
Pl. 36, Figs. 11–14

Macrandrous; dioecious (?). Vegetative cells distinctly capitellate, 8–9.5μ in diameter, 18–33μ long; basal cell elongate, 16–18.5μ long. Oogonia solitary (rarely 2 together); very little wider than the vegetative cells; globose or depressed-globose; operculate; division superior; 11–12.9μ in diameter, 10–11.2μ long. Oospores globose; filling the oogonia; the wall smooth; 11–12μ in diameter. Antheridia not observed.

This plant is similar to *Oe. Howei* Tiff., which is larger and has an inferior division of the oogonium. Although numberless plants were examined, the antheridia were not found. The female characteristics are distinctive and warrant the description of a new species.

In several soft water lakes and acid swamps. Wis.

Oedogonium mitratum Hirn 1895, p. 22
Pl. 44, Figs. 11, 12

Macrandrous; dioecious. Vegetative cells capitellate, (4)–5–10μ in diameter, 18–50–(80)μ long. Oogonia solitary or 2–4 in series; globose; operculate; division superior or supramedian; 18–24–(27)μ in diameter, 20–28–(35)μ long. Oospores globose to subglobose, with a smooth wall; nearly filling the oogonia; 17–23μ in diameter, 17–22–(23)μ long. Antheridia 6–9μ in diameter, 6–8μ long.

Attached to submerged aquatics. Wis.

Oedogonium nanum Wittrock 1875, p. 37
Pl. 36, Fig. 10

Macrandrous; dioecious. Vegetative cells usually cylindric, 6–8–(10)μ in diameter, (15)–18–20–(33)μ long. Oogonia solitary or as many as 3 in a series; ellipsoid; operculate; division superior; 24–28μ in diameter, 30–36μ long. Oospores ovate or ellipsoid; nearly filling the oogonia; wall smooth; 18–22–(27)μ in diameter, (24)–26–28–(30)μ long. Antheridia 7–10μ in diameter, 8–11μ long.

In shallow water of swamp. Wis.

Oedogonium paucostriatum Tiffany 1934, p. 325
Pl. 38, Figs. 1, 2

Macrandrous; dioecious. Vegetative cells cylindric, 13–20μ in diameter, (66)–106–120μ long. Oogonia solitary; ellipsoid; operculate; division superior; 45–48–(52)μ in diameter, (76)–79.8–88μ long. Oospores ellipsoid; not filling the oogonia; middle wall ribbed with about 20 longitudinal costae; (44)–45–47μ in diameter, 53–55–(70)μ long. Antheridia 17–20μ in diameter, 8–12μ long.

This species should be compared with the slightly larger *Oe. paucocostatum* Transeau.

Attached to reeds in a lake of medium hard water. Wis.

Oedogonium pisanum Wittrock 1876, p. 50

Pl. 36, Figs. 8, 9

Macrandrous; dioecious. Vegetative cells cylindric, (5)–6–7.5–(12)μ in diameter, (12)–14.8–18–(72)μ long. Oogonia solitary; ellipsoid-ovate; operculate; division superior; 20–29–(32)μ in diameter, 34–45μ long. Oospores globose; nearly filling the oogonia; wall smooth; 18–21–(25)μ in diameter, 18–26–(37)μ long. Antheridia 8μ in diameter, 6–8μ long.

In a small lake among sand hills. Wis.

Oedogonium poecilosporum Nordstedt & Hirn *in* Hirn 1900, p. 298

Macrandrous; dioecious or monoecious (?). Vegetative cells cylindric, 6–8μ in diameter, 20–47μ long. Oogonia 1 or 2; ellipsoid to depressed-globose; operculate; division median and wide; 24–28μ in diameter, 25–28μ long. Oospores ellipsoid to depressed-globose; nearly filling the oogonia; wall smooth; 23–26μ in diameter, 21–28μ long.

Mich.

Oedogonium porrectum Nordstedt & Hirn *in* Hirn 1900, p. 186

Pl. 36, Figs. 6, 7

Macrandrous; dioecious. Vegetative cells cylindric, 5.8–8–(10)μ in diameter, 23–29–(55)μ long. Oogonia solitary; ellipsoid or oblong-ellipsoid; operculate; division superior; 19.5–22–(27)μ in diameter, (27.3)–39–44–(53)μ long. Oospores ellipsoid; not filling the oogonia; wall smooth; (17.5)–18–24μ in diameter, 25–27.3–(28)μ long. Antheridia 6–7μ in diameter, 6–8μ long.

Our specimens are slightly smaller in the diametric dimensions of the oogonia and of the oospores but otherwise seem to agree with this species.

In shallow water of swamp. Wis.

Oedogonium pratense Transeau 1914, p. 297

Pl. 36, Figs. 4, 5

Macrandrous; dioecious. Vegetative cells cylindric, 9.2–11.7–(17)μ in diameter, 24–35–(95)μ long. Oogonia solitary; globose or subpyriform-globose; operculate; division median; (33)–42–44μ in diameter, (35)–42–44–(50)μ long. Oospore globose; filling the oogonium (not quite filling it in our specimens); wall smooth; 32–38–(40)μ in diameter, (28)–36–42μ long. Antheridia 10–14μ in diameter, 13–18μ long.

This dioecious plant seems to be assignable to *Oe. pratense,* although the relatively smaller oospore (not filling the oogonium completely in some specimens) is unlike that species.

On grass in a wooded swamp; found fruiting in both June and August. Mich., Wis.

Oedogonium Pringsheimii Cramer 1859, p. 17
Pl. 36, Figs. 1–3

Macrandrous; dioecious. Vegetative cells cylindric, (14)–18–20μ in diameter, 43–(100)μ long. Oogonia 1–6; globose or subovate-globose; operculate; division superior; 35–39–(43)μ in diameter, (36)–39–42–(46)μ long. Oospores globose; filling the oogonia; wall smooth, thick; (30)–35–36–(37)μ in diameter, 35–36–(46)μ long. Antheridia (10)–15–16μ in diameter, (6)–8–9μ long.

Common in many lakes and swamps. Mich., Wis.

Oedogonium Pringsheimii var. *Nordstedtii* (Wittr.) Wittrock
in Wittrock & Nordstedt 1877, Algae Exsic. No. 8, p. 22
Pl. 38, Figs. 9, 10

A variety smaller than the typical plant. Vegetative cells 9.5–10μ in diameter, 48–55μ long. Oogonia 37μ in diameter, 42.5μ long Oospores 33.3μ in diameter, 33.3–35μ long.

On grass and on *Isoetes* in soft water lakes. Mich., Wis.

Oedogonium punctatostriatum DeBary 1854, p. 47
Pl. 38, Figs. 5, 6

Macrandrous; dioecious. Vegetative cells cylindric, 18–22μ in diameter, 38–128μ long; wall with spiral punctations. Oogonia solitary, depressed-globose; operculate, the opening narrow and median; the wall spirally punctate; (48)–55–(66.5)μ in diameter, 38–48–(55.5)μ long. Oospores depressed-globose; wall smooth; (40)–51–56μ in diameter, 35–42–(48)μ long. Antheridia 19–20–(23)μ in diameter, 8–14–(19)μ long.

Our specimens are a little larger than the size described for *Oe. punctatostriatum* but agree otherwise.

Oedogonium pusillum Kirchner 1878, p. 59

Macrandrous; dioecious or monoecious. Described in the next section.

Oedogonium Sancti-thomae Wittrock & Cleve *in* Wittrock 1874, p. 40

Macrandrous; dioecious. Vegetative cells cylindric, 7–15μ in diameter, 16–88μ long. Oogonia 1–3; pyriform; operculate; division superior; 28–33μ in diameter, 36–50μ long. Oospores pyriform-ovate; not filling the oogonia; wall smooth; 25–30μ in diameter, 28–35μ long. Antheridia (?).

Mich.

Oedogonium Smithii Prescott 1944, p. 353
Pl. 36, Figs. 17–19

Macrandrous; dioecious (?). Vegetative cells cylindric or irregularly inflated, 3.7–8μ in diameter, 13–25μ long. Oogonia solitary; broadly pyriform-fusiform, with a secondary lateral inflation in the upper portion; operculate; division median and wide; 22–25μ in diameter, 27–32μ long. Oospores depressed-globose; nearly filling the oogonia laterally; wall smooth; 16–18μ in diameter, 12.9–14μ long. Antheridia (?).

This plant should be compared with *Oe. inconspicuum,* from which it is distinguished by the pyriform oogonium with its lateral inflations.

Rare; in a roadside pond. Wis.

Oedogonium spurium Hirn 1900, p. 301
Pl. 37, Figs. 4, 5

Macrandrous; monoecious or sometimes dioecious. Vegetative cells capitellate, 7–13μ in diameter, 20–55μ long. Oogonia solitary; subglobose to depressed-globose; operculate; division supramedian; 26–30μ in diameter, 23–33μ long. Oospores depressed-globose; sometimes filling the oogonia; wall smooth; 23–28μ in diameter, 21–26–(28)μ long. Antheridia 7–8μ in diameter, 8–11μ long.

Mich., Wis.

Oedogonium tapeinosporum Wittrock 1875, p. 40
Pl. 38, Figs. 11, 12

Macrandrous; dioecious (?). Vegetative cells cylindric, (2)–3.7–5.5μ in diameter, 12–25–(40)μ long; basal cell hemispherical. Oogonia solitary; globose, depressed-globose, or subelliptic (shape varies in the same plant); operculate; division median; (14)–18.5–19μ in diameter, (14)–20–23–(25)μ long. Oospores globose or depressed-globose; not filling the oogonia; wall smooth; (13)–14–15μ in diameter, 9–14–(18)μ long. Antheridia unknown.

This plant should be compared with *Oe. inconspicuum* Hirn, especially small specimens, which are easily confused with large individuals of the latter species.

In shallow water of swamps and in a slough. Mich., Wis.

[188]

Oedogonium trioicum Woronichin 1923, p. 99; 1923a, p. 141

Pl. 37, Fig. 10

Macrandrous; dioecious. Vegetative cells variable in proportions; elongate, or short-cylindric; 3.5–5μ in diameter, 10–22μ long. Oogonia solitary (rarely 3 in series); ellipsoid or oblong-ellipsoid; operculate; division superior; 25–27μ in diameter, (13)–17–(26)μ long. Oospores ellipsoid to subovate; wall smooth; (14)–17–20–(21)μ long. Antheridia 4μ in diameter, 3μ long.

Our specimens are assigned here on the basis of the shape and size of the oogonium. The oospores in our specimens are only slightly ellipsoid, and the faint violet color described for *Oe. trioicum* was not observed in the preserved material. ·

In a roadside fosse. Wis.

Oedogonium Welwitschii West & West 1897, p. 5

Pl. 38, Figs. 7, 8

Macrandrous; dioecious. Vegetative cells cylindric, (18.5)–20–28μ in diameter, (25)–37–84μ long. Oogonia 1–3; subglobose or subovate-globose; operculate; division superior; 43–50μ in diameter, 43–52μ long. Oospores globose; wall thick, smooth; (35)–40–42–(43)μ in diameter. Cells of male filament 17–20μ in diameter, 35–80μ long. Antheridia 16–18μ in diameter, 7–9μ long.

Attached to grass and other submerged aquatics. Wis.

Section 4

Macrandrous—Monoecious—Operculate

Oedogonium Ahlstrandii Wittrock *in* Wittrock & Nordstedt 1882, Algae Exsic. No. 401

Macrandrous; monoecious. Vegetative cells cylindric, 10–18μ in diameter, 30–180μ long. Oogonia solitary; ellipsoid; operculate, opening superior; 35–42μ in diameter, 57–69μ long. Oospores ellipsoid; filling the oogonia; wall smooth; 34–41μ in diameter, 53–62μ long. Antheridia 13–17μ in diameter, 9–12μ long.

Mich.

Oedogonium autumnale Wittrock 1875, p. 11

Pl. 34, Figs. 11, 12

Macrandrous; monoecious. Vegetative cells cylindric, (16)–18.5–20μ in diameter, (25)–74–80μ long. Oogonia solitary; globose or obovoid-globose; operculate; division superior; 39–45μ in diameter, 39–45.7μ long. Oospores globose; not filling the oogonia; wall thick, smooth; 37.5–39–(42)μ in diameter, 37.5–39–(42)μ long. Antheridia 1–2, 15.5μ in diameter, 7.4μ long.

On submerged vegetation. Wis.

Oedogonium bohemicum Hirn 1900, p. 169

Pl. 37, Fig. 3

Macrandrous; monoecious. Vegetative cells capitellate, (10)–14.8–15–(16)μ in diameter, (21)–48–53–(66)μ long. Oogonia solitary; globose; operculate; division superior; 40.7–42–(45)μ in diameter, 44–46–(49)μ long. Oospores globose; filling the oogonia; wall smooth; 38–43μ in diameter, 38–43μ long. Antheridia 10.7μ in diameter, (5)–6–7–(8)μ long.

In a roadside fosse. Wis.

Oedogonium crispum (Hass.) Wittrock 1875, p. 10

Pl. 44, Fig. 5

Macrandrous; monoecious. Vegetative cells cylindric, (10)–12–15μ in diameter, 35–42–(80)μ long. Oogonia solitary; subglobose or obovoid-globose; operculate; division superior; (37)–39–42–(45)μ in diameter, 42–50–(53)μ long. Oospores subglobose; the wall smooth; 35–40–(43)μ in diameter, 35–40–(43)μ long. Antheridia 8–14μ in diameter, 7–12μ long.

In small pools on beach of lake, Wis., Mich.

Oedogonium crispum fa. *inflatum* Hirn 1900, p. 161

Vegetative cells 12–16μ in diameter, 35–95μ long. Oogonia obovoid-globose, 40–50μ in diameter, 45–53μ long. Oospores 37–45μ in diameter, 38–45μ long. Antheridia 8–12μ in diameter, 9–12μ long. Mich.

Oedogonium gracilimum Wittrock & Lundell *in* Wittrock 1875, p. 15

Pl. 34, Figs. 13, 14

Macrandrous; monoecious. Vegetative cells cylindric but often irregular, forming crooked filaments, epiphytic on other species of *Oedogonium;* (4)–5.2–5.5–(7)μ in diameter, 15–22–(42)μ long. Oogonia solitary; oblong; operculate; division superior; 14–19μ in diameter, 34–40μ long. Oospores oblong-ellipsoid; not filling the oogonia; 13–17μ in diameter, 25–28–(32)μ long. Antheridia 3–5μ in diameter, 5–7μ long.

In a roadside fosse. Mich., Wis.

Oedogonium Gunnii Wittrock 1875, p. 37

Pl. 34, Figs. 15, 16

Macrandrous; monoecious. Vegetative cells cylindric or slightly capitellate, 6–9.2–(10)μ in diameter, (16.6)–20.3–30–(45)μ long. Oogonia 1–4, depressed-globose; operculate; division median and narrow (sometimes wide in our specimens); (23)–25–26–(29)μ in diameter, (19)–29–30μ long. Oospores depressed-globose; nearly filling the oogonia; wall smooth; 22.5–27μ in diameter, 17–18.5–(23)μ long. Antheridia 7.6–9μ in diameter, 3.8–11–(12)μ long.

Attached to grass in a small pond. Wis.

Oedogonium inclusum Hirn 1895, p. 21

Macrandrous; monoecious. Described in previous section.

Oedogonium Itzigsohnii DeBary 1854, p. 56

Macrandrous; monoecious. Vegetative cells cylindric, 8–10μ in diameter, 25–50μ long. Oogonia solitary; ellipsoid, with a median whirl of cone-shaped projections; operculate; division inframedian; 34–40μ in diameter, 32–40μ long. Oospores globose; not filling the oogonia; wall smooth; 20–23μ in diameter. Antheridia 8–9μ in diameter, 8–15μ long.

Mich.

Oedogonium minisporum Taft 1939, p. 80
Pl. 43, Fig. 1

Macrandrous; monoecious. Vegetative cells capitellate, 6–14μ in diameter, 53–69μ long. Oogonia 1 or 2; subpyriform-globose to subglobose; operculate, opening median; 30–42μ in diameter, 34–42μ long. Oospores globose to subglobose; not filling the oogonia; wall smooth (yellow); 25–30μ in diameter, 24–29μ long. Antheridia 8–11μ in diameter, 7–9μ long.

Presque Isle County, Michigan.

Oedogonium minus (Wittr.) Wittrock 1875, p. 9
Pl. 34, Figs. 7–9

Macrandrous; monoecious. Vegetative cells capitellate; walls spirally punctate; (9)–12–13μ in diameter, (30)–35–74–(78)μ long. Oogonia solitary, globose or pyriform-globose; wall with spiral punctations (in our specimens, with projections, as if mucilaginous concretions had formed at the punctations); operculate; division median; (34)–35–40–(46)μ in diameter, (28)–30–40–(42)μ long. Oospores depressed-globose; not filling the oogonia; wall smooth; 30–35–(42)μ in diameter, (26)–30–33–(36)μ long. Antheridia 9–13μ in diameter, 3–5μ long (in series of up to 10).

In a roadside fosse. Mich.,Wis.

Oedogonium nodulosum Wittrock 1872, p. 22

Macrandrous; monoecious. Vegetative cells with 2 prominent undulations and constrictions; 20–29μ in diameter, 30–140μ long. Oogonia 1 or 2; obovoid-globose or obovoid-ellipsoid; operculate; opening superior; 45–57μ in diameter, 56–73μ long. Oospores globose or subglobose-ellipsoid; nearly filling the oogonia; wall smooth; 46–53μ in diameter, 49–56μ long.

Mich.

Oedogonium oblongum Wittrock 1872, p. 2

Macrandrous; monoecious. Vegetative cells cylindric, 6–11μ in diameter, 20–86μ long. Oogonia solitary; oblong; operculate; division superior; 20–26μ in diameter, 41–60μ long. Oospores ellipsoid to ovate; not filling the oogonia; wall smooth; 19–23μ in diameter, 30–36μ long. Antheridia 6–9μ in diameter, 7–9μ long.

Mich.

Oedogonium oblongum var. *majus* Nordstedt *in* Wittrock 1876, p. 45

Vegetative cells 8–11μ in diameter, 35–75μ long. Oogonia 26–28μ in diameter, 42–50μ long. Oospores 22–26μ in diameter, 31–34μ long. Antheridia 4–9μ in diameter, 9–10μ long.

Mich.

Oedogonium oblongum var. *minus* Taft 1939, p. 81
Pl. 43, Figs. 2, 3

Vegetative cells 3–6μ in diameter, 16–35μ long. Oogonia 13–16μ in diameter, 20–23μ long. Oospores 11–15μ in diameter, 17–21μ long. Antheridia 5–6μ in diameter, 7μ long.

Mich.

Oedogonium pachydermum Wittrock & Lundell
in Wittrock 1871, p. 125

Macrandrous; monoecious. Vegetative cells cylindric, 21–27μ in diameter, 34–120μ long. Oogonia solitary (sometimes 2); ellipsoid; operculate; division superior; 50–70μ in diameter, 75–100μ long. Oospores ellipsoid; not filling the oogonia; wall smooth; 40–60μ in diameter, 50–80μ long. Antheridia 18–21μ in diameter, 10–12μ long.

Mich.

Oedogonium poecilosporum Nordstedt & Hirn *in* Hirn 1900, p. 298

Macrandrous; monoecious or dioecious. Described in previous section.

Oedogonium psaegmatosporum Nordstedt 1877, p. 24
Pl. 34, Fig. 4; Pl. 37, Fig. 6

Macrandrous; monoecious. Vegetative cells cylindric, elongate; 9–10–(14)μ in diameter, (56)–57–80μ long. Oogonia 1–5, pyriform-globose; operculate; division median; (28)–33–39μ in diameter 33–40–(43)μ long. Oospores depressed-globose; nearly filling the oogonia; wall smooth; 27–31μ in diameter, 23–27μ long. Antheridia 9–12μ in diameter, 6–10–(11.7)μ long.

Our plants seem to belong here, although the vegetative cells are slightly larger than described for this species and the oospores sometimes do not completely fill the oogonia.

In a ditch through a *Sphagnum* bog. Wis.

Oedogonia pusillum Kirchner 1878, p. 59
Pl. 37, Figs. 11, 12

Macrandrous; monoecious or dioecious. Vegetative cells cylindric, 6μ in diameter, (10)–25–50–(60)μ long; basal cell hemispheric. Oogonia solitary; subbiconic-ellipsoid to subbiconic-globose, with a slight median constriction when mature; operculate; division median; 14–16μ in diameter, (15)–20–25μ long. Oospores broadly ellipsoid, but deeply constricted in the median portion; wall smooth; 11–13μ in diameter, (13)–14–15–(16)μ long. Antheridia 3–4μ in diameter, 5–6μ long.

On aquatic vegetation in swamps and ditches. Mich., Wis.

Oedogonium pyriforme Wittrock 1875, p. 39
Pl. 34, Figs. 5, 6

Macrandrous; monoecious. Vegetative cells cylindric, 13.6–15–(16)μ in diameter, (48)–74–80–(90)μ long. Oogonia solitary; pyriform; operculate; division superior; 40–44.8–(46)μ in diameter, (44)–52.6–(60)μ long. Oospores usually filling the oogonia and of the same shape; wall smooth; (36)–40–42μ in diameter, (36)–40–44μ long.

On grass and *Eleocharis* in soft water lakes. Wis.

Oedogonium Reinschii Roy in Cooke 1883, p. 160
Pl. 34, Figs. 1–3

Macrandrous; monoecious. Vegetative cells subellipsoid to hexagonal or fusiform, especially the latter shape in the lower portions of the filament; (5)–7.5–8–(11)μ in diameter, 8.5–19.2–(24)μ long. Oogonia 1–2; pyriform-globose; operculate; division median; (17)–19–20μ in diameter, 15–21–(22.8)μ long. Oospores depressed-globose; not filling the oogonia longitudinally; wall smooth; (13)–15–18μ in diameter, 14–15–(17)μ long. Antheridia 4–9.5μ in diameter, 9–11.4μ long.

This species was found to be in a reproductive state in several places during August. It is one of the few species of the genus which can be identified when in the vegetative condition, because of the distinctive cell shape.

Common in many desmid habitats where the water is soft or acid. Mich., Wis.

Oedogonium spheroideum Prescott 1944, p. 353
Pl. 38, Figs. 3, 4

Macrandrous; monoecious. Vegetative cells elongate-cylindric, 16–19μ in diameter, 115–155μ long. Oogonia solitary; broadly ellipsoid to subglobose; operculate; division superior; 55–64μ in diameter, 80–87.5μ long. Oospores spheroidal, the wall thick; outer membrane with 12–15 longitudinal ribs; 57–60μ in diameter, 57–60μ long. Antheridia 1–4, immediately below the oogonia or scattered. Antherozoids 2; the division horizontal; 19–21μ in diameter, 16μ long.

This species should be compared with *Oe. sol* Hirn, which is smaller and has an oospore with the middle, rather than the outer, layer of the wall ribbed.

Attached to grass in a roadside swamp. Wis.

Oedogonium spirostriatum Tiffany 1936a, p. 2
Pl. 44, Figs. 1, 2

Macrandrous; monoecious. Vegetative cells slightly capitellate; 16–24–(28)μ in diameter, 50–164μ long; wall of the vegetative cells, as well as of oogonia, with spirally disposed punctations; basal cell hemispherical to nearly globose. Oogonia solitary; subglobose to depressed-globose; operculate; division supramedian; 49–56μ in diameter, 40–50μ long. Oospores depressed-globose; about the same shape as the oogonia but not filling them; 40–47μ in diameter, 34–40μ long. Antheridia 20–24μ in diameter, 17–20μ long.

This species should be compared with *Oe. punctatostriatum*, which is dioecious and has cylindric cells; also the oogonium of *Oe. punctatostriatum* has a median, rather than a supramedian, division.

Common in many lakes. Mich., Wis.

Oedogonium spurium Hirn 1900, p. 301

Macrandrous; monoecious or dioecious. Described in previous section.

Oedogonium trioicum Woronichin 1923, p. 99; 1923a, p. 141

Macrandrous; monoecious or dioecious. Described in previous section.

SECTION 5

Nannandrous—Idioandrosporous—Poriferous

Oedogonium cyathigerum Wittrock 1871, p. 131

Nannandrous; idioandrosporous. Vegetative cells cylindric, 21–30μ in diameter, 40–300μ long. Oogonia 1–3; subovate; opening by a superior pore; 57–65μ in diameter, (70)–77–100μ long. Oospores subovoid or quandrangular-ellipsoid; outer spore wall smooth middle layer with 16–25 longitudinal ribs; 51–62μ in diameter, 60–75μ long. Dwarf male plants 10–15μ in diameter, 50–58μ long. In swamps. Mich., Wis.

Oedogonium cyathigerum fa. *ornatum* (Wittr.) Hirn 1900, p. 254
Pl. 44, Fig. 13

A form somewhat larger throughout than the typical plant and with dwarf males more elongate.

With the typical plant. Wis.

Oedogonium gallicum Hirn 1900, p. 197
Pl. 39, Fig. 4

Nannandrous; idioandrosporous. Vegetative cells cylindric, 16–18.5–$(22)\mu$ in diameter, 51–65–$(120)\mu$ long. Oogonia solitary (rarely 2 together); globose; opening by a median or supramedian pore; (39)–45–48μ in diameter, 40–45–$(54)\mu$ long. Oospores depressed-globose; filling the oogonia; wall thick, smooth; 36–46μ in diameter, 39–44μ long. Dwarf male plants 2-celled, on the suffultory cells. Antheridia exterior, 11.7μ in diameter, 10–13μ long. Suffultory cell 18μ in diameter, 51μ long.

In waterlily pond. Mich., Wis.

Oedogonium hystricinum Transeau & Tiffany 1919, p. 240

Nannandrous; idioandrosporous. Vegetative cells cylindric, 8–15μ in diameter, 42–100μ long. Oogonia solitary; globose or obovoid; opening by a median pore; 30–40μ in diameter, 35–53μ long. Oospores globose or subglobose; outer wall densely spiny; 23–38μ in diameter, 28–43μ long. Antheridia 5–6μ in diameter, 6–10μ long. Mich.

Oedogonium idioandrosporum (Nordst. & Wittr.)
Tiffany 1934, p. 325

Nannandrous; idioandrosporous. Vegetative cells cylindric, 25–36μ in diameter, 65–200μ long. Oogonia 1–3; globose-obovoid to globose;

opening by a superior pore; 48–59µ in diameter, 57–90µ long. Oospores ellipsoid-globose, ovoid, or angular-globose; wall smooth; 42–57µ in diameter, 50–66µ long. Antheridia 8–10µ in diameter, 10–18µ long.

Mich.

Oedogonium irregulare Wittrock 1871, p. 128

Nannandrous; idioandrosporous (?). Vegetative cells cylindric, 15–20µ in diameter, 40–80µ long. Oogonia solitary; globose or subdepressed-globose; opening by a superior pore; 37–45µ in diameter, 36–47µ long. Oospores globose; filling the oogonium; wall smooth; 36–42µ in diameter, 34–41µ long. Antheridia 10–12µ in diameter, 6–8µ long.

Mich.

Oedogonium magnum (Ackley) Tiffany 1934, p. 325

Nannandrous; idioandrosporous. Vegetative cells cylindric, 14–18µ in diameter, 30–90µ long. Oogonia solitary; subglobose; opening by a supramedian or median pore; 40–43µ in diameter, 33–38µ long. Oospores globose to subglobose; wall smooth; 38–41µ in diameter, 32–36µ long. Antheridia 8–10–(12)µ in diameter, 8–10µ long.

Mich.

Oedogonium multisporum Wood 1869, p. 141

Nannandrous; idioandrosporous (or gynandrosporous ?). Vegetative cells cylindric, 10–15µ in diameter, 10–30µ long. Oogonia 1–3; subovoid or subglobose; opening by a superior pore; 24–35µ in diameter, 27–33µ long. Oospores globose; nearly filling the oogonia; wall smooth; 27–30µ in diameter, 24–30µ long. Antheridia quadrate, 7–9µ in diameter.

Mich.

Oedogonium perfectum (Hirn) Tiffany 1934, p. 326
[Oe. cyathigerum fa. perfectum Hirn]
Pl. 39, Figs. 6, 7

Nannandrous; idioandrosporous. Vegetative cells cylindric, 20–30–(35)µ in diameter, (65)–92–350µ long. Oogonia solitary (or as many as 4 in a series); subovate, subquadrangular-ellipsoid, or ovate; opening by a superior pore; (65)–66–72–(85)µ in diameter, 70–85–(111)µ long. Oospores obovoid; filling the oogonia; outer spore wall smooth, middle layer ridged with 16–24 anastomosing and curved costae; 59–70–(80)µ in diameter, (65)–70–83–(85)µ long. Dwarf male plants on the suffultory cells, 12–16µ in diameter, 50–58–(85)µ long.

In swamps. Wis.

Oedogonium Westii Tiffany 1934, p. 325
Pl. 39, Fig. 8

Nannandrous; idioandrosporous (?). Vegetative cells cylindrical or somewhat capitellate, (17)–19.5–29–(35)μ in diameter, (81)– 117–163–(180)μ long. Oogonia solitary or as many as 3 in a series; obovoid or ellipsoid; opening by a superior pore; 53–68μ in diameter, 67–99μ long. Oospores obovoid or ellipsoid; filling the oogonia; wall smooth; (49)–54.6–65μ in diameter, (49)–68.2–81μ long. Dwarf male plants on suffultory cell. Antheridia 18μ in diameter, 13μ long.

On grass and other submerged aquatics in several soft water and acid lakes. Wis.

SECTION 6
Nannandrous—Gynandrosporous—Poriferous

Oedogonium Braunii Kuetzing 1849, p. 366

Nannandrous; gynandrosporous. Vegetative cells cylindric, 13–15μ in diameter, 25–60μ long. Oogonia solitary; ovate or subglobose; opening by a median pore; 30–37μ in diameter, 33–43μ long. Oospores globose; wall smooth; 27–33μ in diameter. Antheridia 5–8μ in diameter, 9–10μ long.

Mich.

Oedogonium concatenatum Wittrock 1875, p. 25

Nannandrous; gynandrosporous. Vegetative cells cylindric, 25–40μ in diameter, 75–400μ long. Oogonia 1–6, subovate or quadrangular-ellipsoid; opening by a superior pore; 63–83μ in diameter, 76–105μ long. Oospores subovoid or quadrangular-ellipsoid; median wall with pits arranged in longitudinal series; 60–75μ in diameter, 67–95μ long. Antheridia 13–15μ in diameter, 12–25μ long.

Mich.

Oedogonium crassiusculum Wittrock 1871, p. 132

Nannandrous; gynandrosporous. Vegetative cells cylindric, 27–30μ in diameter, 95–105μ long. Oogonia 1–2; globose-ovate or subglobose; opening by a superior pore; 54–60μ in diameter, 60–75μ long. Oospores ellipsoid-globose or globose; wall smooth, thick; 51–57μ in diameter, 52–63μ long. Antheridia 7–9μ in diameter, 9–16μ long.

Mich.

Oedogonium depressum Prigsheim 1858, p. 69

Nannandrous; gynandrosporous. Vegetative cells cylindric, 8–9μ in diameter, 25–54μ long. Oogonia solitary (sometimes 2); globose or subglobose; opening by a median pore; 28μ in diameter, 26μ long. Oospores depressed-globose, not filling the oogonia; wall smooth; 23μ in diameter, 17–18μ long. Dwarf male plants 4–5μ in diameter, 14–16μ long.

Mich.

Oedogonium hispidum Nordstedt *in* Wittrock 1871, p. 128
Pl. 24, Fig. 4

Nannandrous; gynandrosporous. Vegetative cells cylindric, 9–14μ in diameter, 36–130μ long. Oogonia solitary; terminal; subellipsoid or ellipsoid-globose; opening by an inferior pore; 35–44μ in diameter, 42–56μ long. Oospores globose to globose-ellipsoid; not filling the oogonia; outer wall spiny; 32–39μ in diameter, 32–40μ long. Antheridia 5–6μ in diameter, 7–9μ long.

Mich.

Oedogonium multisporum Wood 1869, p. 141

Nannandrous; gynandrosporous or idioandrosporous. Described in previous section.

Oedogonium Sawyerii Prescott 1944, p. 354
Pl. 39, Fig. 1

Nannandrous; gynandrosporous. Vegetative cells cylindric, stout; 30–33.3μ in diameter, 66.6–81μ long. Oogonia solitary; nearly globose; 63–66.6μ in diameter, 55–60μ long; opening by a superior pore. Suffultory cell swollen. Oospores globose; outer membrane with a prominent spiral ridge, continuous from pole to pole, the axis of the spore turned at an angle of about 30 degrees from the longitudinal axis of the oogonium; 50–55μ in diameter (including ridge). Male plants on the suffultory cell. Antheridia 8–10μ in diameter; androsporangia 25.9μ in diameter, 14.8μ long.

This species should be compared with the smaller and idioandrosporous *Oe. latviense* (Tiff.) Tiffany and with *Oe. spiripennatum* Jao, which has a median pore.

In a beach pool cut off from a soft water lake. Wis.

Oedogonium sexangulare Cleve *in* Wittrock 1871, p. 131
Pl. 39, Figs. 2, 3

Nannandrous; gynandrosporous. Vegetative cells cylindric, (9)–16–20–(22.6)μ in diameter, (33)–39–57–(78)μ long. Oogonia solitary; sexangular-ellipsoid; opening by a median pore; 29–33–(40)μ in diameter, (33)–34–39μ long. Oospores the same shape as the oogonia and filling them; wall smooth; (27)–31μ in diameter, (31)–36–38.7–(40)μ long. Dwarf male plants on the suffultory cell. Antheridia exterior, 6–8μ in diameter, 9–12μ long. Suffultory cell somewhat larger than the vegetative cells.

In a lily pond and in acid swamps. Mich., Wis.

Oedogonium stellatum Wittrock 1871, p. 129

Nannandrous; gynandrosporous. Vegetative cells cylindric, 15–35μ in diameter, 40–225μ long. Oogonia 1–3; obovoid-globose; opening by a superior pore; 51–64μ in diameter, 56–70μ long. Oospores globose; filling the oogonia; outer wall spirally striated with ribs; 50–58μ in diameter. Antheridia 6–9μ in diameter, 8–13μ long. Mich.

Oedogonium subsexangulare Tiffany 1934, p. 325
Pl. 39, Fig. 5

Nannandrous; gynandrosporous. Vegetative cells cylindric, (15)–19–24μ in diameter, (20)–30–(68)μ long. Oogonia solitary; sexangular; opening by a median pore; 35–38–(48)μ in diameter, (41)–45–50μ long. Oospores the same shape as the oogonia and filling them; 34–40μ in diameter, (39)–40–43–(48)μ long; the wall smooth. Dwarf male plants with elongated stipes. Antheridia 6–8μ in diameter, 8–10μ long.

Floating clots of filaments in a small pond. Wis.

SECTION 7
Nannandrous—Idioandrosporous or Gynandrosporous—Poriferous

Oedogonium Borisianum (LeCl.) Wittrock 1875, p. 25
Pl. 35, Figs. 8, 9

Nannandrous; gynandrosporous or idioandrosporous. Vegetative cells cylindric, (15)–18.5–24μ in diameter, (45)–55–59–(140)μ long. Oogonia 1–5; obovoid or angularly ellipsoid; opening by a superior pore; (33)–40–50μ in diameter, 55–90μ long. Oospores obovoid; filling the oogonia in diameter but not in length; wall thick, smooth; (35)–47–49μ in diameter, (48)–55.5–57–(60)μ long. Dwarf male plants on the much enlarged suffultory cell. Antheridia exterior; 8–10μ in diameter, (11)–12–15–(16)μ long. Suffultory cell 37μ in diameter, 55–(92)μ long.

Common in several swamps and small lakes. Mich., Wis.

Oedogonium echinospermum A. Braun in Kuetzing 1849, p. 366
Pl. 35, Figs. 10, 11

Nannandrous; gynandrosporous or idioandrosporous. Vegetative cells cylindric, 18–21–(30)μ in diameter, (45)–62–130μ long. Oogonia depressed-globose or ellipsoid-globose; opening by a median pore; (39)–50–54.6μ in diameter, (41)–46–49–(57)μ long. Oospores globose or depressed-globose; the outer wall furnished with short, sharp spines; (38)–46–47μ in diameter, (38)–40–44–(49)μ long. Dwarf male plants on the suffultory cell. Antheridia exterior, 6–9–(12)μ in diameter, 6–11–(15)μ long.

On overhanging grass in a ditch through a Sphagnum bog. Mich., Wis.

Oedogonium spiralidens Jao 1934, p. 84

Pl. 40, Fig. 1

Nannandrous; gynandrosporous or idioandrosporous. Vegetative cells cylindric, (12)–14–16–(18)μ in diameter, (50)–55–76–(85)μ long. Suffultory cell enlarged, 22.5μ in diameter, 70.3μ long. Oogonia solitary; globose or obovoid; opening by a median pore; (42)–44–46–(50)μ in diameter, (40)–48–(50)μ long. Oospores nearly globose, with long axis transverse to long axis of oogonium; outer spore wall with 4–7 spiral costae, irregularly toothed at the edges, the costae meeting at the poles; wall also marked with coarse granulations or crystalline deposits; 41–50μ in diameter, 41–47μ long. Dwarf male plants 2- or 4-celled; on the suffultory cell; 10–12–(13)μ in diameter, 62.9μ long. Antheridia exterior; 6–7.8–(8)μ in diameter, (8)–11–12μ long.

Attached to reeds in lakes. Wis.

Oedogonium striatum Tiffany 1934, p. 326

Pl. 39, Fig. 10

Nannandrous; gynandrosporous or idioandrosporous. Vegetative cells cylindric or slightly capitellate, (18)–30–36μ in diameter, (53)–76–250μ long. Oogonia 1–8–(10); subovate or ellipsoid; opening by a superior pore; (67)–76–80μ in diameter, 79–83–(92)μ long. Oospores the same form as the oogonia; the outer layer of the spore wall with about 40 longitudinal, anastomosing ribs; 64–72–(76)μ in diameter, 74–76–(90)μ long. Dwarf male plants on the much enlarged suffultory cell. Antheridia exterior; (12)–13.3–14μ in diameter, 9.5–12μ long. Suffultory cell 57–68.4μ in diameter, 117μ long.

In a small northern lake among sand hills. Wis.

Oedogonium Wolleanum Wittrock 1878, p. 137

Pl. 35, Figs. 12, 13

Nannandrous; gynandrosporous or idioandrosporous. Vegetative cells long, cylindric; (21)–25–30μ in diameter, (65)–70–180–(235)μ long. Oogonia 1–4, ellipsoid or subquadrangular; opening by a superior pore; 58–65–(68)μ in diameter, (65)–69–80–(89)μ long. Oospores filling the oogonia and of the same shape; the outer layer of the spore wall furnished with 25 or more ribs with entire margins; (56)–58–65–(66)μ in diameter, 65–80.5–(83)μ long. Dwarf male plants, usually several, on the suffultory cell; 2- or 4-celled. Antheridia exterior; (9)–10–12–(14)μ in diameter, (7)–8–10–(11)μ long. Suffultory cell much enlarged, (45)–48–53–(65)μ in diameter.

In a small northern lake among sand hills. Wis.

Nannandrous—Idioandrosporous—Operculate

Oedogonium Ackleyae Tiffany 1937, p. 70

Nannandrous; idioandrosporous (?). Vegetative cells cylindric, 9–11μ in diameter, 27–60μ long. Oogonia 1–3; globose or subglobose; operculate; division superior; 32–35μ in diameter, 30–35μ long. Oospores globose; not filling the oogonia; median wall scrobiculate; 31–33μ in diameter, 31–32μ long. Antheridia 8–9μ in diameter, 6–10μ long.

Mich.

Oedogonium brasiliense Borge 1899, p. 4
Pl. 41, Figs. 3, 4

Nannandrous; idioandrosporous. Vegetative cells distinctly capitellate, (16)–20.3–22μ in diameter, (35)–55–74–(95)μ long. Oogonia 1–4–(9); depressed-globose; operculate; division wide, median or supramedian; 51.8–55.5–(63)μ in diameter, 46.2–52–(59)μ long. Oospores globose or depressed-globose; not filling the oogonia; wall smooth; (44.5)–48–53μ in diameter, 33–35–(45)μ long. Dwarf male plants unicellular; on the oogonia; 11μ in diameter, 12–13–(19)μ long.

Our specimens differ from the original description of *Oe. brasiliense* in having the operculum sometimes supramedian and in having the oogonia in longer series.

In a small pond on grass. Wis.

Oedogonium Kozminskii Prescott 1944, p. 355
Pl. 42, Figs. 4–6

Nannandrous; idioandrosporous. Vegetative cells cylindric to slightly capitellate, 14–15.6μ in diameter, 50–60μ long. Oogonia solitary; globose; operculate; division supramedian; (46)–50.7–52μ in diameter, 46–53.7μ long. Oospores globose or depressed-globose; wall smooth; 43.9–45μ in diameter, 39–42μ long. Suffultory cell not enlarged or scarcely so. Dwarf male plants unicellular; on the oogonia; 11.7–13μ in diameter, 13–14.5μ long.

The distinguishing characteristics of this species are the capitellate vegetative cells and the supramedian opening of the oogonium. It should be compared with *Oe. mirandrium* Skuja, in which the suffultory cell is enlarged and the oogonium smaller.

Attached to grass in a *Sphagnum* bog. Wis.

Oedogonium longatum Kuetzing 1853, Tab. Phyc. 3, p. 11

Nannandrous; idioandrosporous (?). Vegetative cells cylindric, 4–7μ in diameter, 10–35μ long. Oogonia 1–3; ovate or ellipsoid; operculate; division superior; 16–18μ in diameter, 21–25μ long.

Oospores ellipsoid, nearly filling the oogonia; wall smooth; $15–17\mu$ in diameter, $17–20\mu$ long. Antheridia $4–5\mu$ in diameter, $5–6\mu$ long. Mich.

Oedogonium macrandrium Wittrock 1871, p. 130

Nannandrous; gynandrosporous; operculate. Described in the following section.

Oedogonium megaporum Wittrock 1872, p. 3

Nannandrous; idioandrosporous. Vegetative cells cylindric, $13–17\mu$ in diameter, $40–100\mu$ long. Oogonia 1–6; pyriform, with 12–16 longitudinal ribs; operculate; division supramedian; $37–42\mu$ in diameter, $40–45\mu$ long. Oospores subdepressed-globose; not filling the oogonia; wall smooth; $31–35–(38)\mu$ in diameter, $27–30\mu$ long. Dwarf male plants unicellular, $8–12\mu$ in diameter, $13–16\mu$ long. Mich.

Oedogonium polyandrium Prescott 1944, p. 355
Pl. 42, Figs. 7–9

Nannandrous; idioandrosporous (?). Vegetative cells slightly capitellate, $4.5–5.4\mu$ in diameter, $14–30\mu$ long. Oogonia solitary; ovate or broadly ellipsoid; operculate; opening superior; $17–19\mu$ in diameter, $27–28\mu$ long. Oospores ovate; nearly filling the oogonia; outer spore wall with coarse sparsely arranged scrobiculations or shallow pits; middle and inner layers of the spore wall smooth; $15–17\mu$ in diameter, $22–25\mu$ long. Dwarf male plants 2-celled, numerous; on the oogonia; stipe 4.5μ in diameter, $14–16\mu$ long. Antheridia exterior (?).

This species has a combination of characteristics which make it quite unlike any other. It should be compared, however, with Oe. longatum, which is similar in size, but in which the outer layer of the oospore wall is smooth. Also in Oe. longatum the dwarf male plants are distinctly curved or reflexed. Skuja (1932, p. 59) describes the oospore wall as having the middle layer pitted.

Attached to grass in a bog. Wis.

Oedogonium pseudoplenum Tiffany 1934, p. 326
Pl. 40, Fig. 9

Nannandrous; idioandrosporous. Vegetative cells capitellate, (12)–$15.6–16.5–(17)\mu$ in diameter, $(36)–54.6–120\mu$ long. Oogonia 1–8; globose; operculate; division median and wide; $36–40–(42)\mu$ in diameter, $(36)–39–41–(53)\mu$ long. Oospores depressed-globose; not filling the oogonia; wall smooth; $(30)–31.2–33\mu$ in diameter, $(27)–30–31\mu$ long. Dwarf male plants unicellular; on the oogonia; 8μ in diameter, $(12)–14–15\mu$ long.

In a *Sphagnum* bog. Wis.

Oedogonium sinuatum (Trans.) Tiffany 1934, p. 325

Nannandrous; idioandrosporous. Vegetative cells undulate (with 4 undulate constrictions), (13)–19–26μ in diameter, 48–110μ long. Oogonia 1–2, subglobose or ellipsoid-globose; operculate; division inferior; 56–68μ in diameter, 45–80μ long. Oospores globose; not filling the oogonia; wall smooth; 42–60μ in diameter, 42–56μ long. Dwarf male plants elongate-obconic, on the suffultory cell. (Typical plant not found in our collections.)

Oedogonium sinuatum fa. *seriatum* Prescott 1944, p. 354
Pl. 40, Fig. 2

Vegetative cells undulate and capitellate, with 4 median undulations; 22–25μ in diameter, 48–59.2–(140)μ long. Oogonia in series of 4 or 5; operculate; division inferior; 62–67μ in diameter, 62–72μ long. Oospores globose; not filling the oogonia; wall smooth; 55.5μ in diameter. Dwarf male plants usually crowded on the suffultory cell. Antheridia exterior (?), 10.9μ in diameter.

This form has some features resembling *Oe. undulatum,* with which it should be compared. The principal difference is the seriate arrangement of the oogonia in our specimens.

Attached to overhanging grass in a *Sphagnum* bog ditch. Wis.

SECTION 9
Nannandrous—Gynandrosporous—Operculate

Oedogonium ambiceps (Jao) Tiffany 1937, p. 79
Pl. 37, Figs. 7–9

Nannandrous; gynandrosporous. Vegetative cells distinctly capitellate, (9)–12–13μ in diameter, 22–42μ long. Oogonia solitary, depressed-globose, with 8–10 median longitudinal bulges separated by narrow creases, or sometimes by broad depressions; operculate; division inframedian; 32–37–(38)μ in diameter, (19)–29.6–33μ long. Oospores depressed-globose; nearly filling the oogonia; wall thick, smooth; (19)–26–33μ in diameter, (19)–25.9–27μ long. Dwarf male plants not observed. Androsporangia 11–13μ in diameter, 4μ long.

The absence of dwarf male plants from our specimens and the small proportions of the androsporangia make it possible to confuse this with some other monoecious species, but the distinctive form of the oogonium and its markings, together with the gynandrous condition, are helpful in identification.

Attached to logs. Wis.

Oedogonium Areschougii Wittrock 1871, p. 122

Nannandrous; gynandrosporous. Vegetative cells cylindric, (8)–9–12–(13)μ in diameter, 36–38–(75)μ long. Oogonia 1–7; depressed-globose or pyriform-globose; operculate; division median; (34)–35–37–(39)μ in diameter, 36–40μ long. Oospores globose; not filling the oogonia; wall smooth; (22)–23–25–(26)μ in diameter. Dwarf male plants unicellular; on or near the oogonia; 6–7μ in diameter, 12–13–(15)μ long.

In a lily pond. Wis.

Oedogonium Areschougii var. *contortofilum* Jao 1934a, p. 199
Pl. 40, Figs. 6, 7

Somewhat larger throughout (in our specimens) than the typical plant. Vegetative cells slightly capitellate, forming spiral twists especially just above the oogonial series, in which there may be as many as 7; 7–12–(15.6)μ in diameter, 54–60μ long. Oogonia 36–41μ in diameter, 30–31μ long. Dwarf male plants unicellular; on the oogonia or near them. Oospores globose, 31μ in diameter, 29–30μ long.

Considerable variation was noted in the amount of twisting exhibited by this variety in different habitats. The suggestion naturally presents itself that the spiral character of the filaments is related to environmental factors. It is known that reaction to parasitism frequently causes bending in filamentous algae, although in these cases no parasitic organisms were observed.

On submerged wood. Wis.

Oedogonium ciliatum (Hass.) Pringsheim 1856, p. 227

Nannandrous; gynandrosporous. Vegetative cells cylindric, 14–24μ in diameter, 35–92μ long. Oogonia 1–7; ovate or ovate-ellipsoid; operculate; division superior to supreme; 43–50μ in diameter, 55–72μ long. Oospores ovate to subellipsoid-globose; nearly filling the oogonia; wall smooth; 40–47μ in diameter, 44–57μ long. Antheridia 8–10μ in diameter, 10–11μ long.

Mich.

Oedogonium Croasdaleae Jao 1934a, p. 202
Pl. 41, Fig. 11

Nannandrous; gynandrosporous. Vegetative cells cylindrical, (20)–25–28–(30)μ in diameter, 95–105–(230)μ long. Oogonia usually 3–4 in a series (rarely solitary); subovate or ellipsoid (sometimes sub-quadrangular-ellipsoid); operculate; division superior; (56)–58–

62–(77)μ in diameter, 86–96–(116)μ long. Oospores filling the oogonia and the same shape; outer spore wall smooth; middle layer with coarse, anastomosing, longitudinal costae; (54)–55–62–(73)μ in diameter, (77)–79–94–(105)μ long. Dwarf male plants 10–15μ in diameter, 55–60–(62)μ long.

In a roadside swamp; attached to submerged aquatics in a beach pool. Wis.

Oedogonium decipiens Wittrock 1871, p. 126
Pl. 42, Figs. 13, 14

Nannandrous; gynandrosporous. Vegetative cells cylindric or slightly capitellate, (9)–10–12μ in diameter, (28)–30–78–(80)μ long. Oogonia solitary; subglobose; operculate; division median; (30)–33–36–(38)μ in diameter, (27)–30–40μ long. Oospores depressed-globose, (25)–28–33–(34)μ in ·diameter, (23)–25–28–(30)μ long. Dwarf male plants unicellular, 7μ in diameter, 13–14–(15)μ long.

In several soft water and acid habitats. Mich., Wis.

Oedogonium decipiens var. africanum Tiffany 1929, p. 74
Pl. 41, Fig. 2

Vegetative cells capitellate; filaments frequently twisted; 9–9.2–(13)μ in diameter, 25–30–(60)μ long. Oogonia globose; (25)–29.6–32μ in diameter, (23)–27–28.6μ long. Antheridia 6μ in diameter, 7μ long.

On overhanging grass. Wis.

Oedogonium decipiens var. dissimile (Hirn) Tiffany 1937, p. 68
Pl. 42, Figs. 11, 12

Vegetative cells capitellate, 8–11–(14)μ in diameter, (20)–55–(65)μ long; oogonia (28)–33.3–35μ in diameter, (23)–29.6–38μ long; oospores (23)–30–(34)μ in diameter, 21–(30)μ long. Androsporangium 9.2μ in diameter, 8μ long. Antheridia 8μ in diameter.

Common in swamps and lakes. Mich., Wis.

Oedogonium hians Nordstedt & Hirn in Hirn 1900, p. 227
Pl. 40, Fig. 10; Pl. 42, Fig. 10

Nannandrous; gynandrosporous. Vegetative cells slightly capitellate, 9–14.8–(18)μ in diameter, 37–48–(145)μ long. Oogonia 1 or 2; subglobose or subovoid; operculate; division superior; 37–43μ in diameter, (40)–45–60–(80)μ long. Oospores globose; quite or nearly filling the oogonia; wall smooth; 30–31.4–(40)μ in diameter, 32–34–(40)μ long. Dwarf male filaments 2-celled, on the suffultory cell.

Antheridia exterior, 6–8μ in diameter, 5–6μ long. Suffultory cell
(26)–32–34μ in diameter, (46)–50–53.6–(80)μ long.

Attached to grass in a small northern pond in sand hills. Wis.

Oedogonium macrandrium Wittrock 1871, p. 130
Pl. 41, Fig. 1

Nannandrous idioandrosporous (or gynandrosporous?). Vegetative cells cylindric, 14.8–16–(20)μ in diameter, 40–51.8–(100)μ long. Oogonia 1–4; sub-globose or ovate-globose; operculate; division superior; 36–42μ in diameter, (43)–48–154μ long. Oospores globose; wall smooth; (31)–34–37μ in diameter. Dwarf male plants 2- or 4-celled; stipe 14.8μ in diameter, 33.3μ long; scattered on the female plant. Antheridia exterior, 7.4–10μ in diameter, 7–10μ long.

In soft water bog lakes. Mich., Wis.

Oedogonium michiganense Tiffany 1927, p. 205
Pl. 43, Figs. 9–11

Nannandrous; gynandrosporous. Vegetative cells capitellate, 12–24μ in diameter, 80–160μ long. Oogonia 1–7; globose to ellipsoid-globose; operculate; division supreme; 50–64μ in diameter, 50–80μ long. Oospores globose; sometimes filling the oogonia; wall smooth; 44–60μ in diameter. Dwarf males 13–20μ in diameter, 40–56μ long.

Mich.

Oedogonium monile Berkeley & Harvey in Hooker 1859, p. 342

Nannandrous; gynandrosporous (?). Vegetative cells cylindric, sometimes capitellate; 9–15μ in diameter, 50–160μ long. Oogonia 1–8; subovate or subglobose; operculate; division superior; 30–39μ in diameter, 30–56μ long. Oospores globose or subglobose; outer spore wall smooth, median wall scrobiculate; 28–38μ in diameter. Antheridia quadrate, 7μ in diameter. Suffultory cell 21–29–(32)μ in diameter.

Mich.

Oedogonium oelandicum Wittrock 1875, p. 17

Nannandrous; gynandrosporous. Vegetative cells capitellate, 10–15μ in diameter, 25–125μ long. Oogonia 1–7; depressed-globose, with 12–16 prominent longitudinal ribs in the median portion; operculate; division supramedian and broad; (29)–31–40μ in diameter, 25–32μ long. Oospores depressed-globose; almost completely filling the oogonia; wall smooth; 25–36μ in diameter, 23–30μ long. Dwarf male plants unicellular; on the oogonia; 7–8μ in diameter, 12–15μ long.

Mich.

Oedogonium oelandicum var. *contortum* Prescott 1944, p. 355
Pl. 42, Figs. 1–3

A variety differing from the typical by its contorted filaments which sometimes form short spirals, several of which may occur in one filament. Vegetative cells 11–12μ in diameter, distinctly capitellate. Oogonia much shorter than wide; depressed-globose; 29–30μ in diameter, 20–21.5μ long. Oospores depressed-globose; the wall smooth; 25–27μ in diameter, 18–20μ long. Dwarf male plants unicellular; on the oogonia.

Attached to grass in small lakes. Wis.

Oedogonium rugulosum Nordstedt 1877, p. 28
Pl. 44, Figs. 14, 15

Nannandrous; gynandrosporous. Vegetative cells cylindric, (4)–8–9.5μ in diameter, (10)–11.7–19.5–(35)μ long. Oogonia solitary (rarely 2 together); ellipsoid or globose-ellipsoid; operculate; division superior; (16)–20μ in diameter, (22)–25.4–29μ long. Oospores globose or subglobose; wall smooth; 15–17.5–(18)μ in diameter, 17.5–19.7–(25)μ long. Dwarf male plants short; on the oogonia. Antheridia exterior, 5μ in diameter, 6μ long. Basal cell of female filament 7.8μ in diameter, 11–13.6–(14)μ long.

In a roadside fosse. Mich., Wis.

Oedogonium rugulosum fa. *rotundatum* (Hirn) Tiffany
1936, p. 169
Pl. 39, Figs. 9, 11, 12

Vegetative cells cylindric or slightly capitellate, 5–6.8–(8)μ in diameter, 27–30–(31)μ long. Oogonia 1–3; ovate or globose-ellipsoid; division superior; (19)–20–23–(30)μ in diameter, (20)–29–30μ long. Oospores globose or ellipsoid-globose; nearly filling the oogonia; wall smooth; 18–20–(22)μ in diameter, 22–25μ long.

Our plants are in agreement with this variety except that the cells have a tendency to be capitellate.

With the typical plant. Wis.

SECTION 10

Nannandrous—Idioandrosporous or Gynandrosporous—Operculate

Oedogonium acrosporum DeBary 1854, p. 47
Pl. 41, Fig. 7

Nannandrous; gynandrosporous or idioandrosporous. Vegetative cells cylindric, (12)–15–19.5–(21)μ in diameter, (34)–40–68–(125)μ long. Oogonia solitary; ellipsoid; terminal; wall ridged internally with 23–30 longitudinal ribs; operculate; division superior; (30')–35–48µ in diameter, 50–63µ long. Oospores filling the oogonia, with as many ridges on the membrane as the ribs on the wall of the oogonia, and fitting in between them. Dwarf male plants 2 to 4 cells long, the stipe elongate; 2- or 3-celled; attached to the suffultory cell. Antheridia exterior, 7µ in diameter, 11µ long.

This species is separated from its varieties mostly by the stout suffultory cell and by the somewhat longer oogonia, with more ridges.

Common in several lakes and *Sphagnum* bogs. Wis.

Oedogonium acrosporum var. *boreale* Wolle 1887, p. 84

Vegetative cells 7.8–12µ in diameter, 54.6–140µ long. Oogonia elliptical, with 11–15 longitudinal ribs; 30–31µ in diameter, 44–46µ long. Dwarf male plants 2-celled. Antheridia exterior, 9µ in diameter, 11µ long. Suffultory cell 15.6µ in diameter, 39µ long.

In acid and soft water lakes. Wis.

Oedogonium acrosporum var. *bathmidosporum* (Nordst.) Hirn 1900, p. 246
Pl. 41, Figs. 5, 6

Vegetative cells (8)–12–17µ in diameter, 46–54–(125)µ long. Oogonia with few ridges (about 18 in our specimens); thick and sometimes interrupted; 27.3–30–(40)µ in diameter, (37)–39–59µ long. Dwarf male plants 2-celled; on the suffultory cell, which is enlarged to 22µ. Antheridia exterior, 5–8–(10)µ in diameter, 9–12–(13)µ long.

Specimens collected in Wisconsin have the characteristics of this variety except that the ribs are not crenulate as originally described for it.

Common in several lakes and *Sphagnum* bogs. Mich., Wis.

Oedogonium acrosporum var. *majusculum* Nordstedt 1878, p. 21
Pl. 41, Fig. 10

Vegetative cells relatively longer; (14)–16–20–(21)µ in diameter, 50–125–(165)µ long. Oogonia 45–58µ in diameter, 50–65.5–(70)µ long. Oospores 46–55µ in diameter.

Attached to grass in a ditch through a *Sphagnum* bog. Mich., Wis.

Oedogonium macrospermum West & West 1897a, p. 472
Pl. 41, Fig. 12

Nannandrous; gynandrosporous or idioandrosporous. Vegetative cells cylindric, (10)–16–18.5µ in diameter, (30)–55–57–(80)µ long. Oogonia solitary; subglobose; operculate; division median; (39)–

40–44.4–(46)μ in diameter, 35–38–(44)μ long. Oospores depressed-globose; with a smooth wall; 36–38.5–(44)μ in diameter, (32)–36.5–42μ long. Dwarf male plants short; usually 2-celled; on the suffultory cell. Antheridia exterior; stipe of dwarf male 9–14.8μ in diameter. Antheridia 7–10μ in diameter, (6)–11–16–(22)μ long.

On submerged aquatics in shallow water of a slough. Mich., Wis.

Oedogonium subplenum Tiffany 1934, p. 326
Pl. 40, Fig. 8

Nannandrous; gynandrosporous or idioandrosporous. Vegetative cells slightly capitellate, (7)–8–12μ in diameter, 23–80μ long. Oogonia solitary; depressed-globose or pyriform-globose; operculate; division median; 29–35–(38)μ in diameter, (26)–29–33–(41)μ long. Oospores globose; not filling the oogonia; 21–22.4–(28)μ in diameter, 19–26μ long. Dwarf male plants 1-celled; on the oogonia; 6–7μ in diameter, 6–10μ long.

In shallow water at edge of a *Sphagnum* bog. Wis.

Oedogonium undulatum (de Bréb.) A. Braun *in* DeBary
1854, p. 94
Pl. 40, Figs. 3–5

Nannandrous; gynandrosporous or idioandrosporous. Vegetative cells capitellate and 4-undulate, except the basal cell which is elongate and smooth; 15.6–18–(22)μ in diameter, (15.8)–45–100–(110)μ long. Oogonia solitary (sometimes 2 together); globose or ellipsoid-globose; operculate, the division inferior; (48)–50.7–55μ in diameter, (50)–54.6–56–(75)μ long. Oospores globose; filling the oogonia; wall smooth; 42–50μ in diameter. Dwarf male plants on the suffultory cell or nearby. Antheridia interior; 9μ in diameter.

Very common in many soft water and acid habitats. Mich., Wis.

Oedogonium undulatum fa. *senegalense* (Nordst.) Hirn 1900, p. 261
Pl. 44, Fig. 4

Vegetative cells with 3 median undulations and of somewhat narrower proportions than in the typical plant; 18–20μ in diameter, 48–80μ long. Oospores 38μ in diameter.

Attached to overhanging grass in a ditch through a *Sphagnum* bog. Wis.

ORDER CHLOROCOCCALES

This large order is composed of a great variety of plants which are 1-celled or which form colonies of rather definite shape. The cells may be adjoined or merely inclosed by a colonial mucilaginous envelope. In a few forms the cells are connected by strands formed by the remains of old mother-cell walls. The chief characteristic which all forms have in common is a negative one, namely, the inability to multiply by cell division in the vegetative state. Auto-spores are common in vegetative reproduction, as is also the habit of forming daughter colonies within each cell of a mature colony. Zoospores are used by some forms in asexual reproduction and isogametes are the rule in the genera which have sexual reproduction.

The cells vary widely in shape, being globose, ovate, acicular, fusiform or polyhedral. Although most forms are uninucleate, a few are coenocytic and hence are regarded by some phycologists as the likely ancestors of the Siphonales. The form of the chloroplast varies almost as much as the cell shape. There may be numerous ovate discs, parietal plates, networks, or in some genera cup-shaped chloroplasts. Pyrenoids may be lacking, but usually there are 1 to several. One family, the Endosphaeraceae, is unique in being diploid in the vegetative state.

Key to the Families

1. Unicellular, relatively large, and irregular in shape; wall very wide, lamellated, and not uniform in thickness; inhabiting the tissues of higher plants, or free-living_____ENDOSPHAERACEAE
1. Unicellular or colonial; cells varied in shape but not irregular; wall of uniform thickness and not definitely lamellated; free-living or attached, rarely subaerial_____ 2
2. Free-floating, or adherent on soil _____ 3
2. Attached and sessile, unicellular; cells fusiform_____CHARACIACEAE
3. Cells cylindrical and forming a macroscopic network, or triangular or polyhedral and united to form either a flat and circular, or globose coenobium (colony)_____HYDRODICTYACEAE
3. Cells not cylindrical, and not forming colonies as above_____ 4
4. Unicellular, solitary or sometimes gregarious, free-floating (usually on moist soil if adherent), reproducing by zoospores (rarely aplan-ospores) which do not adhere to one another but which are liber-ated separately from the parent cell (See *Chlorella* however) _____CHLOROCOCCACEAE
4. Colonial, or solitary not reproducing as above_____ 5
5. Thallus a hollow, globular coenobium of spherical or pyramidal cells, adjoined to neighboring cells by processes, rarely by direct contact_____ COELASTRACEAE
5. Thallus not as above_____ 6
6. An irregular mass of mucilage, often darkly colored, containing ovate or spherical cells at the periphery (compare with *Dimorphococcus* in the Oocystaceae)_____ BOTRYOCOCCACEAE
6. Not as above_____ 7

7. Cells solitary or in colonies of definite or indefinite shape; cells variable in form (spherical, ovate, lunate, polyhedral, etc.), not adjoined to one another; reproduction by autospores............OOCYSTACEAE

7. Two to eight cells adjoined together or adherent to form a pattern of definite shape (a linear series, stellate, or cruciate); reproduction by the formation of autocolonies within the cells of the parent coenobium.............................SCENEDESMACEAE

FAMILY CHLOROCOCCACEAE

In this family the cells vary in shape from spherical to fusiform or spindle-shaped (represented in our collections by spherical cells only). The family is characterized by the use of zoospores in asexual reproduction. These escape through a pore in the wall and separate immediately. In some forms arrested zoospores (aplanospores) may function.

The plants are mostly solitary and free-floating, but in one genus (*Chlorococcum*) cells are gregarious and sedentary, inhabiting moist soil or other subaerial habitats. The cell wall may be smooth or spiniferous. There is considerable variation in the form of the chloroplast which may be a parietal or massive cup, or axial and stellate, with 1 or more pyrenoids. In some species the cells become much enlarged and in age multinucleate.

In the identification of members of this family a comparison should be made with similarly shaped plants in the Oocystaceae.

Key to the Genera

1. Cells spherical or subspherical, inclosed in a wide, longitudinally striated, spindle-shaped sheath.............................*Desmatractum*
1. Cells spherical, not inclosed in a sheath.. 2
2. Cells free-floating, solitary, the walls setiferous 3
2. Cells sedentary, or rarely free-floating, solitary or gregarious on moist earth or submerged substrates; wall smooth.............*Chlorococcum*
3. Setae gradually tapering from the base to apex ....*Golenkinia*
3. Setae thickened for a short distance in the basal portion, then abruptly narrowed and tapering to apex.................... *Acanthosphaera*

CHLOROCOCCUM Fries 1825, p. 356

Cells spherical, solitary or more often gregarious in amorphous gelatinous clumps, or forming films on moist or submerged substrates; cell wall thin and undecorated; chloroplast a thin parietal plate covering the wall or nearly so, containing 1 pyrenoid; reproduction by 8–16 oblong zoospores with 2 flagella.

Species of *Chlorococcum* should be compared with *Chlorella*. See note under that genus.

[211]

Chlorococcum humicola (Naeg.) Rabenhorst 1868, p. 58

Pl. 45, Fig. 1

Cells spherical, solitary or in small clumps, variable in size within the same plant mass; cells 8–20–(25)µ in diameter.

This species is luxuriantly represented on and about dead fish and animal wastes along shores, forming green films in association with *Scenedesmus* spp. and *Euglena* spp. Common on beach soils and in moist aerial habitats. Mich., Wis.

Without a doubt, another common species, *C. infusionum* (Schrank) Meneghini occurs in our region. It has larger cells than *C. humicola* (15–45µ in diameter) and is ordinarily found on submerged substrates.

DESMATRACTUM (West & West) Pascher 1930b, p. 651

Cells globular, the wall thin, firm, and smooth, inclosed in a wide, transparent or brownish spindle-shaped sheath which is longitudinally striated; and composed of 2 top-shaped halves which adjoin at the midregion of the spindle; chloroplast solitary, a parietal cup with 1 or 2 pyrenoids; reproduction by biflagellate zoospores or by autospores.

This genus, as *Bernardinella,* was once placed in the Heterokontae.

Desmatractum bipyramidatum (Chod.) Pascher 1930b, p. 654

Pl. 46, Fig. 9

Characteristics as described for the genus; cells (with sheath) 12µ in diameter, 22µ long.

In acid waters; *Sphagnum* bogs. Mich.

ACANTHOSPHAERA Lemmermann 1899a, p. 118

Unicellular, spherical; free-floating; wall uniformly beset with 24 long, needle-like setae arranged in 6 tiers, 4 in each tier, about the cell wall; setae thickened for about ⅓ their length from the base, then abruptly narrowed to form slender spines; 1 parietal, lobed chloroplast, covering most of the cell wall, with 1 pyrenoid.

Acanthosphaera Zachariasi Lemmermann 1899a, p. 118

Pl. 45, Figs. 4, 5

Characteristics as described for the genus; cells spherical with numerous long setae with thickened bases; cells 9–14.5µ in diameter without setae; length of setae 30–35µ.

In plankton. Wis.

GOLENKINIA Chodat 1894, p. 305

Cells spherical, solitary and free-floating, the wall furnished with long, slender tapering setae; false colonies sometimes formed by the interlocking of setae; cells rarely inclosed by a thin, mucilaginous envelope; chloroplast a parietal cup covering most of the cell wall, containing 1 pyrenoid; reproduction by autospores and zoospores.

This genus seems to belong with the Oocystaceae, and it should be compared with spherical members of that family. The justification for placing it with the Chlorococcaceae is the report that zoospores are formed in asexual reproduction, a method not used by the Oocystaceae.

Key to the Species

Cells 15–18μ in diameter; setae 12–18μ long _____ *G. paucispina*
Cells 7–15μ in diameter; setae 25–45μ long _____ *G. radiata*

Golenkinia paucispina West & West 1902, p. 68
Pl. 45, Fig. 2

Spherical, free-floating unicells with a few short setae arising from all sides of the cell wall; 1 cup-shaped chloroplast, with 1 pyrenoid; cells 15–18μ in diameter; setae about 16μ long.

Rare, in the plankton of several lakes. Wis.

Golenkinia radiata (Chod.) Wille 1911, p. 57
Pl. 45, Fig. 3

Spherical, free-floating unicells with long and very slender setae; cells usually solitary but often in false colonies of 4 as a result of the interlocking of the setae; cells 7–15μ in diameter; setae 25–45μ long.

Rare; in euplankton. Mich., Wis.

FAMILY ENDOSPHAERACEAE

In this family the plants are unicellular, large, irregularly oblong or ovate in shape, free-living, parasitic, or (in our region) endophytic, embedded in the tissues of higher plants or in the mucilage of other algae. The chloroplasts are parietal in young cells but become massive and axial in older plants, with several pyrenoids. The wall is thick and lamellate, or has knob-like elongations. The family is unique in that the single cells are diploid, being but enlargements of the zygospore formed by the union of isogametes. Reduction division occurs when the cell contents divide to form as many as 256 biflagellate protoplasts. It is possible that zoospores, as well as gametes, are produced in this way.

Key to the Genera

CHLOROCHYTRIUM Cohn 1875, p. 102

Unicellular, oblong or broadly ellipsoid, often irregular in outline, formed when a zygote germinates and sends a tubular elongation into the tissues of *Lemna*, the cell contents migrating into the tube and then enlarging among the host cells, the entrance tube persisting as a knob-like extension of the wall, which is thick and lamellate; chloroplast at first parietal, later becoming radial and massive; reproduction by division of the cell contents into a large number of biflagellate isogametes or zoospores.

Chlorochytrium Lemnae Cohn 1875, p. 102
Pl. 45, Figs. 6, 7

See characters of the genus; cells broadly ellipsoid or ovate, with 1 or more knob-like extensions; wall thick and lamellate; cells 60–100μ in diameter, inhabiting the tissues of *Lemna trisulca*.

In host plants collected from water of marshy lakes; in roadside swamps. Mich., Wis.

KENTROSPHAERA Borzi 1883, p. 87

Unicellular, often crowded and intermingled with other algae, sometimes living in the mucilage of colonial Myxophyceae; cells irregularly ovate, ellipsoid, or sub-cylindric; walls lamellated, irregularly thickened with knob-like outgrowths; chloroplast axial, with extensions flattened at the wall to form irregularly shaped processes; one pyrenoid.

Kentrosphaera gloeophila (Bohlin) Brunnthaler 1915, p. 68
Pl. 45, Figs. 8–10

Characters of the genus; cells broadly ovate, or ovoid or elliptic, with knob-like thickenings of the lamellate wall, 18–20μ in diameter, 25–30μ long.

(For a discussion of the nomenclature of this species see Moore, 1917; G. M. Smith, 1933; Bristol, 1920.)

Among thick clots of blue-green algae. Wis.

FAMILY CHARACIACEAE

This is a small family of which there is but a single genus (*Characium*) represented in our collections. (*Actidesmium*, reported from California and arctic Alaska, has spindle-shaped, free-floating cells which are arranged in stellate clusters, adjoined to form compound colonies by gelatinous strands.) *Characium,* which is much more common, has spindle-shaped or ovoid cells growing on other algae, on submerged aquatic plants, or on microfauna. There are 1 or more parietal chloroplasts, each with a pyrenoid (sometimes several). The cells are mostly uninucleate. Biflagellate zoospores, formed 2-128 in a cell, escape through an apical or lateral pore.

CHARACIUM A. Braun *in* Kuetzing 1849, p. 208

See characteristics as described for the family; cells variously shaped, ovoid, fusiform, or cylindric, attached to a substrate (submerged plants, larger algae, microfauna) by a stipe (usually) and often with a basal attaching disc; rarely sessile; chloroplasts 1 or several parietal plates which sometimes become diffuse; pyrenoids 1 to several, although rarely there are none; food reserve in the form of starch.

Key to the Species

1. Cells epizoic on crustacea, often specific as to host 2
1. Cells epiphytic on miscellaneous plants but especially
on filamentous algae 5
2. Cells rounded at the apex 3
2. Cells narrowed to a spine at the apex 4
3. Cells broadly ovoid or pyriform, on a short stout stalk............*C. Debaryanum*
3. Cells elongate-ellipsoid or narrowly obovoid...........................*C. Hookeri*
4. Cells fusiform or slightly crescent-shaped, on a long, needle-like
stipe without a holdfast at the base .... *C. limneticum*
4. Cells elongate-cylindric, from a stipe which has a
forked rhizoidal holdfast.. *C. gracilipes*
5. Cells broadly pyriform or broadly ovate, or ovoid 6
5. Cells narrowly ovoid, fusiform, lanceolate, falcate or cylindrical............... 8
6. With a very slender stipe, 1 to 1½ times as long
as the cell body .... *C. stipitatum*
6. With a stout stipe, much shorter than the length of the cell body............ 7
7. Cells broadly ovate, 10–12µ wide.................................*C. obtusum*
7. Cells pyriform, 13–15µ wide...................................*C. operculum*
8. Cells elongate-fusiform, narrowed anteriorly but
bluntly rounded at the tip...*C. Rabenhorstii*
8. Cells lanceolate, falcate, or cylindric, ending in
an apiculation or spine.. 9
9. Stipe enlarged at the base to form an attaching disc.......................... 10
9. Stipe without a basal attaching disc... 12
10. Cells straight, erect, the stipe short.........................*C. Pringsheimii*
10. Cells strongly curved or falcate... 11
11. Cells lanceolate or falcate .... *C. rostratum*
11. Cells broadly and unsymmetrically ellipsoid, convex on one
margin, nearly straight on the other......................*C. ornithocephalum*

Characium acuminatum A. Braun *in* Kuetzing 1849, p. 892
Pl. 46, Fig. 7

Cells oblong or narrowly ovate, narrowed anteriorly to form a short apiculation, acuminate; stipe short; cells 15–20μ in diameter, 35–40μ long.

Attached to filamentous algae. Mich., Wis.

Characium ambiguum Hermann 1863, p. 26
Pl. 45, Fig. 11

Cells solitary, lance-shaped, fusiform or ensiform, narrowed to a sharp point anteriorly, tapering posteriorly to a fine hair-like stipe, without an attaching disc; chloroplasts 1–3; cells 4–8μ in diameter, 25–30μ long.

Attached to filamentous algae; tychoplanktonic. Mich., Wis.

Characium curvatum G. M. Smith 1918, p. 641
Pl. 45, Figs. 12, 13

Cells lunate or sickle-shaped, either sharply or bluntly pointed; stipe stout, without an attaching disc; chloroplast with or without a pyrenoid; cells 3–6μ in diameter, 13–22μ long, including stipe.

Epiphytic in the mucilage of colonial algae; tychoplanktonic. Wis.

Characium Debaryanum (Reinsch) DeToni 1889, p. 628
Pl. 46, Fig. 19

Cells oblong or ovoid, broadly rounded anteriorly, narrowed below into a stout stipe with a basal adhesive disc or swelling; cells 20–25μ in diameter, 30–40μ long.

Epizoic on copepods. Mich.

Characium falcatum Schroeder 1898, p. 23
Pl. 45, Fig. 14

Cells sickle-shaped, ending in a long sharp point; stipe long and slender, without an attaching disc; 1 chloroplast without a pyrenoid (?); cells 4.2–6.5μ in diameter, 36–50μ long.

This species is somewhat like *C. rostratum* but is separable on the basis of the attaching disc which that species possesses. Also, *C.*

[216]

falcatum has a long, colorless apical beak not present in the former species. It should be compared also with *Characiopsis longipes*.

On filamentous algae in shallow water of lake margins; swamps. Mich., Wis.

Characium gracilipes Lambert 1909, p. 65
Pl. 45, Fig. 16

Cells elongate cylindric, straight or very slightly curved, abruptly tapering anteriorly and extended to form a long, hyaline hair, and abruptly tapering below to a slender stipe with 2 or 3 fine, rhizoidal branchings at the base; chloroplasts variable, 1–32 in number with a single pyrenoid in each; cells 5–14μ in diameter, (70)–80–480μ long.

Epizoic on the anterior appendages of crustacea. Mich., Wis.

Characium Hookeri (Reinsch) Hansgirg 1888, p. 123
Pl. 45, Fig. 17

Cells mostly gregarious on *Cyclops*, club-shaped to subcylindric; stipe long or short, without an attaching disc; chloroplast 1, with 1–3 pyrenoids; cells 9–12μ in diameter, 27–30μ long.

On *Cyclops* in lakes and ponds; euplanktonic and tychoplanktonic. Wis.

Characium limneticum Lemmermann 1903c, p. 81
Pl. 45, Fig. 18

Cells fusiform or lunate (rarely almost straight), extended anteriorly into a long, sharp, spine-like tip, tapering posteriorly rather abruptly to form a long narrow stipe, without a basal attaching disc; chloroplasts 1–8, arranged to form a series of parietal bands; cells 5–14μ in diameter, 25–110μ long, including stipe.

Epizoic on *Diaphanosoma brachyura* in lakes. Mich., Wis.

Characium obtusum A. Braun 1855, p. 39
Pl. 45, Fig. 20

Cells oblong-ovate; stipe short and fairly thick; cell rounded anteriorly and furnished with a thickened plug at the apex; chloroplast parietal, with a single pyrenoid; cells (8)–10–12μ in diameter, 12.9–14.8–(33)μ long.

Attached to filamentous algae; lakes and *Sphagnum* bogs. Mich., Wis.

Characium operculum Ackley 1929, p. 304
Pl. 46, Fig. 13

Cells broadly pyriform on a short thick stipe with a basal attaching disc, broadly rounded anteriorly and furnished with an apical thickened plug; chloroplast (?); cells 13–15μ in diameter, 12–24μ long.

On filaments of *Desmidium*. Mich.

Characium ornithocephalum A. Braun 1855, p. 42
Pl. 46, Fig. 14

Cells broadly and unsymmetrically ellipsoid, convex on one side, nearly straight on the other, abruptly narrowed anteriorly to form a sharp apiculation, the cell body set at an angle and curved away from a long stipe with a basal attaching disc; chloroplast laminate, parietal, with a conspicuous pyrenoid; cells 25–33μ long, without stipe.

On submerged plants, especially filamentous algae. Mich.

Characium Pringsheimii A. Braun 1855, pp. 37, 106
Pl. 45, Fig. 21

Cells narrowly elongate-ovoid to fusiform, erect but with a short oblique tip; stipe short; chloroplast a laciniate plate with 1 pyrenoid; cells 7.8–9μ in diameter, 13–16μ long.

Attached to *Tribonema* filaments in a roadside fosse. Mich., Wis.

Characium Rabenhorstii DeToni 1889, p. 625
Pl. 46, Fig. 27

Cells elongate-fusiform or lanceolate; narrowed anteriorly but with a bluntly rounded apex; narrowed below to a long slender stipe, about ½ the length of the cell body, with a brown basal attaching disc; cells 8–9μ in diameter, 16–18μ long.

On filamentous algae. Mich.

Characium rostratum Reinhard 1876, *ex* Printz 1914, p. 41
Pl. 45, Figs. 22, 23

Cells lanceolate-falcate with curved apex; stipe long and slender from an attaching disc; chloroplast laminate, nearly covering the entire wall; cells 7.8μ in diameter, 40–45μ long, including the stipe.

Attached to *Tribonema* filaments in a roadside fosse. Mich., Wis.

Characium stipitatum (Bachm.) Wille 1911, p. 45
Pl. 45, Fig. 15

Cells ovate to subspherical or pyriform; stipe slender and tapering from the base of the cell, without an attaching disc; chloroplast parietal along the apical wall, with 1 pyrenoid; cells 5–8μ in diameter; stipe 10–16μ long.

Epiphytic on *Coelosphaerium Naegelianum*; generally distributed. Mich., Wis.

FAMILY HYDRODICTYACEAE

The members of this coenocytic family are morphologically very distinctive, although extremely variable. All forms are free-floating, but some are found only in the tychoplankton. In one genus, *Hydrodictyon*, there are cylindrical cells arranged to form a macroscopic, closed cylindrical net. In other genera the cells are triangular or polyhedric in outline and are arranged to form flat or spherical coenobia. The number of cells in the colony varies from 2 to 64 in the plate type of colony, whereas in *Hydrodictyon* several hundreds of cells are involved, always in multiples of 2. The chloroplast is parietal, either a continuous or perforate sheet, with 1 to many pyrenoids.

Like other families in this order, vegetative reproduction by cell division does not occur. The most common method of reproduction is by the formation of daughter colonies within the parent cell, these developing from retained zoospores. Sexual reproduction is by biflagellate isogametes.

Key to the Genera

1. Thallus a cylindrical closed reticulum of cylindrical cells
   which form 5- or 6-sided meshes_____*Hydrodictyon*
1. Thallus not a cylindrical net _____ 2
2. Thallus composed of 2 triangular or trapezoidal cells with
   their bases adjoined _____*Euastropsis*
2. Thallus composed of more than 2 cells _____ 3
3. Thallus a flat, circular plate of polygonal cells_____*Pediastrum*
3. Thallus a spherical colony of spine-bearing cells on stalks
   radiating from a common center_____*Sorastrum*

HYDRODICTYON Roth 1800, p. 531

Thallus maçroscopic, composed of cylindrical cells which are adjoined at their ends to form a cylindrical net with 5- or 6-sided meshes; chloroplast at first a parietal plate with a single pyrenoid, later becoming a reticulum covering the entire wall and containing many pyrenoids; cells multinucleate.

Hydrodictyon reticulatum (L.) Lagerheim 1883, p. 71
Pl. 47, Fig. 1

Characteristics as described for the genus; cells up to 200μ in diameter, as much as 1 cm. long when fully enlarged, forming a net up to 2 dm. in length; chloroplast a much diffused reticulum, light yellow-green color in the plant mass, especially at maturity.

This is a plant which prefers quiet water and is found in lakes where there is little wave action, in pooled streams, and in the

[219]

shallow water of swamps and marshes. Its rapid rate of reproduction (daughter nets formed within each cell of the parent net) makes it possible for *Hydrodictyon* to develop luxuriant growths in favorable habitats. Thick floating mats often result, and sometimes unbalanced biological conditions are produced. In some sections it becomes an obnoxious weed, clogging filters, drains, etc. It is so definitely confined to hard water that it may be used as an index organism for a high pH. In the far West it finds ideal growing conditions in the alkaline water of irrigation reservoirs and ditches.

Common in a large number of lakes, mostly hard water; generally distributed. Mich., Wis.

EUASTROPSIS Lagerheim 1895, p. 20

Thallus free-floating, composed of 2 flattened, triangular or trapezoidal cells adjoined along one wall, the lateral free margins converging and slightly concave, the apex deeply notched; chloroplast 1, parietal, with 1 pyrenoid.

Euastropsis Richteri (Schmidle) Lagerheim 1895, p. 20
Pl. 47, Fig. 2

Characters as described for the genus; cells 4.5–25μ in diameter, 5–20μ long; 2-celled colony 4.5–25μ wide, 10–40μ long.

Rare, in plankton. Wis.

PEDIASTRUM Meyen 1829, p. 772

Coenobium a free-floating, circular, monostromatic disc of cells which may be continuous or perforate; peripheral cells of the disc with 1 or 2 lobes or processes, or merely emarginate without processes; interior cells either the same shape as the marginal ones or different; chloroplast a parietal reticulum, covering the wall, with 1 pyrenoid; cells multinucleate.

Because the plates of *Pediastrum* are formed by the juxaposition of zoospores developed within a vesicle which is extruded from the mother cell, it not infrequently happens that irregularly formed or abnormal coenobia develop when the zoospores fail to align themselves in one plane. Hence coenobia may be found in which some cells overlie others. For a criticial study of this genus the reader is referred to Bigeard (1933) and Harper (1916, 1918).

Key to the Species

1. Outer free wall of the peripheral cells extended to form a single, horn-like projection ....*P. simplex*
1. Outer free wall of peripheral cells with 2 to 4 projections, or merely emarginate, not forming processes 2

Pediastrum araneosum (Racib.) G. M. Smith 1916, p. 476
[*P. angulosum* var. *araneosum* Raciborski]

Pl. 47, Fig. 4

Colony entire, or with minute interstices; cells 5-sided; peripheral cells 2-lobed; margin concave between the lobes, which are short and are about as far apart as are the lobes of two adjacent cells; wall with reticulate ridges; cells 15–32μ in diameter.

Common in the tychoplankton and euplankton of many lakes; generally distributed. Mich., Wis.

Pediastrum araneosum var. *rugulosum* (G. S. West)
G. M. Smith 1916, p. 476
[*P. Boryanum* var. *rugulosum* G. S. West]
Pl. 47, Fig. 3

A variety differing from the typical in having the adjoined cells distinctly undulated or crinkly.
Euplanktonic and tychoplanktonic. Mich., Wis.

Pediastrum biradiatum Meyen 1829, p. 773
Pl. 47, Figs. 5, 6

Colony perforate, the peripheral cells deeply bilobed, the lobes incised; cells adjoined along the lower part of their lateral walls; inner cells bilobed, the lobes not incised, all walls concave; diameter of cells 10–20μ.
Common in the plankton of many lakes; generally distributed. Mich., Wis.

Pediastrum biradiatum var. *emarginatum* fa. *convexum*
Prescott 1944, p. 356
Pl. 47, Figs. 7, 8

Colony perforate (clathrate), cells bilobed at the periphery, the lobes bifurcate, the inner margin of the lobules convex; peripheral cells adjoined along the lower part of their lateral margins only; lobes of inner cells merely emarginate; cells up to 11.7μ in diameter, 9.7–10μ long; 16-celled colony 44–50μ wide.
Rare, in *Sphagnum* bogs. Wis.

Pediastrum Boryanum (Turp.) Meneghini 1840, p. 210
Pl. 47, Fig. 9; Pl. 48, Figs. 1, 3

Colony entire; cells 5–6-sided with smooth or granular walls; peripheral cells with outer margins extended into 2 blunt-tipped processes; cells up to 14μ in diameter, 21μ long; 36-celled colony 85–90μ wide.
Common in the eu- and tychoplankton of many lakes and swamps; generally distributed. Mich., Wis.

Pediastrum Boryanum var. *longicorne* Raciborski 1889, p. 13
Pl. 47, Fig. 10

Peripheral cells with outer margins extended into longer processes than in the typical plant; apices of lobes swollen; cells 20–35–(40)μ in diameter.
Euplankter. Mich., Wis.

Pediastrum Boryanum var. *undulatum* Wille 1879, p. 28
Pl. 48, Fig. 2

Similar to the typical plant, but the adjoining cell walls are undulate and irregular rather than straight; surface walls with granules or smooth; the lobes of the peripheral cells narrow and longer than in var. *rugulosum,* lobes of one cell about the same distance apart as are the lobes of adjoining cells; cells 17–22μ in diameter.

Euplankter. Mich., Wis.

Pediastrum Braunii Wartmann *in* Wartmann & Schenk
1862, Fasc. 1, No. 32
Pl. 48, Fig. 5

Colony circular in outline, nearly entire but with a few interstices, composed of 4–16 quadrate or 5-sided cells (11 peripheral and 5 central); peripheral cells with 3 or 4 short, sharp projections which are unevenly spaced; interior cells 4–5-sided, the walls without projections or incisions; cells 9–12μ in diameter.

Euplankter. Wis.

Pediastrum duplex Meyen 1829, p. 772
Pl. 48, Fig. 4

Colony 8–128-celled, the walls smooth, with lens-shaped spaces between the inner cells, which are quadrate, the outer margin concave; peripheral cells quadrate, the outer margin extended into 2 tapering, blunt-tipped processes, distance between processes of one cell about one-half the distance between processes of adjacent cells; cells 15.6μ in diameter; 36-celled colony 105μ in diameter.

Common in the eu- and tychoplankton of many lakes and swamps. Mich., Wis.

Pediastrum duplex var. *brachylobum* A. Braun 1855, p. 93

A variety in which the peripheral cells bear 2 widely separated, very short, truncate processes (about 3μ long); colony composed of 16–128 cells, with granular walls; colony up to 300μ, cells up to 40μ, in diameter.

Mich.

Pediastrum duplex var. *clathratum* (A. Braun) Lagerheim 1882, p. 56
Pl. 48, Fig. 6

Colony with larger perforations than in the typical form; walls with deep emarginations; apices of lobes of peripheral cells truncate; cells 12–20μ in diameter.

Very common in a large number of lakes of both hard and soft water; generally distributed. Mich., Wis.

[223]

Pediastrum duplex var. *cohaerens* Bohlin 1897, p. 31
Pl. 48, Fig. 11

Colony with large clathrations; cell walls granular; cells 15–20μ in diameter.

Common in tychoplankton. Mich., Wis.

Pediastrum duplex var. *gracilimum* West & West 1895a, p. 52
Pl. 48, Fig. 12

Colony with large perforations; body of cells narrow, equal in width to the processes of the peripheral cells, which are relatively larger than described for the typical plant.

This is undoubtedly a growth form of the typical plant.

Euplankter. Mich., Wis.

Pediastrum duplex var. *reticulatum* Lagerheim 1882, p. 56
Pl. 49, Fig. 1

Outer margins of the peripheral cells having lobes with subparallel sides; inner cells nearly H-shaped.

This form, like the preceding one, should be interpreted as a growth form of *P. duplex*.

Widely distributed; euplanktonic. Mich., Wis.

Pediastrum duplex var. *rotundatum* Lucks 1907, p. 31
Pl. 48, Fig. 8

Marginal cells with stout lobes which have convex rather than parallel margins; apices of lobes closer together than in the typical plant.

Euplankter; common. Mich., Wis.

Pediastrum duplex var. *rugulosum* Raciborski 1889, p. 24
Pl. 49, Fig. 3

Colony ovoid, entire except for small lens-shaped openings between peripheral and inner cells; walls irregularly crenate and wrinkled, granular; cells 15–22μ in diameter.

Euplankter. Wis.

Pediastrum glanduliferum Bennett 1892, p. 7
Pl. 49, Fig. 4

Colony elliptical, entire or nearly so; peripheral cells 5- or 6-angled with a concave incision between 2 long, capitate projections which are tipped with a globular swelling; cells about 10μ in diameter, 12μ long.

Euplankter. Wis.

Pediastrum integrum Naegeli 1849, p. 97
Pl. 48, Figs. 9, 10

Colony entire; cells 5-sided; outer margin of peripheral cells smooth or with 2 short and much reduced processes, and granular walls, emarginate between the processes; cells 16–25μ in diameter.

A smooth-walled form of this species, fa. *glabra* Racib., is frequently encountered.

Euplankter. Mich., Wis.

Pediastrum integrum var. priva Printz 1914, p. 73
Pl. 48, Fig. 7

Colony smaller than the typical plant; peripheral cells trapezoidal, the outer margins straight or slightly retuse.

Euplankter. Wis.

Pediastrum integrum var. scutum Raciborski 1889, p. 5
Pl. 49, Fig. 2

Colony entire, 8–64-celled, walls thick; interior cells 5- or 6-sided; peripheral cells 5-sided, rhomboidal, the outer wall convex and without processes, surface of walls and free outer margins furnished with numerous, sharp granules; cells 10–18.5–(28)μ in diameter.

Rare, in littoral flora. Mich., Wis.

Pediastrum Kawraiskyi Schmidle 1897, p. 269
Pl. 50, Fig. 1

Colony entire; inner cells 4- or 6-sided; peripheral cells napiform in vertical view, the outer margin extended into 2 projections which are not in the same plane, one usually directly above the other; cells 10–20μ in diameter.

Eu- and tychoplanktonic; common. Mich., Wis.

Pediastrum muticum Kuetzing 1849, p. 193
Pl. 49, Fig. 8

Colony perforate, with 8–64 smooth-walled cells; inner cells 5- or 6-sided; peripheral cells with emarginate outer walls and 2 broadly rounded lobes, which are further apart than the lobes of adjacent cells; cells 20μ in diameter.

The original description of this plant contains no justification for including it with *P. tetras* as in DeToni, 1889, Sylloge Algarum, 1 (1) p. 581.

Rare, in euplankton. Mich., Wis.

Pediastrum muticum var. *crenulatum* Prescott 1944, p. 356
Pl. 49, Fig. 9

A variety differing from the typical in having crenulate or irregularly wavy walls on both the adjoining and the outer free surfaces; colony large, as many as 134 cells (in concentric rows of 34, 31, 27, 21, 15, 6); cells 18–24.5μ in diameter, colony up to 167μ wide; 340μ long.

Rare; in plankton. Wis.

Pediastrum obtusum Lucks 1907 (reprint), p. 13
[*Pediastrum quadricornutum* Prescott 1944, p. 356]
Pl. 49, Figs. 6, 7

Colony nearly entire, with minute interstices formed by the retuse margins of some cells; colony oblong, rarely subcircular (the rows of cells arranged: 7 - 1; 16 - 11 - 5; 16 - 9 - 7), composed of from 8–32 cells which have a deep narrow sinus forming 2 major lobes, the lobes incised to form bluntly rounded lobules, the two central lobules in contact or nearly so, thus closing the sinus outwardly, the two lateral lobules in contact with the lateral lobules of the adjoining cells; interior cells about the same shape as the peripheral cells but with the lobules less prominent, sometimes wanting, with the wall merely emarginate or nearly straight; cells 10.5–18μ in diameter; 8-celled colony up to 144μ wide.

Euplankter. Wis.

According to Bigeard (1935) such a form as this would be included with *P. tetras,* a species which has many variations. *Pediastrum obtusum* is here regarded as separable from *P. tetras* on the basis of the narrow, closed incisions of the cells and the obtuse apices. The form was described by Prescott (1944) as *P. quadricornutum* because it seemed to be separable from the forms included in Bigeard's monograph (1935). It had been described earlier, however, as *P. obtusum* by Lucks (1907).

Pediastrum sculptatum G. M. Smith 1916, p. 475
Pl. 49, Fig. 5

Colony entire or with narrow perforations; internal cells 4–6-sided; peripheral cells with 2 lobes having subparallel margins; cell wall covered with a fine reticulum of ridges; cells 10–15μ in diameter; colony 150–180μ wide.

Euplankter. Wis.

Pediastrum simplex (Meyen) Lemmermann 1897, p. 180
Pl. 50, Fig. 2

Colony entire, composed of 16–32–64 smooth-walled cells; inner cells 5- or 6-sided; peripheral cells with the outer free wall extended to form a single tapering, horn-like process with concave margins; cells 12–18μ in diameter.

Common in the plankton of a number of lakes. Mich., Wis.

Pediastrum simplex var. *duodenarium* (Bailey)
Rabenhorst 1868, p. 72
Pl. 50, Figs. 4, 5

Colony perforate, composed of 36–48–64 cells with their inner margins concave, the outer margin of inner cells forming a long process, peripheral cells forming a stout process; cells 11–15μ in diameter, 27–28μ long; 36-celled colony 137μ in diameter.

Euplankter. Mich., Wis.

Pediastrum tetras (Ehrenb.) Ralfs 1844, p. 469
Pl. 50, Figs. 3, 6

Colony entire; inner cells (frequently none) with 4–6 straight sides but with one margin deeply incised; peripheral cells crenate, with a deep incision in the outer free margin, their lateral margins adjoined along ⅔ of their length; cells 8–12–(16)μ in diameter.

Common and generally distributed in both eu- and tychoplankton. Mich., Wis.

Pediastrum tetras var. *obtusata* Raciborski 1889, p. 32

Cells larger than in the typical plant, the outer margin of the peripheral cells straight, not so emarginate; cells 14–18μ in diameter, 18–22μ long.

Euplankter. Wis.

Pediastrum tetras var. *tetraodon* (Corda) Rabenhorst 1868, p. 78
Pl. 50, Fig.7

Colony 4–8-celled, outer margins of peripheral cells with deep incisions; the lobes extended into sharp, horn-like processes; cells 12–15μ in diameter, 16–18μ long.

Euplankter. Mich., Wis.

SORASTRUM Kuetzing 1845, p. 144

A spherical colony of either loosely or compactly arranged reniform, pyriform, cuneate or pyramidate cells, attached by radiating strands to a common polyhedroid central body of mucilage; outer and free surface of the cell furnished with 1–4 stout, outwardly directed spines; 1 diffuse chloroplast covering most of the wall, containing a single pyrenoid.

Key to the Species

Cells broadly cuneate; spines 4–8μ long _____ S. *spinulosum*
Cells narrowly cuneate; spines 10–15μ long _____ S. *americanum*

Sorastrum americanum (Bohlin) Schmidle 1900d, p. 230
Pl. 50, Fig. 8

A free-floating spherical colony of 16–128 heart-shaped or sub-pyramidate cells with the outer free walls emarginate and furnished at each of the 4 angles with a long, stout, outwardly directed spine; cells narrowed toward the base and attached to the center of the colony by a short, cylindrical stalk which at the base is 5- or 6-sided adjoining the sides of other stalks in such a way as to form a central hollow sphere; cells 7–20μ in diameter, 5–20μ long, 4–8μ thick; spines 10–15μ long.

Rare; in several soft water lakes, especially in northern counties; eu- and tychoplanktonic. Mich., Wis.

Sorastrum americanum var. *undulatum* G. M. Smith 1918, p. 640
Pl. 50, Fig. 10

A variety differing from the typical in having the margins of the facets at the base of the stipe undulate.

Rare; in the euplankton of lakes. Wis.

Sorastrum spinulosum Naegeli 1849, p. 99
Pl. 50, Fig. 9; Pl. 53, Fig.1

A spherical, free-floating colony of 4–32 rhomboidal, reniform, or broadly cuneate cells attached by a very short and broad stipe to a common center; outer free wall straight, furnished at each angle with 2 relatively short spines, 4–8μ long; cells 8–20μ in diameter, 6–18μ long, 5–8μ thick..

Common in the plankton of many lakes; generally distributed. Mich., Wis.

FAMILY COELASTRACEAE

This small family is characterized by cells that are radiately arranged and adjoined, forming globular colonies which may be either hollow or solid. In most species the cells are interconnected by narrow processes or by extensions of the cell membrane to form interstices. The chloroplast is parietal, covering nearly the entire wall. Reproduction is by formation of a definite number of autospores within each cell of the colony. These become adjoined to form daughter colonies before being liberated. There is but one genus, *Coelastrum*, since *"Phytomorula"*[3] has been found not to be an alga.

COELASTRUM Naegeli *in* Kuetzing 1849, p. 195

A hollow, spherical, free-floating colony of as many as 128 globose, ovoid, or pyramidal cells which either are closely adjoined and compressed, or interconnected by narrow processes to form a fenestration. Daughter colonies are formed within the parent cells; the walls of the parent cells may persist about the new colonies, interconnecting them and so forming complexes.

Key to the Species

1. Cells without arms; interconnecting processes extremely
   short, sometimes scarcely evident 2
1. Cells with arms, or with longer and very
   evident interconnecting processes 4
2. Cell walls with wart-like processes ....*C. scabrum*
2. Cell walls without wart-like processes 3
3. Cells spherical or ellipsoidal, closely adjoined, with interstices
   narrower than the diameter of the cells ....*C. microporum*
3. Cells conical, adjoined, but with interstices as wide as the
   diameter of the cells, or wider..................................*C. sphaericum*
4. Cells pyramidal or conical; arms truncate, adjoined within the colony in
   such a way as to form large fenestrations..................*C. proboscideum*
4. Cells spherical 5
5. Cells at the ends of long gelatinous strands
   radiating from a common center..................................*C. speciosum*
5. Cells not at the ends of long radiating strands 6
6. Outer free walls of the cells with a truncate projection;
   interconnecting processes of cells short..................*C. cambricum*
6. Outer free walls of cells without a projection;
   interconnecting processes long..................................*C. reticulatum*

Coelastrum cambricum Archer 1868, p. 65
Pl. 53, Fig. 2

Coenobium spherical, usually composed of 32 globose cells (ranging from 8 to 128 in number), each cell adjoined to neighboring cells by 6 broad, short projections of the sheath so that triangular intercellular spaces result; outer free wall of the cells with a flattened, truncate projection; cells 10–20μ in diameter, including sheath.

Widely distributed and common in the plankton of a great variety of lakes and bogs. Mich., Wis.

---

[3]*Phytomorula regularis* Kofoid, the only species described, has been shown to be pollen of *Acacia* spp. (H. F. Copeland in Madroño, 4, pp. 120-125. 1937); hence the family Coelastraceae is monogeneric, unless Chodat's genus *Coelastrella* should prove to be well founded.

Coelastrum microporum Naegeli *in* A. Braun 1855, p. 70
Pl. 53, Fig. 3

Coenobium spherical, composed of 8–64 sheathed globose cells (sometimes ovoid, with the narrow end outwardly directed); cells interconnected by very short, scarcely discernible gelatinous processes, leaving small intercellular spaces; cells 8–20μ in diameter including the sheath.

Common in the tychoplankton of many lakes and ponds. Mich., Wis.

Coelastrum proboscideum Bohlin 1897, p. 33
[*C. compositum* G. S. West]
Pl. 53, Figs. 4, 5, 8

Coenobium pyramidal or cubical (rarely polygonal), composed of 4–8–16–32 truncate cone-shaped cells with the apex of the cone directed outward, the inner or basal wall of the cell concave, the lower lateral walls of the cells adjoined about a large space in the center of the colony; cells 8–15μ in diameter; 4-celled colony as much as 35μ in diameter.

In both tycho- and euplankton of several lakes; not as common as other species of *Coelastrum*. Mich., Wis.

Coelastrum reticulatum (Dang.) Senn 1899, p. 66
Pl. 53, Fig. 6

Coenobium spherical, free-floating, composed of 8–32 globose cells each inclosed by a gelatinous sheath and adjoined to neighboring cells by 6 long, slender gelatinous processes, leaving large intercellular spaces; outer free wall of the cells without protuberances or processes; cells 8–20–(24)μ in diameter including the sheath.

Euplankter. Mich., Wis.

Coelastrum scabrum Reinsch 1878, p. 238
Pl. 46, Fig. 3

Coenobium spherical, composed of 8–16 angular-globose to angular-depressed-globose cells which bear on their outer faces 4–6 short, wart-like and truncate projections; cells 8–10μ in diameter.

Mackinaw City, Michigan.

Coelastrum speciosum (Wolle) Brunnthaler 1915, p. 197

Coenobium spherical, composed of 16–24 spherical cells, each at the end of a slender gelatinous strand radiating from the center of the colony; outer face of the cell with a single, short-truncate gelatinous projection; cells 10–12μ in diameter.

Cheboygan County, Michigan.

Coelastrum sphaericum Naegeli 1849, p. 98

Pl. 53, Fig. 7

Coenobium ovoid, composed of conical cells, the narrow end directed outward, adjoined without processes along the lower lateral walls, forming interstices which are equal to or greater than the diameter of the cells; cells up to 25μ in diameter.

Euplankter. Mich., Wis.

FAMILY BOTRYOCOCCACEAE

This family is composed of plants which have ovoid or spherical cells embedded and crowded in tough, often foamy, irregularly shaped masses of mucilage which are frequently darkly colored and semi-opaque. In some species the cells are inclosed in a cup of fatty substance with an outer layer of pectic material. The chloroplast is an open or close parietal net-work, usually with 1 pyrenoid. Both starch and oil accumulate as food reserve, the latter often so dense as to obscure the true nature of the cell content. Asexual reproduction is carried on by autospores.

As here defined, this family includes only the genus *Botryococcus* which has been given various taxonomic positions. Because the fatty material in which the cells are embedded is so darkly colored in the type species, *B. Braunii* Kuetz., the exact nature of the cell content and pigmentation has been difficult to determine. Until recently the genus has been placed in the Heterokontae (Chrysophyta) with a few other genera, to comprise the family Botryococcaceae. The critical studies of Blackburn (1936) on *Botryococcus Braunii* Kuetz., however, seem to establish the identity of this species as a member of the Chlorophyta. The morphology of the wall, the presence of a pyrenoid and of starch, and the habit of retaining mother cell membranes and secretions in the building of the colony justify the removal of the genus from the Chrysophyta. Blackburn (*l.c.*) rightly proposes that the Botryococcaceae be placed near the Dictyosphaeraceae. See page 237.

BOTRYOCOCCUS Kuetzing 1849, p. 892

[Ineffigiatus West & West]

Thallus an irregularly globose or bullate colony of ovoid or spherical cells densely arranged somewhat radially in a sticky, often dark-colored mucilage, the cells embedded in a cup-like sheath of fatty material in one species; compound or net-like aggregates of colonies may be formed by long or short strands of rubbery mucilage connecting several clusters of cells; chloroplast a fine or close

[231]

net-work covering only part of the wall, containing 1 pyrenoid; both starch and oil present as food reserves; reproduction by fragmentation and by autospores.

Key to the Species

1. Cells inclosed by a tough, rubbery, often darkly colored mucilage 2
1. Cells invested by a thin, colorless mucilage..B. sudeticus
2. Colonial envelope completely covering the cells; mucilage darkly colored, especially in the older colonies..B. Braunii
2. Colonial envelope leaving the outer face of the cells free.......B. protuberans

Botryococcus Braunii Kuetzing 1849, p. 892
Pl. 52, Figs. 1, 2, 11

Cells ellipsoid, radiately arranged at the periphery of irregularly shaped, usually dark-colored masses of mucilage; free floating; colonial mucilage much folded and extended into tough, foamy strands, often forming colonial complexes by interconnecting strands of mucilage; chloroplast a thin, or dense, parietal net with 1 pyrenoid, covering only a portion of the wall (often masked by the dark color of the mucilage); starch and oil droplets present; individual cells invested by a layer of fatty substance and an outer layer of pectin; cells 3–6μ in diameter, 6–12μ long.

Common, and often abundant, especially in semi-hard water lakes where it frequently is the dominant component of water-bloom associations.

Mich., Wis.

Botryococcus protuberans var. minor G. M. Smith 1918, p. 652
Pl. 52, Figs. 4, 5

Cells ovoid, arranged in few-celled clusters which are connected by long tough, fibrous strands, 4–16 such clusters involved to form multiple colonies; cells embedded in but not entirely surrounded by mucilage, one end protruding at the periphery; cells 5–6.5μ in diameter, 8–9.5μ long.

Rare to common in the euplankton of several lakes, Mich., Wis.

Botryococcus sudeticus Lemmermann 1896a, p. 111
Pl. 52, Fig. 3

Cells spherical, clustered and embedded in a hyaline mucilaginous envelope, forming irregularly shaped or somewhat spherical masses which may be joined together by gelatinous strands to form complexes; cells 6–13μ in diameter.

Rare in the euplankton of several lakes. Mich., Wis.

FAMILY OOCYSTACEAE

This is a large family in which there is a wide range in cell shape and arrangement. The cells may be spherical, ovate, pyramidal, or polygonal. Some forms are unicellular, others colonial. The chief characteristic which unites the 30 or more genera is the autospore method of reproduction; ordinary cell division and zoospore formation are not known. The autospores are small replicas of the mother cell and are usually cut out in a definite number from the parent protoplast. Upon escape they may remain together to form a colony, as in the Coelastraceae, or may separate. Unlike the Coelastraceae and the Scenedesmaceae, however, the colonies are not composed of definitely arranged cells. In most cases the cells are not adjoined but are held together by a gelatinous investment or by the enlarged and persistent mother cell wall, or gelatinized portions of the old wall. In the majority of forms there is a single, laminate chloroplast, but a few species have several to many disclike bodies, each with a pyrenoid. Multinucleate cells are rare.

Key to the Genera

1. Plants endozoic in the cell or body cavities of animals (sponges, *Hydra*, etc.) _____*Zoochlorella*
1. Plants not endozoic _____ 2
2. Plants unicellular _____ 3
2. Plants colonial _____ 21
3. Cells angular, pyramidal, triangular, or polygonal _____ 4
3. Cells spherical, ellipsoid, ovoid, or acicular _____ 8
4. Angles bearing spines or bristles _____ 6
4. Angles not bearing spines; smooth or with the angles produced and extended to form simple or branched processes _____ 5
5. Cell body evident, distinguishable from the extensions of the angles, or with angles smooth and rounded _____*Tetraëdron* (part)
5. Cell body not clearly evident, gradually extended into the processes of the angles _____*Cerasterias* (part)
6. Body of the cell evident, with or without produced angles _____ 32
6. Body of the cell not clearly evident, gradually extended into the processes _. 7
7. Angles of the cell with a thick, stout, and very long spine _____*Treubaria*
7. Angles of the cells gradually narrowed to form a spine-like tip, or with the apices tipped with minute spines _____*Cerasterias* (part)
8. Cells spherical _____ 9
8. Cells ovate, ellipsoid, lunate, or acicular _____ 14
9. Cell wall smooth _____ 10
9. Cell wall not smooth _____ 13
10. Cells with 1 chloroplast (see also *Zoochlorella*) _____ *Chlorella*
10. Cells with several to many chloroplasts _____ 11
11. Cells inclosed by a wide gelatinous investment; chloroplasts not in a reticulum nor in radiating strands _____*Planktosphaeria* (part)
11. Cells not inclosed by a gelatinous investment _____ 12

[233]

12. Chloroplasts numerous irregular plates arranged in a reticulum or in strands of cytoplasm radiating from the center of the cell; wall thin..*Eremosphaera*
12. Chloroplasts cone-shaped, arranged at the periphery and projecting inward; wall thick and lamellate...............................*Excentrosphaera*
13. Cell wall with reticular markings or with short spines .... *Trochiscia*
13. Cell wall with several long, sometimes stout, spines............ *Echinosphaerella*
14. Cells ellipsoid..15
14. Cells lunate, straight and fusiform, or acicular..17
15. Cells without spines or setae..*Oocystis* (part)
15. Cells bearing spines or setae..16
16. Setae distributed over the entire cell wall....................................*Franceia*
16. Setae arising from the poles only, or from the poles and the equator..*Lagerheimia*
17. Cells lunate, distinctly curved...18
17. Cells straight, acicular, or fusiform..19
18. Cells invested by a gelatinous sheath..........................*Kirchneriella* (part)
18. Cells not inclosed by a sheath...........................*Ankistrodesmus* (part)
19. With a fine, needle-like spine at one or both poles of the cell......*Schroederia*
19. Poles of the cell without a spine, although apices may taper to a fine point..20
20. Chloroplast an elongate plate with a row of pyrenoids; cell up to 530μ long ....*Closteriopsis*
20. Chloroplast without pyrenoids, or with but 1; cell much shorter than above..........................*Ankistrodesmus* (part)
21. Cells with a gelatinous investment...22
21. Cells without a gelatinous investment...26
22. Cells spherical or broadly ovate..23
22. Cells not spherical, but elongate, at least twice as long as wide................24
23. Cells arranged in clusters at the ends of radiating strands....*Dictyosphaerium*
23. Cells not adjoined by radiating strands.....................*Planktosphaeria* (part)
24. Cells straight, with long axes parallel in the colony.....................*Quadrigula*
24. Cells curved..25
25. Cells invested by a firm sheath (gelatinized mother cell wall); cells slightly curved or reniform ....*Nephrocytium*
25. Cells in a homogeneous, thin mucilage; sharply curved, lunate or sickle-shaped....................................*Kirchneriella* (part)
26. Cells adjoined by remains of old mother cell walls at the center of the colony..27
26. Cells held together by other means; fragments of old mother cell walls not present at center of colony...28
27. Cells spherical; cell wall fragments curved and unbranched..............*Westella*
27. Cells reniform or ovoid; cell wall fragments forming straight, branching strands...*Dimorphococcus*
28. Cells spindle-shaped; adjoined end to end to form a chain which may branch...*Dactylococcus*
28. Cells not spindle-shaped and not adjoined end to end in a chain-like series..29
29. Cells ovate or spherical, inclosed by enlarged mother cell walls................30
29. Cells elongate, acicular, or spindle-shaped..31
30. Cells separated from one another by a deposit of semi-opaque mucilage which forms cruciately arranged bands about the colony.. *Gloeotaenium*

30. Cells not separated by semi-opaque deposits of mucilage ..... *Oocystis* (part)
31. Cells lunate or sickle-shaped, with their convex
surfaces apposed .... *Selenastrum*
31. Cells straight, in fascicles or irregular clusters, sometimes
twisted about one another .... *Ankistrodesmus* (part)
32. Angles tipped with 4–6 fine, hair-like bristles .... *Polyedriopsis*
32. Angles tipped with 1, 2, or 3 short, stout spines .... *Tetraëdron* (part)

ZOOCHLORELLA Brandt 1882, p. 140

Unicellular; spherical or ovoid; inhabiting the cells and body cavities of animals. Chloroplast (sometimes 2) a parietal plate covering only a portion of the wall; pyrenoid usually present. Reproduction by aplanospores, as in *Chlorella*.

This group, with justification, is regarded by some students as being congeneric with *Chlorella*. It is arbitrarily separated here and the name retained in order to provide a distinct category for the endozoic species. The phenomenon of 'green' animals, such as *Hydra, Ophrydium, Spongilla*, etc., is invariably referred to as being caused by *Zoochlorella*. Long usage, therefore, seems to warrant the separation. The relationship between species of this group and various animals is apparently definite and not haphazard. The symbiosis may vary from commensalism to parasitism. Although the species are described as having no pyrenoid, our specimens usually showed this body very clearly, especially in larger cells.

Key to the Species

Plants inhabiting *Hydra;* cells 3–6µ in diameter .... *Z. conductrix*
Plants inhabiting *Ophrydium, Spongilla*, and *Stentor;*
cells 1.5–3µ in diameter .... *Z. parasitica*

Zoochlorella conductrix Brandt 1882, p. 140
Pl. 53, Fig. 10

Cells globose or broadly ovoid, usually densely compacted with the cells of *Hydra;* chloroplasts 1–2, usually with a pyrenoid; cells 3–6µ in diameter.

Common; in green *Hydra;* inhabiting ponds and swamps where there are dense beds of aquatic vegetation. Mich., Wis.

Zoochlorella parasitica Brandt 1882, p. 140
Pl. 53, Fig. 9

Cells ovoid, inhabiting *Ophrydium*, fresh-water sponges (*Spongilla*), and *Stentor* spp.; chloroplast 1 (rarely 2); cells 1.5–3µ in diameter.

Common in *Ophrydium*, a colonial ciliate which forms floating or attached gelatinous masses 1–10 cm. in diameter. Sometimes the colonials are attached to submerged vegetation. The algal cells vary in abundance so that the colony may be light or very dark accordingly. The protozoan inhabits mostly hard water lakes where it is frequently mistaken for *Nostoc, Tetraspora,* or some other gelatinous alga. Mich., Wis.

CHLORELLA Beyerinck 1890, p. 758

Unicellular, solitary or aggregated in irregular clumps; round or ellipsoid; variable in size in the same habitat. Chloroplast a parietal cup or merely a plate, with or without a pyrenoid. Reproduction by 4 or 8 daughter cells (non-motile) produced from the protoplast of the mother cell.

This small plant may be confused with species of *Chlorococcum,* a soil or subaerial genus, from which it can be differentiated with surety by a study of reproductive habits. It is very similar also to many other unicellular green algae and may be confused with motionless zoospores of some genera. It is necessary, therefore, to study a large number of individuals, or better still to culture the plants in making identification.

Chlorella forms 4 or 8 daughter cells within the mother cell wall whereas *Chlorococcum* produces biflagellate zoospores which escape and immediately separate from one another. In *Chlorococcum* the chloroplast more nearly covers the cell wall than in *Chlorella*. *Chlorococcum* lives almost entirely on or in soil, sometimes at considerable depth, or on old wood and rocks. *Chlorella* is aquatic but may share the same habitat with *Chlorococcum*.

Beyerinck (1890) recommends combining *Chlorella* and *Zoochlorella,* but for the reason mentioned above (under *Zoochlorella*), they are separated here.

Key to the Species

Cells ellipsoidal, 7–8μ in diameter, 9.5μ long .... *C. ellipsoidea*
Cells spherical, usually 5–10μ in diameter .... *C. vulgaris*

Chlorella ellipsoidea Gerneck 1907, p. 250
Pl. 53, Figs. 11, 12

Cells ellipsoidal, sometimes unsymmetrical; chloroplast a folded plate over part of the cell wall; described as producing as many as 32 autospores during reproduction; vegetative cells 7–8μ in diameter, 9–9.5μ long.

Generally distributed in many lakes and ponds. Mich., Wis.

Chlorella vulgaris Beyerinck 1890, p. 758

Pl. 53, Fig. 13

Cells spherical, scattered among other algae or sometimes occurring in almost pure growths; chloroplast a parietal cup, sometimes without a pyrenoid; cells 5–8.5–(10)μ in diameter.

In small lakes and pools, especially where there is a concentration of organic matter. Mich., Wis

WESTELLA de Wildemann 1897, p. 532

A free-floating, globose colony of 30–100 spherical cells without a gelatinous investment; members in groups of 4 and bound together by the persistent remains of old mother cell walls; 1 parietal, cup-shaped chloroplast, often with a pyrenoid.

Key to the Species

Colonies of 40 cells or fewer; cells arranged in
  linear series, 3–6μ in diameter_____*W. linearis*
Colonies of 40–80 cells; cells arranged to form
  quadrate or pyramidate clusters_____*W. botryoides*

Westella botryoides (W. West) de Wildemann 1897, p. 532

Pl. 53, Fig. 14

Colony composed of 40–80 spherical cells, quadrately arranged in groups of 4, the groups loosely connected by the persistent remains of old mother cell walls; cells with 1 parietal, cup-shaped chloroplast; pyrenoid sometimes present; cells 3–9μ in diameter.

Rare but widely distributed, in a large number of lakes, especially in the plankton of soft water. Mich., Wis.

Westella botryoides var. *major* G. M. Smith 1918, p. 628

A variety differing from the typical by having larger cells, 8–13μ in diameter.

Rare in euplankton. Mich., Wis.

Westella linearis G. M. Smith 1920, p. 107

Pl. 53, Figs. 15, 16

An irregularly shaped colony of about 40 spherical cells arranged in a linear series of 4; groups of cells held together by inconspicuous remains of old mother cell wall fragments; cells 3–6μ in diameter.

Rare in euplankton. Wis.

DICTYOSPHAERIUM Naegeli 1849, p. 72

Colony globular or ovoid, composed of spherical or ovoid cells attached by fine, branching strands which radiate from a common

[237]

center, the entire colony invested by a wide, hyaline, gelatinous envelope; cells with 1 or 2 parietal chloroplasts, each with a pyrenoid.

Key to the Species

Cells ellipsoidal or ovoid; colony ovoid_____*D. Ehrenbergianum*
Cells spherical; colony usually globose_____*D. pulchellum*

Dictyosphaerium Ehrenbergianum Naegeli 1849, p. 73
Pl. 51, Figs. 3, 4

Colony ovoid, composed of 8–30 ellipsoidal cells with 1 or 2 parietal or cup-like chloroplasts, cells attached in groups of 2 or 4 at the ends of fine, branched strands; cells 4–6μ in diameter, 8–10μ long.

Common in the plankton of many soft water lakes. Mich., Wis.

Dictyosphaerium pulchellum Wood 1874, p. 84
Pl. 51, Figs. 5–7

Colony spherical or ovoid, composed of as many as 32 spherical cells arranged in series of 4 on dichotomously branched threads, inclosed in mucilage; cells 3–10μ in diameter.

This species is sometimes a conspicuous component of the plankton in acid bog lakes. Taylor (1935) has found it in the leaves of pitcher plants (*Sarracenia purpurea* L.)

Generally distributed in many soft water as well as semi-hard water lakes. Mich., Wis.

TROCHISCIA Kuetzing 1833b, p. 592

Free-floating (or sometimes subaerial), spherical, unicellular plants with thick walls which are either smooth or variously sculptured and decorated (reticulations, warts, spines); with 1 to several plate-like, parietal chloroplasts; pyrenoids 1 or more.

Some care must be used in distinguishing members of this genus from the zygospores of some desmids. The latter have a single, massive chlorophyll-bearing body of indefinite form.

Key to the Species

1. Wall decorated with granular, wart-like or spine-like roughenings _____ 2
1. Wall decorated with ridges which may be concentric
   and parallel, or may form a reticulum_____ 3
2. Granulations sharply pointed and numerous_____*T. aspera*
2. Granulations low and blunt, not so closely
   arranged as above_____*T. granulata*
3. Wall with concentric ridges which form
   low, blunt protuberances_____*T. obtusa*
3. Wall with reticulate ridges_____ 4
4. Reticulations coarse, forming 8–10 visible polygonal areas _____*T. Zachariasii*
4. Reticulations fine, forming as many as 35
   visible areas on the wall _____*T. reticularis*

Trochiscia aspera (Reinsch) Hansgirg 1888a, p. 128
Pl. 53, Fig. 17

Cells free-floating, globose, the wall moderately thick, decorated with evenly distributed, wart-like projections (interconnected by faint lines ?), chloroplasts several, disc-shaped; cells (13)–18–29.5μ in diameter.

Rare in plankton. Mich., Wis.

Trochiscia granulata (Reinsch) Hansgirg 1888a, p. 128
Pl. 53, Fig. 18

Cells aquatic or subaerial, spherical, the wall thick and densely covered with low, granular or wart-like roughenings; cells 10–20–(23)μ in diameter.

In a *Sphagnum* bog. Mich., Wis.

Trochiscia obtusa (Reinsch) Hansgirg 1888a, p. 130
Pl. 52, Fig. 8

Cells spherical, the wall thick, with concentric series of ridges or low, parallel protuberances; 34–37μ in diameter.

Tychoplankter. Mich., Wis.

Trochiscia reticularis (Reinsch) Hansgirg 1888a, p. 129
Pl. 53, Figs. 19, 20

Cells free-floating, spherical, with thick walls which are externally ridged to form a reticulum in which as many as 70 polygonal areas may be marked out; cells up to 39μ in diameter.

This plant also passes under the name of *T. sporoides* (Reinsch) Hansgirg.

Rare; in several lakes and *Sphagnum* bogs. Mich., Wis.

Trochiscia Zachariasii Lemmermann 1903, p. 157
Pl. 53, Fig. 21

Cells free-floating, spherical; wall very thick and decorated externally with a very coarse reticulum of prominent ridges marking out 8–10 irregularly shaped, polygonal areas on the visible side of the cell, forming prominent projections at the periphery; cells 10–20μ in diameter.

Rare, in plankton. Wis.

PLANKTOSPHAERIA G. M. Smith 1918, p. 627

A free-floating colony of spherical cells compactly grouped within a mucilaginous, homogeneous envelope; chloroplasts several, angular, parietal discs, each with a pyrenoid.

Planktosphaeria gelatinosa G. M. Smith 1918, p. 627
Pl. 53, Fig. 23

Characteristics as described for the genus; cells (4.5)–20–25μ in diameter.

This plant should be compared with *Sphaerocystis Schroeteri*, which has a single parietal, cup-shaped chloroplast and in which the cells are usually more distantly arranged. In old colonies of *Planktosphaeria gelatinosa* the cells may become somewhat loosely arranged, but usually they are closely clustered.

Common in the plankton of a variety of lakes and ponds, both in hard and soft water. Mich., Wis.

EREMOSPHAERA DeBary 1858, p. 56

Cells spherical, spheroidal, or somewhat angular-spheroidal (3-angled in face view); solitary or 2–4 together within an old mother cell wall, with or without a gelatinous sheath; free-floating or lying among mixtures of algae in shallow water; chloroplasts numerous, ovate or irregularly shaped discs or pads, with large starch grains, lying in a meshwork along the periphery or in radiating strands of cytoplasm from a central core which involves the nucleus. The chloroplasts are able to shift their position in response to light stimulus.

Key to the Species

Cells spheroidal or angular-spheroidal, 2–4 within an old mother
    cell wall, inclosed by a gelatinous sheath......................*E. oocystoides*
Cells spherical, solitary, sheaths not apparent....................*E. viridis*

Eremosphaera oocystoides Prescott *in* Prescott, Silva & Wade 1949, p. 85
Pl. 46, Fig. 12

Cells spheroidal or triangular-spheroidal in one view, 2–4 (rarely solitary) within old mother cell walls which are ovate or oblate-spheroidal, inclosed in a wide gelatinous sheath in which there are numerous radiating spicules, the old mother cell wall often appearing spiny, and showing flattened, thickened, poles; chloroplasts numerous, small irregularly shaped plates, lumpy with starch grains; cells up to 122μ in diameter; colony 300–450μ in diameter.

In shallow water of an acid swamp. Mich.

Eremosphaera viridis DeBary 1858, p. 56
Pl. 53, Fig. 22

Cells solitary, spherical, not inclosed by a mucilaginous sheath; chloroplasts as described for the genus; cells 50–350μ in diameter.

This plant is so definitely restricted to soft water habitats that it may be used as an index organism for acid conditions in which the pH is 6.0–6.8. It is a common component of a flora in which desmids predominate, and there is some evidence that high organic acid content of the water results in huge *Eremosphaera* cells.

Common in many acid lakes and *Sphagnum* bog ponds. Mich., Wis.

EXCENTROSPHAERA Moore 1901, p. 322

Cells spherical or ellipsoid, free-floating, intermingled with other algae, the wall thick and often lamellate; chloroplasts numerous cone-shaped bodies arranged at the periphery and directed inward, each with many small pyrenoids; reproduction by aplanospores.

Excentrosphaera viridis Moore 1901, p. 322
Pl. 46, Figs. 15, 16

Characteristics as described for the genus; cells 22–55μ in diameter; spores (not observed in our collections) 2–3μ in diameter.

Tychoplankter; in shallow water of lake margins and soft water or acid swamps. Mich.

ECHINOSPHAERELLA G. M. Smith 1920, p. 128

Free-floating, globose cells, entirely covered with long, stout, tapering spines; chloroplast 1, cup-shaped and parietal, containing a single pyrenoid. The genus is monotypic.

Echinosphaerella limnetica G. M. Smith 1920, p. 128
Pl. 51, Figs. 1, 2

Characteristics as described for the genus; cells 9–12μ in diameter exclusive of spines; spines 2.5–3μ wide at the base, 20–25μ long.

This species should be compared with desmid zygospores, many of which have spiny walls and greatly resemble *Echinosphaerella*. Differentiation can be made on the basis of the chloroplast, there being no definitely shaped chlorophyll-bearing body in the desmid zygospore, but a dense, rather shapeless mass.

Rare, in plankton. Wis.

TREUBARIA Bernard 1908, p. 169

Free-floating, pyramidal or flattened 3- to 4-angled unicells, the angles rounded or produced to form a stout, thick-based spine which is either tapering or has subparallel sides; the margins of the cell concave between the angles; chloroplasts 1–4, parietal, cup-shaped in some, becoming massive and filling the cell; 1 or more pyrenoids, usually 1 in each angle of the cell.

This genus should be compared with the pyramidal species of *Tetraëdron*, in which the angles of the cell are sometimes drawn out to form arms. Some species of *Tetraëdon* have the angles bearing spines, but these are relatively short, never equaling the diameter of the cell, whereas in *Treubaria* the angles of the cell are spines, which are much longer than the diameter of the cell body.

Treubaria setigerum (Archer) G. M. Smith 1933, p. 499
[*Tetraëdron trigonum* var. *setigerum* (Arch.) Lemmermann]
Pl. 51, Fig. 8

Cells triangular and flattened in surface view, the angles broadly rounded and then produced to form a long tapering spine; chloroplast a parietal plate, covering the cell wall; cells 7–9μ in diameter; spines 12–15μ long.

Rare; in tychoplankton. Wis.

OOCYSTIS Naegeli *in* A. Braun 1855, p. 94

Unicellular or in colonies of 2–16 individuals inclosed by the persistent and much swollen mother cell wall of the previous generation; several successive generations of cells sometimes inclosed within old membranes; cells ovoid, ovoid-ellipsoid, or rarely subcylindric, with rounded poles which may be smooth or furnished with a conspicuous nodule-like thickening; chloroplasts 1 or many, mostly parietal, of various shapes, ovoid discs, irregular star-shaped plates, or reticular; 1 pyrenoid in each chloroplast (sometimes wanting).

Key to the Species

1. Poles of cells with nodular thickening 2
1. Poles of cells without nodular thickening; apices rounded or pointed.... 9
2. Cells with one pole thickened, the other broadly rounded;
   cells somewhat pyriform ....*O. pyriformis*
2. Cells with nodular thickenings at both poles;
   cells oval, elliptic, or oblong 3
3. Chloroplasts numerous, 4–25–60 4
3. Chloroplasts fewer in number, 1–3 (rarely 4) 7
4. Cells oblong, with lateral walls concave;
   chloroplasts 12–25 ....*O. panduriformis*
4. Cells elliptic or oval (sometimes nearly round)........................ 5
5. Chloroplasts 40–60 irregularly lobed, parietal discs.......*O. Eremosphaeria*
5. Chloroplasts fewer, disciform or oval, laminate 6
6. Chloroplasts relatively large, 4–10; mother cell wall
   much swollen and inclosing 2–4–(8) daughter cells..................*O. crassa*
6. Cloroplasts smaller and more numerous, 12–25;
   mother cell wall not swollen; cells mostly solitary
   (uncommonly as many as 8 in a famiy)..............................*O. solitaria*

Oocystis Borgei Snow 1903, p. 379
Pl. 51, Fig. 10

Unicellular or crowded in groups of 2–8, inclosed by the old mother cell wall; ellipsoid or ovate cells with the poles broadly rounded and smooth; chloroplasts 1 or as many as 4 parietal plates, each with a pyrenoid; cells (9)–12–13μ in diameter, (9)–10–19μ long; colony of 8 cells, up to 31μ in diameter, 46μ long.

Lemmermann (1903) has assigned this species, as a variety, to *O. gigas*.

Common in the plankton of soft water lakes; often appearing among filamentous algae in shallow water. Mich., Wis.

Oocystis crassa Wittrock *in* Wittrock & Nordstedt 1880, p. 117
Pl. 51, Fig. 9

Unicellular or in colonies of 2–8, inclosed by a much swollen and gelatinized mother cell wall; cells ovate, the poles broadly rounded and furnished with a nodular thickening; chloroplasts several (as many as 10) large parietal discs, with pyrenoids usually present; cells 10–20μ in diameter, 14–26μ long.

Rare; in plankton. Mich., Wis.

Oocystis elliptica W. West 1892, p.736
Pl. 51, Fig. 11

Colony composed of 4–8 oblong-ellipsoid cells inclosed by the irregularly swollen old mother cell wall; poles of the cells broadly rounded and without polar thickenings; chloroplasts numerous (as many as 20) parietal discs, apparently without pyrenoids; cells 11–15.6μ in diameter, 20–21.4–(25)μ long.

Common in the plankton of many soft water lakes and ponds; frequent in ditches and swamps, especially where there are luxuriant growths of algae and where the water is rich in organic acids. Mich., Wis.

Oocystis elliptica var. minor West & West 1894, p. 14

Cells smaller than in the typical plant, 7–10μ in diameter, 15–22μ long. Common in plankton. Wis.

Oocystis Eremosphaeria G. M. Smith 1918, p. 630
Pl. 51, Fig. 12

Plants unicellular, usually solitary, sometimes in a group of 2 or 4 within the old mother cell wall; cells narrowly ovate, the poles broadly rounded and furnished with a large nodular thickening; chloroplasts numerous, as many as 60 parietal, lenticular discs, each with a pyrenoid; cells 20–25–(31)μ in diameter, 35–45μ long.

The larger specimens always seem to be found in habitats where there is a rich mixture of algae in shallow, warm water.

Plankter; in many lakes and sloughs. Mich., Wis.

Oocystis gigas Archer 1877, p.105
Pl. 51, Fig. 14

Plant usually a family of 4 broadly ellipsoid or ovate cells inclosed within a much enlarged, elliptical mother cell wall; cells broadly rounded at the poles, which are smooth and without nodules; chloroplasts many parietal discs; pyrenoids not observed; cells 29–35–(40)μ in diameter, 40–51.8μ long.

Rare; in plankton. Mich., Wis.

Oocystis gloeocystiformis Borge 1906, p. 23
Pl. 51, Fig. 13

Plant usually composed of a family of 2 or 4 ellipsoid cells inclosed within the old mother cell wall; cells with narrowed and sharply rounded poles, without nodular thickenings; 1 parietal chloroplast in each cell, pyrenoid lacking; cells (3)–11μ in diameter, 8–18.5μ long.

The poles of the cells of this species are somewhat produced to form blunt points, giving an appearance of nodular thickenings. This may be interpreted as a modification of the nodule character which is common to many species, and from the evidence at hand it would seem logical to include *O. gloeocystiformis* with that section of the genus characterized by the possession of polar nodules. Our specimens compare more closely with the plant figured by Borge (1906) than with those shown by Smith (1920).

Among other algae in a few soft water lakes and swamps. Wis.

Oocystis lacustris Chodat 1897, p. 119; 1897a, p. 296
Pl. 54, Fig. 1

Plants usually in families of 2–8 within enlarged, oval mother cell walls; cells broadly elliptic or moniliform, the poles furnished with large nodular thickenings; chloroplasts 1–3 parietal plates, usually containing 1 pyrenoid; cells 12–20μ in diameter, 16–28μ long.

Common in the plankton of several soft water lakes. Mich., Wis.

Oocystis natans (Lemm.) Wille 1911, p. 58

Cells ellipsoid with sharply pointed poles, without nodular thickenings, united in families of 8; cells 12–15μ in diameter, 23–26μ long; chloroplasts 4–8 star-shaped plates.

Typical plant not observed in our collections.

Oocystis natans var. *major* G. M. Smith 1918, p. 630
Pl. 54, Fig. 2

A family of 2 or 4 ovate cells inclosed in the much expanded old mother cell wall; poles of the cells rather sharply rounded but without polar nodules; chloroplasts 4–8 in number, parietal, lobed or star-shaped plates, each containing a pyrenoid; cells 16–25μ in diameter, 31–38μ long; families about 90μ in diameter, 120μ long.

Plankter; common. Wis.

Oocystis nodulosa West & West 1894, p. 15
Pl. 54, Figs. 6, 7

Cells solitary, or 2 within old mother cell wall; ellipsoid to oblong-ellipsoid, with rounded apices bearing a papillate thickening which projects both inward and outward; 16–18μ in diameter, 25–30μ long.

Rare; in plankton. Wis.

Oocystis novae-semliae Wille 1897, p. 26

Cells ellipsoidal with thick walls; 4 or 8 individuals inclosed by the old mother cell wall; poles of cells without nodular thickenings; cells 5μ in diameter, 8μ long.

Typical plant not represented in our collections.

[245]

Oocystis novae-semliae var. *maxima* West & West 1894, p. 13

A variety differing from the typical plant by its much greater size, 12–15μ in diameter, 19–23μ long; colony 23–42μ in diameter, 40–52μ long.

Plankter; in several lakes. Wis.

Oocystis panduriformis West & West 1894, p. 15

A family of 4 oblong-ovate cells with emarginate, concave lateral walls; cells broadly rounded at the poles and furnished with a conspicuous nodular thickening; chloroplasts numerous, parietal discs, each with a pyrenoid; cells 23–25μ in diameter, 50–61.5μ long.

Typical plant not represented in our collections.

Oocystis panduriformis var. *minor* G. M. Smith 1916, p. 471
Pl. 54, Fig. 11

A variety differing from the typical plant by its smaller size, 12–20μ in diameter, 30–41μ long; colony of 4 cells up to 59μ in diameter, 103μ long.

Euplankter. Wis.

Oocystis parva West & West 1898, Jour. Bot., 36, p. 335
Pl. 54, Fig. 3

One-celled or in families of 2–8 individuals, inclosed by the enlarged mother cell wall of the previous generation; 2–4 generations sometimes involved; cells ellipsoid or fusiform with pointed poles which are not furnished with definite polar nodules; chloroplasts 1 to 3 parietal discs, pyrenoids sometimes present; cells 4–7.5μ in diameter, 6–15.6μ long; colony up to 43.9μ in diameter.

Common in the tycho- and euplankton of several lakes and bogs. Mich.,Wis.

Oocystis pusilla Hansgirg 1890, p. 9
Pl. 51, Fig. 15; Pl. 54, Figs. 4, 5

A colony of 4 ovate cells inclosed by the enlarged mother cell wall; poles of the cells broadly rounded, without nodular thickenings; chloroplasts 1 or 2 parietal plates, pyrenoids sometimes present; cells 3.8–7.5μ in diameter, 6–12μ long.

Plankter. Uncommon but found in several lakes. Mich., Wis.

Oocystis pyriformis Prescott 1944, p. 357
Pl. 54, Figs. 8, 9

Cells broadly pyriform-ovoid, with a prominent apiculation at one pole, the other end broadly rounded; united in families of 2 or 4; chloroplast massive and parietal with 1 pyrenoid; cells 14–16μ in diameter, 16–19μ long; colony of 4 cells up to 36μ in diameter, 48.8μ long.

This species should be compared with *O. apiculata* W. West, a much smaller plant with broadly elliptic cells.

Plankter; in a cedar swamp. Wis.

Oocystis solitaria Wittrock *in* Wittrock & Nordstedt 1879, p. 24
Pl. 54, Fig. 10

Often solitary, or in a family of 2–8 cells inclosed by the old mother cell wall; cells ovate or ellipsoid; poles with nodular thickenings; chloroplasts numerous parietal plates, each with a pyrenoid; cells 3–9μ in diameter, 7–20μ long.

Common in the euplankton of lakes; also in tychoplankton among filamentous algae. Mich., Wis.

Oocystis solitaria var. *major* Wille 1879, p. 26

A form differing from the typical by having sharply pointed poles and by its larger size, about 16.5μ in diameter, 29μ long.

Rare; in plankton. Wis.

Oocystis submarina Lagerheim 1886, p. 45
Pl. 54, Fig. 12

Usually a family of 2–16 oblong-cylindrical cells, rarely solitary; cells narrowed at the poles and furnished with a nodular thickening; chloroplasts 1–3 parietal plates with 1 pyrenoid each; cells 3–9μ in diameter, 7–20μ long.

Rare; in eu- and tychoplankton. Mich., Wis.

GLOEOTAENIUM Hansgirg 1890, p. 10

A free-floating, spherical or quadrangular-ovate colony of 2–8 globose or ellipsoid cells compactly and cruciately arranged within the persistent mother cell wall; cells separated within the colony by dark-colored masses of mucilage containing calcium carbonate, usually appearing as 2 X-shaped bands and sometimes almost entirely masking the inclosed cells, a cap of dark mucilage also appearing between the cells and the colonial membrane; chloroplast massive and indeterminate in shape.

There is but 1 species in this genus; it is rather rare and widely distributed.

Gloeotaenium Loitelsbergerianum Hansgirg 1890, p. 10
Pl. 54, Figs. 13, 14

Characteristics as described for the genus; cells globose or ovoid,
18–25–(30)μ in diameter; 8-celled colony as much as 70μ in diameter, 80μ long.

In tychoplankton of lakes, in soft or semi-hard water. Mich., Wis.

NEPHROCYTIUM Naegeli 1849, p. 79

A colony of 4–8 cells, varied in shape, ovate, fusiform, hemispherical, or oblong-ellipsoid to reniform, inclosed by the much enlarged
persistent mother cell wall, which may gelatinize and coalesce
somewhat, permitting daughter colonies to adhere together, thus
forming colonial complexes; occasionally 2 generations of cells
inclosed by 1 mother cell wall; chloroplast a parietal plate, which
becomes very diffuse in older cells; 1 pyrenoid.

Key to the Species

1. Cells broadly ovate or hemispherical, 1½ times longer than wide_____ 2
1. Cells lunate, fusiform, or reniform, 2–3 times longer than wide_____ 3
2. Old mother cell walls gelatinized and persisting as fragments
   about the colony; cells 13–18μ in diameter,
   broadly ovate or hemispherical_____*N. ecdysiscepanum*
2. Old mother cell wall firm and thick; cells hemispherical or
   very broadly ovate, up to 28μ in diameter_____*N. obesum*
3. Investment of cells formed by gelatinized mother cell
   walls; cells curved or sausage-shaped_____*N. limneticum*
3. Investment of cells formed by persistent and firm mother cell walls_____ 4
4. Cells reniform_____*N. Agardhianum*
4. Cells lunate_____*N. lunatum*

Nephrocytium Agardhianum Naegeli 1849, p. 79
[*N. Naegelii* Grunow]
Pl. 54, Figs. 15, 16

Colony ovate, composed of 2–8 cylindrical or reniform cells,
twisting so as to give a spiral arrangement within the old mother
cell wall; cells 2–7μ in diameter, 8–18μ long.

Rather common in the tychoplankton of several lakes and ponds.
Mich., Wis.

Nephrocytium ecdysiscepanum W. West *in* West & West 1896, p. 161
Pl. 54, Fig. 17

Colony broadly ovate, composed of 4–16 ovate, ovoid, or nearly
hemispherical cells inclosed by the old mother cell wall, the family
adjoined or adhering to other families by the gelatinized and

fragmentary remains of cell walls of previous generations, the complex often forming a fan-like arrangement; cells (13)–15.6–18μ in diameter, 30–32μ long; colony of 4 cells about 60.4μ in diameter. Rare; in lakes and swamps. Wis.

Nephrocytium limneticum (G. M. Smith) G. M. Smith 1933, p. 503
Pl. 54, Fig. 18

Colony subspherical, composed of 4–8 curved, crescent- or sausage-shaped cells with broadly rounded ends; mother cell wall of previous generation completely gelatinized and not persisting as a membrane; cells 7.4μ in diameter, 10–25μ long.

Reported as *Gloeocystopsis limneticus* G. M. Smith from Wisconsin.

Euplankter; in ponds and lakes. Mich.

Nephrocytium lunatum W. West 1892, p. 736
Pl. 54, Fig. 19

Colony ovate, consisting of 4–8 lunate, bluntly-pointed cells inclosed by a thin, hyaline membrane and arranged so that the concave wall is directed toward the center of the colony; chloroplast covering the cell wall; cells 4–5μ in diameter, 14–18μ long.

Tychoplanktonic in swamps; in ditches. Wis.

Nephrocytium obesum West & West 1894, p. 13
Pl. 54, Fig. 20

Colony broadly ovate, composed of 2–4 broadly ovate to hemispherical cells inclosed by a thick membranous integument, the cells broadly rounded at the poles and with one margin strongly convex, the other straight or concave; chloroplast massive, somewhat reticulate and covering the entire wall; cells 14–16–(28)μ in diameter, 30–33–(49)μ long.

This species should be compared with *N. ecdysiscepanum*.

Tychoplankter; in ponds and lakes. Mich., Wis.

LAGERHEIMIA (DeToni) Chodat 1895, p. 90
[*Chodatella* Lemmermann 1898]

A solitary, free-floating, moniliform, ovate, or ellipsoid cell with a rather thick wall beset with long, tapering, needle-like setae which are confined to the polar or to the equatorial region; chloroplasts 1–4 parietal plates, with or without pyrenoids.

Key to the Species

1. Cells moniliform_____*L. citriformis*
1. Cells ovate or ellipsoid_____ 2

2. Setae more than twice the length of the cell .... *L. longiseta*
2. Setae shorter, twice the length of the cell or less 3
3. Cells with 2 diverging setae arising near each apex .... *L. quadriseta*
3. Cells with more than 2 setae, arising at the apices of the cell 4
4. Cells with 2–4 setae arising from each pole; cells ovate .... *L. subsalsa*
4. Cells with 3–8 setae arising from each pole; cells oblong-ovate .... *L. ciliata*

Lagerheimia ciliata (Lag.) Chodat 1895, p. 90
Pl. 55, Fig. 1

Cells oblong-ovate with 3–8 (usually 6) fine, tapering setae at each pole; chloroplasts 1–4 parietal plates, each with a pyrenoid; cells 6–18μ in diameter, 10–21μ long; setae 15–20μ long.
Rare; in plankton. Mich., Wis.

Lagerheimia ciliata var. *minor* (G. M. Smith)
G. M. Smith 1920, p. 129
Pl. 55, Fig. 2

A variety with smaller, ovate, cells, 6–7.5μ in diameter, 8–10μ long; setae up to 20μ long.
Rare; in plankton. Wis.

Lagerheimia citriformis (Snow) G. M. Smith 1920, p. 130
Pl. 55, Fig. 4

Cells ellipsoid, moniliform with knob-like extensions at the poles (giving an *Oocystis*-like appearance to the cell); 4–8 long tapering setae arranged in a whorl at each pole; 1 parietal chloroplast containing a single pyrenoid; cells 8–20μ in diameter, 13–23μ long without the setae, which are 25–35μ long.
Rare; in plankton. Mich., Wis.

Lagerheimia citriformis var. *paucispina*
Tiffany & Ahlstrom 1931, p.462
Pl. 46, Fig. 4

Cells the same shape as the typical but smaller, 8–9μ in diameter, 10–14μ long; each pole provided with 2–4 setae.
Mich.

Lagerheimia longiseta (Lemm.) Printz 1914, p. 60
Pl. 55, Fig. 5

Cells ovate or ellipsoid, with very long setae (more than twice the length of the cell) arranged in a whorl of 4–10 close to the poles; 1 (?) parietal chloroplast without a pyrenoid; cells 5–8μ in diameter, 9–13μ long without setae; setae 40–55μ long.
Rare; in plankton. Mich., Wis.

Lagerheimia longiseta var. *major* G. M. Smith 1920, p. 130
Pl. 55, Fig. 6

A variety differing from the typical by its pointed ovate cells which are considerably larger, 12–15μ in diameter, 15–22μ long without setae; setae 45–60μ long; described as having 1–2 chloroplasts, each with a pyrenoid.

Rare; in plankton. Mich., Wis.

Lagerheimia quadriseta (Lemm.) G. M. Smith
Pl. 46, Fig. 11

Cells ovate, with 2 long, diverging setae arising near the apices; cells 4–6.5μ in diameter, 7.5–12μ long; setae up to 23μ long.

Mich.

Lagerheimia subsalsa Lemmermann 1898, p. 193
Pl. 55, Fig. 7

Cells ovate, with a tuft of 2–4 setae at the poles; 1 parietal chloroplast with a pyrenoid; cells 2.5–8μ in diameter, 5–12μ long without setae; setae 7.5–26μ long.

Rare; in plankton. Mich., Wis.

FRANCEIA Lemmermann 1898c, p. 307

Free-floating ovate or ellipsoid cells, solitary or 2–4 together; walls covered with long, slender bristle-like setae which may show a basal swelling or tubercle; chloroplasts 1–4 parietal plates; pyrenoids present or absent.

This genus should be compared with *Lagerheimia* in which the setae are confined to the polar or equatorial regions of the cell wall.

Key to the Species

Cells ellipsoid; chloroplasts 2–4 _____ *F. Droescheri*
Cells ovate; chloroplasts 1–2–(3) _____ *F. ovalis*

Franceia Droescheri (Lemm.) G. M. Smith 1933, p. 505
Pl. 56, Figs. 1–3

Cells broadly ellipsoid, the wall covered with stiff, straight, spine-like bristles without tubercular thickenings at their bases; chloroplasts 2–4 parietal plates; cells 5–12μ in diameter without setae, 9–16μ long; setae 15–22μ long.

Euplankter. Mich., Wis.

Franceia ovalis (Francé) Lemmermann 1898c, p. 308
Pl. 56, Fig. 4

Cells ovate; chloroplasts 1–2–(3) parietal plates; cells 7–10μ in diameter, 13–17μ long without setae; setae 15–23μ long.

Rare; in plankton. Mich., Wis.

[251]

DIMORPHOCOCCUS A. Braun 1855, p. 44

Colony free-floating; cells arranged in groups of 4 on the branched wall fragments of the previous generation, not inclosed in mucilage; quartets of cells composed of 2 ovate or subcylindric and 2 reniform or cordate individuals; 1 chloroplast, parietal, with 1 pyrenoid.

Dimorphococcus lunatus A. Braun 1855, p. 44
Pl. 55, Fig. 8

Cells in groups of 4 on the ends of fine, branched threads composed of the fragments of the mother cell wall, the 2 inner cells of the quartet ovate or subcylindric, the 2 outer cells cordate; cells 4–15μ in diameter, 10–25μ long; chloroplast 1, a parietal plate nearly covering the entire cell wall in mature individuals.

Common and widely distributed; especially in the plankton of soft water lakes and acid bog ponds. Mich., Wis.

ANKISTRODESMUS Corda 1838, p. 196

Cells acicular, crescent-shaped, or narrowly fusiform; solitary or clustered in fascicles, sometimes straight, usually curved, and often twisted about one another; without a gelatinous envelope. Chloroplast a thin, parietal plate covering most of the cell wall; pyrenoid present or absent.

Members of this genus are frequently found in great abundance in small pools, along with species of *Scenedesmus*, coloring the water green. They are common pioneers in waterlily and other artificial ponds and laboratory aquaria. Care is needed to distinguish some species of *Ankistrodesmus* from the myxophycean genus *Dactylococcopsis*.

Key to the Species

1. Cells sigmoid or spirally twisted, sometimes wound about one another........ 2
1. Cells fusiform, straight or lunate, not twisted.. 3
2. Cells slender and elongate, spirally twisted
   about one another, forming bundles...*A. spiralis*
2. Cells wider and stouter than above, sigmoid-arcuate, twisted
   at the apices only, not forming bundles .... *A. convolutus*
3. Cells straight, or nearly so, broadly fusiform, solitary......................*A. Braunii*
3. Cells narrower than above, curved or lunate, or if straight,
   ending in long needle points... 4
4. Cells fusiform or lunate, straight, or curved,
   usually entangled or clustered...*A. falcatus*
4. Cells arcuate, dorsal walls straight from the midregion to the
   sharply pointed apices; cells always solitary.................................*A. fractus*

[252]

Ankistrodesmus Braunii (Naeg.) Brunnthaler 1915, p. 189

Pl. 46, Fig. 8

Cells relatively broadly fusiform, lateral margins convex but irregularly so, narrowed at either pole to short points (not drawn out into long needle points as in most species of the genus); chloroplasts 2 parietal plates; cells 8–10μ in diameter, 20–25–56μ long.

Tychoplankter. Mich.

Ankistrodesmus convolutus Corda 1839, p. 199

Pl. 55, Fig. 3

Solitary or in groups of 2–4 cells, fusiform in shape, twisted and sigmoid; apices sharply pointed and often twisted in opposite directions; cells 3–4.5μ in diameter, 15–25μ long.

Common in the tychoplankton. Mich., Wis.

Ankistrodesmus falcatus (Corda) Ralfs 1848, p. 180

Pl. 56, Figs. 5, 6

Cells needle-like to somewhat spindle-shaped, solitary or in clusters of 2–32 individuals, not inclosed in a colonial sheath; chloroplast 1, a parietal plate without pyrenoids; cells 2–6μ in diameter, 25–100μ long, sometimes longer.

Ubiquitous; intermingled with other algae and most commonly found in acid water habitats of high temperatures where there is a dense conglomeration of unicellular and colonial algae. Mich., Wis.

Ankistrodesmus falcatus var. *acicularis* (A. Braun)

G. S. West 1904, p. 223

Pl. 56, Fig. 16

Cells solitary and almost straight, the outer wall slightly curved in the median portion, extended into long, finely drawn out apices; chloroplast extending over ⅔ of the cell wall; cells 2.5μ in diameter, 36–65μ long.

Tychoplankter; rare in several lakes. Mich., Wis.

Ankistrodesmus falcatus var. *mirabilis* (West & West)

G. S. West 1904, p.224

Pl. 56, Fig. 10

Cells sigmoid or lunate, apices gradually tapering to fine points; cells solitary, 2–3μ in diameter, as much as 150μ long.

Generally distributed. Mich., Wis.

Ankistrodesmus falcatus var. *stipitatus* (Chod.)

Lemmermann 1908, p. 176

Pl. 56, Figs. 14, 15

Cells lunate (rarely almost straight), attached at one pole to filamentous algae or other submerged aquatics; usually gregarious, forming clusters of 2–8; cells 3–4μ in diameter, 18–22μ long.

Plankter. Wis.

Ankistrodesmus falcatus var. *tumidus* (West & West)

G. S. West 1904, p. 224

Pl. 56, Fig. 9

Cells lunate or fusiform, the ventral margin decidedly tumid in the midregion, 4.5–6.5μ in diameter, 61–73μ long.

Rare; in plankton. Wis.

Ankistrodesmus fractus (West & West) Brunnthaler 1915, p. 189

Pl. 56, Fig. 7

Solitary, arched-fusiform or arcuate cells, the outer wall convex in the median portion only, with almost straight walls extending to the sharply pointed apices, the inner margin concave in the median portion, straight toward the apices; cells 2.8μ in diameter, 40–43.5μ long; chloroplast divided into 4 portions by deep folds or incisions.

Rare; in the plankton of *Sphagnum* bogs. Wis.

Ankistrodesmus spiralis (Turner) Lemmermann 1908, p. 176

Pl. 56, Figs. 11, 12

Cells spindle-shaped, spirally twisted into bundles of 4–16 cells; cells 2–3μ in diameter, 25–35μ long; chloroplast a parietal plate without a pyrenoid.

Common in a variety of ponds and lakes; tycho- and euplanktonic. Mich., Wis.

DACTYLOCOCCUS Naegeli 1849, p. 85

Pseudo-filamentous, consisting of ovate or fusiform-elliptic cells attached end to end, filaments breaking up to form single, scattered cells or small chains of cells; chloroplast a parietal plate, with or without a pyrenoid.

See G. M. Smith 1933, p. 507, for a discussion of the systematic position of this genus.

Dactylococcus infusionum Naegeli 1849, p. 85
Pl. 56, Fig. 13

Fusiform cells, either solitary or attached pole to pole to form false, branched filaments or chains; chloroplast a parietal plate, sometimes with a pyrenoid; cells 2.5–3.5μ in diameter.

From a laboratory culture. Wis. (Smith).

CLOSTERIOPSIS Lemmermann 1899a, p. 124

Cells long and needle-like, tapering to sharp points at both ends; chloroplast a lobed plate extending almost the entire length of the cell and containing a row of pyrenoids.

Closteriopsis should be compared with *Closterium* and *Ankistrodesmus*. It is shaped much like some of the very slender species of the former genus in which, however, there are two chloroplasts, one on either side of a central nucleus. It is differentiated from *Ankistrodesmus* on the basis of its greater size, stouter proportions, and the axial row of pyrenoids.

Closteriopsis longissima Lemmermann 1899a, p. 124
[*Ankistrodesmus longissimus* (Lemm.) Wille]
Pl. 57, Fig. 1

Cells long and very narrowly spindle-shaped, the ends tapering to fine points; chloroplast a parietal, lobed plate; cells 3.5–6μ in diameter, 190–240–(530)μ long.

Rare; in the plankton of a few soft water lakes. Wis.

Closteriopsis longissima var. *tropica* West & West 1905, p. 31
Pl. 57, Figs. 2, 3

A variety of stouter proportions than the typical plant and not tapering to a fine point but bluntly tipped at the poles; cells 6–7.5μ in diameter, 225–370μ long.

Plankter. Wis.

SCHROEDERIA Lemmermann 1898c, p. 311

Free-floating, unicellular, acicular, fusiform or straight, tapering at the poles and forming long fine setae, one of which may terminate in a disc or may be bifurcated near the end to form a pair of recurved, bristle-like spines; 1 parietal chloroplast covering most of the cell wall, with 1–3 pyrenoids.

Key to the Species

Cells as much as 20 times their diameter in length;
spines 13–27μ long_____S. setigera
Cells smaller, not more than 10 times their diameter
in length; spines 10–16μ long_____S. Judayi

Schroederia Judayi G. M. Smith 1916, p. 474
Pl. 57, Figs. 5, 6

Cells fusiform, straight or arcuate, the poles narrowed and extended into long setae, one of which terminates in short bifurcations; 1 chloroplast, with a single pyrenoid; cells 2.5–6µ in diameter, 45–63µ long, including the setae, which are 10–16µ long.

This species resembles an unattached *Characium* and should be compared with some of the species of that genus.

Rare; in euplankton. Mich., Wis.

Schroederia setigera (Schroed.) Lemmermann 1898c, p. 311
Pl. 57, Fig. 4

Cells fusiform, mostly acicular, the poles extended into long, fine setae, one of which is bifurcate near the tip, forming recurved bristles; chloroplast plate-like, covering most of the cell wall, usually with 1 pyrenoid; cells 3–6µ in diameter, 60–85µ long, including the setae, which are 13–17µ long.

In plankton of lakes. Wis.

SELENASTRUM Reinsch 1867, p. 64

A colony of 4–16 lunate or sickle-shaped cells with acute apices, the dorsal or convex walls adjacent; not inclosed by a gelatinous envelope; chloroplast 1, parietal, lying along the convex wall, usually with 1 pyrenoid.

Species of this genus should be compared with *Kirchneriella* which has somewhat scattered lunate cells within a gelatinous envelope.

Key to the Species

1. Cells decidedly sickle-shaped, 19–28µ from tip to tip_____*S. gracile*
1. Cells lunate (crescent-shaped), or arcuate but not
   sickle-shaped, mostly smaller_____ 2
2. Cells arcuate, 1.2–2.5µ in diameter_____*S. Westii*
2. Cells lunate, larger in diameter_____ 3
3. Cells 5–8µ in diameter, 16–42µ from tip to tip_____*S. Bibraianum*
3. Cells (2)–3µ in diameter, 7–9µ from tip to tip_____*S. minutum*

Selenastrum Bibraianum Reinsch 1867, p. 64
Pl. 57, Fig. 9

Colony ovate in outline, composed of 4–16 lunate or sickle-shaped cells with sharp apices and arranged so that the convex surfaces are apposed and directed toward the center of the colony; cells 5–8µ in diameter, 20–38µ long; distance between apices 16–42µ.

Rare; in several lakes, mostly soft water, and in acid swamps. Mich., Wis.

Selenastrum gracile Reinsch 1867, p. 65

Pl. 57, Fig. 11

Colonies of 8–64 sickle-shaped cells in irregular arrangement, but with the convex surfaces apposed; apices of the cells sharply pointed; chloroplast a parietal plate along the convex wall, without a pyrenoid (?); cells 3–5μ in diameter, 19–28μ between apices.

In tychoplankton of lakes and swamps. Mich., Wis.

Selenastrum minutum (Naeg.) Collins 1909, p.171

Pl. 46, Fig. 10

Cells often solitary or in small families, irregularly arranged, crescent-shaped, the poles bluntly pointed; cells 2–3μ in diameter, 7–9μ between apices.

Mich.

Selenastrum Westii G. M. Smith 1920, p. 133

Pl. 57, Fig. 10

Colony small, composed of 2–8 slender, lunate or arcuate (but not sickle-shaped) cells, arranged with their convex walls apposed; chloroplast a parietal plate lying along the convex wall; pyrenoid lacking (?); cells 1.5–2.5μ in diameter; 15–18μ between apices.

Rare; in euplankton. Mich., Wis.

KIRCHNERIELLA Schmidle 1893, p. 83

Free-floating or caught among larger algae; a colony of strongly curved, lunate, sickle-shaped or twisted fusiform, sometimes cylindrical cells, inclosed by a gelatinous envelope in which there is no regular arrangement of individuals although young colonies may have even numbers of individuals, and these are usually arranged so that the convex walls are together; chloroplast a parietal plate along the convex wall, with 1 pyrenoid.

Key to the Species

1. Cells inclosed by the persistent mother cell
   wall of the last generation..*K. subsolitaria*
1. Cells inclosed by a copious mucilaginous sheath.. 2
2. Cells vermiform cylinders, rounded at the poles.. 3
2. Cells lunate, sickle-shaped, sharply or bluntly pointed at the apices........... 4
3. Cells small, 2μ or less in diameter, up to 14μ long ....*K. contorta*
3. Cells larger, 2–3μ in diameter, up to
   25μ long; spirally twisted..*K. elongata*
4. Cells narrowed at the poles, rounded or bluntly pointed...................*K. obesa*
4. Cells sharply pointed at the poles...*K. lunaris*

Kirchneriella contorta (Schmidle) Bohlin 1897, p. 20
Pl. 57, Figs. 7, 8

Free-floating colonies, usually of 16 twisted, arcuate, cylindrical cells with broad, convex apices, lying irregularly scattered throughout the homogeneous, gelatinous envelope; chloroplast covering the entire wall of the cells, which are 1–2μ in diameter, 5.8–10–(14)μ long.

Rare; in plankton of several lakes. Mich., Wis.

Kirchneriella elongata G. M. Smith 1916, p. 473
Pl. 58, Fig. 1

Colonies composed of 4–16 elongate-cylindrical, spirally twisted cells which have rounded apices; individuals much entwined near the center of the homogeneous colonial envelope; 1 parietal chloroplast, without a pyrenoid; cells 2–3μ in diameter, 15–25μ long; colonies up to 100μ in diameter.

Rare; in the plankton of several lakes. Mich., Wis.

Kirchneriella lunaris (Kirch.) Moebius 1894, p. 331
Pl. 58, Fig. 2

Colony composed of numerous cells arranged in groups of 4–16 within a close, gelatinous envelope; cells flat, strongly curved crescents with rather obtuse points; chloroplast covering the convex wall; cells 3–8μ in diameter, 6.5–13μ long; colonies 100–250μ in diameter.

Common in the plankton of open water or among mats of algae in the shallow water of acid ponds and lakes. Mich., Wis.

Kirchneriella lunaris var. *Dianae* Bohlin 1897, p. 20
Pl. 58, Fig. 3

A variety differing from the typical in having very strongly curved cells with sharply pointed apices which are not in the same plane; cells 3–5μ in diameter, 10–18–(21)μ long.

Rare; in plankton of several lakes especially in acid habitats. Mich., Wis.

Kirchneriella lunaris var. *irregularis* G. M. Smith 1920, p. 142
Pl. 58, Fig. 4

A variety differing from the typical by having the apices distinctly twisted and very evidently pointing in different directions so that a spiral sigmoid curve is produced; cells 4–6μ in diameter, 6–13μ long.

Rare; in plankton of a variety of lakes. Wis.

[258]

Kirchneriella obesa (W. West) Schmidle 1893, p. 16 [83]
Pl. 58, Fig. 5

Colony composed of many irregularly arranged cells in a wide gelatinous envelope; cells strongly lunate, the outer margin convex and the inner nearly parallel to it, tapering slightly to bluntly pointed apices; chloroplast covering the entire convex portion of the wall; cells 4–6μ in diameter, 10–14μ long.

Rare but widely distributed; in the plankton of many lakes. Mich., Wis.

Kirchneriella obesa var. *aperta* (Teil.) Brunnthaler 1915, p. 182
Pl. 58, Figs. 6, 7

A variety in which the cells are less strongly lunate, with the inner margin of the cell describing a much greater arc than the outer; cells 7.4–10μ in diameter, 10–14μ long.

Rare; in the plankton of several lakes. Wis.

Kirchneriella obesa var. *major* (Bernard) G. M. Smith 1918, p. 636
Pl. 57, Fig. 12

A variety differing from the typical by having the inner and outer margins nearly parallel, slightly tapering at the apices, which are bluntly rounded; cells 3–5μ in diameter, 10–18–(21)μ long.

Rare; in plankton. Mich., Wis.

Kirchneriella subsolitaria G. S. West 1908, p. 284
Pl. 58, Fig. 8

Plant consisting of 4 strongly curved, crescent-shaped cells arranged together within old mother cell wall, the apices bluntly rounded and not tapering; cells 3–4.5μ in diameter, 10–14μ long.

Euplankter. Wis.

QUADRIGULA Printz 1915, p. 49

A free-floating, ellipsoid colony of 2–4–8 long-cylindrical or fusiform cells with long axis parallel with that of the gelatinous sheath in which they are inclosed; poles of the cells subacute or sharply rounded; chloroplast a parietal plate covering most of the cell wall, or sometimes located along one side; pyrenoid sometimes present.

Some species of this genus will be found treated under *Ankistrodesmus* in a number of manuals. The two genera are separable on the basis of their arrangement in the colony and the common investing sheath, the latter not being present in *Ankistrodesmus*.

Key to the Species

1. Cells spindle-shaped, numerous and scattered within a gelatinous
   investment but with the longitudinal axes parallel..................*Q. lacustris*
1. Cells arcuate, lunate, or straight, arranged in bundles of 4
   within the gelatinous investment, fewer in number than above.................... 2
2. Cells straight, margins subparallel in the
   median portion; poles rounded....................................*Q. closterioides*
2. Cells arcuate or lunate; poles pointed..................*Q. Chodatii*

Quadrigula Chodatii (Tan.-Ful.) G. M. Smith 1920, p. 138
[*Ankistrodesmus Chodati* (Tan.-Ful.) Brunnthaler]
Pl. 59, Figs. 1–3

Free-floating; cells long, fusiform to slightly lunate or arcuate, tapering to subacute points, longitudinally arranged within a broadly fusiform colonial envelope; chloroplast a parietal plate with a median notch, containing 2 pyrenoids; cells 3.5–7μ in diameter, 30–80μ long; colony as much as 250μ long.

Rare; in euplankton of a few lakes as well as in the tychoplankton of shallow water. Mich., Wis.

Quadrigula closterioides (Bohlin) Printz 1915, p. 49
Pl. 58, Figs. 9, 10

Cells long, straight, but with one margin slightly curved, cylindrical in the mid-region, tapering to sharply rounded apices, arranged in longitudinal bundles of 4 within a fusiform colonial envelope; chloroplast parietal, covering almost the entire cell wall, with a median notch; 1 pyrenoid; cells 4–6μ in diameter, 22–35–(45)μ long.

Common in many soft water lakes. Mich., Wis.

Quadrigula lacustris (Chod.) G. M. Smith 1920, p. 139
[*Ankistrodesmus lacustris* (Chod.) Ostenfeld]
Pl. 59, Figs. 4, 5

A free-floating, fusiform-shaped colony containing many short, fusiform cells, mostly arranged in pairs; cells straight, but with slightly convex margins, tapering to blunt points; chloroplast a parietal plate, sometimes twisted in the cell, without a median notch, with 1 pyrenoid; cells 3–5μ in diameter, 20–25μ long.

Rare; in the plankton of many lakes, mostly soft water. Mich., Wis.

TETRAËDRON Kuetzing 1845, p. 129

Cells solitary and unattached; of various shapes, triangular and flat, pyramidal, polyhedric; the angles entire, with or without spines, or variously lobed to form dichotomous or trichotomous spine-tipped processes; chloroplasts one to many parietal discs or plates; pyrenoids usually present.

Key to the Species

[261]

Tetraëdron armatum (Reinsch) DeToni 1889, p. 611
Pl. 59, Figs. 6, 7

Cells irregularly triangular and lobed, the angles scarcely or not at all produced, but furnished with a pair of widely separated spines; the angles of the cell sometimes not all in the same plane, so that 1 or 2 pairs of spines are seen one above the other when viewed from the side; cell 30–47.6μ in diameter.

Rare; in euplankton. Mich., Wis.

Tetraëdron arthrodesmiforme (G. S. West) Wołoszyńska 1914, p. 203
Pl. 59, Fig. 8

Cells quadrate in outline, symmetrically incised to form 2 lobes; a spine on each of the 4 angles; 2 sides of the cell subparallel, convex, the isthmus bordered by a widely open sinus; cells up to 56μ in diameter.

Typical form not reported from our region.

Tetraëdron arthrodesmiforme var. *contorta* Wołoszyńska 1914, p. 203
Pl. 59, Figs. 9, 10

A variety differing from the typical by having the 4 lobes twisted and extending in at least 2 planes, a character which is particularly evident when seen from the 'side'; cell 25–32–(50)μ in diameter, up to 60μ in the longest dimension.
Rare; in euplankton. Wis.

Tetraëdron asymmetricum Prescott 1944, p. 357
Pl. 59, Figs. 11–13

Cell quadrangular in outline, unsymmetrically incised to form 2 major lobes with an isthmus bordered by a widely open sinus, the 2 major lobes slightly bilobed, the lobules tipped with 2 or 3 short spines; cells 10–18μ in their longest dimension.
This species should be compared with *T. irregulare* (Reinsch) DeToni.
Rare; in euplankton and tychoplankton. Wis.

Tedraëdron bifurcatum (Wille) Lagerheim 1893, p. 160
Pl. 59, Fig. 14

Cells irregular tetrahedrons, the lobes tipped by 2 short spine-bearing processes, the margins of the cell concave between the apices of the lobes; maximum diameter of the cell 55–60μ.
Rare; in plankton of lakes; tychoplanktonic in swamps. Wis.

Tetraëdron bifurcatum var. *minor* Prescott 1944, p. 358
Pl. 59, Figs. 15, 16

A form differing from the typical by its small size and in having the lobes bifurcated, the lobules rather stout and tipped with a short spine; cells up to 22.5μ in their maximum diameter.
Rare; in tychoplankton. Wis.

Tetraëdron caudatum (Corda) Hansgirg 1888a, p. 131
Pl. 59, Figs. 17, 24, 25

Cells flat, 5-sided, the angles rounded and tipped with a short, sharp spine, the sides between the angles concave, but with one margin narrowly and deeply incised; cells in their longest dimension 8–15–(22)μ.
Tetraëdron caudatum var. *incisum* Lagerheim, reported from Michigan by Taft (1939), does not seem to be separable from the typical form. The sinus of the incision on the margin is very narrow.
In tychoplankton; in shallow water of lakes and in swamps. Wis.

Tetraëdron caudatum var. *longispinum* Lemmermann 1898d, p. 151
Pl. 59, Figs. 20–22

A variety differing from the typical by having longer spines which are directed at right angles to the flattened surface of the cell, 2 turned in one direction, 3 in the opposite; cells 8–18μ in diameter; spines 3–8μ long.

Euplankter; in lakes. Wis.

Tetraëdron constrictum G. M. Smith 1920, p. 122
Pl. 59, Fig. 28

Cells quadrangular in outline, tetragonal, 2 sides subparallel, the other 2 deeply concave as seen in front view, the angles extended into slightly tapering processes which are dichotomously branched and tipped with a short spine; in side view fusiform, the processes at the superimposed poles of the cell not quite in the same plane but slightly turned at different angles; cells 5–8μ in diameter, without processes, 8μ thick, 18–25μ in their longest dimension.

Rare; in euplankton. Wis.

Tetraëdron cruciatum (Wallich) West & West 1902a, p. 198

Cells cruciately 4-lobed, the lobes bifurcate, one division of 2 lobes usually again divided; lobes and lobules tipped with 2 short spines; margin of the cell deeply concave between the lobes, more deeply so on 2 sides than on the others; cells (larger forms) 42–54μ or (smaller forms) 17μ in diameter.

Typical plant not reported from our region.

Tetraëdron cruciatum var. *reductum* Prescott 1944, p. 358
Pl. 59, Fig. 23

Cell flat, irregularly cruciform or sometimes 3-lobed, the lobes bifurcate, the lobules tipped with a short spine; margins of the cell concave on 2 opposite sides, straight or only slightly concave on the other sides; cells 28–30μ in diameter, up to 54μ in the greatest dimension.

Tychoplankter; in swamps. Wis.

Tetraëdron duospinum Ackley 1929, p. 304
Pl. 46, Figs. 22, 23

This species, described as new from Michigan and illustrated (Ackley, *l.c.*, Pl. 35, Fig. 14), appears to be a *Cystodinium* or some other encysted dinoflagellate. I have not seen type specimens, however.

Mich.

Tetraëdron enorme (Ralfs) Hansgirg 1888a, p. 132
Pl. 52, Figs. 6, 7 (var.); Pl. 59, Fig. 19

Cells poly- or tetrahedric, the angles shortly produced and bilobed, the lobes bifurcate and tipped with short spines; margins of the cell concave between the angles, the processes not all in the same plane; cells (25)–30–(45)μ in diameter.

Common in the tychoplankton of several lakes; generally distributed. Mich., Wis.

Tetraëdron enorme var. *pentaedricum* Prescott 1944, p. 358
Pl. 59, Fig. 18

Cells 5-sided in outline, the sides straight or slightly convex, with pairs of narrow bifurcated processes extending in all planes, the processes tipped with short spines; cells 50–55μ in diameter, without processes.

This form differs from the typical plant by its straight margins and narrow bifurcated processes extending from the angles. It is similar to Borge's figure of *T. enorme*, which I judge to be typical.

Rare; in plankton. Wis.

Tetraëdron gigas (Wittr.) Hansgirg 1888a, p. 131

Cells relatively large, irregularly 5- or 6-angled, the processes broadly rounded, with the margins between the angles broadly concave; cells 35–45μ in the short diameter, 65–75μ long.

Typical form not reported in our region.

Tetraëdron gigas var. *granulatum* Boldt *ex* Brunnthaler 1915, p. 148

A variety differing from the typical by the possession of finely punctate walls.

Mich.

Tetraëdron gracile (Reinsch) Hansgirg 1889, p. 19
Pl. 60, Fig. 1

Cells flat, cruciform, rectangular in outline, the angles extended into narrow, twice furcated processes which are tipped with 1 or 2 short spines, the margins deeply concave between the processes; cells 15–30μ in diameter, without processes, 35–40μ wide including processes; 6–12μ thick.

Rare; in euplankton. Mich., Wis.

Tetraëdron hastatum (Reinsch) Hansgirg 1888a, p. 132
Pl. 59, Fig. 26

Cells pyramidal, the angles extended into narrow, slightly tapering, unbranched processes which are tipped with 2 or 3 short spines,

the margins concave; cells 28–36µ in diameter, processes 8µ wide at the base.
Rare; in plankton. Wis.

Tetraëdron hastatum var. *palatinum* (Schmidle)
Lemmermann 1902, p. (247)
Pl. 59, Fig. 27

Cells pyramidal, the processes longer and more graceful, not tapering, tipped with 3 short spines, the margins of the cell convex; cells 4–14µ in diameter without processes.
Euplankter. Wis.

Tetraëdron limneticum Borge 1900, p. 5
Pl. 60, Figs. 2–4

Cells pyramidal, 4-angled, the angles produced into relatively narrow, once or twice furcated processes which are tipped with short spines, the margins of the cell concave between the angles; cells 30–55–(85)µ in diameter including processes.
Common and generally distributed in many lakes. Mich., Wis.

Tetraëdron limneticum var. *gracile* Prescott 1944, p. 358
Pl. 60, Fig. 5

Cells pyramidal or tetragonal, the angles extended into bifurcate processes which are tipped with 2 or 3 stout spines, the margins of the cell concave between the processes; bases of the processes adjoining so that there is scarcely a cell body; cells 40–46.8µ in diameter; processes 6–8µ wide.
Euplankter. Wis.

Tetraëdron lobulatum (Naeg.) Hansgirg 1888a, p. 132
Pl. 60, Figs. 6, 7

Cells tetragonal, mostly pyramidal (or flattened); processes short and stout, bifurcate at the apices; cells 35–40µ in diameter.
Euplankter. Mich., Wis.

Tetraëdron lobulatum var. *crassum* Prescott 1944, p. 359
Pl. 60, Fig. 8

Cells tetragonal, pyramidal, the angles slightly produced to form relatively wide, short processes which are bilobed, the lobules bifurcate and ending in short curved spine-like tips; cells 25–30µ in diameter.

This form differs from the typical by its broad, bilobed processes and by the lateral walls of the cell being much less concave or emarginate. It differs from var. *polyfurcatum* G. M. Smith in the form and number of processes.

Planktonic in lakes; also found in Manitowish River, Wisconsin.

Tetraëdron lobulatum var. *polyfurcatum* G. M.Smith 1916, p. 480
Pl. 60, Fig. 11

Cells tetragonal, pyramidal or flattened, the angles extended into processes which are dichotomously divided 3 to 5 times, the lobules ending in 2 or 3 minute spines; margin of the cell concave between the processes; cells 15–25μ in diameter without processes, 35–70μ in diameter including processes.

Rare; in the plankton of many lakes. Wis.

Tetraëdron lunula (Reinsch) Wille 1911, p. 60
Pl. 60, Figs. 9, 10

Cells lunate, tapering to sharply pointed poles; the outer margin more sharply curved than the inner, which is concave; cells 11–12μ in diameter, 25–30μ long.

Plankter, in a small inlet of the Wisconsin River, Wisconsin.

Tetraëdron minimum (A. Braun) Hansgirg 1888a, p. 131
Pl. 60, Figs. 12–15

Cells small, flat, tetragonal, the angles rounded and without spines or processes, lobes sometimes cruciately arranged; margins of the cell concave, with one frequently incised; cells (6)–14.5–20μ in diameter.

Common in the tychoplankton and euplankton of many lakes and ponds. Mich., Wis.

Tetraëdron minimum var. *scrobiculatum* Lagerheim 1888, p. 591

A variety differing from the typical by having deeply punctate walls.

Mich.

Tedraëdron muticum (A. Braun) Hansgirg 1888a, p. 131
Pl. 60, Figs. 16, 17

Cells small, flat, triangular, the angles without spines or furcations; sides of the cell emarginate or slightly convex; cells 6–18μ in diameter.

A common species in many habitats, but because of its small size it is easily overlooked in rich tychoplanktonic collections. Mich., Wis.

Tetraëdron muticum fa. *punctulatum* (Reinsch)
DeToni 1889, p. 600
Pl. 60, Fig. 18

Cells flattened, triangular, the angles sharp but without spines; margins slightly convex; wall granular; cells 15–20μ in diameter, 8–10μ thick.
Euplankter. Wis.

Tetraëdron obesum (West & West) Wille *ex* Brunnthaler 1915, p. 154
Pl. 60, Figs. 19, 20

Cells ovate or broadly elliptic in outline, but with 3 lobes which are scarcely produced, one lobe lateral to the long axis of the cell, all lobes tipped with a short sharp spine; cells 15μ in diameter, 31–35μ long.
Plankter; in lakes and ponds. Mich., Wis.

Tetraëdron pentaedricum West & West 1895, p. 84
Pl. 60, Figs. 21–23

Cells irregularly 5-lobed, with 1 lobe extended in a different plane from the others; angles sharply rounded, the apex of each lobe furnished with a sharp spine; diameter of cells 18–21μ.
Rare; in euplankton. Mich., Wis.

Tetraëdron planctonicum G. M. Smith 1916, p. 479
Pl. 60, Figs. 27, 28

Cells polyhedral-pyramidate, 4- or 5-angled, with convex sides, the angles produced into once- or twice-furcate processes, becoming narrower in the furcations, the lobes tipped with 2 or 3 spines; cells 18–30μ in diameter without processes, 45–60μ including the processes.
Common in the plankton of many lakes. Mich., Wis.

Tetraëdron pusillum (Wallich) West & West 1897, p. 237
Pl. 60, Fig. 29

Cells cruciform, deeply 4-lobed, concave between the lobes, the lobes bifurcate at the apices, all in one plane; cells elongate-elliptic in side view; 10μ in diameter, 25μ long.
Plankter; found in several lakes; common. Mich., Wis.

Tetraëdron quadratum (Reinsch) Hansgirg 1889, p. 18
Pl. 46, Figs. 21, 21a

Cells quadrangular in front view, the lateral margins straight with sharp angles which are furnished with a short spine; membrane 2-layered, up to 4.5μ thick; cells 17–34μ in diameter.
Mich.

Tetraëdron regulare Kuetzing 1845, p. 129
Pl. 60, Figs. 24–26

Cells tetragonal, pyramidal, the angles produced to form stout lobes, narrowly rounded and tipped with a single, stout spine; the margins of the lobes convex or straight, lateral walls between the lobes concave; cells (14)–45–51.8μ in diameter.

Plankter; in many lakes and ponds; generally distributed. Mich., Wis.

Tetraëdron regulare var. *bifurcatum* Wille 1884, p. 12
Pl. 61, Fig. 1

Cells tetragonal, pyramidal, the sides convex or slightly concave, the angles broadly rounded and tipped with 2 stout often curved spines; cells 30–36μ in diameter including spines.

Tychoplankter; in shallow water of lakes and sloughs. Mich., Wis.

Tetraëdron regulare var. *granulata* Prescott 1944, p. 359
Pl. 61, Figs. 2, 3

Cells large, pyramidal, the lobes broad and stout with convex margins, the angles broadly rounded and tipped with a single short spine which may be reduced to a mere papilla; wall punctate and covered with small granules or roughenings; cells 35–51.8μ in diameter.

Plankter; in several lakes. Wis.

Tetraëdron regulare var. *incus* Teiling 1912, pp. 274, 277
Pl. 61, Figs. 4–7

Cells tetragonal, flat or pyramidal, with concave lateral margins, the angles slightly produced to form short lobes each tipped by a relatively long spine; cells 15–20μ in diameter without spines, up to 37μ in diameter including spines.

Plankter; in several lakes. Wis.

Tetraëdron regulare var. *incus* fa. *major* Prescott 1944, p. 359
Pl.61, Fig. 13

Cells tetragonal, pyramidal, the margins straight or slightly convex, the angles produced to form long, stout spines; cells 35–50μ in diameter, including spines; spines 12–13.5μ long.

Plankter; lakes and streams. Wis.

Tetraëdron regulare var. *torsum* (Turner) Brunnthaler 1915, p. 150
Pl. 61, Figs. 8–10

Cells tetragonal, pyramidal, the lobes narrow and tapering to a spine-tipped apex, twisted so that they are cruciately arranged;

lateral margins convex; sides of the cell concave between the lobes; cells 25–33–(40)μ in diameter.
Tychoplankter. Mich., Wis.

Tetraëdron trigonum (Naeg.) Hansgirg 1888a, p. 130
Pl. 61, Figs. 11, 12

Cells flat, 3-angled, the angles tapering to sharply rounded, spine-tipped apices; margins convex; sides of the cell body concave or straight; cells 19–29.8μ in diameter.
Common in the tychoplankton of several lakes. Mich., Wis.

Tetraëdron trigonum var. *gracile* (Reinsch) DeToni 1889, p. 598
Pl. 61, Figs. 14–16

Cells flat, triangular, the angles narrower and more produced than in the typical plant, sometimes curved, tapering acutely and ending in a spine; cells 25–40μ in diameter, including the spines.
Euplankter. Wis.

Tetraëdron trigonum var. *papilliferum* (Schroed.)
Lemmermann *ex* Brunnthaler 1915, p. 149

A variety with only slightly concave margins, the angles tipped with a blunt, wart-like papilla; cells 12–15μ in diameter.
Mich.

Tetraëdron tumidulum (Reinsch) Hansgirg 1889, p. 18
Pl. 61, Figs. 17, 18

Cells tetragonal, pyramidal, the margins straight, concave, or convex; the angles bluntly rounded and sometimes with knob-like extensions; cells 30–53μ in diameter.
Plankter; in lakes and sloughs. Mich., Wis.

Tetraëdron verrucosum G. M. Smith 1918, p. 632
Pl. 61, Figs. 24, 25

Cells tetragonal, pyramidal, sometimes with lobes cruciately arranged; margins of the cell convex, the angles ending in a stout, blunt spine; wall coarsely verrucose; cells 65–80μ in diameter including the spines, which are 13–18μ long.
Rare; in euplankton. Wis.

Tetraëdron Victoriae Wołoszyńska 1914, p. 203

Cells deeply lobed to form 2 semicells which are subcruciform in arrangement, the semicells bilobed, with the walls emarginate

between the lobes; apices of the lobes rounded and tipped with a short, blunt spine; cells 10–15μ in diameter, 20–30μ long.
Typical form not reported from our region.

Tedraëdron Victoriae var. major G. M. Smith 1920, p. 119
Pl. 61, Figs. 28, 29

Cells 4-angled, divided into fusiform-shaped semicells, as seen in vertical view, by deep emarginations, the two semicells bilobed and cruciately arranged, each lobe produced into a stout spine; cells 15–20μ in diameter, 30–60μ long including spines.
Euplankter; rare but found in several lakes. Wis.

CERASTERIAS Reinsch 1867, p. 68

Unicellular, free-floating, triangular or pyramidal, the angles extended into long, tapering processes, the bases of which comprise the body of the cell; processes all in one plane or in more than one; chloroplast parietal, without a pyrenoid.

This genus should be compared with Tetraëdron, from which it is separated only on relative size of the cell body. In Tetraëdron the main part of the cell is evident, and it may have spines or processes at the angles. In Cerasterias the body of the cell is practically non-existent, being only the bases of the cell lobes. C. irregulare G. M. Smith is to be expected in this area, but in our collections only the European species, C. staurastroides West & West, has been found. It is sometimes listed as Tetraëdron staurastroides (W. West) Wille.

Cerasterias staurastroides West & West 1895b, p. 268 (fa.)
Pl. 56, Fig. 8; Pl. 61, Figs. 19, 20

Cells tetragonal, the body narrow and gradually extended into 4 long, slightly tapering processes which have 2 or 4 teeth-like spines (in our specimens) at the apices; the wall of the processes covered with sharply pointed granules arranged in transverse series; body of the cell 10μ in diameter; greatest dimension, including processes, 36.5μ.

Our specimens differ from the typical in having the processes tipped with short teeth. The apices are described as rounded by Brunnthaler (1915, p. 159).
Plankter; rare. Wis.

POLYEDRIOPSIS Schmidle 1900a, p. 17

Unicellular, free-floating, tetragonal or pyramidal, the angles truncately rounded and furnished with a tuft of 3–10 long, tapering setae; sides concave, or in some slightly convex; chloroplast a parietal plate covering most of the cell wall, or more massive in old cells, with 1 pyrenoid.

Polyedriopsis spinulosa Schmidle 1900a, p. 17
Pl. 62, Figs. 2, 3

Characteristics as described for the genus; cells 12–25μ in diameter; setae 40μ long.

Rare; in plankton. Wis.

FAMILY SCENEDESMACEAE

In this family the cells are adjoined to form definite patterns and colonial aggregates of regular shape. This arrangement is determined by the autospores which, when cut out of the parent protoplast, become definitely related and oriented to one another to form autocolonies in which there are always multiples of 2. These colonies upon being liberated increase in size to form the mature plant.

There is a great variety of cell shapes (oblong, fusiform, spherical, triangular, trapezoidal) and arrangement. The colony may be a linear series, a flat plate, a trapezoidal aggregate, or a cluster of radiating fusiform individuals.

This family differs from the preceding one (Oocystaceae) in that colonies are formed by the definite adjoining of cells in a regular pattern.

Key to the Genera

1. Cells ovoid, fusiform, crescent-shaped, or oblong, arranged with their long axes parallel to form a single or double series in 1 plane..*Scenedesmus*
(See *S. acuminatus*, with cells in a curved series.)
1. Cells of different shape, or otherwise arranged................................... 2
2. Cells fusiform or cylindrical, with long axes parallel; quadrately arranged in 2 tiers......................................*Tetradesmus*
2. Cells arranged otherwise.. 3
3. Cells spherical, forming pyramidal and multiple colonies of 4; cells bearing long spines......................*Micractinium*
3. Cells not spherical, without spines or with but very short ones................. 4
4. Cells with only their poles adjoined, extending in several planes............. 6
(See *Scenedesmus Bernardii*, however.)
4. Cells, often in 4's, forming a flat coenobium with cells adjoined or not adjoined along their walls................................ 5
5. Cells bearing spines.. *Tetrastrum*
5. Cells without spines..*Crucigenia*
6. Cells cylindrical or fusiform..................................*Actinastrum*
6. Cells sausage-shaped, or crescent-shaped...................*Tetrallantos*

SCENEDESMUS Meyen 1829, p. 774

Colony of 2–4–8–32 ovoid, fusiform, crescent-shaped, or oblong cells lying side by side in a single series, or in a double row with the cells alternating; cell walls smooth or with spines, teeth, and ridges; chloroplast a parietal plate covering most of the cell wall and often showing a median lateral notch; 1 pyrenoid.

This genus contains some species which are perhaps more widely distributed than any other fresh-water algae. Whereas a few are commonly found as euplankters, especially those which bear spines, most forms occur in tychoplankton. In favorable habitats one or two species may completely dominate the flora, and often a small artificial pool or an aquarium will be densely colored by their tremendous numbers. See Chodat (1926) and Smith (1916a) on the taxonomy and pure-culture studies of the genus.

Key to the Species

1. Wall smooth, without decorations such as spines, teeth, or ridges 2
1. Wall decorated with spines, teeth, or ridges 7
2. Poles of cells rounded 3
2. Poles of cells narrowed, sometimes pointed 4
3. Cells definitely arranged in a double series .... *S. arcuatus*
3. Cells arranged in a single series (sometimes in an indefinitely alternating series) .... *S. bijuga*
4. Cells all in one plane 5
4. Cells not all in one plane 6
5. Cells fusiform, all the same shape in the colony .... *S. obliquus*
5. Cells both fusiform and crescent-shaped in the same colony ..... *S. dimorphus*
6. Cells adjoined alternately at their poles only, forming a twisted chain .... *S. Bernardii*
6. Cells adjoined along their longitudinal walls, forming a cirque .... *S. acuminatus*
7. Cells with longitudinal ridges only, no teeth .... *S. acutiformis*
7. Cells with teeth, spines, and sometimes ridges also 8
8. Cells with teeth or spines only 9
8. Cells with both teeth (or spines) and ridges 18
9. Wall uniformly beset with very short teeth .... *S. hystrix*
9. Wall not beset with uniformly distributed teeth 10
10. Cell wall with a longitudinal row of small teeth, as well as teeth at the poles .... *S. serratus*
10. Cell wall without a longitudinal row of teeth 11
11. Cells with only a single, blunt, papilla-like spine at the apex of each cell .... *S. incrassatulus*
11. Cells with long, sharp teeth or spines 12
12. Cells with 2 or 3 sharp teeth at the poles .... *S. denticulatus*
12. Cells with long spines, not teeth alone at the poles 13
13. Spines on only the outer cells of the series 14
13. Spines on both the outer and inner cells of the series 16

Scenedesmus abundans (Kirch.) Chodat 1913, p. 77
Pl. 61, Fig. 21

Cells oblong or ovate, in a linear series of 4, the terminal cells with 1 or 2 polar spines and 2 spines on the lateral wall, the inner cells with a spine at each pole; cells 4–7μ in diameter, 7–12μ long.

Plankter; found in several lakes; common. Mich., Wis.

Scenedesmus abundans var. *asymmetrica* (Schroed.)
G. M. Smith 1916a, p. 468
Pl. 61, Figs. 22, 23

Cells oblong-ellipsoid, outer cells with a spine at each pole and all cells with a median spine arising perpendicularly from the lateral walls; cells 2.5–4.5μ in diameter, 12–15μ long.

Plankter; uncommon. Wis.

Scenedesmus abundans var. *brevicauda* G. M. Smith 1916a, p. 468
Pl. 61, Figs. 26, 27; Pl. 62, Fig. 1

Cells smaller than the typical; spines shorter and fewer; cells 2.5–5μ in diameter, 5–8μ long; spines 1.5–3.5μ long.

Wis.

Scenedesmus abundans var. *longicauda* G. M. Smith 1916a, p. 467
Pl. 62, Figs. 4, 5

Cells smaller than the typical, with relatively longer spines; cells 3–6μ in diameter, 7–9μ long; spines 6–10μ long.

Wis.

Scenedesmus abundans var. *spicatus* (West & West)
G. M. Smith 1916a, p. 468

Colony composed of 2–4 cells, the outer cells with a longitudinal series of 5–7 spines, the inner cells with 1–2 spines at the apices only; cells 4μ in diameter, 7.5–9μ long.

Wis.

Scenedesmus acuminatus (Lag.) Chodat 1902, p. 211
Pl. 62, Fig. 16

Cells arranged in a curved series of 4 (rarely 8) cells strongly lunate, with sharply pointed apices, the convex walls adjoined inwardly, the concave faces directed outward; cells 3–7µ in diameter, 30–40µ long.

Plankter; rare. Mich., Wis.

Scenedesmus acuminatus var. *minor* G. M. Smith 1916a, p. 436

A small variety; cells 3.5–6µ in diameter, 18–28µ between the apices.

Wis.

Scenedesmus acuminatus var. *tetradesmoides*
G. M. Smith 1916a, p. 439

A variety with cells less strongly curved than in the typical; 2.5–4µ in diameter, 11–15µ long; curvature of colony varying from slight to acute.

Wis.

Scenedesmus acutiformis Schroeder 1897a, p. 45
Pl. 62, Figs. 6, 7

Cells arranged in a single series of 4 (2 to 8), fusiform-elliptic, with poles sharply pointed; inner cells with a single facial longitudinal ridge; outer cells with 2–4 longitudinal ridges; cells 7–8µ in diameter, (16)–22.5µ long.

Plankter; found in several lakes and bogs; fairly common. Mich., Wis.

Scenedesmus arcuatus Lemmermann 1899a, p. 112
Pl. 62, Fig. 8

Cells arranged to form a curved (usually double) series of 4–16 oblong-ovate individuals with lateral walls in contact along ⅓ to ½ their length; cell wall without spines or teeth; poles of the cell broadly rounded; cells 4–8–(9)µ in diameter, 10–15–(17)µ long.

Swamps, lakes. Mich., Wis.

Scenedesmus arcuatus var. *capitatus* G. M. Smith 1918, p. 637
Pl. 62, Fig. 9

Similar to the typical form but with a short, blunt-pointed projection at each pole of the cells; cells 5–11µ in diameter, 11–23µ long.

Wis.

Scenedesmus arcuatus var. *platydisca* G. M. Smith 1916a, p. 451
Pl. 62, Figs. 10–12

Plant composed of 8 cells arranged in a flat, rather than a curved, double series; cells oblong-elliptic, 4.5–7.5µ in diameter, 8–17µ long.

Mich., Wis.

Scenedesmus armatus (Chod.) G. M. Smith 1916a, p. 460
Pl. 62, Figs. 13, 14

Plant composed of 2–8 cells arranged in a single, partially alternating series, oblong-ellipsoid but with ends broadly rounded; terminal cells with a single, long, usually curved or unevenly bent spine at each pole; central cells with a median, incomplete longitudinal ridge; cells 6–8μ in diameter, 9–15μ long.

Widely distributed and fairly common in a variety of lakes and ponds. Mich., Wis.

Scenedesmus armatus var. *Chodatii* G. M. Smith 1916a, p. 461

A variety with more slender cells and with proportionately less of the lateral walls in contact so that the notches between the poles of adjacent cells are deeper; cells 4–5μ in diameter, 11–15μ long. Wis.

Scenedesmus armatus var. *major* G. M. Smith 1920, p. 155
Pl. 62, Fig. 15; Pl. 63, Fig. 23

Cells larger than in the typical plant, 9μ in diameter, 25μ long; spines longer, 15μ. Wis.

Scenedesmus armatus var. *subalternans* G. M. Smith 1916a, p. 461

Colony composed of pyriform cells, subalternately arranged in two series; cells 3–5.5μ in diameter, 9–12μ long. Wis.

Scenedesmus Bernardii G. M. Smith 1916a, p. 436
Pl. 63, Fig. 1

Colony composed of 2–8 fusiform, lunate, or sigmoid cells in a single series, but with terminal cells at an angle to the plane of arrangement of the inner cells; cells adjoined alternately by the apex of one cell to the midregion of the next in series; wall without spines or teeth; cells 3–6μ in diameter, 8–17μ long. Mich., Wis.

Scenedesmus bijuga (Turp.) Lagerheim 1893, p. 158
Pl. 63, Figs. 2, 7

Colony composed of 2–8 cells in a single (rarely alternate) flat series; cells ovate or oblong, without teeth or spines; cells 4–8μ in diameter, 8–16μ long.

Widely distributed; often appearing as a prominent component of the littoral plankton. Mich., Wis.

[276]

Scenedesmus bijuga var. *alternans* (Reinsch) Hansgirg 1888, p. 114
Pl. 63, Figs. 3, 4

Cells ovate or elliptic, regularly arranged in 2 alternating series; cells 4–8μ in diameter, 7–16μ long.

Widely distributed; common in the plankton of many lakes and in the tychoplankton of ponds and swamps. Mich., Wis.

Scenedesmus bijuga var. *flexuosus* (Lemm.) Collins 1909, p. 168

A variety differing from the typical by having the cells arranged in a single series only, as many as 32 in one colony; cells broader than in the typical plant.
Wis.

Scenedesmus bijuga var. *irregularis* (Wille)
G. M. Smith 1916a, p. 448

Cells very irregularly arranged, occurring either in alternate or double series; 3.5–6μ in diameter, 7.5–10μ long.
Wis.

Scenedesmus brasiliensis Bohlin 1897, p. 22
Pl. 63, Figs. 5, 6

Colony composed of 2–8 subcylindric or ovate-ellipsoid cells arranged in a single series; apices of cells with 1–4 short teeth and with a longitudinal median ridge extending between the apices of each cell; cells (3)–5–7μ in diameter, 10–22μ long.

Common in many lakes. Mich., Wis.

Scenedesmus denticulatus Lagerheim 1882, p. 61
Pl. 63, Figs. 10, 11

Colony composed of 4 or 8 ovate cells arranged in a single series (rarely alternating); apices of cells with 1–4 short teeth; free walls of cells smooth; cells 6–10μ in diameter, 8–15μ long.

Very common and almost always accompanying other species of *Scenedesmus*. Mich., Wis.

Scenedesmus denticulatus var. *linearis* Hansgirg 1888, p. 268

Colony composed of 4 or 8 ovate cells arranged in a single, straight series, poles of the cells rounded and furnished with 2 small teeth; cells 4–5μ in diameter, up to 15μ long.
Wis.

Scenedesmus dimorphus (Turp.) Kuetzing 1833, p. 608
Pl. 63, Figs. 8, 9

Colony composed of 4 or 8 fusiform cells arranged in a single or alternating series; the inner cells with straight, sharp apices; the outer cells lunate, strongly curved, with acute apices; cells 3–6μ in diameter, 16–22μ long.

Common and widely distributed in many lakes and bogs. Mich., Wis.

Scenedesmus hystrix Lagerheim 1882, p. 62
Pl. 63, Fig. 12

Colony composed of 2–4–8 oblong-cylindric cells arranged in a single series; apices narrowly rounded; wall uniformly beset with short, sharp spines; cells 3–5μ in diameter, 8–18μ long.

Rare; in plankton. Wis.

Scenedesmus incrassatulus Bohlin 1897, p. 24
Pl. 63, Fig. 14

Colony composed of (2)–4–8 fusiform, subacute cells, arranged in either 1 or 2 series (alternating); median cells slightly curved; outer cells definitely curved, with the free walls strongly concave; apices of the cells with a nodular thickening; cells 5–8μ in diameter, 17–24μ long.

Typical plant not reported from our area.

Scenedesmus incrassatulus var. *mononae* G. M. Smith 1916a, p. 440
Pl. 63, Fig. 13

A variety differing from the typical by its smaller, more slender cells, 4.4–5μ in diameter, 11–12μ long.

Wis.

Scenedesmus longus Meyen 1829, p. 774
Pl. 63, Figs. 15, 16

Colony composed of 2–4–8 oblong-cylindric cells arranged in a single series; apices of both inner and outer cells with 1 or 2 sharp spines which are longer on the outer cells; cells 4–6μ in diameter, 8–12μ long.

Rare in the plankton of several lakes. Mich., Wis.

Scenedesmus longus var. *brevispina* G. M. Smith 1916a, p. 471

A variety with more slender cells than the typical and with shorter spines; cells 3–5μ in diameter, 9–11μ long.

Wis.

Scenedesmus longus var. *ellipticus* (West & West)
G. M. Smith 1916a, p. 472

Colony composed of 4 ellipsoid cells arranged in a single series; outer cells bearing 2 outwardly curved spines, the inner cells with a single spine; cells 5μ in diameter, 12μ long.

Wis.

Scenedesmus longus var. *minutus* G. M. Smith 1916a, p. 471

A small variety with short spines; cells 2–3μ in diameter, 8μ long; spines 1.5–2μ long.
Wis.

Scenedesmus longus var. *Naegelii* (de Bréb.)
G. M. Smith 1920, p. 156
Pl. 63, Fig. 24; Pl. 64, Fig. 1

Colony composed of 8 cylindrical cells arranged in a single series; outer cells bearing a long, curved spine at each pole; inner cells with a long spine at one pole only (rarely with no spines); cells 7–12μ in diameter, 16–28μ long.
Plankter; in several small lakes. Mich., Wis.

Scenedesmus obliquus (Turp.) Kuetzing 1833b, p. 609
Pl. 63, Fig. 17

Colony composed of 2–8 (usually 4 or 8) fusiform cells arranged in a single series; apices of cells apiculate; wall smooth; cells 4.2–9μ in diameter, 14–18–(21)μ long.
Rare in tychoplankton of a swamp; rare in many lakes. Mich., Wis.

Scenedesmus opoliensis P. Richter 1896, p. 7
Pl. 63, Fig. 18

Colony composed of 2–4–8 naviculoid cells arranged in a single series, with free walls of outer cells convex, the lateral adjoined walls in contact along 1/3–2/3 of their length; apices of cells with long spines (inner cells with a spine at one pole only, or sometimes without spines); cells 6–8μ in diameter, 14–26μ long.
Rare but widely distributed. Mich., Wis.

Scenedesmus opoliensis var. *contacta* Prescott 1944, p. 359
Pl. 63, Figs. 19, 20

Colony consisting of 4 naviculoid cells arranged in a single series, adjoined along ¾ of the length of their lateral walls; spines on terminal cells either 1 or 2 at each pole, long and curved; spines on apices of inner cells short and straight; cells 6–8μ in diameter, 20–24μ long.
Plankter; rare. Wis.

Scenedesmus perforatus Lemmermann 1904, p. 159
Pl. 46, Figs. 24, 25

Cells subrectangular with convex end walls and concave lateral walls, thus forming biconvex intercellular spaces; end cells of the colony bearing a single long curved spine at each pole arising from the corner of the cells, the outer lateral walls of the end cells straight or umbonate; cells 3–3.5–(5)μ in diameter, 10–13μ long. Mich.

Scenedesmus quadricauda (Turp.) de Brébisson *in* de Brébisson & Godey 1835, p. 66
Pl. 64, Fig. 2

Colony consisting of 2–4–8 oblong-cylindric cells usually in 1 series (sometimes in 2 alternating series); outer cells with a long curved spine at each pole; inner cells without spines or with mere papillae at the apices; cells variable in size, 3–18μ in diameter, 9–35μ long.

Common and widely distributed in a variety of habitats; one of the most nearly ubiquitous algal species. Mich., Wis.

Scenedesmus quadricauda var. *longispina* (Chod.)
G. M. Smith 1916a, p. 480
Pl. 63, Fig. 22

A variety differing from the typical by the greater length of the spines; cells 3.5–5μ in diameter, 8–11μ long; spines 7.5–10μ long.

Plankter; in lakes. Mich., Wis.

Scenedesmus quadricauda var. *maximus* West & West 1895, p. 83
Pl. 64, Figs. 3, 4

A variety differing from the typical by the larger size of cells and relatively longer spines; cells 9–11.5μ in diameter, 27–36μ long; spines 20–30μ long.

Plankter; in lakes; rare. Mich., Wis.

Scenedesmus quadricauda var. *parvus* G. M. Smith 1916a, p. 480
Pl. 64, Fig. 6

Colony composed of 2–16 cylindrical-ovate cells arranged in a single series; outer cells with a long spine at each pole; inner cells with spineless walls; cells 4–6.5μ in diameter, 12–17μ long.

Very common in many lakes and swamps. Wis.

Scenedesmus quadricauda var. *quadrispina* (Chod.)
G. M. Smith 1916a, p. 480
Pl. 63, Fig. 21

Colony composed of 4–8 ovate cells with short spines, usually strongly recurved; cells 4–7.4μ in diameter, 9–16μ long; spines about 3μ long.

Rare, but widely distributed in many lakes and ponds. Mich., Wis.

Scenedesmus quadricauda var. *Westii* G. M. Smith 1916a, p. 480

Pl. 64, Figs.7, 9

Colony composed of 4–8 ovate cells with broadly rounded apices; cells 5–8μ in diameter, 10–18–(22)μ long; spines relatively short, often strongly reflexed.

Rare, but found in the plankton of a great variety of lakes, ponds, and swampy habitats. Mich., Wis.

Scenedesmus serratus (Corda) Bohlin 1901, p. 44

Pl. 64, Fig. 8

Colony composed of 4 oblong-ovate cells arranged in a single series; the outer cells with one, the inner cells with two longitudinal rows of small teeth; apices of all cells bearing 3–4 small teeth; cells 4.5–7μ in diameter, 15–20μ long.

Plankter; in several lakes. Wis.

ACTINASTRUM Lagerheim 1882, p. 70

Colonial, planktonic, composed of 4–16 truncate-fusiform or basidia-like cells, sometimes cigar-shaped with subacute poles, radiating in all planes from a common center, not inclosed by a colonial envelope; chloroplast a parietal, elongate plate covering about ⅓ of the wall in circumference and nearly as long as the cell; 1 pyrenoid present.

Key to the Species

Cells 7–10 times as long as wide, about as wide at the poles
as in the median part of the cell..*A. gracilimum*
Cells 3–6 times as long as wide; median part of the
cell about twice as wide as the poles..*A. Hantzschii*

Actinastrum gracilimum G. M. Smith 1916, p. 480

Pl. 64, Fig. 5

Cells cylindrical, with very slightly narrowed to abruptly truncate poles, forming colonies of individuals with the long axes of the cells radiating in all planes from a common center; cells 1.7–3μ in diameter, 14–21μ long; colonies 30–45μ in diameter.

Rare; in the plankton of several lakes. Mich., Wis.

Actinastrum Hantzschii Lagerheim 1882, p. 70

Pl. 64, Figs. 10, 11

Cells spindle-shaped or cylindrical, narrowed toward the apices, arranged in simple or compound colonies of 4 or 8 with the long axes of the cells radiating from a common center; chloroplast a parietal plate, with 1 pyrenoid; cells 3–5.6μ in diameter, 12–22μ long. Common in plankton. Mich., Wis.

Actinastrum Hantzschii var. *elongatum* G. M. Smith 1918, p. 636
Pl. 65, Fig. 2

Cells cylindrical, very slightly if at all narrowed toward the apices, larger than in the typical plant; cells 4–5μ in diameter, 30–35μ long. Rare; in plankton. Wis.

Actinastrum Hantzschii var. *fluviatile* Schroeder 1899, p. 20
Pl. 65, Fig. 1

A variety differing from the typical in that the cells are sharply pointed; cells 3.3–3.5μ in diameter, 39–42μ long. Rare in a swamp. Wis.

TETRADESMUS G. M. Smith 1913, p. 76

A 4-celled, free-floating colony; cells fusiform, or cylindrical, arranged in 2 planes with their longitudinal axes parallel, the adjoined walls straight, in contact throughout most of their length, the outer free wall straight or concave, the poles of the cell directed away from the center of the colony; cells in vertical view spherical, arranged in a quadrangle; chloroplast a parietal plate with 1 pyrenoid.

Key to the Species

Cells fusiform, attached throughout the length
  of their lateral walls_____*T. wisconsinense*
Cells crescent-shaped, cylindrical, attached along only a
  portion of their lateral walls_____*T. Smithii*

Tetradesmus Smithii Prescott 1944, p. 360
Pl. 64, Figs. 15–17

Cells slightly arcuate or crescent-shaped or subcylindrical, slightly narrowed toward the poles which are broadly rounded, in groups of 4 with their long axes parallel and with the convex walls adjoined in the mid-region only; outer free walls concave or nearly straight; cells in end view spherical, arranged in a quadrangle; chloroplast a parietal plate; cells 3.7–4μ in diameter, 27–29μ long.

This species should be compared with *Quadrigula* spp. The cells are not so straight as in that genus although they have about the same proportions and are arranged in bundles of 4. Also *Tetradesmus Smithii,* unlike *Quadrigula,* has no gelatinous investment inclosing the quartets of cells.

Rare; in plankton. Wis.

[282]

Tetradesmus wisconsinense G. M Smith 1913, p. 76
Pl. 64, Figs. 12–14

Cells fusiform arranged with their long axes parallel; cells adjoined throughout the length of their lateral walls; outer free walls concave; poles of the cell narrowed and directed away from the center of the colony; in end view spherical, the cells arranged in a quadrangle; cells 4–6μ in diameter, 12–14.5μ long.

Rare; in the plankton of lakes. Wis.

CRUCIGENIA Morren 1830, pp. 404, 415

Colony free-floating, consisting of a plate of 4–8–16 trapezoid or rhomboid cells lying in one plane about a small or large central space; chloroplast a parietal plate with 1 pyrenoid in each cell; colony inclosed by a thin, inconspicuous gelatinous envelope which often causes the families to adhere to one another and to form colonial complexes.

Key to the Species

1. Opening at the center of the colony large, approximately equal to the greatest dimension of the cells 2
1. Opening at center of the colony small, less than the greatest dimension of the cells 3
2. Cells nearly hemispherical, old mother cell walls persistent .... *C. Lauterbornii*
2. Cells trapezoidal; outer free walls slightly convex; old mother cell walls not persistent .... *C. fenestrata*
3. Cells triangular; opening at the center of the colony very small 4
3. Cells ovate or polygonal 5
4. Outer free walls straight .... *C. tetrapedia*
4. Outer free walls convex .... *C. quadrata*
5. Cells with an apiculation at the free pole .... *C. apiculata*
5. Cells without an apiculation 6
6. Cells abruptly truncated at the free poles, the walls thickened at the apex .... *C. truncata*
6. Cells not truncated, the wall not thickened at the apex 7
7. Cells somewhat reniform, the outer free walls concave; cells always quadrately arranged .... *C. crucifera*
7. Cells ovate 8
8. Cells regularly arranged in quartets or in multiples of quartets, 5–10μ long .... *C. rectangularis*
8. Cells irregularly arranged within the colony, some in 4's, 8–14μ long .... *C. irregularis*

Crucigenia apiculata (Lemm.) Schmidle 1901, p. 234
Pl. 65, Fig. 3

Colony composed of 4 ovate, rhomboidal or somewhat triangular cells arranged about a 4-sided opening, with 1 short, cone-shaped apiculation on the cell wall at the free outer apex, and one on the lateral walls where the cells adjoin at their 'bases'; cells 3–7μ in diameter, 5–10μ long; colony 6–12.5μ wide, 9–18μ long.

Euplankter. Mich., Wis.

Crucigenia crucifera (Wolle) Collins 1909, p. 170
Pl. 65, Fig. 4

Colony consisting of 4-sided cells arranged about a central square opening, the outer free walls longer and concave, the outer free angles of the cells rounded, the lateral adjoined walls straight and converging inward where they adjoin other cells, the inner walls about the central opening forming a short, straight side; multiple colonies resulting from the adherence of quartets of cells by persisting mother cell walls; cells 3.5–5μ in diameter, 5–7μ long; colony 9–11μ wide, 14–16μ long.

Plankter. Mich., Wis.

Crucigenia fenestrata Schmidle 1901, p. 234
Pl. 65, Fig. 5

Colony consisting of 4 trapezoidal cells arranged about a square opening, the outer free wall longest and convex, the free angles sharply rounded; lateral and inner (the shortest) walls straight; cells 3–5μ in diameter, 5–13μ long; colony 8–14μ wide, frequently adjoined in closely arranged association to form multiple colonies.

Rare; found in the euplankton of a few lakes. Mich., Wis.

Crucigenia irregularis Wille 1898, p. 302
Pl. 65, Fig. 6

Colony free-floating, consisting of 4, or multiples of 4 ovate cells not definitely arranged about a central space as in other species of the genus and not in quadrangular formation, with both lateral and apical walls in contact; chloroplasts broad parietal plates or discs, as many as 4 in a cell; pyrenoid sometimes absent; cells 5–9μ in diameter, 8–14μ long.

This is the most frequently seen species of Crucigenia in our collections. It should be compared with C. rectangularis (Naeg.) Gay which also has ovate cells but in which the cells have a regular arrangement about a central space.

Common in a large number of lakes and ponds. Mich., Wis.

Crucigenia Lauterbornii Schmidle 1901, p. 234
Pl. 65, Fig. 11

Colony free-floating, consisting of 4 subspherical cells arranged in 2 opposite pairs about a large square space bounded by the flat, inner walls of the cells; cells in contact only at their inner corners; 1 chloroplast, parietal along the outer convex wall; pyrenoid present; cells 4.5–9μ in diameter, 8–15μ long; quartets of cells adjoined in multiples by remains of old mother cell walls.

Rare; in the plankton of several lakes. Wis.

Crucigenia quadrata Morren 1830, pp. 415, 426
Pl. 65, Fig.10

Colony free-floating, consisting of a circular plate of 4 triangular cells, cruciately arranged about a small central space, the outer free wall of the cells broadly convex, the lateral walls straight, adjoined throughout their length with neighboring cells and converging toward the center of the colony; walls sometimes with knob-like projections; chloroplasts parietal discs, as many as 4 in a cell; pyrenoids not always present; cells 2.5–6μ in diameter, 3.7μ long; multiple quadrate colonies formed by the close arrangement of component quartets.

Smith (1920, p. 147) considers *Staurogenia multiseta* var. *punctata* Schmidle and *Crucigenia triangularis* (Chod.) Schmidle to be synonymous with this species.

Plankter; found in a large number of lakes in northern counties. Mich., Wis.

Crucigenia rectangularis (A. Braun) Gay 1891, p. 100
Pl. 65, Figs. 7, 8

Colony free-floating, consisting of ovate or oblong cells, very regularly arranged about a rectangular central space in 2 pairs, with the apices adjoining; chloroplasts 1–4, parietal discs, with a pyrenoid in each; cells 4–7μ in diameter, 5–10μ long.

This species should be compared with *C. irregularis* Wille.

Common in both eu- and tychoplankton of a large number of lakes. Mich., Wis.

Crucigenia tetrapedia (Kirch.) West & West 1902, p. 62
Pl. 65, Fig. 9; Pl. 66, Fig. 1

Colony free-floating, consisting of 4 triangular cells cruciately arranged about a minute central space; outer free wall and lateral walls straight, the angles acutely rounded; chloroplast a parietal plate with a single pyrenoid; cells 4.5–9μ in diameter, frequently forming a rectangular plate of 16 cells (4 quartets).

Common in a small lake. Wis.

Crucigenia truncata G. M. Smith 1920, p. 146

Pl. 66, Fig.2

Colony free-floating, consisting of 4 ovate cells arranged about a central, rectangular space, with lateral walls of each pair of cells adjoining and with apical walls in contact at the corners, the outer free walls thick and truncate, straight; chloroplasts 1–4, parietal discs; pyrenoids absent; quartets of cells adjoined to form compound colonies by the adherence of old mother cell walls; cells 4–6μ in diameter; colonies up to 50μ wide, 75μ long.

Rare in the plankton of several lakes. Wis.

TETRASTRUM Chodat 1895a, p. 114

Plant a free-floating colony of 4 triangular, cruciately arranged cells, inner faces straight and adjoined to form a rectangular plate, outer free wall convex and beset with 3 or 4 short setae; colony inclosed by a thin gelatinous matrix; chloroplasts 1–4 in each cell, parietal discs with pyrenoids sometimes absent.

This plant should be compared with *Crucigenia,* a genus with which it has much in common. Some species of *Crucigenia* in the past have been assigned to *Tetrastrum.* The latter genus is characterized by the setae, by its possession of a definite colonial investment, and by its failure to form compound colonies.

Key to the Species

Outer faces of cells with short, knob-like projections.............................*T. punctatum*
Outer faces of cells with long, hair-like setae.......................*T. staurogeniaeforme*

Tetrastrum punctatum (Schmidle) Ahlstrom & Tiffany 1934, p. 504

Colony of 4 angular, or somewhat triangular cells, broadly convex on their outer free walls, arranged about a very small central space; walls furnished with several coarse knob-like projections; chloroplast parietal and plate-like, with a single pyrenoid; cells 8–12μ in diameter.

Uncommon; in plankton. Mich., Wis.

Tetrastrum staurogeniaeforme (Schroeder)
Lemmermann 1900d, p. 95
Pl. 66, Fig. 3

A colony of 4 triangular cells, cruciately arranged about a small rectangular space; lateral margins of the cells straight and adjoined, the outer free walls convex and furnished with as many as 6 fine, hair-like setae; chloroplasts 1–4 parietal discs, sometimes containing pyrenoids; cells 3–6μ in diameter; colony 7–15μ wide without setae, which are 4–8μ long.

This species should be compared with *Crucigenia quadrata*.

Rare in the plankton of several lakes. Mich., Wis.

TETRALLANTOS Teiling 1916, p. 62

A colony of 4 crescent-shaped or sausage-shaped cells which are bluntly rounded at their apices and inclosed by a colonial mucilage, with clusters of daughter cells often held in approximation by old mother cell wall fragments; cells in 2 pairs and in 2 planes, 1 pair facing each other and in contact at their poles, the other pair in a longitudinal plane vertical to these and so arranged that each member has 1 pole at the point of contact of the poles of the other pair; chloroplast a parietal plate with 1 pyrenoid.

Tetrallantos Lagerheimii Teiling 1916, p. 62
Pl. 66, Figs. 4–6

Characteristics as described for the genus; cells 4–8μ in diameter, 10–13μ long.

This rather unusual plant is rare in the United States, apparently having been found only in Wisconsin, Massachusetts, and Mississippi.

Rare; in the plankton of soft water lakes and small ponds. Wis.

MICRACTINIUM Fresenius 1858, p. 236

Free-floating, one-celled or in colonies of tetrahedrally or pyramidally arranged spherical or ovate cells (sometimes in 1 plane); walls beset with 1–7 long, needle-like setae; 1 parietal, cup-shaped chloroplast containing a single pyrenoid. Korschikov (1937) reports observation of sexual reproduction in this genus.

Key to the Species

Cells spherical; setae 20–35μ long_____ M. *pusillum*
Cells ovate; setae 23–40μ long_____ M. *quadrisetum*

Micractinium pusillum Fresenius 1858, p. 236
Pl. 66, Fig. 8

A free-floating colony of 4–16 spherical cells arranged in a pyramid or in a square, groups of 4 in association with other similar groups; free walls beset with 1–5 finely tapering setae; chloroplast a parietal cup with 1 pyrenoid; cells 3–7μ in diameter without setae; setae 20–35μ long.

Rare in the plankton of many lakes, mostly soft water habitats. Mich., Wis.

Micractinium pusillum var. *elegans* G. M. Smith 1918, p. 631
Pl. 66, Fig. 7

A variety differing from the typical by having more numerous and longer setae on the free walls of the cells; setae 5–7 in number.
Rare; in plankton. Wis.

Micractinium quadrisetum (Lemm.) G. M. Smith 1916, p. 479
Pl. 68, Fig. 1

A free-floating colony of 4 ovate cells, adjoined to other groups of 4 about a central rectangular space; wall with 1–4 very long, finely tapering setae; chloroplast a parietal cup with 1 pyrenoid; cells 4–7μ in diameter, 8–10μ long; setae 23–40μ long.
Rare; in the plankton of lakes. Mich., Wis.

ORDER SIPHONALES

In this order the thallus is a coenocytic tube, more or less branched and usually showing a basal-distal differentiation. In marine forms the thallus becomes very elaborate and complex; in the fresh-water genera the vegetative thallus is simplified, although sexual reproduction is of an advanced type. There are no cross walls except where sex organs or zoospores are cut off, although in *Dichotomosiphon* there are frequent constrictions of the filament. There are numerous ovate chloroplasts peripherally arranged in a layer of cytoplasm along the wall, the center of the tube being vacuolate. There are no pyrenoids, but starch is stored in *Dichotomosiphon,* and either starch or oil may accumulate in *Phyllosiphon* and *Vaucheria.**

Asexual reproduction is accomplished by zoospores or aplanospores. In sexual reproduction a high type of heterogamy is involved. Enlarged oogonia, each with a single egg, are cut off by a wall from the vegetative filament, usually near tubular antheridia which produce large numbers of small biflagellate antherozoids. Fertilization is effected through a terminal pore in the wall of the oogonium.

Key to the Families

Plants endophytic_____ _____ PHYLLOSIPHONACEAE
Plants free-living, either aquatic or subaerial _____ VAUCHERIACEAE

FAMILY PHYLLOSIPHONACEAE

In this family the thallus is a much contorted tubular or vesicular coenocyte which is either endozoic or (in our specimens) endophytic. The plants inhabit the tissues of the Araceae, especially in tropical and subtropical climates. There is but a single genus in our region.

----

*Now considered a member of the Chrysophyta.

PHYLLOSIPHON Kühn 1878, p. 24

This genus is parasitic in the tissues of the common Jack-in-the-pulpit, *Arisaema triphyllum* (L.) Schott. The thallus consists of a much twisted and closely compacted coenocytic tubular filament with numerous oval chloroplasts and nuclei. The alga brings about the disintegration of the host tissues and a destruction of the chlorophyll so that large yellow patches develop. Food reserve is in the form of either starch or oil. The only known method of reproduction is by the formation of numerous aplanospores in the tube which, upon being liberated, generate new coenocytic filaments directly.

Phyllosiphon Arisari Kühn 1878, p. 24
Pl. 69, Figs. 1–3

Characters as described for the genus; tubes dichotomously branched, ramifying among the tissues of the host plant and producing discolored areas; tubes 25–35μ in diameter, 60μ in diameter during aplanospore production.

On blades and stalks of Jack-in-the-pulpit. Wis. (Swingle).

FAMILY VAUCHERIACEAE

Thallus long, much-branched, coenocytic tubes, sometimes possessing horizontal, downwardly directed, and vertical sex-organ-bearing branches; chloroplasts numerous ovate or circular discs embedded in a thin sheet of cytoplasm along the wall and about large vacuolated central regions; pyrenoids lacking; reserve food either oil or (less often) starch; reproduction by large multiflagellate zoospores cut off from the ends of branches, by akinetes, or by eggs and antherozoids, the gametes being produced in special sex organs.

Key to the Genera

Regularly branched dichotomously and frequently
   constricted; sex organs terminal..*Dichotomosiphon*

Irregularly branched (sometimes sparsely so), not constricted;
   sex organs lateral on the main filament
   or terminal on lateral branches...*Vaucheria*

DICHOTOMOSIPHON Ernst 1902, p. 115

A multinucleate siphon, forming attached, felt-like masses on the bottom of aquatic habitats, or rarely subaerial on damp soil; branching usually dichotomous with frequent constrictions at the base of the branches; chloroplasts numerous small discs; pyrenoids lacking; sexual reproduction oogamous, the sex organs borne in corymb-like clusters at the ends of branches, the oogonia usually solitary globose; antheridia 1 to several in the cluster, formed at the tip of the branch, becoming cut off by a septation, producing numerous motile antherozoids. Large akinetes are common.

There is but one species in this genus.

Dichotomosiphon tuberosus (A. Braun) Ernst 1902, p. 115
Pl. 68, Figs. 6, 7

Thallus a dichotomously branched tube with constrictions at the base of the branches and with cross walls only where reproductive structures are cut off; forming felt-like or cushion-like mats in the silt of lake bottoms, and consisting of horizontal, downwardly projecting, and erect, sex-organ-bearing branches; much enlarged, elongate, subcylindric or globose akinetes frequent; sex organs monoecious, located at the ends of strongly recurved branchlets which form corymb-like clusters at the ends of vegetative filaments; usually 1 spherical oogonium and several cylindrical antheridia present; the oospores globular, becoming yellow at maturity and easily seen with the unaided eye, oospore wall 3-layered; vegetative siphons $50-100\mu$ in diameter; oogonia $250-300\mu$ in diameter; oospore nearly the same size as the oogonium; antheridia $35-50\mu$ in diameter, 2–4 times the diameter in length.

This plant seems to grow only in lakes with a rich organic silt. The thallus is often nearly buried in loose bottom deposits with only the tips of vertical branches and the sex organs emerging. In Wisconsin the plant has not been collected except from hard water or eutrophic lakes. In Michigan it is common at depths up to 16 meters, but in such habitats it appears to reproduce only by akinetes, sex organs being formed when the plant grows at 2 meters or less. This may be related to water temperature. Like *Vaucheria*, *Dichotomosiphon* forms a habitat for an association of microfauna such as Rotifera, Cladocera, and many protozoa.

From several lakes, mostly from silty bottoms. Mich., Wis.

VAUCHERIA De Candolle 1805, p. 61[*]

Thallus subaerial or aquatic, a much and irregularly branched siphonous coenocyte without cross walls except where reproductive structures are cut off; filaments often compactly interwoven (especially in terrestrial species) to form a felt-like expansion, with colorless rhizoids when attached, or forming entangled clots of coarse threads when floating; branches arising laterally or dichotomously, nearly as large as the main filament and tapering slightly to broadly rounded tips; chloroplasts numerous ovate discs without

---

[*]See footnote, p. 288.

pyrenoids; asexual reproduction by large globose, multiflagellate zoospores cut off singly at the ends of clavate branches; thick-walled akinetes at the ends of branches, or in the tubes of some species; sexual reproduction oogamous; oogonia globose or ovate, sessile, on pedicels, or on long stalks, containing a single egg which may completely fill the oogonium; antheridia on the same or different filaments, clavate, cylindrical, or subcylindrical, coiled or straight, usually reflexed with the terminal opening directed toward the oogonium, borne near the oogonia or at the end of a series, producing many biflagellate, ovoid to fusiform antherozoids; oospores with thick walls, sometimes completely filling the oogonia and the same shape.

Key to the Species

1. Oogonia 262–289μ in diameter _____ _V. Nicholsii_
1. Oogonia smaller _____ 2
2. Oogonia sessile on the main filament _____ 3
2. Oogonia on a pedicel or on a lateral branch _____ 5
3. Oogonia obliquely ovate, large, up to 160μ high
   and 220μ long; wall 6μ thick ____ _____ _V. pachydermum_
3. Oogonia more nearly erect, smaller; wall not thick _____ 4
4. Oogonia erect, the pore vertically directed _____ _V. orthocarpa_
4. Oogonia with the pore directed obliquely upward _____ _V. sessilis_
5. Oogonia on a short pedicel, sometimes nearly sessile _____ 6
5. Oogonia at the end of a long or short lateral branch, stalked _____ 10
6. Oospores not filling the oogonia; oogonia usually
   in pairs, the pores directed oppositely _____ _V. aversa_
6. Oospores filling the oogonia; arranged otherwise _____ 7
7. Pedicel very short, scarcely evident; oogonia
   broadly ovate, the pore nearly erect _____ _V. sessilis_
7. Pedicel evident; oogonia narrowly ovate or ellipsoid,
   the pore oblique or more nearly horizontal _____ 8
8. Oogonia in pairs, or several on a short pedicel,
   the antheridium between _____ _V. geminata_
8. Oogonia arising singly, near the antheridium _____ 9
9. Oogonia 80–150μ in diameter, the pore directed
   horizontally or obliquely downward _____ _____ °V. ornithocephala_
9. Oogonia 60–65μ in diameter; pore directed obliquely upward _V. polysperma_
10. Oogonia 2 to several on the end of a lateral branch
    a millimeter or more in length _____ _V. longipes_
10. Oogonia solitary, on a much shorter branch _____ 11
11. Oogonia 60–103μ in diameter, 85–211μ long, without a pedicel
    from the branch, arising near the base of the antheridia _____ _V. terrestris_
11. Oogonia averaging smaller, 60–75μ in diameter, 75–90μ long, with
    a pedicel, placing it well above the associated antheridium _____ _V. hamata_

Vaucheria aversa Hassall 1843, p. 429
Pl. 66, Figs. 9, 10

Coarse filaments, freely branched and readily collapsing upon being handled, 65–100μ in diameter; oogonia usually in pairs or several in a series on very short pedicels, mostly sessile, ovoid to subglobose, opening by an oblique pore in a narrow beak which faces in an opposite direction from the neighboring oogonium, 100–125μ in diameter, 180–250μ long; antheridia subcylindric, strongly recurved, one on each side of a pair or series of oogonia; oospores globose, with a 3-layered membrane, 80–120μ in diameter, not filling the oogonium.

Forming a soft, felt-like mat in spring seeps and on moist shady banks of streams, etc. Wis.

Vaucheria geminata (Vauch.) De Candolle 1805, p. 62
Pl. 68, Figs. 2, 3

Aquatic or on very moist soil; filaments coarse and freely branched, 80–100μ in diameter; oogonia in pairs, ovate to subglobose, borne laterally near the end of a short stipitate branch of the main axis, with 1 antheridium circinate or strongly reflected; oogonia with pores directed vertically, 60–80μ in diameter, 70–90μ long; oospores with thick, 3-layered membranes, completely filling and the same shape as the oogonia.

Forming floating, tangled mats in marshes and cut-oi s from lakes protected from wave action; in ditches of shallow water Mich., Wis.

Vaucheria geminata var. *depressa* Transeau 1917, . 228

A variety differing from the typical by having the pedicels of the oogonia longer than in the typical, arising from a snort lateral branch and curved so that the oogonia are in contact with the main filament.

Mich.

Vaucheria hamata (Vauch.) De Candolle 1805, p. 63

Filaments rather slender; monoecious; oogonia solitary, or rarely 2 together, ovate to somewhat lunate, with the inner or lower margin somewhat concave, borne on a pedicel at the end of a lateral branch from the main axis, 60–75μ in diameter, 75–90μ long; antheridium tubular, circinate, arising from near the base of the oogonium pedicel; oospore with a 4-layered membrane, completely filling the oogonium, containing a dark granular spot.

Floating, tangled mats in quiet water. Mich., Wis.

Vaucheria longipes Collins 1907, p. 201
Pl. 67, Fig. 5

Filaments rather coarse, 80–90μ in diameter; monoecious; sex organs on a long (1–4 mm.) lateral branch, 30–40μ in diameter; the antheridium distinctly circinate, terminal on the branch; oogonia usually 3 (2–4), ovoid, somewhat oblique on rather long stalks (up to 1500μ) arising from just below the antheridium, 35–40μ in diameter, 70–85μ long.

In pooled streams and quiet water of lakes. Wis.

Vaucheria Nicholsii Brown 1937, p. 283
Pl. 67, Fig. 10

Filaments very coarse, 112–120μ in diameter; monoecious; oogonia globose, sessile, the opening vertical, 262–289μ in diameter; oospore the same shape as and filling the oogonium (except the beak), yellow-brown; antheridia sessile, arising from all sides of the main filament near the oogonium and recurved so as to lie parallel with the filament and opening toward the oogonium, 39–50μ wide, 115–123μ long.

Shore of Douglas Lake, Michigan.

Vaucheria orthocarpa Reinsch 1887, p. 191
Pl. 67, Fig. 1

Filaments slender to moderately coarse, 77–110μ in diameter; monoecious; oogonia sessile, ovoid, erect with the opening vertical; oospore ovate, completely filling the oogonium, the wall thick, 50–65μ in diameter, 65–90μ long; antheridia sessile, arising near the oogonia, distinctly coiled, with the opening directed toward the oogonium.

Mich.

Vaucheria pachyderma Walz 1866, p. 146
Pl. 67, Fig. 2

Filaments variable, slender or stout, 40–123μ in diameter; monoecious; oogonia mostly solitary, globular or transversely ellipsoid, the opening horizontal, or downwardly oblique, the wall thick, up to 6μ, with discolored spots, 69–160μ high, 69–220μ long; oospore filling the oogonium, 145μ in diameter, 180μ long, with a thick wall; antheridium erect beside the oogonium, hooked at the apex.

Mich.

Vaucheria polysperma Hassall 1843, Pl. 6, Fig. 6
Pl. 67, Fig. 13

Filaments very slender, 15–33μ in diameter; monoecious; oogonia in a series of 3–5, each on a short pedicel, ovate, opening upwardly oblique, 60–65μ in diameter; oospores globose, filling the oogonium in width only, 44–60.5μ in diameter; antheridia cylindrical, sessile on a short pedicel, strongly reflexed and opening toward the oogonia.

Mich.

Vaucheria sessilis (Vauch.) De Candolle 1805, p. 63
Pl. 68, Fig. 5

Aquatic or terrestrial; filaments somewhat slender, 50–58μ in diameter, with irregular branching; monoecious; oogonia usually in pairs, ovoid to subglobose with the pore in a short beak and directed obliquely upward, 70–85μ in diameter, as much as 100μ long; antheridia on a short pedicel between 2 oogonia, either straight or circinate, but usually with the opening directed toward the pore of an oogonium, about 25μ in diameter; oospore with a 3-layered membrane, filling the oogonium.

A common species but infrequently found in our collections; forming a felt-like mat on submerged rocks and on sandy bottoms of springs; on rocky outcrops where there is trickling water. Mich., Wis.

Vaucheria sessilis fa. *clavata* (Klebs) Heering 1921, p. 88
Pl. 67, Figs. 3, 4

Filaments stouter than in the typical, 77–110μ in diameter; oogonia broadly ovate with the beak directed vertically; oospore 49.5–66.5μ in diameter, 66–88.5μ long.

Mich.

Vaucheria terrestris (Vauch.) De Candolle 1805, p. 62
Pl. 68, Fig. 4

Either aquatic or terrestrial, usually forming floating clots; filaments rather slender, 50–80μ in diameter, branching dichotomous, or at right angles to the main filament (as in the case of the relatively long branches which bear the sex organs); monoecious; oogonia subglobose to ovoid, at the end of a slightly bent stalk, with the pore directed downward, exceeding the antheridium and appearing to be terminal on the branch, 60–103μ in diameter, 85–211μ long; antheridia strongly circinate, 15–20μ in diameter, terminating the branch but appearing to arise beneath the oogonium; oospore with a thick, 4-layered membrane, completely filling the oogonium which falls with the oospore.

Floating in hard or soft water lakes and small ponds, becoming mature and fruiting abundantly at low temperatures. This species is also found on moist soil, especially in well-shaded habitats. Mich., Wis.

ORDER ZYGNEMATALES

Except for the desmid families in which there are unicellular genera (See Appendix) plants in this order are unbranched filaments without basal-distal differentiation. Rarely, incidental rhizoidal branches may be formed where filaments come in contact with substrates. The cells are long or short cylinders, but in some species the cells become inflated during the reproductive process (conjugation). The cell wall has 1 or 2 layers of firm cellulose and an outer pectose layer of varying thickness and consistency. The mucilaginous sheath present in most forms is responsible for the fact that these plants very seldom become hosts for epiphytes although frequently parasitized by *Lagenidium* and *Myzocytium* (Phycomycetes). The end walls of the cells are separated by a middle lamella and may be either plane or characteristically infolded (replicate). One of the most characteristic features of this order is the relatively large size of the chloroplasts, usually 1 or 2 in each cell, although in *Spirogyra* there may be several (up to 16). Pyrenoids in the chloroplasts are large and conspicuous, but in *Mougeotiopsis* pyrenoids are lacking. The chloroplasts may be axial plates, stellate masses or cushions, or parietal spiral ribbons. In asexual reproduction aplanospores and akinetes are sometimes formed. It is in sexual reproduction that plants in this order show their most distinctive characteristics. Either all or part of the vegetative cell content serves as a gamete, union being achieved by one or both gametes passing through a tube which forms between the cells of two filaments (scalariform conjugation) or between cells of the same filament (lateral conjugation). In a few species, filaments become adjoined or are juxtaposed, and gametic union is achieved without the use of tubes. The resulting zygospore has a wall which is usually 3-layered and thick. It may be smooth or the outer layers may be decorated with scrobiculations, pits, or reticulations, features which are specific and of taxonomic importance. The gametangial cells after conjugation may be empty or may become filled with pectic compounds which are usually deposited in layers.

Motile reproductive cells do not occur. This, together with other fundamental details of the life history, behavior of the germinating zygospore, etc., set the Zygnematales well apart from other orders of the Chlorophyta, so that in some systems of classification they have been placed outside the Chlorophyceae.

Of the 3 families which comprise this order (Zygnemataceae, Mesotaeniaceae, Desmidiaceae*) only the first is considered in this book.

FAMILY ZYGNEMATACEAE

Characteristics as described for the order; cells short- or long-cylindric with plane or folded end walls, usually unbranched and without basal-distal differentiation; chloroplasts few, large, and, except for one genus, with conspicuous pyrenoids.

*See appendix for desmid genera.

Besides conjugation, described above, akinetes (thick-walled resting cells formed by modification of vegetative cells) or parthenospores (aplanospores) may occur. The latter are thick-walled, zygospore-like bodies formed within cells independent of conjugation.

Reproductive material often can be identified in the field, especially in *Spirogyra, Mougeotia,* and *Zygnema,* by the foamy, brownish or 'dirty' appearance of the plant masses. In many forms conjugation regularly occurs in surface mats of filaments, each species fruiting in its own season.

Key to the Genera

1. Cells with 2 broad, disc-like chloroplasts, mostly axial but in part parietal; cell sap deep purple (rarely colorless)_____*Pleurodiscus*
1. Cells with other types of chloroplasts; cell sap colorless (but lilac or purplish-brown in *Mougeotia capucina*)_____ 2
2. Chloroplasts parietal ribbons (usually with laciniate or crenate margins), spiral (rarely nearly straight), with several to many pyrenoids in a single series_____ Spirogyra
   (including *Sirogonium*)
2. Chloroplasts axial, shaped otherwise, broad bands, stellate bodies, elongate pads, or axial polster (cushion-shaped) bodies_____ 3
3. Chloroplasts axial plates or bands, broad and filling the width of the cell in some; pyrenoids none, or 2 to many, in 1 row or scattered_____ 4
3. Chloroplasts (usually 2) axial, star-shaped or pad-like bodies ____ 7
4. Chloroplasts without pyrenoids_____*Mougeotiopsis*
4. Chloroplasts with pyrenoids_____ 5·
5. Conjugating cells formed by a portion of the vegetative cell cut off from one end_____*Temnogametum*
5. Conjugating cells involving the entire vegetative cell_____ 6
6. Conjugating cells becoming filled with pectic substances _____ Debarya
6. Conjugating cells not becoming filled with pectic substances, often containing granular residues_____ Mougeotia
7. Chloroplasts 2 central, polsterform bodies (without, or with very short, radiating processes); cytoplasmic granular material left in conjugating cells and in sporangia _____Zygogonium
7. Chloroplasts 2 star-shaped bodies in each cell (radiating processes long) _____ 8
8. Conjugating cells becoming filled with pectic substances; zygospores always formed in the tube, spheroidal or mostly quadrate, flattened or polsterform in side view _____Zygnemopsis
8. Conjugating cells not becoming filled with pectic substances; zygospores formed in the tube or in one of the gametangia, globose, ovate, or somewhat cylindric_____Zygnema

DEBARYA (Wittr.) Transeau 1934, p. 203

Filaments of slender, cylindrical cells; chloroplast a narrow axial plate containing 2–8 pyrenoids (these sometimes increasing in number prior to conjugation); conjugation scalariform by protuberances from both gametangia; zygospores variable in shape, ovate, quadrangular-ovate, or spheroidal, formed between the gametangia, the median wall yellow, brown, or blue, smooth or variously ornamented; gametangia becoming filled with pectic substances but without residues of cytoplasmic granules; reproduction also by aplanospores and akinetes.

This genus is so much like *Mougeotia* in its vegetative expression that identification cannot be made unless reproductive stages are at hand.

Key to the Species

Zygospores lenticular, with 3 transverse ridges,
  30–48μ in diameter, 42–72μ long_____*D. glyptosperma*
Zygospores compressed-globose, median spore wall
  tricarinate, 50–54μ in diameter, 52–65μ long_____*D. Ackleyana*

Debarya Ackleyana Transeau 1944, p. 244

Vegetative cells 12–15μ in diameter, 90–140μ long; chloroplast an axial ribbon with 8 pyrenoids; zygospores compressed-globose or ovate, median spore wall with 3 ridges, the lateral ones ruffled and with transverse corrugations between the ridges, middle keel 10μ wide and radially striated, polar walls finely pitted, 50–54μ in diameter, 52–65μ long.

Douglas Lake, Michigan.

Debarya glyptosperma (DeBary) Wittrock 1872, p. 35

Vegetative cells 9–16μ in diameter, 50–200μ long; chloroplast an axial plate with several pyrenoids; zygospores lenticular or compressed-ovate, median spore wall with 3 ridges which extend as projections at the poles, the ridges interconnected by transverse striations, 30–48μ in diameter, 42–72μ long.

Douglas Lake, Michigan.

MOUGEOTIA (C. A. Agardh) Wittrock 1872, p. 35

Unattached filaments of cylindrical cells without basal-distal differentiation (rarely with lateral anchoring rhizoidal branches near one end of the filament), forming entangled cottony masses, floating or caught among aquatic plants, sometimes attached and epiphytic on submerged culms of *Scirpus*, etc. Chloroplast occasionally rod-like, usually a broad axial plate, sometimes 2 plates connected by a bridge; with either an axial row of pyrenoids or with pyrenoids scattered over the surface; sometimes twisted in the midregion of the cell. Conjugation usually scalariform, the zygospore formed in the tube between the gametangia; the zygospore and tube sometimes enlarged so as to divide the gametangia,

[297]

giving the sporangium the appearance of being bounded by as many as 4 cells. Zygospore wall smooth or variously decorated; with residues in the gametangial cells outside the zygospore.

The genus should be compared with *Debarya*.

Key to the Species

[298]

Mougeotia abnormis Kisselew 1927, p. 301
[*M. notabilis* Hassall 1842, p. 46]
Pl. 70, Figs. 3, 4

Filaments forming sparse entanglements; vegetative cells long-cylindric, 10–21µ in diameter, 50–111–(250)µ long; chloroplast filling the length of the cell. Zygospores formed almost entirely within the conjugation tube but extending into and filling one of the gametangia; triangular or quadrate-ovate, with margins concave and median spore wall smooth; 24–26µ in diameter, 26–36µ long.

Our specimens are referred to *M. abnormis* on the basis of their agreement with the published partial description.

Among other algae in ponds and lake margins. Wis.

Mougeotia americana Transeau 1918, p. 237

Filaments slender; vegetative cells 4–5μ in diameter, 40–120μ long, becoming geniculate in conjugation. Zygospores formed in the tube, but extending into both the gametangia; irregularly quadrate, the margins concave or convex, with angles produced and truncately rounded; median spore wall colorless and smooth; 13–24μ in diameter, 18–32μ long; sporangium membrane becoming filled with pectic substance.

Douglas Lake, Michigan.

Mougeotia calcarea (Cleve) Wittrock 1872, p. 40

Vegetative cells 8–14μ in diameter, 40–280μ long, filaments becoming geniculate in conjugation. Zygospores formed in the tube but extending into the gametangia; globose or somewhat angular, the wall colorless and smooth; 25–30μ in diameter, or (if angular) 22–28μ in diameter, 30–50μ long.

Mich.

Mougeotia calcarea var. bicalyptra (Wittr.) Transeau 1926, p. 316

Vegetative cells 10–12μ in diameter, 30–110μ long; zygospores with thick end walls adjacent to the gametangia, extending into and at times completely dividing the gametangia.

Mich.

Mougeotia capucina (Bory) C. A. Agardh 1824, p. 84
Pl. 70, Figs. 5, 6

Filaments long and slender, forming purplish, cottony masses; vegetative cells 14–21μ in diameter, 70–150–(280)μ long; chloroplast a narrow axial band with 4–6 pyrenoids (sometimes as many as 12 or 16) in a single series. Zygospores formed in the tube but extending into and dividing both gametangia; irregularly quadrangular with concave margins, the wall brownish-violet and smooth; 50–74μ in diameter, 80–100μ long; with lamellate pectic substances deposited in the angles of the spore.

This species is often found fruiting during late summer along lake margins where water has receded. It forms purple films on moist substrates or purple cloud-like masses about the stems of *Chamaedaphne*.

A collection of *M. capucina* from a *Sphagnum* bog in Cheboygan County, Michigan, showed mature zygospores with minute punctations when viewed under oil immersion magnification (H. K. Phinney manuscript).

Entangled about reeds and in shallow water of beach pools; common in acid habitats and *Sphagnum* bogs. Mich., Wis.

Mougeotia cyanea Transeau 1926, p. 321

Vegetative cells $14–18–(20)\mu$ in diameter; chloroplast one-third to one-half the cell in length. Zygospores formed in the tube, not dividing the gametangia; compressed-globose; at right angles to the tube; wall blue, finely punctate; $30–40\mu$ in diameter, $38–48\mu$ long.

Douglas Lake, Michigan.

Mougeotia elegantula Wittrock 1872, p. 40
Pl. 70, Figs. 7, 8

Filaments very slender, becoming geniculate in conjugation; cells long-cylindric, $4–4.5\mu$ in diameter, $50–135\mu$ long; chloroplast a thin plate, not quite equalling the cell in length, containing 4–8 pyrenoids. Zygospores formed in the tube and dividing both gametangia; quadrate with concave margins, the wall smooth, hyaline; $18–25\mu$ in diameter.

Forming cottony masses in shallow water. Mich., Wis.

Mougeotia floridana Transeau *in*
Transeau, Tiffany, Taft, & Li 1934, p. 224

Vegetative cells $14–20\mu$ in diameter, $60–200\mu$ long; chloroplast with 6–8 pyrenoids in 1 series. Zygospores formed in the tube and extending into one gametangium; globose or triangular; the median wall yellow and smooth; $30–40\mu$ in diameter, $36–48\mu$ in long dimension.

Mich.

Mougeotia genuflexa (Dillw.) C. A. Agardh 1824, p. 83
Pl. 70, Figs. 9, 10

Filaments slender, frequently conjugated by geniculations but not producing zygospores; cells $25–38\mu$ in diameter, $50–100–(225)\mu$ long; chloroplast a broad band filling the length of the cell, with several pyrenoids. Zygospores formed either by lateral or (more rarely) scalariform conjugation, within the tube, not dividing the gametangia; quadrately-ovate or subglobose; median wall smooth and hyaline; $30–35–(40)\mu$ in diameter.

Among beds of vegetation in lagoons and lakes; rather common in *Sphagnum* bogs, growing luxuriantly in shaded habitats. Mich., Wis.

Mougeotia genuflexa var. *gracilis* Reinsch 1867, p. 215

Smaller than the typical; vegetative cells 15–24μ in diameter; zygospores 24–30μ in diameter.
Mich.

Mougeotia gracilima (Hass.) Wittrock 1872, p. 40

Vegetative cells 5–7μ in diameter, 55–140μ long. Zygospores dividing both gametangia; quadrate with concave margins to retuse angles, the wall finely verrucose; 20–25μ in diameter, 20–28μ long.
Mich.

Mougeotia Hirnii Transeau *in*
Transeau, Tiffany, Taft, & Li 1934, p. 218

Vegetative cells 25–28μ in diameter, 60–140μ long. Zygospores formed in the tube, not dividing the gametangia; ovate; the median spore wall smooth, yellow to brown; 40–48μ in diameter, 43–50μ long.
Mich.

Mougeotia laetevirens (A. Braun) Wittrock *in* Wittrock
& Nordstedt 1877, Algae Exsic. No. 58
Pl. 70, Figs. 11–14

Filaments forming light green, cottony growth; cells long-cylindric; (22)–27–40μ in diameter, up to 350μ long; chloroplast a broad band extending the full length of the cell, containing an indefinite number of irregularly arranged pyrenoids. Zygospores formed by scalariform conjugation in the tube, not dividing the gametangia; cylindric or ovate in front view, with lateral walls convex, free walls concave; median wall smooth and brown; 36–50μ in diameter, 45–73μ long.
Mich., Wis.

Mougeotia laevis (Kuetz.) Archer 1866, p. 272
[*Debarya laevis* (Kuetz.) West & West]
Pl. 70, Figs. 1, 2

Vegetative cells elongate-cylindric, 20–26μ in diameter, up to 5 times the diameter in length; chloroplast with 2–4 pyrenoids. Zygospores formed in the conjugation tube, not dividing the gametangia; ovate to broadly ellipsoid; outer wall smooth, median wall coarsely scrobiculate; 20–30–(36)μ in diameter, 42–50μ long.
Shallow water of ponds and ditches. Mich., Wis.

Mougeotia maltae Skuja 1926, p. 111

Vegetative cells 17–22μ in diameter, up to 160μ long; chloroplast with a single row of 4–8 pyrenoids. Zygospores formed in the tube,

not dividing the gametangia; globose; median spore wall blue and smooth; 30–35–(40)μ in diameter.
Mich.

Mougeotia micropora Taft *in*
Transeau, Tiffany, Taft, & Li 1934, p. 218
Pl. 74, Fig. 5

Vegetative cells 18–23μ in diameter, 60–160μ long; chloroplast with 4–6 pyrenoids in 1 series. Zygospores formed in the tube, not dividing the gametangia; globose, ovate, or compressed, parallel with the tube; median spore wall brown and punctate; 26–36μ in diameter, 26–30μ long; sporangium finally becoming inclosed by a thick layer of pectose.
Mich.

Mougeotia nummuloides (Hass.) DeToni 1889, p. 713

Vegetative cells 8–16μ in diameter, 32–160μ long. Zygospores formed in the tube, not dividing the gametangia; globose to ovate; median spore wall brown and scrobiculate; 17–37μ in diameter.
Mich.

Mougeotia parvula Hassall 1843, p. 434

Vegetative cells 6–12μ in diameter, 30–140μ long; chloroplast ⅔ the length of the cell, with 4–6 pyrenoids. Zygospores formed in the tube, not dividing the gametangia; globose; median spore wall brown and smooth; 13–24μ in diameter.
Mich.

Mougeotia pulchella Wittrock 1871, p. 88

Vegetative cells 24–29μ in diameter, 48–150μ long; chloroplast with pyrenoids in a single series. Zygospores formed in the tube, not dividing the gametangia; ovate or ellipsoid, with flattened ends; median spore wall brown and punctate; 28–35μ in diameter, 40–50μ long.
Mich.

Mougeotia punctata Wittrock 1867, p. 21
Pl. 71, Fig. 1

Filaments forming sparse, cottony growths; cells short- or long-cylindric, 8–10μ in diameter, (50)–115–135μ long; chloroplast a broad plate with 4–6 (or more ?) pyrenoids. Zygospores formed in the tube and dividing both gametangia; quadrate with retuse margins; outer spore wall coarsely punctate or pitted; (18)–29μ in diameter, 30–33–(38)μ long.
Among reeds in a small lake of soft water. Wis.

Mougeotia quadrangulata Hassall 1843, p. 434

Pl. 71, Figs. 3–5

Vegetative cells long-cylindric, 14–16μ in diameter, 135–150μ long; chloroplast a broad plate extending the full length of the cell, with 4–6 pyrenoids. Zygospores formed in the tube, dividing both gametangia; quadrate, with straight or slightly retuse margins, ovate when seen from the side; wall finely scrobiculate or punctate, colorless; 28–40μ in diameter.

In shallow water of lake margins and swamps. Mich., Wis.

Mougeotia recurva (Hass.) DeToni 1889, p. 714

Vegetative cells 12–18μ in diameter, 50–180μ long. Zygospores formed in the tube, not dividing the gametangia; globose; median spore wall brown and smooth; 23–33μ in diameter.

Mich.

Mougeotia Reinschii Transeau *in*

Transeau, Tiffany, Taft, & Li 1934, p. 224

Vegetative cells 9–13μ in diameter, 80–160μ long; chloroplast with 5–8 pyrenoids in a single series. Zygospores usually formed by lateral conjugation, or in the tube by scalariform conjugation, not dividing the gametangia; quadrangular-globose or rhomboid; median spore wall yellow and smooth; 25–30μ in diameter.

Mich.

Mougeotia robusta (DeBary) Wittrock *in*

Wittrock & Nordstedt 1884, Algae Exsic. No. 651

Pl. 74, Fig. 7

Vegetative cells 25–33μ in diameter, 75–260μ long; chloroplast with many irregularly placed pyrenoids. Zygospores formed in the tube, not dividing the gametangia; ovate to subglobose; median spore wall brown and scrobiculate; 35–41μ in diameter, 47–54μ long.

Mich.

Mougeotia robusta var. *biornata* Wittrock *in*

Wittrock & Nordstedt 1884, Algae Exsic. No. 615

Vegetative cells 27–30μ in diameter, 25–240μ long. Zygospores with outer wall inwardly verrucose, median spore wall scrobiculate; 30–38μ in diameter, 42–50μ long.

Mich.

Mougeotia scalaris Hassall 1842, p. 45

Pl. 71, Figs. 6, 7

Vegetative cells 20–27–(34)μ in diameter, 40–180μ long; chloroplast a broad plate with 4 pyrenoids. Zygospores formed in the tube by scalariform conjugation, not dividing the gametangia; globose or broadly ovate; walls smooth and golden brown; 25–31μ in diameter, 27–40μ long.

In littoral flora of many lakes. Mich., Wis.

Mougeotia sphaerocarpa Wolle 1887, p. 227
Pl. 74, Fig. 6

Vegetative cells 19–24μ in diameter, 60–120–(240)μ long; chloroplast with 4–6 pyrenoids. Zygospores formed variably, sometimes dividing one or both gametangia; subglobose to ovate; median spore wall brown and smooth; 40–45μ in diameter, or 36–40μ in diameter and 40–55μ long.

Mich.

Mougeotia tumidula Transeau 1914, p. 297
Pl. 71, Fig. 2

Vegetative cells long-cylindric, 6–8μ in diameter, up to 120μ long; chloroplast a broad plate with 4–8 pyrenoids in one series. Zygospores formed in the tube, dividing both gametangia; quadrangular; both inner and outer spore walls minutely scrobiculate; 22–26μ in diameter, 26–30μ long.

Mich.

Mougeotia varians (Wittr.) Czurda 1932, p. 79
Pl. 71, Figs. 11, 12

Vegetative cells 25–27μ in diameter; chloroplast a broad band entirely filling the length of the cell, with 4 pyrenoids. Zygospores formed in the tube, dividing one of the gametangia; cylindric or drum-shaped, the free walls concave, the walls adjoining the gametangia convex; median wall smooth and brown; 48–60μ in diameter, 60–70–(78)μ long.

This species is smaller than *M. laetevirens* (A. Braun) Wittr. and also differs in that the zygospore completely fills the gametangial cell, whereas in *M. laetevirens* the spore is formed entirely within the conjugation tube.

In the tychoplankton of soft water lakes. Mich., Wis.

Mougeotia ventricosa (Wittr.) Collins 1912, p. 69

Vegetative cells 5–8–(9)μ in diameter, 100–140μ long. Zygospores unknown. Aplanospores obliquely ellipsoid to subglobose; median spore wall yellow and smooth; 12–24μ in diameter, 16–29μ long.

Mich.

Mougeotia virescens (Hass.) Borge 1913, p. 43
Pl. 72, Figs. 1, 2

Vegetative cells 8–9–(11)μ in diameter, 30–80–(130)μ long. Zygospores formed in the tube, dividing both gametangia; quadrate with concave margins and rounded angles; wall smooth and colorless; 29–34.5μ in diameter.

Our specimens agree with *M. virescens* except that the vegetative cells are a little longer than described.

In a small pond, Sawyer County, Wisconsin.

Mougeotia viridis (Kuetz.) Wittrock 1872, p. 39
Pl. 71, Figs. 8–10

Filaments slender, becoming geniculate in conjugation; cells 6–8μ in diameter, 24–40–(80)μ long; chloroplast a broad plate extending the full length of the cell with 4–6 pyrenoids. Zygospores formed in the tube, dividing both gametangia; quadrate, the sides concave, corners retuse; median spore wall smooth and colorless; 24–32μ in diameter.

This is the most common species of *Mougeotia* in our collections. It appears in many shallow water situations and in roadside trickles, seeps from banks, etc.

Tychoplankter; in several lakes; in swamps. Mich., Wis.

MOUGEOTIOPSIS Palla 1894, p. 228

Filaments slender, composed of short cylindrical cells; 1 axial, plate-like, folded chloroplast without pyrenoids; conjugation scalariform, the zygospore formed in the tube, protruding into one or both of the gametangia and not cut off from them by a wall; entire contents of the gametangial cells used in the formation of the zygospore; gametangial cells not becoming filled with lamellate pectic substances.

Mougeotiopsis should be compared with *Debarya*, from which it may be differentiated in the vegetative condition by the presence of pyrenoids in the latter. In the reproductive phase *Mougeotiopsis* may be identified by the lack of pectic substances in the old gametangial cells. In our specimens a gelatinous sheath was sometimes present about the filaments.

Mougeotiopsis calospora Palla 1894, p. 228
Pl. 69, Figs. 4–6

Filaments light green, long and loosely entangled. Cells short-cylindric, sometimes quadrate in the vegetative state, becoming elongate in conjugation; 12–14μ in diameter, 14–18μ long. Chloroplast a broad, folded axial plate, almost as long as the cell (sometimes ulotrichaceous in appearance). Zygospores formed in the connecting tube by scalariform conjugation, and extending into the gametangia; oblong or rectangular-oblong; outer spore wall smooth, middle wall with deep pits; $22-25\mu$ in diameter, $33-38\mu$ long (rarely longer).

This species was once described as *Mesogerron fluitans* Brand and included in the Ulotrichaceae because of its *Ulothrix*-like chloroplast. Our specimens were found only in the vegetative condition, but this plant is so distinctive that it can be assigned to *M. calospora*.

Rare in several lakes and *Sphagnum* bogs. The plants seems to be confined to soft water habitats. Mich., Wis.

SPIROGYRA Link 1820, p. 5

Filaments long and unbranched, usually without basal-distal differentiation but sometimes with rhizoidal branches developing laterally where the filament comes in contact with substrate. Cells cylindrical, short, to very long in some species, with plane (even and smooth), replicate, or colligate (exterior H-shaped piece) end walls. Chloroplast a parietal band or ribbon which may be spirally twisted ½ to 3 (rarely 8) turns, or may be nearly straight (as in genus *Sirogonium,* not separated here); 1–16 chloroplasts in a cell. Conjugation either lateral or scalariform, usually by the formation of tubes, rarely by geniculate bendings of the filament so that conjugating cells are brought into juxaposition. Zygospores formed in one of the gametangial cells, which may become swollen, depending upon the species; zygospores ovate, subglobose, ellipsoid, or oblong, with 3-layered wall, of which the middle layer may be smooth or decorated and colored. Aplanospores uncommon, similar to the zygospores in shape and wall markings; rarely aplanospores alone occur.

Spirogyra is the largest genus in number of species and the most common of Zygnemataceae. It is identifiable in the field by its bright green, cottony growths and its slippery mucilaginous texture. In hand, a mass of filaments is easily drawn out into a long fine thread.

In deep cold springs and pools *Spirogyra* flourishes abundantly and vegetatively, forming enormous green 'clouds' several feet in diameter in favorable habitats. In shallow warm water it has a tendency to form floating mats, with conjugation and subsequent disintegration of the filaments occurring. During conjugation the plant masses become dull, dirty-green or brownish, often with a burnt-orange tinge, which is almost invariably macroscopic evidence that reproduction is in progress. Some species of *Spirogyra* seem to prefer hard water habitats with a pH between 7.0 and 8.5 (*S. crassa*, for example). Others are always found in shallow water which is rich in organic acids and where there is a considerable amount of disintegrating vegetation.

As in most other genera of the Zygnemataceae, species identification cannot be made without mature zygospores, or in some cases aplanospores. Of the 258 or more known species of *Spirogyra*, only 55 have been found fruiting in our region, hence the following key is greatly limited.

In those species of *Spirogyra* which have a large number of closely spiraled chloroplasts a count may be made easily by focusing on a band at the upper side of the cell, counting this as 1. Then by focusing down, the number of bands which are seen to be crossed by this one and added to it will give the total number of chloroplasts.

Key to the Species

Spirogyra aequinoctialis G. S. West 1907, p. 105
Pl. 72, Figs. 3, 4

Vegetative cells long-cylindric, 23–29μ in diameter, up to 150μ long, with plane end walls. Chloroplasts 2–3, with crenate margins and large pyrenoids, making 1 to 1½ turns. Conjugation by tubes from both gametangia, the receiving cells becoming symmetrically inflated. Zygospores ovate or elongate-ellipsoid, with broadly rounded poles; median spore wall with deep pits; (40)–41–50μ in diameter, (52)–72–77μ long.

In shallow water of lake margins. Wis.

Spirogyra affinis (Hass.) Petit 1880, p. 18

Filaments of rather stout cylindrical cells, 27–30μ in diameter, up to 90μ long, with plane end walls. Chloroplast solitary, making 1 to 3 1/2 turns. Conjugation mostly lateral, but also scalariform, tubes from both cells; sporangia inflated on both sides. Zygospores ellipsoid; wall layers smooth; 28–33μ in diameter, 30–50μ long.

Common in ponds and swamps. Mich., Wis.

Spirogyra Borgeana Transeau 1915, p. 23
Pl. 77, Figs. 7, 8

Filaments of cylindrical cells, usually slender, 30–35μ in diameter, up to 200μ long, with plane end walls. Chloroplast solitary, making 1½ to 5 turns. Conjugation scalariform; sporangia inflated only on the outer side. Zygospores ellipsoid; wall layers smooth; 33–40μ in diameter, 54–70μ long.

Mich.

Spirogyra borysthenica Kasanowsky & Smirnoff 1913, p. 139

Filaments of slender cylindrical cells, 30–40μ in diameter, 130–450μ long, with replicate end walls; chloroplasts 3–4, making ½ to 2 1/2 turns. Conjugation scalariform, tubes from both cells, fertile cells swollen to twice the diameter of the vegetative cells. Zygospores ellipsoid to fusiform; median wall with papillae; 52–63μ in diameter, 100–180μ long.

Mich.

Spirogyra catenaeformis (Hass.) Kuetzing 1849, p. 438

Filaments of rather stout cylindrical cells, 24–27–(32)μ in diameter and up to 5 diameters in length, with plane end walls; chloroplast solitary, making 1 to 6 turns. Conjugation by tubes from both gametangia; fertile cells swollen; the sporangia inflated on both sides. Zygospores ellipsoid; wall layers smooth; 24–30μ in diameter, 55–90μ long.

Mich., Wis.

[311]

Spirogyra circumlineata Transeau 1914, p. 293
Pl. 74, Fig. 8

Filaments of rather stout cells, 40–50μ in diameter and 3–6 times their diameter in length, with plane end walls; chloroplast solitary, making 4 to 8 turns. Conjugation by tubes from both gametangia; sporangia inflated mostly on the inner (conjugating) side. Zygospores ellipsoid; wall layers smooth; 40–50μ in diameter, 70–125μ long.
Mich.

Spirogyra Collinsii (Lewis) Printz 1927, p. 372
Pl. 77, Figs. 4–6

Filaments of rather slender cells, 15–24μ in diameter, and about 5 times as long as broad, with plane end walls; chloroplast solitary. Conjugation scalariform and lateral, the tube formed by the male gametangium only; sporangia inflated slightly on both sides to contain the spore; the male gametangium formed by a partitioning off of one end of a vegetative cell. Zygospores ellipsoid; median wall coarsely punctate; 35μ in diameter, 60μ long.
Mich., Wis.

Spirogyra communis (Hass.) Kuetzing 1849, p. 439

Vegetative cells slender, cylindric, (18)–20–26μ in diameter, (35)–65–100μ long, with plane end walls; chloroplast solitary, making 1½ to 4 turns. Conjugation by tubes from both gametangia; fertile cells cylindric. Zygospores ellipsoid, with narrowly rounded poles; median spore wall smooth, colorless, or yellowish in age; 19–23μ in diameter, 36–69μ long.
Common in ponds and swamps. Mich., Wis.

Spirogyra condensata (Vauch.) Kuetzing 1843, p. 279
Pl. 72, Figs. 5, 6

Filaments of rather stout vegetative cells, (48)–53–62μ in diameter, 45–94–(120)μ long, with plane end walls; chloroplast solitary, making ½ to 4 turns. Conjugation by tubes from both gametangia, or lateral; fertile cells cylindric. Zygospores ellipsoid; median spore wall smooth and brown; 34–38μ in diameter, 50–75μ long.
In alkaline bog lakes. Mich.

Spirogyra crassa Kuetzing 1843, p. 280
Pl. 72, Figs. 7, 8

Filaments coarse, stout, feeling glassy to the touch; vegetative cells cells (133)–140–160μ in diameter, quadrate or 2 times the diameter in length, with plane end walls; chloroplasts 6–12 (usually 8–10), slender, making ½ to 1 turn. Conjugation by tubes from both gametangia; fertile cells cylindric. Zygospores ovate or laterally flattened, the poles broadly rounded; median spore wall finely pitted and brown; (80)–120–140µ in diameter, 166–175µ long.

Forming dark green masses of coarse filaments in quiet water of bogs and pooled streams; apparently specific for hard water habitats. Mich., Wis.

Spirogyra daedaleoides Czurda 1932, p. 180
Pl. 72, Figs. 9–11

Filaments of rather stout cylindrical cells, 30–35µ in diameter, 70–148–(240)µ long, with plane end walls; chloroplast solitary, making 3 to 4 turns. Conjugation scalariform by tubes from both gametangia, or lateral; fertile cells becoming inflated. Zygospores ellipsoid or ovate-ellipsoid; median spore wall coarsely reticulate and brown; 35–(44)µ in diameter, (46)–59–77µ long.

In hard water lakes. Mich., Wis.

Spirogyra decimina (Mueller) Kuetzing 1843, p. 280

Filaments of rather stout cylindric cells, 34–40µ in diameter, 60–125–(150)µ long, with plane end walls; chloroplasts 2 (rarely 3) in each cell, broad, making 2 turns. Conjugation by tubes from both gametangia; fertile cells cylindric. Zygospores cylindric-ovate, rarely subglobose; median spore wall smooth; 31–40µ in diameter, 31–68–(75)µ long.

Forming cloudy masses on false bottom of an alkaline bog lake. Mich., Wis.

Spirogyra dubia Kuetzing 1855, p. 8. Tab. Phyc. V

Filaments of rather stout cylindrical cells, (40)–43–50µ in diameter and up to 2½ times the diameter in length, with plane end walls. Chloroplasts 2 (sometimes 3), making 1 to 3 turns. Conjugation scalariform by tubes from both gametangia; fertile cells inflated. Zygospores globose or ovate; median wall smooth; 40µ in diameter, up to 80µ long.

Mich., Wis.

Spirogyra ellipsospora Transeau 1914, p. 294
Pl. 72, Fig. 12

Filaments of stout cylindric cells, 125–150µ in diameter, 125–230–(500)µ long, with plane end walls; chloroplasts 3–8 narrow bands, making ½ to 5 turns. Conjugation by tubes from both gametangia;

fertile cells cylindric. Zygospores ellipsoid or cylindric-ellipsoid, not compressed; spore walls smooth, becoming yellow-brown in age; 100–140μ in diameter, 160–255μ long.

This species is readily differentiated from other large forms in our collections (*S. crassa* and *S. maxima*) by the large ellipsoid spores with smooth walls. In our region it has not been collected in pure growths as have many other species of the genus.

Among other filamentous algae in shallow water. Mich., Wis.

Spirogyra fallax (Hansg.) Wille 1900a, p. 16
Pl. 77, Fig. 10

Filaments of rather slender cylindrical cells, 33–45μ in diameter and up to 8 times the diameter in length, with replicate (rarely plane) end walls; chloroplasts 3–5, making $\frac{1}{2}$ to $1\frac{1}{2}$ turns (sometimes nearly straight). Conjugation scalariform, the tubes short but formed from both gametangia; fertile cells inflated (shortened). Zygospores ellipsoid; wall layers smooth; 45–60μ in diameter.
Mich.

Spirogyra Farlowii Transeau 1914, p. 291

Filaments of rather long cylindrical cells 24–30μ in diameter and up to 180μ long, with replicate end walls; chloroplast solitary, making $2\frac{1}{2}$ to 6 turns. Conjugation scalariform by tubes from both gametangia; fertile cells fusiform, inflated. Zygospores ellipsoid; median spore wall smooth; 32–45μ in diameter, 48–93μ long.
Mich.

Spirogyra flavescens (Hass.) Kuetzing 1849, p. 438

Filaments of slender cells, 11–13μ in diameter and up to 4 times the diameter in length, with plane end walls; chloroplast solitary, making 1 to 2 turns. Conjugation scalariform by tubes from both gametangia, the fertile cells inflated. Zygospores ovate to cylindric-ovate; median spore wall smooth; 20μ in diameter, up to 30μ long.
Mich.

Spirogyra fluviatilis Hilse *in* Rabenhorst
1864–1868, Algen No. 1476
Pl. 73, Figs. 4, 5

Filaments of rather stout cells, (30)–36–40–(45)μ in diameter and 5–6 times the diameter in length, with plane end walls; chloroplasts 3–5, making $1\frac{1}{2}$ to $2\frac{1}{2}$ turns. Conjugation scalariform by tubes from both gametangia, fertile cells becoming inflated. Zygospores ovate; median spore wall wrinkled and irregularly pitted; 42–44–(65)μ in diameter, 59–77–(110)μ long.

In pooled streams; common in lakes and ponds. Mich., Wis.

Spirogyra Fuellebornei Schmidle 1903, p. 76

Pl. 73, Fig. 6

Filaments of stout cylindrical cells, 40–44μ in diameter, 120–200–(240)μ long, with plane end walls; chloroplasts 3–4, making 1 to 2 turns. Conjugation by tubes from both gametangia; fertile cells cylindric. Zygospores ellipsoid, with sharply rounded poles; median spore wall smooth and brown; 32–40μ in diameter, 50–80μ long.

In an alkaline bog lake. Wis.

Spirogyra gracilis (Hass.) Kuetzing 1849, p. 438

Filaments of rather stout cells, 16–24μ in diameter and up to 5 times the diameter in length, with plane end walls; chloroplast solitary, making ½ to 3 turns. Conjugation scalariform by tubes from both gametangia; sporangium inflated on the conjugation side only. Zygospores ellipsoid; median spore wall smooth; 27–30μ in diameter and up to 60μ long.

Mich.

Spirogyra gratiana Transeau 1938, p. 528

Pl. 74, Fig. 9

Filaments of elongate-cylindric cells, 28–33μ in diameter, 144–400μ long, with replicate end walls; chloroplasts (2)–3–(4). Conjugation lateral or scalariform by tubes from both gametangia; fertile cells cylindric or merely enlarged. Zygospores ellipsoid or cylindric-ellipsoid; median spore wall smooth and yellow; 35–47μ in diameter, 108–223μ long.

Rock pool from north shore of Lake Superior.

Spirogyra Grevilleana (Hass.) Kuetzing 1849, p. 438

Pl. 74, Fig. 11

Filaments of rather slender cells, 21–25–(28)μ in diameter and up to 10 times the diameter in length, with replicate end walls; chloroplast solitary (rarely 2 in each cell), making 4–5 (up to 9) turns. Conjugation scalariform, the tubes formed from the male gametangium only; fertile cells inflated on the conjugation side. Zygospores ovate; median spore wall smooth; 30–36μ in diameter and up to 2½ times the diameter in length.

Mich.

Spirogyra inconstans Collins 1912, p. 74

Filaments of rather slender cells, 30μ in diameter and up to 15 times the diameter in length, with replicate end walls; chloroplasts 3–4 (rarely only 2), making 1 to 3 turns. Conjugation scalariform

by tubes from both gametangia; fertile cells inflated. Zygospores ellipsoid; median wall reticulate; 45–75μ in diameter and up to 125μ long.
Mich.

Spirogyra inflata (Vauch.) Kuetzing 1843, p. 279

Filaments of rather slender cells, 15–20μ in diameter and up to 8 times the diameter in length, with replicate end walls; chloroplast solitary (rarely 2), making 3 to 8 turns. Conjugation scalariform by tubes from both gametangia; fertile cells inflated, fusiform. Zygospores ellipsoid; median spore wall smooth; 42–48μ in diameter and up to 96μ long.
Mich., Wis.

Spirogyra Juergensii Kuetzing 1845, p. 222
Pl. 73, Figs. 7, 8

Filaments of moderately stout, long or short cylindrical cells, 24–26–(30)μ in diameter, 60–125μ long, with plane end walls; chloroplast solitary, making 2 to 4 turns. Conjugation by tubes from both gametangia; fertile cells cylindric. Zygospores ellipsoid; median spore wall smooth and brown; 28–30–(33)μ in diameter, 40–75μ long.
Floating mats in a marsh; in swamps and ditches. Mich., Wis.

Spirogyra jugalis (Fl. Dan.) Kuetzing 1845, p. 223

Filaments of large, stout cells, 90–100μ in diameter, 1–1½ times the diameter in length, with plane end walls; chloroplasts 3–4, making 1 to 2 turns. Conjugation scalariform by tubes from both gametangia; fertile cells cylindric. Zygospores ellipsoid or cylindric-ellipsoid; wall layers smooth; 87–108μ in diameter and 1½ times the diameter in length.
Mich.

Spirogyra laxa Kuetzing 1849, p. 438

Filaments of rather stout cells, 30–33–(40)μ in diameter and up to 230μ long, with replicate end walls; chloroplast solitary, making 3 to 5 turns. Conjugation by tubes from both gametangia; fertile cells cylindric. Zygospores ellipsoid; median spore wall smooth and yellow; 30–33μ in diameter, 60-82μ long.
Mich.

Spirogyra longata (Vauch.) Kuetzing 1843, p. 279

Filaments of moderately stout cells, 20–36μ in diameter and up to 10 times the diameter in length, with plane end walls; chloroplast solitary, making 2 to 5 turns; conjugation by tubes from both game-

tangia; fertile cells cylindric. Zygospores ovate or elongate-ovate; median spore wall smooth but with a longitudinal suture, brownish; 30–(38)μ in diameter, 50–(83)μ long.
Mich.

Spirogyra majuscula Kuetzing 1849, p. 441
Pl. 74, Fig. 10

Filaments of stout cells, 50–80μ in diameter, 80–500μ long, with plane end walls; chloroplasts 3–8, nearly straight or making less than ½ turn. Conjugation by tubes from both gametangia; fertile cells cylindric (sometimes slightly swollen). Zygospores lenticular or spheroidal, laterally compressed; median spore wall smooth and brown; 57–72μ in diameter, 45–60μ wide.
Mich.

Spirogyra maxima (Hass.) Wittrock 1882, p. 57

Filaments of rather stout, short-cylindric cells (118)–145–153μ in diameter, with plane end walls; chloroplasts 6–8, making ½ to ¾ turn. Conjugation scalariform by tubes from both gametangia; fertile cells cylindric. Zygospores compressed-globose or lentil-shaped; median spore wall finely reticulate; 100–120μ in diameter, 70–95μ wide.
In an alkaline bog lake. Mich., Wis.

Spirogyra micropunctata Transeau 1915, p. 27
Pl. 73, Fig. 9

Filaments of fairly stout cells, 30–33–(36)μ in diameter, 108–114–(300)μ long, with plane end walls; chloroplast solitary, making 2 to 4 turns. Conjugation scalariform by tubes from the male gametangium only; fertile cells becoming slightly inflated. Zygospores ellipsoid, the poles broadly rounded; median spore wall finely and densely punctate; 37–42μ in diameter, 57–70–(100)μ long.
In bogs and ditches. Mich.

Spirogyra mirabilis (Hass.) Kuetzing 1849, p. 438
Pl. 77, Fig. 1

Filaments of slender cells, 24–26–(27)μ in diameter and up to 10 times the diameter in length, with plane end walls; chloroplast solitary, making 4 to 7 turns. Conjugation by tubes from both gametangia; fertile cells inflated. Zygospores ovate to ellipsoid; median spore wall smooth and brown; 24–29μ in diameter, 50–83μ long.
Mich.

Spirogyra nitida (Dillw.) Link 1833, p. 262
Pl. 73, Fig. 10

Filaments of rather stout cells, 60–80µ in diameter, 90–166–(170)µ long, with plane end walls; chloroplasts 3–5, making ½ to 1½ turns. Conjugation by tubes from both gametangia; fertile cells cylindric. Zygospores ellipsoid or cylindric-ellipsoid, with sharply rounded poles; median spore wall smooth and brown; 60–77–(85)µ in diameter, 90–118–(170)µ long.

Tychoplankter; in shallow water of lakes and marshes. Mich., Wis.

Spirogyra novae-angliae Transeau 1915, p. 26
Pl. 75, Figs. 1–3

Filaments of rather stout cells, 49–60µ in diameter, 140–240–(390)µ long, with plane end walls; chloroplasts 3–5, broad, making 1½ to 4 turns. Conjugation by tubes from both gametangia; fertile cells cylindric. Zygospores ovate to ovate-ellipsoid; median spore wall irregularly reticulate and brown; 50–60µ in diameter, 82–92–(120)µ long.

Forming sparse floating clots in several lakes. Mich., Wis.

Spirogyra orientalis West & West 1907, p. 186

Vegetative cells 30–31µ in diameter, 90–160µ long, with plane end walls; chloroplasts 3, making 1 to 1½ turns. Conjugation scalariform by tubes from both gametangia; fertile cells inflated. Zygospores ellipsoid; median spore wall finely scrobiculate; 32–42µ in diameter, 61–67µ long.

Mich.

Spirogyra porangabae Transeau 1938, p. 525
Pl. 77, Figs. 2, 3

Vegetative cells 11–14.5µ in diameter, 65–145µ long, with plane end walls; chloroplast solitary, making 4 to 9 turns. Conjugation scalariform by tubes from both gametangia; fertile cells slightly inflated (or merely enlarged to contain the spore). Zygospores ellipsoid; median spore wall irregularly punctate when mature, yellow; 21–27µ in diameter, 47–54µ long.

Mich.

Spirogyra porticalis (Muell.) Cleve 1868, p. 22
Pl. 75, Fig. 10

Filaments of rather stout cells, 40–50µ in diameter, 68–200µ long, with plane end walls; chloroplast solitary, making 3 to 4 turns. Conjugation scalariform by tubes from both gametangia; fertile cells sometimes inflated. Zygospores ovate to subglobose-ovate; median spore wall smooth and yellow; 38–50μ in diameter, 50–83μ long.

Common in shallow water of lakes, swamps, and roadside ditches. Mich., Wis.

Spirogyra pratensis Transeau 1914, p. 292
Pl. 75, Figs. 4–6

Filaments of rather slender cells, 17–20μ in diameter, 80–95–(240)μ long, with plane end walls; chloroplast solitary (rarely 2), making 1 to 8 turns. Conjugation by tubes from both gametangia; fertile cells inflated. Zygospores ellipsoid to subcylindric-ovate; median spore wall smooth, yellow at maturity; 24–36μ in diameter, 50–60–(70)μ long.

In a small pooled stream. Mich.

Spirogyra protecta Wood 1872, p. 165

Vegetative cells 32–36–(44)μ in diameter, 120–475μ long, with replicate end walls; chloroplast solitary making 4 to 5 turns. Conjugation by tubes from both gametangia; fertile cells cylindric or slightly enlarged, sterile cells becoming inflated during conjugation. Zygospores ovate or cylindric-ovate; median spore wall smooth and yellow, inner scrobiculate; 36–42–(50)μ in diameter, 66–130μ long.

Mich.

Spirogyra pseudofloridana Prescott 1944, p. 360
Pl. 75, Figs. 7–9

Filaments of stout cells, 51–60μ in diameter and 3–5 times the diameter in length, with plane end walls; chloroplasts 4 (rarely 5), narrow, making ½ to 1½ loose turns. Conjugation by geniculate bending of filaments, without tubes being formed; gametangia becoming shortened and thickened and apparently cut off from vegetative cells; fertile cells becoming slightly inflated. Zygospores ellipsoid, with narrowly rounded poles; median spore wall roughened with irregular granulations and wrinkles (not regularly reticulate), brown; 63–70μ in diameter, 100–120μ long.

This species should be compared with S. *illinoisensis* Transeau and S. *floridana* Transeau. It is smaller than the former and has fewer chloroplasts. From the latter it differs chiefly in the decoration of the mesospore.

Floating in a lagoon. Wis.

Spirogyra reflexa Transeau 1915, p. 28

Vegetative cells 30–40μ in diameter, 120–300μ long, with plane end walls; chloroplast solitary, making 3 to 8 turns. Conjugation by tubes from the male gametangia only; fertile cells grouped, in series of 2–4. Zygospores ellipsoid; median spore wall smooth and yellow-brown; 44–54μ in diameter, 90–150μ long.

Mich.

Spirogyra rhizobrachialis Jao 1936a, p. 57
Pl. 76, Figs. 1, 2

Filaments of rather stout cells (40)–45–59μ in diameter, 114–240μ long, with plane end walls; chloroplasts 3–5, crenate and deeply toothed on the margins, making 1½ to 2½ turns. Conjugation by tubes from both gametangia; fertile cells cylindric, sterile cells frequently forming tubes which develop highly branched rhizoidal processes at their ends. Zygospores ellipsoid; median spore wall irregularly and coarsely reticulate, brown; (38)–40–62μ in diameter, 111μ long.

Our specimens agree closely with this species in habit of growth and spore characters, but vary in dimensions from the original description.

Bright green cottony masses in soft water lakes. Wis.

Spirogyra rivularis (Hass.) Rabenhorst 1868, p. 243

Vegetative cells 36–41μ in diameter, 100–400μ long, with plane end walls; chloroplasts 2–3, making 2½ to 3½ turns. Conjugation by tubes from both gametangia; fertile cells cylindric. Zygospores ellipsoid or cylindric-ellipsoid; median spore wall smooth.

Mich.

Spirogyra scrobiculata (Stock.) Czurda 1932, p. 182
Pl. 76, Figs. 3, 4

Filaments of short cells, 30–34–(40)μ in diameter, (30)–90–136μ long, with plane end walls; chloroplast solitary, making 1 to 5 turns. Conjugation by tubes from both gametangia, the fertile cells inflated on the conjugating side; zygospores ellipsoid, median spore wall deeply pitted and brown; 33–35–(38)μ in diameter, 44–50–(68)μ long.

Among other algae in swamps. Mich., Wis.

Spirogyra singularis Nordstedt 1880, p. 23

Vegetative cells 29–39μ in diameter, with plane end walls; chloroplast solitary. Conjugation by tubes from both gametangia; fertile cells cylindric. Zygospores ellipsoid or cylindric-ellipsoid, not laterally compressed; median spore wall smooth; 27–37μ in diameter.

Mich.

Spirogyra Spreeiana Rabenhorst 1863, Algen No. 988

Pl. 77, Fig. 9

Vegetative cells 18–21–(25)μ in diameter and up to 25 times the diameter in length; end walls replicate; chloroplast solitary, making 1 1/2 to 4 turns, Conjugation tubes formed from the male gametangia only; fertile cells inflated on both sides. Zygospores ellipsoid, median spore wall smooth and yellowish; 30–36μ in diameter, 55–100μ long.

Mich.

Spirogyra stictica (Engl. Bot.) Wille 1884, p. 34

Pl. 76, Figs. 5–7

Filaments of short or long cells, 38–56μ in diameter, 80–300μ long, with plane end walls; chloroplasts 2–6, straight or making ½ turn, Conjugation by geniculate bending of the filaments; connecting tubes not formed; the fertile cells becoming slightly swollen. Zygospores ellipsoid; median spore wall smooth; 41–64μ in diameter, 75–118μ long.

In shallow water of lake margins, and in swamps. Mich., Wis.

Spirogyra subsalsa Kuetzing 1845, p. 222

Pl. 73, Figs. 1–3

Filaments of slender cells 26–28μ in diameter, (35)–148μ long, with plane end walls; chloroplast solitary, making 1½ to 3 turns. Conjugation by tubes from both gametangia; fertile cells becoming slightly swollen. Zygospores ellipsoid; median spore wall smooth, inner irregularly reticulate (?), and brown; (18)–33–35μ in diameter, (30)–55–59μ long.

This species should be compared with S. *esthonica* (Skuja) Czurda and S. *daedalea* Lag., from which two species it differs in fundamental details of the spore characters.

In swamps and other shallow water habitats. Wis.

Spirogyra suecica (Borge) Transeau 1934a, p. 420

Vegetative cells 26–29μ in diameter, 80–175μ long, with plane end walls; chloroplast solitary. Conjugation by tubes from both gametangia; fertile cells inflated on both sides. Zygospores ovate; median spore wall smooth; 32–39μ in diameter, 38–60μ long.

Mich.

Spirogyra sulcata Blum 1943, p. 783

Filaments of rather stout cells 37–46μ in diameter, 50–160μ long, with plane end walls; chloroplast solitary (rarely 2), making 2 to 5 turns. Conjugation by tubes from both gametangia, which are shortened, the receiving cell becoming somewhat swollen. Zygospores ovate; median spore wall reticulate and brown; 43–46μ in diameter, 52–62μ long.

Wis.

Spirogyra tenuissima (Hass.) Kuetzing 1849, p. 437

Vegetative cells (8)–9–12–(15)μ in diameter, 4–12 times the diameter in length with replicate end walls; chloroplast solitary, making 3 to 5½ turns. Conjugation by tubes from both gametangia; fertile cells fusiform, inflated. Zygospores ellipsoid; median spore wall smooth and yellowish; 30μ in diameter.

Mich.

Spirogyra Teodoresci Transeau 1934a, p. 420

Vegetative cells 23–30μ in diameter, 42–90μ long, with plane end walls; chloroplast solitary, making 1 to 5 turns. Conjugation by tubes from both gametangia; fertile cells greatly inflated on the conjugating side. Zygospores ellipsoid, varying to ovate or globose; median spore wall smooth; 26–33μ in diameter, 45–55μ long.

Mich.

Spirogyra triplicata (Collins) Transeau 1944, p. 243

Vegetative cells 34–40(48)μ in diameter, 2–4 times the diameter in length, with plane end walls; chloroplasts 3, making 1 to 2 turns. Conjugation by tubes from both gametangia; fertile cells cylindric. Zygospores ovate to subglobose, not compressed; median spore wall smooth; 34–48μ in diameter, 48–54μ long.

Mich.

Spirogyra varians (Hass.) Kuetzing 1849, p. 439
Pl. 76, Figs. 11, 12

Filaments of short cells, (28)–33–(40)μ in diameter, 51–85–(120)μ long, with plane end walls; chloroplast solitary, making ½ to 4 turns. Conjugation by tubes from both gametangia; fertile cells inflated on the conjugation side only. Zygospores ellipsoid or ovate-ellipsoid; median spore wall smooth; 32–40μ in diameter, 50–63–(100)μ long.

Mich.

Spirogyra Weberi Kuetzing 1843, p. 279
Pl. 76, Figs. 8–10

Filaments of long cells, 19–30μ in diameter, 80–480μ long, with replicate end walls; chloroplast solitary, broad, making 3 to 6½ turns. Conjugation by tubes from both gametangia; fertile cells cylindric. Zygospores cylindric-ovate; median spore wall smooth and brown; 21–25μ in diameter, 30–95μ long.

This species has never been found in pure growth; it seems always to be mixed with other filamentous algae. The unusually long, slender cells and the long ovate spores are distinctive features. ,

Entangled among other algae in many lakes and swamps; common. Mich., Wis.

ZYGNEMA C. A. Agardh 1824, p. 77

Unbranched filaments of short or long cylindrical cells with plane end walls, inclosed by a soft (usually) mucilaginous sheath, rarely with irregular rhizoidal outgrowths of a few cells when in contact with the substrate; chloroplasts 2 (rarely 4) axial, stellate masses, each containing a large central pyrenoid with a conspicuous starch sheath. Conjugation mostly scalariform, with the zygospores formed in the connecting tube, or rarely in one of the gametangia, but not cut off by membranes from the gametangial cells. Zygospores spherical, ovate, or ellipsoid, with a thick, 3-layered wall, the outer and middle layers variously sculptured with scrobiculations and punctations. Asexual reproduction by aplanospores and akinetes.

The genus *Zygnema* contains about 85 known species, and many more of these certainly occur in our region than can be listed now. Numerous collections of *Zygema* were made in the sterile condition and are, therefore, unidentifiable. One species was invariably found in soft water lakes attached about the culms of *Scirpus* spp., where it formed pale green, cottony masses. Although this species was collected repeatedly at several different seasons no fruiting specimens were found. This is interpreted as having a distinct ecological significance, and several possible explanations present themselves. One of these has to do with water chemistry. Species of both Zygnemataceae and Oedogoniaceae were found to flourish vegetatively in soft water lakes but were scarcely ever collected in a fruiting condition. In hard water lakes or in shallow ponds where there was a high concentration of organic matter and organic acids, these plants are more luxuriant and fruit abundantly.

Key to the Species

1. Zygospores not formed; conjugation unknown; reproduction by aplanospores; vegetative cells 44–54μ in diameter................................*Z. sterile*
1. Zygospores formed by conjugation; aplanospores present or absent; vegetative cells smaller.. 2
2. Spore wall blue when mature... 3
2. Spore wall yellow, yellow-brown, or colorless when mature 6
3. Spores formed in one of the gametangia......................*Z. chalybeospermum*
3. Spores formed in the conjugation tube, extending into the gametangia or not.. 4
4. Median spore wall smooth......................................*Z. cyanosporum*
4. Median spore wall punctate 5

Zygnema carinatum Taft *in* Transeau, Tiffany, Taft, and Li 1934, p. 210
Pl. 78, Fig. 11

Vegetative cells 16–18μ in diameter, 33–36μ long; fertile cells not inflated. Zygospores formed in the tube; compressed-globose, ovate, or top-shaped, compressed at right angles to the tube; median spore wall blue and punctate, with a conspicuous transverse suture; 23–26μ in diameter, 29–33μ long. Sporangium finally encased in a thick pectic layer.
Mich.

Zygnema chalybeospermum Hansgirg 1892, p. 243
Pl. 74, Fig. 2

Vegetative cells 24–27μ in diameter and up to 3 times the diameter in length; fertile cells cylindrical (shortened). Zygospores formed in one of the gametangia; globose or broadly ovate; median wall blue and smooth; 30–35μ in diameter, 30–38μ long.
Mich.

Zygnema conspicuum (Hass.) Transeau 1934, p. 208

Vegetative cells (18)–22–27–(33)μ in diameter, 50–90–(100)μ long; fertile cells not inflated. Zygospores formed in the tube; globose or ovate; median wall brown and rather coarsely pitted, the pits 1.5–2μ in diameter; the spores 24–32μ in diameter, 26–33μ long.
Mich.

[324]

Zygnema cyanosporum Cleve 1869, p. 28

Vegetative cells (17)–20–(27)μ in diameter and up to 9 times the diameter in length; fertile cells not inflated. Zygospores formed in the tube; globose or depressed-globose, compressed at right angles to the tube; median layer blue and smooth; 34–40μ in diameter.
Mich.

Zygnema decussatum (Vauch.) Transeau 1914, p. 290

Vegetative cells 18–20μ in diameter and up to 100μ long, the wall without a thick layer of mucilage; fertile cells not inflated. Zygospores formed in the tube; globose or depressed-globose; median spore wall brown and scrobiculate; 27–30μ in diameter.
Mich.

Zygnema insigne (Hass.) Kuetzing 1849, p. 444

Vegetative cells 26–30μ in diameter, 1–2 times the diameter in length; fertile cells cylindrical or inflated on one side only. Zygospores formed in one of the gametangia; subglobose to ovate; median wall brown and smooth; 32μ in diameter, or (ovate spores) 26μ in diameter, 32μ long.
Mich.

Zygnema leiospermum DeBary 1858, p. 77
Pl. 78, Fig. 13

Vegetative cells 20–24μ in diameter, quadrate; fertile cells enlarged but not distinctly inflated. Zygospores formed in one of the gametangia; globose; median wall brown and smooth; 23–30μ in diameter.
Mich.

Zygnema micropunctatum Transeau 1934, p. 210
Pl. 78, Fig. 12

Vegetative cells 14–16μ in diameter, 24–52μ long; fertile cells not inflated. Zygospores formed in the tube; depressed-globose or ovate, compressed at right angles to the conjugation tube; median wall yellow-brown and minutely punctate; 28–32μ in diameter, 36–40μ long.
Mich.

Zygnema pectinatum (Vauch.) C. A. Agardh 1817, p. 102
Pl. 69, Figs. 9, 10

Filaments forming light green, cottony masses; vegetative cells 30–37–(40)μ in diameter, up to 80μ long, usually inclosed by a soft mucilaginous sheath; fertile cells not inflated. Zygospores formed in the tube; globose; median spore wall brown and pitted; 35–50μ in diameter.

Rare in a few lakes; forming floating masses among larger vegetation or entangled about the culms of rushes in shallow water, Mich., Wis.

Zygnema stellinum (Vauch.) C. A. Agardh 1824, p. 77

Filaments forming green, mucilaginous masses, floating free or sometimes in pooled seeps on banks; vegetative cells (25)–28–36–(40)μ in diameter, quadrate or up to 3 times the diameter in length (mostly about 70μ); fertile cells not inflated. Zygospores formed in one of the gametangia; broadly ovate or oblong; median layer brown and deeply pitted; 30–35μ in diameter, 35–48μ long.

In Sphagnum bogs and sloughs. Mich., Wis.

Zygnema sterile Transeau in Transeau, Tiffany, Taft, & Li 1934, p. 212

Filaments scattered among other algae and seldom forming pure masses; vegetative cells 44–54μ in diameter, 22–69μ long, with a thick wall and inclosed by a firm pectic sheath which may be as much as 15μ in thickness, the sheath often deeply constricted at the plane of the cross walls; cell contents very dense and so nearly opaque that the individual chloroplasts can scarcely be discerned. Conjugation not known; reproduction by thick-walled, scrobiculate akinetes which fill the cell when mature.

Common; intermingled with other algae in shallow water, especially in small lakes and ponds where there is a high concentration of decomposing organic matter. Mich., Wis.

Zygnema synadelphum Skuja 1926, p. 110
Pl. 74, Fig. 1

Vegetative cells 17–21μ in diameter; fertile cells not inflated Zygospores formed in the tube; globose, or compressed parallel with the conjugation tube; median layer blue and scrobiculate; 33–36μ in diameter.

Mich.

ZYGNEMOPSIS (Skuja) Transeau 1934, p. 203

Filaments slender, composed usually of cylindrical cells which are as much as 10 times their diameter in length; chloroplasts 2 stellate or cushion-like masses, containing a single pyrenoid each. Conjugation scalariform (between dissociated cells in some species ?), the gametangia persisting and becoming filled with cellulose-pectic compounds, usually deposited in layers. Zygospores formed in the enlarged conjugating tube, compressed-spheroid or quadrate in front view, the median spore wall smooth or variously sculptured and decorated, brownish in color.

This genus should be compared with *Zygnema*, especially those species which have stellate chloroplasts. It is separated from that genus chiefly by the presence of swollen and filled gametangia.

Key to the Species

1. Vegetative cells 16–22μ in diameter _____ 2
1. Vegetative cells smaller _____ 3
2. Zygospores ovate or quadrangular-ovate,
   median spore wall scrobiculate _____ Z. *decussata*
2. Zygospores quadrate, outer wall densely punctate_____ Z. *spiralis*
3. Median and outer spore walls smooth _____ 4
3. Median or outer spore walls decorated _____ 5
4. Vegetative cells 8–10–(12)μ in diameter, with
   2 rounded chloroplasts_____ Z. *minuta*
4. Vegetative cells 10–12μ in diameter, with
   1 plate-like chloroplast _____ Z. *Tiffaniana*
5. Median spore wall finely reticulate; spores 20–40μ in diameter,
   30–40μ long; 1 chloroplast with 2 pyrenoids_____ Z. *americana*
5. Median spore wall finely punctate; spores 14–24μ in diameter,
   20–27μ long; 2 cushion-like chloroplasts in each cell_____ Z. *desmidioides*

Zygnemopsis americana (Trans.) Transeau *in* Transeau, Tiffany, Taft, & Li 1934, p. 215

Vegetative cells 9–12μ in diameter, 27–120μ long; chloroplast with 2 pyrenoids. Zygospores formed in the tube but extending into the gametangia; ovate or quadrangular-ovate in face view, the angles retuse or rounded; median wall verrucose; 20–40μ in diameter, 30–40μ long.

Mich.

Zygnemopsis decussata (Trans.) Transeau *in* Transeau, Tiffany, Taft, & Li 1934, p. 214

Pl. 74, Fig. 3

Vegetative cells 16–20μ in diameter, 24–50μ long; chloroplast with 2 pyrenoids. Zygospores irregular in shape, or ovate to quadrate-ovate, somewhat compressed parallel with the conjugation tube; the angles various, either rounded, retuse, or extended; median spore wall scrobiculate; 24–30μ in diameter, 30–48μ long.

Mich.

Zygnemopsis desmidioides (West & West) Transeau *in*
Transeau, Tiffany, Taft, & Li 1934, p. 215

Pl. 69, Fig. 8

Filaments short, slender, and fragile, much constricted at the
cross walls, composed of cylindrical cells, broadly rounded at the
apices, 8–11μ in diameter, 25–40μ long. Zygospores rectangular in
front view, broadly ellipsoid in side view; the median wall finely
and densely punctate; 14–24μ in diameter, 20–27–(30)μ in long
dimension. Gametangia persisting about the spore as 4 horn-like
processes filled with pectic compounds.

Rare; in shallow water of swamps; lake margins. Mich., Wis.

Zygnemopsis minuta Randhawa 1937, p. 312

Vegetative cells 8–10μ in diameter, 36–46μ long; chloroplasts 2
irregular cushion-like bodies. Reproduction mostly by lenticular
aplanospores. Zygospores quadrate in a 4-lobed sporangium (sometimes 3-lobed), formed by remains of gametangia; median spore
wall brown and smooth; 22–24μ in diameter. Conjugation usually
between dissociated cells.
Mich.

Zygnemopsis spiralis (Fritsch) Transeau *in* Transeau,
Tiffany ,Taft, & Li 1934, p. 214

Pl. 69, Fig. 7

Filaments long, composed of short cylindrical cells, 17–22μ in
diameter and up to 130μ long; chloroplasts 2 stellate bodies. Zygospores quadrate in outline, formed in the enlarged connecting tube
but extending into the gametangial cells which form horn-like
enlargements; outer spore wall brown and densely punctate; 30–36μ
in diameter, 48–54μ in long dimension.
Mich., Wis.

Zygnemopsis Tiffaniana Transeau 1944, p. 244

Pl. 74, Fig. 4

Vegetative cells 10–12μ in diameter, 30–60μ long; chloroplasts
with 2 pyrenoids. Zygospore quadrate, the margins either retuse or
straight to angles which may be produced or retuse (concave);
median spore wall smooth; 20–24μ in diameter, 28–32μ long. Conjugation frequently between dissociated cells.
Mich.

ZYGOGONIUM Kuetzing 1843, p. 280

Filaments of short-cylindric or slightly tumid cells with lateral branches, either rhizoidal or several cells in length. Chloroplasts cushion- or pad-like, 2 in a cell, or appearing as 1 duplex body with an interconnecting narrow band; a pyrenoid in each chloroplast; at times the chloroplast showing short radiate processes similar to *Zygnema;* nucleus in the bridge between the 2 chloroplasts; cytoplasm usually colorless but sometimes purplish, becoming brown. Conjugation lateral or scalariform by protuberances from both gametangia; only part of the cell contents serving as a gamete. Zygospore ovate, in a sporangium which is formed between the two gametangia and which splits along a median line; spore wall smooth or decorated; gametangia not becoming filled with pectic substances but with granular residues. Reproduction also by akinetes and aplanospores (more common than zygospores).

Zygogonium ericetorum Kuetzing 1845, p. 224
Pl. 78, Figs. 8–10

Filaments with cells 15–24μ in diameter and $\frac{1}{2}$-$1\frac{1}{2}$-(4) times the diameter in length, cylindrical or slightly constricted at the cross walls; cell walls thick; chloroplasts, cytoplasm, and conjugation as described for the genus; zygospore ovate or globose, 20–25μ in diameter, the median spore wall smooth.

In shallow water of Black Lake, Michigan; on damp soil and tree trunks arising from water along lake margin.

CLASS CHAROPHYCEAE

This unique group of plants occupies an isolated position from a taxonomic point of view. They have no known ancestors nor have they given rise to other living plant forms according to present information. They are alga-like in their reproductive habits and because of their pigmentation there is ample justification for giving them a place in the Chlorophyta. In many characteristics they are quite unlike the green algae, however, and are so unique that in some systems of classification the Charophyceae are considered to be a separate division in the plant kingdom.

The Charophyceae are all macroscopic, having rhizoidal, erect stem-like branches and whorls of secondary branches, or 'leaves'. They vary in height from 2 to 60 cm., growing erect or sprawling in the bottom of lakes or slow-flowing streams. In many forms vegetative proliferation occurs by stolons and special buds or 'bulbils' which develop on subterranean rhizoidal branches. Hence it is customary to find members of this group in compact beds or 'meadows.'

The stem has definite nodes and internodes. From the former, short branches of definite growth (the 'leaves') and longer branches of unlimited growth develop. The leaves and secondary branches may arise in whorls or in a dichotomous or trichotomous plan. The chracteristic manner of growth in the Charophyceae is unique among the Chlorophyta. A meristematic apical cell cuts off node and internodal segments and from the former all lateral branches and sex organs are produced. In one genus cortical cells also develop from the node region and extend both anteriorly and posteriorly along the internodal cell.

Reproduction is heterogamous and the sex organs are relatively complex. There are both monoecious and dioecious species. The oogonia are large, ovoid, or subglobose cells containing a single egg and are inclosed by a definite number of spirally twisted corticating cells which form a crown, the cornula, at the apex. The oogonia, like the antheridia, are produced at a node of the stem or its leaves. The antheridia are globose and usually smaller than the oogonia but are frequently conspicuous because of their red color when mature (as is also the oogonium in some species). The shell of the antheridium is composed of a definite number of flat, shield-like cells which have radiating lobes, these interlocking with lobes from other cells. The shield cells bear internally a large number of multicellular filaments, in each cell of which a swimming antherozoid is produced. The oogonia may be above, below, or side by side with the antheridia, depending upon the genus.

The reader is referred to Groves and Bullock-Webster (1920), Fritsch (1935), and Smith (1938) for detailed discussions of the morphology of the group and of the many characteristics which are of taxonomic importance. It is a class which requires special terminology and much careful study in dealing with its taxonomy.

There is 1 order and 1 family, divided into 2 clearly recognizable tribes.

ORDER CHARALES

FAMILY CHARACEAE

In the taxonomy of this family the arrangement of the sex organs, the presence or absence of cortical cells, and the number and arrangement of these, are the major fundamental characteristics upon which differentiations are made.

[330]

Key to the Tribes

Crown of oogonium composed of 5 cells; oogonium always above
the antheridium (in monoecious species)............................CHAREAE
Crown of oogonium composed of 10 cells (5 pairs, 2 cut off from
the tip of the cortical cells of the oogonium); oogonium below
or beside the antheridium; stem uncorticated................NITELLEAE

TRIBE NITELLEAE

In this tribe the stem bears whorls of short branches and 2 or
more branches of indefinite growth. The plan of branching is dichotomous or trichotomous, and in many forms the secondary branches
or 'leaves' all terminate at about the same level and are usually less
than the internodes in length so that (especially in some species of
Nitella) a beaded appearance results. The plants are entirely uncorticated and in most forms (particularly *Nitella*) they are limp
and flexible. The coronula ('crown') of the oogonium is composed
of 10 cells in 2 tiers at the ends of the 5 corticating cells of the
female organ. The antheridium may be vertical at the end of a
short stalk from the node of a fertile branchlet, or lateral (*Tolypella*)
and either sessile or stalked. In the monoecious species the oogonia
are below the antheridia (*Nitella*) or above and beside them
(*Tolypella*).

Key to the Genera

Branching regular and symmetrical; antheridia terminal and
vertical on a branchlet in the furoations;
oogonia below the antheridia..*Nitella*
Branching irregular or not symmetrical, some branches longer
and giving a scraggly appearance; antheridia lateral in the
furcations; oogonia beside the antheridia or
appearing to be above them...*Tolypella*

NITELLA (C. A. Agardh) Leonhardi 1863, p. 69

Branches of unlimited growth, usually 2 at each node, the sex-
organ-bearing branches repeatedly forked and terminating at the
same level; antheridia terminal on a short stalk among the furcations
of the branchlets; oogonia lateral, either just below an antheridium,
or solitary on the node of a 'leaf.'

Key to the Species

1. Plants small, 2–5–(8) cm. tall; ultimate divisions
   of the branchlets (rays) 2-celled.. 2
1. Plants larger; ultimate divisions of the branchlets 1-celled............ 3

[331]

2. Whorls of verticils at the nodes globular in outline, gradually decreasing in size toward the apex of the main axis, forming minute tufts at the tip _____ *N. tenuissima*

2. Whorls of verticils at the nodes spreading, not forming compact globules, becoming compactly arranged at the anterior end and forming dense clusters cone-shaped in outline _____ *N. Batrachosperma*

3. Plants monoecious _____ *N. flexilis*

3. Plants dioecious _____ *N. opaca*

Nitella Batrachosperma (Reichenb.) A. Braun 1847, p. 10

Pl. 78, Figs. 1–4

Plants minute and very delicate, up to 2 cm. (rarely 3 cm.) tall, with several branches arising from a basal node; internodal cells in the lower part of the thallus 2–3 times the length of the verticils, which are in whorls of 8 at the node, and spreading, the branchlets crowded toward the apex, forming a cone-shaped cluster at the tip; branchlets once or twice divided, the ultimate rays 2-celled, the terminal cell awl-shaped; monoecious; antheridia terminal on a short stalk in the furcation of a 'leaf,' 0.135–0.210 mm. in diameter; oogonia borne laterally to the antheridia and below them, with a persistent coronula; oospore globose, 0.27–0.30 mm. in diameter, dark brown in color, the outer membrane with reticulations.

This species is the smallest and the most delicate one in our collections. Like *N. tenuissima*, it has a gray-green color, is often found embedded in silt in the bottoms of shallow ponds and lagoons and hence is easily overlooked.

Mich.

Nitella flexilis (L.) C. A. Agardh 1824, p. 124

Pl. 79, Figs. 1–3

Plants large (up to 30 cm. tall) and stout, with long internodes (about 2 times longer than the branchlets), repeatedly branched, especially long and sprawling stems in deep water; nodes bearing whorls of 6–8 branchlets with the sex-organ-bearing branchlets usually shorter, forming dense clusters, the branchlets but little divided, usually only one, the ultimate rays 1-celled and ordinarily acuminate; sex organs monoecious, the oogonia 2–3, subglobose or broadly ovoid, 0.55–0.75 mm. in diameter, 0.625–0.9 mm. long, the investing cells showing 8–9 turns; antheridium 0.5–0.75 mm. in diameter.

In shallow water of soft water lakes and *Sphagnum* bogs; from 10–12 meters. Mich., Wis.

Nitella opaca C. A. Agardh 1824, p. 124
Pl. 79, Figs. 4–10

Plants large and robust with very long internodes (2–4 times longer than the branchlets); nodes bearing 6–7 branchlets which may be either simple or once-divided, ultimate rays 1-celled and mucronate; fertile branchlets crowded, forming heads; sex organs dioecious, the oogonia 1–2, broadly ovoid, 0.5–0.565 mm. in diameter, 0.65–0.7 mm. long, the investing cells showing 7–9 turns, the crown 0.25–0.4 mm. high, deciduous; antheridia 0.65–0.75 mm. in diameter.

Common; a very luxuriantly growing, bushy plant, often forming dense beds, especially in soft water lakes; sometimes found at a depth of 5–8 meters. Mich., Wis.

Nitella tenuissima (Desv.) Kuetzing 1843, p. 319
Pl. 80, Figs. 1–7

Plants small, tufted, 2–8 cm. high, with several branches arising from a single basal node; stem very slender, bearing whorls of 6 branchlets which are short, densely crowded and form glomerules, giving a distinct beaded appearance to the plant; the branchlets forking 3–4 times, ending in 2-celled rays; sex organs monoecious, the oogonia spherical or broadly elliptic, about 260μ (0.26 mm.) in diameter, 400μ (0.4 mm.) long, invested by corticating cells that show 9 turns; antheridia about 0.175 mm. in diameter.

Like *N. Batrachosperma*, this species is often overlooked because it grows in silt, with only the tips of the branches emergent.

Growing in shallow water on silty bottoms, mostly in soft water or slightly acid lakes. Mich., Wis.

TOLYPELLA (A. Braun) Leonhardi 1863, p. 72

Thallus relatively coarse, (8)–10–25 cm. high, light green or gray-green in color, usually irregularly branched, presenting a scraggly appearance; sterile branches 6–16 in a verticil, of variable length; fertile branches involving several long, and one head of short, branchlets; internodes of principal filament and of primary laterals long; uncorticated; primary laterals sparsely branched; branches terminating in a series of unbranched ray cells which may be pointed or bluntly rounded at the tip; monoecious (in our specimens), the antheridia sessile or at the ends of short lateral branchlets in the furcations; oogonia usually crowded, appearing to be above and also beside the antheridia on the same node, formed either at the base of a fertile branchlet or on one of the lower nodes, the coronula persistent or not; oospore round in cross section, light to orange-brown in color.

Tolypella intricata Leonhardi 1863, p. 32
Pl. 78, Figs. 5–7

Thallus 8–25 cm. tall, gray-green; sparsely branched with a few primary branches and dense heads of fertile branchlets subtended by laterals of unequal length; the primary ray including but few nodes from which 2 or 3 lateral branches arise, simple or again divided, the laterals but 3 or 4 cells in length, the terminal cell sharp-pointed or sometimes bluntly rounded; fertile branchlets densely clustered and including also long, coarse branchlets of irregular length; the primary branch with 2 or 3 nodes, each bearing 3–(4) lateral branches, the ultimate rays of the fertile branches 3- or 4-celled, the lateral branch rays branched at the first node and again branching, sometimes also branching from the second node, these branches simple if there are but 2 nodes in the branchlet; antheridia sessile, up to 0.3 mm. in diameter, lateral at the nodes of the fertile branchlets; oogonia at the base of or on the nodes of the fertile branchlets, several together, appearing above or beside the antheridia; oospore 0.3–0.318–(0.4)mm. in diameter, light brown when mature, decorated with 10–11 ridges, the outer membrane yellowish, thin, and granular.

In hard and semi-hard water lakes, in shallow water where there is protection from wave action and strong currents. Mich.

Tribe Chareae

In this tribe the stems usually have but a single branch of unlimited growth arising from the nodes of the stem. The whorls of branchlets are simple, having only short bracts or leaflets at their nodes rather than bifurcations. In one genus, *Chara,* most species are characterized by having the internodal cells of the stem corticated. The sex organs may be monoecious or dioecious, in our specimens (*Chara*) with the oogonium borne above the antheridium in the monoecious species. The coronula of the oogonium in this group is composed of but 5 cells, cut off from the tips of the spiral corticating cells of the oogonium.

CHARA Linnaeus 1754, p. 491

These plants are usually stout and coarse of texture, when compared with *Nitella.* They are frequently encrusted with lime and thrive best in hard or semi-hard water lakes and slowly flowing streams. It is this character which has earned for them the common name of Stoneworts. The stem in most species is corticated by elements which develop from the node cells in both directions along the internodal cell and so meet cortical cells from the node above and below. The cortical cells in their development themselves cut off small node cells. These show as small round units in the series; often they are spiniferous. From the node cells of the corticating cells secondary corticals may be cut off and grow down alongside the primary elements. These may be more prominent than the primary, or less so, a specific character of taxonomic value. Sometimes there are two such cells cut off, one on either side of the primary cortical cell. The results of the behavior of the *node cells* of the *cortical elements* are then: 1. The node cells may not produce laterals and the cortical cells are rather large and equal in number to the leaves, which are borne at the node of the stem. This condition is known as *haplostichous cortication.* 2. If the node cell of the cortical series cuts off one lateral so that the cortex is composed of alternating primary and secondary cells the condition is known as *diplostichous,* and there are twice as many cortical cells as there are leaves at the stem node. 3. The node cells of the cortical series may give rise to two laterals, one on either side, so that in the circumference of the stem the primary cells alternate with two secondary cortical cells, and there are three times as many cortical cells as there are leaves in the whorl at the stem node. This condition is known as *triplostichous.* There are irregularities in these plans of arrangement, so that it is often necessary to examine many stem sections to obtain the necessary information for taxonomic considerations. Rarely the stems are *ecorticate.*

In most forms, besides bearing a whorl of leaves, the stem node is encircled by a single or double row of spine-like cells, the *stipulodes.*

The nodes of the leaves may be smooth or they may bear *leaflets* or *bracts* (bracteoles). Some of these may be mere papillae, whereas others at the same node may be much elongated, especially at fertile nodes where there are usually 2 or 4 long bracts about the oogonium. The last 1 to 4 cells of the leaves may be ecorticate and the general form and arrangement of these cells at the tip, and the lateral elements given off just below the uncorticated cells at the end of the leaves are characteristics which are of taxonomic value also.

There are both monoecious and dioecious species. In the former condition the oogonia are always borne above the antheridia, developing, however, from the same initial cell in the node of the branchlet.

Only the more conspicuous species of *Chara* were collected, and in the present treatment I have included one which has been previously reported. Hence only a few of the many forms which undoubtedly occur in the region are included. In order to make an adequate study of this interesting group, dredging and other special methods of collecting would be required. Many species of *Chara* listed by Robinson (1906) occur in the range of this area, but none are specifically referred to Michigan and Wisconsin. See Allen (1888–1896), Robinson (*l.c.*), and Groves and Bullock-Webster (1924) for the taxonomy of *Chara*.

Key to the Species

1. Stems uncorticated (Ecorticata) _____ 2
1. Stems corticated (Corticata) _____ 3
2. Bracts about the oogonium distinctly shorter
   than the mature fruit _____*C. Braunii*
2. Bracts about the oogonium as long as or
   longer than the mature fruit _____ *C. Schweinitzii*
3. Cortication haplostichous (see definition above) _____ *C. canescens*
3. Cortication diplostichous or triplostichous _____ 4
4. Cortications diplostichous _____ 5
4. Cortications triplostichous _____ 7
5. Primary cortical cells more prominent than their secondary laterals _____ 6
5. Lateral cortical cells in pairs and more prominent than the primary
   cell; posterior bracts much shorter than the
   oogonium, sometimes wanting _____ *C. vulgaris*
6. Stipulodes in a double row, the upper longer than the lower
   and persistent; bracts about the oogonium ½ its length _____ *C. excelsa*
6. Stipulodes in a double row but short and blunt, usually deciduous,
   leaving scars; bracts about the oogonium sometimes a little shorter
   than the female organ but usually 6–7 times its length ___ ___ ___ *C. contraria*
7. Leaves (branchlets) uncorticated in the internode region just
   above the node of the stem; oogonia and antheridia on different
   leaf nodes, or sometimes on the same node ___ ___ ___ ___ ___ _____ 8
7. Basal internode region of the leaves corticated; oogonia and
   antheridia always on the same leaf node ___ ___   _____ *C. fragilis*
8. Bracts about the oogonia longer than the mature fruit _____ 9
8. Bracts about the oogonia shorter than the mature fruit_____ *C. sejuncta*
9. Oogonia and antheridia on the same node_____ *C. elegans*
9. Oogonia and antheridia at different nodes_____ *C. formosa*

Chara Braunii Gmelin 1826, p. 646

Pl. 81, Fig. 1

Plants bright green, slightly if at all encrusted with lime, but crisp, (6)–15–20 cm. high; stem long-jointed, with a single whorl of stipulodes at the node, one for each of the leaves, of which there are 10–12; internodes of stem and leaves entirely uncorticated; sex organs monoecious, borne at the same node; oogonia 0.7–0.8 mm. long, subtended by bracts which are shorter than the mature fruit, cortical cells of oogonium showing 9–10 turns; antheridium small, 0.25–0.275 mm. in diameter.

Several collections of *Chara* showed characteristics in agreement with both *C. Braunii* and *C. Schweinitzii*. As Robinson (1906) has pointed out, most of these forms are best assigned to the latter species. *C. Braunii* is less common than *C. Schwenitzii*. Our plants are typical of the former.

In shallow water of a small lake. Wis.

Chara canescens Loiseleur-Deslongchamps 1810, p. 139
Pl. 81, Figs. 2–6

Plants rather coarse but bright green and only moderately rigid inasmuch as they are but very little encrusted with lime; 6–15 cm. high; stems bearing a double whorl of stipulodes and 8–10 leaves at each node, the upper series of stipulodes longer than the lower; cortications of the internodes haplostichous, the node cells of the cortical series bearing 3 spines; terminal cell of the leaves uncorticated, spine-like, sometimes surrounded by several cells from the last node which are equal to the terminal cell in length, or nearly so, giving a forked appearance to the leaf tip; sex organs dioecious; oogonia subtended by 6 bracts, those adjacent to the oogonium shorter than the others; cortical cells of the oogonium showing 13–15 turns; oogonium 0.7–0.8 mm. long.

The branchlets (leaves) in this species are relatively short, with 5–8 joints, and are incurved at the tips. Examination of herbarium material in the University of Minnesota, University of California, and the Chicago Natural History Museum shows that there is a great deal of variation among specimens bearing the label of *C. canescens*.

In ponds of semi-hard water. Mich., Wis.

Chara contraria A. Braun *ex* Kuetzing 1845, p. 258

Plants usually coarse and stiff; stems bearing 7–8 leaves and a double row of short, blunt stipulodes which frequently are deciduous, leaving only scars; cortication of the internode diplostichous, the primary cells more prominent, the secondary laterals irregular; spine cells short, deciduous in the lower parts of the stem; terminal cells of the stem and branchlets ecorticate, the apical cell short and spine-like; monoecious, both organs produced at the same node; oogonia subtended by 3 bracts which may be slightly shorter than the oogonium or as much as 7 times longer, the posterior bracts short and often papilliform; oospores 0.48–0.74 mm. long, with 9–14 ridges, brown in color; antheridia globose, up to 0.58 mm. in diameter.

Walnut Lake, Michigan.

Chara elegans (A. Braun) Robinson 1906, p. 283

[*C. gymnopus* var. *elegans* Allen]

Pl. 82, Figs. 13–15

Plants green, not encrusted with lime; stems triply corticated, with a double row of stipulodes at the nodes, which bear whorls of 9–12 leaves; leaves uncorticated in the internode immediately above the node which bears them, the upper row of stipulodes usually exceeding and covering the uncorticated internode; leaves terminating in a long, uncorticated cell, subtended by 3 spine-like cells from the last node; spine cells from the nodes of the cortical cells prominent, often forming whorls about the stem; sex organs monoecious, borne at the same node; oogonia 0.4–0.5 mm. in diameter, subtended by 2 pairs of bracteoles which exceed it in length; antheridia 0.5 mm. in diameter.

In hard water lakes and ponds. Mich., Wis.

Chara excelsa Allen 1882, p. 43

Pl. 81, Figs. 7–10

Plants coarse and brittle, encrusted with lime, 6–14 cm. high; stems bearing 7–8 leaves and a double whorl of stipulodes of which the upper row is longer than the lower; cortication of the internode diplostichous, the primary cortical cells larger and more prominent than the secondary laterals; 2–3 cells at the tip of the leaves uncorticated; sex organs monoecious, produced on the same node; oogonia 0.8–1.5 mm. long, investing cells showing 7–10 turns; bracts subtending the oogonium longer than the fruit: antheridia 0.32–0.35 mm. in diameter.

In shallow water of lakes and ponds. Wis.

Chara formosa Robinson 1906, p. 296

Plants rather fragile, very little if at all encrusted with lime, 4–30 cm. high; stem triplostichous in cortication, the primary and secondary cells about the same diameter, the cortications bearing spines, some of which are long and recurved, especially in the younger stem internodes; nodes of the stem bearing a whorl of 10–15 leaves (mostly 10–11 in our specimens), the lowest internode of which is uncorticated, and a double whorl of stipulodes, the upper series longer and often completely hiding the uncorticated internode of the leaves; leaves also uncorticated at the apex; sex organs monoecious, antheridia and oogonia developing on separate nodes, the oogonia 0.9–0.96 mm. long, subtended by 2 pairs of bracts which are longer than the mature fruit; antheridia 0.28–0.38 mm. in diameter.

In shallow water of both soft and hard water lakes. Mich., Wis.

Chara fragilis Desvaux *in* Loiseleur-Deslongchamps 1810, p. 137
Pl. 82, Figs. 6–8

Plants moderately stout and of medium coarseness, not heavily encrusted with lime, (2.5)–8–30–(75)cm. high; stem with long internodes and triplostichous cortications, the primary and secondary cortical cells about equal in diameter; the node cells of the primary series of cortications not bearing spines; nodes of the stem with 6–9 leaves and a double whorl of very small, sometimes inconspicuous, papilla-like stipulodes, of which the upper series is a little larger and more prominent than the lower; leaf tips uncorticated in the last two cells, ending in a simple, short spine-like cell, the last node of the leaf from which cortical cells are produced, smooth, not giving rise to leaflets or bract cells, the latter also frequently lacking on the sterile nodes of the leaves; plants monoecious, antheridia and oogonia at the same node and subtended by 2 bracts which are about equal to the mature fruit in length, although there are in the same whorl several shorter, sometimes papilla-like bract cells; oogonia 0.8–0.95 mm. long, investing cells showing as many as 17 turns; antheridia up to 0.5 mm. in diameter.

Common in several hard water lakes, especially in shallow water. Mich., Wis.

Chara sejuncta A. Braun 1845, p. 264
Pl. 82, Figs. 9–12

Plants fragile, 8–15–(60)cm. high, very little encrusted with lime, spotted in our specimens; stem triplostichous in cortication, the primary and secondary cells about equal in diameter, in the upper internodes very short and mosaic-like, bearing many recurved spines but almost smooth in the older stem internodes; nodes bearing a whorl of 9–13 leaves (usually 10), the lowest internode of which is uncorticated, and double whorl of stipulodes, the upper series of which is longer than the lower and exceeds the length of the uncorticated internode of the leaves; sex organs monoecious, but on different nodes; oogonia 0.96–1.26 mm. long, subtended by at least 2 pairs of bracts which are always shorter than the mature fruit; investing cells of the oogonium showing 8–10 turns; antheridia 0.3–0.48 mm. in diameter.

See description of *C. formosa*, a species which should be compared with *C. sejuncta*. The latter has somewhat larger oogonia and the bracts are always shorter than the mature fruit.

In hard water lakes and ponds. Wis.

Chara Schweinitzii A. Braun 1834, p. 353

Pl. 80, Figs. 8–12

Plants bright green, not at all encrusted with lime, 10–15 cm. high; stem long-jointed, with a single whorl of stipulodes at the node, which also gives rise to 8–11 leaves; internodes of both stem and leaves uncorticated; sex organs monoecious, usually borne on the same node; oogonia 0.8–0.9 mm. long, subtended by bracts which are equal in length to the mature fruit or as much as 3 times longer; cortical cells of oogonium showing 7–9 turns; antheridia 0.28–0.3 mm. in diameter.

Herbarium specimens of this species show a very pronounced translucence or sheen.

Collected in standing and running water; semi-hard water lakes. Wis.

Chara vulgaris Linnaeus 1753, p. 1156

Pl. 82, Figs. 1–5

Plants coarse and brittle, usually much encrusted with lime varies greatly with habitat), variable in height from 4 cm. in shallow water and on sand bars to 40 cm. in deep water on muck bottoms; plants especially odoriferous; stems with diplostichous cortication, the secondary laterals wider and more prominent than the primary (in some varieties the primary and secondary corticals about equal), the node cells of the primary cortical series produced into spines which may vary from mere papillae to very long and prominent cells, giving a distinctly spiny appearance to the plant as a whole (at least in some of the varieties); nodes of the stem bearing a whorl of 6–11 leaves and a double whorl of stipulodes, of which those in the upper series are longer than the lower; leaves uncorticated for 3–4 cell lengths at the tip, the cortications of the leaves ending abruptly at a node which bears 3–6 papillae or thorn-like leaflets of differing sizes; sex organs monoecious, borne on the same leaf node, the subtending bracts about 6, of which 4 near the oogonium are longer than the mature fruit, whereas the posterior bracts are very short, even papilla-like; oogonia 0.525–0.8 mm. long, investing cells showing 11–14 or as many as 16 turns; antheridia 0.25–0.55 mm. in diameter.

This species is extremely variable in size, form, and color. In the shallow water expressions it is often short-tufted and sparse, whereas in deep water it forms dense beds or mats with stems as much as 40 cm. long, and with long internodes. The color varies from gray-green to bright green, mostly depending upon the amount of lime deposited. *C. vulgaris* has a stronger fetid odor than perhaps any of the other species in the genus. It has been described as being like that of garlic ("spoiled garlic"), or as skunk-like.

This species is important as a marl-former because of the large amounts of calcium carbonate which are deposited by it. In hard water lake regions through central and southern Wisconsin and southern Michigan it is one of the most common *Chara* species.

Common in a large variety of lakes but mostly in hard water; generally distributed. Mich., Wis.

DIVISION CHRYSOPHYTA

This group, as now recognized, is large and includes an enormous variety of plant forms which have, however, several fundamental characteristics in common. First, their pigmentation is yellowish-green or brown with carotinoids predominating. Second, the food reserve is oil or leucosin rather than starch, and third, there is a prevalent duplex character in structure of the wall, which in many genera is composed of 2 spliced sections. The juncture of the two halves may be along the longitudinal walls, or in the short diameter of the cell.

It is noteworthy that the division includes forms which present a morphological evolutionary series comparable to that noted in the Chlorophyta. There are unicellular non-motile and flagellated forms, and in addition a rhizopodal type of cell which has no counterpart in the Chlorophyta. There are simple, indefinite or definitely formed colonies, simple or branched multicellular filaments, and siphonaceous thalli.

Reproduction varies greatly according to respective classes and families. Besides vegetative multiplication by cell division and fragmentation, there are other non-sexual methods which involve aplanospores, zoospores, or special modifications of these. It is interesting that heterogamy has not been developed in this division, only isogametes being known and these for a limited number of genera.

Key to the Classes

1. Chromatophores yellow-green, or if green not
   responding to iodine test for starch _____ XANTHOPHYCEAE
1. Chromatophores brown or golden brown; oil bodies and
   leucosin granules usually conspicuous _____ 2
2. Cells capsule-like, the wall definitely 2-valved; silicious
   and usually etched with punctae or striations; organs of
   locomotion absent; not forming cysts _____ BACILLARIOPHYCEAE
   (Diatoms—See Appendix p. 939)
2. Cells not capsule-like, the wall not 2-valved; pectic, with silicious
   impregnations not distinct; flagellated or rhizopodal cells common;
   forming endogenous cysts with silicified walls _____ CHRYSOPHYCEAE

CLASS XANTHOPHYCEAE

The most noticeable characteristic of this class is the predominance of yellow pigments in the chromatophores, causing the cells to appear pale green, in contrast to the Chlorophyta. In many forms the cell content possesses a metallic lustre as a result of leucosin accumulations which, together with oil, constitute the chief food reserves.

Although certain amounts of cellulose may be present, the walls are of pectose or pectic acid to which silicious substances may be added. The duplex character of the wall is especially common in this class, there being two halves, one of which overlaps the other in the midregion of the cell or toward one end (rarely sections appearing at both ends). In filamentous forms this results in the formation of characteristic H-shaped pieces which appear when cells dissociate, because they separate at the points of juncture of the wall pieces and not at the cross walls. The cell at the end of a broken filament has adjoined to it half the wall of its previous neighboring cell. (For a discussion of wall structure and other special features of this class, see Fritsch, 1934; Pascher, 1937–1939; Poulton, 1925; Smith, 1933 and 1938.)

Reproduction in this class is by aplanospores, zoospores, and in a few forms by isogametes.

Key to the Orders

1. Plants filamentous; cells adjoined end to end
   to form a uniseriate strand...HETEROTRICHALES
1. Plants not filamentous 2
2. Plants macroscopic (2–3 mm. in diameter); coenocytic
   vesicles; terrestrial ....HETEROSIPHONALES
2. Plants microscopic; not coenocytic vesicles 3
3. Cells motile by means of 2 flagella of unequal length.... HETEROCHLORIDALES
3. Cells not flagellated.. 4
4. Cells amoeboid, or epiphytic, with rhizopodal processes (some-
   times not clearly evident); inclosed by a lorica (outer
   shell) with a stipe-like attaching organ .... RHIZOCHLORIDALES
4. Cells not rhizopodal; without a lorica 5
5. Plants colonial, usually with cells embedded in mucilage and
   adjoined by mucilaginous stalks; non-motile but capable
   of returning directly to a motile condition......................HETEROCAPSALES
5. Plants unicellular (rarely colonial as in Gloeobotrydaceae, or forming
   clusters only incidentally), non-motile in the vegetative condition
   and incapable of returning to motility directly.....................HETEROCOCCALES

ORDER HETEROCHLORIDALES

In this small order the plants are unicellular and are motile by means of 2 flagella (in our specimens) of unequal length. Ordinarily there are 2 elongate, plate-like chromatophores; food reserve in the form of fats, leucosin, and, in some forms, glycogen. The primitive type of cell in this order may assume a rhizopodal state during which food particles are ingested in an amoeboid fashion. Reproductive methods other than simple cell division are unknown. There is 1 family and 1 genus in our collections.

FAMILY CHLOROMOEBACEAE

CHLOROCHROMONAS Lewis 1913, p. 254

Cells pyriform or cordate, with 2 flagella of unequal length attached at the broad anterior end, which is slightly concave; cell wall lacking; protoplast containing 2 elongate-ovate and somewhat curved chromatophores; food reserve in the form of oil droplets and a basal globule of leucosin; cells capable of becoming amoeboid, attached by a posterior pseudopodium-like extension; pigment-spot lacking.

Chlorochromonas minuta Lewis 1913, p. 254
Pl. 93, Figs. 8–10

Characteristics as described for the genus; cells 4.5–9.5µ long. Culture from Lake Mendota, Wisconsin (Lewis).

ORDER RHIZOCHLORIDALES

These organisms have a plasmodial morphology. The protoplast is naked but in some forms at least is inclosed by a definitely shaped hyaline envelope or lorica. Although essentially uninucleate, a multinucleate condition develops in older cells by repeated nuclear division. The chromatophore is a thin, laminate disc. Reproduction is by cell division or by zoospores. There is 1 family.

FAMILY STIPITOCOCCACEAE

Characteristics as described for the order. This group is composed of forms in which variously shaped loricas are secreted about the protoplast. This envelope is usually attached to a substrate by a fine, thread-like stipe. The protoplast often shows 1 or more rhizopodal extensions, at least an apical one. In our collections the family is represented by 1 genus, although organisms probably belonging to a second genus, *Rhizolekane*, have been noted.

STIPITOCOCCUS West & West 1898, Jour. Bot., 36, p. 336

An attached unicell, housed in an envelope of various forms, elliptical, pitcher-shaped, or ovoid, borne on a slender, thread-like stipe which may have a basal attaching disc; chromatophores faintly pigmented, yellow-green bodies, 1–3 in each cell; protoplast showing a fine rhizoidal apical thread; attached to filamentous algae.

Key to the Species

1. Lorica pitcher-shaped when mature..*S. urceolatus*
1. Lorica not pitcher-shaped..2
2. Cells globose with an apiculation..*S. apiculatus*

Stipitococcus apiculatus Prescott 1944, p. 361
Pl. 93, Figs. 11–13

Cells ovoid or fusiform, apiculate, with a slender attaching stipe; chromatophores 1–3; an oil (?) body near the anterior end, where a rhizoidal thread extends; cells gregarious, attached in whorls about filamentous desmids, sometimes 2 or 3 cells in a series on 1 stalk, the protoplasts connected by rhizoidal threads; cells 3.8–4μ in diameter, 18–36μ long, including the stipe.

The arrangement of the cells in dense, transverse zones about the host filament gives a very distinctive appearance to this species. The occurrence of 2 or 3 cells in a linear series on a single attaching stipe is unlike any of the other described forms. It is thought that this condition must be the result of in situ germination of swarmers.

On Hyalotheca filaments. Wis.

Stipitococcus capense Prescott in Prescott & Croasdale 1937, p. 271
Pl. 93, Figs. 14, 15

Lorica flask-shaped on a long slender stipe, narrowed anteriorly into a short, straight neck with parallel margins; chromatophores 1–2; cells 6–11.7μ in diameter, 22–23.4μ long.

This form is suggestive of a Lagynion on a stipe. The chromatophores are more definite in shape and more richly colored than in that genus. It should be noted in Pascher's Heterokonten (Rabenhorst's Kryptogamen-Flora, 11, p. 1062, 1939) that incorrect reference is made to the figures illustrating S. capense and S. vasiformis, both the figure descriptions and the text references being reversed.

On filamentous algae in Sphagnum bogs. Mich., Wis.

Stipitococcus crassistipatus Prescott 1944, p. 362
Pl. 93, Figs. 16–19

Lorica broadly (sometimes narrowly) flask-shaped, attenuated anteriorly to form a short wide neck and reduced posteriorly into a thick stipe which is 1.5–2μ wide; protoplast ovoid to subglobose, with 2 laminate chromatophores; lorica 7.6–8μ in diameter, 18–20μ long.

This species differs in having a stipe which is much stouter and less tapering than in the other described forms. It should be compared with S. *capense,* which has a very similarly shaped lorica but a very slender, tapering stipe, as well as with *Derepyxis amphora,* which it superficially resembles. *D. amphora* has a cross partition through the basal region of the lorica, and the protoplast is attached by fine threads to the sides of the envelope. The gross appearance of S. *crassistipatus* suggests relationship with *Derepyxis,* and subsequent study of living specimens may result in its transference to that genus.

On filamentous algae in acid bogs and soft water lakes. Wis.

Stipitococcus urceolatus West & West 1898, Jour. Bot., 36, p. 336
Pl. 93, Figs. 20–22

Lorica pitcher-shaped, ovoid, with a flaring 2-lipped apex, attached by a fine, thread-like stipe without a basal disc; chromatophores 1–2 parietal plates; lorica 3–4μ in diameter, 6–11μ long; stipe 4–6μ long.

Attached to filamentous algae in *Sphagnum* bogs and acid swamps. Mich.,Wis.

Stipitococcus vasiformis Tiffany 1934a, p. 32
Pl. 95, Figs. 32, 33

Lorica broadly ellipsoid or subglobose, on a short, slender stipe, abruptly narrowed anteriorly into a relatively long neck with parallel or subparallel margins, the apical opening not enlarged; protoplast with 1 faintly pigmented, plate-like chromatophore; cells 4.5–7μ in diameter, 8–13μ long.

In acid and soft water bogs. Mich.

ORDER HETEROCAPSALES

In this order the plants are simple colonies of non-motile cells embedded in a copious mucilage, or attached in cylindrical, gelanous tubes. Like the Tetrasporales in the Chlorophyta, members of this order are able to resume a motile condition directly. Zoospores produced by these forms lose their motility and enlarge to form adult plants. Cells are ovate or globose and contain 2 or more yellow-green, plate-like chromatophores from which fats and leucosin accumulate as food reserves. One family is represented in our collections.

FAMILY MISCHOCOCCACEAE

Cells in this family are arranged in gelatinous tubes. Repeated cell division and subsequent tube formation result in dichotomous or tetrachotomous dendroid colonies. The tubes are formed by the swelling and gelatinization of the old cell membrane, which pushes the daughter cell forward, so that protoplasts are always located at the distal ends of these mucilaginous stalks. Pascher (1937–1939) favors the placing of this family in the Heterococcales, mostly on the basis of cell arrangement and the absence of the copious gelatinous investments that characterize the Heterocapsales. As he also states, this family is one of several whose position in the Heterokontae is uncertain. Additional information is needed before a satisfactory taxonomic disposition can be made.

MISCHOCOCCUS Naegeli 1849, p. 82

Characteristics as described for the family; plant an attached, usually dichotomously branched, gelatinous tube inclosing globular cells which are often distantly removed from one another, or are in 2's and 4's in the distal end of the tubes; chromatophores 1–4, parietal, pale yellow-green discs; asexual reproduction by aplanospores or by uniflagellated zoospores; sexual reproduction by isogametes has been reported.

Mischococcus confervicola Naegeli 1849, p. 82
Pl. 93, Fig. 30

Characteristics as described for the genus; tubes dichotomously or tetrachotomously branched, with 1 or 2 globose cells in the distal end of each cylinder; cells 3.5–5.5μ in diameter.

Adhering to filamentous algae or entangled in the mixture of vegetation in shallow water of bays and small ponds. Wis.

ORDER HETEROCOCCALES

Unlike the Heterocapsales, these plants are permanently non-motile in the vegetative state and can assume motility only through the formation of zoospores. The plants are mostly unicellular (or may form colonies incidentally, as in some species of *Ophiocytium*). In one family, Gloeobotrydaceae, small colonies occur. Although mostly free-floating, a few forms are definitely epiphytic, or otherwise sedentary. The chromatophores are 1 to many, parietal, ovate or irregular plates, and oil and leucosin occur as food reserves. Reproduction, as far as is known definitely, is non-sexual, autospores and zoospores being used, although reports of gametic union have been made.

Key to the Families

1. Plants attached 2
1. Plants not attached 5
2. Plants attached by a stipe or with a broad adhesive base 4
2. Plants sessile, adhering without differentiation of the cell wall 3

3. Cells solitary..PLEUROCHLORIDACEAE (in part)
3. Cells in clusters, colonial 8
4. Cells cylindrical, growing by
   increasing in length[4]..CHLOROTHECIACEAE (in part)
4. Cells fusiform, ovate, globose, or subglobose,
   not growing in length...CHARACIOPSIDACEAE
5. Cells globose, several to many included
   in a gelatinous sheath ....GLOEOBOTRYDACEAE (in part)
5. Cells not inclosed in a gelatinous sheath, of various shapes.......................... 6
6. Cells rectangular, or cylindrical (usually elongate),
   growing by increasing in length 7
6. Cells globose, ovate, triangular, or polyhedral,
   not increasing in length ...............................PLEUROCHLORIDACEAE (in part)
7. Cells cylindrical, circinately
   coiled or S-shaped ....CHLOROTHECIACEAE (in part)
7. Cells quadrate or, if cylindrical, straight
   or only slightly curved..CENTRITRACTACEAE
8. Cells compactly arranged, adjoining walls flattened
   by mutual compression ....BOTRYOCHLORIDACEAE
8. Cells in colonies but not closely
   aggregated; walls not flattened..........................GLOEOBOTRYDACEAE (in part)

FAMILY PLEUROCHLORIDACEAE

Mostly solitary (incidentally clustered because of autospore liberation), mostly free-living cells of various shapes, globose, tetrahedral, short-cylindric, or spindle-shaped, sometimes narrowly so and decidedly needle-like; cells not growing in length; wall smooth or sculptured and spiny, in 1 or 2 sections; chromatophores parietal, varied in shape, disc-like, band-like, or lobed plates; pyrenoids and reddish oil bodies and pigment-spots (?) usually present; reproduction by aplanospores or zoospores.

This is an artificial family erected to include the one-celled Heterococcales which are free-living and which do not increase in length. It no doubt will be divided when more is learned about the life histories and when the significance of structural features of the cell wall are better understood. The sculptured forms especially may constitute a separate group.

Key to the Genera

1. Cells solitary, attached, sessile on submerged plants........................... *Perone*
1. Cells solitary or colonial, free-floating or intermingled with other algae....... 2
2. Cell wall smooth... 3
2. Cell wall sculptured or spiny.. 7
3. Cells cylindrical.. *Monallantus*
3. Cells globose or fusiform.. 4

---

[4]Cells which increase in length usually show very clearly 2 cross breaks in the wall, one near either end of the cell, with an interconnecting cylindrical and newer wall piece. See *Chlorothecium*.

ARACHNOCHLORIS (Pascher) Pascher 1939, p. 480

Cells spherical, solitary, with walls sculptured by broad circular or elongate depressions, sometimes faint, producing serrations at the wall margin; membrane becoming silicified in age; chromatophores 2 or several bands or petal-like plates arising parietally from a thickened common center, sometimes forming H-shaped plates wrapped along the cell wall, a pyrenoid sometimes evident; storage products fats and leucosin; reproduction by autospores or by heterokont zoospores formed 2–4 in a cell.

Arachnochloris minor Pascher 1930, p. 412
Pl. 95, Figs. 9, 10

Cells spherical, the wall firm, finely sculptured (sometimes indistinctly) with closely arranged series of depressions; basal body of chromatophore spongy, with an indistinct pyrenoid; chromatophore forming 2 parietal lobes; red oil drops sometimes present; cells 7–9μ in diameter.

Little Lake Sixteen, Presque Isle County, Michigan, an acid *Sphagnum* bog habitat.

BOTRYDIOPSIS Borzi 1894, p. 169

Cells solitary (or incidentally clustered in families), spherical or compressed-globose, the walls thin and in 2 overlapping sections:

chromatophores 1 or 2–(3) when young, becoming numerous in age; cytoplasm containing oil globules; reproduction by aplanospores or heterokont biflagellate zoospores.

Botrydiopsis arhiza Borzi 1895, p. 170
Pl. 95, Figs. 27, 28

Cells solitary, or in clusters without a gelatinous investment as a result of autospore liberation from mother cell; globose or spheroidal, the walls smooth; chromatophores usually 2–4 parietal plates; oil bodies small and numerous; cells 8–10μ in diameter (on damp soil as much as 70μ in diameter).

This species is more often found on moist soil than in strictly aquatic habitats.

In mixtures of algae in *Sphagnum* bogs. Mich., Wis.

CHLORALLANTHUS Pascher 1930, p. 421

Cells solitary, oblong or broadly ellipsoid, with parallel or subparallel lateral margins and broadly rounded poles (rarely with slightly attenuated poles); cell wall sculptured, sometimes faintly so, with circular or 4–6-sided depressions arranged in transverse or rectilinear series, the thickenings between the depressions often bearing spines; wall divided in 2 equal sections which adjoin in a transverse plane, silicified; chromatophores numerous parietal plates when old (2 in the young cells); reproduction by 2–4 (or as many as 16) zoospores, or by 2–4 autospores in each cell.

Chlorallanthus oblongus Pascher 1930, p. 422
Pl. 95, Fig. 4

Cells broadly ellipsoid or oblong, with rounded poles, margins subparallel, the wall brown, sculptured with reticular thickenings and intervening depressions resulting in teeth-like projections at the wall margin; chromatophores numerous ovate discs or broad parietal plates; cells 5–9μ in diameter, 10–15μ long.

In shallow water of small acid bog lakes. Mich.

CHLOROCLOSTER Pascher 1925, p. 52

Cells solitary or in small families (not inclosed in evident mucilage), elongate-fusiform or club-shaped, straight or more often twisted and sickle-shaped, the poles often dissimilar, one bluntly rounded, the other tapering to a point, the wall smooth; chromatophores 2 to many, either parietal folded plates or (more rarely) ovate discs, with pyrenoids sometimes present; reproduction by autospores and cyst-like aplanospores.

Chlorocloster pyreniger Pascher 1939, p. 459
Pl. 95, Fig. 42

Cells irregularly spindle-shaped, straight or slightly lunate, sometimes sigmoid; chromatophores 2 (rarely 1) parietal plates without pyrenoids; a red pigment-spot (oil body ?) visible; cells 6–8μ in diameter, up to 25μ long.

In *Sphagnum* bog pools. Mich.

DIACHROS Pascher 1939, p. 370

Cells solitary or in small clusters resulting from autospore liberation, spherical, the wall thin but firm, usually reddish-brown, in 2 lightly adjoined sections which separate easily to liberate autospores formed 2–4 in each mother cell; chromatophores 1–3; zoospores unknown.

Diachros simplex Pascher 1939, p. 372
Pl. 95, Fig. 14

Cells globose, solitary or in clusters, wall smooth; chromatophores 1–2 parietal plates; contents with 2 reddish-colored pigment-spots (oil bodies ?); cells 10–12μ in diameter.

In *Sphagnum* bog pools. Mich.

GONIOCHLORIS Geitler 1928, p. 81

Cells solitary or incidentally clustered in 2's and 4's, irregularly or regularly triangular or several-angled, flattened, or twisted with the angles in more than 1 plane, apices sometimes bluntly rounded, sometimes with the wall thickened and extended into prominent points or spines, wall thick and firm, often reddish or brown, sculptured with regularly arranged series of pits which form serrations at the cell margin (possibly some species with smooth walls); chromatophores 2–5 parietal plates; oil bodies and leucosin, and 1 or 2 red pigment-spots usually present; reproduction by autospores.

Goniochloris sculpta Geitler 1928, p. 81
Pl. 95, Figs. 1–3

Cells triangular in face view, compressed and narrowly ovate or oblong-elliptic in side view and showing the juncture of the 2 wall pieces in the long axis; outer membrane sculptured with rounded or hexagonal depressions, which form serrations at the wall margins; chromatophores 3–5 plate-like parietal bodies; cell contents with 1 or 2 reddish-colored oil bodies; cells about 30μ in the long dimension, in face view, 24μ wide.

In shallow water of acid bog. Mich.

MERINGOSPHAERA (Lohmann) Pascher 1932a, p. 200

Cells globose or subglobose, solitary, the cell wall rather thick and firm (in two sections ?), silicified, smooth or sculptured, beset with long or short spines which may be sparse and scattered or numerous and evenly distributed, the spines either tapering or truncate, straight or twisted; chromatophores 1 to many, golden-brown parietal plates, with or without pyrenoids; reproduction by autospores (possibly zoospores also ?).

Meringosphaera spinosa Prescott in Prescott, Silva, & Wade 1949, pp. 87, 93
Pl. 95, Figs. 21, 22

Cells spherical, the wall sparsely beset with relatively long, fine, tapering spines; chromatophores numerous ovate, parietal discs; (pyrenoids ?); cells 10–12.5μ in diameter.

Our specimens are referred to the marine genus *Meringosphaera* on the basis of the wall features and the shape of the cells. The smooth walls (except for the spines) prevent the inclusion of this species with other genera that have spherical cells. It should be compared with *M. brevispina* Pascher, a marine species with 3–4 band-like chromatophores.

In shallow water of acid bog lakes. Mich.

MONALLANTUS Pascher 1939, p. 420

Cells solitary or in unjoined clusters of 2–4, sometimes arranged in a series and inclosed by an inconspicuous film of mucilage, oblong with parallel margins and broadly rounded poles, sometimes short cylinders with slightly convex margins; cell wall smooth, sometimes reddish; chromatophores 2–10, band-like or plate-like (occasionally reticulate), parietal, with or without pyrenoids; leucosin granules and red oil globules usually present; reproduction by heterokont zoospores and autospores.

Monallantus brevicylindrus Pascher 1939, p. 422
Pl. 95, Fig. 24

Cells cylindric, one-third to one-half longer than broad; chromatophores (1)–2–4; cells 6–8μ in diameter, 9–12μ long; zoospores with 2 flagella, amoeboid, ellipsoid, with 1 or 2 chromatophores.

In shallow water of acid bog lake. Mich.

PERONE Pascher 1932b, p. 685

Cells solitary, sessile and epiphytic on leaves or among cells of *Sphagnum* and other aquatic mosses, globose or depressed-globose, somewhat flattened on the side against the substrate; wall thin, firm, smooth, composed of 1 piece, the cytoplasm highly reticulate and vacuolate in older cells; chromatophores 1 (in younger cells) to numerous disc-like or ovate plates, distributed parietally in the cytoplasm; uninucleate at first, becoming multinucleate before the formation of amoeboid, rhizopodal swarmspores; contractile vacuoles, oil bodies, leucosin, and usually a red pigment-spot present.

Perone dimorpha Pascher 1932b, p. 685
Pl. 95, Figs. 25, 26

Cells 13–60μ in diameter; amoeboid swarmers 7–15μ in diameter. On mosses in an acid bog pond. Mich.

PLEUROGASTER Pascher 1939, p. 469

Cells solitary, or incidentally clustered in 2's and 4's, fusiform, ellipsoid, or irregularly lunate, sometimes transversely flattened; wall smooth, thickened at the poles and extended into short and blunt, or long and hair-like points; chromatophores 2–4, parietal; no pyrenoids; several reddish oil bodies present in the cytoplasm; reproduction by autospores and biflagellate zoospores.

Key to the Species

Cells broadly ovate to subcylindric, or
  unsymmetrically reniform .... *P. oocystoides*
Cells fusiform or irregularly lunate .... *P. lunaris*

Pleurogaster lunaris Pascher 1939, p. 470
Pl. 95, Fig. 15

Cells ellipsoid, fusiform, or irregularly lunate, the poles slightly thickened and sometimes extended to form short knobs or horns; chromatophores 2–4 parietal plates; reddish oil bodies usually present in the cytoplasm; cells 8–15μ in diameter, 12–17μ long.
  Plankter; in Douglas Lake, Michigan.

Pleurogaster oocystoides Prescott *in* Prescott,
Silva, & Wade 1949, pp. 87, 93
Pl. 95, Figs. 19, 20

Cells solitary, ovate, unsymmetrically reniform, or broadly elliptic, one side flattened or concave, the other broadly convex, the poles broadly rounded and furnished with a nodular thickening at one or both ends; chromatophores numerous parietal discs; cells 8–10μ in diameter, 12–14μ long.

This species differs from others of the genus in the *Oocystis*-like and *Nephrocytium*-like shape of the cells, and the numerous disc-like chromatophores (rather than plates).

In *Sphagnum* bog pools. Mich.

TETRAGONIELLA Pascher 1930, p. 426

Solitary, tetragonal cells, triangular in outline when seen from one angle, the four lobes in two different planes and cruciately arranged; wall thick, sculptured with shallow depressions between reticulations which produce serrations at the cell margin, the depressions arranged in linear series about the cell, the wall at the apices of the lobes thickened and extended into short, sharp points; cell contents highly vacuolate, with a parietal reticulum in which the numerous disc-like chromatophores are arranged, and with leucosin granules and rod-like bodies; reproduction by zoospores containing 2–5 chromatophores.

Tetragoniella gigas Pascher 1930, p. 426
Pl. 95, Figs. 12, 13

Characteristics as described for the genus; cells (30)–45–50μ in diameter.

In shallow water of an acid bog. Mich.

TRACHYCHLORON Pascher 1939, p. 504

Cells solitary, ovate, ellipsoid, or citriform, rhomboid in end view; wall with reticulate thickenings and intervening depressions, making the margin of the cell serrate; chromatophores 1 to several, elongate band-like or H-shaped bodies, parietal, often with a thickened 'basal' portion from which lobes extend; pyrenoids present or absent; leucosin, fat globules, and reddish oil bodies present; reproduction by aplanospores and zoospores.

Key to the Species

Cells fusiform; chromatophores 2–3 (rarely 1) ....*T. biconnicum*
Cells broadly ellipsoid; 1 chromatophore ....*T. depauperatum*

Trachychloron biconicum Pascher 1939, p. 513
Pl. 95, Fig. 5

Cells broadly fusiform, with bluntly rounded poles; wall sculpturing usually prominent; chromatophores 2–3 or several plate-like bodies; cells 8–10μ in diameter, 16–20μ long.

In shallow water of an acid bog. Mich.

[354]

Trachychloron depauperatum Pascher 1939, p. 507

Pl. 95, Figs. 43, 44

Cells ovate or broadly ellipsoid, with broadly rounded poles; wall finely (sometimes faintly) sculptured, making very close serrations at the wall margin; 1 chromatophore, vase-shaped or ring-like, making a parietal fold within the cell wall; cells 4–8μ in diameter, 8–(10)–12μ long.

In shallow water of an acid bog. Mich.

FAMILY GLOEOBOTRYDACEAE

The cells in this family are spherical or ovate, arranged in 2's and 4's or sometimes many within a hyaline mucilage. Most species are planktonic, but some are sedentary palmelloid gelatinous masses. In the few-celled colonies the mucilage is lamellated but is scarcely or not entirely so in the multi-celled thalli. Reproduction is by zoospores or autospores, formed 2–4 within a cell. Gametic union is unknown.

To this family are assigned the genera *Chlorobotrys* and *Gloeobotrys*. Until recently the former was included with *Centritractus* and *Botryococcus* in the Botryococcaceae, but the latter genus has been transferred to the Chlorophyta and *Centritractus* has been placed in its own family (Pascher 1937–1939).

Key to the Genera

Cells 2–4 (rarely 6–8) in globular or ovoid, gelatinous,
    lamellated sheaths; free-floating_____*Chlorobotrys*

Cells many within unlamellated gelatinous
    sheaths; free-floating or sedentary_____ *Gloeobotrys*

CHLOROBOTRYS Bohlin 1901, p. 34

A colony of 2–4–8 spherical or ovoid individuals inclosed and usually evenly spaced in a wide, gelatinous lamellate envelope; the cell wall thick and impregnated with silicon; chromatophores 2–4, yellow-green, parietal bodies without pyrenoids; starch not present; a red pigment-spot often visible (not interpreted as an eye-spot comparable with the organ present in other algal groups); reproduction by autospores. There is but one species in our collections.

Chlorobotrys regularis (W. West) Bohlin 1901, p. 34

Pl. 93, Figs. 26, 27

A spherical colony of 2–8 (rarely more) globose cells regularly arranged within a hyaline, gelatinous envelope; chromatophores several parietal discs; a conspicuous pigment-spot usually visible (sometimes appearing black); cells 10–27μ in diameter; colony as much as 90μ in diameter.

Rare; in several lakes and bogs. Mich., Wis.

GLOEOBOTRYS Pascher 1930, p. 438

A free-floating or sedentary, gelatinous mass of regular or irregular shape, containing many spherical or slightly ovate cells; the sheath not at all or but very weakly stratified; chromatophores 2–4 parietal plates or discs; reproduction by aplanospores or by zoospores. There is but one species in our collections.

Gloeobotrys limneticus (G. M. Smith) Pascher 1937–1939, p. 637
Pl. 93, Figs. 35, 36

An ovate colony of 10–30 ovate cells in clusters within a wide, gelatinous envelope; chromatophores 3–4, yellow-green, parietal discs; cells 5–6μ in diameter, 6–8μ long; colonies up to 200μ in diameter.

In the tychoplankton of several soft water lakes. Wis.

FAMILY BOTRYOCHLORIDACEAE

Cells clustered, few to many, in small families or colonies (rarely 2–4 in a cluster) without being inclosed by a definite colonial sheath of mucilage; cells round, short-cylindric, or needle-shaped, free living or adherent to other algae; the cells in adherent colonies angular from mutual compression; reproduction by autospores and zoospores.

CHLORELLIDIOPSIS Pascher 1939, p. 683

Cells seldom solitary, mostly in closely arranged, sometimes cushion-like aggregates, sessile on substrates in 2's, 3's or 4's, irregularly globose but flattened by mutual compression along the adjoined walls; a mucilaginous investment sometimes evident; wall smooth; chromatophores 1 or 3 thin parietal plates; reddish globules of waste material present in the cytoplasm; reproduction by autospores and zoospores.

Chlorellidiopsis separabilis Pascher 1939, p. 686
Pl. 95, Figs. 16–18, 23

Cells globose, subglobose, or pyriform, forming extended, loose patches on filamentous algae and other aquatic plants; cells arranged in 2's or 3's, occasionally solitary; chromatophores 2 parietal plates; cells 8–14μ in diameter.

In mixtures of algae in *Sphagnum* bog pools. Mich.

FAMILY CHARACIOPSIDACEAE

This family includes attached, unicellular forms which are unable to multiply by cell division in the vegetative state. The plants are variously shaped, ovoid to fusiform or sickle-shaped and are attached by a long or short stipe to filamentous algae or microfauna. The stalk is formed by an extension of the cell wall which consists of but one piece. There are 1 to several parietal, plate-like, yellowish-green chromatophores. Food reserve is in the form of oil. Reproduction occurs by aplanospores, or more frequently by 8–64 zoospores with 2 flagella of unequal length.

Key to the Genera

Cells ovoid or subglobose, attached by a stipe which usually has no
    basal disc; the stipe longer than the cell body; 1 chromatophore ...*Peroniella*
Cells fusiform, subcylindrical, or sickle-shaped, attached by a short
    or long stipe with a basal disc, the stipe shorter than the cell
    body in most species; chromatophores several (rarely but 1).........*Characiopsis*

CHARACIOPSIS Borzi 1894, p. 151

An attached, ovoid or pyriform, subcylindrical or sickle-shaped cell with a narrow, long or short stipe and usually with a basal attaching disc, growing on filamentous algae or microfauna; chromatophores 2–5, plate-like, yellow-green bodies; zoospores produced many in a cell, with a single flagellum (probably one long and one very short); gametic union reported for at least 1 species.

Characiopsis should be compared with *Characium*, a genus with grass-green chloroplasts and pyrenoids, producing starch and usually having very slender basal stipes. See page 215. Also this genus should be compared with *Harpochytrium*, certain species of which greatly resemble *Characiopsis*. Especially when examining preserved algae this comparison should be made. *Harpochytrium Hyalothecae*, frequently seen in our collections, is illustrated on Pl. 93, Figs.23–25.

Key to the Species

1. Cells cylindrical..*C. cylindrica*
1. Cells not cylindrical 2
2. Cells with a sharply pointed apex.. 3
2. Cells with an obtuse apex 5
3. Cells ellipsoid, with a very short, broad stipe (practically sessile),
    and a short, straight spine-like apex ....*C. spinifer*
3. Cells with a slender stipe 4
4. Stipe as long or longer than the cell body;
    cell narrowly fusiform ....*C. longipes*
4. Stipe less than the cell body in length;
    cells broadly ellipsoid..*C. acuta*

5. Cells pyriform, broadly rounded anteriorly,
   narrowed to a slender stipe below..*C. pyriformis*
5. Cells broadly ovoid in the lower portion, abruptly narrowed an-
   teriorly and then extended to form a produced apex................*C. lageniformis*

Characiopsis acuta (A. Braun) Borzi 1894, p. 153
Pl. 95, Figs. 29–31

Cells ovoid to fusiform or spindle-shaped, on a slender stipe less than the cell body in length, with a basal attaching disc, narrowed anteriorly, sometimes abruptly to a sharp or blunt point; membrane thin, thickened at the apex; chromatophores 1–2 large parietal plates folded along the wall; cells 6–10μ in diameter, 15–28μ long (including stipe).

In soft water lake; tychoplanktonic among other algae. Mich., Wis.

Characiopsis cylindrica (Lambert) Lemmermann 1914, p. 256
Pl. 45, Fig. 19; Pl. 94, Figs. 1, 2

Cells club-shaped to cylindrical, rounded at the anterior end, tapering posteriorly to a narrow base, scarcely forming a stipe (nearly sessile); with a basal attaching disc; in reproduction forming 8–32 or hundreds of minute bodies which escape through a pore in the apex where there is a thickened plug; chromatophores 2, parietal; cells 9–20μ in diameter, 24–55–(430)μ long.

Epizoic on *Daphnia* and other microzoa in small lakes. Wis.

Characiopsis lageniformis Pascher 1930, p. 444
Pl. 93, Fig. 31

Cells solitary or in small groups, fusiform, broad below and then rather abruptly narrowed to a rounded, cone-shaped apex; narrowed below to a short stipe which has a flattened attaching disc; chromatophores 2 parietal bands; cells 7–11μ in diameter, 20–23μ long.

Epiphytic on *Tribonema* filaments. Wis.

Characiopsis longipes (Rab.) Borzi 1894, p. 152
Pl. 93, Fig. 32

Cells fusiform, straight or curved, apiculate, tapering posteriorly into a long, slender stipe, with a basal attaching disc; chromatophores 1–2; cells 5–7.5μ in diameter, 40–50μ long.

Epiphytic on filamentous algae, including diatoms. Mich., Wis.

Characiopsis pyriformis (A. Braun) Borzi 1894, p. 153
Pl. 93, Figs. 33, 34

Cells obovoid, apex broadly rounded, base narrowed gradually into a relatively long stipe with a basal attaching disc; chromatophores

2–4; cells 5–12μ in diameter, 18–25μ long including stipe; stipe 9–13μ long.

Found on members of the Volvocales and on diatoms. Mich., Wis.

Characiopsis spinifer Printz 1914, p. 44
Pl. 94, Figs. 3–5

Cells ovoid to elliptic, with an acute tip, practically sessile on a broad attaching disc; chromatophores several disc-shaped bodies; cells 7–9μ in diameter, 22–30μ long.

On miscellaneous filamentous algae. Wis.

PERONIELLA Gobi 1887, p. 244

An attached ovate, ovoid- or elliptic-pyriform cell with a narrow stipe which may have a basal attaching disc; chromatophores 1 or 2, yellow-green parietal plates.

Species of this genus have always been found on algae which are inclosed in a gelatinous sheath. The stipe of the epiphyte penetrates the mucilage to make contact with the cell wall of the host.

Key to the Species

Cells spherical, stipe fine and thread-like .... *P. Hyalothecae*
Cells ovoid or ellipsoid, narrowed below to form a
slender, but not thread-like stipe..*P. planctonica*

Peroniella Hyalothecae Gobi 1887, p. 244
Pl. 94, Fig. 6

Cells spherical, 15–20μ in diameter, with a very slender hair-like stipe and a basal attaching disc; chromatophores 2 parietal plates.

Common in acid habitats; attached to the filamentous desmid *Hyalotheca*. Mich., Wis.

Peroniella planctonica G. M. Smith 1916, p. 476
Pl. 94, Figs. 7–9

Cells broadly ovate, ovoid, subglobose, or pyriform-globose, with a tapering stipe which has no basal attaching disc; chromatophores 1 or 2 laminate bodies; cells 6–9.5μ long without the stipe, 15–18μ long including the stipe.

Attached to the filamentous desmid, *Sphaerozosma;* in *Sphagnum* bogs and soft water lakes. Wis.

FAMILY CENTRITRACTACEAE

The cells in this family are solitary and uninucleate. In a few species small aggregates of cells are formed, however. The individuals are fusiform, cylindrical, or rectangular in shape, but in the latter case flattened when seen in side view. The wall is in 2 equal or unequal pieces between which a section may be interpolated to bring about a lengthening of the cell. In most forms there is a spine at the poles, or at the corners of the cell. Reproduction is by autospores or, rarely, by zoospores. *Centritractus*[5] should be compared with *Ophiocytium*.

Key to the Genera

Cells furnished with a spine at either end of the
cell, which is usually long-cylindric...*Centritractus*
Cells without spines..*Bumilleriopsis*

BUMILLERIOPSIS Printz 1914, p. 50

Cells solitary or adjoined end to end to form short filaments or radiating clusters; the cells ellipsoid, subcylindric, or fusiform, with poles either smooth or furnished with a blunt apiculation, the two poles symmetrical or unsymmetrical; cell wall thin, or thick and firm, smooth, the 2 sections not clearly apparent except during liberation of autospores or zoospores; chromatophores 2 to many parietal plates.

Bumilleriopsis brevis Printz 1914, p. 50
Pl. 95, Figs. 6–8

Cells cylindric or subcylindric, straight or slightly curved to semilunate, the poles unsymmetrical, one pole sometimes sharply pointed, the other broadly rounded; chromatophores numerous parietal discs; cells 4–10μ in diameter, 10–30–(60)μ long.
In an acid bog lake. Mich.

CENTRITRACTUS Lemmermann 1900d, p. 274

Cells ellipsoid or subcylindrical, with a long or short spine at each pole; wall in 2 portions, the juncture occurring either in the midregion or near one end, or in elongated cells, occurring at two points so that a 'cap' is formed at either end of the cell; chromatophores (1)–2–4–(5), yellowish-brown, plate-like bodies; reproduction by autospores, aplanospores, or zoospores (Pascher 1937–1939, p. 849).

Key to the Species

Spines ½ the length of the cell or less;
cells elliptic to oblong-elliptic...*C. dubius*
Spines as long as the cell body or nearly so; cells
cylindrical (cylindric-ovoid when young)......................*C. belanophorus*

---

[5]Spelling changed to *Centratractus* by Pascher.

Centritractus belanophorus Lemmermann 1900d, p. 274

Pl. 95, Figs. 37, 38

Cells usually elongate-cylindric (rarely elongate-ovoid to ellipsoid when young), straight or slightly curved, with a long, slender spine at each pole; junctures of the wall sections conspicuous, one showing near each end of the cell; chromatophores 1 or 2 parietal plates; pigment-spot sometimes apparent (especially in cells with but 1 chromatophore); cells 8–12–(15)μ in diameter, up to 40μ long; spines about as long as the cell.

In acid bog lakes. Mich., Wis.

Centritractus dubius Printz 1914, p. 72

Pl. 93, Figs. 28, 29

Cells broadly ellipsoid or narrowly ovate to subcylindrical, the poles broadly rounded and furnished with a stout, straight spine; overlapping of the 2 wall sections very evident, the juncture near the midregion of the cell; chromatophores 2–5 parietal plates or folds; cells 5–7.8μ in diameter, 41.6μ long including spines, 10–14μ long without spines.

Rare in plankton of several soft water and acid lakes. Wis.

FAMILY CHLOROTHECIACEAE

This distinctive but small family includes free-floating or attached cylindrical cells which have a thick, often lamellated wall (a character usually determinable only in stained preparations). The wall is formed of 2 pieces decidedly different in size, the longer one of which overlaps the other. In one genus (*Ophiocytium*), the cells elongate by a stretching of one of the pieces, and additional layers of wall material are erected to form a series of telescoping cups. There may be a spine at one or both poles, or the apices may be smooth. The cells are multinucleate, at least in age. Usually members of this family are solitary, but in a few species colonies are formed when successive generations of cells remain attached in tiers by the *in situ* germination of zoospores in or on the old mother cell wall. The plants are incapable of multiplication by cell division. (See Pascher 1937–1939 for a treatment of the taxonomy of this family.)

Key to the Genera

Cells attached by a broad, short stipe, or sessile;
solitary; not growing by increase in length_____*Chlorothecium*

Cells free-living or, if attached, furnished with a slender stipe;
cells elongate-cylindric and increasing in
length; often colony-forming_____*Ophiocytium*

CHLOROTHECIUM (Borzi) Pascher 1939, p. 863

Cells subspherical, clavate, or ellipsoid, attached by a broad flattened base or short, thick stipe to a substrate; cells straight or slightly bent if elongate; cell wall smooth, in 2 sections, the upper longer than the lower; chromatophores 1 to many, without pyrenoids (?); reproduction by autospores and aplanospores.

Chlorothecium Pirottae Borzi 1894, p. 139
Pl. 95, Fig. 11

Cells club-shaped to elongate-ellipsoid, or clavate, narrowed at the base to form a short, stout stipe with an adhesive disc; chromatophores 2–4, parietal; contents divided to form (2)–4 or many aplanospores which are liberated by the gelatinization of the upper part of the cell; cells 6–10μ in diameter, up to 30μ long.

Attached to filamentous algae and other submerged aquatic plants. Mich.

OPHIOCYTIUM Naegeli 1849, p. 87

An attached or free-floating cylindrical or clavate unicell which may be straight, arcuate, or spirally coiled; sometimes with one end swollen and capitate; solitary or in some species forming corymblike clusters; poles of the cell truncately rounded, with or without a spine or stipe; chromatophores (3)–4–16 pale yellow parietal discs or plates, without pyrenoids; oil but not starch formed as a storage product; reproduction by autospores or zoospores, liberated by the lifting away of the upper portion of the cell.

Some species of the genus are attached by the stipe, usually to filamentous algae. It is thought likely that some of the free-floating species are the same as those which are attached and which become planktonic in age, the stipe then appearing as one of the polar spines.

Key to the Species

1. Cells attached, epiphytic 2
1. Cells free-floating 5
2. Plants solitary ....O. desertum
2. Plants colonial 3
3. Cells with an apical spine ....O. mucronatum
3. Cells without an apical spine 4
4. Cells with a slender stipe, 2–4 times the
   diameter of the cell in length ....O gracilipes
4. Cells with a short, stout stipe, equal to or
   1½ times the diameter of the cell in length ....O. arbuscula
5. Cells with a spine at each pole 6
5. Cells with a spine at one pole only, or without spines 7
6. Cells 15–20μ in diameter; spine long, up to 40μ ....O. bicuspidatum
6. Cells smaller, (2.7)–5–10μ in diameter; spines short and sharp ....O. capitatum

Ophiocytium arbuscula (A. Braun) Rabenhorst 1868, p. 68
Pl. 94, Fig. 12

Cells attached by a short, stout stipe, cylindrical, united in corymbose families, several cells with truncate or rounded apices growing from the end of a straight or slightly twisted basal cell; cells 3.5–5µ in diameter.

Tychoplankter; in swamps. Mich., Wis.

Ophiocytium bicuspidatum (Borge) Lemmermann 1899, p. 31
Pl. 94, Fig. 23

Cells free-floating, arcuate or spirally twisted; poles each bearing a stout spine; cells 15–20µ in diameter, 50–55µ long without spines; spines up to 40µ long.

Plankter; in soft water lakes; generally distributed. Mich., Wis.

Ophiocytium capitatum Wolle 1887, p. 176
Pl. 94, Figs. 21, 22

Cells free-floating, cylindrical, strongly curved or sickle-shaped, with a short sharp spine at each pole; cells (2.7)–5–10µ in diameter, 45–150–(2000)µ long.

Common in a variety of lakes. Mich., Wis.

Ophiocytium capitatum var. *longispinum* (Moebius)
Lemmermann 1899, p. 32
Pl. 94, Fig. 19

Cells free-floating, either straight, arcuate, or spiral, each pole bearing a spine (in which character this variety differs from the typical); cells 4.5–6µ in diameter; spines 16–50µ long.

Tychoplankter. Wis.

Ophiocytium cochleare (Eichw.) A. Braun 1855, p. 54
Pl. 94, Figs. 10, 11, 15

Cells free-floating, cylindrical, strongly arched and spirally twisted, one end truncate, the other with a stout, sharp spine; cells 5–9.5µ in diameter.

Common in the tychoplankton of many lakes and swamps. Mich., Wis.

Ophiocytium desertum Printz 1914, p. 47

Cells cylindrical, attached by a short, relatively stout stalk and a thick adhesive disc (usually on filamentous algae); cells truncately rounded at the anterior end, without a spine; 9–14μ in diameter, 30–60μ long.

Mich.

Ophiocytium desertum var. minor Prescott 1944, p. 362
Pl. 96, Figs. 2, 3

Cells attached, cylindrical or sausage-shaped; basal stipe with a flattened disc-like attaching organ; anterior end broadly rounded; 4–9μ in diameter, 58–65μ long.

In swamps; tychoplanktonic in lakes. Wis.

Ophiocytium elongatum West & West 1907, p. 232

Cells free-floating, irregularly curved, twisted at one end, or sometimes nearly straight, with a short spine at one end, truncately rounded at the other; 5–5.5μ in diameter, up to 70 times the diameter in length. (Typical form not found in our region.)

Compare with O. Lagerheimii Lemm. and O. majus.

Ophiocytium elongatum var. major Prescott 1944, p. 362
Pl. 94, Figs. 13, 14

A variety differing from the typical by its much greater size; cells free-floating, cylindrical, straight, curved or hooked at one end which is truncate, the other bearing a stout spine, not coiled; chromatophores 16 parietal discs; cells 10–12μ in diameter, 400–420μ long without the spine, which is 10–12μ long.

This species should be compared with O. cochleare, which is smaller and has arcuate or coiled cells. O. elongatum, originally described from Burma, is coiled although not closely.

In soft water or in acid swamps. Wis.

Ophiocytium gracilipes Rabenhorst 1865, p. 68
Pl. 95, Figs. 35, 36

Cells cylindrical, straight or somewhat curved, attached by a stipe 2–4 times the diameter of the cell in length, and basal adhesive disc, forming colonies by the germination of spores at the rim of the anterior open end of a mother cell; the young plants attached by strongly curved stipes; chromatophores (2)–4 parietal plates; cells 5–7μ in diameter and up to 40μ long.

The basal stipe is longer and more slender than in the common O. arbuscula.

Rare; on filamentous algae. Mich., Wis.

Ophiocytium majus Naegeli 1849, p. 89

Pl. 94, Figs. 17, 18

Cells free-floating, cylindrical, relatively long; S-curved, spiral, or lunate; one end truncate, the other with a short, sharp spine bearing a spherical enlargement at its tip; $7.8-17\mu$ in diameter, 152μ long.

Rare; in bogs and in tychoplankton of lakes. Mich., Wis.

Ophiocytium mucronatum (A. Braun) Rabenhorst 1868, p. 68

Pl. 94, Fig. 16

Cells irregularly cylindrical, curved, attached by a short stipe and a hemispherical disc to filamentous algae; apical region slightly swollen, terminating in a slender spine; older individuals with cells of the second generation attached at the anterior end; diameter $4-7\mu$; $46-48\mu$ long.

Tychoplanktonic in lakes and swamps. Mich., Wis.

Ophiocytium parvulum (Perty) A. Braun 1855, p. 55

Pl. 94, Fig. 20; Pl. 96, Figs. 4, 5

Cells free-floating, cylindrical, long and strongly S-curved or spiral, truncate at both ends, $3-10\mu$ in diameter.

Common in the tychoplankton of many lakes. Mich., Wis.

ORDER HETEROTRICHALES

This well-defined order is composed of the strictly filamentous forms in the Xanthophyceae. In one of the suborders, Tribonematales (Pascher 1937–1939), the filaments are unbranched, whereas in a second suborder (Heterocloniales), they are simply branched. Although most forms are free-floating, some are attached, at least when young, by a basal stipe and adhesive disc. The duplex morphology of the wall is apparent in some genera in the vegetative condition, but in others it is evident only when the cells separate to liberate zoospores or aplanospores. Chromatophores are parietal plates or discs, often faintly pigmented. Reproduction is by zoospores, aplanospores, and in some genera by isogametes, the motile cells bearing 2 flagella of unequal length. Only one family is represented in our region, the Tribonemataceae. Pascher (*l.c.*) separates *Tribonema* from other genera, however, on the basis of wall structure details, recognizing the Tribonemataceae and the Heterotrichaceae to which *Bumilleria* is assigned. According to some views this separation is not justified.

FAMILY TRIBONEMATACEAE

The filaments are unbranched, uniseriate and composed of more or less cylindrical cells. There is basal-distal differentiation in young filaments, which are attached by a stipe and an adhesive disc. In nearly all forms the 2-piece construction of the cell wall is clearly evident, the juncture of the pieces occurring at the midregion of the cell. When the filaments fragment, the cells dissociate at the planes of juncture with the result that H-shaped pieces are formed (as in the genus *Microspora* in the Chlorophyta). There are 2 to several parietal disc-like chromatophores. Reproduction as described for the order.

Key to the Genera

Cells elongate-cylindric or slightly inflated, with overlapping of
  2 wall pieces clearly evident in all cells_____*Tribonema*
Cells short-cylindric, never inflated; 2 wall pieces not in evidence
  except as occasional thick H-shaped bands external
  to the cell wall and usually brown _____*Bumilleria*

BUMILLERIA Borzi 1894, p. 186

Filaments short, or long and entangled; composed of cylindrical, thin-walled cells; duplex character of the wall and H-shaped pieces seldom apparent except in cells liberating reproductive elements; chromatophores 2–8, parietal, yellow-green discs, with pyrenoids demonstrable in stained preparations.

Bumilleria sicula Borzi 1894, p. 186
Pl. 96, Fig. 6

Filaments (in our specimens) short, the ends showing H-shaped pieces; chromatophores 2–4 yellow-green parietal bodies with a metallic lustre; cells 8–13–(20)μ in diameter, 1½–2 diameters in length.

Tychoplankter; in swamps and ponds. Mich., Wis.

TRIBONEMA Derbés & Solier 1856, p. 1

Filaments composed of cylindrical (sometimes slightly swollen) cells, the walls of which are constructed of 2 sections overlapping in the midregion of the cell; cells forming H-shaped pieces when fragmentation of the filament occurs; chromatophores disc-shaped, light yellow-green, 2 to several in a cell, without pyrenoids.

The characteristic overlapping of the two portions of the cell wall is often distinguished with difficulty when living or filled cells are examined, but is apparent in empty cells and at the ends of broken filaments where one-half of a cell remains attached to the adjoining cell of the filament, thus showing one-half of the H.

Key to the Species

1. Filaments 5–7μ in diameter; cells elongate-cylindric;
   chromatophores 2–4, regularly arranged... 2
1. Filaments larger, 7–16–(30)μ in diameter; cells slightly inflated,
   with constrictions at the cross walls; chromatophores many........................ 3
2. Cells cylindrical, not at all constricted at the cross walls, up to
   8 times the diameter in length; chromatophores 2–4 folded plates........T. *affine*
2. Cells slightly inflated, 2–4 (rarely 6) times the diameter in length;
   chromatophores 2–4 irregular discs...T. *minus*
3. Cells 10–17μ in diameter; wall thick, clearly showing
   the overlapping of the 2 wall sections..T. *utriculosum*
3. Cells 6–11μ in diameter; wall thin, not showing
   overlapping of the 2 wall sections..T. *bombycinum*

Tribonema affine G. S. West 1904, p. 208
Pl. 96, Figs. 7–9

Filaments straight and slender; cells long-cylindric with thin walls, 5–5.6μ in diameter, 35–40μ long; chromatophores 4 pale, yellow-green parietal plates with smooth margins.

Forming gray-yellow clouds in ponds, ditches, and small lakes. Wis.

Tribonema bombycinum (C. A. Ag.) Derbés & Solier 1856, p. 18
Pl. 96, Fig. 10

Filaments much entangled, forming a grayish-yellow cloudy mass in quiet water. Cells with thin walls; cylindrical or slightly constricted at the cross walls; 6–11μ in diameter, 15–38μ long. Chromatophores 4–8 small, parietal, pale yellow-green discs, sometimes in contact, giving the appearance of 1 or 2 large, irregularly shaped plates.

Pascher's dropping of this name seems unwarranted, although there is great confusion as to which plants belong to this time-honored name. In his Heterokonten (Rabenhorst's Kryptogamen-Flora, 11, p. 975, 1939) Pascher has transferred T. *bombycinum* Derbés & Solier to T. *viride* Pascher (1925, p. 106.)

This is a common species in cold water of springs, ditches, and dark-colored lakes. In bodies of water rich in humic acid, such as lakes receiving drainage from wooded swamps, this species is often the predominating if not sole component of the algal flora (at least in shallow water of the margin). Mich., Wis.

Tribonema bombycinum var. tenue Hazen 1902, p. 185
Pl. 96, Fig. 11

A variety differing from the typical by its more slender filaments; cells cylindrical, 3–6μ in diameter, 10–36μ long; chromatophores numerous small discs.

Probably a growth form. Forming light green cottony masses entangled in submerged roots and sticks. Occurring with the typical plant.

Tribonema minus (Wille) Hazen 1902, p. 185
Pl. 96, Figs. 12, 13

Filaments slender; cells slightly inflated to subcylindrical, 5–6μ wide, 23–27μ long (rarely longer); chromatophores 2–4 relatively large parietal disc-like plates, symmetrically arranged about the wall (as in *T. aequale* Pascher).

In shallow water of lakes and ponds; often in water with humic acids. Wis.

Tribonema utriculosum (Kuetz.) Hazen 1902, p. 186
Pl. 96, Figs. 14–16

Filaments long or short, fragmenting easily; cells stout with relatively heavy walls, clearly showing the overlapping of the 2 wall pieces in the midregion of the cell; chromatophores many irregular discs; cells 10–17μ in diameter, 15–53.5μ long.

Forming loose cottony masses in shallow water of lake margins, swamps, and marshes; tychoplanktonic. Mich., Wis.

ORDER HETEROSIPHONALES

The plants which compose this small order are vesicular, growing on moist soil with subterranean rhizoidal portions. There are numerous small chromatophores and nuclei. Although pyrenoids are reported, the food reserve is oil rather than starch. Reproduction is by zoospores, aplanospores, or by hypnospores which are formed underground in the rhizoidal portions of the thallus. There is 1 family.

FAMILY BOTRYDIACEAE

Characteristics as described for the order. This family contains 1 genus, and of the 2 species reported from the United States one occurs in our collections.

BOTRYDIUM Wallroth 1815, p. 153

A macroscopic, unicellular coenocyte growing on moist soil, vesicular and globose above, narrowed below to form subterranean rhizoidal branches; chromatophores numerous yellow-green discs; food reserve oil and leucosin; spores formed in the underground portions of the thallus.

Botrydium Wallrothii Kuetzing is to be expected in this region but has not been reported. The membrane of the vescicle in this species is very thick and lamellate. In the subterranean portions of the thallus, rhizoids are transversely folded and wrinkled.

Botrydium granulatum (L.) Greville 1830, p. 196
Pl. 96, Figs. 17, 18

A dark green obovoid or globose vesicle, variable in size from 0.5–2.5 mm. in diameter.

Growing on damp soil and mud, especially along stream banks or near lake shores and swamps where water has recently receded; often found on damp soil in greenhouses. Mich., Wis.

CLASS CHRYSOPHYCEAE

Most of the members of this class are motile, but a few apparently closely related forms are filamentous or palmelloid. The most obvious characteristic is the relatively large, yellow-brown chromatophore which, in addition to chlorophyll, contains an abundance of phycochrysin. In a very few genera pyrenoids are present, but in no case is starch formed as a reserve food, oil and leucosin being the chief storage products. There are 5 orders in this class, which are differentiated by general morphology and on the basis of motility.

Key to the Orders

1. Motile in the vegetative state by 1 or 2 flagella............CHRYSOMONADALES
1. Non-motile in the vegetative state................................ 2
2. Amoeboid, or if stationary showing
   rhizopodal tendencies..RHIZOCHRYSIDALES
2. Not amoeboid or rhizopodal 3
3. Plants palmelloid..CHRYSOCAPSALES
3. Plants not palmelloid 4
4. Filamentous ....CHRYSOTRICHALES
4. Unicellular, cyst-like, forming autospores..............CHRYSOSPHAERALES

ORDER CHRYSOMONADALES

Motile in the vegetative condition; flagella 1 or 2; either unicellular or colonial; cell wall lacking but in many forms possessing a definitely shaped envelope or lorica; three suborders.

Key to the Suborders

1. Swimming by 1 flagellum ....CHROMULINEAE
1. Swimming by 2 flagella, but may be non-motile in
   the vegetative state... 2
2. Flagella of equal length; lorica absent .... ISOCHRYSIDINEAE
2. Flagella of unequal length; protoplast
   inclosed by a lorica...OCHROMONADINEAE

[369]

SUBORDER CHROMULININEAE

Of the 2 families in this group only the Mallomonadaceae is represented in our collections. The Chromulinaceae includes forms which have the cell membrane undecorated. They are undoubtedly of wide occurrence but as yet have not been reported from this region; at least *Chromulina Cienkowski* may be expected here.

FAMILY MALLOMONADACEAE

Plants solitary or colonial; cell membrane decorated or beset with silicious plates or scales and bristles which may be very long and sometimes irregularly diverging from the cells.

Key to the Genera

Unicellular, the membrane covered with variously shaped scales,
  usually bearing long needle-like bristles _____*Mallomonas*
Colonial, the cells furnished with 2 long
  anterior rods set in basal cups _____*Chrysosphaerella*

MALLOMONAS Perty 1852, p. 170

Unicellular, free-swimming, ovoid, elliptical, fusiform, or sometimes nearly cylindrical, the membrane beset with closely arranged or overlapping silicious plates (scales) which may bear very long, slender needles of the same material (also, in some species, with spines near the poles of the cell); scales circular, elliptic, ovoid or polygonal; chromatophores, 2 golden-brown parietal plates; 1 anterior flagellum; food reserve in the form of leucosin, which collects in the posterior end of the cell.

See Conrad (1927, 1933) for monographic treatment of this genus.

Key to the Species

1. Cells with an apical corona or collar _____ 2
1. Cells without an apical corona or collar _____ 3
2. Cells with an apical collar, the margin smooth _____*M. urnaformis*
2. Cells with an apical corona of sharply pointed teeth _____ *M. pseudocoronata*
3. Setae arising from over the entire surface of the cell _____ 4
3. Setae lacking or arising from near one end of the cell_____ 6
4. Cells pyriform, narrower at the anterior end_____*M. fastigata*
4. Cells ovoid or ellipsoid _____ 5
5. Setae projecting at all angles, not recurved at the tips,
  cells narrower at the posterior end_____*M. caudata*
5. Setae mostly directed posteriorly, the tips recurved,
  cells narrower at the anterior end_____*M. acaroides*
6. Long setae not present_____*M. elliptica*
6. Long setae present _____ 7
7. Setae few in number, sparsely scattered posteriorly; scales longitudinally elliptical; cells 50–92μ long _____*M. apochromatica*
7. Setae many; cells smaller _____ 8

Mallomonas acaroides Perty 1852, p. 171

Pl. 96, Fig. 22

Cells ovoid, broadly rounded at both poles but somewhat narrowed anteriorly; scales ovoid to subcircular, arranged in spiral series; needles as long as or a little longer than the cell, mostly directed posteriorly (slightly recurved at the tips); cells (7)–15–(23)µ in diameter, 18–23.4–(45)µ long.

Rare; in euplankton. Wis.

Mallomonas acaroides var. *Moskovensis*
(Wermel) Krieger 1932, p. 293

Pl. 96, Fig. 20

Cells broadly ovoid, 1¼ to 2 times as long as wide; scales elliptical, very slightly overlapping; needles in the anterior region directed forward and outwardly curved, other needles straight and directed posteriorly; cells 12–15µ in diameter, 21–25µ long.

Euplankter. Wis.

Mallomonas alpina Pascher & Ruttner, in
Pascher & Lemmermann 1913, p. 36

Pl. 96, Fig. 19

Cells elongate-ellipsoid or oblong, usually with broadly rounded poles; membrane covered with rhomboidal scales, so disposed as to form diagonal (spiral) rows, those near the anterior end of the cell each bearing a long needle, the needles directed forward and outwardly curved; cells 8–12µ in diameter, 25–45µ long.

Rare; in the plankton of many lakes, mostly semi-hard water. Mich., Wis.

Mallomonas apochromatica Conrad 1927, p. 440

Pl. 97, Fig. 3

Cells oblong to cylindrical, broadly rounded at both poles; scales longitudinally elliptical and imbricate, arranged in spirally transverse series; needles few in number at the posterior end of the cell, straight or slightly curved; cell (22)–32µ in diameter, 58–92µ long.

Euplankter. Wis.

Mallomonas caudata Iwanoff 1899 [1900a], p. 250

Pl. 97, Fig. 1

Cells ovoid, much narrower at the posterior end, membrane covered with oval scales so disposed as to form transverse rows; all scales bearing a long needle, the needles directed outward and back; anterior end furnished with a few sharp teeth; chloroplasts 2 brown, parietal plates; cells 12–30μ in diameter, 40–85μ long.

Rare to common in the plankton of a great variety of lakes. Mich., Wis.

Mallomonas elliptica (Kisselew) Conrad, 1933, p. 17

Pl. 96, Fig. 24

Cells broadly elliptical and broadly rounded posteriorly, narrowed anteriorly; membrane covered with diamond-shaped, rhomboidal or polyhedral scales arranged in somewhat irregular transverse rows, the scales without needles; spines not present except for small projections at the anterior end around the flagellum aperture; cells 28–30μ in diameter, 47–50μ long.

Euplankter, uncommon. Wis.

Mallomonas fastigata var. *macrolepis*

(Conrad) Conrad, 1933, p. 65

Pl. 97, Fig. 2

Cells pyriform, elongate-elliptic, broadest at the anterior end, narrowly rounded at the posterior pole; scales ovoid to subcircular, overlapping and with no apparent order of arrangement; needles numerous, long, posteriorly directed (described as being barbed near the ends but this not observed in our specimens); 20–25μ in diameter; 50–60–(80)μ long.

Euplankter. Wis.

Mallomonas producta (Zacharias) Iwanoff 1899 [1900a], p. 250

Pl. 97, Fig. 4

Cell cylindrical, the lateral walls either straight or slightly convex; membrane covered with diamond-shaped or transversely elongate-elliptic scales so disposed as to form diagonal (spiral) rows; needles produced only in the basal region, posteriorly directed; chromatophores 2 golden-brown, parietal plates; cells 9–13μ wide, 40–70μ long.

Rare to common in the plankton of a variety of lakes. Wis.

Mallomonas producta var. *Marchica* Lemmermann 1903d, p. 106
Pl. 97, Fig. 5

Differing from the typical by having shorter and broader cells, with the needles both anterior and posterior; cells 11–12μ wide, 21–26μ long.
Euplankter. Wis.

Mallomonas pseudocoronata Prescott 1944, p. 363
Pl. 96, Fig. 23

Cells fusiform-elliptic, narrowly rounded at both poles; scales transversely elliptic to rhomboidal or diamond-shaped, not imbricate, arranged in spirally transverse series, at the anterior end forming a corona of sharply pointed projections about the flagellum opening; needles of 2 kinds, stout long ones forming a posterior tuft and short spine-like recurved ones over the surface; cell 20–25μ in diameter, 48–50μ long including needles.
Euplankter. Wis.

Mallomonas tonsurata Teiling 1912, p. 277
Pl. 97, Fig. 6

Cells ellipsoid or ovate, with the posterior end broadly rounded and the anterior end narrowed; membrane covered with irregularly arranged ovoid scales, those in the anterior end bearing a needle; cells 11–12μ in diameter, 21–26μ long.
Euplankter. Wis.

Mallomonas urnaformis Prescott 1944, p. 363
Pl. 97, Fig. 7

Cell elliptic with a corona or neck of erect scales at the anterior end about the flagellum pore, scales of the membrane rectangular, arranged in transverse and longitudinal series, with a few modified scales at the posterior end; needles few, long, slender, and diverging in all directions, evenly scattered; cell 11–14μ in diameter, 25–30μ long (without needles).
Euplankter. Wis.

CHRYSOSPHAERELLA Lauterborn 1896, p. 16

A free-swimming globose colony of ellipsoid or pyriform cells inclosed in a gelatinous envelope in which are embedded many small plates of silicon; anterior ends of the cells all directed outward, bearing 2 vase-like or collar-like extensions through which a long, straight rigid seta projects; 1 flagellum arising from between the two sheathed setae; chromatophores 2, parietal, golden-brown.

Chrysosphaerella longispina Lauterborn 1896, p. 16
Pl. 98, Fig. 1

Characteristics as described for the genus; cells 9μ in diameter, 15μ long; colony up to 250μ in diameter.

Common in the plankton of a variety of lakes; also in *Sphagnum* bogs, roadside ditches, etc.; frequently accompanies *Synura uvella*.

SUBORDER ISOCHRYSIDINEAE

In this group the organisms may be unicellular or colonial, attached or free-swimming. In any case the cells are equipped with 2 flagella of equal length but are difficult of discernment in the sedentary forms. There are 2 elongate, brown chromatophores.

Key to the Families

Cell membrane smooth; plants with or without a lorica
  (unicellular and possessing a lorica in our specimens)............SYNCRYPTACEAE
Cell membrane with silicious scales which are inconspicuous
  except at the anterior end of the cells, where they form barbs
  (plant a globose colony in our specimens)................................SYNURACEAE

FAMILY SYNCRYPTACEAE

Cells in this family have smooth membranes. Although equipped with 2 flagella of equal length, some organisms are sedentary and inclosed in a lorica. *Syncrypta volvox* Ehrenb., a colonial form, has been reported from Michigan (Gustafson, 1942).

DEREPYXIS Stokes 1885, p. 317

Attached; protoplasts inclosed in a vase-like or flask-shaped lorica which usually has a short pedicel and is narrowed anteriorly to form a long or short neck through which 2 long flagella emerge; protoplast globose or hemispherical, suspended from the sides of the lorica by protoplasmic strands, and usually resting on a cross membrane through the median part of the envelope; chromatophores 1 or 2, brown, plate-like.

This genus should be compared with *Lagynion*.

Key to the Species

Lorica vase-shaped, abruptly narrowed anteriorly
  to a slender neck; sessile...*D. dispar*
Lorica elongate-ellipsoid, narrowed gradually
  anteriorly to a wide neck; short-stalked...........................*D. amphora*

Derepyxis amphora Stokes 1885, p. 318
Pl. 96, Fig. 21

Lorica broadly ellipsoid, on a short stipe, gradually narrowed anteriorly to form a short, relatively wide neck; protoplast ovoid, with 1 or 2 parietal chromatophores; lorica 12.9–14μ in diameter, 31–35μ long.

Attached to filamentous algae; common. Mich., Wis.

Derepyxis dispar (Stokes) Senn 1900, p. 161
Pl. 95, Fig. 34

Lorica sessile, vase-shaped, inversely ovoid, abruptly narrowed above to form a slender neck; protoplast globose, suspended on a cross partition of the lorica; flagella about twice the length of the protoplast; lorica 10–14μ in diameter, 18–20μ long; neck 1–2μ wide, 5μ long.

Attached to filamentous algae in tychoplankton of acid swamps and shallow lakes. Mich., Wis.

FAMILY SYNURACEAE

In this family the cell membrane is beset with silicious scales which form projecting barbs, especially near the anterior end. Only the free-swimming colonial genus *Synura* is represented in our region.

SYNURA Ehrenberg 1838, p. 60

A free-swimming globose colony of pyriform cells radiating from a common center, with the broader end directed outward; cell membrane furnished with short spines or apiculations formed by spirally arranged scales, especially evident in the anterior region; chromatophores 2 parietal plates, laterally disposed; flagella 2, of equal length, arising at the anterior end; eye-spot lacking.

Key to the Species

Cells pyriform, densely arranged in ovoid
  or spherical colonies_____*S. uvella*
Cells elongate-pyriform (club-shaped), not compactly arranged
  but rather loosely disposed in a radiating fashion in spherical
  or obovoid colonies_____*S. Adamsii*

Synura Adamsii G. M. Smith 1924, p. 136
Pl. 92, Fig. 1

A free-swimming, globose colony of rather loosely arranged, elongate-pyriform or club-shaped cells, much narrowed to subacute at the posterior end; anterior end broadly rounded and furnished with a few small sharp spines; chromatophores 2 lateral, plate-like bodies, one on either side of the cell; 2 flagella of equal length; cells 8–10μ in diameter, 40–45μ long.

This species appears to be synonymous with *S. uvella* var. *longipes* Virieux (1916, p. 76).

Rare in the plankton of a few lakes and swamps. Wis.

Synura uvella Ehrenberg 1838, p. 61
Pl. 92, Figs. 6, 7

A free-swimming colony of 64–128 short pyriform cells which have several short, sharp spines in the anterior region of the wall; cells 8–17μ in diameter, 20–30–(35)μ long.

Not infrequently this species becomes superabundant and produces the equivalent of a water bloom. In lakes and reservoirs this organism may become obnoxious because of the strong oily taste it imparts to drinking water.

Common in the plankton of many lakes, especially in hard water and in habitats where there is a high concentration of organic matter. Mich., Wis.

SUBORDER OCHROMONADINEAE

These organisms are either solitary or colonial and swim by means of 2 flagella of unequal length. Only one of the families is represented in our region.

FAMILY OCHROMONADACEAE

Organisms with a smooth, undecorated cell membrane; colonial or solitary cells sometimes inclosed in a lorica of definite shape. (See other characteristics in the description of the order.)

Key to the Genera

1. Cells inclosed by a lorica of definite shape; solitary or in arbuscular colonies 2
1. Cells not inclosed in a lorica, arranged in spherical, free-swimming colonies ....*Uroglenopsis*
2. Lorica conical, with transverse growth scars which form lateral bristles ....*Hyalobryon*
2. Lorica conical or cylindrical throughout most of its length; without transverse growth scars....................................*Dinobryon*

DINOBRYON Ehrenberg 1835, p. 279

Free-swimming or attached; rarely solitary, usually forming arborescent colonies of conical or vase-like loricas, each inclosing a single, ovoid or spindle-shaped, pigmented protoplast which is attached by a slender stalk to the base of the envelope; loricas variously tapering at the base in different species, with smooth or undulate margins; arranged in forked chains, 1 or 2 cones fitting into the wide mouth of the lorica below; envelope colorless or brownish, composed of cellulose and silicon (?); protoplast with 1 or 2 plate-like, parietal chromatophores which are yellow-brown, and 2 flagella of different lengths attached apically; pigment-spot and 2 contractile vacuoles in the anterior end; food reserve leucosin, usually in the form of a single basal granule.

See Ahlstrom (1937) for a critical study of American species of *Dinobryon*.

Key to the Species

1. Cells solitary, epiphytic 2
1. Cells adjoined to form arborescent colonies; free-swimming 3
2. Lorica an elongate cone, 6–7 times longer
   than the maximum diameter .... *D. calciformis*
2. Lorica fusiform, 2 times longer than
   the maximum diameter .... *D. Tabellariae*
3. Colony widely diverging, spreading 4
3. Colony with loricas mostly erect, or slightly divergent,
   long axes often nearly parallel, compactly arranged 6
4. Margins of lorica smooth throughout (but often with one
   angular protrusion near the base) .... *D. cylindricum*
4. Margins of the lorica undulate throughout,
   or in the basal or anterior portion 5
5. Upper portion of the lorica with undulate margins; mouth flaring
   decidedly; the basal portion as long or longer
   than the anterior portion .... *D. Vanhoeffenii*
5. Upper portion of the lorica not undulate, mouth slightly flaring,
   the basal portion with undulations above the posterior cone-
   shaped apex; basal portion shorter than the upper .... *D. divergens*
6. Lorica conical with slightly diverging
   sides and flaring at the mouth .... *D. sociale*
6. Lorica campanulate or semi-cylindrical in the upper portion 7
7. Lorica distinctly campanulate but often with unsymmetrical
   swellings at the base of the anterior portion .... *D. sertularia*
7. Lorica cylindrical in the upper portion 8
8. Lorica with margins undulate, often extended posteriorly into a
   long or short acute or subacute point .... *D. bavaricum*
8. Lorica with smooth margins; basal portion shorter
   than the anterior cylindrical portion .... *D. sertularia*

Dinobryon bavaricum Imhof 1890, p. 484

Pl. 98, Fig. 6

Closely arranged loricas in slightly diverging colonies, the loricas elongate-conical, tapering posteriorly to a sharp point (the length of the posterior part varying greatly, sometimes forming a short, sharp point), lateral margins undulate, diverging, gradually enlarging at first and then slightly flaring to a wide mouth; loricas 6.5–8.6μ in diameter, 45–100μ long.

Common in the euplankton of a variety of lakes; mostly in hard or semi-hard water. Mich., Wis.

Dinobryon calciformis Bachmann 1908, p. 82
Pl. 98, Figs. 8, 9

Loricas elongate-conical, solitary, epiphytic in the mucilage of *Coelosphaerium, Microcystis,* and other colonial Cyanophyta, narrowed posteriorly to a sharp point; lateral margins smooth, slightly convex or diverging symmetrically, then converging to a wide mouth; 5–6μ in diameter, 30–40μ long.

Attached in the mucilage of colonial blue-green algae in plankton of many lakes and ponds. Mich., Wis.

Dinobryon cylindricum Imhof 1883 *ex* Ahlstrom 1937, p. 148
Pl. 107, Fig. 1

Loricas closely arranged in divergent but compact colonies, with flaring (sometimes almost campanulate) mouths, irregularly or unsymmetrically tapering posteriorly to a blunt or relatively sharply pointed cone, decidedly and suddenly swollen just above the cone-shaped posterior portion, usually more on one side to produce an angular protuberance, the lorica with one or both margins concave above the swelling; loricas 8.5–12.5μ in diameter at the mouth, 30–77μ long.

Euplankter. Mich., Wis.

Dinobryon divergens Imhof 1887, p. 134
Pl. 98, Fig. 7

United in diverging and much-branched colonies. Loricas densely arranged, cone-shaped, the posterior portion bent at an angle of as much as 90 degrees from the longitudinal axis and blunt-pointed, the lateral margins irregularly undulate, slightly diverging anteriorly to form a campanulate mouth; 7–8μ in diameter, 35–50μ long.

Euplankter; common in many lakes. Mich., Wis.

Dinobryon sertularia Ehrenberg 1835, p. 280
Pl. 98, Fig. 10

Colonies slightly diverging. Loricas fusiform-campanulate; posterior blunt-pointed; lateral margins smooth, convex, narrowed above the midregion and then slightly flaring to a wide mouth; 10–14μ in diameter, 30–40μ long.

Common in the plankton of hard water lakes. Frequently found with *D. sociale*. Sometimes the most conspicuous element in the phytoplankton. Mich., Wis.

Dinobryon sertularia var. *protuberans*
(Lemm.) Krieger 1930, p. 308

Loricas 24–35.5µ long; basal portion with unsymmetrical swellings. Euplankter. Wis.

Dinobryon sociale Ehenberg 1835, p. 279
[*D. stipitatum* Stein]
Pl. 98, Fig. 13

Colonies loosely branched, slightly spreading. Loricas cone-shaped, either straight or bent, blunt-pointed posteriorly, the lateral margins smooth and usually diverging symmetrically to the wide, slightly flaring mouth; 7–8µ in diameter, 30–70µ long.
Common in the plankton of hard water lakes; generally distributed. Mich., Wis.

Dinobryon sociale var. *americanum* (Brunn.)
Bachmann 1911, p. 54

A variety with relatively shorter and wider loricas; the mouth flaring slightly; subcylindrical above, narrowing abruptly posteriorly to a sharply pointed cone which is about one-half the length of the cell; 21–38µ long.
Euplankter. Wis.

Dinobryon Tabellariae (Lemm.) Pascher *in*
Pascher & Lemmermann 1913, p. 66
Pl. 98, Figs. 3–5

Solitary, epiphytic on the diatom *Tabellaria*. Loricas broadly fusiform, extended posteriorly into a short tapering stipe; 7–10µ in diameter, 18–22µ long.
Plankter; in a variety of lakes. Wis.

Dinobryon Vanhoeffenii (Krieg.) Bachmann 1921
ex Ahlstrom 1937, p. 157
[*D. stipitatum* var. *affine* Taylor 1935, p. 88]
Pl. 107, Fig. 14

Loricas in diverging colonies, mouth of the lorica straight or flaring almost imperceptibly, subcylindrical above, with undulate margins, gradually and symmetrically narrowed posteriorly to a long, sharply pointed apex which is one-half or more the length of the cell; lorica 11–13.3μ in diameter, 60–105μ long.

Euplankter. Mich.

HYALOBRYON Lauterborn 1896, p. 17

Solitary or colonial, epiphytic, the protoplast housed in a cone-shaped lorica which is composed of a series of nesting cups representing growth stages, the margin of the cups forming lateral projections or barbs; protoplast with 2 elongate chromatophores.

Hyalobryon mucicola (Lemm.) Pascher in
Pascher & Lemmermann 1913, p. 81
Pl. 98, Figs. 11, 12

Lorica conical, cylindrical in the midregion, with an expanded mouth, tapering posteriorly to form a short stipe which attaches the envelope to the gelatinous investment of various algae, margins of the lorica showing several apiculations marking the zones of growth; lorica 4–6μ in diameter, 24–45μ long.

Rare to common in a number of lakes and swamps. Wis.

UROGLENOPSIS Lemmermann 1899a, p. 107

A free-swimming sphere with hundreds of spherical or ellipsoidal cells arranged at the periphery of the colonial gelatinous envelope; cells with 1 or 2 brownish, parietal, plate-like or disc-like chromatophores; flagella 2, of unequal length, attached in the narrowed anterior end of the cell and extending through and beyond the colonial mucilage; pigment-spot sometimes present in the anterior portion of the cell.

Uroglenopsis americana (Calkins) Lemmermann 1899a, p. 107
Pl. 99, Figs. 1–5

A free-swimming, spherical colony with hundreds of ellipsoid or ovoid cells evenly distributed within the periphery of the gelatinous investment; cells with 1 parietal, plate-like chromatophore; 2 flagella of unequal length and a pigment-spot; cells 3–7μ in diameter; colony 500μ in diameter.

This is a fairly common component of the plankton in a large number of lakes, apparently preferring hard water; especially abundant during late summer. Mich., Wis.

ORDER RHIZOCHRYSIDALES

This small order includes those members of the Chrysophyceae which are essentially rhizopodal, although a few may have a transitory flagellated condition. In morphology and taxonomic position they correspond to the Rhizochloridales of the Xanthophyceae previously treated. Although some genera are colonial, most of them in our region are unicellular, either with or without a lorica.

There are 1 or 2 golden-brown chromatophores and the customary food reserve is leucosin. Some forms are amoeboid in their food habits. Only vegetative reproductive methods are known for this order and resting cysts have been reported as occurring in but few genera.

FAMILY RHIZOCHRYSIDACEAE

Characteristics as described for the order. (Pascher, 1927–1939, recognizes separate families for several of the genera here grouped in the Rhizochrysidaceae.)

Key to the Genera

1. Colonial, 16 ovate cells radially arranged
   in a mucilaginous sheath_____*Chrysostephanosphaera*
1. Solitary, or few cells adjoined by pseudopodia,
   not inclosed in a common mucilage_____ 2
2. Protoplast inclosed by a lorica of specific shape; solitary_____*Lagynion*
2. Protoplast without a lorica; free-swimming_____ 3
3. Protoplasts adjoined by radiating pseudopodia to
   form an aggregate or complex of individuals_____*Chrysidiastrum*
3. Protoplasts not adjoined by pseudopodia
   (or only temporarily and incidentally)_____ 4
4. Amoeboid cells with few, tapering pseudopodia_____*Chrysamoeba*
4. Amoeboid cells with many slender needle-like pseudopodia_____*Rhizochrysis*

CHRYSOSTEPHANOSPHAERA Scherffel 1911, p. 307

Colonies of 2–16 ovate or subspherical cells, inclosed in a spherical or disc-shaped mucilaginous sheath which is densely impregnated with refractive granules of waste (?) material; the cells radiately arranged within the mucilage and often showing several thread-like, simple or branched pseudopodia; chromatophores 2 parietal plates; 2 contractile vacuoles (sometimes not clearly apparent); reproduction by cell division and by fragmentation of the colony.

Chrysostephanosphaera globulifera Scherffel 1911, p. 307
Pl. 95, Fig. 41

Characteristics as described for the genus; cells 10–12μ in diameter, arranged in a girdle within the periphery of the colonial mucilage.

In shallow water of bogs and acid swamps; intermingled with other algae. Mich.

CHRYSAMOEBA Klebs 1893, p. 406

A free-swimming, irregularly radiate amoeboid, sometimes with 1 long flagellum and 2 plate-like, golden-brown crhomatophores, a large noncontractile and 2 smaller contractile vacuoles; in the amoeboid condition solitary or clustered, with radiating pseudopodia.

Chrysamoeba radians Klebs 1893, p. 406
Pl. 99, Fig. 6

Characteristics as described for the genus; cells 8–10μ in diameter, 12–15μ long in the flagellate condition; 35–40μ including pseudopodia in the amoeboid phase.

Rare; in euplankton. Mich., Wis.

RHIZOCHRYSIS Pascher in Pascher & Lemmermann 1913, p. 90

An irregularly shaped, naked, amoeboid unicell with numerous radiating needle-like, or stout pseudopodia, cells sometimes united in temporary colonies and invested in a sheath; chromatophores 1 or 2 golden-yellow plates; vacuoles present or absent; reserve food in the form of leucosin and oil; flagellated stage apparently lacking. Wis.

Rhizochrysis limnetica G. M. Smith 1920, p. 77
Pl. 98, Fig. 2

Cells free-floating, irregularly globose with many radiating, needle-like pseudopodial processes; 1 golden-brown chromatophore; vacuoles numerous and small; cells 35–45μ in diameter without processes.

Rare; in the plankton of many lakes. Wis.

CHRYSIDIASTRUM Lauterborn in Pascher & Lemmermann 1913, p. 91

Cells globose, free-floating, with delicate pseudopodia, joined by radiating processes to form linear colonies of 2–16 individuals; chromatophore a central plate or band.

Chrysidiastrum catenatum Lauterborn in
Pascher & Lemmermann 1913, p. 91
Pl. 99, Fig. 7

Characters as described for the genus; cells 12–15μ in diameter without processes, 45–60μ wide including processes.

Rare; in euplankton of several lakes. Wis.

LAGYNION Pascher 1912, p. 155

An epiphytic flask- or bottle-shaped lorica inclosing a naked, pigmented protoplast; lorica hyaline, or often brown and supposedly composed of cellulose, with a broad base flattened against the substrate, váriously tapering anteriorly to form a long or short neck through which a fine protoplasmic thread extends; chloroplasts 1 or 2 small discs.

Key to the Species

1. Lorica hemispherical, with an annular
thickening about the apical aperture.. *L. reductum*
1. Lorica flask-shaped, globose or pyramidal,
with an elongated, narrow neck.. 2
2. Body of the lorica globose, flattened on the side next to the
substrate, the neck equal to or a little longer than the body ... *L. ampullaceum*
2. Body of the lorica not globose 3
3. Body of the lorica transversely ovate or hemispherical, the neck
equal to the height of the body in length........................... *L. Scherffelii*
3. Body of the lorica not transversely ovate or hemispherical.................... 4
4. Body of the lorica triangular or funnel-shaped, flaring
at the aperture of the neck... *L. macrotrachelum*
4. Body of the lorica unsymmetrically and narrowly triangular;
neck about ½ the height of the body in length; not flaring at
the aperture of the neck................................... *L. triangularis* var. *pyramidatum*

Lagynion ampullaceum (Stokes) Pascher 1912, p. 155
Pl. 97, Fig. 9

Lorica flask-shaped, the body globose, flattened against the substrate and extending into a long neck which flares slightly at the opening; 12–14μ wide, 18–20μ long.

On filamentous algae, usually in acid water. Mich., Wis.

Lagynion macrotrachelum (Stokes) Pascher 1912, p. 155
Pl. 97, Fig. 10

Lorica depressed-ovoid or transversely ovoid, flattened against the substrate, extending into a rather long neck which flares slightly at the opening, 10–12μ wide, 15–20μ long.

Common on *Microspora* and other filamentous algae, especially in soft water lakes. Mich., Wis.

Lagynion reductum Prescott 1944, p. 363
Pl. 97, Figs. 12, 13

Lorica globose to conical, dark brown, with an opening surrounded by an annular thickening through which a fine protoplasmic thread extends; protoplast globose, chromatophore 1, lying along one side of the cell; 10μ high, 11.5μ in diameter.

This organism reminds one of *Heterolagynion Oedogonii* Pascher (Ber. D. D. Bot. Ges., 30, p. 157, Pl. 6, Figs. 1–4, 7–19. 1912), which is, however, colorless and much larger than our specimens.

Growing on filaments of *Tribonema*. Wis.

[383]

Lagynion Scherffelii Pascher 1912, p. 155
Pl. 97, Fig. 14

Lorica depressed-ovate or subpyramidate, flattened against the substrate, extending into a short neck with diverging sides; protoplast with 2 chromatophores.

On filamentous algae in habitats rich in organic matter; in shallow water in bogs and backwashes from several lakes. Mich., Wis.

Lagynion triangularis var. *pyramidatum* Prescott 1944, p. 364
Pl. 97, Fig. 11

Lorica narrowly pyramidate with uneven margins, or subtriangular, tapering from the base to a short or long neck with nearly parallel margins, $10.8–12\mu$ wide, $15–20\mu$ high.

This variety differs from the typical in being narrower, proportionately taller and in having a longer neck.

On filamentous algae. Wis.

ORDER CHRYSOCAPSALES

In this order are included colony-forming, palmelloid organisms. The globose cells are embedded in copious mucilage, forming amorphous masses or thalli of rather definite shape. There are 1 or 2 golden-brown chromatophores. Although non-motile under ordinary conditions these cells may assume a swimming zoospore expression directly, and after scattering initiate the formation of new colonial masses. In the zoospore state the cells have 1 or 2 flagella. Vegetative reproduction by ordinary cell division may be carried on throughout the colony or it may be confined to the distal end. Fragmentation may also be employed by some members. Two families are represented in the known flora of the United States, but only 1 has members in our collections.

FAMILY CHRYSOCAPSACEAE

Characters as described for the order. The cells are embedded in copious mucilage where they multiply by cell division in all planes throughout the colony.

CHRYSOCAPSA Pascher 1913, p. 85

A free-floating colony of spherical, or ellipsoidal cells inclosed in a wide, colorless, gelatinous envelope which is usually homogeneous but may show lamellations; chromatophores one or more golden-brown parietal plates; pigment-spot sometimes present.

Chrysocapsa planctonica (West & West) Pascher 1913, p. 85
[*Phaeococcus planctonicus* West & West]
Pl. 99, Fig. 8

A free-floating colony of globose or subglobose cells in some multiple of 2, up to 64; colonial envelope hyaline, homogeneous, or with radiating fibrils of mucilage; chromatophores 1–2 golden-brown, parietal plates which may completely cover the cell wall; cells 7.2–9.6μ in diameter; colonies up to 250μ in diameter.

Common in the plankton of many lakes, both hard and soft water. Mich., Wis.

ORDER CHRYSOSPHAERALES

In this order the organisms are unicellular and the protoplasts are inclosed by a firm wall of a hard material, the composition of which is apparently unknown. The cells are incapable of division in the vegetative state and in this respect are comparable to the Chlorococcales in the Chlorophyta. In most forms reproduction occurs by the formation of 2 or more individuals within the parent cell in which they may remain for a short time; typical colony formation, however, is not known for this group. Zoospore formation has been observed in some.

FAMILY CHRYSOSTOMATACEAE

Characters as described for the order. This is a little-understood group of organisms which are cyst-like in character. The wall is impregnated with silicon and is variously extended to form slender, radiating, simple or forked, processes. There is an aperture or plug at one end. The chromatophores are yellow-brown and parietal and the food reserve is in the form of oil droplets (probably leucosin is formed also).

CHRYSOSTRELLA Chodat 1921, p. 86

Characters as described for the family. Cells free-swimming (floating ?), globose or subglobose with a firm membrane (possibly impregnated with silicon) in which there is an apical flagellum opening; chromatophores 2, plate-like parietal bodies; stored food in the form of numerous oil bodies.

Chrysostrella paradoxa Chodat 1921, p. 86
Pl. 97, Fig. 8

Cells globose, with a thick, firm membrane which bears a number of radiating processes, either simple or dichotomously divided near

the tips; flagellum opening surrounded by a low collar; chromatophores 2, brown, parietal plates; cells 8–14µ in diameter without
the processes.

Tychoplankter. Wis.

ORDER CHRYSOTRICHALES

This small order includes the truly filamentous Chrysophyceae.
In the adult form they are branched. Palmelloid stages in the shape
of gelatinous strands inclosing uniseriately arranged spherical cells
are common. In the filamentous expression the cells are cylindrical
or quadrate with 2 plate-like chromatophores. In some forms there
are erect branches, in others prostrate discs of cells develop. Reproduction is by zoospores or resting cysts. There is one family.

FAMILY PHAEOTHAMNIACEAE

In this family the thallus is an erect branched filament without
a well-developed horizontal portion.

PHAEOTHAMNION Lagerheim 1884, p. 3

Thallus an attached, erect branched filament showing a central
axis and made up of cylindrical or somewhat inflated cells; basal
holdfast cell hemispherical and thick-walled; chromatophores 2 or
several, yellowish-brown plates; food reserve leucosin.

Phaeothamnion confervicola Lagerheim 1884, p. 3
Pl. 96, Fig. 1; Pl. 99, Figs. 9, 10

Characters as described for the genus; cells 6–11µ in diameter,
14–20µ long.

Growing on *Drepanocladus* in 30 feet of water. Wis.

DIVISION EUGLENOPHYTA
CLASS EUGLENOPHYCEAE

This is a protozoan-like division of the Protista which is sharply defined by unique and highly specialized features. The derivation of the euglenoids is obscure, if not entirely unknown, although there is some evidence that they have evolved from marine ancestors. Most of the members in this division are fresh-water, however. Although a few are sedentary, most forms are motile by 1 or 2 stout flagella of complex structure which arise apically from a small reservoir and emerge through a canal. In the colorless members, and also (though less evident) in the chlorophyll-bearing forms, there is a gullet and a complex vacuolar system. Many euglenoids are highly metabolic, and some may even adopt an amoeboid type of motility and apparently never develop flagella (*Euglena* spp.). In 1 family, the Euglenaceae, there are disc-like, ribbon-like, or star-shaped chloroplasts (chloroleucites) which contain a peculiar type of chlorophyll. Pyrenoids are present in some of the members of this division, as is also a red pigment-spot.

In the holophytic (autotrophic) forms, food reserve is a starch-like polysaccharide, paramylon, which is deposited in variously shaped bodies. Unlike starch, it does not stain blue when treated with iodine. See Fritsch (1935), Dangeard (1902), and Gojdics (1934) on morphology of the cell.

Reproduction is by longitudinal division of the cell, although there are a few reports of conjugation and of isogamete fusion.

The colorless forms are included in the two families Peranemaceae and Astaciaceae, whereas the alga-like genera constitute the Euglenaceae, the only family considered here.

Some authors recognize the family Colaciaceae for the epizoic genus *Colacium*, and place the family in a separate order, Colaciales. Accordingly, the Euglenaceae comprises the Euglenales. Here the simplified arrangement used by Fritsch (1935) is followed.

ORDER EUGLENALES

FAMILY EUGLENACEAE

This family includes the pigmented, holophytic euglenoids which contain a peculiar type of chlorophyll, the chemistry of which is not well known. In addition to this pigment there may be haematochrome which appears when the organisms are subjected to intense illumination or, in a few forms, may be present at all times. The chlorophyll is localized in definitely and specifically shaped chloroplasts (chloroleucites) which may be disc-like, ribbons, or stellar plates scattered through the cell or, rarely, radiating from the center. In some forms lens-shaped pyrenoids can be discerned projecting from either surface of the chloroplast. As mentioned above, food reserve is paramylon, a carbohydrate, which may be deposited about the pyrenoid, or it may collect independently in the cytoplasm. The shape of the paramylon grains is specific, and varies greatly among the different genera and species, and is therefore of taxonomic value. The grains may be minute and numerous rods, a few large sticks, circular plates, or doughnut-shaped rings. The nucleus is usually conspicuous and is centrally located.

Most members of this family have a single thick flagellum, but a few have 2. The flagella are attached at the anterior end, arising from basal granules and emerging through a canal. Placed anteriorly and laterally is a complex red pigment-spot.

The shape of cell varies greatly among the genera of the family. It may be fusiform, cylindrical, pyriform, or ovoid, and in cross section it may be either round or much flattened. The cell membrane (the periplast) may be smooth or, more often, variously decorated with spiral striations, rows of granules, or punctae.

In one genus, *Trachelomonas,* the protoplast is housed in a test of firm gelatinous material, the flagellum emerging through an apical pore. Although most forms are motile, a few are sedentary, occurring as dendroid colonies. Especially in *Euglena* certain species are highly metabolic and may use creeping movements, as well as flagella, for locomotion. On the other hand, the cell is quite rigid and maintains a more or less constant shape.

As mentioned above, the commonly observed method of reproduction is longitudinal cell division (a protozoan attribute). The few cases of sexual reproduction by isogametes or conjugation which have been reported for this family suggest that more life history studies are required. At present there are few observations which indicate other than strictly vegetative reproduction in this group. In *Euglena* many species are known to form thick-walled resting cysts which, however, do not lead to multiplication as far as known. Other genera also enter resting stages as an environmental adaptation.

The family as a whole inhabits shallow water environments, apparently preferring high temperatures and a medium in which there is an optimal concentration of organic matter.

Key to the Genera

1. Cells epizoic, attached by gelatinous
   stalks to microfauna..*Colacium*
1. Cells not epizoic.. 2

2. Cells inclosed in a brown or buff-colored shell or test of various
shapes, with a flagellum aperture ....*Trachelomonas*
2. Cells free-living, not inclosed in a test 3
3. Cells much flattened dorsiventrally, usually spirally twisted
in at least a part of the cell ....*Phacus*
3. Cells not flattened, round or ovoid in cross section 4
4. Cells fusiform, cylindrical, or elongate-fusiform, round
or nearly so in cross section (rarely slightly flattened)......................*Euglena*
4. Cells broadly ovoid or pyriform, usually furnished with a short
caudus; paramylon bodies 2 very large and conspicuous
lateral rings or plates... *Lepocinclis*

EUGLENA Ehrenberg 1838, p. 104

Cells mostly free-swimming, rarely creeping; fusiform, cylindrical,
or ovate, usually round in cross section but rarely slightly flattened;
the posterior end either rounded or produced, sometimes extending
into a fine point or caudus, the anterior end usually narrowed and
sometimes conspicuously 2-lipped; periplast either firm, giving the
cell a rigid shape, or soft and pliable, the cell metabolic and constantly changing shape in its movements; when firm, the periplast
decorated with fine spiral striations or rows of granules; a gullet and
a reservoir in the anterior end from which arises a single flagellum of
variable length; chloroplasts variable, either numerous ovoid discs, a
few ribbon-like bands, or, rarely, star-shaped plates, sometimes with
pyrenoids, which are embedded in the chloroplast and protrude
from either side; chlorophyll sometimes masked by an abundance
of brick-red or blood-red haematochrome, usually only temporarily
present and incident to intense illumination; food reserve paramylon
in the form of a few large or numerous small rods, plates, rings, or
discs.

There are many species of *Euglena*, differentiated and identified
by the shape of the cell, the periplast markings, the form of the
chloroplasts, the shape and arrangement of the paramylon grains,
and the presence or absence of pyrenoids. Considerable discrimina-
tion in taxonomic determinations is required, therefore, and because
important characteristics are often obscure, identification is not easy.

While some species of *Euglena* appear not uncommonly in the
euplankton, most are found in the tychoplankton, in the shallow
water of quiet bays, in ponds and ditches. A few species seem to be
confined to acid water, and in *Sphagnum* bogs they may form a
conspicuous green film over submerged or partly submerged mosses.
In small ponds and sloughs a heavy surface bloom may develop so
that a green film is produced. A pond often appears brick-red because of the production of haematochrome in the cells when exposed
to intense light.

Key to the Species

1. Periplast decorated with spiral rows of pearly granules_____E. Spirogyra
1. Periplast without spiral rows of granules _____ 2
2. Cells a deep blood-red; haematochrome almost entirely
   masking the green pigment_____E. sanguinea
2. Cells normally green (if red, only temporarily
   so and then brick- rather than blood-red)_____ 3
3. Cells with a single, elongate, band-like or plate-like chloroplast_____ 4
3. Cells with other forms of or more than one chloroplast_____ 5
4. Cells 55–60μ long; organism maintaining
   its shape when swimming_____E. elongata
4. Cells 12–14μ long; organism highly metabolic, constantly
   changing shape when swimming _____E. minuta
5. Cells with convolute margins; paramylon bodies saucer-shaped,
   parietal along both sides of the cell_____E. convoluta
5. Cells with other shapes of paramylon bodies;
   margins not convolute _____ 6
6. Cells elongate-fusiform, produced posteriorly into a long, fine,
   tapering point; 140–180μ long_____ E. acus
6. Cells fusiform or somewhat cylindric, not produced into
   a long, fine point posteriorly_____ 7
7. Cells highly metabolic, constantly changing shape in movements_____ 8
7. Cells not highly metabolic, more or less rigid and
   maintaining a constant shape in movements _____ 13
8. Cells minute, 5–6μ in diameter_____E. minuta
8. Cells larger _____ 9
9. Cells stout, less than 5 times as long as wide_____10
9. Cells longer than 5 times their diameter;
   elongate-fusiform or subcylindric_____12
10. Cells nearly cylindrical, or broadly fusiform, with 12–15
    chloroplasts; cells 80–90μ long _____ E. polymorpha
10. Cells smaller, not cylindrical; 37–50–(95)μ long _____11
11. Chloroplasts numerous, as many as 50; cells broadest
    below the midregion; 50–70–(95)μ long_____ E. proxima
11. Chloroplasts not so numerous; broadest at or
    above the midregion; 37–50μ long_____E. gracilis
12. Cells cylindrical, broadly rounded posteriorly _____ 14
12. Cells abruptly tapering posteriorly, forming a blunt tip _____E. deses
13. Paramylon bodies in the form of rods; posteriorly narrowed to
    form a sharply pointed tip; cells small (66)–70–80μ long_____E. tripteris
13. Paramylon bodies in the form of 2 large, oblong
    rings; cells large, up to 500μ long_____ E. oxyuris
14. Cells 76–100μ long _____ E. elastica
14. Cells 250–290μ long _____ E. Ehrenbergii

Euglena acus Ehrenberg 1838, p. 112
Pl. 85, Fig. 28

Cells very slightly metabolic, elongate spindle-shaped, produced
posteriorly into a long, fine tapering point, narrowed and truncate
at the anterior end; membrane indistinctly spirally striated; chloro-

plasts numerous, disc-like; paramylon bodies 2 to several long rods; 10–14μ in diameter, 140–180μ long.

This is a widely distributed but rather uncommon species. It is almost at once identifiable by the narrow and very long, rigid cell.

In *Sphagnum* bogs and swamps. Mich., Wis.

Euglena acus var. *rigida* Huebner 1886, p. 9
Pl. 85, Fig. 27

Cell rigid, swimming slowly and continuously in one direction, spindle-shaped but narrow and elongate, tapering abruptly posteriorly into a sharply pointed tail-piece; paramylon bodies in the form of 2 long rods (rarely more numerous small rods); chloroplasts numerous, plate-like and ovoid bodies, sometimes showing a spiral arrangement within the cell; 5.5–10μ in diameter, 118–125μ long.

Uncommon; in ditches and among dense growths of algae in bays of lakes. Wis.

Euglena convoluta Korshikov 1941, p. 23
[*Euglena breviflagellum* Prescott & Gojdics]
Pl. 86, Figs. 7–9, 14

Cells slightly metabolic, elongate-fusiform, and spirally twisted or curved, seldom straight, elliptic in cross section, rather abruptly narrowed anteriorly and truncate posteriorly, narrowing more gradually to form a long tail-piece. Membrane finely and spirally striate. Flagellum short, about one-sixth the length of the cell. Paramylon bodies of two sorts: 6–8 large, concave or trough-shaped plates laterally arranged, parallel with the long axis, with the pellicle slightly undulate over them; and numerous small disc-like rings irregularly scattered throughout the cell. Chloroplasts numerous ovoid discs evenly distributed throughout the cell; pyrenoids lacking (?); eye-spot elliptic, composed of irregularly arranged crimson granules. Cell 120–145μ long, 10–12μ in diameter; large paramylon bodies 18μ long; small paramylon grains 5μ wide, 7μ long.

This species is bent and spirally twisted but does not turn in its forward movements, and thus appears to be quite rigid. It is, however, metabolic at times. Apparently the bending of the cell and the undulations of the membrane are determined by the position and junctions of the large lateral paramylon bodies. Upon contraction of the cell, the paramylon discs are seen to telescope laterally. The striations of the membrane are extremely fine, sometimes almost undiscernible. They spiral left to right, proceeding posteriorly.

Tychoplankter; in Trilby Lake, Wisconsin. (Also reported by Gojdics in a pond near Woods Hole, Massachusetts, August 1935.)

Euglena deses Ehrenberg 1835, p. 248

Pl. 85, Fig. 20

Cells highly metabolic, twisting and turning continuously; elongate-fusiform or subcylindric, posteriorly tapering rather abruptly to a short, blunt tip; membrane finely striated; chloroplasts numerous, disc-like; paramylon bodies several to many rods of various length; cell $18-20-(24)\mu$ in diameter, $65-125-(200)\mu$ long.

In shallow water of *Sphagnum* bogs and in organic detritis at margins of pools and ponds; frequently found with other species of *Euglena*. Mich., Wis.

Euglena Ehrenbergii Klebs 1883, p. 304

Pl. 86, Fig. 13

Cells straight but highly metabolic, elongate, band-like, truncately rounded at both poles, not or scarcely tapering, flattened-elliptic in cross section; paramylon bodies several to many cylindrical or flattened sticks; chloroplasts many small, ovoid discs; flagellum about ½ the length of the cell; cell $20-26\mu$ in diameter, $250-290\mu$ long.

In shallow water; swamps. Wis.

Euglena elastica Prescott 1944, p. 365

Pl. 86, Figs. 10–12

Cells highly metabolic and constantly changing shape when in motion, mostly spindle-shaped but frequently much swollen in the midregion and abruptly narrowed anteriorly and posteriorly, tapering slightly to conically rounded apices, the basal end often swollen and knob-like, never extended into a caudus; periplast smooth, flagellum about ⅔ the length of the cell; chloroplasts many, irregularly ovoid bodies; pyrenoids lacking (?); paramylon bodies numerous short rods scattered rather evenly throughout the cell; pigment-spot an irregularly shaped body, laterally placed at the anterior end; cells $9.5-11\mu$ in diameter (when the cell is stretched out), $76-100\mu$ long.

In a small pool near Plum Creek at Sayner Fish Hatchery, Wisconsin.

Euglena elongata Schewiakoff 1893, p. 16

Pl. 86, Fig. 3

Cell slightly metabolic but keeping a firm and constant shape when swimming, elongate fusiform-cylindric, tapering gradually to a blunt point posteriorly; one chloroplast, which is band-like and more or less parallel with the long axis of the cell; paramylon grains in the form of small numerous rods; cells 5–8μ in diameter, 55–60μ long.

In tychoplankton; among mats of *Spirogyra*. Wis.

Euglena gracilis Klebs 1883, p. 303
Pl. 85, Fig. 17

Cells metabolic, short-fusiform to ovoid; chloroplasts many, disc-shaped bodies evenly distributed throughout the cell, with pyrenoids; paramylon bodies not observed; cell 8–15–(22)μ in diameter, 37–50μ long.

In *Sphagnum* bogs and in ponds where there is a high concentration of nitrogenous matter; usually found with other species of *Euglena*. Wis.

Euglena minuta Prescott 1944, p. 365
Pl.85, Figs. 23, 24

Cells highly metabolic, fusiform to somewhat pyriform, produced posteriorly into a short, blunt, often curved tip; membrane smooth (?); flagellum ¾ the length of the cell; 1 plate-like chloroplast with a pyrenoid; paramylon bodies many small rods (?); cells 5–6μ in diameter, 12–14μ long.

In tychoplankton; Muskellunge Lake, Wisconsin.

Euglena oxyuris Schmarda var. *minor* Prescott 1944, p. 366
Pl. 85, Fig. 18

Cells slightly metabolic, mostly keeping a constant shape in movement; elongate-cylindric and twisted; tapering posteriorly rather abruptly to form a short tail-piece. Periplast longitudinally striated; chloroplasts numerous, disc-like; paramylon grains 2 large, flattened rings, one anterior and one posterior to the central nucleus. Cells 15–18μ in diameter, 77–85μ long.

This variety differs from the typical in its smaller size, the typical being twice as large (30–45μ in diameter, 375–500μ long).

In shallow water of High Lake, Wisconsin.

Euglena polymorpha Dangeard 1902, p. 175
Pl. 85, Figs. 21, 22

Cells metabolic, ovoid-pyriform to subcylindric, narrowed gradually posteriorly to a short, blunt tip; periplast with spiral striations; chloroplasts many and disc-like with laciniate margins, with 1 pyrenoid; paramylon bodies small ovoid grains (not observed in our specimens); cells 20–26μ in diameter, 80–90μ long.

In roadside ditches. Wis.

[393]

Euglena proxima Dangeard 1902, p. 154

Pl. 85, Fig. 25

Cells metabolic, fusiform, narrowed posteriorly to a blunt tip; periplast spirally striated; chloroplasts numerous, irregularly shaped discs; paramylon bodies numerous small rods scattered throughout the cell; cells 14.5–19–(21)μ in diameter, (50)–70–85–(95)μ long.

Among desmids in pools and in the tychoplankton of lakes. Mich., Wis.

Euglena sanguinea Ehrenberg 1838, p. 105

Pl. 86, Figs. 1, 2

Cells metabolic, ovoid-pyriform to subcylindric, tapering posteriorly to a short, blunt tail-piece; periplast spirally striated; chloroplasts numerous, irregularly notched bands or short ribbons; paramylon bodies several to many ovoid grains; content of cells somewhat obscured by haematochrome, which is normally present; cells 28–33μ in diameter, 55–120μ long.

This species seems never to form the bloom type of growth frequently developed by some other species of the genus, but it often occurs in such numbers as to tinge the water slightly with a blood-red color. This is a different effect from that produced by those species of *Euglena* which develop haematochrome only when subjected to intense illuminations. The color produced by the latter is a dense brick-red, localized in a film at the surface.

Uncommon in ponds, ditches, and swamps. Wis.

Euglena Spirogyra Ehrenberg 1838, p. 110

Pl. 86, Fig. 15

Cells somewhat metabolic; elongate-cylindric and twisted, narrowed posteriorly and extended into a sharp, bent tail-piece; periplast brownish, spirally striated with alternating rows of large and small shining granules; chloroplasts numerous, disc-like; paramylon bodies 2 flattened rings, 1 anterior and 1 posterior to the central nucleus; cells 10–26.6μ in diameter, 80–150μ long.

Not uncommon in ditches and swamps, but never discolors the water or forms surface films. Mich., Wis.

Euglena tripteris (Duj.) Klebs 1883, p. 306

Pl. 86, Figs. 4–6

Cells rigid, elongate-cylindric and twisted, narrowing posteriorly to form a sharp tip; broadly rounded at the anterior end; periplast finely striated; chloroplasts numerous disc-shaped bodies; paramylon in the form of 2 thick rods, one anterior and one posterior to the central nucleus; cells 7–10μ in diameter, (60)–70–80μ long.

Widely distributed in *Sphagnum* bogs and ditches, but sparse in occurrence. Wis.

PHACUS Dujardin 1841, p. 334

Cells ovate, pyriform, fusiform, or orbicular, often twisted or in part spiral, and much flattened, with a long or short caudus in most species; a gullet in the anterior end marked by a fold in the membrane; 1 flagellum arising anteriorly, sometimes through an apical papilla; periplast decorated with longitudinal or spiral striations, rows of granules, or punctations; chloroplasts numerous ovoid discs, rarely bands; paramylon bodies in the form of circular plates or rings, rarely rods; pigment-spot usually present, placed laterally at end; cells never metabolic as in *Euglena*.

Key to the Species

1. Caudus (tail-piece) lacking; cells broadly
   rounded posteriorly_____ *P. Segretii*
1. Caudus present, straight or curved _____ 2
2. Periplast with longitudinal or spiral rows of
   granules or sharp warts_____ 3
2. Periplast longitudinally or spirally striated, or smooth_____ 4
3. Cells pyriform; granules in longitudinal rows _____ *P. suecicus*
3. Cells ovate or fusiform; granules in spiral rows_____ *P. Spirogyra*
4. Cells distinctly pyriform_____ 5
4. Cells globose, subglobose, ovoid-fusiform, or ovoid_____ 7
5. Chloroplasts several longitudinal bands_____ *P. chloroplastes*
5. Chloroplasts circular or ovoid discs _____ 6
6. Protoplast inclosed by a spirally striated periplast
   from which it is remotely separated _____ *P. Nordstedtii*
6. Protoplast not separated from the periplast_____ *P. pyrum*
7. Cells (70)–80–190μ long, with a long caudus nearly
   or quite as long as the cell body_____ 8
7. Cells mostly shorter; caudus much shorter than the cell body_____ 10
8. Cell body flat, ovoid, or nearly round in outline, with a
   straight or nearly straight caudus as long as
   or longer than the cell body_____*P. longicauda*
8. Cells strongly twisted, fusiform in outline _____ 9
9. Cells twisted throughout their length _____*P. helikoides*
9. Cells twisted only in the caudal portion _____ *P. tortus*
10. Cell with a short, straight, almost papilla-like caudus _____*P. acuminatus*
10. Cell with a conspicuous caudus, straight,
    curved, or strongly reflexed_____ 11
11. Cell with evenly undulate margins _____*P. crenulata*
11. Cell with margin entire, irregularly undulate,
    or notched unsymmetrically_____ 12
12. Cell unsymmetrically fusiform, somewhat euglenoid_____ *P. asymmetrica*
12. Cell ovoid or orbicular in outline, symmetrical or nearly so_____ 13

13. Cell with a prominent dorsal flange, decidedly triangular when
    seen in end view (cf. *P. Swirenkoi,* which is somewhat triangular) _____ 16
13. Cell without a dorsal flange, not triangular in end view_____14
14. Margin of cell with prominent notches _____ 15
14. Margin of cell entire _____17
15. Cell with 1 or 2 lateral notches; 1 large
    circular paramylon body _____ *P. pseudoswirenkoi*
15. Cell with several notches in both sides; 1 large
    and several small paramylon bodies_____*P. Birgei*
16. Cell with a strongly decurved caudus_____*P. orbicularis*
16. Cell with the caudus straight or only slightly
    curved away from the longitudinal axis _____ *P. triqueter*
17. Cells 15–25µ in diameter _____ 18
17. Cells 30–50–(60)µ in diameter _____ 21
18. Paramylon plates 2 large oval rings, at least
    ½ the cell body in length_____ *P. alatus*
18. Paramylon plates smaller, 2 or several _____19
19. Cells distinctly twisted in the posterior part, just above the
    caudus, where there is often a swelling; one side of
    the cell much thicker than the other_____*P. Lemmermannii*
19. Cells not distinctly twisted in the posterior portion;
    without a swelling above the caudus _____20
20. Cell ovoid to ellipsoid, with a straight
    or only slightly curved caudus_____*P. caudatus*
20. Cell broadly ovoid or orbicular, with a short
    caudus curving to the left_____ *P. curvicauda*
21. Cell distinctly twisted in the posterior part just above the
    caudus; paramylon bodies usually 2 large
    and several small plates_____*P. Lemmermannii*
21. Cells not distinctly twisted above the caudus;
    paramylon bodies usually 2 large rings _____22
22. Cell orbicular, broadest below the transverse median line;
    caudus deflexed mostly to the right;
    cell angular in end view _____ 23
22. Cell ovoid or nearly so, broadest at the
    transverse median line, or above it _____ 24
23. Cell twisting slightly into the caudus, which is
    prominent and elongate, slightly deflexed_____*P. pleuronectes*
23. Cell not twisting into the caudus, which
    is short and sharply deflexed _____ *P. Swirenkoi*
24. Cell broadly ovoid or orbicular, with a strongly
    curved caudus; cells 50–100µ long _____ *P. orbicularis*
24. Cells narrowly ovoid, somewhat unsymmetrical, with a nearly
    straight caudus; cells up to 48µ long _____ *P. anacoelus*

Phacus acuminatus Stokes 1885a, p. 183

Pl. 88, Fig. 4

Cells suborbicular in outline, broadly rounded posteriorly, with
a short, blunt apiculation; periplast longitudinally striated; paramylon bodies 1–2 ring-like discs; cells 20–22µ in diameter, 23–25µ long.

Plankter; in cedar swamp. Wis.

Phacus acuminatus var. *Drezepolskii* Skvortzow 1928, p. 113

[*P. caudatus* Ehrenberg *ex* Pochmann 1942, p. 146]

Pl. 88, Figs. 17, 18

Cells ellipsoid or ovoid, slightly produced posteriorly, sometimes with the cell margins convolute, forming a short, sharp caudus; periplast longitudinally striated; paramylon bodies 2 large discs; cells $10-15\mu$ in diameter, $21-24\mu$ long.

In swamps and ditches. Wis.

Phacus alatus Klebs 1883, p. 312

Cells very broadly ovoid to nearly circular in outline, with a short caudus which is strongly curved and twisted to the left (when the cell is seen in ventral view); periplast longitudinally striated; paramylon bodies 2 large plates or rings which are at least ½ the cell body in length, lateral and sometimes peripheral, one on either side of the cell; cells $(16)-19-22\mu$ in diameter, $19-24\mu$ long.

In a slough; among dense growths of filamentous algae. Wis.

Phacus anacoelus Stokes 1888, p. 91

Pl. 87, Figs. 7, 8; Pl. 88, Fig. 11

Cells broadly ovoid, narrowed abruptly posteriorly to form a short caudus, which turns to the left (as seen in ventral view); paramylon bodies 1-2 circular plates; lateral margins of cells with 2-3 creases or folds, the membrane convex between the indentations; periplast longitudinally striate; cells $32-36-(40)\mu$ in diameter, $40-48\mu$ long.

Euplanktonic and tychoplanktonic. Wis.

Phacus anacoelus var. *undulata* Skvortzow 1928, p. 109

[*Phacus undulatus* Pochmann 1942, p. 191]

Pl. 87, Fig. 3

Cells broadly ovoid, produced posteriorly into a long (or short) sharply pointed caudus, oblique to the longitudinal axis of the cell, anteriorly broadly rounded but slightly bilobed because of the gullet groove; periplast longitudinally striated; margin of the cell with 2-3 bulges; 1 large centrally located paramylon disc; cells $60-65\mu$ in diameter, $80-111\mu$ long.

Our specimens average much larger than the dimensions recorded for this variety, but otherwise they are in agreement.

Planktonic; also found in swamps and ditches. Wis.

Phacus anacoelus var. *undulata* fa. *major* Prescott 1944, p. 366
Pl. 89, Fig. 20

Cells broadly ovoid; ending posteriorly in a long obliquely directcd caudus; margins of cell with a deep crease on either side, forming 2 broad bulges; cells much larger than in the typical form, 64μ in diameter, 111–115μ long.

Euplankter. Wis.

Phacus asymmetrica Prescott 1944, p. 366
Pl. 88, Fig. 19

Cell irregularly ovoid-fusiform and slightly spiral in the posterior and anterior portions; extended into a curved, bluntly-pointed caudus posteriorly; narrowed anteriorly and with 2 irregular bulges on either side of the apex; periplast finely striated longitudinally; paramylon bodies 2 thick twisted rings, usually lying transversely in the cell; chloroplasts numerous small ovoid discs; cell 22–25μ in diameter, 50–53μ long.

This species should be compared with *Phacus Raciborski* Drez., which is much more slender and more nearly symmetrical.

In a roadside fosse. Wis.

Phacus Birgei Prescott 1944, p. 367
Pl. 87, Fig. 11

Cell broadly ovoid, produced posteriorly to form a long tapering caudus which is oblique to the longitudinal axis of the cell, broadly rounded anteriorly; flagellum as long as the cell; periplast very finely striated; margins of the cell sharply notched with 4 small indentations on either side; paramylon bodies 1 large and numerous small circular plates; chloroplasts many ovoid discs; pigment-spot (?); cell 50–60μ in diameter, 70–80μ long.

In a small pond near Genoa City, Wisconsin.

Phacus caudatus Huebner 1886, p. 5
Pl. 87, Fig. 13

Cells ovoid-pyriform, spirally twisted, produced posteriorly to form a straight, sharp caudus; broadly rounded anteriorly; periplast longitudinally striated; 1 large, disc-like paramylon body; cells 15–27μ in diameter, 30–50μ long.

Euplanktonic and tychoplanktonic. Wis.

Phacus caudatus var. *ovalis* Drezepolski 1925, p. 266
Pl. 88, Fig. 13

Cells elongate-ovoid, with a short, blunt caudus; cells 18.5μ in diameter, 33.3μ long; periplast smooth (?).

With the typical form. Wis.

Phacus chloroplastes Prescott 1944, p. 367

Pl. 87, Figs. 15, 16

Cells broadly pyriform; produced .posteriorly to form a straight or very slightly deflected caudus; broadly rounded anteriorly, with a median papilla; periplast longitudinally striated; margin of the cell entire; chloroplasts several parietal bands lying parallel with the long axis of the cell; paramylon bodies 2 large thin rings or slightly twisted bands lying lengthwise in the cell; eye-spot median, in the apical region; cell 20–22μ in diameter, 29–31μ long.

This form should be compared with *P. hispidula* (Eichw.) Lemm.

Plankter; from an inlet of Trout Lake, Wisconsin.

Phacus chloroplastes fa. *incisa* Prescott 1944, p. 386

Pl. 88, Figs. 5–8

Cells pyriform or napiform in outline, tapering abruptly to a long, straight sharp caudus; periplast longitudinally striated; margin of the cell with 2 sharp notches on either side; cells 25–26μ in diameter, 38–40μ long.

In cedar swamp. Wis.

Phacus crenulata Prescott 1944, p. 368

Pl. 88, Fig. 9

Cells ovoid-pyriform, posteriorly extended to form a gradually tapering, sharp-pointed caudus; anterior end broadly rounded but bilobed, with a convex papilla between the lobes; flagellum as long as the cell or a little longer; margins of the cell distinctly crenulate or undulate; periplast longitudinally striated with undulating lines; paramylon bodies 2 circular discs; cells 14–15μ in diameter, 34–36μ long.

This species should be compared with *P. costata* Conrad, which has spiral entire striations rather than longitudinal wavy ones. The anterior end is different in that species also. *P. setosa* var. *crenata* Skv. has spiral striations.

Plankter; in a cedar swamp. Wis.

Phacus curvicauda Swirenko 1915a, p. 333

Pl. 87, Fig. 14; Pl. 88, Fig. 21

Cells broadly ovoid to suborbicular in outline, slightly spiral in the posterior part, which is extended into a caudus that curves obliquely to the left (when viewed from the ventral side); anterior end broadly rounded; periplast longitudinally finely striated (or

smooth ?); paramylon bodies 2 large discs; chloroplasts numerous ovoid bodies; cell 24–26μ in diameter, (25)–28–30μ long.
Euplanktonic and tychoplanktonic. Wis.

Phacus helikoides Pochmann 1942, p. 212
Pl. 87, Fig. 9

Cells fusiform or elongate fusiform-pyriform, twisted· throughout their entire length (sometimes closely so), briefly narrowed anteriorly and bilobed, the lobes appearing in 2 planes when seen from the side; tapering posteriorly to a spirally twisted, long, straight caudus which is about ½ the cell body in length; margins of the cell entire but with 2 or 3 bulges; periplast longitudinally and spirally striated; 1 large circular paramylon body; cells 39–(40)–54μ in diameter, 70–120μ long.

This species should be compared with *P. tortus* (Lemm.) Skv., which is broader and is twisted only in the posterior portion of the cell.

Not uncommon in the plankton of lakes and ponds but most frequently found in the tychoplankton of shallow water. Wis.

Phacus Lemmermannii (Swir.) Skvortzow 1928, p. 114
Pl. 88, Fig. 12

Cells broadly ellipsoid to ovoid, decidedly twisted in the posterior portion (usually) and somewhat abruptly tapered to a short, sharp caudus which turns to the right (when the cell is seen from the ventral side); slightly retuse at the anterior pole and sometimes rather narrowly rounded (in our specimens); paramylon bodies either 2 moderately large rings or, more commonly, 2 larger rings and many small circular plates; cell (19)–20–30μ in diameter, (27)–32–45–(47)μ long.

Plankter; in sloughs and ponds. Wis.

Phacus longicauda (Ehrenb.) Dujardin 1841, p. 337
Pl. 87, Fig. 1

Cells broadly ovoid to pyriform, tapering gradually posteriorly to form a long, straight, sharply pointed caudus; anteriorly broadly rounded; periplast longitudinally striated; flagellum shorter than the cell in length; paramylon body usually in the form of a single large (or small) circular plate; cells 45–70μ in diameter, 85–170μ long.

Rather common in the euplankton and tychoplankton of lakes and swamps. Mich., Wis.

Phacus Nordstedtii Lemmermann 1904, p. 125

Pl. 88, Fig. 1

Cells napiform, nearly spherical but with a long, straight, sharply pointed caudus; broadly rounded anteriorly; periplast forming an envelope widely separated from an elliptical protoplast, the periplast spirally striated; paramylon bodies not observed; chloroplasts numerous ovoid indistinct discs; cells 18.5μ in diameter, 36μ long.

Our specimens are assigned here because of the cell shape and periplast characteristics. Judging from the original description of *P. Nordstedtii*, it was not clear to the author of the species whether the species actually belonged to *Phacus*. Our specimens are much smaller than the dimensions given for this species and perhaps should be described as a new variety. This should be deferred, however, until more is learned of their cytology.

Plankter; from a cedar swamp. Wis.

Phacus orbicularis Huebner 1886, p. 5

Pl. 87, Fig. 10

Cells orbicular in outline, with a short caudus curved to the right (when seen in ventral view); broadly rounded anteriorly; periplast finely striated longitudinally; flagellum as long as the body; paramylon bodies 2 disc-shaped plates; cells 39–45μ in diameter, 60–70–100μ long.

Plankter; from a cedar swamp. Wis.

Phacus orbicularis var. *caudatus* Skzortzow 1928, p. 112

[*P. platalea* Drezepolski *ex* Pochmann 1942, p. 179]

Pl. 87, Fig.12; Pl. 88, Fig. 15

Cells broadly ovoid to nearly round in outline, spirally twisted, extended posteriorly into a long, straight, sharply pointed caudus; periplast longitudinally striated; paramylon bodies 1–2 (sometimes several) large circular plates; cells 45–47μ in diameter, 65–69μ long.

With the typical form in a cedar swamp. Wis.

Phacus orbicularis var. *Zmudae* Namyslowski 1921

[*P. circulatus* Pochmann 1942, p. 177]

Pl. 88, Fig. 10

Cells orbicular in outline, produced posteriorly to form a short caudus obliquely turned to the left (as seen in ventral view); periplast longitudinally striated; cells 18.5–21μ in diameter, 27–29μ long.

In a roadside fosse. Wis.

Phacus pleuronectes (Muell.) Dujardin 1841, p. 336

Pl. 88, Fig. 16

Cells broadly ovoid to suborbicular in outline, slightly spiral and produced posteriorly to form a stout, sharp-pointed caudus which is obliquely turned to the right (when seen from the ventral side); anterior end broadly rounded; periplast longitudinally striated; flagellum as long as or longer than the body; paramylon bodies 1–2 ring-like discs; cells (30)–37–46.8–$(50)\mu$ in diameter, (42)–50–80–$(100)\mu$ long.

This is a common species in marginal waters of eutrophic lakes, especially where protected from wave action; also frequent in ponds and ditches. Mich., Wis.

Phacus pseudoswirenkoi Prescott 1944, p. 368

Pl. 85, Fig. 26; Pl. 87, Fig. 2; Pl. 88, Fig. 14

Cells orbicular in outline, abruptly narrowed posteriorly and produced to form a short, sharp caudus which curves to the left (when seen from the ventral side); anterior end broadly rounded; flagellum about as long as the body; periplast longitudinally striated, with a deep, sharp, lateral notch medially located on the right side (rarely one on the left side also); paramylon body a large, circular plate; cells 30–33μ in diameter, 37–40μ long.

This species should be compared with *P. Swirenkoi*, a species which is about the same size but which has entire margins and a caudus which turns to the right.

Plankter; from a cedar swamp; in ponds and ditches. Wis.

Phacus pyrum (Ehrenb.) Stein 1878, III, Taf. 19, Figs. 51–54

Pl. 88, Fig. 22

Cells ovoid, narrowed gradually posteriorly to a long, straight, finely pointed caudus; broadly rounded anteriorly, but with 2 papillae between which the flagellum emerges; periplast spirally ribbed; paramylon bodies 2 ring-like plates, laterally situated; cells (7)–15.6–21μ in diameter, 27–30μ long.

Euplanktonic and tychoplanktonic. Mich., Wis.

Phacus Segretii Allorge & Lefevre 1925, pp. 128, 129

Cells broadly ovoid or unsymmetrically orbicular in outline, without a caudus; slightly narrowed anteriorly, with a prominent ventral furrow; broadly rounded posteriorly; periplast longitudinally or slightly spirally striated; paramylon bodies in the form of 1 large and 1 smaller circular plate; cells 20–22μ in diameter, 22–28μ long.

Typical form not observed in our collections.

Phacus Segretii var. *ovum* Prescott 1944, p. 369

Pl. 88, Fig. 23

Cells larger than in the typical form, broadly ovoid; 28–30μ in diameter, 39–41μ long.

In swamps. Wis.

Phacus Spirogyra Drezepolski 1925, pp. 234, 267

Cells unsymmetrically spherical or ovoid, with a sharply pointed caudus arising from the broadly rounded posterior; periplast spirally striated with rows of granules; cells 32μ in diameter, 45μ long, caudus 10μ long.

Typical form not observed in our collections.

Phacus Spirogyra var. *maxima* Prescott 1944, p. 369

Pl. 87, Figs. 4–6

Cells ovoid to somewhat oblong, unsymmetrically spiral or merely twisted once, abruptly narrowed posteriorly into a long straight or curved caudus; broadly rounded anteriorly (narrowly rounded when seen from the side), with a prominent median protrusion; periplast longitudinally striated with spiral rows of granules; chloroplasts numerous discs; paramylon bodies 2 large doughnut-shaped rings; cells 35–40μ in diameter, 70–80μ long.

This species is peculiar in the shape of the cell body which is not very much flattened. In side view it is narrower than when seen from the front.

In a roadside fosse. Wis.

Phacus suecicus Lemmermann *in* Pascher

& Lemmermann 1913, p. 139

Pl. 88, Figs. 2, 3

Cells broadly ellipsoid or ovate, but not quite symmetrical, with a relatively long, sharp caudus which is slightly deflected; truncate or slightly retuse at the anterior end but with a prominent, median, collar-like papilla through which the flagellum extends; flagellum as long as the cell body; cell planoconvex when seen from the side; periplast longitudinally striated with rows of sharp granules; chloroplasts numerous circular discs; paramylon bodies 2 lateral and peripheral plates or rods lying just within the periplast; cells (14)–19–22μ in diameter, 34–36μ long, 6–11μ thick.

Plankter; in a cedar swamp. Wis.

Phacus Swirenkoi Skvortzow 1928, p. 114

Pl. 88, Fig. 24

Cells orbicular in outline, slightly twisted posteriorly and extended into a short, sharp caudus which turns obliquely to the right (when seen from the ventral side); broadly rounded anteriorly; periplast longitudinally striated; margin of the cell entire; paramylon bodies 2 large circular plates; cells 35μ in diameter, 43–46μ long.

Common in the plankton of lakes; in tychoplankton of bays and in swamps. Wis.

Phacus tortus (Lemm.) Skvortzow 1928, p. 110

Pl. 88, Fig. 20

Cells broadly fusiform or napiform, broadest in the anterior third of the cell, conically rounded at the anterior end, tapering and spirally twisted in the posterior portion to form a long, straight (rarely slightly curved) caudus; periplast with spiral striations; paramylon bodies 1 or 2 large, centrally located circular plates; flagellum $\frac{2}{3}$ the length of the cell body; cells (38)–40–50–$(52)\mu$ in diameter, 85–95–$(112)\mu$ long.

In shallow water of many swamps and in small ponds. Wis.

Phacus triqueter (Ehrenb.) Dujardin 1841, p. 338

Pl. 107, Figs. 4–6

Cells broadly ovoid, usually broadest below the median line, broadly rounded and bilobed anteriorly, narrowed unsymmetrically posteriorly to form a prominent, slightly deflected, sharply pointed caudus; the dorsal surface with a high flange, thus making the cell triangular in outline when seen from the end; a deep longitudinal furrow on the ventral side; periplast longitudinally striated, the striations extending slightly into the caudus; paramylon bodies 2 to several large rings (sometimes only 1); cells 30–45μ in diameter, 37–68μ long.

Tychoplankter. Wis.

LEPOCINCLIS Perty 1849, p. 28

Cells ovoid, ovate, elliptical or fusiform, sometimes nearly spherical, with a firm and usually spirally striated periplast, round in cross section; posteriorly extended into an abruptly pointed tail-piece (rarely gradually tapering); a gullet in the anterior end where there arises a single flagellum that is once or twice the cell in length; chloroplasts numerous parietal discs; pigment-spot laterally placed in the anterior region; reserve food in the form of 2 large, lateral paramylon rings, the 2 together sometimes nearly encircling the cell.

Species of this genus are usually found in company with other euglenoids. They are, for the most part, not found in euplankton but occur among dense growth of algae in shallow bays, swamps, and in ponds. They nearly always appear in samples from water which is rich in organic acids and nitrogenous substances.

The nature of the periplast decoration is of taxonomic value because it varies according to species. This character is often obscured by the density of cell contents, and it is necessary to manipulate a specimen so that it can be seen from various angles.

Key to the Species

1. Cells narrowly pyriform or narrowly ovoid,
   gradually tapering posteriorly..*L. acuta*
1. Cells broadly ovoid, or broadly ellipsoid,
   without a long caudus 2
2. Cells ovoid, 39–58μ long, with a short caudus................*L. fusiformis* var. *major*
2. Cells subglobose, ovoid, or fusiform; smaller.. 3
3. Cells with a bipapillate protrusion at the anterior
   end from which the flagellum emerges 4
3. Cells without a bipapillate protrusion... 5
4. Cells broadly ovoid, 19–21μ in diameter.......................................*L. glabra*
4. Cells ellipsoid, or narrowly ovoid, 8–10μ in diameter..............*L. sphagnophila*
5. Cells 15–17μ in diameter...*L. fusiformis*
5. Cells larger, 22–30μ in diameter 6
6. Cells 22–25μ in diameter; flagellum emerging
   at the anterior end...*L. ovum*
6. Cells 28–30μ in diameter; flagellum arising
   subapically to nearly laterally...*L. Playfairiana*

Lepocinclis acuta Prescott *in* Prescott, Silva, & Wade 1949, p. 89

Pl. 89, Figs. 8, 9

Cells ovoid-pyriform, tapering posteriorly to a long, sharply pointed caudus, slightly narrowed anteriorly and rounded at the apex; periplast spirally striated downward to the right; flagellum about as long as the body; paramylon in the form of 2 curved plates, 1 on either side of the cell; chloroplasts several ovoid discs; cells 11–13μ in diameter, 30–34μ long.

Conrad in his monograph (1934) does not record any species which combine the characteristics of our specimens. The size of the cell and the long, tapering caudus are distinctive.

Among other algae in a fosse. Wis.

Lepocinclis fusiformis (Carter) Lemmermann 1901, p. 89

Pl. 89, Figs. 1–4

Cells broadly fusiform or pyriform, slightly produced posteriorly to form a blunt basal point; membrane spirally striated; paramylon bodies 2 to several circular plates; flagellum about as long as the cell; 15–17μ in diameter and up to 36μ long.

In a roadside fosse. Wis.

Lepocinclis fusiformis var. *major* Fritsch & Rich 1930, p. 72

Pl. 89, Figs. 7, 15

Cells elongate-ovoid to subfusiform, broadest below the midregion, produced posteriorly into a very short obtuse tail-piece; usually with a bipapillate protrusion at the anterior end; periplast sometimes with extremely fine spiral striations (almost straight in our specimens); paramylon bodies 2 very large oval rings, sometimes overlapping one another; chloroplasts numerous irregularly shaped discs; cells 25–29–(39)μ in diameter, 39–58μ long.

This variety is originally described as having, at times, many small paramylon bodies, but our specimens showed only the large rings. The periplast is very faintly striated, a character seen only under favorable conditions. This species should be compared with *L. Steinii* Lemm. and *L. costata* Playf. These species are somewhat similar in shape but differ in size and details of the periplast features, as well as in the form of the paramylon bodies.

Tow from a small pond. Wis.

Lepocinclis glabra Drezepolski 1925, p. 269

Pl. 89, Fig. 14

Cells broadly ellipsoid or ovoid, broadly rounded posteriorly but with a short, blunt caudus; very slightly narrowed anteriorly, with a bipapillate protrusion through which the flagellum arises; flagellum about as long as the body; periplast smooth (?); paramylon in the form of 2 very large, curved plates, one on either side and in certain positions appearing as 4 plates; cells 19–21μ in diameter, 25–31μ long.

In a roadside fosse. Wis.

Lepocinclis glabra fa. *minor* Prescott 1944, p. 370

Pl. 89, Fig. 10

Cells broadly ovoid, with a short papilla-like caudus, broadly rounded anteriorly and ending in a bipapillate protrusion through which the flagellum emerges; flagellum about as long as the body; periplast smooth; paramylon in the form of 2 semicircular bands, curving transversely at the periphery of the cell, one on either side; chloroplasts numerous, oval discs; cells 14–16μ in diameter, 20–22μ long, smaller than the typical form.

In a tow sample from a cedar swamp. Wis.

Lepocinclis ovum (Ehrenb.) Lemmermann 1901, p. 88
Pl. 89, Figs. 5, 6

Cells broadly ovate, with a short, blunt caudus, rounded both anteriorly and posteriorly; periplast spirally striated to the right; flagellum about as long as the body; paramylon in the form of 2 rings, 1 on either side of the cell; cells 22–25μ in diameter, 28–30μ long.

Common in ditches, swamps and small ponds; also found in the shallow water of bays and lagoons among dense growths of algae; rarely euplanktonic. Mich., Wis.

Lepocinclis Playfairiana Deflandre 1932, p. 227
Pl. 89, Fig. 16

Cells broadly oval with a short caudus, slightly narrowed and sharply rounded anteriorly, the gullet and flagellum attachment lateral to the apex, where there is a slight invagination on the right side; periplast smooth; paramylon bodies 2 large circular or oval rings; cells 28–30μ in diameter, 46–48μ long.

In tows from swamps and ponds. Wis.

Lepocinclis sphagnophila Lemmermann 1904, p. 124
Pl. 89, Figs. 11–13

Cells fusiform or ovoid, narrowed posteriorly into a short caudus, tapering anteriorly and forming a bluntly rounded apex which is bipapillate (in our specimens); paramylon bodies 4 plates, 2 on either side; chloroplasts relatively few ovoid discs; flagellum length (?); cells 8–10μ in diameter, 22–25μ long.

Our specimens are assigned here because of their general agreement with Lemmermann's description. Conrad (1934) reports this as a doubtful or little known species.

Not infrequent in soft and acid water habitats. Wis.

TRACHELOMONAS Ehrenberg 1835, p. 315

In this genus euglenoid cells are enclosed in a firm gelatinous shell which has an opening for the flagellum. The shell or test has an almost endless variety of shapes and forms of decoration, and since these features are specific the taxonomy of the genus is based upon characteristics of the test rather than on those of the protoplast. The test is brown, often opaque, or tan to nearly colorless, according to the amount of iron compounds deposited in it. The test may be smooth or decorated with spines, warts, reticulations, punctations, or combinations of these. The protoplast inside is highly metabolic and has the general features of the euglenoids. There is 1 flagellum, a red pigment-spot, and numerous ovoid, disc-like chloroplasts which may have pyrenoids. Reproduction is by cell division, which takes place within the test, one of the new cells escaping through the aperture and secreting its own shell.

Although a few species may appear in the euplankton, most species of *Trachelomonas* occur in shallow water of swamps, ditches, and lagoons as tychoplankters, especially where there is a high concentration of organic matter and where temperatures are high. The organisms may be so abundant as to color the water brown, although they never form a conspicuous surface film as does *Euglena*.

Key to the Species

1. Test with the flagellum opening in a neck, or
surrounded by a collar 2
1. Test without a neck or collar around the flagellum aperture 22
2. Flagellum opening in a distinct neck 3
2. Flagellum opening in a collar or thickened ring (*) 12
3. Test globose, with 4 or 5 long, sharp spines ....*T. aculeata*
3. Test with shorter, more numerous spines 4
4. Test extended into a long, spine-tipped caudus ....*T. speciosa*
4. Test without a caudus, or if present not spine-tipped 5
5. Test sexangular-ellipsoid ....*T. hexangulata*
5. Test some other shape 6
6. Test broadly ovoid, wrinkled and rugose;
neck twisted or curved ....*T. scabra*
6. Test shaped otherwise; not rugose· 7
7. Test rectangular-fusiform, margins retuse, extended into a
caudus ....*T. Girardiana*
7. Test some other shape, not extended into a caudus 8
8. Test elongate-ellipsoid 9
8. Test oblong-cylindric or oblong 10
9. Test with numerous, minute spines, punctate;
margin of collar smooth ....*T. bulla*
9. Test with scattered, stout spines; collar
toothed at the margin ....*T. sydneyensis*
10. Test oval to oblong, collar curved ....*T. similis*
10. Test some other shape; collar not curved 11

(*) The thickened ring is a variable feature in some species. For questionable forms, follow through both No. 2 choices.

11. Test angularly oblong, bottle-shaped ....*T. euchlora*
11. Test oblong-cylindric, lateral margins parallel...................*T. dubia*
12. Test beset with long or short spines 13
12. Test without spines; either smooth or with granules or warts.............. 16
13. Rim of collar beset with stout spines..*T. armata*
13. Rim of aperture smooth 14
14. Test oval, with long, stout spines ....*T. horrida*
14. Test broadly oval to subspherical, with short spines or sharp warts.... 15
15. Test subspherical, beset with sharp warts or very short
    spines..*T. hispida*
15. Test oval, beset with stout spines ....*T. charkowiensis*
16. Test smooth 17
16. Test granular, rugose, or spiny 20
17. Test with mammillate collar; spherical ....*T. mammillosa*
17. Test without a mammillate collar; cylindric or oval 18
18. Test cylindrical ....*T. cylindrica*
18. Test oval or spherical... 19
19. Test spherical with an inward projecting flagellar tube............*T. varians*
19. Test broadly ellipsoid or oval, with short curved collar..........*T. Playfairii*
20. Test oval, (19)—23—25μ in diameter, 31—33μ
    long, uniformly granular ....*T. crebea*
20. Test ellipsoid to ovoid, smaller, (5)—19μ in diameter...................... 21
21. Test oval, 5—11—17μ in diameter, 17μ long ....*T. pulchella*
21. Test ellipsoid, 19μ in diameter, 21μ long ....*T. granulosa*
22. Test triangular, flagellum aperture occupying the entire
    apex...*T. triangularis*
22. Test some other shape; aperture narrower............................... 23
23. Test spherical or subspherical... 24
23. Test elongate, ovoid or cylindrical.. 28
24. Test smooth 25
24. Test warty or spiny 27
25. Test broadly oval, 16—18μ in diameter..............................*T. intermedia*
25. Test spherical 26
26. Test spherical to subspherical; wall thick,
    coarsely punctate ....*T. rotunda*
26. Test perfectly spherical, wall thin, smooth or finely
    punctate ....*T. volvocina*
27. Test nearly spherical, with a few teeth in the vicinity
    of the flagellum aperature ....*T. acanthostoma*
27. Test broadly oval, evenly beset with short, sharp spines........*T. robusta*
28. Test cylindrical 29
28. Test elliptic, oval or subcylindric-oval 30
29. Test with margins nearly parallel, 12—16μ in diameter,
    26—29μ long ....*T. lacustris*
29. Test subcylindric, the margins slightly convex, test
    15.6 x 31μ ....*T. erecta*
30. Test elliptic.. 31
30. Test oval or subcylindric-oval 33
31. Test broadly elliptic, 23—34μ in diameter;
    wall granular ....*T. Kelloggii*
31. Test smaller; wall smooth 32
32. Test narrowly elliptic, twice as long as broad ....*T. pulcherrima*
32. Test broadly elliptic to oval, 1 1/3 as long as broad.............*T. Dybowskii*

33. Wall spiny 34
33. Wall punctate or scrobiculate; test oval to subcylindric,
15.6 x 27.3μ ....*T. abrupta*
34. Test with prominent, long, blunt spines, 31–44μ in
diameter ....*T. spectabilis*
34. Test with sharp spines; flagellum opening with a
ring of spines; 23–25μ in diameter..*T. superba*

Trachelomonas abrupta (Swir.) Deflandre 1926, p. 93

Pl. 83, Figs. 18, 19

Test oval to subcylindric, truncate at the anterior end; flagellum aperture very wide; wall coarsely punctate, light tan in color; test 15.6μ in diameter, 27.3μ long.

In swamps. Wis.

Trachelomonas acanthostoma (Stokes) Deflandre 1926, p. 60

Pl. 83, Fig. 13; Pl. 85, Fig. 3

Test subglobose or ovoid; wall densely punctate, sometimes with minute spiny projections about the flagellum aperture which has a low collar; test 21.4μ in diameter, 32.4μ long.

In shallow water of lakes and in ponds. Wis.

Trachelomonas aculeata fa. *brevispinosa* Prescott
in Prescott, Silva, & Wade 1949, p. 89

Pl. 85, Fig. 4

Test spherical; flagellum aperture in a short neck; wall furnished with 5 spines, which are stouter and much less produced than in the typical form, which has 5 very long and finely tapering spines; cells 19–20μ in diameter.

In *Sphagnum* bogs. Wis.

Trachelomonas armata (Ehrenb.) Stein 1883, Pl. 22, Fig. 37

Pl. 83, Fig. 32

Test broadly ovate, flagellum aperature in a collar, surrounded by a circle of erect spines in some varieties; wall spiny in the anterior region with sparsely scattered spines over the midregion, and with long backwardly directed spines in the posterior part; test 22μ in diameter, 38–40μ long, including spines.

Euplankter and tychoplankter; in ponds. Wis.

[410]

Trachelomonas armata fa. *inevoluta* Deflandre 1926, p. 88
Pl. 83, Fig. 33

Test broadly ovate; wall smooth; collar a low, flat ring; test 29.6–30μ in diameter, 36.5–38μ long.
From swamps. Wis.

Trachelomonas armata var. *longispina*
(Playf.) Deflandre 1926, p. 88
Pl. 83, Fig. 27

Test broadly obovate; flagellum aperture without a collar, but with a circle of erect spines at the margin; anterior region with short spines, posterior portion with stout spines; both short and long; test 30–31μ in diameter, 41–48μ long.
Plankter; in lakes. Wis.

Trachelomonas armata var. *Steinii* Lemmermann 1906, p. 165
Pl. 83, Fig. 26

A variety differing from the typical by having more numerous spines anteriorly and spines stouter posteriorly.
Plankter; with the typical form. Wis.

Trachelomonas bulla (Stein) Deflandre 1926, p. 110
Pl. 84, Fig. 15

Test ovoid, narrowed rather gradually anteriorly to form a broad collar; wall with minute spines, punctate; a flange at the base of the neck and projecting inwardly to form a pore which is narrower than the outer opening of the collar; test 23–24μ in diameter, 39μ long.
In a *Sphagnum* bog. Wis.

Trachelomonas charkowiensis Swirenko *ex* Deflandre 1926, p. 85
Pl. 85, Fig. 14

Test oval; flagellum aperture with a short collar; wall brown, uniformly beset with stout conical spines; test 20μ in diameter, 32.5μ long.
Tychoplankter; in swamps. Wis.

Trachelomonas crebea (Kellicott) Deflandre 1926, p. 103

Test symmetrically ellipsoid, irregularly punctate and sometimes roughened; flagellum aperture in a short, wide collar which is either straight or slightly expanded at the outer rim; shell yellowish- or reddish-brown, 19μ in diameter, 19–25μ long.
Typical form not reported from our region. Wis.

Trachelomonas crebea var. *brevicollaris* Prescott
in Prescott, Silva, & Wade 1949, p. 89
Pl. 84, Fig. 17

Test ovate; flagellum aperture in a very short, ring-like collar; wall uniformly granular and roughened; test 23–25μ in diameter, 31–33μ long.

The chief difference between this and the typical form is the very short neck, reduced to a collar; other characteristics, such as wall decoration and size, are similar to those of the typical form.

In a swamp near Boulder Junction, Wisconsin.

Trachelomonas cylindrica Ehrenberg 1833, p. 315
(Sec. Playfair); Deflandre 1926, p. 75
Pl. 83, Figs. 11, 20

Test oblong-cylindric; broadly rounded at the posterior end but somewhat flattened anteriorly; wall smooth, yellowish; flagellum opening surrounded by a short collar; test 8–10μ in diameter, 14.8–20μ long.

In roadside swamps and ditches. Wis.

Trachelomonas dubia (Swir.) Deflandre 1926, p. 106
Pl. 85, Figs. 1, 2

Test cylindrical, broadly rounded posteriorly, truncate at the anterior end and abruptly narrowed to form a short cylindrical neck; wall smooth, thickened at the base of the collar; test 11–14μ in diameter, 26–28μ long.

Euplanktonic and tychoplanktonic. Wis.

Trachelomonas Dybowskii Drezepolski 1922
ex Deflandre 1926, p. 70
Pl. 83, Fig. 21; Pl. 84, Fig. 6

Test broadly ellipsoidal to ovoid; flagellum opening without a collar, sometimes with an inner thickening of the wall about the aperture; wall smooth; test 10–18μ in diameter, 16–32μ long.

Euplanktonic and tychoplanktonic. Wis.

Trachelomonas erecta Skvortzow 1925, p. 62
Pl. 85, Fig. 16

Test cylindrical, broadly rounded both posteriorly and anteriorly; flagellum aperture without a collar; wall coarsely and densely punctate; test 15.6μ in diameter, 31.2μ long.

Tychoplankter. Wis.

[412]

Trachelomonas euchlora (Ehrenb.) Lemmermann 1906, p. 165

Pl. 89, Fig. 21

Test cylindrical with subparallel sides, broadly truncate both posteriorly and anteriorly; wall smooth, brown; flagellum aperture usually oblique in a neck; test 18–20μ in diameter, 25–30μ long.

In swamps and ponds. Wis.

Trachelomonas Girardiana (Playf.) Deflandre 1926, p. 126

Pl. 84, Fig. 14

Test subhexagonal with emarginate lateral walls, narrowed abruptly posteriorly into a long, stout caudus, anteriorly tapering abruptly into a long or short neck; wall brown, roughened; test 21–26μ in diameter, 38–45–(57)μ long.

In swamps. Wis.

Trachelomonas granulosa Playfair 1916, p. 18

Pl. 89, Fig. 17

Test broadly ellipsoidal; flagellum opening usually furnished with an exterior thickening; wall brown, densely granular; test 19μ in diameter, 21μ long.

Plankter; in sloughs and ponds. Wis.

Trachelomonas hexangulata Swirenko 1914, p. 646

Pl. 85, Figs. 5, 6, 11

Test hexagonal-cylindric, the lateral walls nearly parallel, narrowed with slightly concave margins posteriorly, and rounded at the base; anteriorly narrowed and extended into a long neck with an annular thickening internally at the opening into the neck; wall smooth, brown; test 14–16μ in diameter, 30–36μ long, 3.8μ wide at the posterior pole, 3.6μ wide at the aperture.

Plankter; in swamps and ponds. Wis.

Trachelomonas hexangulata var. *repanda* Prescott 1944, p. 370

Pl. 84, Fig. 16

Differing from the typical by having the lateral margins of the test more convex and the posterior lateral margins more concave so that a blunt apiculation is produced posteriorly; test 14.4–15μ in diameter, 36–38μ long.

Tychoplankter. Wis.

[413]

Trachelomonas hispida (Perty) Stein 1883, Pl. 22, Figs. 21, 24–33

Pl. 83, Fig. 35

Test ovate, narrowed anteriorly; flagellum aperture slightly raised; wall uniformly beset with minute, sharp-pointed warts; test 24–26μ in diameter, 29–31μ long.

This species and *T. volvocina* are the most commonly found members of the genus in our region.

Generally distributed in a variety of ponds, swamps, and ditches; in tow samples from lakes. Mich., Wis.

Trachelomonas hispida var. *coronata* Lemmermann

ex Deflandre 1926, p. 79

Pl. 83, Fig. 30

Test oblong-oval; flagellum aperture surrounded by a short collar with the margin bearing a circle of spines; wall uniformly beset with short spines; test 20μ in diameter, 29–32μ long.

In shallow water of ponds and ditches. Wis.

Tachelomonas hispida var. *crenulatocollis*

fa. *recta* Deflandre 1926, p. 78

Pl. 83, Fig. 31

Test ovoid; flagellum aperture in a short collar with a coarsely toothed margin; wall punctate and unevenly beset with short sharp spines; test 25–26μ in diameter, 33–34μ long.

Euplanktonic and tychoplanktonic. Wis.

Trachelomonas hispida var. *papillata* Skvortzow 1925, p. 36

Pl. 84, Fig. 7

Test oval; flagellum aperture without a collar or thickening; wall brown or pink-brown, smooth except for a few minute spines about the flagellum aperture; 28–30μ in diameter, 34–40μ long.

Euplankter; with the typical form. Wis.

Trachelomonas hispida var. *punctata* Lemmermann 1906, p. 165

Pl. 84, Figs. 3, 4

Test broadly oval; flagellum aperture without a distinct collar but with a slightly raised rim; wall coarsely and densely punctate; test 29μ in diameter, 32–34μ long.

Tychoplanktonic and euplanktonic. Wis.

Trachelomonas horrida Palmer 1905, p. 674
Pl. 84, Fig. 1

Test oval, flagellum aperture with a short broad collar; wall uniformly beset with long, stout, bluntly pointed spines interspersed by short, sharp spines; test 27.5μ in diameter, 35–40μ long.

Uncommon; in several swamps, ponds, and ditches. Wis.

Trachelomonas intermedia Dangeard 1902, p. 231
Pl. 83, Fig. 10

Test subspherical to oval, slightly narrowed anteriorly; flagellum aperture with a thickening but without a distinct collar; wall brown, densely punctate; test 16–18μ in diameter, 20–25μ long.

Tychoplankter; in ponds and ditches. Wis.

Trachelomonas Kelloggii (Skv.) Deflandre 1926, p. 87
Pl. 83, Figs. 16, 17

Test broadly elliptic to subspherical; flagellum aperture without a collar but occasionally with an annular thickening; wall brown, punctate and roughened with conical granulations which usually are more pronounced around the poles; test (23)–31–34μ in diameter, (27)–35–39μ long.

Tychoplanktonic and euplanktonic. Wis.

Trachelomonas lacustris Drezepolski 1925, p. 217
[*T. cylindrica* var. *punctata* Skvortzow]
Pl. 83, Figs. 14, 15; Pl. 85, Fig. 15

Test cylindrical, the lateral margins almost parallel, broadly rounded both posteriorly and anteriorly; flagellum aperture usually without a collar but sometimes with a slightly raised rim; wall coarsely and densely punctate, golden yellow-brown; test 12–16.5μ in diameter, 26–29.6μ long.

Euplanktonic and tychoplanktonic. Mich., Wis.

Trachelomonas mammillosa Prescott 1944, p. 370
Pl. 85, Fig. 12

Test spherical; flagellum aperture in a mammillate swelling; wall yellowish, smooth but with a thick annular ridge encircling the anterior end; test 24–26μ in diameter.

This species is distinguished by the prominent ridge which encircles the test anteriorly, and the papillate swelling about the flagellum aperture. It should be compared with *T. peridiniformis* Skv., reported from Manchuria.

Tychoplankter; in swamps. Wis.

Trachelomonas Playfairii Deflandre 1926, p. 110
Pl. 85, Figs. 8, 9

Test broadly ellipsoid or ovate and rounded both anteriorly and posteriorly; flagellum aperture in a short curved collar; wall smooth, almost colorless or light yellow; test 19–21–(23)μ in diameter, 23–30μ long.

Tychoplanktonic and euplanktonic. Wis.

Trachelomonas pulchella Drezepolski 1925, p. 221
Pl. 83, Fig. 28

Test oval to ovoid, small; flagellum aperture with a short ring-like collar; wall uniformly beset with blunt, wart-like roughenings; test (5)–11.7–17μ in diameter, about 15μ long.

Tychoplankter. Wis.

Trachelomonas pulcherrima Playfair 1916, p. 13
Pl. 83, Figs. 22, 23

Test elliptic or subcylindric-elliptic; flagellum aperture without a collar; wall yellow-brown, smooth; test 14.8μ in diameter, 22μ long.

Euplankter. Wis.

Trachelomonas pulcherrima var. *minor* Playfair 1916, p. 14
Pl. 83, Figs. 24, 25

Test oval or elliptic; flagellum opening without a collar; wall brown, smooth; test 7.5μ in diameter, 12.5μ long.

A variety similar to the typical except for the smaller size.

Trachelomonas robusta Swirenko 1914, p. 636
Pl. 83, Fig. 29

Test subglobose or oval; flagellum aperture without a collar but with a thickened rim; wall dark brown, evenly beset with short, sharp spines; test 14–16μ in diameter, 20–25μ long.

Tychoplankter. Wis.

Trachelomonas rotunda Swirenko 1914, p. 636
Pl. 83, Fig. 9

Test subspherical or spherical; flagellum aperture without a collar; wall coarsely and densely punctate; test 26–30μ in diameter, 33.5μ long.

Tychoplankter. Wis.

Trachelomonas scabra var. *longicollis* Playfair 1916, p. 28
Pl. 85, Fig.7

Test ovoid; flagellum aperture in a short, twisted collar; wall irregularly and rather coarsely roughened; test 19.5μ in diameter, 27.3μ long.
Tychoplankter. Wis.

Trachelomonas similis Stokes 1890, p. 76
Pl. 84, Fig. 12; Pl. 85, Figs. 10, 13

Test oblong-ellipsoid; flagellum aperture in a curved collar; wall uniformly roughened by irregularly shaped granulations; test $(13.4)-14-19\mu$ in diameter, $39-41\mu$ long.
Tychoplankter. Wis.

Trachelomonas speciosa Deflandre 1926, p. 122
Pl. 84, Fig. 13

Test ovate-fusiform, abruptly narrowed posteriorly into a short or long caudus which is trifurcated at the apex to form 3 stout spines; narrowed anteriorly to form a short neck with 3–4 teeth around the margin of the flagellum aperture; wall uniformly beset with moderately long, slender spines; test $20-25\mu$ in diameter, $51-56\mu$ long.
Tychoplanktonic and euplanktonic. Wis.

Trachelomonas spectabilis Deflandre 1926, p. 86
Pl. 85, Fig. 19

Test oval, elongate; flagellum aperture without a collar but with a crenulate margin; wall minutely punctate, with irregularly scattered, stout, long spines; test $31.2-44\mu$ in diameter, $50-65\mu$ long.
Plankter; in both lakes and swamps. Wis.

Trachelomonas superba (Swir.) Deflandre 1926, p. 84
Pl. 84, Fig. 10

Test broadly oval; flagellum aperture without a collar but often with a circle of stout spines at the rim; wall uniformly beset with short, sharp spines; test $23-25\mu$ in diameter, $31-46.8\mu$ long.
Tychoplankter; in swamps. Wis.

Trachelomonas superba var. *duplex* Deflandre 1926, p. 85
Pl. 84, Fig. 11

Test broadly oval, furnished with spines distinctly longer in the polar regions; test $28-30\mu$ in diameter, $35-40\mu$ long.
Tychoplankter; in swamps. Wis.

[417]

Trachelomonas superba var. *spinosa* Prescott 1944, p. 370

Pl. 84, Fig. 5

Test broadly oval; wall spiny, with the posterior part beset with much longer and more sharply pointed spines; flagellum aperture without a collar but encircled with a coronula of sharp, erect spines; test 32.5–36μ in diameter, 39–48μ long.

This variety differs from the typical form in its greater size, the longer spines at the posterior pole, and the coronula about the flagellum aperture.

Euplankter and tychoplankter. Wis.

Trachelomonas superba var. *Swirenkiana* Deflandre 1926, p. 84

Pl. 83, Fig. 34; Pl. 84, Figs. 8, 9

Test subglobose; flagellum aperture in a low, ring-like collar; wall spiny in the anterior and posterior portions with a few minute spines in the midregion; the posterior spines longer and stouter than in the anterior region; test 31μ in diameter, 40μ long.

Euplankter and tychoplankter. Wis.

Trachelomonas sydneyensis Playfair 1916, p. 22

Pl. 84, Fig. 2

Test elongate-ellipsoid, broadly rounded both anteriorly and posteriorly; flagellum aperture in a short collar with a spiny margin; wall brown, rather evenly beset with short, sharp spines in the posterior and anterior regions but with only sharp granules in the midregion; test 25μ in diameter, 32–40μ long.

Tychoplankter; in swamps. Wis.

Trachelomonas triangularis Deflandre 1924, p. 1128

Pl. 83, Fig. 6

Test subtriangular, broadly convex posteriorly, lateral walls sharply convex from the broad base, converging to a truncate apex; flagellum aperture occupying the entire diameter of the apex; wall light brown; test 12–14μ in diameter, 14–16μ long.

In swampy habitats and in roadside ditches. Wis.

Trachelomonas varians (Lemm.) Deflandre 1924, p. 1124

Pl. 83, Figs. 4, 5

Test globose or subglobose; flagellum aperture surrounded by a low flat ring from which a cylindrical canal extends inwardly to

the test cavity; wall smooth or lightly punctate, golden- or reddish-brown; test 23μ in diameter, 23–26μ long.
Tychoplankter; in swamps. Wis.

Trachelomonas volvocina Ehrenberg
1833, pp. 315, 331; 1838, p. 48
Pl. 83, Figs. 1, 7, 8

Test globose; flagellum aperture without a collar; wall yellowish, sometimes colorless, smooth; test 16–20μ in diameter.
Generally distributed; common in ponds and ditches. Mich., Wis.

Trachelomonas volvocina var. compressa
Drezepolski 1925, p. 224
Pl. 83, Figs. 2, 3

Test depressed-globose or spheroidal; flagellum aperture surrounded by a thickening of the wall, which is yellow and smooth; test 18.5μ in diameter, 20.3μ long.
Tychoplankter; in swamps. Wis.

Trachelomonas volvocina var. punctata Playfair 1916, p. 9
Pl. 83, Fig. 12

Test with a distinctly punctate wall, 10μ in diameter, 20μ long; otherwise similar to the typical.
Tychoplankter; in swamps. Wis.

COLACIUM Ehrenberg 1832b, p. 115

Cells losing their flagellum and becoming attached by a stalk-like extension of the membrane, with the anterior end downward, to small animals (Crustacea, etc.); chloroplasts many ovoid discs, with or without a pyrenoid; pigment-spot usually evident in the lower (apical) end; cells solitary or in arbuscular colonies.

Key to the Species

Cells in plume-like colonies, stalks as long
  as or longer than the cells_____C. arbuscula
Cells solitary, or 2–4 on short, thick stalks_____C. vesiculosum

Colacium arbuscula Stein 1878, III, p. 1
Pl. 89, Fig. 22

Cells elliptic or fusiform, joined by a branched, gelatinous stalk to form plume-like, arbuscular colonies; chloroplasts many ovoid

[419]

bodies without a pyrenoid; pigment-spot sometimes evident; cells 8–10μ in diameter, 12–16μ long.

This species is more rarely seen than *C. vesiculosum*. When present it produces dense green growths which are barely discernible to the unaided eye on microzoa such as Crustacea. The colony usually forms a plume on the head region.

Wis.

Colacium vesiculosum Ehrenberg 1832b, p. 115
Pl. 89, Figs. 18, 19

Cells fusiform to somewhat pyriform, solitary or 2–4 together, attached by short stalks to microfauna; cells 8–15μ in diameter, 18–25–(29)μ long; chloroplasts several to many ovoid discs without pyrenoids.

Not widely distributed but common in habitats where it appears; usually on Cladocera and Copepoda. Mich., Wis.

DIVISION CHLOROMONADOPHYTA

CLASS CHLOROMONADINEAE

This is a little-understood group of the Protista which is represented by only a few known forms. Some of the characteristics they possess indicate an affinity with the Euglenophyta, while others are suggestive of the Pyrrhophyta. In general, the Chloromonadophyta are distinctly protozoa-like, and there are no filamentous or coccoid expressions known in the division.

The organisms are motile, ovoid, or pyriform unicells, often dorsiventrally flattened, with a ventral furrow. There are 2 apically attached flagella, 1 of which is usually trailing, as in some of the Euglenophyta and Pyrrhophyta. In the pigmented members (2 genera are colorless), there are numerous ovate and disc-like chloroplasts in which xanthophyll is a predominant pigment. Neither starch nor paramylon occurs as a food reserve, but instead, fats and oils.

A characteristic common to several forms is the presence of radially disposed trichocysts in the peripheral region of the cell. These throw off threads upon stimulation.

As far as is known, reproduction occurs by longitudinal cell division (as in the somewhat common *Vacuolaria virescens* Cienk.).

FAMILY CHLOROMONADINACEAE

Characteristics as described for the class. Only one genus is represented in our collections.

GONYOSTOMUM Diesing 1866, pp. 298, 332

Cells motile, dorsiventrally flattened, obovate or obovate-lanceolate in front view and often showing a short caudus; dorsal surface convex, the ventral surface flattened and with a longitudinal furrow extending posteriorly from an opening which leads into a colorless 3-cornered cavity in the anterior region; flagella 2, usually longer than the body, 1 projected forward, the other trailing; chloroplasts numerous ovoid discs, crowded at the periphery; short radiating, rod-like trichocysts also at the periphery, extending toward the center of the cell (often only a few of these show in the unstained, living cell); pigment-spot wanting; food reserve in the form of oil.

Gonyostomum semen (Ehrenb.) Diesing 1866, p. 332
Pl. 99, Figs. 11, 12

Characters as described for the genus; cells 23–69µ in diameter, 36–92µ long; nucleus central; flagella as long as the cell body.

Drouet and Cohen (1935, 1937) have made very critical observations on this organism and have described its morphology and reproductive process.

In swamps and acid ponds. Mich., Wis.

DIVISION PYRRHOPHYTA

By far the majority of the Pyrrhophyta are swimming unicells, but there are a few sedentary forms, and in one of the orders, the Dinotrichales, there is a filamentous expression. Some genera in the plankton of the sea form simple colonies. The division in its present definition includes three classes (Pascher, 1931; Smith, 1938), and in one of these, the Dinophyceae, there is an approach to the same evolutionary series which characterize some of the other algal divisions. There are, for example (besides the filamentous tendency mentioned above), palmelloid forms comparable to the Tetrasporales of the Chlorophyta, and a Chlorococcales parallel is seen in the Dinococcales.

Morphologically the division is extremely heterogeneous, but the diverse forms are bound together by fundamental similarities. The more significant of these are their brown pigment, food reserve in the form of starch, and the presence of cellulose in the cell wall. Oil may be present in addition to starch, however, and some forms do not possess a definite cell wall.

Of the three classes in the Pyrrhophyta, the class Dinophyceae is much the largest, including most of the known fresh-water species of the division, although the majority of the Dinophyceae are marine. In the sea, this class exhibits a great diversity and there are many bizarre forms, most of which are holozoic or saprophytic, and are red or yellow in color.

The Desmokontae, mostly marine, have no representatives reported from our region.

Although but few members of the third class, Cryptophyceae, have been recorded in our region, many species of this almost altogether fresh-water class are to be expected there. Most forms are biflagellated protozoa-like organisms, but 2 non-motile genera, colonial in expression, are known. Filamentous forms are lacking in this class.

Key to the Classes

Chromatophores numerous brown discs_____DINOPHYCEAE
Chromatophores 1 or 2 brown, elongate, parietal plates_____ CRYPTOPHYCEAE

CLASS DINOPHYCEAE
(Dinoflagellates)

The cells in this class contain numerous disc-like or spindle-shaped chromatophores (at least in the fresh-water forms) in which several pigments have been identified. The predominating one is

[423]

peridinin, which is responsible for the brown color exhibited by the autotrophic forms. Marine holozoic organisms are commonly red, purple, or yellow. In some groups there are pyrenoids. Reserve food ordinarily collects as starch, although in their nutrition these organisms may be holozoic, holophytic, or saprophytic.

In most of the free-swimming species the protoplast contains a red pigment-spot which is unusually large and conspicuous and may be either simple or complex with lens-like structures.

The cell is either a naked protoplast or is inclosed by a thin or thick wall. In the latter case (the armored dinoflagellates), the envelope is complex, being composed of a varying number of plates, which may be smooth or rough and spiny. The size, arrangement, and number of these plates are of taxonomic value.

The motile forms have 2 flagella attached on the ventral surface in a more or less conspicuous *longitudinal furrow* or *sulcus*. One of these trails behind the cell while the other is wrapped about it in a *transverse furrow* in which the flagellum vibrates, causing the organism to rotate on its axis as it swims forward. The transverse furrow marks the juncture of the two halves of which the wall (in most forms) is composed. In the anterior part of the cell (*epicone*), the plates comprise the *epitheca*, and those in the posterior part (*hypocone*) form the *hypotheca*. See Eddy (1930) for figures illustrating plans of arrangement and nomenclature of the plates.

In the epitheca the plates adjoining the transverse girdle are called the *precingulars*. Not always present are a few *anterior intercalary* plates interspersed between the precingulars and the plates at the apex which are known as the *apicals*. Correspondingly, the plates of the hypotheca adjacent to the girdle are called the *postcingulars*, with 1 or 2 *antapicals* at the posterior pole. Rarely there may be a *posterior intercalary* plate between the postcingulars and the antapicals. In addition to the components mentioned, there may be a more or less prominent *ventral* plate which lies just above the anterior end of the longitudinal furrow. It may or may not extend to the anterior pole.

When viewed from the ventral side so that the longitudinal furrow is seen, the right side of the organism is on the left of the observer, and is at the right of the observer, of course, when seen dorsally with only the transverse furrow in view.

In one order, Dinococcales, the cells are not motile in the vegetative phase and do not carry on cell division. Unlike members of the other orders they reproduce by forming 2–8 autospores or zoospores. It is significant that the sedentary cells are sometimes very similar

[424]

in shape to the temporary resting cysts produced by many of the motile Peridiniales.

The Pyrrhophyta are both euplanktonic and tychoplanktonic. It is presumed that they are important in the food chain of fresh-water animals, as they are in the sea, although in fresh water they seldom occur in such tremendous 'blooms' as they do in salt water at certain seasons. The ubiquitous *Ceratium hirundinella* (O. F. M.) Duj., however, frequently appears in such numbers as to give an entire lake a definite coffee-color.

Of the 7 recognized orders in the class Dinophyceae, 3 are represented in our collections.

Key to the Orders

1. Motile 2
1. Non-motile 3
2. Cells without walls; naked protoplasts with an
   envelope not divided into plates .... GYMNODINIALES
2. Cells with walls; membrane with plates (obscure
   in *Glenodinium* and *Hemidinium*) .... PERIDINIALES
3. Cells arranged to form a filament .... *DINOTRICHALES
3. Cells solitary, attached or free-floating .... DINOCOCCALES

ORDER GYMNODINIALES

These are forms which, as their name implies, have no definite cell wall but occur as naked protoplasts. Some observers, however, have described a fine periplast in which platelets have been discerned. Fresh-water species are ovoid or subrhomboidal and usually are flattened when seen in side view. There is a longitudinal furrow which may or may not extend into the epicone from the transverse furrow. The latter is wound to the left (descends on the right side of the organism when seen in ventral view) and joins the longitudinal sulcus where the flagella are attached. There is 1 fresh-water family.

FAMILY GYMNODINIACEAE

Characteristics as described for the order.

GYMNODINIUM (Stein) Kofoid & Swezy 1921, p. 158

Cells ovoid, ellipsoid, or pyriform, the transverse furrow complete, spirally turning to the left and dividing the cell into 2 equal (or slightly unequal), differently shaped portions; longitudinal furrow extending to the poles or only part way into the epicone and hypocone, but always farther into the latter than the former; pigmented species with numerous, golden-brown, elongate or ovoid chromatophores which are radially arranged; membrane smooth (in our specimens) or with longitudinal striations.

Most of the species of *Gymnodinium* are marine, but a few of the known fresh-water forms have been recorded for this country.

Key to the Species

1. Cells broadly rounded posteriorly, emarginate
   at the antapical pole..*G. palustre*
1. Cells extended posteriorly to form a cone, or a caudus......................... 2
2. Cells extended posteriorly into a curved caudus.....................*G. caudatum*
2. Cells extended into a short, cone-shaped portion posteriorly............*G. fuscum*

Gymnodinium caudatum Prescott 1944, p. 371
Pl. 90, Figs. 1–3

Cells large, ovoid to inversely conical or top-shaped, broadly rounded at the anterior end, narrowed and produced into a curved caudus at the posterior pole; very much flattened dorsiventrally; transverse furrow prominent and median, spirally turned to the left; chromatophores numerous golden-brown, ovoid, or elongate plates, radially disposed; pigment-spot present near the sulcus in the hypocone; longitudinal furrow extending about half the length of the hypocone and for a short distance into the epicone; cell 65–70μ in diameter, 104–118μ long.

The large size of the cell and the narrowed, tail-like hyocone are the distinguishing features of this species.

In a *Sphagnum* bog. Wis.

Gymnodinium fuscum (Ehrenb.) Stein 1878, p. 95
Pl. 89, Fig. 23

Cells large, ovoid, the epicone dome-shaped, the hypocone as broad as or broader than the epicone, narrowed posteriorly to form an inverted cone with a slightly produced tip; transverse furrow slightly spiral; the longitudinal furrow extending about half way into the hypocone, but scarcely at all into the epicone; chromatophores numerous ovoid discs or rods, radially arranged; cells 55–60μ in diameter, 80–100μ long.

Our specimens are slightly smaller than the dimensions given for *G. fuscum* but are otherwise in agreement.

Common in lily ponds and acid bogs. Wis.

Gymnodinium palustre Schilling 1891, pp. 248, 277, 278
Pl. 107, Fig. 3

Cells relatively small, ellipsoid, the anterior end sharply rounded or somewhat cone-shaped, the posterior pole broadly rounded;

epicone about twice the length of the hypocone so that the transverse furrow is inframedian; longitudinal furrow narrow, extending about half way into the epicone, broader in the hypocone; 27–30μ in diameter, 40–60μ long.

Mich.

ORDER PERIDINIALES

In this group the cells have a definite, thick membrane which is constructed of plates (see p. 424). There is a definite epitheca and hypotheca separated by a broad transverse furrow which sometimes completely encircles the cell. In most of the fresh-water species the plates are thick and are separated by wide sutures, but in one family (Glenodiniaceae) the plates are thin and close-fitting.

Key to the Families

1. Cell wall thin, plates obscure..GLENODINIACEAE
1. Cell wall with conspicuous plates, usually separated by sutures.............. 2
2. Cells with anterior half extended into a long,
   horn-like process..CERATIACEAE
2. Cells with anterior half broadly rounded or
   conical but not extended into a horn..PERIDINIACEAE

FAMILY GLENODINIACEAE

These organisms are globose or somewhat flattened dorsiventrally, ellipsoid or top-shaped in front view. The cells have a very thin wall in which there are delicate, scarcely discernible plates. There are numerous brown chromatophores and a pigment-spot is usually conspicuous. The transverse furrow does not extend completely around the cell in some forms.

Key to the Genera

With a transverse furrow that extends completely
around the cell..*Glenodinium*

With a transverse furrow that extends only
part way around the cell...*Hemidinium*

GLENODINIUM (Ehrenb.) Stein 1883, p. 91

Cells globose (very slightly flattened dorsiventrally), with a very thin theca in which there are faintly marked-out plates separated by narrow sutures (best seen in plasmolyzed or stained specimens); transverse furrow complete, either in one plane or slightly spiral in some species; epicone broadly rounded or somewhat apiculate, with a variable number of plates; hypotheca with 5–6 postcingulars and usually 2 antapical plates (rarely 1); chromatophores numerous, brown, oval or circular bodies which are frequently radially arranged; pigment-spot usually present in the broad longitudinal sulcus which lies almost entirely in the posterior half of the cell.

Key to the Species

1. Theca with posterior spines or teeth_____ 2
1. Theca not furnished with posterior spines or teeth_____ 4
2. Theca with 2 posterior spines and 2 lateral processes_____G. quadridens
2. Theca with a single posterior tooth or apiculation _____ 3
3. Plates distinctly visible; longitudinal furrow with a flange that
   terminates in a posterior tooth; cells 35μ in diameter_____G. Gymnodinium
3. Plates scarcely visible; longitudinal furrow without
   a flange; cells 19–28μ in diameter_____G. armatum
4. Epicone conical with an apiculation _____ 5
4. Epicone broadly or narrowly rounded, convex; not apiculate_____ 6
5. Cells 36–40μ in diameter; longitudinal furrow
   broad (10–12μ wide)_____G. Borgei
5. Cells 20–25μ in diameter; longitudinal furrow
   narrower than above _____ G. Penardiforme
6. Cells 25–31μ in diameter; plates of theca conspicuous_____ 7
6. Cells 13–19–(29)μ in diameter; plates not visible_____G. pulvisculus
7. Longitudinal furrow extending to the apex of the
   hypocone; 6 postcingulars, 2 antapicals_____G. Kulczynskii
7. Longitudinal furrow not extending entirely to apex
   of hypocone; 5 postcingulars, 1 antapical_____G. palustre

Glenodinium armatum Levander 1900, p. 103
Pl. 90, Fig. 7

Cells spherical in outline, unsymmetrically divided by a broad, transverse furrow, the epicone longer, almost hemispherical but sharply rounded at the apex; the hypocone short, broadly rounded at the pole and with a short conical projection on the left side (right side as seen from the ventral surface); plates scarcely visible in the thin but firm theca; chromatophores radially arranged ovoid plates; pigment-spot present in the longitudinal sulcus which is hardly visible but which extends from the transverse furrow almost to the posterior pole; cells 19–28μ in diameter, 16–29.7μ long.
Tychoplankter. Wis.

Glenodinium Borgei (Lemm.) Schiller 1935–1937, p. 112
[Peridinium Borgei Lemmermann]
Pl. 90, Figs. 8, 9

Cells broadly ovoid to subglobose, the epicone high and shortly apiculate; not dorsiventrally compressed but round in polar view; epitheca with 1 apical, 2 intercalary, and 6 precingular plates; the

[428]

apical plate on the dorsal side not extending to the apex; hypotheca with 5 postcingular and 2 antapical plates; cells 36–40μ in diameter, 40–46μ long.

Tychoplankter. Wis.

Glenodinium Gymnodinium Penard 1891, p. 54
Pl. 90, Figs. 10, 11

Cells broadly oval as seen in the ventral view, dorsiventrally flattened as seen vertically; transverse furrow broad, turning spirally to the left; longitudinal furrow extending from the epicone to the apex of the hypocone, the left margin of the longitudinal furrow with a flange which ends in a tooth at the posterior pole; epitheca with 1–(2?) apical, 4 intercalary, and 7 precingular plates; hypotheca with 5 postcingular and 2 antapical plates; chromatophores brownish-green; cells 35μ in diameter, 40μ long.

Tychoplankter. Wis.

Glenodinium Kulczynskii (Wolosz.) Schiller 1935–1937, p. 96
Pl. 90, Figs. 12–14

Cells broadly ovoid or nearly round as seen in ventral view, flattened in polar view, the dorsal margin broadly convex; epitheca with 1 apical, 3 intercalary, and 6 precingular plates; hypotheca with 6 postcingular and 2 antapical plates; longitudinal furrow extending to the apex of the hypocone; cell 30–31.5μ in diameter, 35μ long.

Tychoplankter. Wis.

Glenodinium palustre (Lemm.) Schiller 1935–1937, p. 99
[Gonyaulax palustris Lemmermann]
Pl. 90, Figs. 15, 16

Cells globose with the transverse furrow slightly but clearly spiral; longitudinal furrow extending from the epicone through the hypocone; epitheca with 1 apical plate, 3 intercalary and 6 precingular plates; hypotheca with 5 postcingular and 1 antapical plate; cells 25–30μ in diameter, 27–34μ long.

Plankter; in several, mostly soft water, lakes and acid bogs. Wis.

Glenodinium Penardiforme (Linde.) Schiller 1935–1937, p. 113
Pl. 90, Fig. 21

Cells small, ovoid, the epicone sharply rounded and slightly apiculate, dorsiventrally flattened; the hypocone broadly rounded and emarginate at the pole; transverse furrow broad; longitudinal furrow scarcely extending into the epicone, broadening into the hypocone and reaching the posterior pole; cells 20–25μ in diameter, 30–35μ long.

The plates are very inconspicuous in the specimens seen and their assignment is questionably made on the basis of present information. *G. Penardiforme* is described as having 4 intercalary and 6 precingular plates in the epitheca, 5 postcingular and 2 antapical plates in the hypotheca; the cell with or without chromatophores.

Not uncommon; in several soft water lakes, ponds, and swamps. Wis.

Glenodinium pulvisculus (Ehrenb.) Stein 1883, III, part 2
Pl. 90, Figs. 17, 18

Cells ovate to subglobose, the epicone and hypocone both broadly rounded at the poles; transverse furrow winding to the left; longitudinal furrow extending into the epicone and posteriorly almost to the pole of the hypocone; chromatophores numerous, golden-brown bodies; cells 13–19–(29)μ in diameter, 23–35μ long.

The plates of the theca of this species are as yet incompletely known, and the assignment to the genus *Glenodinium* is questionable. As suggested by Eddy (1930) it may belong to *Gymnodinium*. Tychoplankter. Mich., Wis.

Glenodinium quadridens (Stein) Schiller 1935–1937, p. 117
Pl. 90, Figs. 19, 20

Cells ovate, the epicone apiculate, the hypocone broadly rounded and furnished with 3–5 short, sharp spines, laterally and posteriorly placed; transverse furrow not spiral, usually median and equally dividing the cell; longitudinal furrow extending into the epicone, widening posteriorly and reaching the apex of the hypocone; epitheca with 1 apical, 5 intercalary, and 7 precingular plates; hypotheca with 5 postcingular and 2 antapical plates with a stout spine on each; cells 20–35μ in diameter, 24–30μ long. Tychoplankter. Wis.

HEMIDINIUM Stein 1883, p. 90

Cells unsymmetrically ellipsoid, much flattened dorsiventrally, both poles broadly rounded, the anterior less so and somewhat cone-shaped; transverse furrow incomplete, spirally descending to the left; membrane covered by a very thin theca in which there are indistinctly marked areolate plates; epitheca with 6 apical, 6 precingular plates; hypotheca with 5 postcingular, 1 intercalary, and 1 antapical plate; chromatophores golden-brown fusiform bodies, radially arranged.

The plates in this genus can be discerned only under favorable optical conditions.

Hemidinium nasutum Stein 1883, p. 91
Pl. 90, Figs. 4–6

Cells elliptical or narrowly ovoid; transverse furrow incomplete, curving down to the right as seen from the ventral side; longitudinal furrow forming a narrow sulcus which extends from the transverse furrow to the posterior pole which is broadly rounded; cell 16–20μ in diameter, 24–28μ long.

Fairly common in the plankton of several lakes, especially in marginal waters among dense beds of other algae. Wis.

FAMILY PERIDINIACEAE

This family has cells which are globose, or only slightly flattened, fusiform, or top-shaped. The transverse furrow is broad and horizontal, definitely dividing the cell into epicone and hypocone. Although usually broadly rounded anteriorly, the epicone may be narrowed and pointed at the apex. The hypocone likewise is usually broadly convex, but in a few forms it may be somewhat produced to form one or more lobes or conical projections. Reproduction is by cell division. Resting cysts of specific shape are used during periods of adverse environmental conditions.

PERIDINIUM Ehrenberg 1832a, p. 38
[*Peridinium* Ehrenb., Stein 1883]

Cells globose, ovoid, or fusiform (in fresh-water species), usually somewhat dorsiventrally flattened, either broadly rounded at the poles or produced to form apiculations or short horns; transverse furrow infra-median and slightly spiral, the epicone sometimes with a true apex and a pore at the anterior pole, or with a false apex that is produced into a horn without a pore and is longer than the hypocone; longitudinal furrow usually broad in the hypocone and extending to the posterior pole, or not, and into the epicone slightly; flagella attached in the ventral sulcus, one winding about the cell in the transverse furrow, the other trailing; arrangement and number of plates in the epitheca variable, usually 4 apical, 3 intercalary and 6–7 precingular plates, one of the apical plates extending from the top of the longitudinal sulcus to the apical pole (the rhomboid or ventral plate); hypotheca with 5 postcingulars and 2 antapical plates; all plates conspicuously marked with reticular thickenings and sometimes other decorations, such as small spines, and with narrow or wide sutures between the plates which are usually striated, as is also the transverse furrow; in some species with a conspicuous flange or wing-like rim about the cell through which small ribs or concretions radiate to the margin from the surface of the plates.

Key to the Species

1. Cells broadly fusiform, extended posteriorly into 1 or more processes............ 2
1. Cells broadly rounded posteriorly.. 3
(See *P. cinctum* var. *tuberosum*, however.)
2. One posterior horn-like extension.................................... *P. wisconsinense*
2. Two posterior horn-like extensions.................................... *P. limbatum*
3. Cells 13–20μ in diameter 6
3. Cells larger.. 4
4. Cells nearly circular in outline 5
4. Cells distinctly longer than broad.................................... *P. Willei*
5. Cells 35–55μ in diameter; longitudinal furrow extending
for some distance into the epicone.................................... *P. cinctum*
5. Cells 55–80μ in diameter; longitudinal furrow
scarcely extending into the epicone.................................... *P. gatunense*
6. Cells with 3 small teeth at the posterior pole.................... *P. inconspicuum*
6. Cells with broadly rounded smooth antapical poles.................... *P. pusillum*

Peridinium cinctum (Muell.) Ehrenberg 1838, p. 253
Pl. 91, Fig. 1–4

Cells globose, subglobose, or broadly ovoid in ventral view, very slightly flattened dorsiventrally as seen in polar view; transverse furrow broad, spiral, dividing the cell almost equally on the left side (as seen ventrally) but spiralling to a supramedian position on the right; plates thick and coarsely reticulate; epicone high and broadly rounded, epitheca with 4 apicals (including the rhomboid plate), 3 intercalary, and 7 precingular plates; hypocone broadly rounded posteriorly, hypotheca with 5 postcingular and 2 antapical plates; cells 35–55μ in diameter, 40–60μ long.

Fairly common in both euplankton and tychoplankton. Mich., Wis.

Peridinium cinctum var. *Lemmermannii*
G. S. West 1909, p. 190

Cells 62–70μ in diameter, 56–70μ long, 52–53μ thick; a variety in which the right antapical plate is distinctly larger than the left.
Euplanktonic and tychoplanktonic. Mich., Wis.

Peridinium cinctum var. *tuberosum* (Meunier)
Lindemann 1928, p. 260
Pl. 91, Figs. 7–12

A variety larger than the typical, 63μ in diameter, 66.6μ long, and more nearly globose, scarcely if at all dorsiventrally flattened; in ventral view the epicone broadly rounded in general outline, with angulations at the margin where it is interrupted by the sutures of the plates, sometimes apiculate at the pole; plates variable, usually with 4 apical, 3 intercalary, and 7 precingular plates; the 2 hypothecal plates produced posteriorly to form 3 stout, blunt horns (the variety is described as having 3 antapical plates, but Wisconsin specimens seem to have but 2 in every case); the cell showing a flange that extends from the transverse furrow around to the poles; plates coarsely reticulate.

Tychoplankter; in ponds and swamps. Wis.

Peridinium gatunense Nygaard *in* Ostenfeld
& Nygaard 1925, p. 10 (reprint)
Pl. 90, Figs. 25, 26

Cells globose to elliptic, with angulations at the marginal sutures; (as seen ventrally), the poles broadly rounded; transverse furrow spiral with a wide border, unequally dividing the cell into a greater epicone and a shorter hypocone; the longitudinal furrow extending from high in the epicone to near the posterior pole; plates with wide, striated sutures between them, coarsely reticulate; epitheca with 13 plates; hypotheca with 2 large antapicals and 5 postcingular plates; cells 55–80μ in diameter, 45–80μ long.

Tychoplanktonic and euplanktonic. Wis.

Peridinium inconspicuum Lemmermann 1900, p. 350
Pl. 90, Figs. 22–24

Cells small, ovoid, with the apical region slightly produced and pointed, the posterior pole broadly rounded with 2 or 3 short, sharp, horn-like projections; in polar view slightly flattened dorsiventrally; transverse furrow broad, without a marginal ridge, or with a very narrow one (although the furrow is very deep), not spiral, dividing the cell into a tall epicone and a short hypocone; longitudinal furrow very broad in the hypocone, extending from the posterior pole into the epicone a short distance; epitheca with 13 plates and a true apex; hypotheca with 2 large antapical and 6 postcingular plates; cells 18.5–20μ in diameter, 22–25μ long.

The plants are small and the plate characteristics are seen with difficulty unless empty cells are found. This species often appears in great numbers, although it is less widely distributed than some other species of *Peridinium* in our collections. Several of the described varieties have been noted in our collections, but according to Schiller (1935) these should be referred to the typical form and the varietal names not retained.

Plankter; found in several, especially soft water, lakes and in desmid habitats. Wis.

Peridinium limbatum (Stokes) Lemmermann 1900c, p. (120)
Pl. 91, Figs. 16–18

Cells ovate, the epicone narrowed and produced to form a prominent apiculation which is bifurcate and often turned to the left when viewed from the ventral side; hypocone broad, with 2 stout posterior horns; transverse furrow broad, slightly spiral, unsymmetrically dividing the cell into a high epicone and a short hypocone; longitudinal furrow very broad in the hypocone, extending from the posterior pole to well within the epicone; rhomboid plate extending from the top of the longitudinal furrow to the apical pole, which has a true apex and pore; epitheca with 10 plates; hypotheca with 5 (?) postcingulars and 2 antapical plates (these two produced to form the posterior horns); sutures and transverse furrow striated; plates reticulate; cells 60–65μ in diameter, 80–85.5μ long.

Rare; in the plankton of soft water lakes and in *Sphagnum* bogs. Wis.

Peridinium pusillum (Penard) Lemmermann 1901d, p. 65
Pl. 107, Figs. 7–9

Cells ovoid, somewhat flattened dorsiventrally, the epicone slightly longer than the hypocone so that the transverse furrow is inframedian, and not spiral; epitheca slightly produced at the apex and emarginate, with 7 precingular and 6 apical plates; hypotheca with 5 postcingular and 2 antapical plates; chromatophores golden-brown; 13–20μ in diameter, 18–24μ long.

Mich.

Peridinium Willei Huitfeld-Kaas 1900, p. 5
Pl. 91, Figs. 22–25

Cells large, subglobose, very little compressed dorsiventrally, broadly rounded at both poles, with a wing-like flange which forms a crest anteriorly and two lobes posteriorly, and with raised edges along the margins of the sutures of the plates (especially in mature cells); transverse furrow broad, spiral, dividing the cell unsymmetrically into a high epicone and a short hypocone, with a wide border that often extends down along the edge of the longitudinal furrow, producing a wing-like flange; longitudinal furrow broad in the hypocone, extending into the epicone from the posterior pole; rhomboidal plate broadly wedge-shaped, widest at the top and reaching from the margin of the longitudinal furrow to just below the anterior pole where there is not a true apex; epitheca with 14 plates, 7 precingulars, 3 apicals (median), 2 ventral apicals, 1 dorsal apical, and a rhomboidal plate; hypotheca with the usual arrangement of 5 postcingular and 2 large antapical plates; cell 49–55μ in diameter, 50–70μ long.

Plankter; in a variety of lakes; widely distributed but seldom occurring in abundance. Wis.

Peridinium wisconsinense Eddy 1930, p. 300
Pl. 91, Figs. 13–15

Cells large, spindle-shaped, slightly flattened dorsiventrally when seen from the poles; epicone greatly produced to form a prominent cone and the hypocone likewise produced to form a single, stout sharply-pointed horn; transverse furrow broad, slightly spiral (in our specimens, but described as strongly spiral), almost equally dividing the cell into conical epi- and hypocones; longitudinal furrow extending from about half way to the posterior pole to the transverse furrow but not into the epicone; rhomboidal cell extending from the top of the longitudinal furrow to the apical pole which has a true apex; epitheca with 14 plates (including the rhomboidal), 1 median apical, 2 ventral apicals, 1 right lateral apical (on the left as seen from the top), and 2 dorsal apicals; hypotheca with 5 postcingular and 2 antapical plates, one of which (left, as seen from the posterior pole) forms the posterior horn; plates coarsely reticulate; cells 48–56μ in diameter, 55–64μ long; cyst broadly ovoid with one pole sharply and the other bluntly pointed, the membrane thick and lamellate at the poles.

Originally described from Lake Oconomowoc, Wisconsin.

Common in a variety of lakes; frequently abundant in favorable habitats. Mich., Wis.

FAMILY CERATIACEAE

This family (erected for the genus *Ceratium*) has cells which are fusiform in general outline. As described below, there is a prominent apical horn in the epicone and 2–3 posterior horn-like processes in the hypocone. The longitudinal sulcus is very broad and short. The cell undergoes division in such a way that one of the new protoplasts inherits 4 apical, 2 precingular and three post-cingular plates, while the other portion retains the remaining 2 precingular, the 2 antapical and 2 postcingular plates. This means that the plane of division and separation of plates is oblique. The daughter protoplasts continue to move about and gradually build in the necessary complement of plates.

CERATIUM Schrank 1793, p. 34

In this genus there are broadly fusiform cells which have 3 or 4 horns, one anterior and 2 or 3 posterior. The epivalve of the theca (broad just above the girdle) soon narrows abruptly to form the apical horn, which is composed of 4 plates. The hypotheca has 5 postcingular and 2 antapical plates, the latter forming the longest posterior horn. In forms which have 3 posterior horns, one is very short. There are no broad sutures between the plates as in some of the related genera. The transverse furrow opens into a broad longitudinal sulcus. The entire theca is uniformly marked with a fine reticulum, the meshes of which are 5- or 6-sided. There are numerous brown disc-like chromatophores which are often obscured by the semi-opaqueness of the theca.

Most species of *Ceratium* are marine but there are a few freshwater plankters, usually occurring more abundantly in hard water than in soft water lakes.

Key to the Species

1. Apical horn long and tapering, as long as or longer than the
   cell body and the posterior horns _____*C. hirundinella*
1. Apical horn shorter than the remainder of the cell _____ 2
2. Apical horn sharply curved and tapering
   to a blunt point _____ *C. carolinianum*
2. Apical horn straight but directed at an angle from the longitudinal
   axis; squarely truncate at the apex _____*C. cornutum*

Ceratium carolinianum (Bailey) Jörgensen 1911, p. 14
[*C. curvirostre* Huitfeldt-Kaas]

Pl. 92, Figs. 2, 3

Cells broadly fusiform in outline; epivalve broad above the transverse furrow, narrowed abruptly to form a stout, curved apical horn, with a shoulder on each side at the base; transverse furrow relatively narrow; hypotheca broad, with a short diverging horn on the left (as seen from the ventral surface), and a longer central horn which is somewhat obliquely directed; cells 65–80μ in diameter, about twice as long as broad.

Plankter; in *Sphagnum* bogs, ponds and ditches. Wis.

Ceratium cornutum (Ehrenb.) Claparède
& Lachmann 1858, p. 394
Pl. 92, Figs. 8, 9

Cells broadly fusiform in outline, stout, the epitheca broad above the transverse furrow, the sides rapidly converging and narrowed to form a short, stout anterior horn which extends obliquely and is truncate at the apex; transverse furrow relatively broad; hypotheca broad below the furrow, extended into 2 horns, 1 short lateral horn and 1 longer and median; cells 75–80μ in diameter, about as long as wide, or slightly longer.

Rare; in the plankton of soft water lakes. Mich., Wis.

Ceratium hirundinella (O. F. Muell.) Dujardin 1841, p. 377
Pl. 92, Figs. 4, 5

Cells broadly or narrowly fusiform in outline, depending upon the degree of divergence of the horns; very much flattened dorsiventrally; epitheca with sharply converging margins from just above the transverse furrow, then narrowed more gradually to form a long horn; transverse furrow relatively narrow; body of the hypotheca broad and short below the transverse furrow, divided into a varying number of posterior horns, usually 3, sometimes only 1, the central or median horn the longest and formed by the antapical plates; plates coarsely reticulate; cells varying in size depending upon environmental conditions, 100–400μ long.

This species is very common, especially in hard water lakes, where occasionally it may become so abundant as to color the lake a deep brown. Such blooms develop and disappear suddenly.

This species shows a great variation in the form of the cell, number of horns, etc., and it is often the subject of ecological and limnological studies. It shows a remarkable periodicity and may exhibit a vertical distribution which is accompanied by some interesting relationships between the length of the horns and buoyancy; form of the cell and temperature, etc.

The tremendous amount of nitrogen, phosphorus, and products of photosynthesis which accumulate in these organisms when they develop a bloom must certainly produce interesting limnological effects in a lake. In spite of the wealth of literature on this genus, very little seems to have been published on the role that these species play in lake biology.

Mich., Wis.

ORDER DINOCOCCALES

These are forms which are not motile in the vegetative state and which are incapable of cell division. They exist as either free-floating or sedentary attached unicells of various forms, crescent-shaped, quadrangular, or pyramidal, with the angles extended into horns or spines. Usually the wall is thick and shows lamellations where it is thickened at the poles or angles. Many have an expression similar to the encysted phase of the motile Peridiniales. In their reproductive methods the Dinococcales employ autospores or zoospores. There are 2–8 of these formed in a cell. In some forms the zoospores show a transverse furrow and other *Gymnodinium* features. The spores, upon escape, enlarge and assume the expression of the nonmotile parent cell. One family is recognized.

FAMILY DINOCOCCACEAE

Characteristics as described for the order.

Key to the Genera

1. Cells free-floating, lunate or arcuate ....*Cystodinium*
1. Cells attached, transversely ellipsoid or inversely
   triangular in front view.. 2
2. Cells triangular or tetrahedral (especially when
   seen from above)..*Tetradinium*
2. Cells ellipsoid..*Raciborskia*

CYSTODINIUM Klebs 1912, pp. 384, 442

Cells free-floating, lunate or arcuate, the poles extended to form sharp, usually recurved spines; longitudinal and transverse furrows lacking, although the position of the furrows is represented in the swarmers formed by the division of the protoplast within the parent cell; chromatophores several to many, brown, more or less pointed or fusiform discs; nucleus conspicuous and centrally located, pigment-spot usually lacking.

Key to the Species

1. Cells broadly crescent-shaped, the outer margin broadly convex,
   the inner slightly tumid or straight ....*C. iners*
1. Cells narrowly crescent-shaped, the outer margin convex, the
   inner margin concave (sometimes straight in the midregion) 2
2. Each pole of the cell ending in a curved spine which is twisted
   away from the longitudinal axis of the
   cell; cells 65–110μ long...*C. Steinii*
2. Each pole of the cells ending in a spine, 1 straight, the other
   twisted away from the longitudinal axis of
   the cell; cells 40–60μ long .... *C. cornifax*

Cystodinium cornifax (Schill.) Klebs 1912, pp. 384, 442
Pl. 91, Figs. 5, 6

Cells lunate, the dorsal margin strongly convex, the inner margin concave (slightly straight in the midregion); poles extended into

[438]

colorless, somewhat twisted horns, one of which is recurved and is directed at an angle from the longitudinal axis; protoplast forming 2 (or only 1) *Gymnodinium*-like swarmers which have a wide transverse furrow, dividing the zoospore into a broadly rounded anterior portion and a broadly conical or sharply pointed posterior, with pigment-spot showing in the longitudinal furrow; cells 28–36μ in diameter, 40–60μ long (sometimes longer); swarmers about 20μ in diameter, 25μ long.

In the tychoplankton of several lakes and swamps; frequently found in desmid habitats. Wis.

Cystodinium iners Geitler 1928a, p. 5
Pl. 91, Figs. 19–21

Cells crescent-shaped, strongly convex on the dorsal margin, tumid (or straight) on the ventral or inner margin, ending in sharp points at the poles, with the wall much thickened at the base of the horns, which are in the same plane with the longitudinal axis of the cell; protoplast usually showing a transverse furrow, appearing as a *Gymnodinium*-like cell dividing to form two swarmers; chromatophores numerous ovoid plates; cells 25–28–(30)μ in diameter, 60–80μ long, including the apical spines.

Mich.,Wis.

Cystodinium Steinii Klebs 1912, pp. 382, 442
Pl. 93, Figs. 1, 2

Cells crescent-shaped, the dorsal margin more strongly convex than the ventral; apices terminating in curved and slightly twisted points, each projecting at a different angle from the longitudinal axis of the cell; upon dividing producing 2 *Gymnodinium*-like swarmers with a broad transverse furrow and with both poles broadly rounded; pigment-spot in the longitudinal furrow; cells 25–35μ in diameter, 65–100–(110)μ long; swarmers 30–35μ wide, 40–50μ long.

Rare; in the tychoplankton of lakes and acid swamps. Mich., Wis.

RACIBORSKIA Wołoszyńska 1919, p. 199

Cells attached, inversely triangular-ellipsoid as seen from the front, ellipsoid when seen in vertical view, the poles tipped with a single stout spine; attached by a short stalk to the substrate; in side view the upper margin straight, the 2 lateral margins straight or slightly convex, converging to the thick stalk; reproduction (?).

Raciborskia bicornis Wołoszyńska 1919, p. 199

Pl. 93, Figs. 4–7

Characteristics as described for the genus; cells 25–35μ long, including the spines, 9–12μ in diameter.

Rare; attached to the aquatic moss *Drepanocladus* in 35 feet of water; on large filamentous algae. Wis.

TETRADINIUM Klebs 1912, p. 408

Cells triangular or tetrahedral, attached by a short stalk to a substrate, the angles tipped with 1 or 2 short, stout spines; chromatophores many small ovate discs; nucleus central; reproduction by the formation of 2 swarmers in each cell.

Key to the Species

Angles of the cells tipped with 2 spines _____ *T. javanicum*
Angles of the cells tipped with 1 spine _____ *T. simplex*

Tetradinium javanicum Klebs 1912, p. 408

Pl. 93, Fig. 3

Cells inversely pyramidate when seen from the front, the dorsal margin straight or slightly convex, the lateral margins convex, converging to a short, stout stalk which attaches the cell to the substrate; angles of the cell furnished with 2 short curved spines; cells 35–50μ in diameter.

Attached to filamentous algae. Mich., Wis.

Tetradinium simplex Prescott *in* Prescott, Silva, & Wade 1949, p. 89

Pl. 107, Fig. 2

Cells inversely triangular, sessile, with scarcely any stipe, on filamentous algae, the dorsal margin broadly convex in front view, the angles tipped with a single, downward projecting spine; triangular in top view, the angles bearing a short spine; cells 12–25μ in diameter, 12–20μ high.

On filamentous algae in shallow water of acid ponds. Mich.

CLASS CRYPTOPHYCEAE

In this group the organisms are mostly motile by means of 2 apical or lateral flagella (Cryptomonadales), but coccoid forms (Crytococcales) have been placed here also. The cells are dorsiventrally flattened, ovoid, slipper-shaped, or reniform, and possess a longitudinal furrow. In some, a gullet extends inwardly from the furrow in the anterior end of the cell. The pigments are dark golden-brown, localized in (usually) 2 parietal and (in our specimens) laminate chromatophores which may possess pyrenoids. Both starch (staining blue with iodine) and oil are produced as food reserves. The cells are uninucleate and possess a contractile vacuole. In some forms trichocysts border the furrow. There are 3 subgroups, one of which is without pigmentation.

Key to the Genera

Gullet absent ....*Chroomonas*
(Cryptochrysideae)

Gullet present ....*Cryptomonas*
(Cryptomonadeae)

CHROOMONAS Hansgirg 1885, p. 230

Cells swimming by 2 apical flagella, dorsiventrally flattened, elongate-ellipsoid or pyriform, broader toward the anterior end, which is unsymmetrically bilobed, narrowed but broadly rounded at the posterior end; longitudinal furrow narrow and shallow, without a gullet, extending farther on the ventral surface than on the dorsal; chromatophores 2 lateral parietal bands.

Chroomonas Nordstedtii Hansgirg 1885, p. 230
Pl. 95, Fig. 45

Cells slipper-shaped, broader toward the anterior end, which is unsymmetrically bilobed; narrowed posteriorly but broadly rounded at the pole; chromatophores 2 broad, parietal bands; cells 9–16μ long, 4–8μ in diameter.

Common in shallow water of lakes and among algae masses and decaying vegetation; in shallow pools and bogs. Wis.

CRYPTOMONAS Ehrenberg 1838, p. 40

Cells slipper-shaped, dorsiventrally flattened, convex on the dorsal surface, flat or concave ventrally, with a broad and conspicuous longitudinal furrow from which a gullet extends inwardly from the anterior end; flagella 2, attached on the ventral surface at the anterior end; chromatophores 1 or 2, lateral and parietal; starch grains often present in the form of short rods; trichocysts sometimes discernible along the margins of the furrow; contractile vacuoles 1–3.

Key to the Species

Gullet extending scarcely to the middle of
the cell; cells 15–32μ long .... *C. erosa*

Gullet longer, extending nearly ¾ the length of
the cell; cells larger, up to 80μ long .... *C. ovata*

Cryptomonas erosa Ehrenberg 1838, p. 41

Pl. 95, Fig. 39

Cells broadly ovate or ellipsoid, with the left hand margin (as seen from the ventral side) arcuate and more convex than the right; apex almost evenly bilobed, the apical depression deep, the gullet broad, extending about ½ or less the length of the cell; chromatophores 2 parietal elongate plates, brown (in our specimens), blue-green or reddish; cells 8–16μ in diameter, 15–32μ long.

In stagnant waters; swamps; tychoplanktonic in small lakes. Mich., Wis.

Cryptomonas ovata Ehrenberg 1838, p. 41

Pl. 95, Fig. 40

Cells broadly ellipsoid or ovate, the left hand margin (as seen from the ventral side) symmetrically convex, the right nearly straight; apex unsymmetrically bilobed, the apical depression broad and shallow, gullet extending about ¾ the length of the cell; chromatophores 2 elongate parietal plates, brown; cells 5–18μ in diameter, 20–80μ long.

Euplankter; in lakes and ponds. Mich., Wis.

DIVISION CYANOPHYTA

In this division the cells are without chromoplastids, the pigments being diffused generally throughout the peripheral portion of the protoplast. In some forms the pigments occur as granules crowded and somewhat localized just within the cell membrane. Besides the usual complement of pigments found in the green algae (although chlorophyll-b is lacking in the Cyanophyta), phycocyanin (water-soluble) and myxophycean phycoerythrin may be present. Different concentration and combinations of these pigments are responsible for the multitudinous colors exhibited by the blue-green algae.

Photosynthetic products are glycogen and glycoproteins rather than starch. Frequently proteinaceous granules (cyanophycin) are present. There is no definite nucleus, although the presence of chromatin bodies has been proved in the central region of the cell.

Usually the cells or colonies of individuals are invested by muci-laginous substances, which may be either soft and watery or firm enough to form a definite sheath. The cell membrane is thin and is composed of two layers, the outer one gelatinous and contributing to the investing mucilage. Many forms contain pseudovacuoles which are dark and refractive and sometimes cause the cells to appear black, reddish, or purple. According to some investigators, these are gas vacuoles; others identify them as pockets of mucilage.

Reproduction occurs principally by fission and by fragmentation, but in some of the filamentous members, *akinetes*, sometimes referred to as *gonidia,* function as reproductive cells. Sexual reproduction is unknown in the Cyanophyta. In a few forms, *endospores* may be employed. These are especially characteristic of the Chamaesipho-nales where gonidia-like bodies are formed from the protoplast by either simultaneous or successive constrictions or divisions.

Colonial organization is very simple, and the range of architecture is limited, the branched trichome being the climax of structural complexity.

As interpreted here, the Cyanophyta include 2 classes, the blue-green algae or Myxophyceae, and the Chlorobacteriaceae, a group of pigmented, bacteria-like organisms.

CLASS MYXOPHYCEAE

The Chamaesiphonales and Chroococcales constitute the tribe Coccogoneae, and the Hormogonales the tribe Hormogoneae of some authors.

Key to the Orders

1. Cells club-shaped unicells (in our specimens) showing basal-distal differentiation; solitary, or forming rather definite layers on rocks and shells, or epiphytic; reproduction by non-motile endospores .... CHAMAESIPHONALES
1. Cells other shapes; not reproducing by endospores 2
2. Cells coccoid; solitary or united in colonies of definite or indefinite shape; reproduction by fission .... CHROOCOCCALES
2. Plants filamentous; reproduction by fission, by hormogonial fragmentation, or by gonidia .... HORMOGONALES

ORDER CHROOCOCCALES

This group includes plants which are unicellular or which form simple colonies of cells. The colonies may be definite or indefinite in shape, but there is no differentiation of cells, or interdependence. A copious gelatinous investment is present in most forms. See Daily (1942) and Drouet and Daily (1939) for critical studies of this group.

FAMILY CHROOCOCCACEAE

Unicellular or colonial, free-floating or attached to submerged or aerial substrates. There are no pseudofilamentous arrangements or expanses produced as in the Entophysalidaceae, another family in this order, which is not represented in our region.

Key to the Genera

1. Plants unicellular or forming small aggregates of 2–8 (rarely up to 32) cells 2
1. Plants composed of many cells embedded in copious mucilage, with or without apparent cell sheaths 8
2. Cells spherical, forming small clusters of 2–4–16–32 individuals[6] .... _Chroococcus_ (in part)
2. Cells longer than their diameter 3
3. Cells occurring as blue-green chromoplast-like bodies in colorless host cells 4
3. Cells not occurring as chromoplast-like bodies in colorless host cells 5
4. Host cell adherent, bearing long bristle-like setae; usually 2–4 host cells inclosed in a common mucilage .... _Gloeochaete_
4. Host cell free-floating, not bearing setae, not inclosed in colonial mucilage .... _Glaucocystis_
5. Cells with a gelatinous sheath; several individuals inclosed by a common mucilage .... _Chroococcus_ (in part)
5. Cells solitary or clustered in small groups, without a mucilaginous investment 6

[6]Cf. the symbiotic genera _Glaucocystis_ and _Gloeochaete_, in which the host cells may be grouped in small families.

6. Cells pear-shaped, radiately arranged.._Marssoniella_
6. Cells some other shape, not radiately arranged.................................... 7
7. Cells cylindrical and strongly curved through ⅔ of a circle,
   often lying parallel and compact within the mucilage of other
   algae; minute, 0.5–1μ in diameter.._Cyanarcus_
7. Cells ovate or oblong; larger, up to 15μ in diameter................._Synechococcus_
8. Cells 10 or more times their diameter in length; cylindrical,
   vermiform, reniform, or fusiform 9
8. Cells round, ovate, or short-cylindric 1C
9. Cells narrowly fusiform, with tapering
   and pointed apices ...._Dactylococcopsis_
9. Cells reniform or vermiform, rounded at the apices................._Rhabdoderma_
10. Cells oblong or short-cylindric, with rounded ends, many
    individuals irregularly and densely crowded in copious
    mucilage; individual cell sheaths evident or not................._Anacystis_ (in part)
    Including:
        a. _Aphanothece_ (see p. 465) with individual
           cell sheaths not evident
        b. _Gloeothece_ with individual cell sheaths distinct
10. Cells spherical or ovate, sometimes ellipsoid, not cylindrical.................... 11
11. Cells round, embedded in copious mucilage, and forming
    shapeless masses on submerged or more
    frequently aerial substrates ...._Gloeocapsa_
11. Cells of other shapes, or if round not forming
    shapeless masses on substrates 12
12. Cells round or ovate, dividing in 2 directions
    to form rectangular plates 13
12. Cells dividing in 3 planes to form spherical,
    ovate, or shapeless colonial masses 14
13. Cells regularly arranged in rectilinear series ...._Merismopedia_
13. Cells irregularly arranged to form
    somewhat rectangular plates ...._Holopedium_
14. Colony hollow, the cells arranged toward the periphery....................15
14. Colony not hollow; cells distributed throughout
    the colonial mucilage 16
15. Cells at the ends of branching gelatinous strands which radiate
    from the center of the colony ...._Gomphosphaeria_
15. Colonies without radiating gelatinous strands....................._Coelosphaerium_
16. Cells longer than wide, distributed throughout the colonial muci-
    lage, with or without evident individual cell sheaths........._Anacystis_ (in part)
    Including:
        a. _Aphanothece_ (see p. 465) without evident cell sheaths
        b. _Gloeothece_ with individual cell sheaths evident
16. Cells globose 17
17. Cells evenly and remotely distributed within the colonial
    mucilage; pseudovacuoles wanting...................................._Aphanocapsa_
17. Cells crowded, usually very densely so, not evenly distributed
    throughout the colonial mucilage;
    pseudovacuoles usually present ...._Microcystis_

[445]

CHROOCOCCUS Naegeli 1849, p. 45

One-celled, or an association of 2–32 spherical, hemispherical or ovate individuals, either free-floating, adhering to submerged substrates, or forming expansions in moist aerial habitats; each cell with a sheath which may be distinct from or (as in most planktonic species) confluent with the common mucilage investing a group of cells; several generations of sheaths present as a result of successive cell divisions; sheaths either hyaline or ochraceous; cell contents homogeneous or granular, not vacuolate, light to bright blue-green, olive-green, or yellowish.

The sedentary species, especially, should be compared with *Gloeocapsa*, a genus which in some conditions and stages of development might be confused easily with *Chroococcus*. *Gloeocapsa* forms attached, gelatinous masses on either submerged substrates or, more commonly, in aerial habitats. In *Gloeocapsa,* many more cells are associated in families and clusters of families than in *Chroococcus;* the individual cell sheaths are usually thick and conspicuous, and the gelatinous matrix in which the cells are embedded is formed of several concentric layers. A small, isolated, and little-developed clump of *Gloeocapsa* resembles certain species of *Chroococcus*. It is desirable, therefore, to see a number of plants in a collection before attempting determinations.

Key to the Species

1. Cells large, 13–70μ in diameter... 2
1. Cells smaller, 1.5–10μ in diameter... 3
2. Maximum diameter of cell, including sheath, 50μ...........................*C. turgidus*
2. Cells larger, diameter 67–70μ including the sheath...................*C. giganteus*
3. Colonial mucilage or individual cell sheaths lamellate........................... 4
3. Colonial mucilage or individual cell sheaths not lamellate................... 5
4. Cells arranged in cubical (sarciniform) packets.....................*C. Prescottii*
4. Cells not in cubical packets...*C. varius*
5. Cells arranged in cubical packets of from 4–8, or in multiple
   packets of 32 cells in *Sarcina*-like families.........................*C. Prescottii*
5. Cells not arranged in cubical packets.. 6
6. Colonies free-floating in the euplankton 7
6. Colonies adhering to substrates, or entangled
   among other algae in tychoplankton 9
7. Colony of many cells within a homogeneous sheath,
   cells 2–3μ in diameter...*C. minimus*
7. Colony of 24 or fewer cells in a homogeneous sheath, cells
   usually more than 3μ in diameter... 8
8. Cells 3–4.5μ in diameter, arranged at
   some distance from one another.......................................*C. dispersus*
8. Cells 6–12–(22)μ in diameter, arranged close together ....*C. limneticus*

9. Cells (5)–6–8–(11)μ in diameter; contents pale yellow............._C. pallidus_
9. Cells mostly smaller than above; contents blue-green....................10
10. Cells oblong; 5–7–(10)μ in diameter; in groups of 2
   inclosed in a homogeneous sheath.._C. minutus_
10. Cells angular or irregularly globose, 3–4μ in diameter; solitary
   or 2 together within homogeneous sheaths, sometimes forming
   small masses on submerged aquatic plants.................._C. minor_

Chroococcus dispersus (Keissl.) Lemmermann 1904, p. 102
Pl. 100, Fig. 7

A free-floating, flattened, ovate or irregularly-shaped colony of
4–16 spherical cells which are either single or arranged in small
clusters, evenly distributed at some distance from one another in
the mucilaginous envelope; individual cell sheaths not evident; cell
contents bright blue-green (sometimes gray-green or pale blue-
green); cells 3–4.5μ in diameter.

This species should be compared with _C. limneticus_, in which the
colonies are globular and the cells are larger.

Euplankter. Found in many lakes of both hard and soft water.
Mich., Wis.

Chroococcus dispersus var. minor G. M. Smith 1920, p. 28
Pl. 100, Figs. 1–3

A variety differing from the typical in having smaller cells, 1.7–
2.5μ in diameter.

Rare, but has been found in several lakes. Mich., Wis.

Chroococcus giganteus W. West 1892, p. 741
Pl. 100, Fig. 16

Cells hemispherical or ovate, solitary or in groups of 2–5, inclosed
by a wide, hyaline, lamellate envelope of mucilage in which individual cell sheaths are evident; cell contents bright blue-green and
densely granular; cells, without sheath, 54–58μ in diameter, 67–70μ
including the sheath.

This species is, by far, the largest of the genus in our region.
Except for its greater size it is not unlike _C. turgidus_ with which it
should be compared. Specimens of _C. giganteus_ collected in Vilas
County, Wisconsin, are so much like a large form of _C. turgidus_ that
I am inclined to regard the former as a variety maximum of the latter.

Tychoplankter. Rare; in mixtures of other algae in shallow water.
Mich., Wis.

Chroococcus limneticus Lemmermann 1898d, p. 153

Pl. 100, Figs. 4, 5

A free-floating, spherical or ovate colony of 4–32 spherical cells rather closely and evenly arranged, sometimes in groups of 2–4 cells as a result of rapid cell division; individual cell sheath usually indistinct and confluent with the hyaline, mucilaginous colonial envelope; cell contents dull to bright blue-green, not conspicuously granular; cells 6–12–22μ in diameter, without sheath.

This is one of the most common of all planktonic species found in our region. Its distribution in acid or soft water habitats suggests a specificity similar to that of *C. turgidus* in the tychoplankton of highly acid mediums.

Euplankter. Found in many lakes, especially soft or semi-soft water. Mich., Wis.

Chroococcus limneticus var. *carneus* (Chod.)

Lemmermann 1904, p. 101

Pl. 100, Fig. 6

A variety differing from the typical by its smaller size and the irregularity of cell distribution within the colonial envelope; cells 4–16 in number, 7–9μ in diameter without sheath.

Euplankter. Found in several lakes. Mich., Wis.

Chroococcus limneticus var. *distans* G. M. Smith 1916, p. 481

Pl. 100, Fig. 8

A free-floating ovoid colony of 8–32 globose or hemispherical cells, rather widely separated (or in widely separated groups of individuals) within a hyaline, homogeneous, gelatinous colonial envelope; cell sheaths confluent with the colonial mucilage; cell contents homogeneous, gray to light blue-green; cells 6–8μ in diameter.

Euplankter. Found in several soft water lakes. Mich., Wis.

Chroococcus limneticus var. *elegans* G. M. Smith 1916, p. 619

Pl. 100, Fig. 11

A free-floating colony of ovoid cells which are circular in one view but flattened when seen from the side; cells irregularly scattered in a wide, gelatinous colonial envelope; cell contents bright blue-green and non-granular; cells 18–22μ in diameter without sheaths, 20–26μ in diameter including the sheath.

Euplankter. Mich., Wis.

Chroococcus limneticus var. *subsalsus* Lemmermann 1901c, p. 84

Pl. 100, Fig. 10

A globose or ovoid to ellipsoid colony of 8–32 spherical cells, evenly scattered within a wide, hyaline, and homogeneous colonial envelope of mucilage; individual cell sheaths not evident; cell contents bright blue-green and non-granular; cells smaller than in the typical plant, 3–4.5μ in diameter without sheaths.

Euplankter. Found in a number of lakes; rare but widely distributed in our region. Mich., Wis.

Chroococcus minimus (Keissl.) Lemmermann 1904, p. 102

A globose or elliptical colony of 4–8 spherical or ovoid cells in a wide, hyaline, non-lamellated colonial envelope; cells 2–3μ in diameter without sheaths; contents blue-green, non-granular.

Euplankter. Wis.

Chroococcus minor (Kuetz.) Naegeli 1849, p. 47

Pl. 100, Fig. 12

A small gelatinous attached and amorphous mass in which cells (spherical or angular from mutual compression) are irregularly scattered, singly, in pairs, or in larger groups resulting from repeated cell division; individual cell sheaths scarcely visible, confluent with the colonial envelope; cell contents pale to bright blue-green, non-granular; cells 3–4μ in diameter without sheath.

Growing on moist substrates or intermingled with dense clots of miscellaneous algae; often forming small masses on *Potamogeton* spp. or other submerged aquatics; sometimes buried in the decaying tissues of higher plants. Wis.

Chroococcus minutus (Kuetz.) Naegeli 1849, p. 46

Pl. 100, Fig. 9

A small, amorphous, mucilaginous mass in which spherical or hemispherical cells are compactly arranged within a wide hyaline envelope; individual cell sheaths indistinct, not lamellated; cell contents blue-green, either homogeneous or finely granular; cells 5–7–(10)μ in diameter without sheaths.

Common in a great variety of both hard and soft water lakes; tychoplankter; found among dense growths of algae and higher aquatics in shallow water of lakes, cut-offs from lakes, and in swamps; sometimes appearing incidentally in tow samples from *Sphagnum* bogs. Mich., Wis.

Chroococcus pallidus Naegeli 1849, p. 46

Pl. 100, Fig. 14

Single-celled or, more frequently, a small colony of 2–4–(8) spherical individuals inclosed by an oval or globose, wide, hyaline or yellowish, homogeneous envelope of mucilage; individual cell sheaths indistinct; contents pale blue-green; cells (5)–6–11μ in diameter without sheath.

Plants of this species are to be found on moist aerial substrates or scattered among algae in shallow water tychoplankton. Mich., Wis.

Chroococcus Prescottii Drouet & Daily *in*

Drouet 1942, p. 127

Pl.100, Fig. 13

A free-floating colony of 4–16–32 spherical cells arranged in 2 planes to form cubes or sarciniform clusters, inclosed in a rectangularly shaped, hyaline, colonial envelope which is often lamellated, with individual cells or quartets of cells inclosed by a sheath; cell contents bright blue-green; finely granular, cells 5–8μ in diameter; colony (of 16 cells) 18–22μ wide, 30–42μ long, and about as thick as wide.

This plant was questionably listed as *Eucapsis alpina* Clements and Schantz by Prescott and Croasdale (1937). It should be compared with that species, the cells of which are similarly arranged but more numerous in the colony and in which the colonial sheath is without lamellations.

Not uncommon in the tychoplankton of acid habitats, intermingled with dense growths of other algae, especially desmids, and commonly associated with *C. turgidus*. Mich., Wis.

Chroococcus turgidus (Kuetz.) Naegeli 1849, p. 46

Pl. 100, Fig. 19

A free-floating colony of 2–4 ovoid or hemispherical cells inclosed by a very wide (usually), hyaline, and lamellate colonial sheath; cells bright blue-green, contents sometimes coarsely granular, inclosed by individual sheaths, 8–32μ in diameter without sheath, 15–50μ wide including sheath.

Tychoplankter. Common in many lakes and in bogs. This is a relatively large species, attaining maximum size and abundance in *Sphagnum* bogs. Mich., Wis.

Chroococcus varius A. Braun *in* Rabenhorst
1861–1878, Nos. 246, 248, 252
Pl. 100, Fig. 15

An irregularly shaped colony of 2–8 spherical cells inclosed by a
hyaline, sometimes colored, gelatinous envelope, forming dark-green
or brownish masses on moist aerial substrates, or among other algae
in shallow water; colonial envelope lightly lamellate, individual cell
sheaths not distinctly evident; cell contents blue-green or olive, not
granular; cells 2–4μ in diameter.

Most of the records of this species in North America are from
moist substrates near geysers and hot springs, or from sulphur water.

Not infrequent in the tychoplankton of a variety of both hard and
soft water lakes. Wis.

GLOEOCAPSA Kuetzing 1843, p. 174

Essentially unicellular but with many individuals aggregated to
form amorphous gelatinous masses of spherical cells, or as associations of families of irregularly arranged cells, each individual inclosed by a lamellate, mucilaginous, and usually thick sheath; plant
mass blue-green, reddish, yellowish, or brown; cell contents blue-
green or yellowish to olive-green, homogeneous or (more often)
granular, without pseudovacuoles.

This genus should be compared with those attached or sedentary
species of *Chroococcus* in which the colonial envelopes of the
families are persistent and do not become confluent with the general
investing mucilage. In general, *Gloeocapsa* masses contain many
more cells than *Chroococcus,* and the lamellate, thicker sheaths are
more conspicuous, whereas in some (especially planktonic) species
of the latter genus they tend to become confluent.

Key to the Species

1. Sheaths yellowish or brownish to orange..*G. rupestris*
1. Sheaths colorless... 2
2. Cells 6–9μ in diameter without sheaths, 11–12μ
   in diameter with sheaths ....*G. calcarea*
2. Cells smaller 3
3. Plants encrusting on moist substrates; cells 2–4μ in diameter ..... *G. aeruginosa*
3. Plants free-floating (tychoplankton); cells
   0.7–2.3μ in diameter..*G. punctata*

Gloeocapsa aeruginosa (Carm.) Kuetzing
1845–1849, Tab. Phyc., Pl. 21, Fig. 2
Pl. 101, Fig. 6

Plant mass with firm or leathery mucilage, blue-green; cells
spherical, with blue-green, homogeneous contents, arranged in small

families and inclosed by wide, colorless sheaths which are only slightly lamellate; cells 2–4μ in diameter, with sheaths 4–8μ wide.
On shore and in tychoplankton of shallow lake. Mich., Wis.

Gloeocapsa calcarea Tilden 1898, p. 29

Plant mass light gray-green to blue-green, forming a calcareous crust on moist substrates; cells spherical, in families of 4–16 individuals inclosed in thin, colorless sheaths, 6–9μ in diameter, with sheaths 11–12μ wide.
On wet boards, Osceola, Wisconsin.

Gloeocapsa punctata Naegeli 1849, p. 51
Pl. 101, Fig. 7

Plant mass blue-green, floating or entangled among other algae, consisting of small aggregates of 4–16 individuals which are spherical and inclosed by thick sheaths that are weakly lamellate outwardly but which break down and become confluent with the colonial mucilage internally; cells 0.75–2.3μ in diameter; contents blue-green, homogeneous.

This species may be identical with *G. aurata* Stiz., a species described as having yellowish envelopes that are not lamellate. Sheath color and presence or absence of lamellations seem to be such variable characters that alone they are inadequate for the separation of species.
On soil and in tychoplankton of soft water lakes. Wis.

Gloeocapsa rupestris Kuetzing 1845–1849, Tab. Phyc., 1, p. 17
Pl. 107, Fig. 13

Plant mass dark-colored, brownish, encrusting; cells blue-green, spherical, in few-celled colonies; cell sheaths thick and but slightly lamellated, yellowish or orange-brown; cells 6–9μ in diameter; families 15–75μ in diameter.
Mich.

APHANOCAPSA Naegeli 1849, p. 52

A globular, ovate, or sometimes amorphous mass, gelatinous, and free-floating, in which spherical cells are usually widely and evenly distributed through a yellowish or hyaline, homogeneous colonial mucilage; individual cell sheaths not evident; cells often in pairs as a result of recent division; contents homogeneous or finely granular, pale gray-green to bright blue-green. See description of *Microcystis*, page 455.

These plants are common in plankton and frequently appear with *Microcystis aeruginosa* in water blooms, but they never become dominant components of such blooms in our region. Most species show a preference for soft water and acid habitats.

Key to the Species

1. Cell endophytic in the mucilage of other algae .... *A. endophytica*
1. Cells free-living 2
2. Cells 5–6µ in diameter, colony usually free-floating,
   sometimes attached .... *A. rivularis*
2. Cells smaller 3
3. Cells bright blue-green; rather crowded .... *A. Grevillei*
3. Cells gray-green or bluish-green, colonial mass not deeply colored;
   cells not crowded (except var. *conferta* of *A. elachista*) 4
4. Cells 3.5–4.5µ in diameter .... *A. pulchra*
4. Cells less than 3µ in diameter 5
5. Cells minute, coccoid, 1µ in diameter or less .... *A. delicatissima*
5. Cells 1.5–2.5µ in diameter .... *A. elachista*

Aphanocapsa delicatissima West & West 1912, p. 431
Pl. 101, Figs. 8, 9

Colonies spherical or elliptical, free-floating; cells minute, bluish, evenly distributed throughout copious, colorless mucilage, 0.5–0.8µ in diameter.

Common in the tychoplankton of many lakes. Most frequent in soft or acid water. Mich., Wis.

Aphanocapsa elachista West & West 1895b, p. 276

Colonies spherical or ellipsoid, free-floating or intermingled with other algae, small and few-celled, the colonial mass pale blue-green; cells small, globose, often in pairs and widely separated in colorless mucilage, 1.5–2.5µ in diameter.

Mich., Wis.

Aphanocapsa elachista var. *conferta* West & West 1912, p. 432
Pl. 101, Figs. 10, 11

Colonies ovate or globose, frequently irregular in shape (in our specimens commonly very large) up to 150µ in diameter; cells spherical, crowded within a hyaline colonial mucilage, often with many cells in pairs, 1.6–2.0µ in diameter.

Euplankter. Rare to common in several soft water lakes. Mich., Wis.

[453]

Aphanocapsa elachista var. *planctonica* G. M. Smith 1920, p. 42
Pl. 101, Fig. 12

Cells less crowded than in var. *conferta,* evenly dispersed throughout a colorless, colonial mucilage, 2–3μ in diameter.
Euplankter. Rare in several, mostly soft water, lakes. Mich., Wis.

Aphanocapsa endophytica G. M. Smith 1920, p. 42
Pl. 101, Fig. 13

Endophytic in the colonial mucilage of *Microcystis;* cells solitary or
arranged in small clumps which are evenly dispersed and remote
from one another; cell contents homogeneous, pale to bright blue-
green; cell 2μ in diameter.
Reported as common in Poor Farm Lake, Wisconsin.

Aphanocapsa Grevillei (Hass.) Rabenhorst 1865, p. 50
Pl. 101, Figs. 15, 16

Free-floating colonies, sometimes on moist soil, spherical or, in
age, irregularly shaped; cells in pairs, in groups of four and crowded,
or solitary, evenly dispersed through colorless mucilage, blue-green,
with pseudovacuoles, 3.8–5.5μ in diameter.
Rare; in the tychoplankton of several lakes. Mich., Wis.

Aphanocapsa pulchra (Kuetz.) Rabenhorst 1865, p. 49
Pl. 101, Fig. 14

Colonies ovate or globose, free-floating; cells spherical, loosely
and evenly dispersed within a copious mucilage, contents blue-
green, finely granular, 3.4–4.5μ in diameter.
This is the most common species of the genus in our collections
of phytoplankters. It is often a component of water blooms in hard
water lakes although not infrequently found intermingled and
attached among other algae in shallow water of *Sphagnum* bogs.
The colonies often attain macroscopic size. Mich., Wis.

Aphanocapsa rivularis (Carm.) Rabenhorst 1865, p. 49
Pl. 101, Fig. 17

A free-floating or sessile, amorphous, or tubular to spherical
colony of globose cells which have bright blue-green, granular
contents; cells solitary or in pairs and scattered at some distance
from one another within the colonial mucilage; cells 5–6μ in diameter.
The slightly larger size of the cells, and the more scattered arrangement separate this species from *A. Grevillei.*
Euplankter. Mich., Wis.

MICROCYSTIS Kuetzing 1833a, p. 372[7]

A free-floating or sedentary colony of numerous spherical cells closely and irregularly arranged within copious mucilage, forming ovate, globose, or irregularly shaped masses which are often lacerate or perforate; individual cell sheaths confluent with the colonial mucilage; cell contents pale or bright blue-green, or appearing black or purplish because of pseudovacuoles, present in most species, which are large and conspicuous, or sometimes numerous and small.

This genus should be compared with *Aphanocapsa* in which the spherical cells are evenly and widely spaced within a definitely shaped (usually spherical) colonial investment of mucilage. Unlike most of the species of *Microcystis*, the cells of *Aphanocapsa* are always without pseudovacuoles.

The reader is referred to Elenkin (1924), to Drouet and Daily (1939), and to Teiling (1946), for critical remarks on the synonymy of species in this genus. In the following key those species which have been reassigned by students of the genus are given in parentheses.

Key to the Species

1. Colonies saccate, lobed and clathrate, the colonial mucilage
   thick and refractive in young plants _____ *M. aeruginosa*
1. Colonies globular, or ovate, definite in shape,
   not perforate or clathrate _____ 2
2. Cells without pseudovacuoles or, if present,
   small and inconspicuous _____ 4
2. Cells with large and conspicuous pseudovacuoles _____ 3
3. Colonies simple, a large mass of much crowded cells inclosed
   by a transparent, mucilaginous envelope _____ (*M. flos-aquae*)
   M. aeruginosa
3. Colonies compound, several groups of cells, each with a colonial
   envelope, inclosed within a common mucilage _____(*M. ichthyoblabe*)
   M. aeruginosa
4. Cells 1–2μ in diameter, small and numerous but uniformly
   distributed within the colonial mucilage _____ *M. incerta*
4. Cells 2–3μ in diameter, compactly arranged
   within the colonial mucilage _____(*M. pulverea*)
   M. incerta

---

[7]See notes by Drouet and Daily (Daily, 1942, p. 638) in which they explain the use of the generic name *Polycystis* Kuetz. for the species grouped under *Microcystis* Kuetz. I prefer to retain the latter name because it is generally accepted and well understood. Although *Microcystis* was used originally for a miscellany of organisms, and at one time only for flagellates, those species to which it referred in earlier times have all been transferred to their proper places in other genera. Since the name *Microcystis* no longer applies to any of them, there is no danger of taxonomic confusion. In any case, the creation of *Polycystis* as a genus by Kuetzing in 1849 was antedated by the use of that name for a genus of Uredineae (*Polycystis* Leveille 1846, Annales Sci. Nat. Bot., 5 (Ser. 3), p. 269). This precludes the revival of the name for the species now grouped under *Microcystis*.

Microcystis aeruginosa Kuetz.; *emend.* Elenkin 1924, p. 14

[*M. aeruginosa* var. *major* G. M. Smith; *M. flos-aquae*

(Wittr.) Kirchner; *M. ichthyoblabe* Kuetzing]

Pl. 102, Figs. 1–4

An ovate, spherical, or irregularly lobed, saccate and clathrate colony of numerous spherical cells which are much crowded within a gelatinous matrix (several colonies sometimes invested by a common tegument); colonial mucilage hyaline and homogeneous, retaining a definite shape; cell contents blue-green, highly granular and with conspicuous pseudovacuoles; cells 3–4.5μ in diameter.

Very common in hard water lakes, becoming especially abundant during late summer periods and appearing in such dense growths in favorable habitats as to color the water. Mich., Wis.

This species is a frequent component of water blooms, especially in lakes with eutrophic characteristics, although it is common to a great variety of aquatic habitats. The tendency to float high in the water results in the formation of large, macroscopic clots and floating crusts which develop as the plants push each other above the surface. Like *Aphanizomenon flos-aquae,* this species is notorious as a spoiler of water for domestic uses, swimming, and recreation and often causes the death of fish in heavily infested lakes.

In assigning species of *Microcystis* collected in this region, I have followed the nomenclature recommended by students who have given special attention to the genus. There long have been recognized two species names for the very common planktonic forms of *Microcystis,* which show considerable variation in colony form. The name *M. aeruginosa* Kuetz. has been used for the plant which has a perforated or clathrate and much lobed colony. The name *M. flos-aquae* (Wittr.) Kirch. has been applied to the form with globose, non-perforate or non-clathrate colonies. Elenkin (1924, p. 14), after a critical study, reduced this latter species to synonymy with *M. aeruginosa* Kuetz. At the same time he recognized two forms: fa. *minor* Elenkin, cells 3–5μ in diameter, and fa. *major* (Wittr.) Elenkin, cells 4–7μ in diameter. It is held by some that the perforate condition of the colony is merely a character accompanying age and that the many intergrading variations are related to physical conditions in the habitat such as water currents, or to methods of collecting. Virieux (1916) and others (Drouet and Daily, 1939) also have advocated uniting *M. aeruginosa* and *M. flos-aquae.* Drouet and Daily (*l.c.*) have published on the synonymy of *Microcystis aeruginosa* and have discussed the fresh-water species of the genus critically. Teiling (1946) advocates the retention of the two names.

If the interpretations of Elenkin (*l.c.*), Drouet and Daily (*l.c.*) and others are followed, the name *M. flos-aquae* (Wittr.) Kirch. will be discarded. The view which holds that the clathrate condition is a result of age only, is not compatible with the many observations which I have made on collections of these forms in which very large, globose, solid colonies dominate the habitat, forming almost pure growths in some lakes. Such colonies mature and disintegrate without assuming the perforate and clathrate condition which one might expect to develop if age were responsible for the *aeruginosa* form. Illustrations of some of the various expressions which this plankter assumes are illustrated on Plate 102, Figs. 1–4. See also Fjerdingstad (1945) on the retention of these two names.

Microcystis incerta Lemmermann 1899a, p. 132
[*M. pulverea* (Wood) Migula]
Pl. 102, Fig. 5

A spherical or lobed colony, consisting usually of many small, spherical, closely arranged cells, inclosed by a thin, mucilaginous envelope; cells 0.5–2μ in diameter; cell contents gray-green to light blue-green; pseudovacuoles lacking or minute and inconspicuous; colonies either tychoplanktonic, or forming blue-green granular masses on the bottom.

Not uncommon, occurring in both hard and soft water lakes. Mich., Wis.

The small size and compact arrangement of the cells, and the minute pseudovacuoles are characteristics which aid in the identification of this species.

I follow Drouet and Daily (*l.c.*) in assigning forms ordinarily listed under the name of *M. pulverea* (Wood) Migula to *M. incerta* Lemm. The plant listed by other authors as *Anacystis pulverea* Wolle has been transferred to *M. glauca* (Wolle) by Drouet and Daily (*l.c.*). Apparently it has not been collected in our region. It inhabits hard water lakes rich in lime and is to be expected in lakes of southern Michigan and Wisconsin.

MERISMOPEDIA Meyen 1839, p. 67

A plate-like colony of ovate or globose cells compactly or loosely arranged in rows both transversely and longitudinally, inclosed by a hyaline, homogeneous, mucilage; colony quadrangular (becoming distorted in age) or with margins rolled and convolute; cell contents homogeneous (rarely with pseudovacuoles); individual cell sheaths

[457]

indistinct in most species and confluent with the colonial mucilage.

The plate-like form of the *Merismopedia* colony and the regularity of cell arrangement make identification of this genus certain. Only in rare instances are *Chroococcus* cells found in a somewhat plate-like colony, and the examination of a number of individuals will confirm the identification.

Key to the Species

1. Colony a very broad, membranaceous plate with
   margins convolute and enrolled_____ *M. convoluta*
1. Colony a flat plate _____ 2
2. Cells with refractive vacuoles _____ *M. Trolleri*
2. Cells without refractive vacuoles, usually homogeneous and
   finely granular, sometimes with a few conspicuous granulations _____ 3
3. Cells light blue-green, finely granular _____ 4
3. Cells bright blue-green, frequently with coarse granulations _____ *M. elegans*
4. Cells forming small rectangular colonies;
   1.3–2.2µ in diameter_____ *M. tenuissima*
4. Cells larger _____ 5
5. Cells 3–7µ in diameter_____ *M. glauca*
5. Cells averaging smaller than above_____ 6
6. Cells blue-green or gray-green, 2.5–4µ
   in diameter; sheaths thin_____ *M. punctata*
6. Cells violet or somewhat pink, inclosed by
   thick, cartilaginous sheaths_____ *M. chondroidea*

Merismopedia chondroidea Wittrock & Nordstedt 1878, No. 200

A colony of 4–8 (rarely 16) cells with thick individual sheaths, arranged in a rectangular plate; cell contents violet or somewhat pink; cells 2–3.5µ in diameter.

Geitler (1928) refers to this plant as an abnormal expression of some other species. It has appeared too seldom in our collections to provide a satisfactory basis for a final decision, but I use the name for forms of *Merismopedia* that have thick sheaths.

In the tychoplankton of several soft water lakes and *Sphagnum* bogs. Wis.

Merismopedia convoluta de Brébisson *in* Kuetzing 1849, p. 472
Pl. 103, Fig. 13

Colony irregularly quadrangular, forming extensive sheets with convolute margins, 1–4 mm. in width and usually visible to the unaided eye; cells spherical or oblong, 4–5µ in diameter, 4–8µ long, arranged in multiple families of 64 individuals.

Among other algae in tychoplankton; in a dense film of miscellaneous algae on submerged wood. Mich., Wis.

Merismopedia elegans A. Braun *in* Kuetzing 1849, p. 472
Pl. 101, Fig. 1

Colony irregularly quadrangular, composed of as many as 4000 compactly arranged, ovate cells, with the rows of cells becoming distorted in older and larger colonies; cells 5–7.5μ in diameter, 7–9μ long; contents bright blue-green.

Among other algae in shallow water but commonly found in euplankton of several soft water lakes; in *Sphagnum* bogs. Mich., Wis.

Merismopedia elegans var. *major* G. M. Smith 1920, p. 32
Pl. 100, Fig. 18

A variety differing from the typical by the larger size of the cells, 10–11μ in diameter, 12–14–(17)μ long.

This variety is interpreted by Geitler (1930–31, p. 265) as a separate species.

Euplanktonic and tychoplanktonic. Mich., Wis.

Merismopedia glauca (Ehrenb.) Naegeli 1849, p. 55
Pl. 101, Figs. 2–4

Colony of 16–64 ovate or hemispherical cells, very regularly arranged to form quadrangular colonies; 3–5–(7)μ in diameter; 30-celled colony 30μ wide; cell contents bright blue-green, homogeneous.

Very common in many lakes, especially soft water; scattered among other algae (tychoplankton), rarely in euplankton. Mich., Wis.

Merismopedia aeruginea de Bréb. is here included with *M. glauca*. The former name refers to a species which has compactly arranged cells, violet-green in color, and with contents finely granular. Under this name the plant was reported from Troutmere, Wisconsin, by Macmillan.

Merismopedia punctata Meyen 1839, p. 67
Pl. 102, Fig. 10

A rectangular plate of 32–128 ovate cells, usually loosely arranged, sometimes in compact groups of 4–8 individuals, the groups widely separated within a broad gelatinous envelope; cells 2.5–4μ in diameter; cell contents homogeneous, blue-green.

Scattered among other algae in several lakes. Mich., Wis.

Merismopedia tenuissima Lemmermann 1898d, p. 154
Pl. 100, Fig. 17

A small rectangular plate of (usually) 16 minute ovate cells which are rather evenly and closely spaced within a wide gelatinous investment; cells 1.3–2.2μ in diameter, cell contents pale blue-green or gray-green, homogeneous; colony 16–18μ wide.

The small size of both the cells and the colony help in identification.

Very common in acid habitats and invariably found in association with desmids. Mich., Wis.

Merismopedia Trolleri Bachmann 1920, p. 350
Pl. 101, Fig. 5

A colony of 8–16 spherical cells, each with a distinct sheath and evenly arranged within a transparent colonial mucilage; cell contents with pseudovacuoles (gas vacuoles ?), appearing brownish or purplish because of light-refraction; cells 2–3.5μ in diameter.

Uncommon; in plankton and among other algae in tychoplankton; and in *Sphagnum* bogs. Wis.

Judging from Lemmermann's description of *M. Marssonii* it is not different from *M. Trolleri* except in its smaller size, a character which is insufficient to separate the two species. *M. Trolleri* has been reported previously in this country by Prescott and Croasdale (1937), from Massachusetts.

HOLOPEDIUM Lagerheim 1883, p. 42

Cells subglobose to subcylindric, or ellipsoid, either closely or somewhat distantly arranged to form flat plates which are quadrate, or subquadrate and lobed, the cells forming linear series in part, but in general irregularly disposed.

The cells appear round when seen on end, but appear elongate and subcylindric when seen from the side, especially in *H. Dieteli* (Richter) Migula, a species not reported from this country.

Holopedium irregulare Lagerheim 1883, p. 43
Pl. 107, Figs. 10, 11

Cells subcylindric, irregularly arranged in flat plates, with long axes mostly parallel, contents pale blue-green; cells 2–3μ in diameter.

Tychoplankter. Found in acid lakes. Mich.

SYNECHOCOCCUS Naegeli 1849, p. 56

A cylindrical oblong, or elliptical unicell; or sometimes 2 to 4 cells seriately united as a result of cell division in one plane; free-floating, without a sheath; cell contents pale blue-green or some shade of yellow, highly granular.

This genus should be compared with *Anacystis* (*Aphanothece, Gloeothece*), a genus with elongate cells inclosed in hyaline mucilage and with cells usually aggregated in large numbers to form colonies.

Synechococcus aeruginosus Naegeli 1849, p. 56
Pl. 102, Figs. 6–8

Cells oblong to cylindric, 2–3 times their diameter in length, poles broadly rounded; solitary or in pairs; 7–15μ in diameter, 14–25μ long.

Rare in tychoplankton and in films of algae on sandy beaches. Mich., Wis.

GLOEOTHECE Naegeli 1849, p. 57

Ovate or cylindrical cells inclosed by definite, often lamellated sheaths and embedded in copious mucilage to form amorphous gelatinous masses, either free-floating or attached, often occurring with *Aphanothece* spp. See notes under that genus, p. 465, concerning the combining of *Gloeothece* and *Aphanothece* under *Anacystis* Meneghini.

Key to the Species

1. Colonial mucilage and cell sheaths
   golden- or yellow-brown_____*G. fusco-lutea*
1. Colonial mucilage colorless_____ 2
2. Cells 1.2–2.5μ in diameter, up to 18μ long, cylindrical with
   rounded apices, each cell faintly sheathed_____*G. linearis*
2. Cells 4–6μ in diameter, up to 15μ long; individual cell sheaths
   conspicuous, sometimes several cells inclosed by one sheath_____*G. rupestris*

Gloeothece fusco-lutea Naegeli 1849, p. 58

Cells oblong-cylindric, inclosed in amorphous mucilage with individual sheaths thick and golden-brown in color; cell contents blue-green; cells 4–5.5μ in diameter, 7.4–9μ long.

Tychoplankter. Wis.

Gloeothece linearis Naegeli 1849, p. 58
[*Anacystis Peniocystis* (Kuetz.) Drouet & Daily *in* Daily 1942, p. 651]
Pl. 102, Fig. 9

Cells cylindrical, vermiform, or bacilliform, about 10 times their diameter in length, loosely scattered in small, free-floating, irregularly saccate or elongate-bulbous colonies, with long axes of the cells approximately parallel, ends of the cells rounded; colonial mucilage hyaline or yellowish and faintly lamellated, each cell inclosed by a sheath; cell contents usually pale blue-green, rarely brightly colored; cells 1.2–2.5μ in diameter, 10.5–18μ long.

Our specimens have not been collected from strata on rocks as described for *Anacystis Peniocystis* (Kuetz.) Drouet & Daily (Daily, 1942), but always as small planktonic colonies of more or less definite shape. Our plants are assigned to this species on the basis of cell size and shape, sheath characteristics and color.

Rather common in the tychoplankton of lakes. Wis.

Gloeothece linearis var. composita G. M. Smith 1920, p. 46
Pl. 103, Fig. 1

Differs from the typical form in having shorter, stouter cells, and in the small number of individuals (2–8) within the broad colonial sheath; cell sheaths not confluent; cells 3–3.5μ in diameter, 4–8μ long; plants 10–12μ wide, 20–35μ long.

Appearing with the typical form in tychoplankton. Wis.

Gloeothece rupestris (Lyngb.) Bornet in
Wittrock & Nordstedt 1880, No. 2456
[*Anacystis rupestris* (Lyngb.) Drouet & Daily *in* Daily 1942, p. 650]
Pl. 103, Figs. 2, 3

Cells ovate or cylindric-ovate, irregularly scattered throughout a copious colorless or brownish gelatinous matrix, solitary or in 2's and 4's in small families surrounded by definite sheaths; plant mass usually attached, at least when young, becoming free-floating; cells 4–6–(9)μ in diameter, up to 15μ long.

Tychoplankter. Wis.

RHABDODERMA Schmidle & Lauterborn in Schmidle 1900e, p. 148

A free-floating, ovate or fusiform colony of 8–32 sigmoid or arcuate cylindrical cells with rounded poles; individual sheaths entirely confluent with the colonial mucilage which is thin, transparent, without lamellations, and often scarcely discernible.

Key to the Species

1. Cells short, 5μ or less in length, distinctly sigmoid .... *R. irregulare*
1. Cells more than 5μ long, straight, weakly sigmoid or contorted 2
2. Cells strongly twisted and contorted .... *R. sigmoidea*
2. Cells straight or slightly sigmoid 3
3. Cells straight or somewhat curved, 8–10μ long .... *R. lineare*
3. Cells curved or sigmoid, 10–14μ long .... *R. Gorskii*

Rhabdoderma Gorskii Wołoszyńska 1918, p. 127

Pl. 103, Fig. 4

A fusiform colony with uneven margins; cells cylindrical, 7–10 times their diameter in length, arcuate or somewhat sigmoid, the poles broadly rounded, loosely scattered with their longitudinal axes approximately parallel with that of the colony, inclosed in a wide, hyaline, mucilaginous envelope; cell contents bright blue-green, homogeneous; cells $1.5–2\mu$ in diameter, $10–14\mu$ long.

Euplankter; in soft water lakes. Wis.

Rhabdoderma irregulare (Naumann) Geitler 1925a, p. 113

Pl. 103, Figs. 9, 10

An ovate colony of sigmoid, cylindrical cells irregularly arranged within a copious, gelatinous envelope; cells $1.5–2\mu$ in diameter, $4.5–5–(6)\mu$ long.

Euplankter; in semi-hard water lakes. Wis.

Rhabdoderma lineare Schmidle & Lauterborn *in*

Schmidle 1900e, pp. 148, 149

Pl. 103, Figs. 11, 12

A fusiform colony of cylindrical, nearly straight cells arranged with their longitudinal axes parallel with that of the colony, sometimes several cells end to end in a series; colonial envelope transparent and wide; cells $1.8–2.0\mu$ in diameter, $8–10\mu$ long; cell contents blue-green, homogeneous.

Uncommon in the euplankton of several soft water and acid lakes. Wis.

Rhabdoderma sigmoidea fa. *minor* Moore & Carter 1923, p. 398

Pl. 103, Figs. 5, 6

Cells arcuate and much twisted, sigmoid and lunate, irregularly arranged in a hyaline envelope; cell contents pale blue-green; cells $1.5–1.6\mu$ in diameter, $15–16\mu$ long.

The much twisted and contorted shape of the cells is a constant character; cells more slender than in the typical plant.

Euplankter. Wis.

DACTYLOCOCCOPSIS (Reinsch) Hansgirg 1888b, p. 590

Cells fusiform, solitary or colonial, of various shapes, straight, sigmoid, arcuate, or spirally twisted; when colonial usually inclosed by a fusiform gelatinous envelope, the individual cell sheaths inconspicuous and confluent with the colonial mucilage; cell contents nearly colorless to light blue-green, homogeneous.

This genus should be compared with *Ankistrodesmus* in the Chlorophyta. Cells of some species are shaped very similarly, but differentiation can be made on the presence of the chloroplast, which in *Ankistrodesmus*, however, is often indefinite. Most species of *Ankistrodesmus* have a pyrenoid which can be detected even though the chloroplast is indistinct.

Key to the Species

1. Cells stout, not more than 5 times their diameter in length................*D. Smithii*
1. Cells elongate, needle-like, with apices sharply pointed or much
   narrowed and narrowly rounded...2
2. Cells much twisted about one another to
   form fascicles or bundles ....*D. fascicularis*
2. Cells not twisted about one another..3
3. Cells lunate, arcuate or sigmoid, sometimes
   nearly straight; apices rounded...*D. rhaphidioides*
3. Cells straight, needle-like, sharply pointed at the apices...........*D. acicularis*

Dactylococcopsis acicularis Lemmermann 1900, Ber. d. Deutsch.
Bot. Ges., 18, p. 309

A free-floating colony of few (rarely solitary) acicular or straight cells with extremely finely pointed poles, inclosed by a wide gelatinous envelope; cells 2–3μ in diameter, 45–60–(80)μ long.

Euplankter. Rather rare but found in several lakes. Wis.

Dactylococcopsis fascicularis Lemmermann 1898d, p. 153
Pl. 105, Figs. 10–12

Colonies fusiform, composed of 4–8 elongate, arcuate or spirally sigmoid cells tapering to fine points at the poles, rather compactly twisted and inclosed by a thin, mucilaginous envelope; cells 1.5–2μ in diameter, 19.5μ long.

Euplankter. Wis.

Dactylococcopsis rhaphidioides Hansgirg 1888b, p. 590
Pl. 105, Figs. 13–15

Cells elongate-fusiform, seldom straight, usually arcuate or sigmoid, narrowed but not sharply pointed at the poles, arranged in colonies of 4–8 within a hyaline, gelatinous envelope; cells 1–3μ in diameter, 5–25μ long.

From squeezings of *Utricularia*. Mich., Wis.

Dactylococcopsis Smithii Chodat & Chodat 1925, p. 455

Pl. 105, Figs. 3, 4

Colony ovate or broadly fusiform, containing 4–8–16 fusiform cells which are nearly straight or slightly arcuate, sometimes paired and lying end to end with one pole pointed and the other bluntly rounded; cells 3.8μ in diameter, 11–15μ long.

This species (listed as *D. rhaphidioides* Hansg. by Smith, 1920, p. 47) was more frequently found in the region than any other species of the genus.

Common in the euplankton of lakes and ponds; also in rich mixtures of algae in acid bogs and small lakes. Mich., Wis.

CYANARCUS Pascher 1914, p. 351

Unicellular, solitary or gregarious in the mucilage of other algae, or free-floating; cells curved rods, describing ½ to ⅔ of a circle, sometimes lying in compact series with longitudinal axes parallel; not tapering toward the apices, which are bluntly rounded; cell contents blue-green, homogeneous.

Cyanarcus hamiformis Pascher 1914, p. 351

Pl. 103, Figs. 7, 8

Characteristics as described for the genus; cells 0.5–0.75μ in diameter, 3–4μ long; strongly curved, describing nearly a complete circle, several cells lying together and parallel so as to form a short cylinder.

In a mixture of algae in a *Sphagnum* bog. Wis.

APHANOTHECE Naegeli 1849, p. 59

Cells ovate, oblong or subcylindrical, densely but evenly arranged and scattered throughout firm and copious mucilage, forming masses which are often macroscopic and either amorphous or definite in shape, free-floating or sedentary, sometimes subaerial; cell contents either gray, olive, or bright blue-green, granular but not vacuolate; cell sheaths indistinct and confluent with the homogeneous colonial mucilage.

This genus should be compared with *Gloeothece* which has been differentiated on the basis of the definite, individual cell sheaths. Because of the otherwise great similarity which exists between species of these two genera, and because even the presence of cell sheaths is sometimes demonstrable in *Aphanothece*, they have been combined recently (Daily, 1942) and reassigned to the genus

Anacystis Meneghini. This name, dating ırom 1837, has priority (Drouet and Daily, *in* Daily 1942, p. 648). This greatly simplifies the nomenclature and serves as a basis for assigning names to species heretofore referred to both *Aphanothece* and *Gloeothece*. Some of the species of these two genera not treated by Daily (*l.c.*) require consideration. In the present study, type materal has been examined for some of the species, but not for all. It is considered best, therefore, to retain the names commonly used for the plants referable to these genera. The reader should see Daily (*l.c.*) for an analysis of synonymy. In the following key the species which have been transferred to synonymy in *Anacystis* are so indicated by the name in parentheses.

Key to the Species

1. Colonies clathrate, irregularly expanded, with large perforations ... *A. clathrata*
1. Colonies not clathrate; globular or amorphous ... 2
2. Colonies globular or hemispherical, either free-floating or attached ... 3
2. Colonies amorphous, gelatinous masses, usually adherent, becoming free-floating ... 4
3. Cells short-cylindric, stout, (3.6)–7μ in diameter; colony free-floating ... (*A. prasina*—see *A. stagnina*)
   Anacystis rupestris var. *prasina*
3. Cells cylindric with rounded ends, 3–5μ in diameter; colony adherent to bottom, sometimes free-floating ... (*A. stagnina*)
   Anacystis rupestris
4. Cells minute, 2μ or less in diameter ... 5
4. Cells larger than 2μ in diameter ... 6
5. Cells 1–1.5μ in diameter, about twice the diameter in length ... *A. nidulans*
5. Cells larger, (1)–1.8–2μ in diameter, slender, up to 3 times the diameter in length ... *A. saxicola*
6. Cells ovate to nearly spherical, not cylindric ... *A. gelatinosa*
6. Cells cylindrical, up to 3 times the diameter in length ... 7
7. Plant mass very pale, gray to light blue-green ... 8
7. Plant mass brightly colored ... 9
8. Cells 3.3–3.7–(4.5)μ in diameter, up to 7μ long; densely arranged ... *A. microscopica*
8. Cells larger, 4.5–5.6μ in diameter, up to 8.5μ long; loosely arranged ... (*A. pallida*—see *Gloeothece rupestris*)
   Anacystis rupestris
9. Cells elongate-cylindric, 2.4–3μ in diameter, up to 3 times the diameter in length; loosely arranged ... *A. microspora*
9. Cells short-cylindric, 2–3.5μ in diameter, up to 2 times the diameter in length; densely arranged ... (*A. Castagnei*)
   Anacystis marginata

Aphanothece Castagnei (de Bréb.) Rabenhorst 1865, p. 76

[*Anacystis marginata* Meneghini 1837]

Pl. 105, Figs. 5, 6

Cells ellipsoid or ovate to subcylindric, densely arranged within a gelatinous, amorphous mass which is olive-green or brownish; cells of various shapes and sizes within the same colony, oblong or polygonal when compressed; $2–3.5\mu$ in diameter, $4–8\mu$ long; cell contents finely granular and olive-green.

In ditches; in tychoplankton of lakes. Wis.

Aphanothece clathrata G. S. West *in* West & West 1906, p. 111

Pl. 104, Figs. 6, 7

Colonies free-floating, irregular in shape and usually clathrate with large perforations; cells cylindrical or elongate-elliptic, straight or slightly curved, scattered through a transparent mucilage; cells $0.8–1.2\mu$ in diameter, $3–6\mu$ long.

The small size of this species and the clathrate colony are characters which separate this species from most of the other free-floating forms of *Aphanothece*. Its lack of pseudovacuoles differentiates it from *A. pulverulenta* Bachmann, another species with minute cells (ellipsoid in shape) which possess pseudovacuoles.

Floating in several soft water lakes. Mich., Wis.

Aphanothece gelatinosa (Henn.) Lemmermann 1910, p. 69

Pl. 104, Fig. 8

Cells ovate, nearly spherical, compactly arranged in globular, blue-green to brown gelatinous attached masses; cell contents blue-green; cells $3.8–4\mu$ in diameter, $4–4.5\mu$ long.

This plant is differentiated by the color of the colonial mass and by the size of the cells from *Aphanothece stagnina*. It is possibly only a variation of that species, and the assigned name is used here tentatively to designate a form which does not agree with typical *A. stagnina*. I have not seen type specimens of *A. gelatinosa* for comparison.

In a hard water swamp and in lakes with a high calcium carbonate content. Wis.

Aphanothece microscopica Naegeli 1849, p. 59

Pl. 104, Figs. 9, 10

Cells ovate to subglobose, densely arranged in small, free-floating or attached ovate colonies; cell sheaths not evident; cell contents light blue-green, finely granular; cells 3.3–3.7–(4.5)μ in diameter, 5.5–7.5μ long.

This plant has smaller cells than those described for *Aphanothece prasina,* and they are not cylindrical.

Euplankter. Mich., Wis.

Aphanothece microspora (Menegh.) Rabenhorst 1863, p. 76
Pl. 105, Figs. 7–9

Cells short-cylindric with rounded ends, loosely arranged, solitary or in pairs in small, amorphous, olive or yellow-green gelatinous masses; cells 2.4–2.7μ in diameter, 6–10μ long.

Fairly abundant in a few hard water lakes; entangled in tycho-plankton, among filamentous algae. Wis.

Aphanothece nidulans P. Richter 1884, p. 128
Pl. 104, Figs. 2, 3

Cells short-cylindric, broadly rounded at the apices, densely and evenly distributed in small ovate or spherical colonies, inclosed by a colorless mucilage in which individual cell sheaths are not distinct; cells small, 1–1.5μ in diameter, 3–3.5μ long; cell contents pale blue-green.

This is a euplanktonic species, often forming a major portion of a rich flocculent algal population in shallow water, especially in hard water lakes. The minute bacilliform cells give colonies the appearance of a bacterioidal mass. Mich., Wis.

Aphanothece nidulans var. *endophytica* West & West 1912, p. 432
Pl. 105, Fig. 16

Cells within the mucilage of other colonial Cyanophyta, such as *Coelosphaerium* and *Microcystis,* where they are evenly distributed throughout the envelope of the host; cells 0.8–1.5μ in diameter, 2.5–4.5μ long.

Rare; in the euplankton of lakes of fairly soft water. Wis.

Aphanothece saxicola Naegeli 1849, p. 60
Pl. 104, Fig. 1

Cells cylindrical with rounded ends, 2–3.5 times longer than wide, loosely arranged, solitary or in pairs within amorphous, homo-geneous, and almost colorless mucilage; colonies free-floating or attached; cell contents pale blue-green; cells (1)–1.5–1.8–(2)μ in diameter, 2.8–6μ long.

The cells of this species are bacilliform and are almost colorless.

Because of their minute size they may easily be mistaken for a colony of bacteria. Their faint bluish-green pigmentation is scarcely to be differentiated from the apparently similar color of unstained bacteria caused by light refraction in microscopical examination. The name *A. saxicola* Naeg. is used tentatively for this small plant. It is nearest *A. nidulans* P. Richt. in size but is more slender and the cells are more loosely arranged in the colonial mucilage than described for *A. nidulans*. According to Drouet and Daily (*l.c.*) *Aphanothece saxicola* is synonymous with *Anacystis marginata* Meneghini, the original description of which does not agree with our specimens. The former name is used here, therefore, to refer to a plant which agrees with the description of *A. saxicola*.

In *Sphagnum* bogs; tychoplankter in lakes. Mich., Wis.

Aphanothece stagnina (Spreng.) A. Braun *in* Rabenhorst 1864–1869, Algen No. 1572

[*Anacystis rupestris* (Lyngb.) Drouet & Daily *in* Daily 1942, p. 650]
Pl. 103, Figs. 14–16

Cells short cylindric, evenly distributed throughout an ovate or irregularly globose gelatinous mass; colonies bright green, attached and attaining macroscopic size; cell contents usually bright blue-green (sometimes pale), homogeneous; cells sheaths diffluent and not evident; cells $3.7–7\mu$ in diameter, $5–8\mu$ long.

Free-floating colonies with larger cells are usually referred to *Aphanothece prasina* A. Braun. In his treatment of the genus, Daily has assigned the name *Anacystis rupestris* var. *prasina* (A. Braun) Drouet & Daily to this form and does not separate it from *Aphanothece stagnina* (Spreng.) A. Braun.

Common in many lakes; usually in shallow water; often forming almost continuous gelatinous expanses on the bottom of favorable eutrophic habitats. Mich., Wis.

COELOSPHAERIUM Naegeli 1849, p. 54

A free-floating, globular, ovate, or irregularly shaped colony of spherical or subpyriform cells arranged in the colonial mucilage, in a single peripheral layer, producing a hollow sac; cell contents pale to bright blue-green, either homogeneous or with numerous refractive pseudovacuoles; colonial envelope homogeneous, or with radiating, gelatinous fibrils.

This genus should be compared with *Aphanocapsa*, in which the cells are scattered throughout the colonial mucilage.

Key to the Species

1. Cells 5–7μ in diameter, spherical .... *C. dubium*
1. Cells smaller, either spherical or ovate 2
2. Cells round, up to 4μ in diameter .... *C. Kuetzingianum*
2. Cells ovate to ellipsoid 3
3. Cells appearing dark and granular because of pseudovacuoles;
   2–3μ in diameter, 3.5–6μ long .... *C. Naegelianum*
3. Cells pale blue-green, without pseudovacuoles,
   1–2.5μ in diameter, 2–3.2μ long .... *C. pallidum*

Coelosphaerium dubium Grunow *in* Rabenhorst 1865, p. 55
Pl. 106, Fig. 1

Plant a spherical or sometimes irregularly-shaped colony of spherical cells, or an aggregate of colonies in a common gelatinous envelope; free-floating; cells densely arranged in the colonial mucilage to form a peripheral layer, thus producing a hollow sphere; cell contents blue-green, either homogeneous or with pseudovacuoles; cells 5–7μ in diameter; compound colonies as much as 300μ in diameter.

Rare in euplankton. Wis.

Coelosphaerium Kuetzingianum Naegeli 1849, p. 54
Pl. 106, Fig. 2

A free-floating spherical, or ovate, gelatinous colony of spherical or subspherical cells arranged at some distance from one another (usually) at the periphery of the colonial envelope; cell contents homogeneous (rarely with pseudovacuoles), light blue-green; cells 2.5–4μ in diameter.

This species is not quite so common in our collections as *C. Naegelianum*. It is, however, widely distributed in a variety of lakes, mostly hard or semi-hard water habitats. It seems never to become conspicuous in water blooms as does *C. Naegelianum*. It is to be differentiated from that species by the shape of the cells and by their lack of the reddish-brown color produced by many pseudovacuoles. It also lacks the radiating gelatinous fibrils in the colonial mucilage possessed by *C. Naegelianum*.

Mich., Wis.

Coelosphaerium Naegelianum Unger 1854, p. 196
Pl. 106, Fig. 4

A free-floating, spherical, ovate, or lobed colony of ovate or ellipsoid cells arranged to form a dense peripheral layer in the

[470]

colonial mucilage; cell contents with many pseudovacuoles, giving a dark reddish-brown or black granular appearance to the cell and making the colony opaque when viewed microscopically; colonial mucilage with many radiating fibrillar concretions which clearly show when the colony disintegrates with age; cells 2–3μ wide, 3.5–6μ long.

This species is very common and occurs in abundance in suitable habitats such as hard water, highly nitrogenous lakes with adequate carbon dioxide content. In late summer periods these plants are often conspicuous components of water blooms. *Coelosphaerium Naegelianum* Unger is associated with *Microcystis aeruginosa* Kuetzing *emend.* Elenkin, *Lyngbya Birgei* G. M. Smith, *Coelosphaerium Kuetzingianum* Naeg. and *Gloeotrichia echinulata* (J. E. Smith) P. Richter (see *C. Kuetzingianum* above). When the colony is disintegrating the cells and the fibrils have a distinct radiate appearance and the cells seem to be at the ends of fine strands from the center of the colony.

The original description of this plant agrees with our specimens. In DeToni (1907, p. 100), the name is regarded as synonymous with *C. Kuetzingianum* Naeg.

Coelosphaerium pallidum Lemmermann 1898d, p. 154
Pl. 106, Fig. 3

A spherical or ovate colony of small, ovate cells crowded, but evenly arranged, within the periphery of the colonial mucilage; cell contents pale blue-green, without pseudovacuoles; cells 1–2.5μ in diameter, 2–3.2μ long; colony 30–40μ in diameter.

This species has smaller and more crowded cells than others in our collections. These characters, together with the lack of pseudovacuoles, are sufficient for identification.

Rare. Found in a *Sphagnum* bog and in pooled streams. Wis.

MARSSONIELLA Lemmermann 1900d, p. 275

A colony of 8–12 ovoid or pyriform cells, radiately arranged, with their narrow ends directed outward, inclosed by a thin, transparent, scarcely discernible investment (usually requiring a stain to demonstrate).

Marssoniella elegans Lemmermann 1900d, p. 275
Pl. 107, Fig. 12

Characteristics as described for the genus; cells 1.3–5μ in diameter, 5–6μ long.

Euplankter. Mich.

GOMPHOSPHAERIA Kuetzing 1836, Dec. XVI, No. 151

A globose or ovate colony of globular or pyriform cells arranged singly or in pairs at the ends of gelatinous strands which radiate from a common center, the cells at the periphery of a colorless, mucilaginous envelope; individual sheaths of the cells usually confluent.

Following cell division in this genus, the cells lie side by side in pairs (or in 4's) for some time. The division is accompanied by a forking of the stalk at base of cell, which thus forms the radiating branched stalks of the colony. The cells, especially in some species, appear heart-shaped because fission begins at the outer, free pole of the cell, whereas division of the attached end of the cell is delayed.

Key to the Species

Cells 4–12μ in diameter (some varieties
    smaller), pyriform or cordate _____G. aponina
Cells 1.5–2.4μ in diameter, spherical or somewhat reniform _____G. lacustris

Gomphosphaeria aponina Kuetzing 1836, Dec. XVI, No. 151
Pl. 106, Fig. 5

Cells pyriform, or cordate in stages of division, arranged at the periphery of a globular and usually wide gelatinous sheath, and at the ends of stout radiating, gelatinous strands; cells 4–5μ in diameter, 8–12μ long.

Tychoplankter; common in many lakes. Mich., Wis.

Gomphosphaeria aponina var. cordiformis Wolle 1882,
Bull. Torr. Bot. Club, 9, p. 25
Pl. 106, Fig. 6

Cells decidedly cordate, compactly arranged within a thick gelatinous envelope, individual sheaths distinct; cells 6–12μ in diameter, 12–15–(20)μ long.

Occurring with the typical plant. Mich., Wis.

Gomphosphaeria aponina var. delicatula Virieux 1916, p. 69
Pl. 106, Fig. 7

A variety differing from the typical by the smaller size of the cells, which are 2–3.5μ in diameter, 4.5–6μ long; colonies globose or ovate and often lobed.

Euplankter; uncommon. Wis.

Gomphosphaeria aponina var. *gelatinosa* Prescott
in Prescott, Silva, & Wade 1949, p. 89
Pl. 106, Fig. 10

Cells pyriform, arranged in 2's and 4's in multiple, irregularly lobed or vermiform colonies, each group of cells entirely or partially enclosed by a thick gelatinous integument, the radiating gelatinous strands common to the typical form not in evidence; cells $3.7-4\mu$ in diameter, $6-7.4\mu$ long.

This variety should be compared with *Gomphosphaeria aponina* var. *multiplex* Nygaard.

Plankter; in soft water lakes. Wis.

Gomphosphaeria lacustris Chodat 1898, p. 180
Pl. 106, Fig. 9

Cells spherical or sometimes reniform, arranged in clusters of 4-8 individuals at the ends of fine gelatinous strands, clusters at some distance from one another in copious gelatinous envelopes; cells $1.5-2.4\mu$ in diameter.

This species is sometimes abundant as a euplankter, but it is more commonly found among other algae in the tychoplankton. Although generally distributed, this species seems to prefer hard or semi-hard water lakes. It should be compared with *Coelosphaerium Kuetzingianum*.

Euplankter. Mich., Wis.

Gomphosphaeria lacustris var. *compacta* Lemmermann 1900, p. 339
Pl. 106, Fig. 8

Cells oblong, very compactly arranged within a wide, gelatinous envelope, $1.5-2.0\mu$ in diameter, $4-6\mu$ long.

Rather common in the euplankton of both hard and soft water lakes. Wis.

GLAUCOCYSTIS Itzigsohn, No. 1935 *in* Rabenhorst 1866,
Die Algen Europas; *emend.* Geitler 1923a

A colony of 4-16 cells inclosed by the persistent mother cell wall (as in *Oocystis*); cells spherical or ellipsoidal, containing numerous vermiform or sometimes irregularly shaped chromatophore-like bodies which may be either peripheral or somewhat radiating and axially arranged.

This interesting plant is now interpreted by most students of algae as a colorless member of the Oocystaceae (Chlorophyta) containing protoplasts which belong to the Chroococcaceae. It is a little-understood genus and rather rare, although some species seem to be widely distributed. There appears to be some confusion in the records of the plants assigned to the type species, G. Nostochinearum. Evidence at hand appears to warrant the separation of spherical from elliptical plants and the assignment of only the latter to the type species if they possess vermiform, radiating 'chromatophores.' See Geitler (1923a) and Hieronymus (1892a) on the morphology of these plants.

Key to the Species

1. Cells ellipsoidal_____ 2
1. Cells spherical_____G. duplex
2. Cells broadly elliptical with nodular thickenings
    at the poles_____ G. oocystiformis
2. Cells elliptical, without nodular thickenings
    at the poles_____G. Nostochinearum

Glaucocystis duplex Prescott 1944, p. 371
Pl. 108, Fig. 1

Colony composed of 8–16 spherical cells inclosed by a much enlarged spherical mother cell wall; chromatophore-like bodies in the form of 2 stellate masses with long or short vermiform blue-green protoplasts radiating from 2 separate points; cells 40–44μ in diameter; colony 150–170μ in diameter.

This species differs from G. Nostochinearum by its spherical shape and by the dual arrangement of the colored protoplasts. From G. cingulata Bohlin it differs in the morphology of the cell wall. In that species the cells are spherical, but the wall has a median annular thickening. The chromatophores are numerous and parietal. Some forms of G. Nostochinearum are described as spherical, but other features which they possess seem to warrant the assignment of the Wisconsin plants described above to a different species.

Among dense clots of algae in Manitowish River, Wisconsin.

Glaucocystis Nostochinearum (Itz.) Rabenhorst 1868, p. 417
Pl. 108, Fig. 2

A free-floating colony of 4–8 elliptical cells inclosed by the old mother cell wall; chromatophores axial and stellate in arrangement, bright blue-green; host cell reproducing by autospore formation; cells 10–18μ in diameter, 18–23.4–(28)μ long; colony of 4 individuals up to 50μ long.

Intermingled with miscellaneous algae in soft water ponds and acid swamps; especially common in desmid habitats. Wis.

[474]

Glaucocystis oocystiformis Prescott 1944, p. 372

Pl. 108, Fig. 3

Cells solitary (or in colonies ?), broadly elliptic, with nodular thickenings of the cell wall at the poles; chromatophores numerous, irregular pads at the periphery of the cell about a central, spherical, colorless vacuole (?); cells 20–27.3µ in diameter, 40–45µ long.

This species differs from the others in the shape of cell, the form of the chromatophores, and in its possession of polar nodules. Whether the absence of colonial association or the retention of autospores within the mother cell wall is a constant feature is un-determined, but in all cases observed, the cells were solitary. In the developmental stages of *G. Nostochinearum* as described by Hieronymus (1892a) the chromatophores show much the same character as exhibited in *G. oocystiformis*. I have not found examples of the latter species showing any form of chromatophore other than that described.

In a pooled stream, northern Wisconsin.

GLOEOCHAETE Lagerheim 1883, p. 39

Either a single colorless cell or a group of 2–4 such individuals endophytized by ovate, blue-green protoplasts which form a cup-shaped body within the host cell; colorless cell spherical, with a single long and very fine gelatinous hair; plants inclosed in a copious, homogeneous gelatinous envelope, attached to the walls of fila-mentous algae.

The genus is similar to *Gloeocystis* in respect to its symbiotic composition. The host cell is regarded as a colorless member of the Tetrasporaceae (Chlorophyta). As in the genus mentioned above, the colorless host cell is not well understood and merits a critical study.

Gloeochaete Wittrockiana Lagerheim 1883, p. 39

Pl. 108, Fig. 9

Characters as described for the genus; cells 4–8µ in diameter, usually in groups of 4; gelatinous setae about 20 times the diameter of the cell in length; endophytic cells 1 (or 2 ?), ovoid, forming a blue-green cup within the host cell.

Attached to filamentous algae in soft water lakes. Mich., Wis.

ORDER CHAMAESIPHONALES

FAMILY CHAMAESIPHONACEAE

Members of this family are solitary, or gregarious and form families attached as epiphytes or develop as encrusting expansions on stones, shells, and other submerged objects. In many there is a definite basal-distal differentiation, with the lower part of the cell narrowed to form an attaching stipe. Although cell division is used by a few forms, the characteristic method of reproduction is by endospores (gonidia), i.e., spore-like bodies cut out simultaneously from the entire protoplast or by successive constrictions at the anterior end of the cell. There is but a single genus represented in our collections.

CHAMAESIPHON Braun & Grunow *in* Rabenhorst 1865, p. 148

A slender, club-shaped (sometimes ovate or pyriform) sheathed cylinder from a narrow attaching basal portion, growing epiphytically on other algae or larger aquatics; sheath open at the widened apex when the cell is mature to permit the escape of 1-celled gonidia (endospores) which are cut off successively from the anterior end of the protoplast; cell contents pale to bright blue-green, homogeneous; sheath thin (usually), hyaline or yellowish; plants nearly always gregarious and often forming extensive patches and showing all stages of development, the germinating endospores sometimes forming a layer more than one cell in thickness on the substrate. Of the many species recognized for this genus, only three are identifiable in our collections.

Key to the Species

1. Cells long and strongly curved from a stipe-like base _____*C. curvatus*
1. Cells short, or elongate, straight, not strongly curved _____ 2
2. Entire content of the cell becoming divided to
   form many gonidia simultaneously_____*C. confervicola*
2. Gonidia cut away from the apex of the protoplast
   by successive constrictions _____ *C. incrustans*

Chamaesiphon confervicola A. Braun *in* Rabenhorst 1865, p. 148
Pl. 108, Fig. 4

Cylindrical to claviform, usually straight, sometimes curved; $1-2\mu$ in diameter at the base, $3-9\mu$ at the apex; sheath thin, expanded above; $\frac{2}{3}$ to $\frac{3}{4}$ of the protoplast divided to form endospores, which are $2-4\mu$ in diameter and which may occur in double series or in groups of 4; plant either solitary or gregarious.

Epiphytic on *Cladophora* and on submerged mosses and other aquatic plants. Wis.

Chamaesiphon curvatus Nordstedt 1878, p. 4
Pl. 108, Figs. 5, 6

Several-celled, violet in color, solitary or gregarious, cylindrical, strongly curved and twisted, sometimes club-shaped, with a narrow, stipe-like base, 3.8–4μ in diameter, 14–65μ long.

Growing on *Drepanocladus* in deep water (5–15 m.). Wis.

Chamaesiphon incrustans Grunow in Rabenhorst 1865, p. 149
Pl. 108, Figs. 7, 8

Cylindrical, gregarious, usually straight (sometimes slightly curved), attached to filamentous algae or leaves of aquatic plants; cells 3–6–(8)μ in diameter, 10–25μ long.

This plant was found growing on mosses and other vegetation taken from a depth of 30 feet. Mich., Wis.

ORDER HORMOGONALES

In contrast to the Chroococcales and Chamaesiphonales, plants in this order are filamentous, comprising a "tribe" known as the Hormogoneae, the other orders making up the "tribe" Coccogoneae. The plant may consist of a trichome of cells inclosed by a sheath which is extremely variable in character, or there may be no sheath. In one suborder, the Homocystineae, there is no differentiation of the cells within the trichome, and, also, there may or may not be basal-distal differentiation. In the other suborder, the Heterocystineae, there is a specialization of certain cells in the filament to form two types of structures which are of taxonomic value. One of these is the *heterocyst*, a thick-walled cell, usually somewhat larger and often different in shape from the vegetative cells. The contents are ordinarily homogeneous. In many cells, the wall at either pole is thickened by a plug of mucilage. The heterocyst may be terminal only, intercalary, or lateral to the trichome. Another special cell is the spore or *gonidium*, sometimes termed *akinete*. This cell is usually much-enlarged and thick-walled and has an adventitious reproductive function.

The presence or absence of the heterocyst and spore, the position of these in the trichome, together with form and size, are all-important in the recognition of species in this order. Heterocysts are incapable of cell division, but they assist in vegetative reproduction by facilitating fragmentation of the trichome, or by determining points of proliferation of the trichome through branch formation. In some forms heterocysts are known to function as spores.

Branching of the trichome may be *false*, or there may be *true* branching as a result of cell division in two planes. Reproduction by fragmentation of the trichome to form hormogonia is common to nearly all forms, whereas gonidia are employed only in certain families or genera.

Key to the Families

1. Heterocysts lacking; trichomes with or without a sheath; sometimes with several trichomes within a single sheath_____ OSCILLATORIACEAE
1. Heterocysts present (rarely absent in some genera which are not represented in our collections; see *Amphithrix*)_____ 2
2. Trichomes exhibiting true branching (branches arising as a result of cell division in 2 planes)_____ 3
2. Trichomes exhibiting false branching, or without branches _____ 4
3. Trichomes and lateral branches uniseriate; heterocysts lateral, usually at the ends of short branches; sheaths confluent____*NOSTOCHOPSACEAE
3. Trichomes and lateral branches multiseriate, or if uniseriate with thick, firm sheaths which are not confluent_____ . STIGONEMATACEAE
4. Trichomes decidedly tapering toward the apex, usually from a basal heterocyst _____RIVULARIACEAE
4. Trichomes not tapering toward the apex _____ 5
5. Trichomes with a definite, firm sheath; false branching frequent _____ SCYTONEMATACEAE
5. Trichomes without a sheath, or with only a thin one; no branching _____ NOSTOCACEAE

SUBORDER HOMOCYSTINEAE

Simple trichomes, without cellular differentiations, with dissepiments (sometimes granular) except in the unicellular genus *Spirulina,* and usually sheathed. The sliding, spiral, or oscillating movement shown by most members is characteristic of this suborder but not confined to it. Trichomes reproduce by fission or by fragmentation (to form hormogonia), sometimes breaking by means of dead cells (necridia), into sections that then increase in length by fission. The suborder comprises 1 family.

FAMILY OSCILLATORIACEAE
Key to the Genera

1. Trichomes spiralled or regularly coiled_____ 2
1. Trichomes straight, bent, or entangled, but not regularly coiled_____ 4
2. Trichomes with a sheath_____*Lyngbya* (in part)
2. Trichomes without a sheath _____ 3
3. Trichomes 1-celled, usually relatively short _____ *Spirulina*
3. Trichomes much longer, many-celled, with the dissepiments sometimes indistinct_____ *Arthrospira*
4. Trichomes without an evident sheath (though hormogonia may sometimes show a thin sheath)_____*Oscillatoria*
4. Trichomes with an evident sheath _____ 5
5. Sheath containing a single trichome_____ 6
5. Sheath containing several to many trichomes_____ 9
6. Sheaths firm and definite, not sticking to or confluent with sheaths of other plants_____*Lyngbya* (in part)
6. Sheaths mucous and sticky, confluent with those of other plants, often indefinite_____ 7

7. Plant mass forming erect tufts from a horizontal expanse,
   especially when growing on moist substrates................................. *Symploca*
7. Plant mass not forming erect tufts 8
8. Trichomes lying parallel, forming planktonic fascicles........ *Trichodesmium*
8. Trichomes entangled, forming mucous, sometimes
   thick, layers on a substrate.. *Phormidium*
9. Sheaths wide, mucous, soft and sticky; freely branching 10
9. Sheaths firm and narrow; not freely branching;
   trichomes densely compacted and entwined .... *Schizothrix*
10. Trichomes loosely arranged, 2–4 in a sheath.................... *Hydrocoleum*
10. Trichomes densely entangled, many within a sheath................. *Microcoleus*

SPIRULINA Turpin 1827, p. 309

A spirally twisted, unicellular trichome, cylindrical throughout
and not tapering toward the apices (although briefly attenuated in
some species); spiral loose and lax, or close and tightly coiled according to species, the spiral usually very regular; trichomes free-
floating and planktonic or intermingled with other algae in tychoplankton, sometimes forming layers on moist soil, especially where
water has subsided.

This genus should be compared with *Arthrospira*, in which the
trichomes are multicellular. According to the interpretations of some
phycologists the two genera should not be separated. This would
seem to be justifiable when the dissepiments of *Arthrospira* cannot
be demonstrated and the trichome appears to be unicellular. See
Crow (1927) on the characteristics of these two genera.

Key to the Species

1. Trichomes very tightly coiled..*S. subsalsa*
1. Trichomes loosely coiled... 2
2. Spirals 10–12–(16)μ or more wide.................................. *S. princeps*
2. Spirals less than 10μ wide.. 3
3. Spirals 4–6μ wide, very loose 4
3. Spirals averaging less in width, more tightly coiled............................. 5
4. Trichome 2–2.5μ in diameter... *S. laxa*
4. Trichome 0.7–0.8μ in diameter......................................*S. laxissima*
5. Spirals 5μ wide; trichomes 2μ wide..................... *S. Nordstedtii*
5. Spirals 2.5–4μ wide; trichomes 1.2–1.7μ wide, very long.............. *S. major*

Spirulina laxa G. M. Smith 1916, p. 481
Pl. 108, Fig. 10

Trichomes loosely spiralled, forming a dark blue-green mass,
2–2.5μ in diameter, spiral 4–6μ wide; distance between spirals 15–20μ
wide; cell contents blue-green.

Tychoplankter. Wis.

Spirulina laxissima G. S. West 1907, p. 178

Pl. 107, Fig. 17

Trichomes very slender, 0.7–0.8µ in diameter, twisted in a very loose spiral, 4.5–5.3µ wide; distance between spirals 17–22µ; apex bluntly rounded.

Euplankter. Mich.

Spirulina major Kuetzing 1843, p. 183

Pl. 108, Fig. 11

Trichomes loosely spiralled, scattered among other algae, or when aggregated forming a dark, blue-green mass; trichomes 1.2–1.7µ in diameter; spiral 2.5–4µ wide; distance between spirals 2.7–5µ.

This is a very active species of great length. It is commonly found among *Oscillatoria* species on soil from which water has recently subsided, or on muddy shores and margins of springs, etc.

Wis.

Spirulina Nordstedtii Gomont 1892a, p. 252

Pl. 108, Fig. 12

Trichomes rather closely and regularly spiralled, 2µ in diameter, spiral 5µ wide, distance between spirals 5µ; cell contents pale or bright blue-green.

Plankter; also found on bottom of soft water lakes discolored by humic acids. Wis.

Spirulina princeps (West & West) G. S. West 1907, p. 179

Pl. 108, Fig. 13

Trichomes loosely spiralled, either straight or bent, 3–5µ in diameter; spirals 8.8–16µ wide; distance between spirals (9.5)–10–12–(16)µ; cell contents bright blue-green, homogeneous or slightly granular.

Among other algae in tychoplankton. Wis.

Spirulina subsalsa Oersted 1842, p. 17

Pl. 108, Fig. 14

Trichomes both closely and loosely spiralled in the same individual, 1–2µ in diameter; spiral 3–5µ wide, often so tightly coiled that there is no space between the turns.

Tychoplankter. Wis.

ARTHROSPIRA Stizenberger 1852, p. 32

Trichome a long, loosely spiralled, many-celled plant, not at all or only very briefly tapering toward the apex, which is broadly rounded; sheath wanting; cells quadrate or a little longer than wide, the dissepiments sometimes granular, sometimes scarcely discernible.

See note under *Spirulina* (p. 479). These plants may form thin expansions, but more usually are found intermingled with other algae, especially *Oscillatoria* spp.

Key to the Species

Trichomes 2.5–3.2μ in diameter _____ A. *Gomontiana*
Trichomes 6–8μ in diameter _____ A. *Jenneri*

Arthrospira Gomontiana Setchell 1895, p. 430
Pl. 108, Fig. 21

Trichomes very loosely spiralled, entangled to form free-floating flakes, bright blue-green, 2.5–3.2μ in diameter; cells 4–5μ long, with the dissepiments often scarcely discernible; cell contents vacuolate (?); width of spiral 4–6μ; distance between turns 16–18μ; forming floating patches of much entangled and actively twisting trichomes. Tychoplankter. Wis.

Arthrospira Jenneri (Kuetz.) Stizenberger 1852, p. 32
Pl. 108, Figs. 22, 23

Trichomes blue-green, scattered or gregarious, loosely coiled, not tapering toward the apices, 6–8μ in diameter; cells quadrate, dissepiments granular, 4–5μ long; spiral 10–15μ wide, distance between turns 12–14μ.

Intermingled with other Cyanophyta filaments on mud, or in organic sediment which has collected on submerged plants. Common. Mich., Wis.

OSCILLATORIA Vaucher 1803, p. 165

Filamentous and elongate, without a sheath (except in hormogonous stages of filament development); straight, or twisted and entangled; the mature plant showing a polarity with an apical region, which is often attenuated, the basal end truncate; trichomes solitary and scattered, or forming expanded plant masses and slimy layers on submerged objects or on the bottom; microscopically usually showing an oscillating or gliding movement, especially active in the anterior portion of the trichome; apical cell smoothly rounded, or swollen and capitate, sometimes with a distinct sheath-like membrane, the calyptra; most species having cells much shorter than their width, with or without constrictions at the cross walls, which sometimes have a row of granules on either side; plants often living under semi-anaerobic conditions in stagnant water.

In examining species of *Oscillatoria* care must be used not to confuse them with *Phormidium*, a genus in which there are sticky but sometimes very thin sheaths, which are best seen by staining with an aqueous dye or with chlor-zinc-iodide (see Drouet, 1937).

Key to the Species

[482]

19. Cells granular at the cross walls _____ *O. Agardhii*
19. Cells not granular at the cross walls (rarely granular) _____ 20
20. Apical cell with a flattened calyptra _____ *O. prolifica*
20. Apical cell with a cone-shaped calyptra _____ *O. amoena*
21. Trichomes tapering in the apical region _____ 22
21. Trichomes not tapering in the apical region _____ 24
22. Trichomes straight throughout _____ *O. Agardhii*
22. Trichomes twisted and bent, or straight in the basal portion and
    hooked or curved at the apex _____ 23
23. Trichomes crooked or spirally twisted at the
    apex, cross walls not granular _____ *O. terebriformis*
·23. Trichomes curved but not hooked or twisted
    at the apex; cross walls granular _____ *O. granulata*
24. Cells not granular at the cross walls _____ *O. subbrevis*
24. Cells with distinctly granular cross walls _____ 25
25. Cells with rows of granules at the cross walls _____ *O. tenuis*
25. Cells with 1 or 2 conspicuous granules at the cross walls _____ *O. amphibia*
26. Apical cell capitate, usually with a calyptra _____ 27
26. Apical cell not capitate _____ 29
27. Trichomes bent or hooked at the apex, forming a plant mass _____ *O. anguina*
27. Trichomes scattered in tychoplankton or euplankton, straight _____ 28
28. Cells 6–8μ in diameter, trichomes usually scattered,
    appearing red or purple when in bundles _____ *O. rubescens*
28. Cells 4–6μ in diameter, trichomes solitary, or,
    when in bundles, appearing blue-green _____ *O. Agardhii*
29. Trichomes straight _____ 30
29. Trichomes spirally twisted, undulate, or at
    least hooked or curved at the apex _____ 36
30. Trichomes constricted (sometimes slightly) at the cross walls _____ 34
30. Trichomes not constricted at the cross walls _____ 31
31. Trichomes not appearing red or purple _____ 32
31. Trichomes appearing red or purple, coloring the water when
    abundantly present; solitary or in bundles _____ *O. rubescens*
32. Cells 8–9.2–(10)μ in diameter (sometimes curved at the apex) _____ *O. nigra*
32. Cells (3.5)–5–6μ in diameter _____ 33
33. Cells granular at the cross walls, with pseudovacuoles _____ *O. Agardhii*
33. Cells not granular at the cross walls, without pseudovacuoles __ *O. subbrevis*
34. Trichomes in parallel, free-floating bundles _____ *O. lacustris*
34. Trichomes not in parallel, free-floating bundles _____ 35
35. Cells long, cylindrical _____ *O. Hamelii*
35. Cells shorter than wide, or about quadrate _____ *O. tenuis*
36. Cells long, cylindrical _____ *O. Hamelii*
36. Cells shorter than wide, or slightly longer
    than broad, but nearly quadrate _____ 37
37. Trichomes 8–9–(10)μ in diameter _____ 38
37. Trichomes less than 8μ in diameter _____ 40
38. Trichomes crooked and much twisted in the apical region _____ *O. ornata*
38. Trichomes regularly curved at the apex (often
    straight or only slightly bent) _____ 39
39. Cells granular at the cross walls, very little or
    sometimes not at all constricted _____ *O. nigra*
39. Cells not granular at the cross walls, definitely
    constricted at the cross walls _____ *O. chalybea*

[483]

Oscillatoria acutissima Kufferath 1914, p. 264
Pl. 109, Fig. 1

Trichomes solitary and scattered, or loosely entangled in the mucilage of other algae; gradually tapering to the apex, which is curved or bent slightly. Apical cell acute-conical, with a calyptra. Cells 1.5–2μ in diameter, 1½ to 3 times longer than wide; not constricted at the cross walls, which are not granular.

Although I have not seen type specimens of *O. acutissima*, I have assigned our plants to this species on the basis of their agreement with Kufferath's description.

Tychoplankter; in mucilage of colonial diatoms and egg masses. Mich., Wis.

Oscillatoria Agardhii Gomont 1892a, p. 205
Pl. 108, Figs. 15, 16

Trichomes interwoven to form a blue-green plant mass; occasionally found floating free; straight throughout their entire length, briefly tapering at the anterior end, which is usually capitate, but frequently smooth. Apical cell truncate-conical, with or without a calyptra. Cells (3.4)–5.5–6μ in diameter and not constricted at the cross walls, which are granular; their length from ½ to approximately equal their width (sometimes 1⅓ times their width in length).

This species shows a great deal of variation in the morphology of the apex of the trichome. The straight interwoven filaments, the cell proportions, and the granular cross walls help to identify it.

Abundant in tychoplankton; generally distributed. Mich., Wis.

Oscillatoria amoena (Kuetz.) Gomont 1892a, p. 225
Pl. 109, Figs. 2–4

Trichomes usually forming a thin, submerged, weft-like, blue-green mass, or sometimes scattered among other algae; usually straight but not rigid, slightly tapering toward the apex. Apical cell broad, capitate, with a cone-shaped calyptra. Cells (2.5)–4–5μ in diameter, 2.5–4.2μ long; usually slightly constricted at the cross walls, which are granular.

In tychoplankton of littoral flora; in springs. Mich., Wis.

Oscillatoria amphibia C. A. Agardh 1827, p. 632

Pl. 109, Fig. 6

Trichomes straight or curved and interwoven to form a thin, blue-green plant mass on submerged objects or in moist aerial habitats; not tapering toward the apex. Apical cell broadly rounded, smooth, with a convex outer membrane. Cells (1.5)–2–2.8–$(4)\mu$ in diameter, 2–4 times their diameter in length $(4$–$8\mu)$; not constricted at the cross walls, which have a single large granule on either side, a series of paired granules showing throughout the length of the trichome.

In shallow water of lakes, ponds, and swamps; on submerged objects. Mich., Wis.

Oscillatoria anguina (Bory) Gomont 1892a, p. 214

Pl. 108, Fig. 24

Trichomes entangled and interwoven to form a dark green plant mass on submerged objects, or intermingled among other algae; straight for most of their length but bent and sometimes twisted in the apical region, slightly tapering toward the apex. Apical cell slightly narrowed and capitate, with a thickened outer membrane. Cells 7–8μ in diameter, short, as little as $\frac{1}{6}$ of their diameter in length; not constricted at the cross walls, which are granular. Swollen refringent cells common throughout the length of the trichome.

Forming films on bottom in shallow water. Wis.

Oscillatoria angusta Koppe 1924, p. 641

Pl. 109, Fig. 7

Trichomes loosely entangled to form a thin plant mass, or solitary; not tapering toward the apex; apical cell bluntly rounded, without a calyptra and not capitate; cells (0.8)–1.1–1.3μ in diameter, (5)–7–8–$(10)\mu$ long, not constricted at the cross walls; contents nearly colorless, without pseudovacuoles or conspicuous granules.

Entangled and intermingled with other species of *Oscillatoria* and miscellaneous blue-green algae, forming a slimy layer in shallow water. Wis.

Oscillatoria angustissima West & West 1897, p. 300

Pl. 109, Fig. 5

Trichomes much entangled to form a thin, light blue-green plant mass, not tapering toward the apices; apical cell bluntly rounded, not capitate and without a calyptra; cells 0.6–1.0μ in diameter, $1\frac{1}{2}$–3 times their diameter in length; not constricted at the cross walls, which are scarcely discernible, especially in the anterior end of the trichome; cell contents almost colorless.

This is the smallest species of *Oscillatoria* appearing in our collections. It is easily mistaken for a filamentous bacterium because of its size and pale color. In mass, however, it clearly shows its blue-green algal identity. Not infrequently this species is found entangled in the mucilage of colonial Cyanophyta.

Tychoplanktonic and euplanktonic. Mich., Wis.

Oscillatoria articulata Gardner 1927, p. 34
[*Oscillatoria Grunowiana* var. *articulata* (Gard.) Drouet]
Pl. 107, Fig. 22

Trichomes entangled, flexuous, forming a thin blue-green plant mass, or scattered among other algae, not tapering to the apices; apical cell rounded, not capitate and without a calyptra, but with a thickened outer membrane; cells $2.8-3.2\mu$ in diameter, quadrate or $\frac{1}{2}-\frac{1}{3}$ as long as broad, not constricted at the cross walls, which are conspicuously thickened, sometimes as much as the length of the cell cavity.

Mich.

Oscillatoria Bornetii Zukal 1894, p. 260
Pl. 108, Figs. 19, 20

Trichomes forming a slimy, expanded plant mass, or intermingled among other algae; more or less straight but often bent or slightly sigmoid in the apical region, not tapering toward the apex. Apical cell smoothly rounded, not capitate, and without a calyptra. Cells $(10)-12-16\mu$ in diameter, $3.7-4\mu$ long; not constricted at the cross walls; cell contents pale, almost colorless, with large quadrangular alveolations or vacuoles.

Tychoplankter; in lakes and slowly flowing water. Wis.

Oscillatoria chalybea Mertens *in* Jürgens 1822, Dec. 18, No. 4
Pl. 109, Figs. 8, 9

Trichomes aggregated to form a dark blue-green plant mass; straight for a portion of their length but much entangled and sometimes spirally twisted, gradually tapering toward the apex. Apical cell conical, with a smooth, unthickened outer membrane. Cells $(6)-8-12-(13)\mu$ in diameter, $4-6.8\mu$ long; slightly constricted at the cross walls, which are not granular.

Tychoplankter. Mich., Wis.

Oscillatoria curviceps C. A. Agardh 1824, p. 68
Pl. 108, Figs. 17, 18

Trichomes forming an expanded blue-green plant mass; straight for at least a portion of their length, twisted and much entangled, scarcely tapering to the apex. Apical cell broadly rounded, not capitate, without a calyptra. Cells 10–14–(17)μ in diameter, 3–5μ long; not constricted at the cross walls, which may be granulate.

Forming floating clots; tychoplanktonic. Mich., Wis.

Oscillatoria formosa Bory 1827, p. 474
Pl. 109, Figs. 10, 11

Trichomes aggregated to form a dark blue-green plant mass; straight and rather firm, curved and slightly tapering toward the apex. Apical cell conical, not capitate, without a calyptra. Cells 4–6μ in diameter, 2.5–5μ long; constricted at the cross walls, which are granular.

Rather common on wet soil at margins of lakes, and about swamps; tychoplanktonic in shallow water of ponds. Mich., Wis.

Oscillatoria granulata Gardner 1927, p. 37
Pl. 109, Figs. 12, 13

Trichomes aggregated to form an expanded plant mass; straight or somewhat curved, especially at the apex, which is slightly attenuated. Apical cell not capitate and without a calyptra. Cells 3–5μ in diameter, ½–1½ times their diameter in length; not constricted at the cross walls, which are distinctly granular.

Occurring as small, slimy flakes, or scattered among other algae. Wis.

Oscillatoria Hamelii Frémy 1930, p. 218
Pl. 109, Fig. 14

Trichomes solitary among other algae, or sparsely aggregated to form blue-green masses; straight or undulate, not attenuated at the apices. Apical cell truncately conical, without a calyptra. Cells 7.2–8.5μ in diameter, 1½–2 times the diameter in length; distinctly constricted at the cross walls, which are not granular.

This plant is assigned here on the basis of its agreement with Frémy's description. The type habitat of *O. Hamelii* is in Africa, but the universal distribution of many species of the genus makes its appearance in North America not unusual.

Forming a film on dead leaves in a stream. Wis.

?*Oscillatoria lacustris* (Kleb.) Geitler 1925a, p. 362

[*Trichodesmium lacustre* Klebahn 1895, p. 13]

Pl. 109, Fig. 15

Trichomes straight, lying parallel in free-floating, flake-like bundles or fascicles, not tapering at the apices; apical cell broadly rounded, without a calyptra; cells compressed globose or barrel-shaped, sometimes semiquadrate, or a little longer or shorter than wide, 5–7μ in diameter, 3–7μ long; cell contents with many pseudo-vacuoles.

The specimens assigned here are enigmatic. The bundles of trichomes strongly suggest *Trichodesmium* because of their arrangement and lack of heterocysts. They are not like *Trichodesmium lacustre* Klebahn, however, in respect to the morphology of the apical cell which in that species is long and attenuate, but which in our specimens is short and rotund. The suggestion has been made that the plant found in our collections is a juvenile form of *Aphanizomenon,* which would appear reasonable because of the similarity in respect to trichome arrangement, cell shape, and cytology. As I have pointed out elsewhere (1942, p. 665), however, the occurrence of these bundles of trichomes in what certainly appears to be a mature condition and without any suggestion of nostochaceous characters (heterocysts, gonidia), precludes such a disposition. Geitler has assigned Klebahn's species to *Oscillatoria* and relegates the Wisconsin plant previously reported by Smith (1920) to *Aphanizomenon.* There is scarcely enough evidence at present to justify giving a new name to the Wisconsin plant, but it is possible that subsequent study will establish it as a new fresh-water species of *Trichodesmium.*

Plankter; in hard or semi-hard water, especially eutrophic, lakes. Wis.

Oscillatoria limnetica Lemmermann 1900, Ber. d. Deutsch.

Bot. Ges., 18, p. 310

Pl. 109, Fig. 16

Trichomes solitary and planktonic or intermingled with other algae in littoral waters; straight or flexuous, not tapering toward the apex. Apical cell bluntly rounded and without a calyptra. Cells 1.5–1.8μ in diameter, 3⅙ times the diameter in length; not constricted at the cross walls, which are scarcely visible and are not marked by granules.

In shallow water of swamps and bogs; among submerged aquatics. Wis.

Oscillatoria limosa (Roth) C. A. Agardh 1812, p. 35
Pl. 109, Fig. 17

Trichomes usually forming a very dark blue-green or brownish plant mass attached to submerged objects or forming films on sandy bottoms, although rarely solitary or loosely entangled among filamentous algae; straight, tapering little or not at all toward the apex. Apical cell rotund, the outer membrane thickened but without a definite calyptra. Cells $12–18–(20)\mu$ in diameter, $3.7–5\mu$ long, not constricted at the cross walls, which are usually granular. Trichomes not infrequently inclosed in a hormogonous sheath.

Common in stagnant water of ditches and small ponds; tychoplanktonic in lakes. Mich., Wis.

Oscillatoria minima Gicklhorn 1921, p. 4
Pl. 107, Fig. 24

Trichomes somewhat coiled and spirally twisted, golden-colored, inclosed in a delicate mucilaginous sheath, not tapering toward the apex; apical cell not capitate and without a calyptra; cells 2μ in diameter, $5–6\mu$ long.

Mich.

Oscillatoria nigra Vaucher 1803, p. 192
Pl. 109, Fig. 18

Trichomes aggregated to form a thick, mucilaginous blackish-green plant mass on submerged objects, becoming free-floating; straight or slightly twisted and entangled, slightly tapering toward the apex and curved (or straight). Apical cell rotund, not capitate and without a calyptra. Cells $8–10\mu$ in diameter, $3.7–4.5\mu$ long; slightly constricted at the cross walls, which are sometimes granular; cell contents dark olive-green.

Common in the shallow water of many lakes and ponds. Mich., Wis.

Oscillatoria ornata Kuetzing 1845–1849, p. 30

Trichomes forming a dark, blue-green plant mass; spirally twisted at the end, not at all or scarcely tapering toward the apex. Apical cell broadly rounded, not capitate and without a calyptra. Cells $9–11\mu$ in diameter, short, $\frac{1}{2}–\frac{1}{6}$ times as long as broad ($2–5\mu$ long), constricted at cross walls which are granular.

Mich.

Oscillatoria princeps Vaucher 1803, p. 190
Pl. 110, Fig. 1

Trichomes solitary or loosely entangled to form small floating plant masses, which are black-green in color; individual plants visible to the unaided eye; trichomes very slightly and briefly tapering at the apex. Apical cell usually not capitate, sometimes very slightly so, the outer membrane broadly convex and smooth. Cells 32–55–(80)μ in diameter, 4–8.7μ long; not constricted at the cross walls, which are not granular; cell contents densely granular.

Common in tychoplankton of a variety of lakes and small ponds; in marshes. Mich., Wis.

Oscillatoria prolifica (Grev.) Gomont 1892a, p. 205
Pl. 110, Figs. 2, 3

Trichomes aggregated to form a floating, purple-black expanded mass; straight, but flexible, slightly tapering toward the apex. Apical cell capitate, with a broadly flattened calyptra. Cells 2.5–5μ in diameter, 4–6μ long, without constrictions at the cross walls, which are sometimes granular; cell contents densely granular. Plant described as becoming lilac-colored upon drying.

Tychoplanktonic and euplanktonic. Mich., Wis.

Oscillatoria rubescens De Candolle 1825, Mém. Soc. Phys.
Nat. Genève, 2, p. 29
Pl. 107, Fig. 21

Trichomes solitary or forming small fascicles, appearing red or purple in the plankton; very slightly if at all tapering toward the apex. Apical cell often capitate, with a calyptra, but (in our specimens) as often broadly rounded and smooth. Cells 6–8μ in diameter, 2–4μ long; not constricted at the cross walls, which are usually granular; cell contents with pseudovacuoles.

Our specimens definitely appear to belong to this species, but the lack of capitate apical cells in most plants observed, and the non-tapering trichomes are in disagreement with the original description.

Euplanktonic and tychoplanktonic. In hard water lakes of southern Michigan; forming blooms during late winter immediately after the disappearance of ice.

Oscillatoria sancta (Kuetz.) Gomont 1892a, p. 209
Pl. 110, Fig. 4

Trichomes aggregated to form a dark gray-green plant mass (in our collections), usually on submerged vegetation; straight, not at all or scarcely tapering toward the apex. Apical cell somewhat capitate, with a calyptra, and with a much thickened outer membrane. Cells 11–13–(20)μ in diameter, 4–5μ long; slightly constricted at the cross walls, which are conspicuously granular; cell contents coarsely granular, olive- or gray-green in color.

On submerged aquatics. Mich., Wis.

Oscillatoria sancta var. *aequinoctialis* Kuetzing 1845–1849, p. 30

A questionable variety, with a diameter in the upper limits of the species' range (14–20µ).
Mich.

Oscillatoria splendida Greville 1824, p. 305
Pl. 110, Figs. 5–7

Trichomes solitary and scattered, rarely aggregated in small, flake-like masses; straight or curved, tapering for a long distance to a fine hair at the apex. Apical cell conical and capitate. Cells 2.2–2.8µ in diameter, 7.2–9µ long, not constricted at the cross walls; cell contents finely granular or homogeneous, pale blue-green.

Common in a variety of lakes with a high pH; generally distributed. Mich., Wis.

Oscillatoria subbrevis Schmidle 1901b, p. 243
Pl. 107, Fig. 23

Filaments solitary, not occurring in a plant mass; straight and not tapering toward the apices. Apical cell rounded, not capitate and without a calyptra. Cells short, 5–6µ in diameter, 1–2µ long, with frequent necridia in evidence; cross walls not granular; cell contents pale gray-green.
Mich.

Oscillatoria tenuis C. A. Agardh 1813, Algarum Decades, p. 25
Pl. 110, Figs. 8, 9, 14

Trichomes aggregated to form a blue-green mass, sometimes becoming scattered and appearing singly among other algae. Straight or slightly flexuous, especially at the anterior end, which does not taper; hormogonous sheath frequently present. Apical cell convex, smooth, and not capitate; outer membrane sometimes slightly thickened. Cells (4)–5–8–(10)µ in diameter, 2.5–3.2–(5)µ long; constricted at the cross walls (sometimes only slightly so), which are granular.

Generally distributed and very common in tychoplankton of a variety of lakes and ponds; in swamps and roadside ditches. Mich., Wis.

Oscillatoria tenuis var. *natans* Gomont 1892a, p. 221
Pl. 110, Figs. 10, 11

A variety differing from the typical by having stouter trichomes (in our specimens), which are 7.4–10µ in diameter; cells 3.4–4.6µ long; apical cell truncately rounded.

Forming a blue-green algal film on the bottom; tychoplanktonic. Wis.

Oscillatoria tenuis var. tergestina (Kuetz.) Rabenhorst 1865, p. 102
Pl. 110, Figs. 12, 13

A variety differing from the typical by its smaller proportions, 5.5–6μ in diameter; apical cell convex or cone-shaped.

Drouet (1938, p. 269) states that both this variety and var. *natans* may be found in the same collection, suggesting that the differences in size hardly justify the use of two varietal names. Gomont in his monograph (1892, p. 221) recognizes the variety.

Euplanktonic and tychoplanktonic. Wis.

Oscillatoria terebriformis C. A. Agardh 1827, p. 634
Pl. 107, Figs. 25, 26

Trichomes forming a plant mass, dark steel-blue in color; spirally twisted, especially at the apex, slightly tapering in the apical region. Apical cell round or pointed, not capitate, and without a calyptra. Cells 4–6.5μ in diameter, 2.5–6μ long; not constricted at the cross walls.

Mich.

PHORMIDIUM Kuetzing 1843, p. 190

Plant mass consisting of simple, unbranched filaments within agglutinated and diffluent sheaths which form mucilaginous layers or penicillate tufts (streaming in flowing water). Trichomes cylindrical throughout, except for a slight and brief tapering in the apical region; either parallel or entwined. Apical cell conical, blunt-pointed or capitate, with or without a calyptra. Individual sheaths usually indistinct and difficult of demonstration, although the diffluent sheaths of the plant mass are clearly in evidence. Cells shorter than wide, or quadrate; constricted at the cross walls in some species.

Under certain conditions of preservation the sheath structure of species in this genus may become so difficult of demonstration that it is possible to confuse them with some forms of *Oscillatoria*. It is the sheath which fundamentally separates the two genera. In the field and in macroscopic appearance they may be differentiated usually on the basis of the compact, felt-like layer constructed by *Phormidium*. Whereas masses of some species of *Oscillatoria* may form somewhat similar mats, the trichomes dissociate easily when the collection is made. In *Phormidium*, the mat when present is compact and does not dissociate.

[492]

Key to the Species

1. Trichomes short, living within the mucilage
   of other Cyanophyta (e.g. *Microcystis*)..................................*P. mucicola*
1. Trichomes long, forming plant masses, not
   living within the mucilage of other algae 2
2. Trichomes with constrictions at the cross walls 3
2. Trichomes without constrictions at the cross walls.............................. 6
3. Trichomes capitate at the apex...*P. lucidum*
3. Trichomes not capitate 4
4. Apical cell decidedly tapering and elongate ....*P. tenue*
4. Apical cell not elongate, not or slightly tapering 5
5. Cells 2.5µ in diameter, 2–4µ long ....*P. minnesotense*
5. Cells 4–6µ in diameter, 1.2–2.7µ long ....*P. ambiguum*
6. Trichomes decidedly twisted or hooked at the apex.............*P. uncinatum*
6. Trichomes not twisted, straight or slightly curved at the apex........... 7
7. Apical cell capitate ...., ... 8
7. Apical cell not capitate 11
8. Trichomes with a conical, sharply pointed calyptra........*P. Setchellianum*
8. Trichomes with a broadly rounded or convex calyptra...................... 9
9. Trichomes straight 10
9. Trichomes curved, flexuous...*P. autumnale*
10. Cells longer than wide ....*P. favosum*
10. Cells shorter than wide ....*P. subfuscum*
11. Plant mass incrusted with lime ....*P. incrustatum*
11. Plant mass not incrusted with lime.. 12
12. Cross walls granular..*P. inundatum*
12. Cross walls not granular.. 13
13. Trichomes curved; cells 3–4.5µ in diameter, 3.4–8µ long ......*P. Corium*
13. Trichomes straight; cells 4.5–12µ in diameter,
    4–9µ long...*P. Retzii*

Phormidium ambiguum Gomont 1892a, p. 178
Pl. 111, Fig. 1

Filaments forming a blue-green, mucilaginous layer; straight or gracefully curved, either parallel or somewhat entwined; individual sheaths usually distinct and lamellate but becoming confluent with the mucilage of the plant mass; trichomes curved or rarely straight at the apices, which are not tapering; apical cell broadly rounded, not capitate, but with a thickened outer membrane, which may give a slightly pointed appearance; cells short, disc-like constricted at the cross walls, 4–6µ in diameter, 1.2–2.7µ long; cell contents finely granular.

Among other algae and floating free in tychoplankton. Wis.

Phormidium autumnale (C. A. Ag.) Gomont 1893, p. 207
Pl. 107, Figs. 19, 20

Plant mass forming a broadly expanded, dark-green, mucilaginous layer; filaments much entangled but may be either straight or curved and flexuous; sheaths at first distinct, becoming diffluent

[493]

and confluent with the mucilage of the plant mass; apex slightly tapering, either straight or somewhat curved and capitate, with a calyptra; cell contents blue-green; cells 4–7μ in diameter, 2–5μ long, not constricted at the cross walls, which are granular.
Mich.

Phormidium Corium (C. A. Ag.) Gomont 1890, p. 355

Filaments compactly intertwined and entangled to form a soft but tough membranous layer, dark bluish-green to black; sheaths thin and becoming confluent with the mucilage of the plant mass, trichomes curved (or straight) and slightly tapering at the apex, but not capitate and without a calyptra; cells 3–4.5μ in diameter, 3.4–8μ long, not constricted at the cross walls; cell contents granular.
Mich.

Phormidium favosum (Bory) Gomont 1892a, p. 180
Pl. 111, Fig. 2

Filaments forming a dark green expanded, thin or thick plant mass; individual sheaths not clearly evident; trichomes straight or flexuous and sometimes coiled in the distal region which tapers slightly; apical cell capitate, with a conical or hemispherical calyptra; cells 4.5–9μ in diameter, 3–7μ long, not constricted at the cross walls but with a double row of granules at the partitions; cell contents blue-green.
In trough, at Osceola, Wisconsin.

Phormidium incrustatum (Naeg.) Gomont *in* Bornet & Flahault 1889, p. CLIV

Filaments forming a dark red or violet stratum, encrusted with lime. Trichomes parallel, or curved and entangled in thin mucous sheaths; straight at the apex and tapering slightly, not capitate. Apical cell obtuse-conical. Cells quadrate or slightly longer than wide; not constricted at the cross walls, which are sometimes granular; 4–5μ in diameter, 3.5–5.2μ long.
In a stream at Osceola, Wisconsin.

Phormidium inundatum Kuetzing 1849, p. 251
Pl. 111, Fig. 3; Pl. 107, Fig. 15

Filaments forming a blue-green, gelatinous, membranous expansion; individual sheaths scarcely discernible, diffluent. Trichome straight and parallel, tapering at the apices to form a conical apical cell, which is not capitate. Cells quadrate or short-cylindric, 3–5μ

[494]

in diameter, 4–8μ long; not constricted at the cross walls, which are granular; cell contents granular, especially at the cross walls. Tychoplanktonic; on submerged vegetation. Wis.

Phormidium lucidum (C. A. Ag.) Kuetzing 1843, p. 194

Filaments forming thick, firm mats which are dark green above but colorless within. Trichomes somewhat parallel, either curved or (at least at the ends) straight, and slightly tapering, sometimes ending in a point but with the apical cell capitate; calyptra broadly rounded; sheath diffluent and not colored by chlor-zinc-iodide reagent. Cells very short, 7–8μ in diameter, 2–2.5μ long; slightly constricted at the cross walls, which are granular.
Mich.

Phormidium minnesotense (Tilden) Drouet 1942, p. 136

Filaments forming a blue-green, thin expanse; individual sheaths indistinct, confluent with the mucilage of the plant mass; trichomes straight or slightly curved, parallel or somewhat entangled, not tapering at the distal end; apical cell broadly rounded, not capitate, and without a calyptra; cells short-cylindric, 2.5μ in diameter, 2–4μ long, constricted at the cross walls.
Tychoplankter. Wis.

Phormidium mucicola Naumann & Huber-Pestalozzi *in* Huber-Pestalozzi & Naumann 1929, pp. 67, 68
Pl. 111, Figs. 4, 5

Filaments short, clustered or scattered in the mucilage of other blue-green algae (*Microcystis*). Sheaths thin, inconspicuous, diffluent. Trichomes parallel or scattered; up to 50μ long; not tapering at the apices, which are broadly rounded or conical. Cells quadrate to short-cylindric, 1.3–2μ in diameter, 1.8–3μ long; constricted at the cross walls, often separated from one another; cell contents pale blue-green.

This species is a frequent inhabiter of colonies of *Microcystis aeruginosa*, in which there may be far fewer *Microcystis* cells than *Phormidium* filaments.

Rather common in hard water; euplanktonic. Mich., Wis.

Phormidium Retzii (C. A. Ag.) Gomont 1892a, p. 175
Pl. 111, Fig. 6

Filaments forming thin, dark blue-green skeins or tufts on submerged aquatics, or floating free; sheaths thin and inconspicuous, diffluent; trichomes straight, parallel, not tapering at the apices, or very slightly so; apical cell truncate, with the outer membrane thickened; cells quadrate, or longer (sometimes shorter) than wide, 4.5–12μ in diameter, 4.8μ long, usually not constricted at the cross walls except in the distal end of the trichome; cell contents granular.

On submerged aquatics or floating in small tufts in hard water lakes; forming thick, streaming tufts in flowing water; forming a membrane on casing of a spring. Mich., Wis.

Phormidium Setchellianum Gomont 1892a, p. 156

Filaments forming a thin, weft-like, dark purple layer; sheaths thin and generally confluent with the mucilage of the plant mass; trichomes curved or straight, often hooked at the apex, which is not tapered, or but very slightly so; apical cell capitate with a conical calyptra; cells 4–4.8μ in diameter, 3–6μ long, constricted at the cross walls; cell contents purplish.

On muddy shores. Mich.

Phormidium subfuscum Kuetzing 1843, p. 195
Pl. 107, Fig. 16

Filaments forming a widely expanded, thin and lamellate plant mass, dark green (or olive) in color. Trichomes straight, agglutinated and more or less parallel, relatively short; straight at the apex and briefly tapered; sheath becoming diffluent with the mucilage of the plant mass. Apical cell capitate, with a broadly rounded calyptra. Cells 5.5–11μ in diameter, 2–4μ long, granular, not constricted at the cross walls. Cell contents sometimes granular and blue-green in color.

On log near shoreline of lake, Mich.

Phormidium tenue (Menegh.) Gomont 1892a, p. 169
Pl. 111, Fig. 7

Filaments forming a blue-green, membranous expanse; sheaths diffluent, mucilaginous and indistinct; trichomes straight except at apices, where they are bent and attenuated; apical cell conical, smooth, neither capitate nor furnished with a calyptra; cells 1.2–3μ in diameter, 2.5–5μ long, constricted at the cross walls, which are not granulate; cell contents homogeneous.

Common, forming thin films on submerged aquatics and intermingled with decaying vegetation in shallow water. Mich., Wis.

Phormidium uncinatum (C. A. Ag.) Gomont 1890, p. 355
Pl. 107, Fig. 18

Filaments forming an expanded, thin but firm plant mass, either floating or adherent to a substrate, dark green or brownish; trichomes straight or curved, briefly tapered at the apex, which is hooked or spiralled; sheaths sticky, distinct finally but becoming confluent with the mucilage of the plant mass; apical cell capitate, with a rotund or conical calyptra; cells not constricted, 6–9μ in diameter, 2–6μ long, granular at the cross walls; cell contents blue-green.

On mud near stream, Mich.

LYNGBYA Agardh 1824, p. XXV

Filamentous, composed of a uniseriate, unbranched trichome of cells inclosed by a non-gelatinous, more or less firm sheath; planktonic and solitary, or aggregated, forming entangled masses on substrates or intermingled among other algae; some species spirally coiled; trichomes mostly cylindrical throughout and tapering very slightly, if at all, toward the apices, which are usually not capitate.

In favorable habitats some of the planktonic species may become superabundant, but unlike *Aphanizomenon flos-aquae* and *Microcystis aeruginosa,* the plants remain distributed throughout the water and do not form sticky masses and floating scums; hence they seldom figure in water bloom disturbances.

Key to the Species

1. Filaments spirally coiled or twisted, sometimes
   entwined about other algae 2
1. Filaments straight, curved, or entangled,
   but not definitely coiled 5
2. Filaments wound about and creeping over
   other filamentous algae .... *L. epiphytica*
2. Filaments not entwined about other algae 3
3. Trichomes very loosely spiralled, or merely
   wavy (often straight) .... *L. spirulinoides*
3. Trichomes closely coiled and twisted 4
4. Trichomes irregularly twisted and coiled .... *L. Lagerheimia*
4. Trichomes regularly spiralled .... *L. contorta*
5. Filaments 20–58μ in diameter 6
5. Filaments less than 20μ in diameter 8
6. Filaments euplanktonic, 20–24μ in diameter;
   sheath 0.5–4μ thick; solitary .... *L. Birgei*
6. Filaments tychoplanktonic, intermingled with
   other algae, or forming a plant mass 7
7. Filaments 44–58μ in diameter; sheaths up to
   5μ thick; intermingled with other algae .... *L. latissima*
7. Filaments 8–24–(28)μ in diameter; sheaths thinner; usually
   forming entangled plant masses .... *L. aestuarii*
8. Plants euplanktonic and solitary 9
8. Plants epiphytic, adherent and forming plant
   masses, or entangled among other algae, tychoplanktonic 12

Lyngbya aerugineo-caerulea (Kuetz.) Gomont 1892a, p. 146
Pl. 111, Figs. 10, 11

Plants aggregated, forming masses of curved and loosely entangled filaments among other algae, or expansions on submerged substrates (solitary filaments frequently found scattered among other plants); filaments (4)–6–(7.5)µ in diameter; trichomes 4–7µ in diameter; cells varying in length from a little less to longer than the width, 2.7–7.8µ long, not at all or but very little constricted at the cross walls; apices of trichomes straight, with cone-shaped or slightly capitate terminal cells. Sheaths firm, thin, sometimes with regularly

[498]

spaced bands of roughenings; colorless; extending far beyond the apices of the trichomes.

In a variety of lakes, both acid and hard water; in *Sphagnum* bogs. Mich., Wis.

Lyngbya aestuarii (Mert.) Liebmann 1841, p. 492
Pl. 111, Fig. 8

Plants aggregated, entangled, forming extensive layers on submerged substrates, or upon moist earth and stones; sometimes becoming free-floating. Filaments varying greatly in diameter, $10-26\mu$ wide. Trichomes $8-20-(28)\mu$ in diameter, tapering a little at the apices, which vary in shape, conical, truncate, or somewhat capitate. Cells $2.5-5\mu$ in length, not constricted at the cross walls. Sheaths firm, becoming thickened, lamellose, and discolored with age.

This species sometimes forms very thick, felt-like layers, yellow-gray or olive-green in color, the color ordinarily masked by accumulated silt and debris.

On stones and moist earth. Mich., Wis.

Lyngbya Birgei G. M. Smith 1916, p. 482
Pl. 111, Fig. 9

Plants solitary, planktonic, scattered among water bloom organisms; filaments straight, $(18)-24-(25)\mu$ in diameter, with many hormogonia when aged; sheaths thick and firm, not lamellated, extending far beyond the apices of the trichomes, which are broadly rounded; trichome $20-24\mu$ in diameter, not constricted at the cross walls; cells very short and disciform, $3-7\mu$ long.

This species is frequently a prominent element in the composition of water blooms which develop in lakes with a pH of 7.4–9.0. It is almost invariably associated with *Microcystis aeruginosa, Aphanizomenon flos-aquae, Anabaena flos-aquae, Stephanodiscus* spp. and *Melosira* spp. In fact, its association with these species in eutrophic waters is so constant that during the months of July and August, at least, the relative abundance of *Lyngbya Birgei* G. M. Smith can be used as an approximate index of alkalinity. Although abundant in hard water lakes it does not play an important role in the water bloom disturbances of which *Aphanizomenon* and *Microcystis* are capable, because of its failure to form clots and floating masses.

Common in the euplankton of many hard and semi-hard water lakes. Mich., Wis.

[499]

Lyngbya contorta Lemmermann 1898, p. 202

Pl. 112, Fig. 1

Plants solitary and planktonic, spirally twisted or coiled (rarely straight); trichomes not tapering at their apices and without constrictions at the cross walls; cells 1.5–2μ in diameter, 3.5–5.6μ long; sheaths thin but firm.

This plant sometimes becomes dominant in the plankton of a hard water lake and so abundant as to color the water a brownish-green or a rusty-gray. In some small Iowa lakes it has been found in almost pure growth with scarcely any other phytoplanktonic species present. The dispersed habit of the plant and its failure to agglutinate account for its inability to produce the unbalanced conditions produced by other blue-green plankters.

Eu- and tychoplanktonic. Wis.

Lyngbya Diguetii Gomont *in* Hariot 1895, p. 169

Pl. 112, Fig. 8

Plants solitary or entangled, sometimes forming bundles, frequently adhering to and growing out from filamentous algae which have non-mucilaginous walls; filaments up to 3.2μ in diameter, sheaths thin; trichomes 2.5–3μ in diameter, cells 1.5–3.5μ long; apical cell convex, smooth.

This is a very common species in hard water habitats and is invariably found associated with *Cladophora* and *Rhizoclonium*. It is similar in some characters and in habitat to *Lyngbya epiphytica* Wille (Nyt Mag. f. Natur., 1913, p. 25), a synonym of *L. Nordgaardii* Wille, but in our region is slightly larger than that species.

Mich., Wis.

Lyngbya epiphytica Hieronymus *in* Engler & Prantl 1900, p. 67

Pl. 112, Figs. 2, 3

Plants epiphytic, entangled and spirally twisted about other filamentous algae to which they are adjoined throughout their entire length; filaments 1.5–2.5μ in diameter; trichomes without constrictions at the cross walls; cells 1.2–2μ in diameter, 1–2μ long; apical cell convex, not capitate; sheath thin and close.

This species is not to be confused with *L. epiphytica* Wille, which is synonymous, apparently, with *L. Nordgaardii* Wille (Frémy, Soc. Arch. et Hist. Nat. Manche, 47, p. 44, 1936).

On filamentous algae. Tychoplankter. Wis.

Lyngbya Hieronymusii Lemmermann 1905, p. 146
Pl. 112, Fig. 4

Plants solitary, scattered among other algae or in littoral plankton. Trichomes straight and not tapering at the apices, which are broadly convex; 11–13μ in diameter. Cells ⅕–⅓ as long as wide (2.7–4μ long); usually with pseudovacuoles; not constricted at the cross walls, which are granular. Sheath rather thick, but homogeneous, not lamellose. Filaments (12)–14–19μ wide.

This species should be compared with *L. major* Menegh. and *L. Birgei* G. M. Smith. From the former it differs in the convex, nontapering apices, the homogeneous sheaths, and its failure to form agglutinated masses. From the latter species it differs in size and in its possession of granular cross walls.

Tychoplankter. Mich., Wis.

Lyngbya Lagerheimia (Moebius) Gomont 1890, p. 354
Pl. 112, Figs. 5, 6

Plants solitary or somewhat entangled, bent and twisted, sometimes spiral; trichomes not at all or but very slightly tapering toward the apices, which are broadly conical or convex; cells 2.2–3μ in diameter, 1.5–2.8μ long; cell contents coarsely granular; sheaths thin; filaments 2–2.5μ wide.

Among other algae in shallow water of lakes and in roadside ponds. Mich., Wis.

Lyngbya latissima Prescott 1944, p. 372
Pl. 112, Fig. 9

Plants solitary, planktonic, entangled among other floating algae; trichomes straight, not tapering toward the apices; cells disc-like, with contents finely and evenly granular (sometimes with coarse granules in old plants), 37–40.7μ in diameter, 3.7–7.4μ long; sheaths thick, 3.7–5μ wide, lamellated, with outer layers wrinkled and roughened in age; filaments 44–58μ in diameter.

This species, found in but two habitats, may be a planktonic and unbranched expression of *Plectonema Wollei*. The plants described by Prescott (1944, p. 372) are about the same diameter as this large species of *Plectonema*, and they have some of the same sheath characteristics. The filaments are entirely unbranched and solitary, however, whereas *Plectonema Wollei* is branched (although infrequently) and occurs in woolly mats. *Lyngbya latissima* should be compared also with *Oscillatoria princeps* when the latter is in a hormogonous condition and inclosed by a sheath. The sheath is not thick and lamellated as in our plant, nor are the trichomes so long.

[501]

L. gigantea Lewis, Zirkle, and Patrick (1933), referred by Drouet (1938) to *Oscillatoria princeps,* differs in having thin smooth sheaths characteristic of the hormogonial phase of the latter. Our specimens are not at all tapering at the apices, and the contents of the cells are granular.

Lyngbya Hummellii Borge (1934), a large species, differs from *L. latissima* in its smaller size (37μ, maximum width) and in the longer cells (6–11μ). Also the sheath of Borge's species is thinner and apparently not lamellated as in our specimens.

Euplanktonic and tychoplanktonic. Wis.

Lyngbya limnetica Lemmermann 1898d, p. 154
Pl. 112, Fig. 7

Plants straight, solitary, planktonic; trichomes 1–2–(2.5)μ in diameter, not tapering at the apices; cells 6–12μ long, not constricted at the cross walls; cell contents coarsely granular; sheaths thin and colorless; filaments 2–2.2μ wide.

Euplankter. Wis.

Lyngbya major Meneghini 1837, p. 12
Pl 112, Fig. 10

Plants solitary among other algae, or somewhat gregarious, but not forming expansions or plant masses; filaments straight; trichomes not or but very slightly tapering to the apices, which are indistinctly capitate in older plants, 11–17μ in diameter; cells 1/5–1/4 as long as wide, (2)–3.5–4μ in length, not constricted at the cross walls, which are definitely granulose; cell contents homogeneously granular; sheaths thick (3–3.7μ), firm, and usually lamellated, becoming roughened in age; filament 22–26μ in diameter.

Caught about *Utricularia* and other vegetation; widely distributed in a variety of lakes, mostly hard water; tychoplanktonic. Mich., Wis.

Lyngbya Martensiana Meneghini 1837, p. 23
Pl. 112, Fig. 11

Plants much entangled and interwoven to form an expanded, dark blue-green mass; trichomes 6–10–(12)μ in diameter, not tapering toward the apices, which are broadly convex; cells about 1/4 as long as wide, 2.5–2.8μ long, not constricted at the cross walls, contents homogeneous except for 1 or 2 conspicuous granules at the cross walls; sheaths firm, moderately thick (1.5–2μ); filaments mostly 6–10μ (up to 14μ) in diameter.

This plant is assigned here on the basis of size, lack of constrictions at the cross walls, and the tendency to form plant masses. It is similar to *L. putealis* Montagne, but that species has trichomes constricted at the cross walls. Our specimens should be compared also with *L. major*.

Rare; in tychoplankton. Mich., Wis.

Lyngbya Nordgaardii Wille 1918, p. 32
[*Lyngbya epiphytica* Wille 1913, p. 25]
Pl. 113, Figs. 1, 2

Plants solitary or forming minute patches on the walls of larger filamentous algae (*Oedogonium, Rhizoclonium*), curved and vermiform, sometimes recurved from a basal attachment; trichomes graygreen, not tapering at the apices, $1.2–2\mu$ in diameter, about as long as wide or a little shorter; sheaths very thin and transparent.

On *Drepanocladus* from a depth of 35 feet; on filamentous algae, and in tychoplankton. Wis.

Lyngbya purpurea (Hook. & Harvey) Gomont 1892, p. 49

Plant mass highly mucilaginous, purplish red; trichomes sometimes scattered among other algae, curved and flexuous, not constricted at the cross walls, $1.4–1.8\mu$ in diameter; sheath thin and transparent, not stained blue by chlor-zinc-iodide; cells quadrate.
Mich.

Lyngbya spirulinoides Gomont 1890, p. 355; 1892a, p. 146
Pl. 131, Fig. 1

Plant mass planktonic, olive-green; filaments entangled, loosely spiralled through most of their length (or all of it), rarely straight; cells light blue-green, with homogeneous or slightly granular contents; sheaths thin and homogeneous, sticky and colorless; trichomes $14–16\mu$ in diameter, not constricted at the cross walls nor tapering toward the apices; apical cell broadly rounded, not capitate, and without a calyptra; cells $3.4–6.8\mu$ long.
Tychoplankter. Wis.

Lyngbya Taylorii Drouet & Strickland *in* Strickland 1940, p. 631
Pl. 113, Fig. 3

Plants forming tufts of parallel but flexuous filaments on submerged substrates, or floating free. Trichomes not tapering toward the apices; very little or not at all constricted at the cross walls; $4–7\mu$ in diameter. Terminal cell broadly convex. Cells quadrate, about as long as wide or a little shorter; cell contents granular. Sheaths thin and colorless; filaments long, $6–9\mu$ in diameter.

Forming a bright blue-green film on mud; tychoplankter. Wis.

Lyngbya versicolor (Wartmann) Gomont 1892a, p. 147
Pl. 113, Fig. 4

Plants forming a mucous expansion on submerged objects, becoming detached and floating; filaments much entangled; trichomes not tapering toward the apices and not constricted at the cross walls, which are not granular; cells 2.8–3.4μ in diameter; filaments 3–3.8–(5)μ in diameter; sheaths thick (up to 2μ), mucous.

Forming compact films on submerged logs; tychoplankter. Mich., Wis.

SYMPLOCA Kuetzing 1843, p. 201

Unbranched sheathed filaments, united in branching bundles or fascicles which are erect or growing out and away from the substrate to which they are attached (rarely free-floating); trichomes uniseriate and straight, tapering distally but very slightly; apical cell conical or broadly rounded, sometimes with a thickened outer membrane; sheaths firm and close, or confluent in the median portion of the filament only, thus producing the effect of false branching; cells quadrate or cylindric, slightly, if at all, constricted at the cross walls.

Symploca muscorum (C. A. Ag.) Gomont 1890, p. 354
Pl. 113, Fig. 7

Filaments forming brownish-green, erect or procumbent tufts or fascicles (often producing *Phormidium*-like expansions); trichomes straight or wavy, parallel; cells quadrate to cylindrical, not constricted at the cross walls, 5–8μ in diameter, 5–11μ long; cell contents densely granular; apical cell broadly rounded or obtuse-conical; sheaths firm, thin, close.

Along sides of ditches and in *Sphagnum* bogs; rare in our collections, although a widely distributed and common species. Mich., Wis.

HYDROCOLEUM Kuetzing 1843, p. 196

Trichomes few to several in relatively wide, lamellate, and colorless sheaths, which are in part close and definite, becoming diffluent, the sheaths sometimes branching; forming a cushion-like expanse (sometimes lime-encrusted); individual trichomes tapering slightly at the apices, the terminal cell usually capitate and sometimes with a calyptra; cells quadrate or shorter than wide.

Hydrocoleum oligotrichum A. Braun *in* Rabenhorst 1865, p. 294

Plant mass cushion-like, lime-encrusted, and brownish in color; trichomes clustered in bundles, 2–6 within a lamellate sheath, golden-brown in color, tapering toward the apex, which is capitate; cells 6–8μ in diameter, 3–9μ long.

In small pools on rock cliffs, Pictured Rocks, Michigan.

MICROCOLEUS Desmazières 1823, p. 7

Plant mass consisting of many parallel trichomes inclosed by a wide, gelatinous, homogeneous and sticky sheath; trichomes with basal-distal differentiation, tapering anteriorly to conical or capitate apices, closely entwined, sliding upon one another in and out of the sheath; cells quadrate or elongate-cylindric; contents granular but without pseudovacuoles; cross walls sometimes granular; plants mostly on moist soil, sometimes submerged on old wood in a gelatinous mixture of miscellaneous blue-green algae.

This genus should be compared with *Schizothrix*, which has firm colored sheaths, often forms erect tufts or fascicles of filaments, and is seldom aquatic.

Key to the Species

1. Apical cell capitate..*M. vaginatus*
1. Apical cell not capitate.. 2
2. Trichomes 4–5μ in diameter, constricted
   at the cross walls; aquatic ....*M. lacustris*
2. Trichomes 5–7μ in diameter, not constricted at the cross walls;
   plants usually on moist soil ....*M. paludosus*

Microcoleus lacustris (Rab.) Farlow *in* Farlow, Anderson, & Eaton 1877, Algae Amer. Bor. Exsic., No. 227
Pl. 113, Fig. 6

Aquatic; forming dark blue-green patches on submerged wood or on bottom. Sheaths colorless, confluent with the sheaths of other filaments, thin and evanescent at the ends; not stained by chlor-zinc-iodide reagent. Trichomes with bluntly tapering apical cells, not capitate; 4–5μ in diameter. Cells distinctly cylindrical, constricted at the cross walls; 8–14μ long; contents finely granular, blue-green.

Among other filamentous blue-green algae in tychoplankton and adhering to submerged substrates. Mich., Wis.

Microcoleus paludosus (Kuetz.) Gomont 1892, p. 358
Pl. 113, Fig. 5

Filaments either solitary among other algae or entangled to form dark green, thready masses; sheaths either closed and pointed (sometimes forked) or open; sheaths sticky but not especially confluent, not colored by chlor-zinc-iodide reagent; trichomes compactly entwined, tapering to blunt, conical apices, which are not capitate;

[505]

cells 5–7μ in diameter, 7–13–(14)μ long, not constricted or granular at the cross walls; cell contents bright blue-green.

On moist soil at margins of lakes; tychoplanktonic. Mich., Wis.

Microcoleus vaginatus (Vauch.) Gomont 1890, p. 353
Pl. 131, Fig. 2

Plants solitary or, more often, forming dark green and shiny horizontal layers; twisted and branched. Sheath colorless and either cylindrical throughout or irregularly undulate and wrinkled; not stained by chlor-zinc-iodide reagent; agglutinated and either open at the end or closed and diffluent. Trichomes numerous within the sheath; not constricted at the cross walls, which are often granular; tapering slightly and briefly at the apex, which is straight. Apical cell capitate, with a calyptra. Cells 3.5–7μ in diameter, ½–2 times as long as wide.

Mich.

SCHIZOTHRIX Kuetzing 1843, p. 230

Plant mass consisting of several to many trichomes inclosed by a copious sheath of mucilage, which is usually firm and not sticky, the sheath colorless or yellowed, especially in age, frequently forked towards the ends with but a single trichome in the ultimate divisions; filaments either single, in fascicled tufts, or in an expanded layer; trichomes twisted and intertwined, cylindrical throughout but with the apical cell tapering to a blunt or sharp point; cells cylindrical, or shorter than wide, sometimes constricted at the cross walls.

This genus should be compared with some species of *Phormidium* in which the sheaths are agglutinated and diffluent.

Key to the Species

1. Sheaths colored.. 2
1. Sheaths colorless... 3
2. Trichomes 2.8–3μ in diameter, not tapering
   at the apices, the end bluntly rounded..*S. fuscescens*
2. Trichomes 6–13μ in diameter, tapering slightly toward the
   apices, the end conically rounded..*S. Muelleri*
3. Filaments compactly agglutinated to form erect tufts.................*S. Friesii*
3. Filaments not agglutinated to form erect tufts............................ 4
4. Filaments branching but very little,
   united to form horizontal layers...*S. lardacea*
4. Filaments forming cushion-like masses, or
   penicillate, streaming tufts... 5
5. Trichomes 5–11μ in diameter...*S. rivularis*
5. Trichomes narrower... 6

6. Cells shorter than broad..S. *vaginata*
6. Cells quadrate or longer than broad 7
7. Filaments forming streaming penicillate tufts................................S. *tinctoria*
7. Filaments forming cushion-like or thick, expanded masses 8
8. Plant mass encrusted with lime; trichome 1.4–3µ in diameter; cells 1.2–3.5µ long; apical cell briefly tapering................................S. *fasciculata*
8. Plant mass not at all or but very little encrusted with lime; trichomes 1–1.5µ in diameter; cells 4µ long; apical cell bluntly rounded, not tapering..S. *lacustris*

Schizothrix fasciculata (Naeg.) Gomont 1893, p. 298

Filaments united to form a pulvinate, sometimes expanded mass, thickly encrusted with lime, often forming pebbles; filaments densely entangled, expanding and forked above and involving many trichomes, but narrower below (toward the base of the plant mass); sheaths thick; cells 1.4–3µ in diameter, 1.2–3.5µ long, constricted at the cross walls; apical cell sharply conical; cell contents blue-green. Mich.

Schizothrix Friesii Gomont 1892, p. 316
Pl. 114, Fig. 5

Trichomes solitary or 2–3 (rarely 4–5) within dichotomously branching sheaths which taper at the apices, the envelopes colorless and smooth although roughened in age, sticky and united to form branched and anastomosing, erect tufts; cells cylindrical, constricted at the cross walls; apical cell bluntly conical; cells 3–6µ in diameter, 4–6–(12)µ long.

On submerged logs. Wis.

Schizothrix fuscescens Kuetzing 1843, p. 230
Pl. 114, Fig. 4

Trichomes few and entwined within a soft, gelatinous sheath which usually is colorless without but golden-yellow within, forming mucilaginous masses on moss or on partly submerged substrates; trichomes not at all tapering toward the apices, which are bluntly rounded; cells 2.8–3µ in diameter, 8–13µ long, constricted at the cross walls.

Forming thin, golden-colored or brownish strands on mosses in a *Sphagnum* bog. Wis.

Schizothrix lacustris A. Braun *in* Kuetzing 1849, p. 320
Pl. 131, Fig. 6

Filaments united to form a pulvinate mass, not encrusted with lime, expanded and containing more numerous trichomes above

[507]

than in the basal portion; branched and contorted above. Sheaths thick and colorless, stained violet by chlor-zinc-iodide reagent. Cells 1–1.5μ in diameter, 4μ long; constricted at the cross walls; cell contents blue-green.

Mich.

Schizothrix lardacea (Cesati) Gomont 1892, p. 307

Filaments forming a thick, layered, expanded plant mass, firm but not encrusted with lime; filaments entangled but little-branched; sheaths close, firm, narrowed and pointed at the ends; trichomes not tapering, bluntly rounded at the apex. Cells 1.5–2μ in diameter, 2–3μ long; not constricted at the cross walls, which are usually granular; cell contents blue-green.

Mich.

Schizothrix Muelleri Naegeli in Kuetzing 1849, p. 320
Pl. 114, Fig. 1

Filaments free-floating or attached and entangled among other algae; trichomes 1 or 2 within much lamellated, golden-colored sheaths which are attenuate at the apices; cells stout, 6–13μ in diameter, 4–9μ long, slightly constricted at the cross walls; apical cell conically rounded.

Tychoplankter; in ponds. Wis.

Schizothrix rivularis (Wolle) Drouet 1942, p. 131
Pl. 114, Figs. 2, 3

Trichomes parallel and much entwined, forming cable-like strands or fascicles in copious mucilage; cells quadrate, 5–11μ in diameter, not constricted at the cross walls, which are not granular; apical cell bluntly pointed; cells frequently and easily dissociating within the filament, forming interrupted series; sheaths wide and diffluent; plant mass dark blue-green; individual trichomes bluish or rose-colored.

When collections of this plant are allowed to stand in water for a short time (overnight), especially in a closed container, large quantities of a water-soluble blue pigment are released. The solution has a beautiful fluorescent property.

Forming streaming masses in flowing water; attached to submerged aquatics. Wis.

Schizothrix tinctoria Gomont 1890, p. 351
Pl. 131, Figs. 7, 8

Plants forming blue-green penicillate tufts from soft, expanded, gelatinous masses; usually streaming in flowing water. Filaments branched in the apices; sheaths close, becoming diffluent; trichomes numerous and twisted within the sheath, which is stained by chlor-zinc-iodide reagent; trichomes not tapering toward the apices, which are bluntly rounded. Cells 1.4–2.4μ in diameter, 1.4–3μ long; constricted at the cross walls; cell contents pale blue-green.

Attached to submerged aquatics. Mich., Wis.

Schizothrix vaginata (Naeg.) Gomont 1892, p. 302

Filaments forming a cushion-like mass, sometimes calcified and gray-brown in color; filaments coalesced below but becoming forked above; sheath thin, close, and slightly lamellate, narrowed toward the apex and closed (sometimes expanded), coloring by chlor-zinc-iodide reagent; trichomes single or few within the sheath, not tapering toward the apices, which are broadly rounded; cells 2–3μ in diameter, nearly quadrate or shorter than wide, not constricted at the cross walls, which are granular; cell contents pale yellow-green.

On rocks and entangled among colonial, mucilaginous algae. Wis.

SUBORDER HETEROCYSTINEAE

The chief characteristic of plants in this group is the *heterocyst,* a differentiated cell in the trichome, although in a few rare cases it is lacking. In such genera the habit of branching or some other morphological feature of the trichome definitely relates them to plants possessing a heterocyst. The trichomes may taper toward the apex, but usually they are the same diameter throughout (Rivulariaceae an exception). Although many forms do not branch, especially in the Nostocaceae, there are both true and false branchings. The filaments may be uni- or multiseriate. (See remarks referring to the Order Hormogonales and the key to the families, p. 477 *et seq.*)

FAMILY NOSTOCACEAE

In this family the plants are uniseriate, unbranched filaments which do not taper toward their apices (or scarcely so). The sheath is soft, diffluent and usually indistinct and nearly always without structural conformity (as, for example, in *Lyngbya* of the Oscillatoriaceae, or *Tolypothrix* in the Scytonemataceae). Sometimes the sheath is close, but not firm and rigid. In many forms there is a copious secretion of mucilage with a multitude of trichomes enclosed in a common gelatinous matrix in which individual sheaths are confluent (e.g., *Nostoc*). All genera in this family have heterocysts, which may be either terminal or scattered in the trichome, solitary or (rarely) in series. Vegetative cells are globose, barrel-shaped, or

[509]

cylindrical, with either granular or homogeneous contents. In some there are pseudovacuoles. Of great taxonomic value is the shape and location in the trichome of the gonidia (akinetes) which are enlarged reproductive cells with thick walls. The outer membrane of the gonidia may be smooth or granular, punctate, etc.

Key to the Genera

1. Heterocysts at one or both ends of the trichome 2
1. Heterocysts scattered and intercalary (incidentally at the ends of trichomes after fragmentation) 3
2. Heterocysts at one end of the trichome; gonidia adjacent to the heterocysts .... *Cylindrospermum*
2. Heterocysts at both ends of the trichome; gonidia intercalary, remote from the heterocysts .... *Anabaenopsis*
3. Trichomes lying parallel 4
3. Trichomes solitary, or if gregarious, entangled, not parallel 6
4. Trichomes surrounded by copious mucilage, lying in gelatinous, hollow tubes or in bullate masses .... *Wollea*
4. Trichomes not in hollow tubes; planktonic 5
5. Trichomes many within a free-floating flake of definite shape; trichomes slightly tapering at the apices; gonidia solitary .... *Aphanizomenon*
5. Trichomes forming flakes of irregular outline, embedded in mucilage; trichomes not tapering toward the apices; gonidia in a series (rarely solitary) .... *Anabaena* (in part)
6. Trichomes solitary, planktonic 7
6. Trichomes aggregated in gelatinous masses of definite or indefinite shape 8
7. Cells disc-shaped, much shorter than wide; heterocysts compressed .... *Nodularia*
7. Cells not disc-shaped; globose to cylindrical; heterocysts not compressed .... *Anabaena* (in part)
8. Plant mass of definite shape, the periphery of the colonial mucilage forming a tegument .... *Nostoc*
8. Plant mass not definitely shaped, not bounded by a firm tegument 9
9. Trichomes forming small packets, entangled, sometimes subparallel, inclosed in definite rather firm sheaths .... *Aulosira*
9. Trichomes not forming packets, individual sheaths lacking, or not definite .... *Anabaena* (in part)

ANABAENA Bory 1822, p. 307

Filamentous, mostly gregarious, much entangled and inclosed in amorphous mucilage, solitary and planktonic in a few species, sometimes attached and forming films and gelatinous expansions on moist substrates; trichomes straight, flexuous, or spirally coiled, either with or without a sheath; cells torulose, barrel-shaped, or (in a few species) cylindrical; heterocysts usually numerous and scattered in the trichome, spherical, ovate, or cylindrical; gonidia round, ovate, or cylindrical (sometimes elongate-ovate), either adjacent to or remote from the heterocysts.

See notes under *Nostoc,* which point out the chief characteristics separating these two genera.

Key to the Species

1. Filaments endophytic _____ A. Azollae
   (See also A. cycadearum Reinke, not reported from this region.)
1. Filaments free-living, planktonic, epiphytic, or on moist earth _____ 2
2. Euplanktonic, mostly solitary or forming free-floating fascicles _____ 3
2. Tychoplanktonic, entangled among other algae;
   epiphytic or on moist soil _____ 20
3. Trichomes contorted and twisted, regularly or irregularly spiralled _____ 4
3. Trichomes straight or flexuous but not coiled _____ 8
4. Trichomes coiled or spiralled _____ 5
4. Trichomes irregularly twisted and snarled; gonidia
   formed near the center of the tangle _____ A. flos-aquae
5. Spiral regular; trichome forming a definite coil _____ 6
5. Trichome sigmoid or twisted irregularly _____ A. circinalis
6. Gonidia subglobose to oblong _____ A. spiroides
6. Gonidia cylindrical _____ 7
7. Vegetative cells 3.5µ in diameter; gonidia
   up to 17µ long _____ A. helicoidea
7. Vegetative cells 4–6–(8)µ in diameter;
   gonidia 24–30µ long _____ A. flos-aquae
8. Gonidia adjoining the heterocysts on one or both sides _____ 9
8. Gonidia scattered, near or remote from the
   heterocysts but not adjoining _____ 10
9. Cells globose; gonidia on both sides of the heterocysts _____ A. Bornetiana
9. Cells rectangular, elongate; gonidia on one
   side of the heterocyst only _____ A. unispora
10. Trichomes lying parallel in bundles or forming loose fascicles;
    with 1, rarely 2, gonidia in a trichome _____ A. wisconsinense
10. Trichomes not in a bundle or fascicle; with
    2 or more gonidia in a trichome _____ 11
11. Gonidia globose, sometimes slightly ellipsoid _____ 12
11. Gonidia ellipsoid, oblong or cylindrical _____ 13
12. Cell contents highly vacuolate; gonidia mostly globose _____ A. Scheremetievi
12. Cell contents not vacuolate; gonidia globose,
    (sometimes ovate or elongate) _____ A. planctonica
13. Gonidia ovate or ellipsoid _____ 14
13. Gonidia cylindrical _____ 16
14. Vegetative cells round, sometimes barrel-shaped _____ 15
14. Vegetative cells barrel-shaped to short-cylindric _____ A. Viguieri
15. Gonidia oblong, separated from the heterocyst
    usually by a single cell _____ A. limnetica
15. Gonidia spheroidal or broadly ovate, separated from the
    heterocyst by 2 or more cells _____ A. planctonica
16. Gonidia short-cylindric, not more than twice the diameter in
    length, hexagonal in optical cross section _____ A. macrospora
16. Gonidia usually more than twice the diameter in
    length, round in optical cross section _____ 17

Anabaena aequalis Borge 1907, p. 65
Pl. 115, Figs. 1, 2

Trichomes straight, forming a small plant mass, or scattered among other algae; cells somewhat quadrate or barrel-shaped, (4.5)–5.5–7.5μ in diameter, 7.6–8.5μ long; heterocysts ovate to sub-cylindric, (5.5)–8μ in diameter, (10)–13–(15.2)μ long; gonidia cylindrical, remote from the heterocysts, the wall smooth and color-less, 5–7.6μ in diameter, (21)–35–41–(49.4)μ long.

Tychoplanktonic; intermingled with other algae in shallow water in *Sphagnum* bogs. Wis.

Anabaena affinis Lemmermann 1898a, p. 261

Pl. 115, Figs. 10, 14, 15

Trichomes straight or flexuous, solitary and free-floating, either planktonic or intermingled with other algae in the littoral flora, inclosed in a thin, wide, mucilaginous sheath (often indistinct); cells spherical to spheroidal with either homogeneous contents or with pseudovacuoles, especially the latter when plants are solitary in the plankton, 5–6–(7)μ in diameter; heterocysts spherical, slightly larger than the vegetative cells, 7.5–10μ in diameter; gonidia usually short-cylindric, sometimes broadly ovate and truncately rounded at the poles, scattered, solitary, 9.5–12μ in diameter, 17–24–(26)μ long.

Rare to common in euplankton and tychoplankton of several lakes. Mich., Wis.

Anabaena Augstumalis Schmidle 1899a, p. 174

Trichomes twisted and flexuous, free-floating, solitary; cells barrel-shaped or somewhat cylindric, 4–5μ in diameter, 5–6μ long; heterocysts cylindrical, slightly greater (6μ) in diameter than the vegetative cells; gonidia narrowly cylindric, 6μ in diameter, 30–50–(56)μ long, adjacent to the heterocysts.

This species should be compared with *A. circinalis*, also a plankter. Euplankter. Wis.

Anabaena Augstumalis var. *Marchica* Lemmermann 1905, p. 147

Pl. 115, Fig. 11

Trichomes flexuous (not circinate), planktonic; cells spherical to cylindric with many conspicuous pseudovacuoles, 5–7μ in diameter, 5–9.5μ long; gonidia cylindrical, 9.5–12μ in diameter, 40–70μ long, remote from the heterocysts.

In the plankton of several hard water lakes. Mich., Wis.

Anabaena Azollae Strasburger 1884, p. 352

Pl. 115, Figs. 12, 13

Trichomes straight or coiled, often in small clusters but more frequently solitary, inhabiting the tissues of *Azolla*; cells subglobose to ellipsoid, the contents granular, 4–5μ in diameter, 6–8–(9.5)μ long; heterocysts ovate, 6–9.5μ in diameter, 9–10–(11.5)μ long; gonidia not known.

The lack of gonidia in these plants makes their identification questionable. It is possible that they are only a sterile condition of a free-living species called by another name.

In the tissues of *Azolla*; shallow water and sloughs. Wis.

Anabaena Bornetiana Collins 1896, p. 120
Pl. 115, Figs. 8, 9

Trichomes straight, planktonic and solitary; cells spherical or compressed globose, contents densely granular or homogeneous, 11–12μ in diameter; heterocysts nearly spherical, 10–12–(14)μ in diameter, 12–14–(20)μ long; gonidia cylindrical, adjacent to the heterocysts (often one on either side) or scattered, (12.8)–14–(20)μ in diameter, (50)–66–90μ long.

Plankter; in lakes. Wis.

Anabaena circinalis Rabenhorst 1852, p. 209
Pl. 116, Figs. 1, 2

Trichomes planktonic, flexuous and contorted; solitary or entangled to form floating clots which are easily visible to the unaided eye. Cells spherical or depressed-globose from contact; 8–12–(14)μ in diameter. Heterocysts spherical or compressed, 8–10μ in diameter. Gonidia remote from the heterocysts, rarely adjacent; cylindric, straight or curved; (14)–16–18μ in diameter, 22–30–(32)μ long.

This species is very common and widely distributed. It is often found associated with A. spiroides in the plankton of hard water lakes. These two species, together with Microcystis aeruginosa and Gloeotrichia echinulata, are conspicuous components of water blooms during late summer periods.

Anabaena circinalis may be differentiated from A. spiroides by the shape of the spore when in the reproductive condition, by the lack of regularity in the twisting of the trichome, and by the size of the cells in the vegetative state.

Mich., Wis.

Anabaena circinalis var. macrospora (Wittr.) DeToni 1907, p. 445
Pl. 116, Figs. 5, 6; Pl. 120, Fig. 1

A variety with smaller vegetative cells and narrower, more elongate gonidia. Cells 7–8μ in diameter; heterocysts 7.5–10μ in diameter; gonidia 9–10.5μ in diameter, 28–42μ long.

Euplankter. Wis.

Anabaena Felisii (Menegh.) Bornet & Flahault 1888, p. 232
Pl. 116, Figs. 3, 4

Trichomes straight; solitary or in small clusters. Cells short-cylindric, 6–7μ in diameter, 7–11μ long. Heterocysts ovate to subcylindric, 7μ in diameter, 12–14μ long. Gonidia scattered; solitary or in short series; remote from the heterocysts; 10–12–(14)μ in diameter and up to 70μ long.

This species should be compared with *A. oscillarioides,* from which it differs in having spores remote from the heterocysts, which are subcylindric rather than round. The cells in *A. Felisii* are cylindrical, whereas those of *A. oscillarioides* are barrel-shaped.

Tychoplankter. Wis.

Anabaena flos-aquae (Lyngb.) De Brébisson *in*
De Brébisson & Godey 1836, p. 36
[*A. Lemmermannii* P. Richter]
Pl. 116, Fig. 7

Trichomes planktonic; very flexuous and contorted, sometimes coiled in an irregular spiral fashion; either solitary or entangled in a twisted mass. Cells spherical to subcylindric; (4)–5–6–(8)μ in diameter, 6–8–(12)μ long; cell contents granular with conspicuous pseudovacuoles. Heterocysts globose or somewhat depressed at the poles; 7–9μ in diameter, 6–10μ long. Gonidia cylindrical or sausage-shaped; solitary, or sometimes in a series, crowded near the center of a tangle of filaments; usually adjacent to the heterocysts; (6)–8–12–(13)μ in diameter, (20)–24–30–(50)μ long.

Common in the plankton of hard and semi-hard water lakes; sometimes producing conspicuous water bloom growths during the warm summer months, often in association with *Microcystis aeruginosa* and *Gloeotrichia echinulata*. Mich., Wis.

Anabaena flos-aquae var. *Treleasei* Bornet & Flahault 1888, p. 230
[*A. Mendotae* Trelease 1889, p. 123]
Pl. 120, Fig. 2

A variety differing from the typical by the somewhat smaller size of the vegetative cells and by the more slender gonidia; vegetative cells 4μ in diameter. Heterocysts 5μ in diameter, 10μ long. Gonidia 6μ in diameter, 40μ long.

Forming dense water blooms. Wis.

Anabaena helicoidea Bernard 1908, p. 52
Pl. 116, Fig. 8

Trichomes free-floating; solitary or entangled in a group; spirally twisted throughout their length. Cells ovate or somewhat barrel-shaped, with large granules of food reserve, 3.5–3.8μ in diameter, 4–5μ long. Heterocysts globose, 5–6μ in diameter, 6μ long. Gonidia small, cylindrical, 5μ in diameter, 17μ long.

This species is quite similar to *A. flos-aquae* but is separated pri-

marily on the form of the plant, which is a loose spiral, not a tangled knot. It also should be compared with *A. circinalis* which has gonidia of quite different shape, relatively longer and larger.
Euplankter. Wis.

Anabaena inaequalis (Kuetz.) Bornet & Flahault 1888, p. 231
[*A. laxa* (Rab.) Braun *ex* Bornet & Flahault 1888, p. 120]
Pl. 116, Figs. 9, 10

Trichomes straight or slightly twisted; lying parallel and entwined and inclosed by a definite sticky sheath, $7.4–8\mu$ wide; forming gelatinous strands, entangled among other algae and adherent (sometimes floating free). Cells short barrel-shaped or truncate-globose, $3.7–4.2–(5)\mu$ in diameter. Heterocysts globose or ovate, $4–6\mu$ in diameter, 7.2μ long. Gonidia cylindrical, scattered, with wall often golden-brown when mature; $6–8\mu$ in diameter, $15–16–(17)\mu$ long.

Among other algae and floating free in marginal waters. Mich., Wis.

Anabaena lapponica Borge 1913a, p. 101
Pl. 116, Fig. 11

Trichomes straight, somewhat entangled; cells globose, $7.4–9.2\mu$ in diameter; heterocysts globose, $7.4–10\mu$ in diameter; gonidia cylindrical, $(11.5)–13–14–(17)\mu$ in diameter, $40.7–63–(85)\mu$ long, developing on one or both sides of the heterocysts.

Type specimens of this plant have not been seen for confirmation, but our material agrees with Borge's description. The spherical shape of the vegetative cells and heterocysts separate this species from *A. oscillarioides,* which has barrel-shaped or elongate-ovate vegetative cells and heterocysts.

Tychoplanktonic in lakes; in roadside ditches. Wis.

Anabaena Levanderi Lemmermann 1906b, p. 536
Pl. 117, Figs. 1, 2

Trichomes planktonic, solitary, straight or flexuous. Cells cylindrical, $4–6\mu$ in diameter, $11–33\mu$ long; constricted at the cross walls, which are rounded; contents with pseudovacuoles. Heterocysts spherical to ellipsoid, $6.5–8\mu$ in diameter, $6.5–9.5–(14)\mu$ long. Gonidia solitary, ellipsoid, $8–15\mu$ in diameter, $19–45\mu$ long.
Euplankter. Wis.

Anabaena limnetica G. M. Smith 1916, p. 481
Pl. 117, Fig. 3

Trichomes planktonic, solitary, straight or flexuous, inclosed by a mucilaginous sheath. Vegetative cells spherical or compressed at the poles, (10)–12–14–(15)μ in diameter. Heterocysts globular, 10–14μ in diameter. Gonidia broadly ovate, near to the heterocysts or scattered, 17–20μ in diameter, 20–30μ long.

Euplankter. Mich., Wis.

Anabaena macrospora Klebahn 1895, p. 269
Pl. 117, Figs. 4–6

Trichomes planktonic, straight or flexuous, solitary; cells globose or somewhat ellipsoid, 5–6.5μ in diameter, (5)–6–8–(9)μ long; heterocysts spherical, about 6μ in diameter; gonidia globose to ovate, angular in optical section, not adjoining heterocysts, 17–18.5μ in diameter, 24–26μ long.

Plankter; in many hard and semi-hard water lakes. Wis.

Anabaena macrospora var. *robusta* Lemmermann 1898d, p. 154
Pl. 117, Fig. 7

Trichomes planktonic and solitary. Cells globose or ellipsoid, 9.7–11μ in diameter. Heterocysts globose, 11.5μ in diameter, 11–12μ long. Gonidia globose or ovate; scattered, or adjacent to the heterocysts; 13.2–15μ in diameter, 27–28–(34)μ long.

Plankter; in several hard water lakes; often appearing in water bloom associations in late summer. Wis.

Anabaena oscillarioides Bory 1822, p. 308
Pl. 117, Figs. 8–10

Filaments straight, or entangled in a thin gelatinous layer or solitary. Cells barrel-shaped or truncate-globose, 4–6μ in diameter, 7.8–8μ long. Heterocysts round or ovate; 6–8μ in diameter, (6)–9.2–(10)μ long. Gonidia cylindrical; developing on both sides of the heterocyst (rarely on one side only); 8–10–(15.2)μ in diameter, 20–40–(76)μ long.

Spores in our specimens are larger than those originally described for this species.

Forming thin films on submerged aquatics, or subaerial in swampy places and along margins of lakes. Mich., Wis.

Anabaena planctonica Brunnthaler 1903, p. 292
Pl. 118, Figs. 1–3

Trichomes solitary, free-floating, inclosed in a wide gelatinous sheath; cells barrel-shaped or spherical, 9–15μ in diameter, 6.5–10μ long, with pseudovacuoles; heterocysts spherical, with lateral 'wings' of mucilage, 9–11μ in diameter; gonidia ellipsoid, 10–14μ in diameter, 15–30μ long, near or remote from the heterocysts.

Plankter; in lakes. Wis.

Anabaena Scheremetievi Elenkin 1909, p. 125

Pl. 117, Figs. 11, 12

Trichomes planktonic; mostly straight, sometimes flexuous with a gelatinous sheath. Cells spheroidal or barrel-shaped; with pseudo-vacuoles; 8.5–9–(11)μ in diameter, 8–11–(12)μ long. Heterocysts spherical, 8–10.8μ in diameter. Gonidia spherical to ellipsoid, sometimes angular in optical section, not adjacent to heterocysts, (18) –20–22.6μ in diameter, 21–24μ long.

Euplankter. Wis.

Anabaena spiroides Klebahn 1895, p. 268

Trichomes spiral, solitary, inclosed in a thin mucilaginous sheath. Cells spherical or compressed-spheroidal, 6.5–8μ in diameter. Heterocysts spherical, slightly smaller than the vegetative cells. Gonidia spherical, 14μ in diameter; adjacent to the heterocysts.

Typical form not reported from our region.

Anabaena spiroides var. *crassa* Lemmermann 1898d, p. 155

Pl. 117, Fig. 13; Pl. 118, Figs. 4, 5

Trichomes solitary, spirally twisted, planktonic. Cells spherical, 10–11.5μ in diameter. Heterocysts subspherical, 10μ in diameter, 12μ long. Gonidia oblong; remote from the heterocysts; 19–20μ in diameter, 25–30μ long.

Plankter; in many lakes; especially abundant in late summer, appearing in water blooms with *A. circinalis* and *A. flos-aquae*. Wis.

Anabaena subcylindrica Borge 1921, p. 12

Pl. 118, Figs. 6–8

Trichomes straight; solitary or forming a thin layer; adherent on submerged aquatics and entangled among other algae. Cells short-cylindric, 4–4.5μ in diameter, 5.5–8–(10)μ long. Heterocysts cylindrical, 5–7.5–(10)μ in diameter, 15–(18)μ long. Gonidia cylindrical, adjacent to heterocysts, 7–8.5μ in diameter, 54–57μ long.

Sphagnum bogs; tychoplanktonic in soft water lakes. Wis.

Anabaena torulosa (Carm.) Lagerheim 1883, p. 47

Filaments somewhat straight or irregularly bent (not coiled); forming sparsely clustered flakes. Cells subspherical or barrel-shaped, 4.2–5μ in diameter; the terminal cell conical. Heterocysts globular, 6μ in diameter. Gonidia elongate-ovate to subcylindric, with smooth convex lateral walls; solitary or in a series, on either side of the heterocyst; 7–12μ in diameter, 18–28μ long.

Mich.

Anabaena unispora Gardner 1927, p. 59

Pl. 131, Fig. 5

Filaments straight or slightly curved, mostly solitary. Cells rectangular, 2–4 times longer than wide; 4–5μ in diameter, 11–20μ long; slightly constricted at the cross walls. Heterocysts elongate-ovate or subcylindric, 6μ in diameter, 11μ long. Gonidia solitary; developing near the middle of the filament and close to the heterocyst; elongate-ovate, the margins subparallel or slightly convex; 11–15μ in diameter, 31–35μ long.

Mich.

Anabaena variabilis Kuetzing 1843, p. 210

Pl. 118, Figs. 9, 10

Trichomes entangled in a gelatinous plant mass, on damp soil, or floating entangled among other algae. Cells compressed-globose, 3.7–4–(6.5)μ in diameter. Heterocysts globular or ovate; 5.5–5.8–(8)μ in diameter, 5.8–6.5μ long. Gonidia ovate; in series; remote from the heterocysts; 6.8–9μ in diameter, 7.5–8.2–(14)μ long.

In seeps and ditches. Mich., Wis.

Anabaena verrucosa Boye-Petersen 1923, p. 299

Pl. 118, Figs. 11, 12

Trichomes straight, parallel, with a wide gelatinous sheath; growing on and adherent to other filamentous algae. Cells short-cylindric, 3.3–4μ in diameter, 3.3–6–(8)μ long. Heterocysts cylindrical, 3.6μ in diameter, 5μ long. Gonidia cylindrical; remote from the heterocysts; 4–7μ in diameter, (10.5)–12–(15)μ long.

Tychoplankter. Wis.

?*Anabaena Viguieri* Denis & Frémy 1923, p. 122

Pl. 119, Figs. 1–3

Trichomes planktonic; straight. Cells barrel-shaped to short-cylindric; 7–7.8μ in diameter, (4)–9–10μ long; with pseudovacuoles. Heterocysts globose to subglobose; 7.6μ in diameter and up to 9μ long; smaller than the vegetative cells. Gonidia broadly ovate; 12–14–(15)μ in diameter, 17–18.5μ long; solitary or in 2's; not adjacent to the heterocyst.

This interesting plant was found in but one collection made in our area. It agrees in most respects with the description of *A. Viguieri*, but the cells are slightly longer.

Euplankter. Wis.

[519]

Anabaena wisconsinense Prescott 1944, p. 373

Pl. 115, Figs. 3–7; Pl. 119, Figs. 4–8

Trichomes planktonic; straight or slightly flexuous; solitary or (more often) aggregated in parallel fashion to form small, loose, flake-like bundles; without a sheath; not tapering at the apices. Cells quadrate to cylindrical; constricted at the cross walls; $3.6–4\mu$ in diameter, $3.6–10.8\mu$ long; with large pseudovacuoles. Heterocysts spherical or compressed-globose, $3.6–4.2\mu$ in diameter; only 1 in each trichome, centrally located. Gonidia elliptic-ovate to broadly oval, $7.2–8\mu$ in diameter, $10–13\mu$ long; beginning their development as a series of 3 enlarged vegetative cells, of which usually only 1 matures, so that each trichome has but a single gonidium (if more than 1, the gonidia in pairs); remote from the heterocysts.

This plant is remindful of *Aphanizomenon flos-aquae*. It should be compared with *Anabaena aphanizomenoides* Forti, from which it differs in its smaller size throughout, in the shape of the gonidia, and in the location of the gonidia (remote from, rather than adjacent to, the heterocysts).

Both euplanktonic and tychoplanktonic. Wis.

ANABAENOPSIS (Wołosz.) Miller 1923, p. 125

Trichomes planktonic; short and coiled, with a heterocyst at either end. Cells elongate-ovoid to subcylindric. Akinetes intercalary, remote from the heterocysts.

Anabaenopsis Elenkinii Miller 1923, p. 125

Pl. 131, Fig. 4

Trichomes composed of ellipsoid or elongate-ovoid cells which contain pseudovacuoles. Heterocysts spherical, $4.6–6.7\mu$ in diameter. Akinetes broadly ovoid, $8.3–10.5\mu$ in diameter, $9.3–12\mu$ long; sometimes nearly spherical, $8.3–10.7\mu$ in diameter. Cells $4.6–5.7\mu$ in diameter.

Cheboygan County, Michigan.

NOSTOC Vaucher 1903, p. 203

Membranous or globular or irregularly lobed colony of tangled, uniseriate unbranched trichomes of globose and bead-like, barrel-shaped, or cylindrical cells, inclosed in copious, thick mucilage which (in many species) outwardly forms a firm integument, giving the colony a fixed and definite shape; individual sheaths of the trichome confluent with the colonial mucilage; trichomes without basal-distal differentiation, made up of vegetative cells, frequent heterocysts and, when mature, gonidia which are either solitary or in series.

This genus should be compared with *Anabaena* in which some species have trichomes similarly inclosed in a thick mucilage but for which there is no definite shape. The colonial mass in *Anabaena* is soft, spreading, and does not retain its shape when removed from the water.

Key to the Species

1. Plants inhabiting the tissues of *Ricciocarpus* and other liverworts..*N. sphaericum*
   (See also *N. punctiforme*.)
1. Plants free-living, aquatic, or subaerial 2
2. Colonies globular masses of microscopic size, attached or entangled among other algae....................*N. paludosum*
2. Colonies of macroscopic size 3
3. Colony a membranous expanse, usually subaerial..................*N. muscorum*
   (See also *N. Linckia* and *N. commune*.)
3. Colony globular, regular in shape or lumpy and warty; mostly aquatic...... 4
4. Trichomes inclosed in a thick, tough, wrinkled mucilage, at first globular and solid, later becoming hollow and irregularly tubercular; colonies olive-green or brownish; trichomes densely entangled at the periphery of the colonial mass....................*N. verrucosum*
4. Trichomes not in leathery, hollow, tubercular colonies....................5
5. Colonies spherical, planktonic, blue; 2–5 mm. in diameter..*N. caeruleum*
5. Colonies not definitely planktonic; not blue............................... 6
6. Colonies with a firm outer membrane; definite in shape; usually globular 7
6. Colonies without a firm outer membrane or integument; usually soft and amorphous, although retaining their shape when removed from the water 11
7. Plants growing on moist soil...9
7. Plants growing in water..8
8. Cells 4–5μ in diameter; gonidia elliptic or spherical, 5–7μ in diameter; colonies tuberculate or expanded irregularly............*N. sphaericum*
8. Cells 4–6μ in diameter; gonidia spherical, 10μ in diameter; colonies firm, globular pellets,. sometimes several adhering together; usually gregarious ....*N. pruniforme*
9. Colonial mass membranaceous, expanded (although at first forming globular masses)..*N. commune*
9. Colonial mass not membranaceous...10
10. Cells cylindrical; constricted at the end walls, which are truncate; gonidia ellipsoid to cylindric, 6–7μ in diameter, 6–14μ long *N. ellipsosporum*
10. Cells barrel-shaped, short; gonidia oval, 5μ in diameter, 7μ long...*N. sphaericum*
11. Trichomes densely entangled, filamentous arrangement not clearly discernible ....*N. punctiforme*
11. Trichomes not so densely entangled that the filamentous arrangement is not easily discernible 12

Nostoc caeruleum Lyngbye 1819, p. 201
Pl. 119, Figs. 10, 11

Colony spherical, planktonic, 5–10 mm. in diameter, appearing as bright, sky-blue globules dispersed through quiet water; colonial sheath firm and tough; trichomes densely entangled; cells subspherical or barrel-shaped, 5–7μ in diameter; heterocysts frequent, subglobose or spherical, 8–10μ in diameter; gonidia apparently never described.

Rather uncommon in plankton of lakes with eutrophic characteristics. Mich., Wis.

Nostoc carneum C. A. Agardh 1824, p. 22
Pl. 119, Fig. 9 (showing an atypical form)

Colony olive-green or blue-green, globular, becoming irregularly lobed in age and finally expanded soft to firm; trichomes twisted and entangled but not crowded. Cells subglobose to short-cylindric, sometimes twice as long as wide, 3–4μ in diameter, 6–8μ long; constricted at the cross walls. Heterocysts ovate, 6–7μ in diameter, 8μ long. Gonidia ovate to oblong, 6–7μ in diameter, 8–10μ long.

On the bottom, and floating at the surface of quiet water; forming soft gelatinous expansions when old but retaining a firm tegument. Wis.

Nostoc comminutum Kuetzing 1849–1869, Tab. Phyc., 2, p. 3
Pl. 119, Fig. 12

Colony an irregularly lobed and membranaceous mass, golden-brown in color, the investing mucilage soft but retaining a definite shape when removed from the water. Trichomes twisted or somewhat entangled. Cells globose or compressed-globose; 3.7–4μ in diameter, 3–4μ long; either adjoined or separated (in different parts of the colony). Heterocysts spherical, 6μ in diameter. Gonidia not observed (unknown ?).

Tychoplankter; also found on bottom in shallow water. Mich., Wis.

Nostoc commune Vaucher 1903, p. 222
Pl. 119, Fig. 13

Plant at first a brown, globular, firm, gelatinous mass, later, especially when growing on moist soil, becoming expanded; lobed and clathrate; forming tough leathery layers of considerable extent (20 cm. wide). Trichomes closely entangled and intertwined, especially compact in the outer, brown, layer, less so in the colorless, softer, inner region of the colony. Cells subglobose or barrel-shaped 4–6μ in diameter, 7μ long; constricted at the cross walls. Heterocysts frequent, spherical, 7–8.4μ in diameter. Gonidia the same shape and about the same size as the vegetative cells.

On the bottom and on submerged objects; collected from depth of 20 feet in soft water lakes; on damp soil at the margin of lakes and swamps. Mich., Wis.

Nostoc ellipsosporum (Desmaz.) Rabenhorst 1865, Vol. 2, p. 169

Plant mass reddish-brown, irregularly globular. Trichomes loosely entangled. Cells subcylindric to cylindric; 4μ in diameter, 6–14μ long; constricted at the cross walls, which are truncate; cell contents yellowish or olive. Heterocysts subglobose or oblong, 6–7μ in diameter, 6–14μ long. Gonidia ellipsoid or cylindric-oblong; 6–8μ in diameter, 14–19μ long; with smooth walls.

On grass at margin of lakes; on clay banks. Mich.

Nostoc Linckia (Roth) Bornet & Thuret 1880, p. 86
Pl. 119, Figs. 14–16

Colonies firm and globular when young, becoming irregularly expanded, clathrate, and membranous, soft in age; blue-green in color, becoming dirty green. Trichomes much entangled, twisted. Cells subglobose or barrel-shaped, 3–4.5μ in diameter. Heterocysts subspherical to ovate, 6–7.5μ in diameter. Gonidia subglobose; 6–7μ in diameter, 7–8μ long; with dark, smooth membrane.

Among clots of filamentous algae in hard water lakes; sometimes on moist earth at margin of lakes. Mich., Wis.

Nostoc microscopicum Carmichael (see Harvey in Hooker 1833, p. 399)
Pl. 120, Figs. 3–5

Colonies minute, blue-green or olive-green, globose or ovoid to somewhat irregular. Trichomes relatively loosely entangled in a colorless mucilage. Cells globose, (4.5)–5–8μ in diameter; frequently not adjoined but loosely arranged in a series. Heterocysts subspherical or ovate, 7.3μ in diameter. Gonidia ovate or subspherical, 6–7μ in diameter, 10–15μ long; with smooth walls. Colony 1–9 mm. in diameter.

Subaerial or growing on pebbles in running water or floating and entangled among filamentous algae; common.
Mich., Wis.

Nostoc muscorum C. A. Agardh 1812, p. 44
Pl. 120, Fig. 6

Colony a brown, lumpy or tuberculose membrane, firm and leathery when growing·on moist soil. Trichomes crowded and much entangled. Cells variable in shape, subcylindrical, barrel-shaped, or subglobose; constricted at the cross walls; 3–4μ in diameter, 5.4–6.5μ long. Heterocysts globose or compressed-globose, 6–7μ in diameter. Gonidia ovate, in a series, with smooth ochraceous membranes.

Occurring in swamps and in shallow water of lakes, mostly soft water; common. Mich., Wis.

Nostoc paludosum Kuetzing 1850, p. 1
Pl. 121, Figs. 1–3

Plant a minute, oblong or subspherical colony in which a few trichomes are loosely or (when young) tightly coiled in a wide and copious gelatinous investment. Cells barrel-shaped, 3–4μ in diameter; cell contents yellowish or olive-green. Heterocysts ovate, 4–5μ in diameter, 6μ long. Gonidia ovate, in short series; with a smooth membrane; 4–4.5μ in diameter, 6–8μ long. Colony 1 mm. or less in diameter.

In ditches and Sphagnum bogs; caught among mosses and mats of filamentous algae. Wis.

Nostoc pruniforme C. A. Agardh 1812, p. 45
Pl. 120, Figs. 7, 8

A spherical or ovate colony of loosely entangled or sometimes radiating trichomes inclosed in a copious and firm gelatinous matrix; olive-green when young and changing to a black-olive in age. Cells spherical or compressed-spherical to barrel-shaped; 4–6–(7.5)μ in diameter, 4–7μ long; cell contents blue-green or gray-green. Heterocysts globose or compressed-globose, 6–7μ in diameter. Gonidia spherical, about 10μ in diameter.

This species is common in hard water lakes and slow-flowing

streams, rare on recently inundated soil and on moist earth from which the water has receded. The colonies often appear as marble-like bodies scattered over the bottom among submerged grass, reeds, etc., sometimes in large numbers so that one can scoop them in double handfuls. Although the average size is 1–2.5 cm., the colonies may attain a diameter of 5 cm. Not infrequently they are mistaken for reptile eggs.

Mich., Wis.

Nostoc punctiforme (Kuetz.) Hariot 1891, p. 31
Pl. 121, Figs. 4, 5

A small, usually attached, colony of very compactly entangled trichomes in a colorless, soft mucilage; the linear arrangement of the cells frequently not discernible. Cells compressed-globose, 3.2–4μ in diameter. Heterocysts globose, 4.5–6μ in diameter. Gonidia ovate or oblong; 5–6μ in diameter, 5–8μ long.

Attached to large filamentous algae and to leaves and stems of submerged aquatics in hard water lakes. This species also occurs as an endophyte or a symbiont with lichens and some cycads. Mich., Wis.

Nostoc sphaericum Vaucher 1803, p. 223
Pl. 121, Figs. 6–9

A globose or tubercular, olive-green colony when young, becoming flattened and somewhat membranous and brown in age; trichomes densely entangled; cells globose, 4–5μ in diameter; heterocysts spherical, 7.4μ in diameter; gonidia solitary or in very short series (3–4 together), ovate, 5–7μ in diameter, 10μ long, with a smooth brown wall.

The colonies become as much as 5–6 cm. wide under favorable conditions. The species should be compared with *N. pruniforme,* an aquatic species, but one which sometimes appears in the same habitats as *N. sphaericum.*

Growing on soil at the margins of lakes; in marshy places among grasses; in thalli of *Ricciocarpus.* Mich., Wis.

Nostoc spongiaeforme C. A. Agardh 1824, p. 22
Pl. 121, Fig. 10

A globular colony of loosely entangled trichomes when young, becoming lobed, expanded, warty and bullate, especially when growing on damp soil, the color changing from blue-green to brownish-green. Cells variable in shape within the same colony, subglobose to barrel-shaped and cylindrical; 3.4–5μ in diameter, 5.4–6.5μ long. Heterocysts ovate to oblong or subglobose, 4.8–8μ in diameter, 7.2μ long. Gonidia oblong or ovate; formed in a series and becoming loosely arranged; 6–7μ in diameter, 8–10μ long.

Growing on damp soil in marshy places; near margins of lakes. Mich., Wis.

Nostoc verrucosum Vaucher 1803, p. 225
Pl. 121, Figs. 11–13

A globular or bullate, verrucose and warty, leathery mass, many colonies sometimes coalescing to form a large olive-green or brown, somewhat membranous expansion on soil or on submerged substrates, solid at first but becoming hollow. Trichomes densely entangled, especially in the outer firm layers of the colonial mucilage, less compact inward; straight and radiating, frequently with individual sheaths distinct. Cells compressed-spherical or disc-shaped, 3–4μ in diameter, 2.5–4μ long. Heterocysts spherical, 6μ in diameter. Gonidia ovate, 5μ wide, 7μ long.

Growing in 27–35 feet of water in semi-hard water lakes; sometimes large colonies are found floating or washed onto beaches of lakes; also reported growing on rocks near a waterfall. Mich., Wis.

WOLLEA Bornet & Flahault 1888, p. 223

An attached tubular, saccate-cylindric, gelatinous colony of macroscopic size in which unbranched, simple trichomes of ovate or cylindrical cells lie parallel, their sheaths confluent with the soft colonial mucilage; heterocysts intercalary, or terminal through vegetative fragmentation of the trichome; gonidia ovate, solitary or in a series, either adjoining the heterocyst or distantly removed from it.

Wollea saccata (Wolle) Bornet & Flahault 1888, p. 223
Pl. 122, Figs. 1, 2

Characteristics as described for the genus. Plant mass irregularly tubular or bullate, closed at the top, at first attached (usually in shallow water), later expanding and forming soft, gelatinous masses floating at the surface. Trichomes compactly arranged, mostly parallel with the long axis of the colony, not contorted and twisted but commonly curved. Cells ovate to subcylindric; constricted at the cross walls; varying in their diameter throughout the length of the trichome; 3.6–4.2–(5)μ in diameter, 5–10μ long. Heterocysts ovate to subcylindric; solitary; terminal or intercalary; 4–5μ in diameter, 6.5–9μ long. Gonidia oblong or subcylindrical, with thin, smooth walls; usually in a series of 3–5, rarely solitary; either near the heterocysts or distant from them.

This plant, although rare, has wide distribution in the United

States (Massachusetts and New Jersey to South Dakota). I have collected the species in southern Louisiana and in Panama.

Attached to the sandy bottom of lakes in shallow water. Wis.

NODULARIA Mertens, in Jürgens 1822, Dec. 15, No. 4

A sheathed filament, either solitary among other algae or forming thin expansions or tufts, aquatic or subaerial, on moist soil; cells disc-shaped or compressed spheroidal, constricted at the cross walls; heterocysts similarly compressed, about ⅓ of the width in length; gonidia spherical or disc-shaped, occurring in short (sometimes long) series, intercalary.

Key to the Species

Filaments 4–6µ in diameter; gonidia 6–8µ in diameter_____N. *Harveyana*
Filaments 8–12–(18)µ in diameter; gonidia 12µ in diameter_____N. *spumigena*

Nodularia Harveyana (Thw.) Thuret 1875, p. 378

Filaments usually solitary; nearly straight, sometimes flexuous but not entangled or coiled. Sheaths colorless and thin, usually close but sometimes diffluent and becoming indistinct. Cells 4–6µ in diameter, ⅓ the diameter in length or, before division, nearly as long as broad. Apical cell obtusely conical. Gonidia nearly spherical or compressed-spheroidal; about 8µ in diameter; yellowish-brown in color.

Tychoplankter; in shallow water. Wis.

Nodularia spumigena Mertens in Jürgens 1822, Dec. 15, No. 4
Pl. 122, Figs. 3–5

Filaments usually entangled and clustered in a loose, gelatinous mass; sometimes solitary; 8–12µ in diameter. Cells disc-shaped, very much compressed; constricted at the cross walls; 6–7.8–(10)µ in diameter, 5.6µ long. Gonidia intercalary but not necessarily near the heterocysts; 12µ in diameter, 8–9µ long.

Uncommon; found among algae in lakes of especially hard water; also adhering to the culms of rushes submerged in shallow water. Wis.

APHANIZOMENON Morren 1838, p. 11

Filamentous; united to form fusiform or plate-like bundles and flakes of parallel trichomes, which are free-floating. Trichomes relatively short, tapering very slightly at both ends. Cells quadrate-rectangular, constricted at the cross walls. Heterocysts cylindric, usually but one (rarely 2) in each trichome. Gonidia cylindrical, truncate at the apices; only one in each trichome; located in the median region but not adjacent to the heterocyst.

Aphanizomenon flos-aquae (L.) Ralfs 1850, p. 340
Pl. 122, Figs. 6–8

Trichomes parallel, tapering at both ends; united in bundles or flakes to form macroscopic colonies of few or hundreds of plants. Cells 5–6μ in diameter, 8–12μ long. Heterocysts oblong or cylindrical; scattered in the midregion of the trichome; 7μ in diameter, 12–20μ long. Gonidia cylindrical; formed near the middle of the trichome but not adjacent to the heterocyst; 8μ in diameter, 60–75μ long.

This plant is a frequent component of water blooms and in favorable habitats may become super-abundant. Hard water lakes in which there is a high nitrogen content and an adequate supply of carbon dioxide, either free or available in half-bound carbonates, may become biologically unbalanced by excessive growth of this plant. The cells have pseudovacuoles which permit the trichomes to float high in the water, where they form sticky masses, that are sometimes many square feet in extent. Either alone or in accompaniment with *Microcystis. aeruginosa* and *Anabaena spiroides,* this plant is not infrequently responsible for oxygen depletion in small lakes and bays, resulting in great loss of fish. The occurrence of this species is so consistently related to hard water lakes that it may be used as an index organism for high pH, and usually a high nitrogen and carbonate content (especially when the plant appears as a water bloom). *Aphanizomenon flos-aquae* is rarely found except in eutrophic lakes or in polluted, hard water, slow-flowing streams. An exception to this was found in Rahr Lake, Vilas County, Wisconsin, where there was a visible, although not abundant, bloom in August, Rahr Lake is a semi-hard water body with an acid marginal mat. This species may remain alive all winter in the vegetative state, sometimes thriving under ice; as with *Oscillatoria rubescens,* there is some evidence that such growths bring about depletion of oxygen in shallow lakes, poorly illuminated because of coverage by ice and snow. The blue-green algae are poor oxygenators in any case. Also the gonidia may carry the plant over a period of unfavorable environmental conditions. Their germination and the relation of the gonidium to bundle-formation have been carefully studied under laboratory conditions by Rose (1934).

Mich., Wis.

[528]

CYLINDROSPERMUM Kuetzing 1843, p. 211

Filaments straight, curved, or loosely entangled, each surrounded by a soft film of mucilage which is confluent with others, forming an expanded mass of indefinite shape on soil or on submerged substrates. Heterocysts ovate or ellipsoid, one at either end of the trichome, or at only one end. Cells cylindric or barrel-shaped and constricted at the cross walls. Gonidia ovate, ellipsoid, or subcylindric, adjoining the heterocyst, solitary or several in a series with smooth, punctate, or granular calls; inclosed by a thick, close sheath.

Key to the Species

1. Gonidia occurring in a series 2
1. Gonidia solitary, rarely 2 together 3
2. Cells 4–5μ in diameter; gonidia 8–10μ in diameter .... *C. catenatum*
2. Cells 2.3–3.5μ in diameter; gonidia 4–5.5μ in diameter .... *C. Marchicum*
3. Gonidia cylindrical or subcylindric 4
3. Gonidia ellipsoid or ovate 6
4. Cells 1.8–2μ in diameter; gonidia subcylindric,
   3.5–3.8μ in diameter .... *C. minimum*
4. Cells larger, 3.8–4.5–(6)μ in diameter; gonidia
   cylindrical, or subcylindric 5
5. Gonidia cylindrical, with smooth walls .... *C. stagnale*
5. Gonidia subcylindric, with roughened, punctate walls .... *C. majus*
6. Gonidia with punctate walls when mature 7
6. Gonidia with smooth walls 8
7. Gonidia 6–7μ in diameter .... *C. minutum*
7. Gonidia 14.8μ in diameter .... *C. majus*
8. Cells 2–2.5μ in diameter; gonidia 8–9μ in diameter .... *C. minutissimum*
8. Cells and gonidia larger 9
9. Gonidia 9–12μ in diameter, 10–20μ long .... *C. muscicola*
9. Gonidia 12–14μ in diameter, 20–38μ long .... *C. licheniforme*

Cylindrospermum catenatum Ralfs 1850, p. 338
Pl. 122, Figs. 9, 10

Filaments united by their confluent mucilage to form dark green patches on submerged aquatics or on damp soil. Cells rectangular to short-cylindric; slightly constricted at the cross walls; 4–5μ in diameter, 4–7μ long. Heterocysts ovate to ellipsoid, 4–5μ in diameter, 4–7μ long. Gonidia oblong; formed in a series adjacent to the heterocysts; with a smooth brownish wall when mature; 8–10μ in diameter, 14–18μ long.

On aquatic vegetation; tychoplanktonic. Mich., Wis.

Cylindrospermum licheniforme (Bory) Kuetzing 1847, p. 197
Pl. 131, Fig. 14

Filaments entangled and forming an expanse of macroscopic

proportions, dark green in color. Cells short cylindric; constricted at the cross walls; 2.5–4.2μ in diameter, 4–5μ long. Heterocysts elongate, 5–6μ in diameter, 7–12μ long. Gonidia solitary, elongate-ellipsoid to oblong; the wall thick and smooth; 12–14μ in diameter, 20–38μ long.

On submerged aquatic plants or on stones which are encrusted with sediment. Mich., Wis.

Cylindrospermum majus Kuetzing 1843, p. 212
Pl. 122, Figs. 11, 12

Filaments entangled to form dark green mucilaginous patches. Cells short-cylindric; slightly swollen and constricted at the cross walls; 3.7–5μ in diameter, 4–6μ long. Heterocysts elongate, little larger than the vegetative cells, up to 10μ long. Gonidia ellipsoid to subcylindric, with a roughened and punctate wall; 14.8μ in diameter, 27μ long, including the sheath.

In several soft water and acid lakes and pools. Wis.

Cylindrospermum Marchicum Lemmermann 1910, p. 196
Pl. 122, Fig. 13

Filaments entangled, forming small mucilaginous patches. Cells short-cylindric; slightly constricted at the cross walls; 2.5–3.5μ in diameter, 7.4–8.5μ long. Heterocysts ovate to subquadrate-ovate, 2.5–3μ in diameter, 3–4μ long. Gonidia ovate to subcylindric; in a catenate series adjoining the heterocyst; with thick smooth walls; 4–5.5μ in diameter, (12)–14.8–16μ long.

This plant should be compared with *C. catenatum* from which it differs but very slightly, chiefly in size. It was originally described as a variety of that species.

On moist substrates and on vegetation in shallow water. Wis.

Cylindrospermum minimum G. S. West 1914, p. 1016
Pl. 122, Figs. 14, 15

Filaments solitary, or in small clusters, straight or gracefully curved; cells rectangular to short cylindric, 1.8–2μ in diameter, 1.8–3.5μ long; heterocysts subglobose to ellipsoid, 2μ in diameter, 2.5–2.7μ long; gonidia solitary subcyclindric, 3.5–3.8μ in diameter, 8–9μ long, with a thick smooth wall.

This species was originally described from high altitudes in the Andes. Such a record naturally casts doubt on the assignment of our specimens, but they agree so well with West's description that the disposition seems justified. I have not seen the type specimens for comparison.

Rare in tychoplankton. Wis.

Cylindrospermum minutissimum Collins 1896, p. 120
Pl. 131, Fig. 13

Filaments loosely entangled, forming a thin blue-green skein. Vegetative cells quadrate-cylindric; not constricted at the cross walls; 2–2.5μ in diameter, 4–5μ long. Heterocysts elongate, 4μ in diameter, 6–8μ long. Gonidia solitary or in pairs; ellipsoid; the wall smooth; 8–9μ in diameter, 18–20μ long.

On mats of algae in shallow water; tychoplankter. Wis.

Cylindrospermum minutum Wood 1874, p. 39

Filaments much entangled in a mucilaginous expanse; forming bright blue-green to dark green patches on submerged aquatics; frequently scattered in minute clusters among other algae. Cells short-cylindric or slightly swollen, with constrictions at the cross walls; 3–4μ in diameter, 3.5–4.8μ long. Heterocysts ovate or subglobose, 5–7μ in diameter, 7–8μ long; hirsute, with long radiating gelatinous fibrils. Gonidia ovate, 6–7μ in diameter, 16–19μ long, with a punctate or granular wall.

Common in several acid or soft water lakes and small ponds. Mich., Wis.

Cylindrospermum muscicola Kuetzing 1845, p. 173
Pl. 122, Fig. 16

Filaments entangled in a mucous expanse, forming dark green patches on submerged aquatics (*Potamogeton, Elodea, Ceratophyllum*). Cells quadrate to cylindric; with slight constrictions at the cross walls; 3.5–5.5μ in diameter, 4–6.5μ long. Gonidia broadly ovate; with thick, smooth wall; 9–12μ in diameter, (9)–16–20μ long.

A rather common species, occurring mostly in hardwater habitats, alkaline swamps, and shallow lakes. The broadly ovate gonidia are characteristic. Mich., Wis.

Cylindrospermum stagnale (Kuetz.) Bornet & Flahault 1888, p. 250
Pl. 122, Figs. 17, 18

Filaments entangled or parallel in a mucilaginous expanse, attached or floating. Trichomes with cells constricted at the cross walls. Cells slightly swollen, 3.8–4.5–(6)μ in diameter, 7–13.4μ long. Heterocysts globular or elongate, 6–7μ in diameter, 7–16μ long. Gonidia ovate or subcylindric; with thick, smooth wall, (8)–10–15–(16)μ in diameter, 19–21.6–(40)μ long.

This is the most common species of the genus in our collections. It is found on or among aquatic vegetation such as submerged mosses, and in shallow water on dead and decaying grasses and culms of rushes. At first the plant mass is attached and spreading over the substrate, but soon becomes free-floating, forming mucilaginous flakes.

Mich., Wis.

Cylindrospermum stagnale var. *angustum* G. M. Smith 1916, p. 481
Pl. 123, Fig. 1

A form with gonidia smaller than in the typical plant; vegetative cells 4–4.5μ in diameter, 8–10μ long; heterocysts 5.5–5.6μ in diameter, 7–11μ long; gonidia 7–9μ in diameter, 18–25μ long.

Benthic and tychoplanktonic. Wis.

AULOSIRA Kirchner 1878, p. 238

Trichomes solitary or loosely clustered in small bundles, inclosed in a thin but definite sheath which is closed at the ends. Trichomes the same diameter throughout or narrowed in the midregion and larger toward the apices. Vegetative cells rectangular to short-cylindric, or somewhat barrel-shaped. Heterocysts intercalary; round, ovate, or subcylindric. Gonidia 1 to several in a series, sometimes adjacent to the heterocysts.

Aulosira laxa Kirchner 1878, p. 238
Pl. 123, Figs. 2, 3

Filaments straight or slightly curved; 8μ wide; usually solitary but sometimes in 2's or 3's, entangled and parallel, with thin, colorless, and close sheaths which are somewhat diffluent and not lamellate. Cells short and discoid or as long as wide (rarely a little longer); 6–7.2μ in diameter, 3–8μ long; much constricted and often not adjoined at the cross walls; sometimes forming a double series for a short distance in the sheath. Heterocysts quadrate to angular-globose, 7.5μ in diameter. Gonidia solitary or in series of 2–3; cylindrical with rounded ends; 5–7.5μ in diameter, 16–19μ long.

Entangled with other algae, forming soft gelatinous expanses on submerged sticks, etc. Wis.

FAMILY SCYTONEMATACEAE

The chief characteristic of the sheathed plants which comprise this family is their habit of forming false branches. The filaments are all uniseriate, but in *Desmonema* and *Diplocoleon* (not represented in our collections), more than one trichome is inclosed by a single sheath. All the genera except 2 (*Plectonema* and *Spelaeopogon*) have heterocysts. These determine the point of branch development in some forms, whereas in others the branching occurs between the heterocysts. The branch arises when hormogonia in the primary filament proliferate and produce series of cells that push out laterally through the sheath, often continuing to form successive branches. Occasionally branches arise in pairs when adjacent ends of two hormogonia proliferate.

The sheath is usually firm and definite and sometimes lamellate. It may be colorless or ochraceous. In general, the cells are quadrate or short-cylindric, although in some species they are somewhat barrel-shaped and constricted at the cross walls.

Key to the Genera

1. Heterocysts wanting_____*Plectonema*
1. Heterocysts present_____ 2
2. Heterocysts basal (with intercalary heterocysts sometimes also present; branching rare_____*Microchaete*
2. Heterocysts all intercalary; false branching frequent_____ 3
3. Branches arising in unilateral pairs, about midway between two heterocysts (sometimes branches at the heterocysts also); sheath usually lamellate_____*Scytonema*
3. Branches arising singly, just below a heterocyst or a series of them_____ 4
4. Filaments aggregated, somewhat radially arranged in a mucilaginous layer; branching regularly dichotomous; heterocysts solitary_____*Diplonema*
4. Filaments solitary or aggregated, sometimes forming free-floating, cottony tufts; branching irregular; heterocysts solitary or 2–4 in a series_____*Tolypothrix*

SCYTONEMA C. A. Agardh 1824, p. xxii

A falsely branched, usually thick-sheathed, filament, the false branches ordinarily developing in pairs (rarely singly) between the heterocysts (and sometimes also at the heterocysts); forming wooly mats or tangled clots. Trichomes·solitary within the sheath, forming hormogonia in the branches. Cells quadrate or short-cylindric. Heterocysts subglobose or quadrangular-globose. Gonidia rare; globose or ovate; about the same size as the vegetative cells. Sheaths sometimes homogeneous but in most species definitely lamellated, with the layers either parallel or diverging; hyaline or, especially in the main filament, ochraceous.

This genus should be compared with *Tolypothrix*. *Scytonema mirabile*, for example, seldom forms branches in pairs but singly, as in *Tolypothrix*.

Key to the Species

1. Sheaths very wide, forming lateral, wing-like expansions_____*S. alatum*
1. Sheaths not forming wing-like expansions_____ 2

Scytonema alatum (Carm.) Borzi 1879, p. 373
Pl. 123, Figs. 4, 5

Filaments forming dark olive-brown, wooly mats or tufts. Branches of trichomes in pairs between the heterocysts, branches relatively short. Cells short cylindric or barrel-shaped; 9–15μ in diameter, 8–15μ long. Heterocysts subglobose, tinged with yellow-brown. Sheaths wide; much lamellated, with the layers diverging, forming 'wings'; with decided constrictions here and there, especially at the heterocysts. Filaments 24–66μ in diameter.

Tychoplankter. Mich., Wis.

Scytonema Archangelii Bornet & Flahault 1887, p. 92
Pl. 123, Figs. 6, 7

Filaments in fascicles or tufts, forming brownish or gray mats and cushions. Trichomes with long, gracefully curved branches arising singly at the heterocysts, or more commonly in pairs between the heterocysts. Cells quadrate; without constrictions at the cross walls; 12–18μ in diameter, 14–20μ long. Heterocysts quadrate or cylindrical; either colorless or ochraceous. Sheaths thin, close, hyaline. Filaments 12–16μ in diameter.

Tychoplanktonic and on shore. Wis.

Scytonema coactile Montagne in Kuetzing 1849, p. 305
Pl. 124, Figs. 1–3

Filaments forming thick, blue-green skeins or film-like expansions. Trichomes frequently branched, with the solitary habit predominating; false branches long and spreading. Cells quadrate or compressed barrel-shaped, 12–18μ in diameter, 5.8–7.5μ long; cell contents a deep blue-green or yellow-green, especially in the distal ends of the branches. Heterocysts scattered and infrequent; olive-brown in color; ovate or subglobose; 15.6μ in diameter, 19.5μ long. Sheaths close and firm; colorless or light olive; not lamellate. Filaments 18–23.4μ in diameter.

All our specimens of this plant have been collected in *Sphagnum* bogs and soft water lakes. Wis.

Scytonema crispum (C. A. Ag.) Bornet 1889, p. 156
[*S. cincinnatum* Thuret]
Pl. 124, Figs. 4–6

Filaments forming dark brown or gray-brown wooly mats; seldom branched; coarse and wiry. Trichomes straight or somewhat bent, not tapering, frequently constricted and forming hormogonia. Cells very short, disc-like; 14–30μ in diameter, 2.4–3μ long. Heterocysts spherical, frequent, olive-green or yellowish, 19μ in diameter. Sheath thick (3.5μ), firm, brown, not lamellated. Filaments 16–36 (mostly 20–30μ) in diameter.

Frequent in hard water lakes. Forming tangled, brown clots among filamentous algae or submerged aquatics. In sections of the filament which are unbranched and in which no heterocysts occur the plant has the appearance of a coarse *Lyngbya*. Wis.

Scytonema mirabile (Dillw.) Bornet 1889, p. 155
[*S. figuratum* C. A. Agardh]
Pl. 124, Figs. 7, 8

Filaments forming brown or dark green wooly tufts, either aquatic or terrestrial. Trichomes with long, infrequent branches usually arising singly either at the heterocysts or between heterocysts. Cells quadrate in the main filaments, cylindrical in the branches; 6–12μ in diameter, 8–14μ long. Heterocysts quadrate-globose to cylindric; about the same size as the vegetative cells. Sheaths thin and close in the branches, thick and with diverging lamellations in the main filaments. Filaments 15–20μ in diameter.

One of the most common species of *Scytonema* found in our region. It occurs in both soft and hard water lakes. Many times the plants have the appearance of a *Tolypothrix,* especially in the habit of branching.

Mich., Wis.

Scytonema myochrous (Dillw.) C. A. Agardh 1812, p. 38
Pl. 124, Fig. 9; Pl. 125, Figs. 1, 2

Filaments forming dark brown turfy or tomentose patches. Trichomes long and flexuous in wide sheaths. Cells quadrate to cylindric in the older portions, disc-shaped or compressed-globose in the

[535]

distal ends of the branches; 6–12μ in diameter, 4–14μ long. Heterocysts quadrangular-globose, yellow-brown in color, the contents yellow-green, sheaths thick and lamellated, with layers diverging; brown in color. Filaments 18–36μ wide.

This species is recorded frequently from aerial habitats.

On logs and stones; tychoplankter. Mich., Wis.

Scytonema tolypothricoides Kuetzing 1849, p. 307
[*S. mirabile* var. *tolypothricoides* (Kuetz.) Lobik 1915, p. 42]
Pl. 123, Figs. 8, 9

Filaments forming dark blue-green or brown floating, cottony clots. Trichomes more or less radiating from a common center; freely branched, the branches mostly in pairs. Cells quadrate to subcylindric in the older portions, compressed and much shorter than wide in the branches; 6.8–12μ in diameter. Heterocysts quadrate or ovate; about 10μ in diameter. Sheaths wide, lamellate, at first colorless, becoming brown or orange colored. Filaments 10–15μ in diameter.

Common in the plankton of a variety of lakes, mostly soft water. Appearing as *Tolypothrix*-like clots floating among aquatic vegetation near shore. Mich., Wis.

TOLYPOTHRIX Kuetzing 1843, p. 227

A sheathed, falsely branched trichome; solitary or, more usually, forming cottony tufts and expansions; the false branches mostly long and flexuous, arising from just below a heterocyst. Cells quadrate to cylindric or barrel-shaped, constricted at the cross walls. Heterocysts quadrangular, globose, or subglobose, single or in series. Sheath firm and thin, or somewhat gelatinous and lamellated. Gonidia ovate to elliptic, or subglobose; with a thin membrane; often occurring in a series.

Key to the Species

1. Sheaths thick, about as wide, or wider than
   the diameter of the trichome_____ 2
1. Sheaths thin, usually close, but lamellated in some; less than the
   diameter of the trichome in width_____ 3
2. Trichomes 5.5–9μ in diameter; cells barrel-shaped;
   sheaths not sticky_____*T. limbata*
2. Trichomes 8–10μ in diameter; cells quadrate, not at all or but very
   little constricted at the cross walls; sheaths sticky_____*T. conglutinata*
3. Cells very short, disc-like, 9–12μ in diameter_____*T. distorta*
3. Cells longer than wide, or quadrate_____ 4
4. Cells 8–10μ in diameter; heterocysts 7μ in diameter, quadrate or
   cylindrical; filaments up to 18μ wide_____*T. lanata*
4. Cells smaller, 5–8μ in diameter; heterocysts globose, subglobose
   to subcylindric; filaments up to 10μ wide_____*T. tenuis*

Tolypothrix conglutinata Borzi 1879, p. 371
Pl. 125, Figs. 3, 4

Sparsely-branched filaments, closely entangled to form cottony masses which adhere together by their sticky sheaths. Trichomes bent and curved, with false branches arising from prostrate main axes. Cells quadrate, only slightly constricted at the cross walls, (7.2)–8–10μ in diameter, 3.7–5μ long. Heterocysts ovate or globose, 9.2μ in diameter, 3.7–5μ long; basal and intercalary. Sheaths wide, mucilaginous, not lamellate, somewhat diffluent at the base of the plant mass. Filaments 12–14–$(18)\mu$ wide.

Although type specimens or authentically named material have not been seen, the Wisconsin plants are assigned here because of their close agreement with the original description of this species.

Rare; in the tychoplankton. Wis.

Tolypothrix distorta Kuetzing 1843, p. 228
Pl. 125, Figs. 5, 6

Filaments forming cottony tufts or cushion-like expansions; trichomes repeatedly branched, the branches spreading and flexuous, or erect; cells 9–12μ in diameter, shorter than wide, slightly constricted at the cross walls; heterocysts subglobose, usually solitary or in series of 2–3; sheath thin, firm, not lamellate, slightly swollen at the base of the branches; filaments 10–15–$(25)\mu$ wide.

This is a species which frequently becomes planktonic. It forms macroscopic growths in many lakes. Mich., Wis.

In our observations of material the plant seems to intergrade with *T. tenuis*. The consistently shorter cells, however, and the average greater width of the filaments in *T. distorta* help to separate the two.

Tolypothrix lanata Wartmann in Rabenhorst 1858, No. 768
Pl. 125, Fig. 7

Filaments forming cottony tufts or brownish layers. Trichomes, 9–13μ in diameter, repeatedly branched, the branches long and flexuous. Cells quadrate to cylindric, longer than wide, 8–10μ in diameter, 10–12μ long; cell contents homogeneous, blue-green. Heterocysts subovate or subcyhndric; solitary or 2–3 in a series; 7.4 in diameter, 8–11 long. Sheaths thin and firm, sometimes inflated at the base of the branches. Filaments 9–12–(18) wide.

This species should be compared with *T. tenuis*, which is a more slender form. J. Schmidt (1899) redescribes the latter species and includes *T. lanata* Wartmann.

Common in many lakes, especially in soft or acid water. Mich., Wis.

Tolypothrix limbata Thuret *in* Bornet & Flahault 1887, p. 124
Pl. 126, Figs. 1, 2

Filaments forming dense wooly tufts; coarse. Trichomes repeatedly branched, the branches variously disposed, erect or spreading and flexuous, rarely two unilateral branches arising from near the base of a heterocyst. Cells quadrate or slightly longer than wide; 5.5–9μ in diameter, 5–7μ long; cell contents gray-green. Heterocysts relatively large; globose; up to 11μ in diameter; occurring singly or in pairs. Sheaths wide, thick, lamellated; becoming golden-brown in age.

This is a common species, usually entangled about or attached to submerged aquatics; in tychoplankton in a variety of lakes. Mich., Wis.

Tolypothrix tenuis Kuetzing; *emend.* J. Schmidt 1899, p. 383

A long, slender, frequently and repeatedly branched trichome with thin sheaths; either solitary or forming thick brown mats in full development. Cells cylindrical, quadrate, or a little longer than wide; 5–8μ in diameter, usually not constricted at the cross walls. Heterocysts subglobose to subcylindric; 8μ in diameter, 11μ long; occurring singly or 2–5 in a series. Sheath thin, firm, somewhat swollen at the base of the branches. Filaments 8–10μ wide.

When young, the plants are attached in cottony masses about the culms of rushes, later floating free. There often appears in our collections an expression of this species which agrees with the description of *T. tenuis* var. *Wartmanniana* (Kuetz.) Hansgirg.

This species appears in a great variety of lakes, commonly in tychoplankton. Mich., Wis.

DIPLONEMA Borzi 1917, p. 103

A dichotomously branched, tortuous, radiating and prostrate trichome inclosed in a hyaline or brownish sheath which may be lamellated in the older portions, or homogeneous; the branches arising near a heterocyst, which is globose or ovate, and either basal or intercalary. Vegetative cells torulose or short-cylindric, much constricted at the joints in the basal part of the trichome but with parallel lateral walls in the distal portion, tapering slightly toward the apex.

Diplonema rupicola Borzi 1917, p. 103
Pl. 126, Fig. 3

Characteristics as described for the genus; cells 3.2–4.5μ in diameter, 3.5–5μ long; trichomes dichotomously branched in hyaline,

non-lamellated sheaths, scarcely tapering toward the apices; heterocysts the same size as the vegetative cells.

Forming prostrate patches on submerged logs and stones. Wis.

PLECTONEMA Thuret 1875, p. 375

A falsely branched, sheathed trichome, occurring either free and
solitary or in wooly mats, or embedded and attached in the mucilage
of other algae; cells short, disc-like or barrel-shaped, constricted at
the cross walls or not, forming long trichomes (usually) which
taper but very little, if at all, toward the apices; branches arising
singly or in pairs, often becoming free or extending loosely away
from the main filament; sheaths thin and close, or thick in some
species, homogeneous or lamellate, usually colorless, sometimes
yellowing or becoming brown with age; heterocysts wanting.

Key to the Species

1. Filaments coarse, seldom branched, 28–50µ in diameter_____*P. Wollei*
1. Filaments frequently branched, less than 28µ in diameter_____ 2
2. Plants forming tufts or fascicles_____*P. tenue*
2. Plants solitary or forming mucous layers or expansions_____ 3
3. Plants inhabiting the mucilage of other
   algae, especially *Nostoc*_____*P. nostocorum*
3. Plants free-living; solitary, gregarious, or forming thin wefts_____ 4
4. Filaments 3.7–4µ in diameter; purplish_____*P. purpureum*
4. Filaments less than 3.7µ in diameter_____ 5
5. Trichomes reddish_____*P. carneum*
5. Trichomes not red_____*P. notatum*

Plectonema carneum (Kuetz.) Lemmermann *ex* Geitler 1925a, p. 249
[*P. roseolum* (P. Richt.) Gomont]

Filaments matted and entangled, forming thin, reddish, gelatinous
layers; false branches frequent, solitary or in pairs; sheaths thick,
uneven and colorless, not colored by chlor-zinc-iodide reagent; cells
1.2–1.8µ in diameter, 1.7–5µ long, not constricted at the cross walls,
which are marked by 2 granules; apical cell broadly rounded.

Tychoplankter; on moist aerial substrates. Wis.

Plectonema nostocorum Bornet *in* Bornet & Thuret 1880, p. 137
Pl. 126, Figs. 4, 5

A slender, frequently branched filament in the mucilage of *Nostoc*
and other blue-green algae, or forming small gelatinous masses;
cells quadrate or slightly longer than wide, frequently separated
from each other, 0.7–1.5µ in diameter, 2–3µ long; sheaths thin, colorless; branches usually solitary; filaments 2–4µ in diameter.

Common in many lakes and swamps, almost invariably found in

the mucilage of aquatic species of *Nostoc* which occur intermingled among other algae. Wis.

Plectonema notatum Schmidle 1902a, p. 84
Pl. 126, Figs. 6, 7

Free-living, solitary or forming thin mucous wefts; cells cylindric, little if at all constricted at the cross walls, which are marked by 2 conspicuous but small granules, $1.2-2\mu$ in diameter, $2-3\mu$ long; sheath thin but definite; branches solitary or in pairs; filaments $1.7-2\mu$ in diameter.

Forming a weft on filamentous algae such as *Microspora* and *Rhizoclonium* and on sheathed blue-green algae such as *Lyngbya* and *Tolypothrix*. Wis.

Plectonema purpureum Gomont 1892a, p. 101
Pl. 126, Fig. 8

A much-branched filament, united in bundles or forming slimy, reddish or purplish patches; branches solitary or in pairs, much bent and recurving; cells short-cylindric, or disc-shaped, slightly constricted at the cross walls, $3.5-3.8\mu$ in diameter, $2.8-3.5\mu$ long; apical cell broadly rounded; sheath thin but definite; filaments $3.7-4\mu$ in diameter.

Growing on filamentous algae and on debris in shallow water. Wis.

Plectonema tenue Thuret 1875, p. 380
Pl. 126, Fig. 9

A much-branched, thickly-sheathed trichome, forming wooly masses (sometimes only a few filaments together); cells disc-shaped or quadrate, a little shorter than wide, not constricted at the cross walls, or very rarely so, $6-7.6-(10)\mu$ in diameter, $2-6\mu$ long; apical cell slightly tapering; sheaths thick, colorless at first, becoming yellow and lamellate; branches solitary or in pairs; filaments up to 16.6μ in diameter.

Among other algae in tychoplankton. Wis.

Plectonema Wollei Farlow 1877, p. 77
Pl. 127, Fig. 1

A coarse, sparsely branched filament, forming brown or gray-green wooly mats; cells disc-shaped, much shorter than wide, not constricted at the cross walls, $28-50\mu$ in diameter, $4-9\mu$ long; apical cell broadly or truncately rounded; sheaths thick and lamellate; colorless at first but becoming discolored in age; trichomes straight, frequently constricted or interrupted to form hormogonia; branches single or in pairs (seldom seen unless a great deal of material is examined).

The infrequency with which this species develops false branches gives it the general appearance of a very coarse and thick-sheathed *Lyngbya.*

Forming wooly, brown, tangled clots, either floating or caught among submerged aquatics, especially in hard water habitats. Mich., Wis.

MICROCHAETE Thuret 1875, p. 378

A uniseriate non-tapering trichome with a basal heterocyst, as well as intercalary heterocysts, inclosed by a firm, thin sheath; false branching sometimes present; cells barrel-shaped, shorter than wide, quadrate or, in a few species, slightly longer than wide; basal heterocyst globose, the intercalary ones short- or long-cylindric with truncate poles; sheaths firm, thin, rarely lamellated; filaments solitary or in small stellate tufts attached along their basal portion to larger algae or other aquatics, bent and becoming free from the substrate in the distal portion of the plant.

The occasional false branch in this genus justifies its inclusion in the Scytonemataceae. Lemmermann has set aside *Microchaete, Aulosira,* and *Hormothamnion* to form the Microchaetaceae.

Key to the Species

1. Trichomes with spirally lamellated sheaths..*M. spiralis*
1. Trichomes with parallel lamellated sheaths, or sheaths unlamellated.......... 2
2. Sheath lamellated, double, with an inner and
   an outer firm layer..*M. diplosiphon*
2. Sheath single, thinner than above, either homogeneous or lamellated.......... 3
3. Heterocysts at the base of the trichome only....................*M. Goeppertiana*
3. Heterocysts both basal and intercalary... 4
4. Filaments 16–18µ wide; sheath lamellate................................*M. robusta*
4. Filaments 12–14µ wide; sheath not lamellate.............................*M. tenera*

Microchaete diplosiphon Gomont 1885, p. 212
Pl. 127, Fig. 2

Filaments curved or straight, appressed to substrate for but a short distance; vegetative cells 3.5–6µ in diameter, 3.7–4µ long; basal heterocyst globose to ovate, 7.4µ in diameter, 11µ long; intercalary heterocysts quadrate to cylindrical; sheath lamellated and with 2 or more layers; filament 10–12µ wide; gonidia (not observed in our collections) in a series and about the same size as the vegetative cells.

On *Pithophora* filaments in a slow-flowing stream. Wis.

Microchaete Goeppertiana Kirchner *in* Engler & Prantl 1900, p. 76
Pl. 127, Figs. 3, 4

Filaments usually solitary or a few together, straight or slightly curved away from the substrate to which they adhere; cells short cylindric, 3.7–6μ in diameter, often slightly separated from one another; heterocyst basal only, ovate or globose, 6.5μ in diameter; sheath thin and close, without lamellations; filaments 5.7μ wide.

On filamentous green algae. Wis.

Microchaete robusta Setchell & Gardner 1903, p. 194
Pl. 127, Fig. 5

Filaments solitary or several (4) radiating from a common center, enlarged at the base, slightly tapering distally; cells spheroidal or quadrate to slightly longer than wide, 12μ in diameter, (6)–10–16μ long; cell contents granular at the cross walls; basal heterocyst globose, intercalary heterocysts quadrate; sheath thin but lamellated; filament 16–18μ wide.

Our specimens do not show granulations at the cross walls, but they have been assigned to this species on the basis of size and other characteristics which are in agreement.

On filamentous algae. Wis.

Microchaete spiralis Ackley 1929, p. 302
Pl. 131, Fig. 3

Filaments in small tufts, straight or curved, with spirally lamellose, rather close, thick sheaths; vegetative cells 6–8μ in diameter, somewhat quadrate-cylindric at the base of the trichome, becoming subglobose in the apical region; heterocysts ovate, 4–4.5μ in diameter, 6μ long.

Tychoplankter; in a roadside ditch. Mich.

Microchaete tenera Thuret 1875, p. 378
Pl. 127, Fig. 6

Filaments slender, long, but not tapering, straight or little-curved, either solitary or more usually in stellate tufts on larger algae, and other submerged aquatics; cells quadrate, shorter or a little longer than wide, 4–5μ in diameter; basal heterocysts quadrate-cylindric; gonidia short-cylindric, 6.8μ in diameter, 6.8–8μ long; arranged in a basal series; sheaths thin, firm, close, without lamellations; filaments 12–14μ in diameter.

Common on large filamentous algae, on *Utricularia, Myriophyllum,* etc.; usually in soft water or acid lakes. Mich., Wis.

[542]

FAMILY STIGONEMATACEAE

In this family the cells are arranged in uniseriate or multiseriate branched filaments. The trichomes have definite sheaths which may be close and firm or wide, lamellate, and mucilaginous. Whereas cells may be quadrate or cylindrical in some genera, they are globose or transversely elliptic in others, and in some species intercellular connections are conspicuous. The heterocyst in this family is extremely variable in shape. In some genera it is characteristically quadrate or cylindrical, with truncate apices, but in others it is globose or ellipsoidal. It may be intercalary or lateral, in which case it develops by longitudinal division of a vegetative cell. The habit of branching in this family clearly differentiates it from the Scytonemataceae. The branches (also sheathed) arise by cell division in a plane at right angles to the longitudinal axis of the principal trichome. In some genera the lateral proliferations are more slender than the main filament, and special hormogonia may occur in the apices of the branches.

Key to the Genera

1. Filaments uniseriate, rarely biseriate in part; heterocysts intercalary; sheaths (in our specimens) relatively thin, firm, and close _____ *Hapalosiphon*
1. Filaments composed of 2 to several series of cells (rarely uniseriate); heterocysts lateral and intercalary_____ 2
2. Branches narrow, erect, mostly unilateral, with hormogonia formed in their apices _____*Fischerella*
2. Branches nearly or quite as wide as the main filament, and arising from all sides; not regularly producing hormogonia in the apices of the branches_____*Stigonema*

HAPALOSIPHON Naegeli 1849, p. 894; *emend.* Borzi 1917, p. 90

Creeping, branched, uniseriate trichomes inclosed in a wide and lamellated, or a close, firm sheath; branches usually at right angles to and about the same diameter as the main filament but with thinner sheaths; cells cylindrical in most species, sometimes elliptical and much constricted at the cross walls; heterocysts oblong or quadrate-cylindrical, the contents homogeneous.

The uniseriate trichome, bearing true branches which seldom rebranch and which are about the same diameter as in the main filament characterize this genus. The branches are usually unilateral, but there is considerable variation in this, and one must be careful in using keys to species which employ the arrangement of branches as a point for differentiation.

After studying species in this genus and after examining herbarium material, including several type species, it immediately becomes apparent that there is much confusion in the nomenclature. *Hapalosiphon pumilus* in nature shows great variation in size, in habit of branching, and in color of the sheaths. Some of the expressions cannot be separated from herbarium specimens bearing other names, and it seems likely that a critical study of the genus will reduce some names to synonymy. It seems best to retain the present names for the forms which appear in our collections, pending the appearance of a specialist's monographic study.

Key to the Species

1. Filaments irregularly branching from all sides of the main axis............ 2
1. Filaments mostly branching from one side of the main axis; bilateral branches not infrequent.. 3
2. Heterocysts and cells elliptical; filament up to 8μ in diameter......*H. flexuosus*
2. Heterocysts and cells quadrate to cylindrical; filaments up to 20μ in diameter..*H. confervaceus*
3. Sheath ochraceous or golden-brown, filaments 10–25μ wide............ 4
3. Sheath colorless; filaments averaging mostly less than 10μ wide............ 6
4. Filaments up to 11μ wide; branches narrower than the main filament ....*H. brasiliensis*
4. Filaments larger, 11.5–25μ wide.. 5
5. Main filaments 11–12.5μ in diameter; sheath golden-brown, thick over the branches..*H. aureus*
5. Main filaments up to 25μ in diameter; sheath colorless to ochraceous, thin over the branches ....*H. pumilus*
6. Branches crooked, arising at various angles from the main axis; cells up to 3 times their diameter in length............................*H. intricatus*
6. Branches straight, arising at right angles to the main axis; cells up to 8 times their diameter in length ....*H. hibernicus*

Hapalosiphon aureus West & West 1897, p. 241
Pl. 128, Figs. 1–3

Creeping, forming a loosely entangled mat with numerous, mostly short, branches arising from one side (rarely from both sides) of the main filament. Cells ellipsoid, quadrate, or cylindrical, especially in the apices of the branches, 6–9μ in diameter, 12–24μ long; sheath, thin, close, colorless in the branches, golden-brown in the main filament, which is 11–12.5μ in diameter.

Sometimes our specimens had colorless sheaths throughout a part of the plant, with the cell membrane ochraceus. Many herbarium specimens of this plant have been studied critically. I believe that these cannot be separated from the many expressions of *H. pumilus*, which is extremely variable.

In *Sphagnum* bogs and other soft water habitats. Mich., Wis.

Hapalosiphon brasiliensis Borge 1918, p. 94

This species, like *H. aureus,* is here considered to be a small form of *H. pumilus.* One of the characteristics which might be used to separate it from the latter species is the difference in size between the branches and the main filament. The cells are 7–9µ in diameter, up to 27µ long; filaments up to 11µ in diameter.

Plants which agree with the description of *H. brasiliensis* Borge are found in the same habitat with the larger *H. pumilus.*

In *Sphagnum* bogs and soft water habitats. Wis.

Hapalosiphon confervaceus Borzi 1892, p. 43
Pl. 128, Fig. 4

Filaments prostrate and creeping over submerged aquatics, branching freely from both sides of the principal trichome; cells quadrate or cylindrical, 8–12µ in diameter, 1–3 times the diameter in length; heterocyst short- or long-cylindric, about the same size as the vegetative cells; sheath thin, colorless, non-lamellated; filament 15–20µ wide.

Our plants are assigned here because of the habit of branching and the shape and size of the cells, characters which agree with the description of *H. confervaceus* Borzi. This species is described as having calcareous deposits on the sheath, but the presence or absence of such depositions is not a specific characteristic. Wis.

Hapalosiphon flexuosus Borzi 1892, p. 43
Pl. 128, Figs. 5, 6

Filaments tortuous, creeping and entwining about strands of submerged grass or bits of other aquatic plants, giving rise to long, curved branches from both sides; cells ellipsoid in the main trichome, becoming somewhat cylindric in the apices of the branches, 5.8–6.2µ in diameter; heterocysts ellipsoid, 6.2µ in diameter, 7–8.5µ long; sheath thin, hyaline and without lamellations; filament 7.4–8µ wide.

In shallow water of a small grassy lake. Mich., Wis.

Hapalosiphon hibernicus West & West 1896, p. 163

A prostrate filament, either solitary or forming small entangled tufts on submerged aquatics, branches unilateral and long, narrower than the main filament and slightly tapering; cells quadrate-spherical to long-cylindric, especially in the apices of the branches, 8.5–9.2µ in diameter in the main trichome; heterocysts short- or long-cylindric,

5.8–8μ in diameter, 11.7–15μ long; sheath thin, colorless, and not lamellate; filament 7.5–10–(12)μ wide.

Like other species in this genus, *H. hibernicus* seems to be confined to shallow water where there is a concentration of organic matter and considerable bacterial decomposition in progress.

Among other algae in soft water lakes. Wis.

Hapalosiphon intricatus West & West 1895b, p. 271
Pl. 129, Fig. 1

Trichomes with unilateral, rather short branches which are flexuous, densely entangled, and equal in diameter to the main filament; sheaths close; cells ovate, barrel-shaped or short-cylindric, 3.8–6.8–(7.2)μ in diameter.

Forming a blue-green weft over *Sphagnum;* in swampy margins of lakes. Wis.

Hapalosiphon pumilus (Kuetz.) Kirchner 1878, p. 231
Pl. 129, Figs. 2–4

Filaments prostrate and much entangled, forming dense and very extensive mats on submerged aquatics, freely branching, the branches arising mostly unilaterally; cells globose, quadrate or short-cylindric, 6–10μ in diameter, 1–3 times the diameter in length; heterocysts short- or long-cylindric, 10μ in diameter, 12–22μ long; sheath thin in the older parts of the plant, lamellate, either hyaline or yellow-brown; main filament, 12–25μ wide, branches 10–15μ wide.

Common in shallow water at margins of reed-filled lakes and in acid swamps. In the latter habitat this species may be the dominant form, producing brown cottony mats and clots about culms of rushes, dead grasses, etc., sometimes acres in extent. Mich., Wis.

The characteristics of this plant are best determined by studying the older portions of the plant. Young branchings show color, cell-shape and sheath characters unlike the main body of the plant and, when isolated, may become identified as some of the other species of *Hapalosiphon*. Indeed, it is possible that some of the names and descriptions applied to expressions of *Hapalosiphon* may be based on young portions of *H. pumilus*. See notes on *H. aureus* above.

STIGONEMA C. A. Agardh 1824, p. xxii

Multiseriate (rarely uniseriate), branched and irregularly spreading filaments with wide, firm, mucilaginous sheaths which may be either homogeneous or lamellated, hyaline or colored; plants either scattered among other algae or forming cushion-like clumps or turfy patches, free-floating, or on soil and moist substrates; cells globose, depressed-globose, or ovate, often with intercellular connections; heterocysts either intercalary or lateral; branches often developing hormogonia in the distal portion.

Stigonema is commonly terrestrial, but there are a few aquatic and amphibious species. This genus should be compared with *Hapalosiphon,* although the two are ordinarily easily separable on the basis of the number of series of cells in the filament. *Stigonema* spp. are sometimes uniseriate and *Hapalosiphon* spp. tend to become biseriate, but not throughout the entire plant. Occasionally *Hapalosiphon* branches will rebranch as they do in *Stigonema.* The contents of the *Stigonema* cell are usually more nearly homogeneous than in *Hapalosiphon.* The laterally developed heterocysts are typical of *Stigonema.* One comes to differentiate the two genera by their respective combinations of characteristics.

From *Fischerella, Stigonema* is differentiated by the slender erect branches of the former which terminate in homogonia. Some authors include species of *Fischerella* in a subgenus of *Stigonema.*

Key to the Species

1. Filaments uniseriate; individual cell sheaths conspicuous; intercellular connections evident_____*S. ocellatum*
1. Filaments multiseriate_____ 2
2. Filamentous habit scarcely discernible; lateral clusters of cells inclosed by lamellate sheaths and forming short, bullate branches_____*S. mesentericum*
2. Filamentous arrangement of cells apparent; more elongate branches_____ 3
3. Filaments 40–70μ wide; plants mostly aquatic; branches short and broad_____*S. mamillosum*
3. Filaments 27–37μ wide; plants mostly terrestrial; branches long and curved_____*S. turfaceum*

Stigonema mamillosum (Lyngb.) C. A. Agardh 1824, p. 42
Pl. 130, Figs. 1–3

Filaments much-branched, forming attached, dark green wooly tufts, or scattered in small entanglements among other floating algae, composed of several series of globose or ellipsoid cells; branches short, irregularly developing, narrowed at both the base and in the distal region; heterocysts numerous, compressed-ovate, cut off laterally from the vegetative cells; sheath wide, lamellate, becoming yellowish or olive-brown in age; cells 14–17μ in diameter; filaments 40–70μ wide; hormogonia developing in special short branches.

Our collections have all been made from soft water habitats.

Common in several lakes, usually attached to submerged wood; sometimes forming small clots among floating algae. Mich., Wis.

Stigonema mesentericum Geitler 1925a, p. 184
Pl. 130, Fig. 4

A gelatinous, cushion-like mass, composed of filaments with very short, broad, irregularly developed branches in which series of globose or ovate cells are arranged without definite order; heterocysts compressed globose, intercalary or lateral; cells 6–12μ in diameter; sheath close, thick and lamellate, inclosing small groups of cells which form irregular lobes from the main axis; filaments 25–35μ wide.

Tychoplankter; in semi-hard water lakes. Wis.

Stigonema ocellatum (Dillw.) Thuret 1875, p. 380
[Incl. *S. tomentosum* (Kuetz.) Hieronymus 1895, p. 166]
Pl. 130, Figs. 5, 6

Filaments forming brown tufts or cottony masses, with long, narrow and curved branches; trichomes partly uniseriate; heterocysts mostly lateral; cells quadrate-globose to globose, with intercellular connections, 20–30μ in diameter in the principal filament, each cell inclosed by a conspicuous individual sheath which is either colorless or brown; cell contents blue- or olive-green to bright marine-green in the young cells of the branches; sheath wide and lamellated, brown in the older parts, colorless in the branches; filaments 35–45μ wide.

Stigonema ocellatum is a very common species, appearing in a great variety of fresh-water and aerial habitats. It is often a conspicuous component of the algal flora in habitats where desmids abound, forming brown wooly mats on and over submerged aquatics such as the culms of *Scirpus, Utricularia,* decaying leaves, etc.

This is the only common species of *Stigonema* which has but one series of cells in the filament (rarely showing a double series for short distances).
Mich., Wis.

Stigonema turfaceum (Berkeley) Cooke 1884, p. 272
Pl. 129, Fig. 5

Filaments much-branched, forming dark-colored, cushion-like masses, the branches about the same diameter as the principal filaments, long and curved, with hormogonia produced distally; trichomes of from 2–4 series of globose or much compressed-globose cells which in the hormogonia are 12μ in diameter; heterocysts intercalary or lateral, much compressed; sheaths wide, lamellate and yellow-brown in age; filaments 27–37μ in diameter.

Tychoplankter. Mich., Wis.

[548]

FISCHERELLA (Bornet & Flahault) Gomont 1895, p. 52

A branched and sheathed filament with a stouter, prostrate portion giving rise to vertically elongate, much narrower, curved or straight branches in which 1 or more hormogonia are formed; cells subglobose, quadrate, or cylindrical, usually loosely arranged in 1 to several series in the principal filament, in a single series only in the branches; hormogonia with cells closely adjoined and usually increasing in diameter toward the apices; heterocysts globose, barrel-shaped, or quadrate; sheaths either colorless or brownish, homogeneous or lamellated.

This genus is considered by some to be unseparable from *Stigonema* and is, therefore, often included with it as a subgenus. When given genus rank it is differentiated principally by the unilateral arrangement of the branches, which are distinctly smaller than the main filament, and also by the habit of forming hormogonia in the apices of the branches.

Key to the Species

Main filament mostly uniseriate..*F. ambigua*
Main filament multiseriate ....*F. muscicola*

Fischerella ambigua (Naeg.) Gomont 1895, p. 49

Plant mass consisting of prostrate mats of interwoven filaments from which vertical fascicles arise; filaments $6-9\mu$ in diameter, giving rise to unilateral branches, which are grouped; sheaths colorless when young, becoming brownish; cells $2-3\mu$ in diameter, ovate or subglobular to quadrate in the main axis, rectangular in the branches, 4–6 times longer than wide; heterocysts cylindrical.

On moist soil. Mich.

Fischerella muscicola (Borzi) Gomont 1895, p. 52
Pl. 130, Figs. 7, 8

Plant mass consisting of prostrate, irregularly spreading filaments, containing several series of cells, from which mostly unilateral and uniseriate branches arise; cells quadrate or subglobose in the main axis; branches $4-6\mu$ in diameter, developing hormogonia up to 100μ in length; heterocysts globular or barrel-shaped, about the size of the vegetative cells; sheaths colorless or brownish, without lamellations; filaments $10-14\mu$ in diameter.

In shallow water at the margin of ponds among filamentous algae and larger vegetation. Mich., Wis.

FAMILY RIVULARIACEAE

The outstanding characteristic of plants belonging to this family is the pronounced tapering of the trichomes, which exhibit a distinct basal-distal differentiation. The sheath is firm, at least in the basal portion, and may be lamellate or homogeneous. There may be one or more trichomes within the sheath. In most forms there is a basal heterocyst or a short series of them (and rarely intercalary heterocysts as well), whereas in 2 genera some species are without heterocysts. The trichomes may be solitary or they may form colonial aggregates of spherical or hemispherical shape, or the thalli may be amorphous. In most forms there is an evident false branching which occurs immediately below an intercalary heterocyst. In at least one genus the branches lie semiparallel with the original trichome in the same sheath for some distance before they emerge. Branches may arise also by *in situ* proliferation of hormogonia. The presence or absence of gonidia is of taxonomic interest. These, if present, are adjacent to the heterocysts.

Key to the Genera

1. Filaments numerous, closely arranged in radiate or parallel series within copious mucilage to form globular or hemispherical, free-floating or attached colonies_____ 2
1. Filaments arranged otherwise _____ 3
2. Mucilage firm, often hard and lime-encrusted; akinetes not present; trichomes often parallel, compacted_____*Rivularia*
2. Mucilage soft (especially when the plants are mature); akinetes present; trichomes radiately arranged_____*Gloeotrichia* (in part)
3. Trichomes contained in amorphous gelatinous mucilage; attached or free-floating_____ 5
3. Trichomes not contained in amorphous mucilage; more or less solitary, or forming plant masses of definite shape_____ 4
4. Colonial mass small, saccate and torn, with the investing mucilage lamellate and much folded_____*Sacconema*
4. Colonial mass otherwise, large and expanded, at first attached, later free-floating, mucilage not lamellate or folded_____*Gloeotrichia* (in part)
5. Akinetes absent_____ 6
5. Akinetes present_____ 7
6. Trichomes many, arising from a basal pseudoparenchymatous portion of the thallus_____*Amphithrix*
6. Trichomes few together, not arising from a basal pseudoparenchymatous thallus _____*Calothrix* (in part)
7. Filaments freely branched, the branches inclosed within the sheath of the primary filament, forming dichotomously branched tufts; not epiphytic _____*Dichothrix*
7. Filaments seldom branched; solitary or gregarious, sometimes forming stellate tufts; plants epiphytic on walls of other algae or inclosed in colonial mucilage; forming encrustations in aerial habitats _____*Calothrix* (in part)

[550]

AMPHITHRIX Kuetzing 1843, p. 220

Thallus composed of erect, parallel, tapering trichomes from a basal pseudoparenchymatous tangle of closely appressed trichomes; heterocysts and akinetes wanting; plant mass often purplish.

Amphithrix janthina (Mont.) Bornet & Flahault 1886, p. 344
Pl. 131, Fig. 9

Characters as described for the genus; trichomes tapering to a fine, hair-like extremity, composed of rectangular cells; sheaths thin and colorless; cells 1.5–2.5μ in diameter.

Mich.

CALOTHRIX C. A. Agardh 1824, p. xxiv

Trichomes tapering from basal heterocyst (rarely wanting) to a fine point in most species, abruptly ending in others. In some species the lower part of the trichome is cylindrical, only the apical region tapering. Vegetative cells shorter than wide below, longer than wide toward the apices; heterocysts subglobose or hemispherical, basal but sometimes intercalary also; gonidia (akinetes) often present, 1 or more in a series, adjacent to the basal heterocyst; sheaths firm, close, either homogeneous or lamellated, but not flaring away from the trichome (see *Calothrix adscendens*); filaments usually simple, sometimes with false branches from the midregion; plants either solitary or clustered to form stellate tufts, the basal portion of the plant lying approximately parallel with the substrate and then bending away at a sharp angle (in most species); either epiphytic or endophytic (in the mucilage of other algae), growing on submerged or on exposed and moist rock surfaces, where extensive patches may be produced, sometimes becoming encrusted with lime.

Key to the Species

1. Akinetes present..*C. stagnalis*
1. Akinetes absent.. 2
2. Filaments definitely enlarged in the basal portion; sheaths sometimes inflated below.. 3
2. Filaments very gradually tapering, or cylindrical throughout much of their length and then tapering.. 5
3. Filaments compactly arranged in common mucilage, forming a colonial expanse on aquatic substrates...............................*C. Braunii*
3. Filaments solitary, or in small tufts, intermingled among other algae, or epiphytic.. 4
4. Sheath close, without lamellations; scattered among other algae...*C. stellaris*
4. Sheath wide, lamellated; plants attached in the mucilage of other algae...*C. fusca*

5. Trichomes not tapering to a hair; short, abruptly ending _____ *C. atricha*
5. Trichomes decidedly tapering, sometimes to a long hair _____ 6
6. Filaments associated to form a colonial expanse _____ *C. parietana*
6. Filaments solitary, or few together, scattered or epiphytic _____ 7
7. Cells very short, ¼–⅕ as long as wide; sheath brown _____ *C. breviarticulata*
7. Cells longer; sheath colorless _____ 8
8. Trichomes slender, 3.5–4μ in diameter at the base; filaments 5–7μ in diameter _____ *C. epiphytica*
8. Trichomes stouter, 12μ in diameter at the base; filaments 18–24μ in diameter _____ *C. adscendens*

Calothrix adscendens (Naeg.) Bornet & Flahault 1886, p. 365
Pl. 130, Figs. 9–11

Filaments solitary or in small clusters, tapering from the base to apex, sheath wide, lamellated; heterocysts basal, 11μ in diameter, 11.8μ long; vegetative cells 9.2μ in diameter, 7.4–8μ long at the base; filament 12–18–(24)μ wide at base.

Attached to larger filamentous algae and other aquatic plants. Wis.

Calothrix atricha Frémy 1930, p. 261
Pl. 129, Fig. 6

Trichomes short, solitary or in clusters of 3–4, curved and torulose, sheaths thin, colorless, not lamellated, slightly tapering to a blunt apical cell; heterocysts basal, usually in pairs, spherical, 9μ in diameter; vegetative cells 7.4–8μ in diameter at the base, 1–1½ times as long as wide.

Our plants are questionably assigned to this species originally described from Africa. The torulose character of the filaments and the shape of the cells, together with the characteristics of the sheath and the form of the apical region of the trichome, agree with the description.

Wis.

Calothrix Braunii Bornet & Flahault 1886, p. 368
Pl. 131, Fig. 12

Trichomes parallel, gradually tapering to a point, compactly arranged to form a colonial expanse on submerged substrates; sheath thin and colorless; heterocysts hemispherical, basal; vegetative cells shorter than broad or about as long, constricted at the cross walls, 6–7μ in diameter at the base.

On submerged vegetation and stones in hard water lakes. Wis.

Calothrix breviarticulata West & West 1897, p. 240
Pl. 132, Fig. 1

Filaments mostly solitary, tapering gradually from a broad base to a long hair, 16μ in diameter; sheaths thick, lamellate, discolored in age; heterocysts basal, hemispherical, 12μ in diameter; cells 11–14μ in diameter, very short, ⅓–¼ as long as wide, contents blue-green.

Attached to larger filamentous algae. Wis.

Calothrix epiphytica West & West 1897, p. 240
Pl. 132, Figs. 2, 3

Filaments either single or in small clusters, gradually tapering from base to apex, ending in a long hair; 5–7.5–(7.8)μ in diameter; sheaths wide, not lamellate; heterocysts basal, 4–5μ in diameter; cells 4–5μ in diameter at the base of the trichome, about as wide as long.

On filamentous algae and submerged aquatics. Mich., Wis.

Calothrix fusca (Kuetz.) Bornet & Flahault 1886, p. 364
Pl. 132, Figs. 4, 5

Filaments strongly curved from short horizontal basal portions, attached in the mucilage of other algae, bulbous at the base, 11–14μ in diameter, tapering to a long hair; vegetative cells 7–11μ in diameter, ⅓ as long as wide; heterocysts basal, hemispherical, 9–10μ in diameter.

Attached in the mucilage of *Coleochaete, Batrachospermum,* and other algae inclosed in mucilage. Wis.

Calothrix parietana (Naeg.) Thuret 1875, p. 381
Pl. 132, Fig. 6

Trichomes solitary or gregarious, forming dark brown patches on submerged substrates or in aerial habitats, tapering from the base, much twisted and contorted, with the basal portion of the trichome appressed on the substrate; vegetative cells very short, 5–10μ in diameter, 2.5–3μ long; heterocysts 6–10μ in diameter, usually basal, quadrate-globose to hemispherical; sheaths firm, relatively thick and close, not lamellated, becoming yellowish-brown with age; filaments 10–12μ wide.

Attached to old logs and stones in running water; tychoplankton. Mich., Wis.

Calothrix stagnalis Gomont 1895a, p. 197
Pl. 132, Fig. 7

Filaments usually gregarious in stellate clusters or tufts, rarely solitary, appressed to the substrate in the basal region but bent sharply or twisted to form an erect apical portion; trichomes tapering gradually to a hair-like point from a basal heterocyst; cells short, rectangular to slightly swollen, with constrictions at the cross walls, 5–9μ in diameter, shorter than wide below, becoming longer than wide in the apical region; heterocyst spherical or subspherical, basal, solitary or in pairs, 6–11μ in diameter; sheaths thin, firm, gradually narrowed with the trichomes; gonidia 1–3 in series, adjacent to the heterocyst, 10.8μ in diameter, 14–16μ long; filament 8–(9)–10–(11)μ wide at the base.

Common; attached to large filamentous algae such as *Cladophora, Rhizoclonium,* and *Oedogonium.* Mich., Wis.

Calothrix stellaris Bornet & Flahault 1886, p. 365

Filaments solitary or clustered and radiately arranged, bent from the basal swollen portion and tapering to a fine hair from a hemispherical, basal heterocyst; sheaths thin, firm and close, colorless; cells 6–7μ in diameter, constricted at the cross walls, ½–⅓ times as long as broad; heterocysts either solitary or in a series of 2–3; filaments 15–21μ in diameter at the base.

Attached to submerged plants. Wis.

DICHOTHRIX Zanardini 1858, p. 297

In this genus the plant is composed of 2–6 tapering trichomes inclosed within a single sheath for at least a part of their length. They are usually solitary but sometimes form macroscopic, cushion-like masses or feathery tufts on submerged wood and stones, or on moist substrates; trichomes with basal heterocysts (sometimes intercalary also), and with dichotomous false branching, a branch extending for some distance within the same sheath as the principal trichome, then emerging in its own sheath and usually rebranching successively; cells quadrate, slightly swollen, or shorter or longer than their diameter, either constricted or not at the cross walls; tapering at least in the distal portion of the trichome; basal heterocysts connate or hemispherical; sheaths either thin and close or lamellated, sometimes with a bulbous base, tapering with the trichome or widely diverging toward the apex to form a funnel, according to the species.

Key to the Species

1. Filaments 10–14μ in diameter, with flexuous,
   spreading branches ....*D. Orsiniana*
1. Filaments larger, with straight or curved branches 2
2. Filaments coarse, 20–28μ in diameter; branches bulbous
   at the base ....*D. Hosfordii*
2. Filaments narrower, (12)–15–18μ in diameter;
   branches not bulbous at the base....................................*D. gypsophila*

Dichothrix gypsophila (Kuetz.) Bornet & Flahault 1886, p. 377
Pl. 133, Figs. 1, 2

Either solitary among other algae or forming tufts and expanded strata, frequently encrusted with calcium carbonate; filaments repeatedly branched, the branches parallel with the principal trichome and inclosed in the same sheath with it for a considerable distance; vegetative cells shorter than wide at the base and with convex walls, longer than wide toward the distal end and cylindrical without constrictions at the cross walls, $6-8\mu$ in diameter in the basal portion of the trichome; heterocysts subglobose or hemispherical, $10-12\mu$ in diameter; sheaths lamellated, at first close, then becoming funnel-shaped toward the distal end; filament $(12)-15-18\mu$ wide at the base; penicillate tufts as long as 2 mm.

This species varies in its sheath characters, apparently, for authentically named material which was compared with Wisconsin plants shows both close, tapering sheaths as well as flaring, funnel-forming sheaths. It should be compared with *D. Hosfordii*, a much larger plant with sheaths bulbous at the base.

Forming tufts of filaments entangled among other filamentous algae in shallow water at the margin of marshy lakes. Wis.

Dichothrix Hosfordii (Wolle) Bornet *in* Setchell 1896a, p. 190
Pl. 133, Figs. 3, 4

Plants penicillate tufts of stout, dichotomously branched filaments, $20-28\mu$ in diameter at the base; vegetative cells much shorter than their diameter, $10-15\mu$ in diameter at the base, $3-5\mu$ long, becoming cylindrical and several times their width in length in the distal region, which tapers to a hair-like point; heterocyst a short, broad cone, or hemispherical, olive or blue-green, $15-18\mu$ in diameter; sheaths lamellated and bulbous at the base, several trichomes within a sheath, the branches appressed for some distance, then emerging in their own sheath.

This species is more common in our collections than *D. gypsophila.* It occurs among other algae in a number of both hard and soft water lakes. The greater size and the bulbous-inflated sheaths help to identify it. Mich., Wis.

Dichothrix Orsiniana (Kuetz.) Bornet & Flahault 1886, p. 376
Pl. 133, Figs. 5, 6

Gelatinous, penicillate tufts, composed of slender trichomes in close and thick, lamellated, tapering sheaths; filaments branching freely, the branches extending for most of their length within the sheath of the principal trichome; trichomes subcylindric below,

[555]

tapering to a fine point distally; vegetative cells very short, 5–8μ in diameter, 2–4μ long, or quadrate; heterocysts subglobose or hemispherical, 8–10μ in diameter; filaments 10–14μ wide at the base.

On moist earth or attached to or entangled among filamentous algae. Mich., Wis.

RIVULARIA (Roth) C. A. Agardh 1824, p. 19

Filaments semiparallel or radiately arranged in copious, very firm mucilage, forming either semi-microscopic globose colonies or macroscopic, bullate or expanded masses which may be either solid or hollow; heterocysts all basal and the trichome tapering from them to fine points; frequently branched, the branches sometimes so disposed as to form transverse zones through the colonial mass; individual sheaths definite at the base but becoming diffluent toward the apex of the filament; gonidia lacking.

Key to the Species

Cells 4–7.5μ in diameter; colonies lime encrusted......................................R. haematites
Cells 9–12.5μ in diameter; colonies not conspicuously lime encrusted...R. minutula

Rivularia haematites (D. C.) C. A. Agardh 1824, p. 26
Pl. 131, Figs. 10, 11

Filaments united in attached, hemispherical colonies, inclosed by a firm mucilage and encrusted with lime, colonies frequently gregarious and agglutinated to form an expanse as much as 3 cm. thick; filaments closely arranged and semiparallel, the false branches forming transverse tiers or zones; individual sheaths conspicuous below, firm and close, either colorless or yellow, becoming expanded and funnel-form above toward the periphery of the colony; cells 4–7.5μ in diameter, twice the diameter in length in the lower part of the trichome, becoming ½ as long as wide in the apical region.

On stones in lakes and flowing water. Mich.

Rivularia minutula (Kuetz.) Bornet & Flahault 1886, p. 348
Pl. 136, Fig. 9

Filaments arranged in brownish, globular or hemispherical colonies, enclosed in firm mucilage, but rather loosely and radiately arranged within the colony and inclosed in wide, hyaline or brownish, lamellate sheaths, becoming funnel-form toward the periphery of the colony; trichomes tapering to a stout hair above from oblong or hemispherical heterocysts; cells 9–12.5μ in diameter, quadrate below, becoming 3–4 times as long as wide in the apical region.

Attached to submerged plants and wood. Mich.

[556]

GLOEOTRICHIA J. G. Agardh 1842, p. 8

A free-floating or attached hemispherical or globose colony of radiating trichomes, tapering from basal heterocysts and much attenuated at the apices; colonial mucilage soft or rather firm according to species (but not rubbery and not so tough as in the genus *Rivularia*), either colorless or becoming ochraceous with age in some species; sheath of the trichome usually confluent but often evident in the basal part of the trichome; heterocysts solitary (rarely 2), basal as well as intercalary, globose to oval; vegetative cells short in the basal portion of the trichome but becoming barrel-shaped, longer and cylindrical distally; gonidia cylindrical, usually single, adjoining the heterocyst, rarely in a short series, the membrane thick and smooth.

Species of *Gloeotrichia* are included with *Rivularia* by some authors. Separation is here arbitrarily made on the presence of the gonidia, *Rivularia* lacking them. The latter genus includes species which are always attached and which have very firm, sometimes hard mucilage, often encrusted with lime. The hemspherical colonies of both genera are macroscopic in size and similar in general appearance. In *Rivularia* the colony may be hollow, and the radiating filaments are in concentric zones as a result of false branching. In some species of *Rivularia* agglutinated and expanded gelatinous attached masses are formed. In *Gloeotrichia* the colonial mucilage is softer and the trichomes definitely radiate and not zoned. Branching is less common. Whereas some *Gloeotrichia* may remain attached, most species become planktonic or free-floating, especially *G. echinulata* and *G. natans*.

Key to the Species

1. Colonies globular, planktonic .... *G. echinulata*
1. Colonies not planktonic or, if free-floating, not globular and burr-like 2
2. Colonies containing only a few trichomes; cells very long and cylindrical, rounded at the ends; a conspicuous granule at each cross wall .... *G. longiarticulata*
2. Colonies containing numerous trichomes; cells quadrate or slightly longer than wide, or shorter than wide in the basal portion; end walls not rounded or marked by conspicuous granules 3
3. Colonies globular or hemispherical, 1–5 mm. in diameter; attached, sometimes completely coating aquatic plants ....*G. Pisum*
3. Colonies irregularly globose or bullate, 5 mm. to 10 cm. across, becoming soft and irregularly expanded and floating when old ....*G. natans*

Gloeotrichia echinulata (J. E. Smith) P. Richter 1894, p. 31
Pl. 134, Figs. 1, 2

A free-floating, spherical, gelatinous colony of many sheathed trichomes radiating from a common center; trichomes tapering from a basal heterocyst to a fine hair-like point extending beyond the limits of the colonial mucilage and so giving a burr-like appearance; cells spherical or barrel-shaped at the base of the trichome, 8–10μ in diameter, becoming long and cylindrical in the distal portion; cell contents with many pseudovacuoles; heterocysts spherical, 10μ in diameter; gonidia cylindrical, 10–18μ in diameter, up to 50μ long, adjacent to the heterocyst; sheaths colorless, wide, without lamellations, covering approximately the lower third of the trichome.

The colonies are macroscopic and appear as minute, dark, egg-like or burr-like bodies, opaque in the center and translucent at the periphery. The planktonic habit is associated with the pseudovacuoles, which are often numerous and large. As is well-known, those blue-green species which have a high degree of vacuolization show a great buoyancy, often floating at the very surface. *Gloeotrichia echinulata,* like *Aphanizomenon flos-aquae* and *Microcystis aeruginosa,* often forms a dense suspension of thalli in upper lake levels. Such superabundant growths are frequently followed by unbalanced biological conditions as a result of the death and decay of plant masses. During mid-summer and throughout the warm season *Gloeotrichia echinulata* makes periodic blooms, sometimes becoming concentrated near the shore line and in shallow bays in such numbers as to form a veritable purée.

This species undoubtedly begins its life cycle in a sedentary or attached condition, developing from gonidia of the previous generation. The mechanics involved in the germination which determines the filament arrangement, the soft consistency of the colonial mucilage, and the volume of the cell contents occupied by pseudovacuoles no doubt are responsible for the ready adoption of the planktonic habit. Hence conspicuous growths make a sudden appearance in lake plankton when large numbers of colonies become free-floating. Wind and water currents and probably a change in physiology also act to bring about a scattering and vertical distribution so that a dense surface bloom may disappear as quickly as it developed.

Common in the plankton of many lakes, especially in hard water habitats. Mich., Wis.

?*Gloeotrichia longiarticulata* G. S. West 1907, p. 183
Pl. 134, Figs. 3–5

Thallus hemispherical and attached, containing relatively few, widely separated, and loosely arranged trichomes which taper to a very fine point; sheaths confluent with the colonial mucilage; cells elongate-cylindric with rounded ends, (4.5)–9.5μ in diameter, 3–7 times the diameter in length (in our specimens, with cells separated slightly from each other), with a conspicuous granule at each cross wall, contents not vacuolate; heterocyst subglobose to elongate-elliptic or ovate; gonidia short-cylindric, 14.8μ in diameter, 27.3–(44)μ long with a yellowish membrane.

The plant, found but once, is scantily represented in the collection. The characteristics are distinctive, however, and agree closely with the description given by West; hence it is tentatively assigned to *Gloeotrichia longiarticulata* G. S. West. Subsequent collections are needed to confirm this identification.

Attached to submerged aquatics. Wis.

Gloeotrichia natans (Hedwig) Rabenhorst 1847, p. 90
Pl. 134, Figs. 6, 7

A soft, gelatinous, globose or bullate, attached colony, brown or olive-green in color, becoming free-floating and expanded to form irregularly shaped mucilaginous masses at maturity; filaments at first somewhat radiate, becoming irregularly arranged and entangled, very long and tapering from a basal heterocyst; cells barrel-shaped or subglobose below, becoming quadrate or subcylindrical distally, 7–10μ in diameter; heterocysts globose or ovate, 8–12μ in diameter; gonidia solitary, adjacent to the heterocyst, 12–18μ in diameter, up to 250μ long, with a thick wall and a sheath; basal sheath of the filament covering about a third of the length, lamellated, wrinkled, wide and funnel-shaped above.

This species forms attached colonies as much as 10 cm. across under favorable conditions (quiet hard water and high temperatures). The mucilage is very soft, and the colonies expand and become floating masses by the time gonidia have reached maturity. Inasmuch as the plant mass soon fragments, this species is frequently collected in plankton catches, where it appears as irregular flakes of entangled filaments. Under such circumstances it may be differentiated from old colonies of *Gloeotrichia echinulata* by the form of the sheath, the larger size of the gonidia, and by the greater length of the flagelliform trichome. At maturity the vegetative cells dissociate, leaving the spore and the heterocyst adjoined.

Common in many hard or semi-hard water lakes. Mich., Wis.

Gloeotrichia Pisum (C. A. Ag.) Thuret 1875, p. 382
Pl. 134, Figs. 8–10

A firm, mucilaginous, brown or olive-green, globular or hemispherical colony, attached to submerged aquatics; colonies from 1 mm. to 1 cm. in diameter (usually about 5 mm.), composed of compactly arranged filaments radiating from a common center and tapering from a basal heterocyst to a very fine point; colonial mucilage bounded by a leathery integument; cells short, barrel-shaped or quadrate below, becoming cylindrical in the distal portion, $4-7\mu$ in diameter, $8-12\mu$ long; heterocysts spherical or ovate, $8-11-(15)\mu$ in diameter; gonidia cylindrical with broadly rounding poles, the membrane thick and sheathed, $10-15\mu$ in diameter, up to 400μ long.

This species is attached throughout its entire development, rarely or only incidentally becoming free-floating. In suitable hard water habitats its brown or olive globular colonies are thickly clustered and sometimes completely coat over submerged aquatics such as *Potamogeton* spp. and *Ceratophyllum demersum*. Because of the firm texture of the colonial mucilage and the compact arrangement of the filaments, the species may be confused easily with *Rivularia* when the plants are young, before gonidia have developed.

Common in many hard or semi-hard water lakes and streams. Mich., Wis.

SACCONEMA Borzi 1882, pp. 282, 298

Colonial mass amorphous or somewhat tubercular, the mucilage soft and irregularly lobed and folded, and lamellate; trichomes radiating irregularly, 2 or several within the same sheath, which is wide, lamellate, and expanded at the extremities; heterocyst and akinetes basal, the trichome tapering to fine hair-like points; plants attached to stones and other submerged substrates; one species.

Sacconema rupestre Borzi 1882, pp. 282, 298
Pl. 136, Figs. 1, 2

Characteristics as described for the genus; trichomes $8-10\mu$ in diameter at the base; heterocysts globose or compressed-spheroidal; akinetes globose, 15μ in diameter, with a granulose wall.

On stones from a depth of 20 feet, Douglas Lake, Michigan.

CLASS CHLOROBACTERIACEAE

In this group of the Cyanophyta are classified minute, bacteria-like organisms of uncertain position which are weakly pigmented. The cells are spherical or bacilliform and are arranged to form amorphous, gelatinous colonies in which the cells have no definite arrangement, or the cells may form false filaments or reticulate associations. The colonies may vary greatly in size from 4-celled aggregates to gelatinous masses containing hundreds of individuals. See p. 36 in connection with chlorophyll tests involving a member of this class.

PELOGLOEA Lauterborn 1913, p. 99

Cells bacilliform, straight or slightly twisted, often knobby and irregular (in our specimens), solitary or in short linear series; crowded within an amorphous or irregularly globular gelatinous matrix.

Pelogloea bacillifera Lauterborn 1917, p. 430
Pl. 104, Figs. 4, 5

Characteristics as described for the genus; cells bacilliform, straight or curved rods, sometimes elliptic, slightly tapering at the poles, solitary or 2–3 in linear series; densely crowded in a gelatinous, saccate or clathrate mucilage; cells 0.6–1.5μ in diameter, 2–4μ long.

When this plant was collected in Scaffold Lake, Wisconsin, it was so abundant as to color the entire lake, although ordinary plankton catches failed to disclose the presence of the organism. It was found that the gelatinous colonies dissociate within the net, so that individuals or small clumps of cells only occur, these appearing as bacteria. Repeated collections and laboratory culture permitted the determination of the presence of *Pelogloea bacillifera* together with *Plectonema nostocorum*.

Nannoplankter; in semi-hard water lakes; often in tychoplankton but usually found at great depths; sometimes occurring in a stratum near the bottom of a lake. Mich., Wis.

DIVISION RHODOPHYTA

In this division the cells contain a variety of pigments, chlorophyll, phycocyanin, and phycoerythrin. The latter, a red pigment, is usually predominant, especially in the marine forms, but varying amounts of this and the other pigments produce violet, gray-green, or blue-green colors. This is especially true for the fresh-water Rhodophyta which are almost any color except red. The chromatophore, usually axial, contains a central pyrenoid which collects starch as a food reserve. In one of the subgroups the end walls of the cells have a pore which permits intercellular cytoplasmic connections.

The primary distinguishing characteristics of the division are the structure of the sex organs, the sexual methods of reproduction, and the types of life history entailed.

Throughout the division the range of plant forms discloses an evolutionary series which has counterparts in other algal groups. There are unicellular, palmelloid, simple and branched filamentous, and frond-like expressions. In the higher forms there is often found considerable differentiation among the cells to form what might be regarded as tissues.

The majority of the Rhodophyta are marine, but a few genera are either fresh-water or have representatives in inland habitats. Many of these are found in streams in alpine or subalpine situations.

There are 2 subclasses, the Bangioideae and the Florideae. The former, which is the more primitive, contains 3 families in fresh water. The Florideae, a much larger group, includes the majority of species and is represented by 4 families in fresh water.

CLASS RHODOPHYCEAE
SUBCLASS BANGIOIDEAE

In this group, the fresh-water members possess a thallus which is a branched or unbranched filament, or a ribbon-like or plate-like expanse one cell in thickness. The cell walls are thick and gelatinous and often somewhat lamellate. Unlike some of the Florideae, plants in this group do not have intercellular protoplasmic connections. The chromatophore, which is axial and stellate, contains a single pyrenoid. Pigmentation as described for the division.

Asexual reproduction is by nonmotile spores. In the few known cases of sexual reproduction, divisions of the vegetative protoplast give rise to spermatia which fuse with vegetative cells, after which reproductive cells known as carpospores are formed.

This subclass contains but a single order, the Bangiales, which is represented in our region by 2 genera.

ORDER BANGIALES

Characters as described for the subclass. The three families which comprise this order are the Bangiaceae, in which spores are formed by divisions of unspecialized vegetative cells, the Erythrotrichiaceae, in which spores are borne in special sporangia, and the Goniotrichaceae, in which spores are simply modified vegetative cells formed without division of the protoplast. Only the latter family is represented in our collections.

FAMILY GONIOTRICHACEAE

In this family the plants are simple or branched, pseudofilamentous thalli. Reproduction occurs as described above, sexual reproduction being unknown.

ASTEROCYTIS (Thwait.) Gobi 1879, p. 93

Filaments simple or branched, composed of globose or oblong cells inclosed in broad gelatinous sheaths, arranged in a more or less irregular uniseriate manner. The cells may be closely arranged, or at some distance from one another. The chloroplast is axial and stellate and contains a central, usually conspicuous pyrenoid.

Asterocytis smaragdina (Reinsch) Forti 1907, p. 691
Pl. 135, Fig. 3

Characters as described for the genus; filaments simple or branched, occasionally somewhat palmelloid, the branches developing by a cell slipping to one side of the series and continuing to divide in another plane; cells 6–11μ in diameter, 8–16μ long.

Attached to stones and to strands of coarse filamentous algae, North Trout Lake and Fishtrap Lake, Vilas County, Wisconsin; also reported (C. E. Allen correspondence) from Lake Mendota, Wisconsin.

BANGIOIDEAE OF UNCERTAIN POSITION
FAMILY PORPHYRIDACEAE

PORPHYRIDIUM Naegeli 1849, p. 139

Unicellular but with many individuals aggregated to form an irregularly expanded, thin, gelatinous layer. Cells mostly spherical, with individual gelatinous sheaths and embedded in a common gelatinous matrix; with dark red, stellate chromatophore and small, excentric nucleus. Reproduction by cell division. Forming blood-red film on moist soil and walls, especially in greenhouses.

Porphyridium cruentum Naegeli 1849, p. 139
Pl. 136, Fig. 6

Characters as described for the genus. Size of cells variable: 5–9µ, 7–12µ, or up to 24µ.

On soil in greenhouse, University of Wisconsin, Madison.

SUBCLASS FLORIDEAE

In this advanced group of the red algae the thallus has a multiplicity of expressions, ranging from slightly branched filaments to complex plants of macroscopic size, involving complexes of filaments which may be differentiated to form tissues. Growth in all these forms occurs by the activity of one or more meristematic apical cells.

The sex organs, especially the female, are characteristic of the group. The carpogonium has a definite neck-like extension, the trichogyne, the shape of which varies in different genera and species and is, therefore, of taxonomic value. See Smith (1933, 1938) and Taylor (1937) for a description of morphological characteristics, methods of reproduction, and outlines of life histories.

ORDER NEMALIONALES

There are four fresh-water families in this order, of which three have representatives in the Wisconsin collections. The fourth family, Thoreaceae, undoubtedly is present in the plant *Thorea ramosissima* Bory, but as far as known this species has not been reported from the region. Sexual reproduction involves specialized female sex organs (carpogonia), and antheridia which develop non-motile spermatia. In addition to gametangia, the sexual plant may produce non-motile monospores cut off from the tips of branches, especially in juvenile stages of development.

FAMILY CHANTRANSIACEAE

In this family the thallus is a filament which has repeated alternate branching and is without a conspicuous central axis.

AUDOUINELLA Bory 1823, p. 340

Thallus consisting of sparingly branched filaments of cylindrical cells from rhizoidal holdfasts, the branches about equal in diameter to the main filament which more or less becomes lost in the branchings; branches of the second and third order about equal in diameter to those of the first order; all branches ending in bluntly rounded apical cells; chromatophores discoid or plate-like bodies, without pyrenoids; color gray or violet-green; reproduction by monospores borne singly or in clusters at the ends of short branches. Sexual reproduction is known for a least one species.

Members of this genus should be compared with juvenile states of *Lemanea* and *Batrachospermum*, especially if *Audouinella*-like plants are collected nearby, or with adult stages of other red algae. Most of the plants previously referred to species of *Chantransia* have been assigned to *Audouinella* or redefined as juvenile stages of *Batrachospermum*.

Audouinella violacea (Kuetz.) Hamel 1925, p. 46
Pl. 135, Figs. 1, 2

Plants forming violet-green tufts from horizontal holdfast branches; filaments sparingly branched; branches scarcely tapering, varying in length from one cell to as long as the main filament; cells cylindrical, with 2–3 plate-like chromatophores which are violet-green in color and rather metallic in appearance; filaments 8–12μ in diameter.

Attached in flowing water. Wis.

FAMILY BATRACHOSPERMACEAE

In this family the thallus has a definite axis of cells which becomes corticated by downward growing elements from node regions. Branches are given off in more or less dense and definite whorls so that a beaded effect is produced in the macroscopic appearance of the thallus. Monospores are produced at the ends of branches in juvenile stages, whereas carpogonia and clusters of antheridial cells are borne in the adult phase only. The sex organs may be monoecious or dioecious.

BATRACHOSPERMUM Roth 1797, p. 36

An attached, much branched thallus consisting essentially of an axial row of large cells which cut off lateral units at definite intervals, thus determining node and internode regions; from these laterals a longitudinal investment of cortical filaments develops which more or less (depending upon the species) completely covers the axial row; also from the nodal units as well as from the cortical elements themselves, out-turned fascicles of branches develop, those at the node region forming primary whorls which in many species produce a distinctly beaded appearance; cells in the axial row cylindrical, ovoid, ellipsoid, or fusiform in the branches; branching of the fascicles dichotomous, the ultimate branches terminating in short or long colorless hairs; entire thallus inclosed in a soft amorphous hyaline mucilage; a single massive chromatophore in each of the principal cells, and two to five disc-like or irregular chromatophores, each with a pyrenoid, in each cell of the branches; plant mass gray- or violet-green or brownish.

In this genus sexual reproduction involves female (carpogonial) cells and male (antheridial) units. The latter are small, non-motile cells produced in clusters at the tips of lateral branches. The carpogonium is a flask-like cell with an elongate tip, the *trichogyne*, which receives the spermatia. The shape and location of the carpogonium and the form of the trichogyne are specific characters and are of taxonomic value. The trichogyne may be spatula-shaped, oblong, or lanceolate. See Kylin (1912), Sirodot (1884), and Skuja (1931) for a description of sex-organ morphology in this genus.

When reproductive organs are absent, identification of species in *Batrachospermum* is practically impossible in most cases, and even when such organs are present, experienced judgement is often required to make satisfactory determinations. Although there are more than five species of *Batrachospermum* in our collections, only those are listed here which have been observed in the fruiting condition. An interesting problem involving the ecology and taxonomy of this genus in this area awaits further studies.

Batrachospermum forms dark gray-green or blue-green masses, streaming from stones or submerged wood in flowing or standing water, usually at low temperatures. Some species are less widely distributed than others and seem to be confined to acid ponds in *Sphagnum* bogs, where they produce growths up to 30 cm. in length on the submerged stems of *Chamaedaphne* or on overhanging grasses and sedges. Early in the summer, juvenile or *Chantransia*-stages predominate in certain habitats such as stones in flowing water. In this condition the young plants cover submerged objects with a blue-green gelatinous film. As mentioned under *Audouinella* above, comparison should be made between these juvenile stages of *Batrachospermum* and what may appear to be true *Audouinella* plants.

Key to the Species

1. Lateral whorls of branches lacking or scarcely developed; internodes long..*B. Dillenii*
1. Lateral whorls of branches well-developed, crowded; internodes short 2

Batrachospermum Boryanum Sirodot 1884, p. 246
Pl. 136, Fig. 5

Thallus densely branched and embedded in copious mucilage, gray-green to golden-green in color; whorls conglomerate, usually closely arranged to form a decided beaded appearance; secondary branches either few or many; corticating branches many, loosely arranged; apical hairs few, slightly swollen at the base; dioecious; carpogonia on a primary lateral branch or rarely on the branches from the corticating filaments, the trichogyne ellipsoid or oval; carpospore masses numerous, scattered throughout the branch-whorls.

Walnut Lake, Michigan.

Batrachospermum Dillenii Bory 1823, p. 226
Pl. 135, Figs. 4–6

Thallus irregularly and sparingly branched, the branches rather rigid, straight or slightly curved; plant 2–5 cm. long; cortical filaments highly developed and inclosing the axial filament with a parenchymatous layer; lateral branching system poorly developed, the branches short with few repeated branchings, forming nodal clusters a considerable distance apart so that a jointed appearance is produced macroscopically; in the apical region the abbreviated out-turned branches numerous, compactly clustered, composed of subglobose or ovoid cells and ending in long cylindrical cells but without terminal setae; plants dioecious, the carpogonia on very short branches, produced directly from the main axis, not in whorls of branches, triangular in shape, narrowed above and then slightly inflated to form a claviform or oblong trichogyne; antheridial cells formed in transverse zones from short, out-turned branches, many occurring in one cluster.

Scrapings from a log in flowing water. Wis.

Batrachospermum ectocarpum Sirodot 1884, p. 222
Pl. 136, Fig. 4

Thallus much-branched, the whorls of branches well-developed, lobed and broadly rounded, close together, the internodes short; inclosed in copious rather firm mucilage, gray- or olive-green, up

[567]

to 12 cm. long; hairs few or lacking, short with bulbous bases; corticating branches few or lacking; monoecious; carpogonia on primary lateral branches in the outer part of branch-whorl, subtended by large cells and numerous lateral branches; trichogyne clavate.

In *Sphagnum* bog pools; attached to stones in slowly flowing water. Mich., Wis.

Batrachospermum moniliforme Roth 1800, p. 450
Pl. 136, Fig. 3

Plants stout, richly branched, with well-developed whorls of branches presenting a distinct beaded or moniliform appearance macroscopically; plant mass gray-green, violet-green, or brownish; plant masses up to 10 cm. long, forming streaming tufts (frequently in swiftly running water); inclosed by copious, soft mucilage; plants annual; monoecious; carpogonia developed in inner part of the branch-whorls, terminal on short lateral branches in the axils, with a clavate or lageniform trichogyne; carpospore masses, dense, scattered throughout the plant; branches ending in long setae with a swollen base.

This is the most common species of the genus in the region. It often occurs in flowing water, where it may form extensive beds on stones and gravelly bottoms.

On submerged wood in streams; also in lakes. Mich., Wis.

Batrachospermum vagum (Roth) C. A. Agardh 1824, p. 52
Pl. 135, Figs. 7–11

Plants freely branched, as much as 20 cm. long, forming dark olive- or gray-green arborescent masses inclosed in copious mucilage and forming soft, streaming thalli; whorls of branches well-developed, forming globose nodal masses, the branches composed of ovoid or ellipsoid-ovoid cells, ending in long hairs; the whorls quite separated in the lower part of the plant, becoming closer and coalesced distally; plants monoecious, the branch bearing the carpogonium consisting of 7–14 cells, developing centrally in a whorl of branches, the carpogonial cell bottle-shaped with a spatula-shaped trichogyne; antheridial units globose, few in a cluster, cut off from the tips of lateral branches; carpospores many, forming a dense mass within the center of a whorl.

Attached to submerged logs in flowing water; fruiting late in summer. Mich., Wis.

FAMILY LEMANEACEAE
In this family the thallus is a branched, solid or hollow cylinder

and does not show the axial plan of the Batrachospermaceae. Other essential characteristics are found in the behavior of the zygote and the method by which carpospores are formed.

LEMANEA Bory 1808, p. 181; *emend.* C. A. Agardh 1828, p. 1

Juvenile stage composed of a branching filament, attached to rocks and other objects in swift-running fresh water; mature plant consisting of tufts of macroscopic, tubular reproductive strands which have regularly placed swellings (nodes) distributed from the tip to the basal stipe; strands generally olive-green, green, or purple, leathery, 1–40 cm. long, with nodes 0.2–2.0 mm. in diameter; antheridia produced at the nodes and carpogonia developed internally, with trichogynes extending to the outside; carpospores formed within the thallus, which is hollow except for an axial filament which is either naked or closely covered with enveloping filaments; juvenile stage maturing during winter; fruiting strands reaching their mature size in the spring and spores becoming evident in late spring.

Lemanea fucina (Bory) Atkinson 1890, p. 222
Pl. 136, Fig. 7

Juvenile stage a mat or tuft 1–2 mm. high, of blue-green or green filaments; fruiting strands generally olive or yellow-green, 2–40 cm. long, with a stipe which is usually cylindric and passes abruptly into the wider portion of the strand above, strands simple or much branched, very delicate to stout, tips sometimes capillary; antheridial papillae and nodes either plane, or prominently raised or swollen; papillae 2–7 at each node; carpospores not developed in the internodes.

Collected from Stevens Point, Wisconsin, by L. S. Cheney; specimen in University of Wisconsin Herbarium.

TUOMEYA Harvey 1858, p. 64

A macroscopic, cartilaginous and firm thallus with antler-like, dichotomous branching, brownish-green or gray-green, essentially composed of an axial row of large cells heavily invested by a mass of longitudinal, cortical filaments from which out-turned branches of ellipsoidal cells arise, thus producing a crowded pseudoparenchymatous cortication; thallus without nodes or whorls of branches; plants monoecious, the carpogonia and antheridia developing in different regions of the same plant, the female near the meristematic apex in the main axils of the young branches.

[569]

Tuomeya fluviatilis Harvey 1858, p. 64
Pl. 132, Figs. 8–11

Characters as described for the genus; plant gray-green, 2–5 cm. high, cartilaginous and firm, retaining its shape when lifted from the water.

Attached to logs and on the rim of a dam in swiftly flowing water. Wis.

AN ANALYTICAL KEY
TO THE GENERA

Genera that are to be expected to occur in our region but have so far not been reported there are indicated by asterisks. (See also Note 2, page 92.)

1. Plants macroscopic, 5–40 cm. high, growing erect from rhizoidal attaching organs and showing stem-like branches with internodes and nodes from which whorls of 'leaves' arise (Pl. 79, Fig. 1); not inclosed in mucilage _____Characeae 170
1. Plants smaller, mostly microscopic, if macroscopic and showing whorls of branches, inclosed in copious, sometimes firm, mucilage _____ 2
2. Cells with pigments confined to 1 or more definite chloroplasts or chromatophores[8] _____ 3
2. Cells with pigments diffused throughout the protoplast (sometimes more dense in the peripheral region)_____252
3. Chloroplasts grass-green, chlorophyll predominating; plants forming starch or paramylon as a reserve food (starch-iodine test usually positive)_____ 4
   (Cf. *Euglena, Sphaerella,* and *Trentepohlia,* which may have green chloroplasts masked by red pigment.)
3. Chloroplasts or chromatophores some color other than grass-green, or with green masked by presence of other pigments; food reserve mostly oil or glycogen; carbohydrates not stained blue by iodine _____176
                                   (cf. the motile unicell *Cryptomonas,* however)
4. Plants unicellular, solitary (See Desmids: Appendix)..................... 5
4. Plants not solitary unicells_____12
5. Cells motile in the vegetative state (sometimes non-motile in microscope mounts, with organs of locomotion obscure)_____ 6
5. Cells non-motile in the vegetative state _____81
6. Cells with numerous small, green, ovoid chromatophores; food reserve paramylon or oil; swimming by means of 1 or 2 long, whip-like flagella (Pl. 86, Figs. 1, 8.) _____172
6. Cells with 1 plate-like, cup- or star-shaped chloroplast; food reserve starch; swimming by 2 or 4 short flagella (Pl. 1, Figs. 3, 17.)_____ 7
7. Flagella 2 _____ 8
7. Flagella 4 _____11
8. Cells ovoid to ellipsoid, with the protoplast situated at some distance within the cell wall and connected to it by radiating protoplasmic strands; chloroplast often masked by a red pigment (hacmatochrome)_____ *Sphaerella* (in part)
8. Cells with or without a gelatinous sheath but without protoplasmic strands connecting the protoplast to the cell wall_____ 9

---

[8]See *Trachelomonas* and *Dinobryon;* species are identified by shape and markings of brown or colorless empty tests or lorioas.

9. Cells round in end view; the wall simple and in 1 piece, sometimes inclosed by a mucilaginous sheath_____*Chlamydomonas*
9. Cells compressed when seen in end or side view; the wall bivalved and laterally extended on either side of the protoplast to form an expansion or flange, especially noticeable when seen from the side_____10
10. Cells lenticular or elliptical in side view; valves of wall, when viewed from the side, apparent in the vegetative condition; cells often rectangular in front view, with horn-like processes at the angles_____*Phacotus*
10. Cells ovate in side view; the valves of the wall evident only during cell division or release of swarmers; cells circular or ovoid in front view_____*Pteromonas*
11. Cells elliptical, ovoid, or somewhat heart-shaped, with 4 flagella arising from the midregion of the anterior end_____ *Carteria*
11. Cells ovoid in front view, quadrate in end view, with 4 rounded lobes; flagella 4, each attached in a depression of the anterior end_____*Pyramimonas*
12. Plant a motile colony; cells inclosed by colonial mucilage; swimming by means of 2 or 4 flagella _____ 13
12. Plant non-motile in the vegetative condition; filamentous, or consisting of a definitely or indefinitely formed colony or aggregate of cells (See Desmids: Appendix)_____ 20
13. Colony composed of cells arranged to form a flat or twisted plate_____14
13. Colony spherical, spheroidal, or ovoid_____15
14. Colony a circular or rectangular plate _____ *Gonium*
14. Colony an ovoid or horseshoe-shaped plate, broadly rounded anteriorly, truncate posteriorly, with 3 prominent projections of the colonial investment _____*Platydorina*
15. Colony oblong, without a gelatinous investment; cells pyriform, all directed toward the anterior end of the colony; flagella 4____*Spondylomorum*
15. Colony ovoid or spherical, with a gelatinous investment; flagella 2_____16
16. Cells with sharply pointed lateral extensions of the protoplast, arranged to form a median girdle within a spheroidal colonial sheath _____*Stephanosphaera*
16. Cells not arranged as above _____17
17. Cells pyriform, broadest at the anterior end, compactly arranged in ovoid or ellipsoidal colonies_____ *Pandorina*
17. Cells ovoid or spheroidal, not compactly arranged within the colonial mucilage, colonies globular or ovoid _____18
18. Colony spherical, involving hundreds of cells (500 to 5000 individuals); all the vegetative cells the same size and sometimes interconnected by protoplasmic strands _____*Volvox*
18. Colony spherical or obovoid, involving but a few cells (usually 32–64, rarely up to 256), without intercellular connections _____19
19. Colony spherical, containing cells of 2 sizes which are evenly distributed at the periphery of the colonial mucilage _____ *Pleodorina*
19. Colony obovoid or spheroidal, containing cells all the same size and often arranged in tiers_____ *Eudorina*
20. Plant a pair of trapezoidal cells adjoined along their bases _____*Euastropsis*
20. Cells otherwise arranged, or of different shape _____ 21

[573]

31. Colonies shaped differently from above_____32
32. Fragments of old mother cell walls lying scattered about and
    partly inclosing spherical daughter cells; colonial mass soft and
    shapeless, usually floating at the surface_____*Schizochlamys*
32. Fragments of old mother cell walls lacking or, if present, not
    scattered among daughter cells; colonial mass of definite shape_____33
33. Colonies irregularly globose or spherical; cells arranged in groups
    of 4, the clusters remote from one another within copious muci-
    lage; cells bearing long pseudocilia (visible only under favor-
    able optical conditions)_____*Tetraspora* (in part)
33. Colonies of various shapes; cells not arranged in groups of 4,
    and without pseudocilia_____34
34. Cells ovoid, compactly arranged in semi-opaque mucilage, form-
    ing dense, simple or compound masses, adhering to one another
    by branching strands of mucilage (Pl. 52, Figs. 1, 2); individual
    cells often not apparent in older colonies because of dark muci-
    lage and density of cell contents_____*Botryococcus* (in part)
34. Cells not arranged in semi-opaque, irregularly shaped colonies_____35
35. Chloroplast a stellate mass with radiating processes__*Asterococcus* (in part)
35. Chloroplast not stellate_____36
36. Cells arranged in groups of 4 at the ends of branching strands
    formed by the remains of old mother cell walls; colony ovoid
    or globose _____37
36. Cells not arranged at the ends of branching strands; colony of
    various shapes_____38
37. Cells reniform to sausage-shaped and some also appearing ellip-
    soid in each group of 4, at the ends of branching strands (gela-
    tinous investment usually lacking)_____*Dimorphococcus* (in part)
37. Cells spherical or broadly ovoid, all the same shape, in groups of
    4 at the ends of branching strands_____ *Dictyosphaerium*
38. Cells spherical_____39
38. Cells of various shapes, fusiform, ovoid, reniform_____42
39. Cells arranged in linear series (single or double) within branched
    gelatinous strands; either with or without individual lamellate
    sheaths_____ *Palmodictyon* (in part)
39. Cells arranged otherwise _____ 40
40. Colonies spherical or irregularly shaped, sometimes triangular,
    with cell sheaths distinct and not confluent with the colonial
    mucilage_____ *Gloeocystis* (in part)
40. Colonies spherical; cells without individual sheaths, or with
    sheaths confluent with the colonial mucilage and not apparent_____41
41. Cells with cup-shaped chloroplasts containing a conspicuous
    pyrenoid; colony usually showing daughter colonies of smaller
    cells resulting from cell division _____ *Sphaerocystis*
41. Cells with several peripheral, polygonal chloroplasts, each with a
    pyrenoid (when cells are young with but 1 cup-shaped chloro-
    plast; in this condition to be compared with *Sphaerocystis*);
    colonies never containing daughter colonies, but frequently dis-
    integrating so that cells become solitary_____*Planktosphaeria* (in part)
42. Cells lunate or sickle-shaped, with narrow poles_____ 43
42. Cells reniform or fusiform, with rounded apices _____ 44

[574]

43. Cells strongly curved so that the poles nearly touch, scattered throughout the colonial mucilage in groups of 4, generally with the convex walls apposed...*Kirchneriella*

43. Cells crescent-shaped, arranged in groups of 4, 2 of which are in one plane facing each other, and 2 at right angles to this plane, each of the latter adjoined to one pole of the cells in the other pair...*Tetrallantos* (in part)

44. Cells fusiform 46

44. Cells ovate, reniform, or oblong...45

45. Cells ovate, arranged in 4's within a gelatinous sheath, forming a flat plate...*Dispora*

45. Cells reniform or oblong, reproducing by autospores usually retained within the old mother cell wall which may gelatinize and appear as a mucilaginous sheath.........................*Nephrocytium* (in part)

46. Cells solitary or in linear pairs within a fusiform, gelatinous envelope, multiplying by cell division.........................*Elakatothrix* (in part)

46. Cells arranged in parallel bundles of 4, reproducing by autospores ....*Quadrigula*

47. Cells, or some of them, in clusters, bearing gelatinous bristles or setae 48

47. Cells not bearing gelatinous bristles with or without spines..............49

48. Cells compactly arranged to form an adherent, dome-shaped cluster within the old mother cell wall which bears a dichotomously branched seta. (This cluster of cells results from the formation of zoospores and not from division to form successive generations of vegetative cells.)........................*Dicranochaete* (in part)

48. Cells globose, epiphytic, loosely arranged side by side to form a cluster (often solitary however), each bearing a sheathed, unbranched seta...*Chaetosphaeridium* (in part)

49. Cells attached at the ends of branching gelatinous stalks, epizoic on microscopic animals..50

49. Cells not so arranged, not epizoic...51

50. Cells ellipsoid or spindle-shaped, chloroplasts 1 or 2 parietal bands ....*Chlorangium* (in part)

50. Cells ovate or oblong, with numerous disc-like chromatophores (sometimes referred to as chloroplasts)........................*Colacium* (in part)

51. Cells broadly fusiform or elliptic, attached end to end to form loose, branching chains..*Dactylococcus* (in part)

51. Cells not so arranged...52

52. Cells globose or angular from mutual compression; aerial; forming clumps on moist substrates...................................*Protococcus* (in part)

52. Cells differently shaped, not forming expansions on moist substrates.......53

53. Cells acicular or slightly lunate 54

53. Cells differently shaped...55

54. Cells strongly curved, arcuate or lunate, not entangled but closely aggregated in families of crescent-shaped individuals.............*Selenastrum*

54. Cells straight or slightly crescent-shaped, loosely entangled or twisted about one another; often solitary.............*Ankistrodesmus* (in part)

55. Cells adjoined by their lateral or end walls to form definite patterns or arrangements...56

55. Cells grouped otherwise, not adjoined by their lateral walls or, if so, not forming definite patterns 71

56. Cells cylindrical, adjoined at each end by 2 other similar cells ·in successive order to form a network of coenocytic units, the meshes of which are 5- or 6-sided _____ *Hydrodictyon*
56. Cells attached by their lateral walls, or clustered to form other types of thalli_____57
57. Cells forming flat, circular or rectangular plates_____58
57. Cells not forming flat plates _____61
58. Cells forming circular or subcircular plates which may be perforate or continuous; marginal cells with a deep or shallow incision or sinus; cells within the plate usually somewhat different in shape from those at the margin_____ *Pediastrum*
58. Cells not arranged to form circular plates_____59
59. Cells triangular or ovoid, the walls bearing 1 or more spines, forming quadrate plates of 4 cells each_____ *Tetrastrum*
59. Cells not bearing spines _____60
60. Cells rectangular or trapezoidal, the outer free walls smooth and entire, cruciately arranged to form quadrate plates of 4 cells or multiples of 4 _____*Crucigenia*
60. Cells trapezoidal, the outer free walls deeply incised, cruciately arranged to form subquadrate plates of 4 or 8 _____ *Pediastrum tetras*
61. Cells bearing spines_____62
61. Cells without spines _____65
62. Cells ellipsoid, bearing many needle-like spines, adjoined side by side to form clusters of indefinite number (usually 2 to 8), sometimes solitary_____*Franceia* (in part)
62. Cells with few spines (1 to 4, rarely as many as 7); cells definitely arranged _____63
63. Cells ovoid, adjoined side by side, forming a linear series (single or double); spines usually few in number and mostly confined to the poles of the cells or with 1 or 2 on the lateral free walls (many minute spines in *Scenedesmus hystrix*)_____ *Scenedesmus* (in part)
63. Cells spherical, arranged in groups of 4 and multiples of 4 to form compound colonies; outer free walls bearing 1–7 very long slender spines_____ 64
64. Compound colony triangular in outline; spines 1 to 7 in number_____ *Micractinium*
64. Compound colony always pyramidal in shape, outer free wall of cells bearing a single, stout long spine_____ *°Errerella bornhemiensis*
65. Cells spherical or trapezoidal, arranged to form hollow, spherical, or polyhedral colonies, the cells adjoined by interconnecting protuberances_____*Coelastrum*
65. Cells not arranged in hollow colonies _____ 66
66. Colony composed of narrowly fusiform cells radiating from a common center where they are adjoined at their poles _____ *Actinastrum*
66. Colony not composed of fusiform cells radiating from a common center_____ 67
67. Cells elliptical or fusiform, attached end to end to form branching, chain-like series_____ *Dactylococcus* (in part)
67. Cells not forming such branching chains _____68
68. Cells ovoid, elliptical, or fusiform, adjoined by their lateral walls to form a series of 4 or more cells lying side by side in one plane (rarely in a curved plate) _____ *Scenedesmus* (in part)

79. Cells spherical, not bearing spines; subaerial or terrestrial, sometimes gregarious and densely clustered _____80
79. Cells aquatic, fusiform, acicular or needle-like, loosely clustered or entangled_____*Ankistrodesmus* (in part)
80. Cells gregarious (although sometimes solitary), but not adjoined, usually in several-celled clusters on damp soil or moist substrates; chloroplast not lobed_____*Chlorococcum* (in part)
80. Cells in dense clumps and adjoined, rarely solitary; spherical, or angular from mutual compression; chloroplast a dense, lobed plate nearly filling the cell_____*Protococcus* (in part)
(*Pleurococcus*)
81. Cells bearing spines or setae _____82
81. Cells without spines or setae_____93
82. Cells bearing a simple, sheathed seta_____*Chaetosphaeridium* (in part)
82. Cells not bearing a sheathed seta_____83
83. Cells bearing a single dichotomously branched hair_____*Dicranochaete* (in part)
83. Cells not bearing a dichotomously branched hair_____84
84. Cells ellipsoid or ovate, bearing 1 to 4 teeth or short spines, mostly at the poles; cells usually attached side by side, but sometimes solitary_____*Scenedesmus* (in part)
84. Cells fusiform or some other shape than above or, if ellipsoid, bearing long spines over the entire surface of the wall_____85
85. Cells triangular, pyramidal, quadrangular, or polygonal_____86
85. Cells ovate, round, fusiform, or acicular_____88
86. Cells pyramidate or tetragonal (rarely pentagonal), with 4 to 6 fine, needle-like spines radiating from each angle (see, however, *Polyedriopsis quadrispina*)_____*Polyedriopsis*
86. Cells pyramidate or polyhedral, without a tuft of needle-like spines at each angle_____87
87. Cells triangular, polygonal, or pyramidal, consisting of a definite body with 3 short, stout spines at the angles or at the apices of processes _____*Tetraëdron* (in part)
87. Cells pyramidal, each angle extended into a long spine-like process, the body of the cell small in diameter and not distinguishable from the bases of the processes _____*Treubaria*
88. Cells acicular or fusiform, the poles extended to form a long, finely-pointed seta, one of which may fork at the tip and serve as an attaching organ _____ *Schroederia*
88. Cells not acicular or fusiform _____ 89
89. Cells globose, with radiating spines_____90
89. Cells ovate or elliptical _____92
90. The entire wall beset with long, stout, tapering spines which are broad at the base _____*Echinosphaerella*
90. Cells bearing needle-like, slender spines_____91
91. Spines needle-like throughout, gradually tapering to a fine point_____*Golenkinia* (in part)
91. Spines with basal portion thickened, then tapering abruptly to a long, finely pointed tip _____ *Acanthosphaera*
92. Cells elliptical, with fine, needle-like spines arising from all parts of the wall _____*Franceia* (in part)
92. Cells ovate or ellipsoid, with a few long spines at the poles or localized at both poles and equator_____*Lagerheimia*

93. Cells irregularly globose or ovate, endophytic, buried within the tissues of higher aquatic plants..*Chlorochytrium*

93. Cells not endophytic...94

94. Cells endozoic, inhabiting the tissues of sponges, *Hydra,* and protozoa ....*Zoochlorella*

94. Cells not endozoic...95

95. Cells epizoic, attached to small crustaceans such as *Cladocera* and copepods...96

95. Cells not epizoic...98

96. Cells fusiform or acicular, with a single diffuse chloroplast; attached by a slender stipe........................*Characium* (in part)

96. Cells ovate or elliptic; chloroplast not a diffused sheet; attached by a thick stalk...97

97. Cells with 1 or 2 laminate, elongate chloroplasts.....*Chlorangium* (in part)

97. Cells with many ovate, disc-like chloroplasts (usually in branched colonies, sometimes solitary).......................*Colacium* (in part)

98. Cells free-living, not epiphytic or endophytic.......................100

98. Cells epiphytic...99

99. Cells globose, gregarious, attached by the anterior end, which is elongated to form a narrow stipe; with a massive chloroplast in the upper (posterior) end of the cell; growing in the mucilage of blue-green algae.......................................*Stylosphaeridium*

99. Cells fusiform or cylindrical, attached to filamentous algae or higher aquatic plants...............................*Characium* (in part)

100. Cells fusiform to acicular, much longer than their diameter.......101

100. Cells not spindle-shaped but of various other forms: spherical, ovate, oblong, pyramidal, or polygonal.......................102

101. Cells narrowly fusiform, 3–6µ in diameter, 50 (or more) times longer than wide.......................................*Closteriopsis*

101. Cells much smaller than above, length less than 25 times the diameter.......................................*Ankistrodesmus* (in part)

102. Cells spherical, inclosed in a wide, spindle-shaped, 2-part envelope (the parts adjoined at the equatorial plane).......*Desmatractum*

102. Cells not inclosed in a spindle-shaped envelope.......................103

103. Cells spherical, wall decorated with a reticulum of ridges which form blunt or sharply pointed projections at the periphery.......*Trochiscia*

103. Cells variously shaped; if spherical, without a reticulum.......104

104. Cells broadly and irregularly ellipsoid or subspherical, with thick uneven stratified walls.......................*Excentrosphaera*

104. Cells spherical or of other shapes, without thick stratified walls.......105

105. Cells spherical...106

105. Cells not spherical...111

106. Cells containing a single axial, stellate chloroplast with radiating processes which become flattened at the periphery of the cell.......................................*Asterococcus* (in part)

106. Cells not containing a stellate chloroplast.......................107

107. Cells large (50–300µ in diameter), globular, containing numerous ovate or disc-like chloroplasts arranged in radiating cytoplasmic strands and in a layer about the wall; chloroplasts shifting their position in response to light intensity.......*Eremosphaera*

107. Cells smaller, without numerous ovate chloroplasts.......................108

[579]

119. Gametangia (conjugating cells, Pl. 74, Fig. 4) becoming filled with lamellated pectic substances; zygospores cushion-like, compressed spheroid, or quadrate _____ *Zygnemopsis*

119. Gametangia not becoming filled with pectic substances during conjugation; zygospores globose, compressed globose, or ovate _____ 120

120. Axial chloroplasts 2 definite stellate bodies in each cell; species common _____ *Zygnema*

120. Axial chloroplast without radiating processes, sometimes bridged to form an apparent single, dumb-bell-shaped mass _____ *Zygogonium*

121. Chloroplast a parietal ribbon or band (sometimes only slightly twisted, or nearly straight); 1 to several such ribbons in a cell; pyrenoids several to many at rather regular intervals _____ *Spirogyra*
(including *Sirogonium*)

121. Chloroplast an axial plate or a band, with 2 to several pyrenoids, or with none _____ 122

122. Chloroplast without pyrenoids _____ *Mougeotiopsis*

122. Chloroplast with several pyrenoids _____ 123

123. Gametangia becoming filled with pectic substances during conjugation; granular residues absent in the gametangial cells; plants of slender proportions _____ *Debarya*

123. Gametangia not becoming filled with pectic substances; granular residues of the protoplast occurring in the conjugating cells; plants usually relatively stout _____ *Mougeotia*

124. Filament consisting of more than one series of cells, at least in a portion of its length _____ 125

124. Filament consisting of a single series of cells _____ 126

125. Plant uniseriate at the base, with cylindrical cells, becoming multiseriate above and composed of box-like or brick-like units compactly arranged _____ *Schizomeris*

125. Plant multiseriate, or uniseriate in part; a false filament composed of loosely arranged globose cells in a gelatinous strand _____ *Palmodictyon* (in part)

126. Chloroplast a parietal network covering the entire wall, sometimes very dense and difficult of determination, with many starch grains _____ 127

126. Chloroplast not covering entire wall; axial, or if parietal a folded plate, band, or meshwork _____ 128

127. Cells cylindrical, several to many times their diameter in length; wall thick in most forms, lamellated, sometimes with short rhizoidal branches _____ *Rhizoclonium* (in part)

127. Cells not cylindrical but slightly larger at the anterior end (sometimes inconspicuously so), where 1 or more ring-like scars are formed as a result of cell division (Pl. 29, Fig. 1); enlarged female cell conspicuous when plants are in reproductive condition _____ *Oedogonium*

128. Chloroplast a longitudinally narrow parietal net, plate, or band, which encircles the wall or nearly so _____ 129

128. Chloroplast massive, not a distinct parietal plate or band _____ 141

129. Filament composed of long, coenocytic units in which ovate chloroplasts or reticulate strands are arranged to form narrow, parietal, ring-like bands that encircle the cell; sexual reproduction by eggs and antherozoids _____ *Sphaeroplea*

129. Filament not a series of long cylindrical coenocytes; chloroplast otherwise; sexual reproduction isogamous or by motile heterogametes _____ 130

130. Filaments creeping on large filamentous algae, cells in continuous series _____ *Aphanochaete* (in part)
130. Filaments free-floating, or with basal attachment; if prostrate, with cells in interrupted series_____131
131. Filaments short, up to 20 cells in length; series of cells often interrupted _____132
131. Filaments longer than 20 cells; series continuous_____133
132. Chloroplast a parietal plate covering but a small part of the wall; filaments composed of few cells, frequently interrupted _____ *Stichococcus*
132. Chloroplast a broad parietal plate covering most of the cell wall; filaments continuous_____ *Hormidiopsis*
133. Filaments composed of cylindrical units inclosing 2 protoplasts, arranged in pairs, with the space between the protoplasts and the end walls filled with lamellated, gelatinous material_____ *Binuclearia*
133. Cells not in pairs as above _____134
134. Filaments inclosed by a gelatinous sheath _____135
134. Filaments not inclosed by a gelatinous sheath _____139
135. Cells oblong, broadly elliptic or quadrate, rather loosely arranged in a narrow or wide gelatinous sheath in which the individual cell sheaths are conspicuous and lamellate _____ *Cylindrocapsa*
135. Cells without conspicuously lamellated sheaths _____136
136. Cells cylindrical, subcylindrical, or globose; adjoined at the cross walls _____137
136. Cells oblong, not adjoined at the cross walls_____ *Geminella* (in part)
137. Cells quadrate, short- or long-cylindric _____138
137. Cells subglobose or elliptical; wall usually composed of 2 parts which overlap or adjoin in the midregion of the cell _____ *Radiofilum*
138. Chloroplast a parietal ring or band that encircles the wall or nearly so _____ *Ulothrix* (in part)
138. Chloroplast a laminate plate covering but a small portion of the wall and not encircling it _____ *Geminella* (in part)
139. Filaments without basal-distal differentiation; chloroplast a parietal plate encircling one-half the wall or less _____ *Hormidium*
139. Filaments with basal-distal differentiation, often attached by a basal hold-fast _____140
140. Cells long-cylindric, the terminal cell tapering unsymmetrically to form a blunt point _____ *Uronema*
140. Cells short-cylindric or quadrate, the terminal cell not tapering to a point _____ *Ulothrix* (in part)
141. Plants orange- or brick-red from an abundance of haematochrome which often masks the chlorophyll; chloroplasts discoid or band-like; walls usually roughened externally; plants of aerial habitats, usually branching_____ *Trentepohlia* (in part)
141. Plants without haematochrome; wall usually composed of 2 portions which overlap or adjoin in the midregion (Pl. 8, Figs. 1, 5), forming H-shaped pieces upon fragmentation; chloroplast massive, a branched band or a thick, parietal plate, or a cushion   *Microspora*
(cf. *Tribonema*)
142. Filaments branched, coenocytic and tubular, without cross walls except where reproductive cells are cut off _____168
142. Filaments not coenocytic and tubular, but having cross walls_____143

169. Plants forming felt-like mats on moist soil, attached to submerged substrates, or floating entangled masses; coenocytic and tubular, cylindrical and irregularly branched, reproductive organs lateral or on the ends of short branches _____*Vaucheria*

169. Plants forming submerged, felt-like mats with horizontal, rhizoidal, and erect freely-branched portions (possibly growing on moist soil also); branching dichotomous, with constrictions at the base of the branches and at the place where long, hooked sex organ-bearing branches originate _____*Dichotomosiphon*

170. Plants usually corticated (columnar cells investing the main axial row of cells—Pl. 82, Figs. 7, 13); antheridia below the oogonia, which have five cells in the coronula _____ *Chara*

170. Plants without cortical cells; antheridia lateral at the nodes or apical on short stalks; oogonium with 10 cells in the coronula, arranged in 2 tiers _____171

171. Antheridia terminal on short stalks in the furcations of branchlets; plants symmetrically branched _____*Nitella*

171. Antheridia lateral at the nodes, beside the oogonia; branching unsymmetrical, some branches long and coarse, giving the plant a scraggly appearance _____*Tolypella*

172. Cells flattened dorsiventrally, broadly ovate or ovoid, subspherical, or fusiform in outline (Pl. 80, Figs. 1, 2) _____173

172. Cells not dorsiventrally flattened; round in cross section (some spp. of *Euglena* in exception); round, ovoid, pyriform or elongate in longitudinal view, sometimes fusiform or subcylindric _____ _____ 174

173. With 1 flagellum and 1 or more large and conspicuous paramylon grains; eye-spot usually clearly evident _____ *Phacus*

173. With 2 flagella, one trailing; food in the form of oil; eye-spot lacking _____ *Gonyostomum*

174. Cells inclosed by a firm brown shell or test (Pl. 83, Fig. 1), of many shapes and with various decorations _____*Trachelomonas*

174. Cells not inclosed by a test _____175

175. Cells ovoid or pyriform, rigid, not changing shape in movement; paramylon bodies 2 large lateral rings _____ *Lepocinclis*

175. Cells elongate-fusiform, or nearly cylindrical, mostly metabolic (changing shape in movement), or rigid in some species; paramylon bodies of various shapes but mostly small and numerous _____*Euglena*

176. Chromatophores violet-green, gray-green (plants sometimes appearing blue-green in mass); macroscopic branched thalli, or microscopic cell clusters, or filaments _____177
(see also 183)

176. Chromatophore or protoplast some other color than gray-green or violet-green_____180

177. Plants attached, macroscopic, multicellular, usually highly branched thalli_____178

177. Plants microscopic, filamentous, growing erect from an attached portion and alternately branched; branches usually simple, and tapering slightly toward the apices_____*Audouinella*

178. Thallus embedded in a soft, copious mucilage, exhibiting a regular plan of branching, with internodes and nodes from which fascicles of branches arise; plants limp and formless when removed from the water_____*Batrachospermum*

178. Thallus not embedded in soft mucilage but tough and cartilaginous, somewhat rigid, and maintaining its shape when removed from the water_____179
179. Thallus much branched, the branches antler-like and irregularly dichotomous; axes gradually tapering throughout_____ *Tuomeya*
179. Thallus not at all or but very little branched, stiff and spinelike with definite nodal swellings and intervening contractions ____ *Lemanea*
180. Plants yellow, yellow-brown, or dark golden-brown (see Diatoms: Appendix)_____226
180. Cells with chromatophores or protoplasts of other colors than above_____181
181. Chromatophores pale yellow-green (often appearing grassgreen; iodine test required; see illustrations of representative forms), with xanthophyll predominating, often showing a metallic lustre; reserve food oil or glycogen, the iodine test for starch negative; cell wall often composed of 2 pieces; mostly nonmotile _____189
181. Cells with protoplasts or chromatophores not yellow-green_____182
182. Cells with bright blue-green protoplasts or chromatophores_____183
182. Cells with protoplasts or chromatophores some other color _____185
183. Plants consisting of 1 or 4 spherical cells with a cup-shaped, blue-green protoplast, inclosed by a mucilaginous sheath, each cell bearing a long, gelatinous bristle_____ *Gloeochaete*
183. Plants some other form; not bearing setae _____184
184. Plant a linear series of globose or oblong cells within a gelatinous strand; chromatophores stellate_____ *Asterocytis*
184. Plant an aquatic unicell, or composed of cells clustered in small, spherical families within the old mother cell wall; protoplasts blue-green, chromatophore-like bodies (blue-green algal cells endophytic in colorless host cells)_____*Glaucocystis* (in part)
185. Cells appearing gray or brownish, in compact colonies and inclosed by an orange-colored or brown, rubbery mucilage which obscures the pigmentation of the cells _____*Botryococcus* (in part)
185. Cells reddish, red, or violet-red _____186
186. Plant a gelatinous colony of ovate or globose cells with lamellate sheaths, the green chloroplast masked by an abundance of haematochrome _____ *Gloeocystis* (in part)
186. Plant not a gelatinous colony; cells solitary or gregarious but not invested by a colonial envelope _____187
187. Plants terrestrial; solitary or gregarious; spherical unicells forming blood-red patches or layers on damp soil, especially in greenhouses _____ *Porphyridium*
187. Plants aquatic_____188
188. Cells fusiform, with 1 long (rarely short) flagellum; green chloroplasts masked by haematochrome; sometimes forming red films on the surface of ponds _____*Euglena* (in part)
188. Cells round or ellipsoid; flagella 2, or wanting when cell is encysted and quiescent; usually forming a rusty-red layer on the bottom in shallow rain-water pools, etc._____*Sphaerella* (in part)
189. Plants filamentous_____190
189. Plants not filamentous; cells solitary or colonial _____192
190. Filaments false, consisting of branched gelatinous tubes with 1 or 2 spherical cells at the distal ends of the segments____*Mischococcus* (in part)
190. Filaments not false; unbranched_____191

[9]Cf. *Dinobryon*; species are differentiated by the shape of empty loricas.

241. Cells broadly fusiform in outline, with a long or short anterior horn and 2 or 3 posterior horns; wall heavy and reticulate, composed of plates (sometimes not easily discerned)................_Ceratium_
241. Cells not broadly fusiform and without prominent anterior and posterior horns 242
242. Cells with a definite membrane but without a true wall; not showing plates; possessing a transverse furrow which completely encircles the cell .... _Gymnodinium_
242. Cells with a definite wall which usually shows plates; with a transverse furrow sometimes completely encircling the cell 243
243. Wall heavy, plates easily discerned; transverse furrow completely encircling the cell; cell very little flattened dorsiventrally............245
243. Wall thin, plates often seen with difficulty; transverse furrow complete or not; cell sometimes flattened dorsiventrally 244
244. Cells strongly flattened dorisventrally (Pl. 90, Figs. 4-6); plates scarcely showing; transverse furrow incompletely encircling the cell.._Hemidinium_
244. Cell little or not at all flattened dorsiventrally; plates readily discernible; transverse furrow completely encircling the cell........_Glenodinium_
245. Cells not flattened dorsiventrally, with 1 antapical plate (plate at the posterior pole)..°_Gonyaulax_
245. Cells with 2 antapical plates, slightly flattened dorsiventrally....._Peridinium_
246. Colony actively swimming by means of flagella 248
246. Colony non-motile, or cells with rhizopodal processes 247
247. Cells 2, or 4–8, irregularly arranged in a common mucilage......_Chrysocapsa_
247. Cells 16 (rarely 32) radially arranged in a wide gelatinous sheath which is heavily impregnated with granular waste products ...._Chrysostephanosphaera_
248. Colony spherical, composed of ovoid or pyriform cells arranged at the periphery of a colonial mucilage................................249
248. Plant not a spherical colony of ovoid or pyriform cells 251
249. Cells each with 2 apical cylindrical receptacles from which a long silicious rod extends.............................._Chrysosphaerella_
249. Cells not bearing silicious rods 250
250. Cells elongate-ellipsoid, or elongate-pyriform, with silicious scales in the apical region; swimming by 2 flagella of equal length ...._Synura_
250. Cells small, ovoid or pyriform, without apical silicious scales; flagella 2, unequal in length ...._Uroglenopsis_
251. Cells amoeboid, without loricas, adjoined in loose linear series by their long, thin pseudopodia ...._Chrysidiastrum_
251. Cells with vase-shaped or conical loricas, forming arbuscular or diverging colonies, with 1 or 2 loricas emerging from the mouth of the lorica below.............................._Dinobryon_ (in part)
252. Plant an attached parenchymatous mass in which filamentous arrangement of cells is not clearly evident; endospores formed in the upper or outer cells of the plant mass, or of the branches....°_Pleurocapsa_
252. Plants otherwise, not a parenchymatous mass 253
253. Plants unicellular or colonial, usually with an evident sheath, which may be lamellated..254
253. Plants filamentous; cells arranged in 1 or more series and inclosed or not inclosed by a sheath (Pl. 112, Figs. 1–8). (The series of cells is termed a _trichome_ and this, together with its sheath, is called a _filament_ in this group of the algae.) 274

254. Plant a spirally twisted, long or short unicell, usually showing oscillating or spiral movements _____*Spirulina* (in part)
254. Plant otherwise _____255
255. Plant an epiphyte, a sheathed, club-shaped unicell usually showing endospores (Pl. 108, Figs. 5, 6), which are cut off successively from the apex of the protoplast _____*Chamaesiphon*
255. Plant solitary or colonial, not forming endospores; not a club-shaped unicell _____256
256. Cells embedded in a mucilaginous sheath which may be lamellate_____262
256. Cells not embedded in a common mucilaginous or gelatinous matrix____257
257. Cells globose_____258
257. Cells longer than wide, oblong or cylindrical_____259
258. Cells minute, 1–5μ in diameter, solitary or gregarious (usually with a sheath, but this is often not apparent)_____*Chroococcus* (in part)
258. Cells larger, up to 50μ in diameter (colorless host cells with vermiform, endophytic blue-green protoplasts)_____*Glaucocystis* (in part)
259. Cells solitary or sometimes in families of 2–4; oblong or broadly ovate to subcylindrical, up to 50μ in diameter_____261
259. Cells in small colonies or rarely solitary, cylindrical, strongly curved or pyriform_____260
260. Cells in small clusters, sometimes solitary, strongly curved, describing nearly a complete circle, sometimes lying with long axes parallel in compact series within the mucilage of other algae _____*Cyanarcus*
260. Cells pyriform, radiately arranged in small colonies and inclosed by an inconspicuous gelatinous investment, which is invisible unless stained_____*Marssoniella*
261. Cells ovate, solitary or in families of 2 to 4, inclosed by old mother cell wall (colorless host cell with endophytic blue-green protoplasts), up to 50μ in diameter_____*Glaucocystis* (in part)
261. Cells oblong or subcylindrical, up to 15μ in diameter, not symbiotic as above _____*Synechococcus*
262. Cells globose, 2–16 in a mucilaginous sheath in which individual cell sheaths are visible; free-floating or adherent, sometimes subaerial _____*Chroococcus* (in part)
262. Cells globose, cylindrical, or elongate, forming many-celled colonial aggregates of more than 16 individuals, inclosed by copious mucilage which may or may not be lamellated_____263
263. Cells 10 or more times their diameter in length, cylindrical, reniform, or fusiform_____264
263. Cells 2 or 3 (rarely as much as 8) times their diameter in length; round, ovate, or short cylindric _____265
264. Cells narrowly fusiform, with tapering, blunt-pointed apices _____*Dactylococcopsis*
264. Cells reniform or vermiform, straight or variously curved_____*Rhabdoderma*
265. Cells minute, 0.6–1.5μ in diameter, bacilliform, crowded within a colorless colonial mucilage; pigment scarcely discernible_____*Pelogloea*
265. Cells larger, or not bacilliform; pigment readily discernible _____266
266. Cells oblong or short cylindric, with poles rounded, crowded and irregularly arranged in copious mucilage; individual cell sheaths sometimes evident_____(*Anacystis*, in part)
Including: a. *Aphanothece*, with individual cell sheaths not apparent; b. *Gloeothece*, with individual cell sheaths apparent.

[593]

296. Trichomes and lateral branches multiseriate with wide mucilaginous sheaths, or uniseriate with close, firm sheaths; heterocysts not on the ends of short lateral branches _____297
297. Filaments uniseriate; sheaths firm, close; heterocysts oblong
to cylindrical _____*Hapalosiphon*
(cf. *Stigonema ocellatum*)
297. Filaments multiseriate˙ (rarely uniseriate in part), with wide
mucilaginous sheaths; heterocysts compressed, spheroidal, usually
lateral on a vegetative cell _____298
298. Branches as wide or nearly as wide as the main filament; hormogonia not formed in the apices of the branches _____ *Stigonema*
298. Branches narrow, erect, with hormogonia formed in their apical
region _____ _____ _____ *Fischerella*
299. Trichomes without branches _____300
299. Trichomes with false branches _____310
300. Trichomes with a basal heterocyst (sometimes intercalary heterocysts also); sheath firm and definite _____ *Microchaete*
300. Trichomes without a firm sheath; heterocysts either always terminal or always intercalary _____301
301. Heterocysts always terminal _____302
301. Heterocysts always intercalary _____303
302. Heterocysts at one end, rarely at both ends, of the trichome;
gonidia formed adjacent to the heterocysts _____*Cylindrospermum*
302. Heterocysts at both ends of the trichome; gonidia remote from
the heterocysts _____ *Anabaenopsis*
303. Plant formed of many trichomes, often lying parallel to one
another _____304
303. Trichomes solitary or, if gregarious, entangled, not parallel _____306
304. Trichomes surrounded by copious mucilage, forming hollow,
attached, tubular or bullate masses _____*Wollea*
304. Trichomes not forming attached, tubular or bullate masses, but
occurring in free-floating bundles or fascicles _____305
305. Trichomes very slightly tapering toward both apices; many
within free-floating macroscopic flakes of definite shape; gonidia
always solitary _____ *Aphanizomenon*
305. Trichomes not tapering toward the apices; forming flakes of
irregular outline; gonidia usually in a series (solitary in some
species) _____*Anabaena* (in part)
306. Trichomes solitary, planktonic among other algae _____307
306. Trichomes aggregated in a gelatinous mass of definite or indefinite shape _____308
307. Cells disc-shaped, much shorter than wide; heterocysts compressed _____ ____ _____ ____ ____ _____*Nodularia*
307. Cells not disc-shaped but globose to cylindrical; heterocysts
not compressed _____ *Anabaena* (in part)
308. Plant mass of definite shape, the periphery of the colonial
mucilage forming a tegument _____*Nostoc*
308. Plant mass not of definite shape; colonial mucilage soft, not
bounded by a firm tegument _____309
309. Trichomes forming small packets, entangled, sometimes subparallel, inclosed in a gelatinous sheath _____ *Aulosira*
309. Trichomes not forming packets, individual sheaths lacking, or
not definite_____ *Anabaena* (in part)

[594]

310. Branches usually arising in unilateral pairs about midway between the heterocysts of the main filament; sheath firm and lamellate, rarely homogeneous..*Scytonema*

310. Branches arising singly, just below a heterocyst or a series of them...... 311

311. Filaments aggregated, somewhat radially arranged in a mucilaginous layer; branching regularly dichotomous; heterocysts solitary..*Diplonema*

311. Filaments solitary or aggregated, sometimes forming free-floating, cottony tufts; branching not dichotomous, arising from beneath a heterocyst or series of heterocysts................................*Tolypothrix*

Glossary

Terms Relating to Fresh-water Algae

Abscission: separation of a branch or portion of a thallus by degeneration of cells at its base, or by constriction.

Achromatic: without color.

Achromatin: the material of the nucleus exclusive of the chromatin.

Acicular: needle-shaped.

Adnate: joined along a relatively broad surface.

Aerobic: using free oxygen in respiration.

Agglutinate, Agglutinated: sticking together; adherent, as with mucilaginous sheaths.

Akinęte: a spore produced from a vegetative cell which has developed a thick wall about a concentrated food reserve.

Akontae (Akontean): plants in which neither vegetative cells nor reproductive cells have flagella.

Alveolar: with cavities or pits.

Amoeboid: like an amoeba in locomotion or in nutrition; creeping by pseudopodia.

Amorphous: without definite shape.

Anabaenin: a pigment found in the blue-green algal genus *Anabaena*.

Anaerobic: carrying on respiration without the use of free oxygen.

Anastomose: referring to sheaths, filaments, or thalli which intermittently join and separate; sometimes joining in such a way as to form a network.

Androsporange, Androsporangium: box-like cell which produces a special spore, androspore, which develops into a dwarf male plant (Oedogoniaceae).

Androspore: a spore which gives rise to an epiphytic dwarf male plant (Oedogoniales).

Anisogametes: sex cells of a plant slightly dissimilar in size, shape, or behavior.

Alternation of generations: a life cycle in which both asexual and sexual plants occur, one giving rise to the other by the production of spores, and by the fusion of gametes.

Annular: ring-like.

Antapical: posterior; basal; opposite the apex.

Antapical plates: sections of the cell wall of Dinoflagellatae at the posterior pole.

Antheridium: a male gametangium or sex organ.

Antherozoid: a male gamete; sperm, or spermatozoid.

Apex (Apical): forward tip; anterior end.

Apical plates: sections of the cell wall of Dinoflagellatae at the anterior pole.

Apiculate: abruptly tapered to a fine point.

Aplanogametes: non-flagellated gametes.

Aplanospore: non-motile asexual spores, formed one to several in but not the same shape as a parent cell.

Aplanosporangium: cell which gives rise to aplanospores.

Apposed: paired; opposite in definite relation to one another.

Appressed: pressed together; closely adjoined.

Arborescent, Arbuscular: branched in tree-like fashion; bushy.

Arachnoid: like a web.

Arcuate: arched, bow-shaped, sharply crescent-shaped; strongly curved as in a drawn bow.

Areolate: with openings; with thin areas (areolae), usually circular, in the wall.

Articulate, Articulated: jointed; with segments.

Asexual: referring to reproduction in which spores rather than gametes are used.

Asexual auxospore: a resting stage formed without union of gametes (diatoms).

Attenuated: narrowed or tapering toward the ends.

Autocolony: colony of cells formed by the division of one or more cells of a mother colony; or by internal division of a cell to form a miniature colony (see *Pediastrum, Oocystis, Volvox*).

Autospore: a small replica of the parent cell formed internally, one or several together.

Autotrophic: self-feeding; able to manufacture food.

Auxospore: a resting spore formed by some diatoms, either sexual or asexual.

Axial chloroplasts: chloroplasts in the median plane of a cell, arranged along a median line.

Axis: the central or median plane of a figure, cell, or plant.

Azygote, Azygospore: a spore similar in shape and wall markings to a zygospore (q.v.) but formed without the union of sex cells.

Bacillar: rod-shaped.

Basidia-like: club-shaped.

Basipetalous: developing from apex toward the base.

Benthon: organisms attached on the bottom of an aquatic habitat; deep-water life.

Biconic: in the shape of two cones with their bases together.

Bifurcate: divided into two portions, or branches, as in the forking of spines or lobes.

Bilateral: on two sides; arising on two sides; the same on two sides.

Biseriate: in two rows; with two series of cells.

Blepharoplast: small body (the central body) associated with the nucleus; in some flagellates, the body from which the flagellum arises.

Bulbous: bulb-like, swollen at one end.

Caespitose (or *Cespitose*): clustered; in fascicles; forming a mat or tangle.

Calose: a substance appearing in the walls of the Siphonales which replaces cellulose.

Calyptra: a thickening; a thick covering or membrane at the tip of a trichome or organ (e.g. in *Oscillatoria* spp., *Phormidium* spp.).

Canal: tube; fine channel, as in the wall of diatoms.

Capitate: with a head; swollen at one end, or at both ends.

Capitellate: slightly swollen or enlarged at one end.

Carotene, Carotin: an orange-colored pigment, usually associated with chlorophyll.

Carpogone, Carpogonium: female sex organ in the Rhodophyceae.

Carpospore: spore arising from the fertilized egg in some Rhodophyceae.

Cartilaginous: tough but pliable.

Catenate: joined to form a chain.

Caudus: a tail-piece.

Central body: the central region of the blue-green algal cell, which upon staining shows the presence of chromatin granules; a granule associated with the nucleus in flagellated organisms.

Central nodule: the thickening on the inner face of the wall of some diatoms.

Centricae: diatoms which are radially symmetrical.

Centrifugal: developing from the center outward, or from a point outward.

Centripetal: developing from without inward, or from exterior to interior.

Centrosome, Centriole: a small body, usually lying just outside the nucleus; in flagellates a granule functioning in the neuromotor system.

Cespitose: *See* caespitose.

Chitin: a hard substance, $C_{15} H_{26} O_{10} N_2$, found in skeletons of lower animals and in cell walls of some algae.

Chloroplast: a body (plastid) in the cell containing chlorophyll as the predominating pigment.

Chlorococcine tendency: evolutionary trend toward the Chlorococcales in the green algae (or in other groups) from a solitary motile cell which has ability to reproduce vegetatively by cell division to a nonmotile type of cell (uninucleate or coenocytic) in which vegetative cell division is not used.

Chromatophore: a colored body in a cell which has a pigment other than chlorophyll predominating.

Chromatic: colored.

Chromatin: the material in the nucleus which takes up dyes readily; nuclear material composing chromosomes.

Chromoplasm: the portion or part of cell content containing pigments, not involving plastids; in Myxophyceae the cytoplasm just within the cell wall and exterior to the "central body."

Chromulinad: a type of cell similar to *Chromulina* which has one flagellum.

Chroococcoidal: in shape or arrangement similar to *Chroococcus*; cluster of round cells.

Chrysochrome: brown pigment found in Chrysophyceae.

Cilium (pl., *Cilia*): fine, hair-like extensions, usually from the outer membrane of a cell; used in locomotion by ciliated protozoa; fibrils on the flagella of the Heterokontae.

Cingulum: band within the diatom cell which holds the two overlapping sections of the wall together.

Circinate: coiled, rolled; twisted.

Cirque: arranged in a circle or nearly so.

Citriform: lemon-shaped.

Clathrate: with openings; intermittent spaces.

Clavate, Claviform: wedge-shaped.

Coalesced, Coalescent: joined, united; grown together.

Coccoid: round; spherical; cells as in *Chroococcus, Aphanocapsa*.

Coenobe, Coenobium: a colony of cells arranged to form a hollow sphere.

Coenocytic: with many nuclei; a thallus constructed of multinucleate cells; a thallus in which there are no cross walls.

Collar: narrow neck around the flagellum-opening in a shell or lorica; sometimes a sheath at the base of a bristle or hair.

Colligate: united, joined, as in some species of *Spirogyra* which have an external collar-like piece about the cells at the cross walls.

Colony: a group of individuals, joined together or merely inclosed by a common sheath or investing material; a group of cells joined together to form a filament (rarely used in this sense); a cluster of individual plants, closely associated in growth.

Commensal: referring to two or more species living in close association and deriving mutual benefits.

Complanate: level, smooth, even, plane.

Concentric: layers or structures with a common center.

Confluent: growing into one another; soft sheaths which run together or which become intermingled.

Conidium: a spore cut off from the tip of a cell, or from a filament.

Connate: pointed; united for a short distance as in the basal portion of branches.

Constricted: pinched in; deeply incised.

Contiguous: near-by, adjoined.

Conjugation: union of gametes from cells or from plants which become joined, the gametes moving together in an amoeboid fashion; literally, a yoking together.

Contorted: irregularly twisted.

Contractile: able to expand and contract.

Contractile vacuole: cavity in the cytoplasm surrounded by a membrane which shows pulsating actions, compressing and expanding.

Convolute: rolled together; rolled inward from a margin.

Cordate, Cordiform: heart-shaped.

Coronula: a crown of cells at apex of oogonium in Characeae.

Cortex, Corticating: a layer of cells or filaments which invest or grow around a central core (cell or filament), forming an inclosing layer (e.g., some Rhodophyceae, *Chara*).

Corymb (Corymbose): a flat-topped cluster (especially when sequence of development is from outside toward the center).

Costa (Costate): rib (adj., ribbed).

Craticular stage: a condition in diatoms in which successively formed cell walls nest within one another.

Crenate: with a wavy surface or margin.

Crenulate: finely crenate; with small scallops.

Cuspidate: furnished with a tooth.

Cruciate: cross-like in arrangement.

Cryoplankton, Cryovegetation: plants which live in snow, especially perpetual snow banks of alpine situations.

Cuneate: wedge-shaped.

Cushion-like: said of a thallus composed of a mound of cells, two to many layers of cells; parenchymatous.

Cylindrical: elongate and round in cross section with parallel lateral margins.

Cyst: a dormant, vegetative reproductive cell, usually with a heavy wall.

Cystocarp: a structure that develops around the fertilized egg in the Rhodophyceae in which spores (carpospores) are formed.

Cystosome: soft portion of periplast of flagellates in the food-absorbing region.

Cytopharynx: a canal extending back from the anterior opening in flagellates; narrow part of gullet in euglenoids.

Daughter cells, Daughter segments: cells or portions of thallus that are descended from the same mother cell or parent plant.

Decumbent: growing horizontally but with the segment ascending (c.f. prostrate).

Deliquescent: degenerating; dissolving.

Dendroid: tree-like, branching as in a tree.

Dentate: toothed; with blunt-pointed projections.

Depressed-globose: not quite spherical; like a slightly flattened sphere.

Diastole: period of expansion in action of contractile vacuole.

Diatomaceous earth: grayish-colored silicious deposit of diatom shells.

Diatomin: brown pigment found in diatoms.

Dichotomous, Dichotomy: divided or forked into two parts; forking branches.

Dioecious:"two households"; with male and female organs on separate plants.

Diffluent: flowing off; dissolving away.

Diploid: referring to nucleus with double number of chromosomes; a generation of plant life cycle before reduction division (cf. haploid).

Disarticulate: unjointed; with segments separated.

Disc (*Discoid*): a circular, flat body; a plate.

Dissepiment: a cross partition; a cross wall.

Distal: referring to the forward end; opposite from basal.

Distromatic: occurring in two layers, or at two levels.

Divaricate: widely separating; spreading.

Diverging: extending from a common point in different directions.

Dolioform: barrel-shaped.

Dwarf male: a 1-celled or few-celled male plant epiphytic on the female, usually on or near the oogonia.

Echinate: spiny.

Egg: female gamete; non-motile heterogamete.

Emarginate: a margin which is not even, but notched or with concavities.

Endocellular: within the cell.

Endogenous: arising from within.

Endophyte (*Endophytic*): plant living within another plant but not necessarily parasitic.

Endospore: a spore formed within a cell; a spore cut off from the tip of a protoplast as in *Chamaesiphon*.

Endozoic: living within an animal but not necessarily parasitic.

End piece: the unsheathed tip of a flagellum; a tail piece.

Entire: smooth, not toothed or roughened.

Envelope: a sheath or mass of mucilage which incloses a cell or colony.

Epicone: the upper or anterior half of a dinoflagellate cell.

Epiphyte (*Epiphytic*): plant growing on another plant but not necessarily parasitic.

Epitheca: the part of the cell wall of a dinoflagellate above the transverse furrow.

Epivalve: the upper or larger of the two parts of the wall of diatom cells; sometimes the upper part of dinoflagellate cells.

Epizoic: attached to or growing on animals.

Erect oogonium: oogonium (in the genus *Bulbochaete*) borne at the end of a suffultory cell (q.v.) that has been divided by a transverse wall.

Euplankton: true plankton; open-water drifting organisms.

Eutrophic: referring to older, shallow lakes; highly productive.

Evanescent: disappearing, vanishing, especially with advanced age.

Evection: to set aside or to push one part above another.

Excentric (or *Eccentric*): off center.

Exospore: the outer membrane of a zygospore wall.

Eye-spot: pigment-spot; granule which is sensitive to light and usually dark red in color; found in some swimming spores or in motile vegetative cells.

False branch: a branch formed by a slipping to one side of a section of a filament; a branch not formed by lateral division of a cell.

Family: an aggregation of cells or of similar plants.

Fascicle (*Fasciculate*): a bundle or cluster.

Fastigiate: narrowed to a point.

Fenestrate (*Fenestration*): windowed; with openings.

Fibrils (*Fibrillate, Fibrillose*):fine fibers; slender strands.

Filament: a linear arrangement of cells; thread of cells, together with sheath (Myxophyceae).

[600]

Filiform: thread-like.
Fission: division of a cell by splitting to form two, not necessarily equal, parts; cell division without mitosis.
Flaccid: soft, drooping, not rigid.
Flagellum: a stout, whip-like organ of locomotion which arises within the cell.
Flagelliform: whip-shaped.
Flange: a longitudinal ridge extending vertically from a cell wall.
Flexuous: pliable; not firm or rigid.
Floccose, Flocculent: cottony, or wooly; matted.
Floridean starch: a carbohydrate food reserve in the Rhodophyceae.
Foliaceous, Foliose: like a leaf.
Frond: a flat, leaf-like plant; a foliaceous thallus.
Frustule: the shell of diatoms.
Fusiform: an elongate figure broadest in the middle and tapering at each end; spindle-shaped.
Gametangium: a gamete-producing cell; sex organ.
Gamete: a sex cell, male or female reproductive cell.
Gelatinous envelope: a sheath or investment of mucilage-like substance.
Geniculate: with knee-bendings.
Germling: young plant developed from a spore or zygote.
Gibbous: swollen in a regular curve.
Girdle: a band or belt, usually median; part of the structure just within the wall, and lateral in the cell, which holds the valves of diatoms together.
Girdle view: a lateral or side view of a diatom, showing the overlapping of the two wall sections.
Glaucous: grayish-green; green with a whitish overcast or 'bloom.'
Glomerate: in compact clusters.
Glomerule: a small compact cluster.
Glycogen: a white carbohydrate, amorphous, similar to starch; a food reserve.
Gonidium: a spore-like, thick-walled reproductive cell (see akinete).
Gonimoblasts: short filaments developing from the zygote in certain Rhodophyceae which cut off spores (carpospores) at their tips.
Granulose: furnished with granules.
Gregarious: growing in clusters or in close associations; not solitary.
Gullet: an opening through the membrane at anterior end of flagellates (euglenoids).
Gynandrosporous: in Oedogoniaceae, a condition in which androspores (spores which produce male plants) are developed in the same filament in which oogonia (female organs) occur.
Gypsum: granules of calcium sulphate found in the cells of some desmids.
Haematochrome: a red pigment apparently functioning as a light screen, appearing occasionally in green algae, sometimes permanently present.
Haploid: containing the half number of chromosomes (nucleus with the 1-n number); referring to a generation in the life history following reductive division.
Haplontic: a haploid or 1-n generation; referring to a cell containing the reduced number of chromosomes.
Hapteron (pl. *Haptera*): an anchoring, finger-like organ at the base of a young plant.
Heleoplankton: floating organisms in a small, shallow pond.
Helotism: a form of symbiosis; two different species in close association (lichens).

[601]

Hemicellulose: a hard carbohydrate somewhat similar to cellulose in walls of some algae; more common in cell walls of higher plants.

Heterocyst: a specialized cell in some filamentous Myxophyceae which is usually larger than and a different shape from the vegetative cells.

Heterogametes: sex cells unlike in size, shape, and behavior.

Heterothallic: from two different thalli; of reproductive structures or cells borne on different parents.

Heterotrophic: obtaining food in soluble or particulate form; not photosynthetic.

Heterotypic division: reductive division of a nucleus; segregation of chromosomes.

Hirsute: hairy.

Holdfast cell: the basal cell of a filament modified to form an attaching organ.

Holophytic: obtaining food by photosynthesis.

Holozoic: ingesting food like an animal.

Homothallic: from similar thalli; of gametes from the same parent.

Homotypic division: nuclear division (mitosis) involving a splitting of chromosomes; the chromosome division immediately following first meiotic division.

Hormogonium, Hormogone: a fragment of a filament; a short section broken away from a mature trichome (Myxophyceae).

Hormospore: a vegetative spore-like body formed from a short section of a filament that becomes invested by a thick membrane.

H-shaped pieces: sections formed when a filament of cells dissociates; the H-shaped pieces formed as a result of the fact that cell walls are in two pieces which overlap in the midregion, the line of cleavage being here rather than at the cross walls of the filament.

Hyaline: colorless; transparent.

Hypocone: the lower part or posterior half of a dinoflagellate below the median girdle.

Hypotheca: the lower half of the cell wall of a dinoflagellate below the median girdle.

Hypovalve: the lower or smaller of the two parts of a diatom cell wall.

Hypha, Hyphal filaments: threads which inclose the central, axial filament in some Rhodophyceae (*Lemanea*).

Hypnospore: small, thick-walled, asexual spore; especially the spores formed underground in *Botrydium*.

Idioandrosporous: having androspores formed in filaments separate from those in which the female organs (oogonia) are produced (e.g., in *Oedogonium*).

Imbricate: overlapping; joined in an overlapping series.

Incised: cut, with narrow slits.

Indurate: hard.

Inferior pore: a pore in the wall in the lower part of an oogonium (Oedogoniaceae).

Initial cell: cell which generates other cells, or which gives rise to tissue.

Inner fissure: the inner part of the raphe in the pennate diatoms.

Integument: a covering, sheath, or envelope.

Intercalary: appearing between, inserted (as between cells), rather than terminal or marginal.

Intercalary bands: bands which help to hold the two valves of the diatom cell together.

Interpolate: to place between.

Intestiniform: shaped like an intestine; tubular.

Intravitam: within living tissue; e.g., to stain a living cell.

Intricate: tangled.

Investment: an inclosing membrane or envelope.

Isochrysid: cells bearing two flagella of equal length in Chrysophyceae.

Isodiametric: having diameters equal.

Isogamous: sex cells similar to one another in size, shape, and behavior.

Isokontae (*Isokontean*): plants which have vegetative or reproductive cells equipped with flagella (usually 2) of equal length.

Isthmus: narrow part of the desmid cell connecting two semicells (cell halves).

Karyokinesis: division of the nucleus; segregation of nuclear material in cell division.

Keel: a flange on the valve of some diatoms.

Laciniate: torn; with a cut or lacy margin, or lace-work surface.

Lacuna (*Lacunate*): an opening (with spaces).

Lageniform: flask-shaped.

Lamellate, Lamellated, Lamellose: layered, with layers.

Laminate: plate-like.

Lanceolate: lance-shaped; long and narrow with subparallel margins but tapered at the apex.

Lateral conjugation: sexual reproduction involving a joining to two contiguous cells in the same filament (e.g., in some species of *Spirogyra*).

Lenticular: lens-shaped; with two convex surfaces.

Leucosin: a white food reserve material found in most Heterokontae.

Limnoplankton: drifting organisms in lake water.

Littoral: in shallow water near shore; on the shore.

Longitudinal furrow: a groove in dinoflagellates lying parallel with the long axis, at right angles to the transverse furrow.

Loculiferous: with small chambers or compartments.

Lorica: a shell or case built around but separate from the living protoplast.

Lumen: a cavity, especially the space left in a cell after spores or gametes have escaped.

Lubricous: slippery.

Lunate: crescent-shaped; moon-shaped.

Macrogamete: the larger of two sizes of swimming gametes (e.g., *Stichococcus*).

Macrandrous: having male plants that are as large or nearly as large as the female plants (Oedogoniaceae).

Macrozoospores: the larger of two sizes of zoospores (e.g., *Ulothrix*).

Mammillate: with nipple-like protuberances.

Marl: calcareous deposit formed by some algae, especially *Chara*.

Matrix: investing or surrounding matter, especially mucilaginous material surrounding cells.

Median constriction: a pinched-in or narrowed region in central portion of cell or thallus.

Membranous, Membranaceous: like a membrane, a thin layer.

Meristematic: referring to cells with the ability to divide rapidly.

Mesospore: middle one of three layers in the wall of zygospores.

Metabolic: changeable in form, varying in shape from time to time (e.g., *Euglena*).

Microgamete: the smaller of two sizes of swimming gametes (e.g., *Stichococcus*).

Microspores: minute, spore-like bodies formed by some diatoms, questionably sexual or asexual.

Microzoospores: smaller of two sizes of zoospores in *Ulothrix*; spores which swarm for 2 to 6 days without germination.

[603]

Mitosis (Mitotic): nuclear division by formation of spireme thread and chromosomes.

Moniliform: resembling a string of beads.

Monaxial: with one axis or with one row of cells.

Monoecious: "of one household"; with both male and female sex organs on the same plant.

Monosiphonous: formed of a single tube or filament, without cross walls.

Monospores: asexual spores cut off from tips of branches, or from vegetative cells (e.g., some Rhodophyceae).

Monostromatic: referring to a prostrate thallus, one cell in thickness.

Mother cell: the cell which divides itself (often internally) into daughter cells.

Motile: able to move; swimming.

Multicellular: composed of many cells.

Multiaxial: with more than one axis; with more than one row of cells.

Multinucleate: with many nuclei.

Multiseriate: with more than one row of cells; with many filaments.

Nannandrous: with dwarf male plants, minute male filaments growing epiphytically on the female plant (Oedogoniaceae).

Nannoplankton: very minute aquatic organisms (see plankton).

Nannospores: very small vegetative cells arising from rapid cell division.

Napiform: turnip-shaped.

Naviculoid: like *Navicula;* like a little boat.

Necridium: a dead cell; a somewhat differentiated cell in some filamentous Myxophyceae which permits fragmentation to occur readily.

Nekton: organisms capable of swimming against water currents.

Neuromotor apparatus: the bodies and fibrils interconnecting flagella and attaching them to the centriole and the nucleus (e.g., euglenoids).

Neutral spore: a vegetative spore arising from increased cell division in certain Rhodophyceae.

Nodule: a small knob.

Nonparticulate: referring to substances in solution.

Obconic: cone-shaped with the broader end foremost.

Obovoid: inversely ovoid; with the broader end anterior or outermost.

Obpyriform: inversely pear-shaped, with the broader end anterior or outermost.

Ochromonad: a type of cell similar to *Ochromonas* (with two flagella of unequal length).

Ocelli: raised thickenings on the walls of diatoms.

Ocrea: a sheath; a layered envelope.

Oligotrophic: referring to younger, deep lakes; poor in production.

Ontogeny (Ontogenetic): life history of an organism.

Oogamy: reproduction involving gametes of which one is an egg.

Oogone, Oogonium: one-celled female reproductive organ, usually containing a single egg.

Oolith: a stone-like concretion involving a fossil surrounded by deposits of calcareous material.

Oospore: a thick-walled spore formed from a fertilized egg.

Operculum: a lid or cap.

Orbicular: spherical.

Orbiculate: circular in outline.

Oval: an elongate figure with convex margins and equally rounded at the ends.

Ovoid: shaped like an egg; an elongate figure with unequal curvature at the poles, one being broader than the other.

Ovate: see oval.

Outer fissure: the upper part of the raphe (q.v.) in pennate (bilaterally symmetrical) diatoms.

Packet: compact cluster or aggregate of cells, often cubical.

Palmella stage: a condition resembling *Palmella,* in which a motile cell has lost organs of locomotion, become quiescent, and undergone division to form clumps of daughter cells encased in mucilage.

Palmelloid: similar to *Palmella;* forming clumps of mucilage-encased cells.

Panduriform: fiddle-shaped; an elongate figure, broadest at the anterior end and with concave lateral margins.

Papilla (Papillose): a small nipple-like swelling (adj.: bearing papillae).

Paramylon: a solid carbohydrate food reserve formed by certain euglenoids.

Parenchymatous: cushion-like; composed of a mound of cells.

Parietal: lying along the wall; peripheral in the cell.

Parthenospore: a zygote-like spore produced from a single gamete which develops a thick wall.

Patent oogonium: oogonium (in *Bulbochaete*) borne on a division of the suffultory cell (q.v.) that has been cut off obliquely from the lower cell rather than by a transverse wall; free; free spreading.

Pectin, Pectose: gelatinous substance (carbohydrate) found in the wall of many algae.

Pedicel: a stalk or stem, often delicate and short.

Pelagic: floating organisms, especially in the ocean; surface organisms.

Pellicle: a thin membrane or sheet.

Pellucid: translucent, clear.

Penicillate: brush-like.

Pennatae: diatoms which are bilaterally symmetrical.

Pericentral cell: a cell (one of several) inclosing a central cell or filament.

Peridinin: a reddish pigment found in some dinoflagellates.

Periphyton: organisms attached at the water level to aquatic plants.

Periplast: the bounding membrane, especially the cell membrane of euglenoids.

pH: relative amount of free hydrogen ions; indicator of acidity or alkalinity.

Pharyngeal rods: bodies lying parallel with the gullet (e.g., *Peranema*).

Phototactic: movement or orientation with respect to light stimulus.

Phycochrysin: brown pigment found in Chrysophyceae (chrysochrome).

Phycocyanin: a blue pigment in solution in cells of Myxophyceae and some Rhodophyceae.

Phycoerythrin: red pigment in Rhodophyceae and some Myxophyceae.

Phycopyrin: brownish-red pigment in some dinoflagellates.

Phylogeny: racial development: racial history.

Pigment-spot: See eye-spot.

Piliferous, Pilose: hairy.

Placoderm desmid: desmid usually constricted in the midregion, with wall in two sections.

Plakea: plate of cells formed by successive divisions from mother cell.

Plane: smooth and even, not folded.

Planoconvex: with convex surface opposite a flat surface.

Planogamic heterogamy: condition of having gametes of different size, motile and non-motile.

Plankton (Planktonic): floating organisms unable to swim against currents, drifting.

Plasmodium: naked protoplasm as in slime molds.

Plastid: any one of several kinds of bodies in the cytoplasm of a cell.

Plicate: folded.

Plurilocular gametangium: closely arranged cluster of cells, each producing a gamete.

Polar: at the end of an axis.

Polar nodule: the body on the inner wall at the ends of some diatoms.

Polygonal: with many sides.

Pore: a hole or opening in a wall or membrane; mucilage pore; pore for entrance of antherozoid, etc.

Postcingular plates: sections of the wall of dinoflagellates lying between the median girdle and the antapical plates; posterior plates.

Precingular plates: sections of the wall of dinoflagellates lying between the median girdle and the apical plates; anterior plates.

Processes: extensions; lobes, arms, etc.

Proliferate: to develop a new thallus or branches by vegetative cell division.

Prostrate: lying down; horizontal.

Protonema; Protonema stage: prostrate filaments arising from germination of spore, sometimes giving rise to upright branches.

Protophyte, Protophyta: simplest of plants; often referring to organisms with both plant and animal-like characteristics.

Protoplast: the living material (protoplasm) of a cell.

Psammon: microorganisms inhabiting beaches or sandy shoals.

Pseudocilia: false cilia; hair-like extensions similar to flagella in shape but not used for locomotion.

Pseudofilament:a thread of cells incidentally arranged in a linear series; not a true filament.

Pseudoparenchymatous: resembling a mound of cells but actually constructed of closely grown filaments.

Pseudoraphe: a false raphe (q.v.); a clear median area in the valves of some diatoms which forms a line resembling a raphe.

Pseudopodium: a false foot; a root-like extension of protoplasm usually involved in locomotion (see *Chrysomoeba*).

Pseudovacuoles: false vacuoles; pockets of gas or mucilage in the cytoplasm resembling vacuoles, and usually light-refracting (Myxophyceae).

Pulsating vacuoles: vacuoles which contract suddenly and expand slowly.

Pulsule: non-contracting vacuole (as in dinoflagellates).

Pulverulent: finely granular; powdery.

Pulvinate: cushion-shaped.

Punctate: with minute points or dots; with cylindrical pores.

Pyramidal: in the shape of a pyramid.

Pyrenoid: a proteid granule which collects starch, either within a chloroplast, on its surface, or free within the cytoplasm.

Pyriform: pear-shaped, with narrow end foremost.

Quadrate: square; arranged to form a rectangle.

Quadripartition: division to form four units.

Raceme: a cluster of reproductive structures which mature inwardly from without, the youngest structure being in the center or at the top of the cluster; racemose (adj.), arranged like a raceme.

Radial: along the radius; radiating.

Raphe: a fissure, slit, or channel in the wall of some diatoms.

Rectilinear: arranged in straight rows in two directions.

Reniform: bean-shaped; kidney-shaped.

Repand: referring to cells having the lateral walls concave or undulate.

Replicate: folded, especially the end walls of some species of *Spirogyra*.

Reservoir: posterior, enlarged portion of gullet in flagellates (euglenoids).

[606]

Reticulate: netted; arranged in a net-work; covered with thickenings in the form of a net.

Retuse: rounded at the apex but with an incision (as in heart-shape).

Rhabdosomes: small rods in the periphery of cells in some dinoflagellates.

Rhizoidal: root-like, resembling rhizoids.

Rhizoplast: fibril connecting flagellum base with centrosome; part of the neuromotor apparatus in flagellated organisms.

Rhizopodal: moving as an amoeba.

Rhizopodal tendency: evolutionary trend from a swimming cell to a condition in which the organism is amoeboid.

Rhomboid: a parallelogram with oblique angles and adjacent sides unequal.

Rostrate: with a beak.

Rostrate-capitate: with a beak which has a swollen tip.

Rugose: roughened, as with ridges and furrows.

Saccate: like a sac; balloon-shaped.

Saccoderm desmids: desmids unconstricted in the mid-region and with the wall in one piece (cf. placoderm desmids).

Saggitate: arrow-shaped.

Saprophyte: organism that obtains food from dead organic matter.

Sarciniform: in the shape and arrangement of a cubical packet.

Scalariform: ladder-like, referring to conjugation by tubes connecting two filaments.

Scale-like: like a small husk or membrane.

Schizophycean phycoerythrin: red pigment in the Myxophyceae.

Scrobiculate: pitted, usually with round, shallow depressions.

Scytonemin: a pigment found in the sheath of some *Scytonema*.

Semi-anaerobic: *see* anaerobic.

Semicell: cell-half of a desmid.

Semilunar: somewhat crescent-shaped.

Septa: a cross wall or partition.

Seriate: in a linear sequence or series.

Seta: a hair or bristle; sometimes a tail-piece.

Setiferous: bearing a seta or hair.

Sexual auxospore: spore formed by union of gametes, or from parthenogenetic development of gametes (diatoms).

Sheath: a covering, an envelope, usually relatively thin and composed of mucilage.

Sigmoid: like the letter S.

Silicious: containing silicon.

Sinus: the incision of a desmid cell in the midregion; any conspicuous invagination.

Siphon: organ involved in the digestive apparatus of some flagellates.

Siphonaceous: referring to a tubular thallus which has no cross walls (e.g., *Vaucheria*).

Spatulate: elongate, gradually enlarged and bluntly rounded at one end.

Spermatia: cells acting as male gametes; non-motile male cells, as in Rhodophyceae.

Spermatozoid: a male gamete.

Spermocarp: one of the investing cells developed about the fertilized egg (*Coleochaete*).

Spongiose: like a sponge; like a soft, thick mat.

Spicules: needle-like scales or hard bristles.

Spinescence: spines; spine arrangement.

Sporangium: a cell in which spores are produced (often zoospores).

Spore: a one-celled, asexual reproductive element, with or without a wall.

Statolith: granule functioning as a balancing organ relating the cell to gravity.

Statospore: spore smaller than the parent cell, formed within the shell (frustule) of diatoms.

Stauros: a stake; a stout, pole-like extension; an external central nodule in some diatoms.

Stellate: star-shaped.

Stephanokontae: plants which have motile reproductive cells furnished with a crown of flagella.

Stigma: the red granule or group of granules making up the light-sensitive spot in zoospores and flagellates.

Stipe: a stalk.

Stratum: a layer.

Striae: delicate, long, narrow markings.

Stroma: supporting tissue or mass of cells serving as a base for upright branches or other organs.

Sub—: slightly or nearly, as subglobular; under; beneath.

Subbiconic: nearly or somewhat double cone-shaped.

Subhexagonal: somewhat six-sided.

Subparenchymatous: somewhat cushion-like; approaching the mound-like arrangement of cells, in two or more layers.

Subpyriform: somewhat pear-shaped.

Suffultory cell: a cell resulting from the division of a vegetative cell, the upper segment of which forms an oogonium, the lower segment a somewhat enlarged suffultory cell.

Sulcus: the longitudinal furrow in dinoflagellates.

Superior pore: a pore in the upper part of an oogonium (Oedogoniaceae).

Supramedian: slightly above the median plane.

Suture: furrow or groove; trough between plates in wall of dinoflagellates.

Symbionts: two dissimilar organisms living together in close association.

Symbiotic: a condition in which two different organisms live together.

Systole: contraction period in action of pulsating vacuoles.

Tangential: section or cut made at right angles to the radius.

Tegument: a sheath or envelope.

Terebriform: twisted or twist-hooked, augur-shaped.

Test: an external shell inclosing the protoplast (e.g. *Trachelomonas*).

Tetrad: four cells formed by two divisions from a spore mother cell.

Tetrasporine tendency: evolutionary trend in green algae from a motile unicell through a palmelloid condition to a *Tetraspora*-like expression, and then to a filamentous form.

Thalloid: like a plant body which has no roots, stems, or leaves.

Thallus: a plant body in which there is little or no differentiation of cells to form tissues.

Tie cells: cells in the thallus of some red algae which connect peripheral cells to a central axis.

Tomentose: covered with numerous fine hairs.

Torulose: twisted; flexuous, as in irregularly spiralled species of *Anabaena*.

Transverse: across the short diameter.

Transverse furrow: groove extending (at least partly) around the dinoflagellate cell in the midregion.

Trapezoid: a plane figure which has two parallel sides.

Trichites: silicious spicules; a tuft of bristles.

Trichocyst: an organelle in the cell which throws off a fibril; a stinging thread.

Trichogyne: narrow extended part of female sex organ (carpogonium) in the Rhodophyceae.

Trichome: a hair; a thread of cells without the investing sheath in Myxophyceae.

True branching: branched by lateral division of a cell in a main filament.

Truncate: flat at the top; flatly rounded.

Tubercle (Tuberculate): small raised thickenings on the wall, or at the base of spines.

Tychoplankton: floating or free-living organisms in shallow water of a lake intermingled with miscellaneous vegetation, usually near shore.

Travertine: a deposit of chalk-like calcareous material.

Umbonate: with a cone-shaped protrusion.

Undulate: wavy.

Uncinate: with a hooked apex.

Unilateral: on one side; arising from one side only.

Unilocular sporangium: a solitary, one-celled spore-producing organ.

Uniseriate: arranged in a single row or series.

Uninucleate: with one nucleus.

Utricle: a small sac; a tubular bag or vesicle.

Vacuole: a space in the cytoplasm filled with cell sap, sometimes containing granules.

Valves: the two parts of the wall of diatoms, one of which is larger and fits over the smaller as a lid; the two parts of a dinoflagellate cell.

Valve view: view from the top or bottom of a diatom cell so that the broader surface of the valve is seen.

Ventricose: bulged or swollen on one side.

Vermiform: worm-like.

Verrucae: short, stout projections, smooth or armed with teeth.

Verrucose: warty.

Vertical canals: canals which connect both outer and inner fissures of the raphe (q.v.) in one part of the diatom cell with the fissures in the other part.

Vesicle: minute sac or cavity.

Volvocine tendency: evolutionary trend in green algae from a single motile cell toward simple colonies, and to colonies containing differentiated or specialized cells.

Water bloom: a conspicuous and abundant growth of planktonic algae, sometimes appearing suddenly, often forming a surface scum.

Xanthophyll: yellow pigment associated with chlorophyll.

Zonate: with bands; with concentric layers.

Zoospore: a motile, animal-like spore without a cell wall.

Zygospore: a thick-walled resting spore resulting from the union of gametes.

Zygote: a fertilized egg; a cell resulting from the union of gametes.

Bibliography

† Important reference work
* Deals with Michigan and Wisconsin algae

ACKLEY, ALMA B. 1929.* New species and varieties of Michigan algae. Trans. Amer. Microsc. Soc., 48: 302–309; Pls. 35, 36. 1929a.* The algae of Michigan. Doctoral thesis, Ohio State University. Abstract. 1930.* The algae of Michigan. Doctoral thesis, Ohio State University. 1932.* Preliminary report on Michigan algae, exclusive of desmids and diatoms. Pap. Mich. Acad. Sci., Arts, and Letters, 15(1931): 1–49.

ACTON, ELIZABETH. 1914. Observations on the cytology of the Chroococcaceae. Ann. Bot., 28: 434–454; Pls. 33, 34. 1916. On the structure and origin of "Cladophora balls." New Phytol., 15: 1–10; Figs. 1–5.

AGARDH, C. A. 1810. Dispositio algarum Suecicae, Part I. Lund. 1812. Dispositio algarum Suecicae, Parts II and III. Lund. 1812–1816. Algarum decades, I–IV. Lund. 1817. Synopsis algarum Scandinaviae, adjecta dispositione universali algarum. 135 pp. Lund. 1824. Systema algarum, Vol. I. Lund. 1827. Aufzählung einiger in den östreichischen Ländern gefundenen neuen Gattungen und Arten von Algen, nebst ihrer diagnostik und beigefügten Bemerkungen. Flora, 10: 625–640. 1828. Species algarum, Vol. 2. Lund. 1828–1835. Icones algarum Europaearum. Leipzig.

AGARDH, J. G. 1842. Algae maris Mediterranei et Adriatici. Paris. 1848. Nya Alger från Mexico. Oefv. Kongl. Sv. Vet.-Akad. Förhandl., 4(1847): 5–17. 1899. Analecta algologica. Observationes de speciebus algarum minus cognitis earumque dispositione. Continuatio V. Lund.

AHLSTROM, E. H. 1936.* The deepwater plankton of Lake Michigan, exclusive of the crustacea. Trans. Amer. Microsc. Soc., 55: 286–299. 1937.* Studies on variability in the genus Dinobryon (Mastigophora). Ibid., 56: 139–156.

AHLSTROM, E. H., and TIFFANY, L. H. 1934.* The algal genus Tetrastrum. Amer. Jour. Bot., 21: 499–507; Figs. 1–36.

ALÉXÉNKO, M. A. 1888. Précis des algues chlorosporées des environs de Kharkow. Trav. Soc. Nat. Univ. Imp. Kharkow, 21: 141–278. 1891. Matériaux pour servir à la flore des algues du gouvernement de Poltava. Ibid., 25: 47–88. 1894. Flore algues des maris et des tourbes de la vallée du Dnieper dans les limites du gouvernement de Poltava. Ibid., 27: 59–118. 1895. Matériaux pour servir à la flore des algues du gouvernement de Kharkow. Ibid., 28: 81–132.

ALLEGRE, CHARLES, and JAHN, T. L. 1943. A survey of the genus Phacus Dujardin (Protozoa): Euglenoidina. Trans. Amer. Microsc. Soc., 62: 233–244; Pls. 1–3.

ALLEN, T. F. 1880. The Characeae of America, 1–2: 1–14, Pls. 1–6. Boston. 1882. Development of the cortex in Chara illustrated by a series of American species. Bull. Torr. Bot. Club, 9: 37–47. 1883. Notes on the American species of Tolypella. Ibid., 10: 109–117. 1888–1896.† The Characeae of America. Pls. 1–27. New York. 1900. Three new Charas from California. Bull. Torr. Bot. Club, 27: 299–304.

ALLISON, F. E., and MORRIS, H. J. 1930. Nitrogen fixation by blue-green algae. Science, 71: 221–223.

ALLORGE, P., and LEFÈVRE, M. 1925. Algues de Sologne. Bull. Soc. Bot. France (Session Extraord., Sologne, 1925), 72(Suppl.): 123–150. (This paper is sometimes to be found bound with Vol. 77, 1930. Published bibliographies occasionally cite the latter, rather than the former, volume of this journal, giving either 1930 or 1931 as the date of publication.)

ALTEN, H. VON. 1910. Beiträge zur Kenntnis der Algenflora der Moore der Provinz Hannover. Hannover Jahrb. Nat. Ges., 59: 47–69.

ANDERSON, EMMA N., and WALKER, ELDA R. 1920. An ecological study of the algae of some sandhill lakes. Trans. Amer. Microsc. Soc., 39: 51–85; Figs. 1–17.

ANDERSSON, O. F. (O. Borge). 1890. Bidrag till kännedomen om Sveriges Chlorophyllophyceer. I. Chlorophyllophyceer från Roslagen. Bih. Kongl. Sv. Vet.-Akad. Handl., 16, Afd. 3, (No. 5): 1–19.

ANDREESEN, H. 1913. Beitrag zur Kenntnis der Physiologie von *Scenedesmus acutus* Meyen. Inaug. Diss. Kiel.

ARCHER, W. 1861. *In* A. Prichard, A history of infusoria including the Desmidiaceae and Diatomaceae, 4th ed., London. 1866. [Remarks before meeting of Dublin Microscopical Club, May, 17, 1866]. Quart. Jour. Microsc. Sci., 14 (Vol. 6, n. s.): 268–272. 1867. On the conjugation of *Spirotaenia condensata* (Bréb.) and of *Spirotaenia truncata* (Arch.). *Ibid.*, 7: 186–193; Pl. 8, Figs. 1–3. 1868. [No title]. *Ibid.*, 8: 65. 1872. The genus *Tetrapedia* (Reinsch) with two new forms. Grevillea, 1: 44–47. 1872a. Notice of the genus *Tetrapedia* (Reinsch) and of two kindred new forms. Quart. Jour. Microsc. Sci., 12(n.s.): 351–366. 1874. Algae and Rhizopoda from the hot springs of Azores. *Ibid.*, 16: 107. 1874a. Notes on some collections made from Furnas Lake, Azores, containing algae and a few other organisms. *In* J. D. Hooker, Contributions to the botany of the expeditions of H. M. S. "Challenger." Jour. Linn. Soc. Bot., 14: 328–340. 1877. New species of *Oocystis*. Quart. Jour. Microsc. Sci., 17(n.s.): 104–105.

ARTARI, A. 1913. Zur Physiologie der Chlamydomonaden. Versuche und Beobachtungen an *Chlamydomonas Ehrenbergii* Gorosch. und verwandten Formen. Pringsh. Jahrb. f. Wiss. Bot., 52: 410–466.

ARWIDSSON, TH. 1938. Ueber *Asterocytis, Astrocystis* und *Asterocystis*. Bot. Notiser, 1938: 190–192.

ATKINS, W. R. G. 1923. The phosphate content of fresh and salt waters in its relationship to the growth of the algal plankton. Jour. Marine Biol. Assoc., 13: 119–150.

ATKINS, W. R. G., and HARRIS, G. T. 1924. Seasonal changes in the water and heleoplankton of fresh-water ponds. Sci. Proc. Roy. Dublin Soc., 18(n. s.): 1–21 (reprint).

ATKINSON, G. F. 1890. Monograph of the Lemaneaceae of the United States. Ann. Bot., 4: 177–229; Pls. 7–9. 1931. Notes on the genus *Lemanea* in North America. Bot. Gaz., 92: 225–242.

ATWELL, C. B. 1889. A deep-water *Nostoc*. Bot. Gaz., 14: 291–292.

AVERINTZEV, S. 1899. Zur Kenntnis der Protozoen-Fauna in der Umgebung von Bologoje. Trav. Soc. Imp. Natur. St. Pétersb., 30, Lvr. 1, No. 6: 238–251.

BACH, E. B. 1907.* The Characeae of Michigan. Pap. Mich. Acad. Sci., Arts, and Letters, 9: 126.

BACHMANN, H. 1908. Vergleichende Studien über das Phytoplankton von Seen Schottlands und der Schweiz. Arch. f. Hydrobiol. u. Planktonk., 3: 1–91; Figs. 1–12, I–XI. 1911. Das Phytoplankton des Süsswassers mit besonderer

Berücksichtigung des Vierwaldstättersees. Mitt. Naturf. Ges. Luzern, 6: 1–213. 1920. *Merismopedia Trolleri* Nov. Spec. Zeit. f. Hydrol., 1: 350. 1923. Charakterisierung der Plankton-vegetation des Vierwaldstättersees mittels Netzfängen und Zentrifugenproben. Mitt. Naturf. Ges. Basel, 35: 148–167. 1928. Das Phytoplankton der Pioraseen nebst einigen Beiträgen zur Kenntnis des Phytoplanktons schweizerischer Alpenseen. Zeit. f. Hydrol., 4: 50–103.

BAILEY, J. W. 1841. A sketch of the infusoria, of the family Bacillaria, with some account of the most interesting species which have been found in a recent or fossil state in the United States. Amer. Jour. Sci. and Arts, 41: 284–305. 1847. Notes on the algae of the United States. *Ibid.*, 3 (Ser. 2): 80–85, 399–403. 1848. Continuation of the list of localities of algae in the United States. *Ibid.*, 3(Ser. 2): 37–42. 1851. Microscopical observations made in South Carolina, Georgia and Florida. Smiths. Contrib. Knowledge, 2(Art. 8): 1–48; Pls. 1–3. 1855. Notes on new species and localities of microscopical organisms. I–XIV. *Ibid.*, 7, Art. 3: 1–15.

BAKER, W. B. 1926. Studies in the life history of *Euglena*. I. *Euglena agilis* Carter. Biol. Bull., 51: 321–362; Pls. 1, 2, Figs. A, B.

BALDWIN, H. B., and WHIPPLE, G. C. 1906. Observed relations between dissolved oxygen, carbonic acid and algal growths in Weequahic Lake, N. J. Rep. Amer. Publ. Health Assoc., 32: 167–182.

BEARDSLEY, A. E. 1901. Notes on Colorado protozoa, with descriptions of new species. Trans. Amer. Microsc. Soc., 23: 49–59; Pl. 11.

BENNETT, A. W. 1886. Freshwater algae (including chlorophyllaceous protophyta) of the English Lake District; with descriptions of twelve new species. Jour. Roy. Microsc. Soc. 1886: 1–15. 1888. Fresh-water algae (including chlorophyllaceous protophyta) of the English Lake District. II. With descriptions of a new genus and five new species. *Ibid.*, 1888: 1–6. 1890. Freshwater algae and Schizophyceae of Hampshire and Devonshire. *Ibid.*, 1890: 1–10. 1892. Freshwater algae and Schizophyceae of South-west Surrey. *Ibid.*, 1892: 4–12.

BERGQUIST, S. G. 1936. The Pleistocene history of the Tahquamenon and Manistique drainage region of the northern Peninsula of Michigan. Mich. State Dept. Conserv., Publ. 40(Geol. Ser., 34): 1–137.

BERKELEY, M. J. 1833. Gleanings of British algae; being an appendix to the supplement to English Botany. London.

BERKELEY, M. J., and HARVEY, W. H. 1855–1859. *In* J. D. Hooker. The botany of the antarctic voyage. Part III. Flora Tasmaniae.

BERNARD, C. 1908. Protococcacées et desmidiées d'eau douce récoltées à Java. Dépt. Agric. Ind. Néerland. Batavia. Pls. 1–16. 1909. Sur quelques algues unicellulaires d'eau douce récoltées dans le domaine Malais. *Ibid.*, Buitenzorg. 1910. Algues d'eau douce. Nova Guinea, 8: 253–270.

BERTHOLD, G. 1878. Untersuchungen über die Verzweigung einiger Süsswasseralgen. Nova Acta Acad. Caes. Leop.-Carol. Germ. Nat. Curiosorum, 40: 167–230; Pls. 1–4.

BERTRAND, PAUL. 1927. Les Botryococcacées actuelles et fossiles et les conséquences de leur activité biologique. Comp. Rend. Soc. Biol., 96: 695–697.

BEYERINCK, M. W. 1890. Culturversuche mit Zoochlorellen, Lichenengonidien und anderen niederen Algen. Bot. Zeit., 48: 725–739, 741–754, 757–768, 781–785; Pl. 7.

BHARADWAJA, Y. 1933. False branching and sheath-structure in the Myxophyceae, with special reference to the Scytonemataceae. Arch. f. Protist., 81: 243–283; Figs. 1–9. 1933a. Contributions to our knowledge of the Myxophyceae of India. Ann. Bot., 47: 117–143. 1934. The taxonomy of *Scytonema* and *Tolypothrix* including some new records and new species from India and Ceylon. Rev. Algol., 7: 149–178. 1935. The Myxophyceae of the United Provinces, India. I. Proc. Indian Acad. Sci., 2(Sec. B.): 95–107.

BIGEARD, E. 1933.† Les *Pediastrum* d'Europe. Etude biologique et systématique. Trav. Lab. Bot. Univ. Cathol. Angers, 5: 1–192. 1934–1936. Les *Pediastrum* d'Europe. Etude biologique et systématique. Rev. Algol., 7: 1–94, 327–418.

BIRGE, E. A. 1898. Plankton studies on Lake Mendota. II. Trans. Wis. Acad. Sci., Arts and Letters, 11: 274–448.

BIRGE, E. A., and JUDAY, C. 1911. The inland lakes of Wisconsin. The dissolved gases of the water and their biological significance. Bull. Wis. Geol. and Nat. Hist. Surv., Sci. Ser., 22: 1–259; Figs. 1–142. 1912. A limnological study of the Finger Lakes of New York. Bull. U. S. Bur. Fisheries, 32(Doc. No. 791): 525–609. 1914. The inland lakes of Wisconsin. The hydrography and morphometry of the lakes, by C. Juday. Bull. Wis. Geol. and Nat. Hist. Surv., Sci. Ser., 27: 1–137. 1922. The inland lakes of Wisconsin. The plankton. I. Its quantity and chemical composition. *Ibid.*, 64(Sci. Ser. No. 13): 1–222.

BISHOP, AMELIA SAMANO. 1934. Contribución al conocimiento de las algas verdes de los lagos del valle de México. Ann. Inst. Biol., 5(No. 2): 149–177; Pls. 1–3 (reprint).

BJELJAËVA, A. I. 1922. De sectione *Aegagropila* Kütz. generis *Cladophorae* Kütz. et de nonnullis speciebus hujus sectionis in Rossia inventis. Not. Syst. Inst. Crypt. Horti Bot. Petropol., 1(No. 6): 86–94.

BLACKBURN, K. B. 1936. *Botryococcus* and the algal coals. Part I. A reinvestigation of the alga *Botryococcus Braunii* Kützing. Trans. Roy. Soc. Edinburgh, 58(pt. 3): 841–854.

BLACKMAN, F. F. 1900. The primitive algae and the flagellata. An account of modern work bearing on the evolution of the algae. Ann. Bot., 14: 647–688; Figs. 1, 2.

BLACKMAN, F. F., and TANSLEY, A. G. 1902. A revision of the classification of the green algae. New Phytol., 1: 17–24, 47–48, 67–72, 89–96, 114–120, 133–144, 163–168, 189–192, 218–220, 238–244.

BLANCHARD, FRANK N. 1913. Two new species of *Stigonema*. Rhodora, 15: 192–200; Pl. 105.

BLUM, J. R. 1943.° New species of *Spirogyra*. Amer. Jour. Bot., 30: 782–783; Figs. 1–11.

BOERGESEN, F. 1894. Ferskvandsalger fra Ostgrönland. Medd. om Grönland, 18: 3–41; Pls. 1, 2; Figs. 1, 2. 1898. Nogle Ferskvandsalger fra Island. Bot. Tids., 22: 131–138. 1899. Conspectus algarum novarum aquae dulcis, quas in insulis Faeroensibus invenit. Vidensk. Medd. fra den Naturhist. Foren. i Kjöbenhavn, 1899: 317–336. 1901. Freshwater algae. Botany of the Faeröes, Part I. pp. 198–259. Copenhagen.

BOERGESEN, F., and OSTENFELD, C. H. 1903. Phytoplankton of lakes in the Faeröes. Botany of the Faeröes, Part II. pp. 613–624; Figs. 147–150. Copenhagen.

BOHLIN, KNUT. 1897. Die Algen der ersten Regnell'schen Expedition. I. Protococcoideen. Bih. Kongl. Sv. Vet.-Akad. Handl., 23, Afd. 3, No. 7: 3–47; Pls. 1, 2. 1897a. Zur Morphologie und Biologie einzelliger Algen. Oefv. Kongl. Sv. Vet.-Akad. Förhandl., 1897(No. 9): 507–529; Figs. 1–10. 1897b. Studier öfver några slägten af Alggruppen Confervales Borzi. Bih. Kongl. Sv. Vet.-Akad. Handl., 23, Afd. 3, No. 3: 1–56; Pls. 1, 2. 1901. Etude sur la flore algologique d'eau douce des Açores. *Ibid.*, 27, Afd. 3, No. 4: 1–85; Pl. 1.

BOLD, H. C. 1931. Life history and cell structure of *Chlorococcum infusionum*. Bull. Torr. Bot. Club, 57: 577–604; Pls. 32–36, Figs. 1–5.

BOLDT, R. 1885. Bidrag till kännedomen om Sibiriens Chlorophyllophycéer. Oefv. Kongl. Sv. Vet.-Akad. Förhandl., 42(No. 2): 91–128. 1893. Några sötvättens-alger från Grönland. Bot. Notiser, 1893: 156–158.

BOLOCHONZEW, E. 1903. Ueber das Phytoplankton einiger Seen im Rostowshen Kreise des Gouvernement Jaroslawe und zweier Seen des Gouvernement Wadimir. Jahrb. d. Biol. Walgastation Saratow, 1903: 251–269.

BORGE, O. 1891. Ett litet bidrag till Sibiriens Chlorophyllophycé-Flora. Bih. Kongl. Sv. Vet.-Akad. Handl., 17, Afd. 3, No. 2: 1–16. 1892. Chlorophyllophyceer från Norska Finmarken. Ibid., 17, Afd. 3, No. 4: 3–15. 1894. Süsswasser-Chlorophyceen gesammelt von Dr. A. Osw. Kihlman im nördlichsten Russland, Gouvernement Archangel. Ibid., 19, Afd. 3, No. 5: 1–41. 1894a. Ueber die Rhizoidenbildung bei einigen fadenförmigen Chlorophyceen. 61 pp., 2 pls. Upsala. 1895. Bidrag till kännedomen om Sveriges Chlorophycéer. II. Chlorophyllophyceen aus Falbygden in Vestergötland. Bih. Kongl. Sv. Vet.-Akad. Handl., 21, Afd. 3, No. 6: 1–26. 1896. Australische Süsswasserchlorophyceen. Ibid., 22, Afd. 3, No. 9: 1–32. 1899. Ueber tropische und subtropische Süsswasser-Chlorophyceen. Ibid., 24, Afd. 3, No. 12: 1–33. 1900. Schwedisches Süsswasserplankton. Bot. Notiser, 1900: 1–26. 1901. Süsswasseralgen aus Süd-Patogonien. Bih. Kongl. Sv. Vet.-Akad. Handl., 27, Afd. 3, No. 10: 1–40; Pls. 1, 2. 1906. Süsswasser-Chlorophyceen von Feuerland und Isla Desolacion. Bot. Stud. t. F. R. Kjellman, 1906: 21–34. 1907. Beiträge zur Algenflora von Schweden. Arkiv f. Bot., 6(1906), No. 1: 1–88. 1906. [1907]. Algen aus Argentina und Bolivia. Ibid., 6(1907), No. 4: 1–13; Figs. 1–5. 1909.° Nordamerikanische Süsswasseralgen. Ibid., 8, No. 13: 1–29. 1913. Zygnemales, Spezieller Teil. In A. Pascher, Die Süsswassserflora Deutschlands, Oesterreichs und der Schweiz, Heft 9: 12–51, Figs. 1–79; Jena. 1913a. Beiträge zur Algenflora von Schweden. 2. Die Algenflora um den Torne-Träsksee in Schwedisch-Lappland. Bot. Notiser, 1913: 1–32, 49–64, 97–110; Pls. 1–3; Figs. 1, 2. 1918 [1919]. Die von Dr. A. Löfgren in Sao Paulo gesammelten Süsswasseralgen. Arkiv f. Bot., 15(No. 13): 1–108; Pls. 1–8. 1921. Die Algenflora des Tåkernsees. Sjön Takerns Fauna och Flora. Kongl. Sv. Vet.-Akad., 1921(No. 4): 3–48; Pls. 1, 2; Figs. 1–3. 1922 [1923]. Beiträge zur Algenflora von Schweden. 3. Arkiv. f. Bot., 18(No. 10): 1–34; Pls. 1, 2; Figs. 1, 2. 1925. Die von Dr. F. C. Hoehne wahrend der Expedition Roosevelt-Rondon gesammelten Süsswasseralgen. Ibid., 19(No. 17): 1–56; Pls. 1–6; Figs. 1–3. 1928. Süsswasseralgen. In B. Schröeder, Zellpflanzen Ostafrikas, gesammelt auf der Akademischen Studienfährt 1910. Teil VIII. Hedwigia, 68: 93–114; Pls. 1, 2; Fig. 1. 1933. Schwedische-chinesische wissenschaftliche Expedition nach den nordwestlichen Provinzen. Arkiv f. Bot., 25A(No. 17): 1–18.

BORGE, O., and PASCHER, A. 1913. (See Borge, 1913.)

BORNET, E. 1889. Les Nostocacées hétérocystées du Systema Algarum de C. A. Agardh (1824) et leur synonymie actuelle (1889). Bull. Soc. Bot. France. 36: 144–157.

BORNET, E., and FLAHAULT, CH. 1885. Note sur le genre Aulosira. Bull. Soc. Bot. France, 32: 119–122. 1885a. Tableau synoptique des Nostocacées filamenteuses hétérocystées. Mém. Soc. Nat. Sci. Nat. et Math. Cherbourg, 25: 195–223; Ibid., 26: 137–152. 1886.† Révision des Nostocacées hétérocystées contenues dans 'les principaux herbiers de France. Ann. Sci. Nat. Bot., 3(Sér. 7): 323–381. 1886a.† Part II., Ibid., 4 (Sér. 7): 343–373; 1887. Part III. Ibid., 5(Sér. 7): 51–129. 1888.† Part IV. Ibid., 7(Sér. 7): 177–262. 1888a. Note sur deux nouveaux genres d'algues perforantes. Jour. Bot., 2:

161–165. 1889. Sur quelques plantes vivant dans le test calcaire des mollusques. Bull. Soc. Bot. France, 36: cxlvii-clxxvi; Pls. 6–12.

BORNET, E., and THURET, G. 1876-1880. Notes algologiques, recueil d'observations sur les algues. Paris.

BORY DE ST. VINCENT, J. B. 1808. Mémoire sur le genre *Lemanea* de la famille des Confervés. Ann. Mus. Hist. Nat. Paris, 12: 177–190. 1808a. Mémoire sur le genre *Draparnaldia* de la famille des Confervés. *Ibid.*, 12: 399–409. 1822–1831. *In* Dictionnaire d'histoire naturelle. Paris.

BORZI, A. 1878. Note alla morfologia e biologia delle alghe ficocromacee. Nuovo Giorn. Bot. Ital., 10: 236–288. 1879. *Ibid.*, 11: 347–388. 1882. *Ibid.*, 14: 272–315. 1883. Studi algologici. Fasc. 1: 1–112; Pls. 1–9. Messina. 1889. *Botrydiopsis*, nuova genre di alghe verdi. Boll. Soc. Ital. Microsc., 1: 66–70. 1892. Alghe d'acqua dolce della Papuasia raccolte su cranii umani dissepolti. Nuova Notarisia, 3(1892): 35–53. 1894. Studi algologici. Fasc. 2: 121–378; Pls. 10–31. Palermo. 1895. Probabili accenni di conjugazione presso alcune Nostochinee. Boll. Soc. Bot. Ital., 1895, No. 6: 208–210. 1914. Studi sulle Mixoficee. I. Nuovo Giorn. Bot. Ital., 21(n. s.): 307–360. 1916. Studi sulle Stigonemaceae. *Ibid.*, 23(n.s.): 559–588. 1917. *Ibid.*, 24(n.s.): 65–112.

BOURRELLY, P., and FELDMANN, J. 1946. Une algue méconne: *Sphaeroplea Soleirolii* (Duby) Montagne. Bull. Mus. Paris, 18(No. 5): 412–415; Figs. 1–11.

BOYE-PETERSEN, JOHN. 1923. The Botany of Iceland. Vol. 2, Part 2, No. 2: 249–324.

BRACHER, R. 1919. Observations on *Euglena deses*. Ann. Bot., 33: 93–108.

BRAND, F. 1899. *Mesogerron*, eine neue Chlorophyceen-Gattung. Hedwigia, 38: [181–184]. 1899a. *Cladophora*-Studien. Bot. Centralbl., 79: 145–152, 177–186, 209–221, 287–311; Pls. 1–3. 1901. Ueber einige Verhältnisse des Baues und Wachsthums von *Cladophora*. Beih. Bot. Centralbl., 10: 481–521; Figs. 1–10. 1902. Zur näheren Kenntnis der Algengattung *Trentepohlia* Mart. *Ibid.*, 12: 200–205; Pl. 6. 1902a. Die *Cladophora-Aegagropilen* des Süsswassers. Hedwigia, 41: 34–71; 1 pl. 1905. Ueber die Anheftung der Cladophoraceae, und über verschiedene polynesische Formen dieser Familie. Beih. Bot. Centralbl., 18: 165–193. 1907. Ueber charakteristische Algen-Tinktionen, sowie über eine *Gongrosira* und eine *Coleochaete* aus dem Würmsee. Ber. d. Deutsch. Bot. Ges., 25: 497–506. 1908. Zur Morphologie und Biologie des Grenzgebietes zwischen den Algengattung *Rhizoclonium* und *Cladophora*. Hedwigia, 48: 45–73. 1909. Ueber die Süsswasserformen von *Chantransia* (DC.) Schmitz, einschliesslich *Pseudochantransia* Brand. *Ibid.*, 49: 107–118. 1909a. Ueber die morphologischen Verhaltnisse der *Cladophora*-Basis. Ber. d. Deutsch. Bot. Ges., 27: 292–300. 1913. Ueber *Cladophora humida* n. sp., *Rhizoclonium lapponicum* n. sp., und deren bostrychoide Verzweigung. Hedwigia, 53: 179–183.

BRAND, F., and STOCKMAYER, S. 1925. Analyse der aerophilen Grünalgenanflüge, insbesondere der proto-pleurococcoiden Formen. Arch. f. Protist., 52: 265–355; Pl. 11.

BRANDT, K. 1882. Ueber die morphologische und physiologische Bedeutung des Chlorophylls bei Thieren. Arch. Anat. Physiol. Abth., Heft 1: 125–150.

BRAUN, ALEXANDER. 1834. Esquisse monographique du genre *Chara*. Ann. Sci. Nat. Bot., 1(Sér. 2): 349–357. 1845. Additional notices of the North American Charae. *In* G. Englemann and A. Gray, Plantae Lindheimerianae. Boston Jour. Nat. Hist., 5: 264. 1847. Uebersicht der Schweizerischen Characeen. Neue Denkschr. d. Schweiz. Ges. d. Natur., 10: 1–23 (reprint,

1849). 1849. *In* F. T. Kuetzing, Species algarum. 1851. Betrachtungen über die Erscheinung der Verjüngung in der Natur. Leipzig. 1855.† Algarum unicellularum genera nova vel minus cognita. Pls. 1–6. Leipzig. 1856. Ueber *Chytridium*, eine Gattung einzelliger Schmarotzergewächse auf Algen und Infusorien. Abh. K. K. Akad. d. Wiss. z. Berlin, 1855: 21–83. 1865. *In* L. Rabenhorst. Florae Europaea algarum aquae dulcis et submarinae. 2. Leipzig.

BRAUN, ALEXANDER, and GRUNOW, A. 1865. *In* L. Rabenhorst. Florae Europaea algarum aquae dulcis et submarinae. 2. Leipzig.

BRÉBISSON, A. DE. 1844. Description de nouveaux genres d'algues fluviatiles. Ann. Sci. Nat. Bot., 1 (Ser. 3): 25–31. Pls. 1, 2.

Brébisson, A. de, and Godey, P. 1835. Algues des environs de Falaise décrites et dessinées. pp. 1–66. Falaise. 1836. *Ibid.* Mém. Soc. Acad. sci. arts et bell. lettr. de Falaise Bot., 1835: 1–62, 266–269.

BREHM, V. 1910. Ueber tropisches Süsswasserplankton. Die Kleinwelt, 1: 171–175.

BRETSCHNEIDER, L. H. 1926. Ueber den feineren Bau von *Phacus costata* Conrad. Arch. f. Protist., 53: 131–134.

BRISTOL, B. MURIEL. 1920. A. review of the genus *Chlorochytrium*, Cohn. Jour. Linn. Soc. Bot. London, 45: 1–28; Pls. 1–3. 1920a. On the alga-flora of some desiccated English soils. Ann. Bot., 34: 35–80; Pl. 2.

BRITTON, M. E. 1943. New species of Chlorophyceae. Amer. Jour. Bot., 30: 799–800; Figs. 1–3.

BRITTON, M. E., and SMITH, B. H. 1942. A new species of *Spirogyra*. Ohio Jour. Sci., 42: 70.

BROWN, C. J. D. 1943. How many lakes in Michigan? Mich. Conserv., 12(5): 6–7.

BROWN, HELEN JEAN. 1929.† The algal family Vaucheriaceae. Trans. Amer. Microsc. Soc., 48: 86–117; Pls. 15–20. 1937.° A new species of *Vaucheria* from northern Michigan. *Ibid.*, 56: 283–284; Fig. 1.

BROWN, W. H. 1909. The plant life of Ellis, Great, Little, and Long Lakes in North Carolina. Contrib. U. S. Nat. Herb., 13(1909–1913): 323–341.

BRUNEL, JULES. 1932. Etudes sur la flora algologique du Québec. I. Contrib. Lab. Bot. Univ. Montreal, No. 22: 3–19; Figs. 1–3. 1947. *Vaucheria Schleicheri* in North America. Contrib. Gray Herb., 165: 62–69; Figs. 1, 2.

BRUNNTHALER, J. 1901. Die koloniebildenden *Dinobryon*-Arten. Ver. d. K. K. Zool.- Bot. Ges. in Wien, Math.-Nat. Kl., 51: 293–306. 1903. Phytoplankton aus Kleinasien. Sitz. K. K. Akad. Wiss. Wien, Math.-Nat. Kl., 112(1902), Abt. 1: 289–293. 1907. Die Algen und Schizophyceen der Altwässer der Donau bei Wien. Ver. K. K. Zool.-Bot. Ges. Wien, Math.-Nat. Kl., 57: 170–223. 1912. Systematische Uebersicht über die Chlorophyceen-Gattung *Scenedesmus* Meyen. Hedwigia, 53: 164–172. 1913. Die Algengattung *Radiofilum* Schmidle und ihre systematische Stellung. Oesterr. Bot. Zeit., 63(No. 1): 1–8; Figs. 1–3. 1914. Beitrag zur Süsswasser-Algenflora von Aegypten. Hedwigia, 54: 219–225. 1915.† Protococcales. *In* A. Pascher, Die Süsswasserflora Deutschlands, Oesterreichs und der Schweiz. Heft 5. Chlorophyceae 2: 52–205; Figs. 1–330. Jena.

BUCHANAN, R. E. 1907. Notes on the algae of Iowa. Proc. Iowa Acad. Sci., 14: 47–84.

BUDDE, H. 1940. Beiträge zur Kenntnis der bayerischen *Batrachospermum*-Arten aus der Umgebung von Tölz. Ber. Bayr. Bot. Ges., 24: 87–94.

BUELL, HELEN F. 1938. The taxonomy of a community of blue-green algae in a Minnesota pond. Bull. Torr. Bot. Club, 65: 377–396; Figs. 1–12.

BUETSCHLI, O. 1878. Beiträge zur Kenntnis der Flagellaten und einiger verwandter Organismen. Zeit. f. Wiss. Zool., 30: 205–281. 1883–1887. Mastigophora, Protozoa. *In* H. G. Bronn, Klassen und Ordnungen des Tier-Reiches, 1, Abt. 2; Pls. 39–55. Leipzig and Heidelberg.

BURKHOLDER, PAUL R. 1930. Microplankton studies of Lake Erie. Bull. Buffalo Soc. Nat. Sci., 14: 73–91. 1931. Studies in the phytoplankton of the Cayuga Lake basin, New York. *Ibid.*, 15: 21–179.

BURR, GEO. O. 1941. Photosynthesis of algae and other aquatic plants. *In* A Symposium on Hydrobiology. Madison.

CALKINS, G. N. 1892. On *Uroglena*, a genus of colony-building infusoria observed in certain water supplies of Massachusetts. 23rd Ann. Rep. State Bd. of Health, Mass., 1892: 647–657; Pls. 1–4. 1926. Biology of the Protozoa. New York.

CAMPBELL, D. H. 1886.° Plants of the Detroit River. Bull. Torr. Bot. Club, 13: 93–94.

CARTER, NELLIE. 1919. On the cytology of two species of *Characiopsis*. New Phytol., 18: 177–186; Figs. 1–3.

CARTER, H. J. 1856. Notes on the freshwater infusoria of the Island of Bombay. No. 1. Organization. Ann. and Mag. Nat. Hist., 18(Ser. 2): 115–132, 221–249. 1859. On fecundation in the two Volvoces, etc. on *Eudorina Spongilla, Astasia, Euglena* and *Cryptoglena. Ibid.*, 3(Ser. 3): 1–20.

CAVANAUGH, W. J., and TILDEN, JOSEPHINE. 1930. Algal food, feeding and case-building habits of the larva of the midge fly, *Tanytarsus dissimilis*. Ecology, 11: 281–287.

CAVERS, F. 1913. Recent work on flagellata and primitive algae. New Phytol., 12: 28–36, 78–83, 107–123, 177–187, 225–232; Figs. 1–10.

CEDERCREUTZ, CARL. 1924. Finnländische Zygnemalen. Acta Soc. Fauna et Flora Fenn., 55(No. 2): 1–7. 1931. Zwei neue Heterokontenarten. Arch. f. Protist., 75: 517–522. 1934. Die Algenflora und Algen-vegetation auf Åland. Acta Bot. Fenn., 15: 1–120; Pls. 1–5; 2 maps.

CEDERGREN, G. R. 1926. Beiträge zur Kenntnis der Süsswasseralgen in Schweden. II. Die Algen aus Bergslagen und Wästerdalarne. Bot. Notiser, 1926: 289–313. 1932. Die Algenflora der Provinz Härjedalen. Arkiv f. Bot., 25A(No. 4): 1–107.

CHADEFAUD, M. 1938. Nouvelle recherches sur l'anatomie comparée des Eugleniens: les Peranémines. Rev. Algol., 11: 189–220.

CHAMBERS, C. O. 1912. The relation of algae to dissolved oxygen and carbon dioxide, with special reference to carbonates. 23rd Ann. Rep. Missouri Bot. Gard., 1912: 171–207.

CHANDLER, D. C. 1937. Fate of typical lake plankton in streams. Ecol. Monogr., 7: 445–479, 1939.° Plankton entering the Huron River from Portage and Base Line Lakes, Michigan. Trans. Amer. Microsc. Soc., 58: 24–41. 1944. Limnological studies of western Lake Erie. IV. *Ibid.*, 63: 203–236.

CHAPMAN, F. B. 1934. The algae of the Urbana (Ohio) raised bog. Ohio Jour. Sci., 34: 327–332.

CHAPMAN, V. J. 1941. An introduction to the study of algae. New York. 1943. The aims of future research in the algae. Farlowia, 1: 5–8.

CHMIELEWSKI, V. 1890. Matériaux pour servir à la flora des algues du governement de Kharkow. Trav. Soc. Nat. Univ. Imp. Kharkow, 23: 79–105.

CHODAT, R. 1894. *Golenkinia*, genre nouveau des Protococcoidées. Jour. Bot., 8: 305–308. 1894a. Matériaux pour servir a l'histoire des Protococcoidées. Bull. Herb. Boiss., 2: 585–616; Pls. 22–29. 1894b. Algues des environs de Genéve. Comp. Rend. Soc. Phys. et Hist. Nat. Genéve, *In* Arch. Sci. Phys. et Nat., 32: 623–625. 1895. Sur le genre *Lagerheimia*. Nuova Notarisia, 6: 86–90. 1895a. Matériaux pour servir à l'histoire des Protococcoidées. II. Bull.

Herb. Boiss., 3: 109–114. 1895b. Ueber die Entwickelung der *Eremosphaera viridis* de By. Bot. Zeit., 53: 137–142; Pl. 5. 1896. Sur la structure et la biologie de deux algues pélagiques. Jour. Bot., 10: 333–349, 405–408; Pl. 3. 1897. Algues pélagiques nouvelles. Bull. Herb. Boiss., 5: 119–120. 1897a. Etudes de biologie lacustre. A. Recherches sur les algues pélagiques de quelques lacs suisses et français. *Ibid.*, 5: 289–314. 1898. Etudes de biologie lacustre. B. Nouvelles remarques sur la flore pélagique superficielle des lacs suisses et français. *Ibid.*, 6: 49–77, 155–188. 1898a. Etudes de biologie lacustre. C. Recherches sur les algues littorales. *Ibid.*, 6: 431–475; Pls. 14, 15. 1900. Sur trois genres nouxeaux de Protococcoidées et sur la florule planktonique d'un étang du Danemark. Mém. Herb. Boiss., 1(No. 17): 1–10; Figs. 1–20. 1902. Algues vertes de la suisse. Pleurococcoïdes-Chroolépoïdes. Matér. pour la Flore Crypt. Suisse, 1(No. 3): 1–373; Figs. 1–264. 1913. Monographie d'algues en culture pure. *Ibid.*, 4(Fasc. 2): 1–226; Pls. 1–9. 1919. Sur un *Glaucocystis* et sa position systématique. Bull. Soc. Bot. Genève, 11: 42–49; Figs. 1, 2. 1921. Matériaux pour l'histoire des algues de la Suisse. I–IX. *Ibid.*, 13: 66–114. 1926.† *Scenedesmus*. Etude de genetique, de systématique expérimentale et d'hydrobiologie. Rev. d'Hydrol., 3: 71–258; Figs. 1–162.

CHODAT, R., and CHODAT, F. 1925. Esquisse planctologique de quelques lacs français. Festschr. Carl Schröter, 3: 436–459; Figs. 1–14.

CHODAT, R., and GRINTZESCO, J. 1900. Cultures pure d'algues Protococcacées. Comp. Rend. Soc. Phys. et Hist. Nat. Genéve, *in* Arch. Sci. Phys. et Nat., 10: 386–387.

CIENKOWSKI, L. 1855. Algologische Studien. 2. *Protococcus botryoides* Kuetz. Bot. Zeit., 13: 780–782; Pl. 11. 1865. Ueber einige chlorophyllhaltige Gloeocapsen. *Ibid.*, 23(No. 3): 21–27; Pl. 1. 1870. Ueber Palmellaceen und einige Flagellaten. Archiv f. Mikro. Anat., 6: 421–438; Pls. 23, 24. 1876. Zur Morphologie der Ulothricheen. Bull. Acad. Imp. Sci. St. Péters. 21: 529–557; Pls. 1, 2. 1881. [Algologische excursion an das Weiss Meer]. Arb. d. Kais, St. Petersb. Ges. d. Naturf., 12: 130–171.

CLARKE, G. L., and GELLIS, S. S. 1935. The nutrition of copepods in relation to the food cycle of the sea. Biol. Bull., 68: 231–246.

CLAPARÈDE, ED., and LACHMANN, J. 1857–1861. Etudes sur les infusiores et les rhizopodes. Mém. Instit. Nat. Genevois, 5(1858): 1–260; *Ibid.*, 6(1860): 261–482.; *Ibid.*, 7(1861): 1–291.

CLEVE, P. T. 1868. Försök till en monografi öfver de Svenska arterna af Algfamiljen Zygnemaceae. Nova Acta Reg. Soc. Sci. Upsala, 6(Ser. 3), No. 11: 1–38.

COCHRAN, L. C. 1932.* A thermophilic *Calothrix* in Michigan. Pap. Mich. Acad. Sci., Arts, and Letters, 15: 63–64.

COHN, F. [1852]. Ueber eine neue Gattung aus der Familie des Volvocinen. Zeit. f. Wiss. Zool., 4: 77–116. 1856. Mémoire sur le développement et le mode de reproduction du *Sphaeroplea annulina*. Ann. Sci. Nat. Bot., 5(Sér. 4): 187–208; Pls. 12, 13. 1875. Ueber parasitische Algen. Beitr. Biol. Pflanzen, 1(No. 2): 87–108. 1875a. Die Entwickelungsgeschichte der Gattung *Volvox. Ibid.*, 1(No. 3): 93–115; Pl. 2.

COHN, F., and WICHURA, M. 1858. Ueber *Stephanosphaera pluvialis*. Nova Acta Caes. Leop.-Carol. Germ. Nat. Curiosorum, 26: 1–32; Pls. 1, 2.

COKER, W. C. 1919. A parasitic blue-green alga. Jour. Elisha Mitchell Sci. Soc., 35:9.

COLLINS, F. S. 1896. New Cyanophyceae. Erythea, 4: 119–121. 1897. Some perforating and other algae on fresh water shells. *Ibid.*, 5: 95–97. 1899.

Notes on algae. I. Rhodora, 1: 9–11. 1901. *Ibid.* III. *Ibid.*, 3: 132–137. 1904. Algae of the flume. *Ibid.*, 6: 229–231. 1905. *Chlorochytrium Lemnae* in North America. *Ibid.*, 7: 97–99. 1907. Some new green algae. *Ibid.*, 9: 197–202. 1909.†* The green algae of North America. Tufts College Studies, Sci. Ser., 2: 79–480, Pls. 1–18 (reprinted and repaged by G. E. Stechert, New York, 1928). 1912.†* The green algae of North America. Supplementary Paper. *Ibid.*, 3(No. 2): 69–109; Pls. 1, 2 (reprinted by G. E. Stechert, New York, 1928). 1918.† Notes from the Woods Hole Laboratory. Rhodora, 20: 141–143. 1918a.† The green algae of North America, 2nd Suppl. Tufts College Studies, Sci. Ser., 4: 1–106; Pls. 1–3 (reprinted by G. E. Stechert, New York, 1928).

COMÈRE, J. 1911. Additions a la flore des algues d'eau douce du pays toulousain et des Pyrénées centrales. Bull. Soc. d'Hist. Nat. Toulouse, 44: 9–60.

CONN, H. W., and WEBSTER, LUCIA W. 1908. A preliminary report on the algae of the fresh waters of Connecticut. Conn. State Geol. and Nat. Hist. Surv., Bull. 10: 1–78; Pls. 1–44.

CONRAD, W. 1913. *Errerella bornhemiensis* nov. gen., une Protococcacée nouvelle. Bull. Soc. Roy. Bot. Belgique, 52: 237–242; Figs. 1–3. 1914. Contributions à l'étude des flagellates. I. Arch. f. Protist., 34: 79–94. 1914a. Algues, Schizophycées et flagellates récoltés par M. W. Reckert aux environs de Libau (Courlande, Russie). Ann. Biol. Lacustre, 7: 126–152. 1916. Révision des espèces indigènes et françaises du genre *Trachelomonas* Ehrenbg. *Ibid.*, 8: 193–212. 1920. Contributions à l'étude des Chrysomonadines. Acad. Roy. Belgique, Cl. des Sci., 1920: 167–189; Figs. 1–11. 1922. Contributions à l'étude des Chrysomonadines. Rec. Inst. Léo Errera, 10: 333–353; Figs. 1–11. 1926. Recherches sur les flagellates de nos eaux saumâtres. 2. Chrysomonadines. Arch. f. Protist., 56: 167–231. 1927. Essai d'une monographie des genre *Mallomonas* Perty (1852) et *Pseudomallomonas* Chodat (1920). *Ibid.*, 59: 423–505; Pls. 8–11. 1932. Flagellates nouveaux ou peu connus. III (Formes nouvelles du genre *Trachelomonas* Ehrbg.). *Ibid.*, 78: 463–472. 1933.† Révision du genre *Mallomonas* Perty (1851) incl. *Pseudo-Mallomonas* Chodat (1920). Mém. Mus. Roy. d'Hist. Nat. de Belgique, 56: 1–82; Figs. 1–70. 1934.† Matériaux pour une monographie du genre *Lepocinclis* Perty. Arch. f. Protist., 82: 203–249. 1934a. Euglenacées nouvelles ou peu connues. Ann. Protist., 4: 171–180. 1935.† Etude systématique du genre *Lepocinclis* Perty. Mém. Mus. Roy. d'Hist. Nat. Belgique, 1(Sér. 2): 1–84. 1940. Notes protistologiques. 15. Sur une *Euglena* du psammon de l'escaut. Bull. Mus. Roy. Hist. Nat. Belgique, 16(No. 29): 1–12. 1940a. Notes protistologiques. 16. Sur *Peridinium Woloszynskae* n. sp. *Ibid.*, 16(No. 32): 1–8.

CONRAD, W., and KUFFERATH, H. 1912. Addition à la flore algologique de la Belgique. Bull. Soc. Roy. Bot. Belgique, 49(Pt. 1): 293–335.

COOKE, M. E. 1882–1884.† British freshwater algae, exclusive of Desmidieae and Diatomaceae. 329 pp.; Pls. 1–130. London.

CORDA, A. J. C. 1835–1839. Observations sur les animalicules microscopiques, qu'on trouve auprès des eau thermales de Carlsbad. Almanach de Carlsbad, 1835–1839.

CORRENS, C. 1893. Ueber *Apiocystis Brauniana* Naeg. *In* A. Zimmermann, Beitr. z. Pflanzenzelle. 1(Heft 3): 241–259; Figs. 1, 2.

COUEY, FAYE M. 1935.* Fish food studies of a number of northwestern Wisconsin lakes. Trans. Wis. Acad. Sci., Arts, and Letters, 29: 131–172.

COYLE, ELIZABETH. 1930. The algal food of *Pimephales promelas*. (Fathead minnow). Ohio Jour. Sci., 30: 23–25.

CRAMER, C. E. 1859. *Oedogonium Pringsheimii* Cramer. Hedwigia, 2: 17–19.
CROASDALE, HANNAH T. 1935. The fresh water algae of Woods Hole, Massachusetts. 134 pp.; Pls. I–VII; maps. Philadelphia.
CROW, W. B. 1922. A critical study of certain unicellular Cyanophyceae from the point of view of their evolution. New Phytol., 21: 81–102; Fig. 1. 1923. Fresh-water plankton algae from Ceylon. Jour. Bot., 61: 110–114, 138–145, 164–171. 1924. Variation and species in Cyanophyceae. Jour. Genetics, 14: 397–424; Figs. 1–8. 1924a. Some features of the envelope in *Coelastrum*. Ann. Bot., 38: 398–401; Figs. A, B. 1925. The reproductive differentiation of colonies in Chlamydomonadales. New Phytol., 24: 120–123. 1927. The generic characters of *Arthrospira* and *Spirulina*. Trans. Amer. Microsc. Soc., 46: 139–148. 1927a. Abnormal forms of *Gonium*. Ann. and Mag. Nat. Hist., 19(Ser. 9): 593–601; Figs. A–G. 1928. The morphology of the filaments of Cyanophyceae. Ann. Protist., 1: 19–36.
CURTIS, J. T., and JUDAY, C. 1937.* Photosynthesis of algae in Wisconsin lakes. III. Observations in 1935. Inter. Rev. Ges. Hydrobiol., 35: 122–133; Figs. 1, 2; Tab. 1–2.
CZURDA, V. 1932.† Zygnemales. *In* A. Pascher, Die Süsswasserflora Mitteleuropas, Oesterreichs und der Schweiz. Heft 9: 1–232; Figs. 1–226. Jena. 1939. Zygnemales der Deutschen Limnologischen Sunda-expedition. Archiv. f. Hydrobiol. Suppl., 16: 398–427.
DA CUNHA, A. M. 1913. Contribuição para o conhecimento da fauna de protozoarios do Brasil. Mem. Inst. Oswaldo Cruz, 5: 101–122. 1914. Beitrag zur Kenntnis der Protozoen-fauna Brasiliens. II. *Ibid.*, 6: 169–175.
DADAY, F. 1907. Plankton-Tiere aus dem Victoria Nyanza. Sammelausbeute von A. Bogert, 1904–1905. Zool. Jahrb. Abt. System, 25(Heft 2): 245–262.
DAILY, FAY K. 1944. The Characeae of Nebraska. Butler Univ. Bot. Studies, 6: 149–171; Figs. 1A–5C. 1946. Species of *Tolypella* in Nebraska. *Ibid.*, 8: 113–116; Figs. 1A–1C.
DAILY, WM. A. 1938. A quantitative study of the phytoplankton of Lake Michigan collected in the vicinity of Evanston, Ill. Butler Univ. Bot. Studies, 4: 65–83. 1942. The Chroococcaceae of Ohio, Kentucky, and Indiana. Amer. Midl. Nat., 27: 636–661; Pls. 1–6.
DAMANN, K. E. 1938. Quantitative study of the phytoplankton of Lake Michigan at Evanston, Illinois. Butler Univ. Bot. Studies, 5: 27–44.
DANGEARD, P. A. 1888. Recherches sur les algues inférieures. Ann. Sci. Nat. Bot., 7(Sér. 7): 105–175; Pls. 11, 12. 1889. Recherches sur les Cryptomonadinae et les Euglenae. Le Botaniste, 1: 1–38. 1889a. Mémoire sur les algues. *Ibid.*, 1: 127–174;Pls. 6, 7. 1899. Mémoire sur les Chlamydomonadinées ou l'histoire d'une cellule. *Ibid.*, 6: 65–290; Figs. 1–19. 1900. Observations sur le développement du *Pandorina morum*. *Ibid.*, 7: 192–211; Pl. 5. 1901. Etude sur la structure de la cellule et ses fonctions, le *Polytoma uvella*. *Ibid.*, 8: 5–58; Figs. 1–4. 1902. Recherches sur les Eugléniens. *Ibid.*, 8(1901): 97–360. 1911. Un nouveau genre d'algues. Bull. Soc. Bot. France, 58: 309–311. 1912. Recherches sur quelques algues nouvelles ou peu connues. Le Botaniste, 12: I–XIX; Pls. 1, 2. 1938. Mémoire sur la famille des Péridiniens. *Ibid.*, 29: 1–180. 1939. Le genre *Vaucheria*, spécialement dans la région du sud-ouest de la France. *Ibid.*, 29: 183–264. 1939a. Second mémoire sur la famille des Péridiniens. *Ibid.*, 29: 267–308. 1939b. Sur les algues *Vaucheria* observées dans la région du sud-ouest et sur une nouvelle espèce de ce genre. Comp. Rend. Acad. Sci. Paris, 208: 297–299.
DAVIS, B. M. 1894. *Euglenopsis*, a new alga-like organism. Ann. Bot., 8: 377–

390; Pl. 19. 1896. The fertilization of *Batrachospermum*. *Ibid.*, 10: 49–76; Pls. 6, 7. 1904. Oogenesis in *Vaucheria*. Bot. Gaz., 38: 81–98; Pls. 6, 7.

DAVIS, C. A. 1900.* A contribution to the natural history of marl. Jour. Geol., 8: 485–497. 1908. The flora. A biological survey of Walnut Lake, Michigan. Ann. Rep. Mich. Geol. Surv., 1907: 217–231.

DE, P. K. 1939. The rôle of blue-green algae in nitrogen fixation in rice fields. Proc. Roy. Soc. London (B), 127: 121–139.

DEBARY, A. A. 1854. Ueber die Algengattungen *Oedogonium* und *Bulbochaete*. Abh. Senck. Nat. Ges. Frankfurt A. M., 1: 29–105. 1858. Untersuchungen über die Familie der Conjugaten (Zygnemeen u. Desmidieen). 91 pp.; Pls. 1–8. Leipzig.

DECANDOLLE, A. P. 1802. Rapport sur les Conferves. Jour. de Phys. et Chimie et d'Hist. Nat., 54: 421–441. 1805. Flore Française, II. 3rd ed. Paris.

DEFLANDRE, G. 1924. Additions à la flore algologique des environs de Paris. III.—Flagellées. Bull. Soc. Bot. France, 71: 1115–1130. 1924a. A propos de l'*Euglena acus* Ehrenb. Rev. Algol., 1: 235–243. 1926.† Monographie du genre *Trachelomonas*. Pls. 1–15. Nemours. 1926a. Contribution à la flore algologique de la Basse-Normandie. Bull. Soc. Bot. France, 73: 701–717. 1926b. Algues d'eau douce du Vénézuela (Flagellées et Chlorophycées) récoltées par la Mission M. Grisol. Rev. Algol., 3: 211–241. 1927. Remarques sur la systématique du genre *Trachelomonas* Ehr. I. Bull. Soc. Bot. France, 74: 285–288. *Ibid.* II. Quarte *Trachelomonas* nouveaux. *Ibid.*: 657–665. 1930. *Strobomonas*, nouveau genre d'Euglenacées (*Trachelomonas* Ehrb. pro parte). Archiv f. Protist., 69: 551–614. 1932. Contributions à la connaissance des Flagellés libres. I. Ann. Protist., 3: 219–239.

DE LACERDA, F. S. 1946. Oedogoniaceae de Portugal. Portugal Acta Biol., 11(Ser. B): 1–142; Figs. I–LXVIII.

DENIS, M., and FRÉMY, P. 1923. Une nouvelle Cyanophycée heterocystée *Anabaena Viguieri*. Bull. Soc. Linn. Normandie, 6(Sér. 7): 122–125.

DENNISTON, R. H. 1921.* A survey of the larger aquatic plants of Lake Mendota. Trans. Wis. Acad. Sci., Arts, and Letters, 20: 495–500.

DERBÉS, A., and SOLIER, A. J. J. 1850. Sur les organes reproducteurs des algues. Ann. Sci. Nat. Bot., 4(Sér. 3): 261–282. 1856. Mémoire sur quelques points de la physiologie des algues. Paris.

DESMAZIÈRES, J. B. H. J. 1823. Catalogue des plantes omises dans la botanographie belgique. Lille. 1825–1860. Plantes cryptogames de France. Ed. I, Fasc. 1–44 (1825–1836). Ed. II, Fasc. 1–37 (1836–1851). Ed. Novae. Fasc. 1–16 (1853–1860). Lille.

DESVAUX, A. N. 1818. Observations sur les plantes environs de Angers. Paris.

DETONI, G. B. 1889.† Sylloge algarum omnium hucusque cognitarum. I. Padua. 1907. *Ibid.* Myxophyceae. V. (A. Forti). Padua.

DE TONI, G. B., and FORTI, A. 1899–1900. Contributo alla conoscenza del plancton del Lago Vetter. Atti Reale Istit. Veneto Sci., Lett. ed Arti, 59: 537–561, 779–829. (Note: pages 537–561 erroneously occur twice in Vol. 59. The citation refers to the first series of these pages.)

DETONI, G. B., and SACCARDO, FR. 1890. Revisione de alcuni generi di Cloroficee epifite. Nuova Notarisia, 1: 3–20.

DE WILDEMANN, E. 1888. Observations algologiques. Bull. Soc. Roy. Bot. Belgique, 27: 71–80 *bis*. 1892. Quelques mots sur le genre *Scenedesmus* Turpin. *Ibid.*, 31(Pt. 2): 218–224. 1893. Le genre *Scenedesmus* Meyen. Notarisia, 1893: 85–106. 1893a. Contribution a l'étude des algues de Belgique. *Ibid.*, 32(Pt. 2): 88–101. 1895. Le genre *Palmodictyon* Näg. Bull.

Herb. Boiss., 3: 328–333. 1897. Encore le *Pleurococcus nimbatus* de Wild. *Ibid.*, 5: 532.

DIESING, K. M. 1866. Revision der Prothelminthen. Abtheilung Mastigophoren. Sitz. K. K. Akad. Wiss. Wein, Math.-Nat. Kl., 52(1865), Abt. 1: 287–401.

DILL, O. 1895. Die Gattung *Chlamydomonas* und ihre nächsten Verwandten. Pringsh. Jahrb. f. Wiss. Bot., 28: 323–358; Pl. 5.

DILLWYN, F. 1802. British conjugates. London .

DIWALD, KARL. 1969. Ein Beitrag zur Variabilität und Systematik der Gattung *Peridinium*. Arch. f. Protist., 93: 121–148.

DOFLEIN, F. 1916. Lehrbuch der Protozoenkunde. IV. Auflage. Jena. 1921. Mitteilungen über Chrysomonadinen aus dem Schwarzwald. Zool. Anz., 53: 153–173; Figs. 1–4. 1922. Untersuchungen über Chrysomonadinen. Arch. f. Protist., 44: 149–213. 1923. Untersuchungen über Chrysomonadinen. III. Arten von *Chromulina* und *Ochromonas* aus dem Badischen Schwarzwald und ihre Cystenbildung. *Ibid.*, 46: 267–327; Pls. 15–21. Figs. A–E.

DOLLEY, JOHN S. 1933.* Preliminary notes on the biology of the St. Joseph River. Amer. Midl. Nat., 14: 193–227.

DOMOGALLA, B. P. 1926.* Treatment of algae and weeds in lakes at Madison, Wisconsin. Eng. News Record, Dec. 9, 1926: 950–954. 1935.* Eleven years of chemical treatment of the Madison lakes: its effect on fish and fish foods. Trans. Amer. Fish. Soc., 65: 115–120.

DOMOGALLA, B. P., and FRED, E. B. 1926. Ammonia and nitrate studies of lakes near Madison, Wisconsin. Jour. Amer. Soc. Agronomy, 18: 897–911.

DOROGOSTAÏSKY, V. 1905. Matériaux pour servir à l'algologie du lac Baïkal et de son bassin. Bull. Soc. Imp. Nat. Moscou, 1904(No. 2/3): 228–265.

DREŻEPOLSKI, R. 1923. De Eugleninis se ipsis sustinentibus ex collectione facta a Dr. J. Grochmalicki in Podlachi et Lithuania. Obd. z Rozpraw i wradomosci z Muzeum im Dzied, 7/8(1922): 1–19. 1925. Przycznek do znajomości polskich Euglenin. (Supplément à la connaissance des Eugléniens de la Pologne.) "Kosmos," Jour. Soc. Polonaise Nar. "Kopernik," 50(Fasc. 1.A): 173–270; Pls. 1–6.

DROUET, F. 1937. The Brazilian Myxophyceae. I. Amer. Jour. Bot., 24: 598–608; Figs. 1–5. 1938. *Ibid.* II. *Ibid.*, 25: 657–666. 1938a. The Oscillatoriaceae of southern Massachusetts. Rhodora, 40: 221–241, 255–273. 1939. Francis Wolle's filamentous Myxophyceae. Field Mus. Bot. Ser., 20: 17–64; Fig. 1. 1939a. The Myxophyceae of Maryland. *Ibid.*, 20: 3–14. 1942. Studies in Myxophyceae. I. *Ibid.*, 20: 125–141. 1943. New species of Oscillatoriaceae. Amer. Midl. Nat., 29: 51–54.

DROUET, F., and COHN, A. 1935. The morphology of *Gonyostomum semen* from Woods Hole, Massachusetts. Biol. Bull., 68: 422–439. 1937. Further observations on *Gonyostomum semen*. Bot. Gaz., 98: 617–618.

DROUET, F., and DAILY, WM. A. 1939. The planktonic freshwater species of *Microcystis*. Field Mus. Bot. Ser., 20: 67–83.

DUJARDIN, M. F. 1841. Histoire naturelle des Zoophytes. Infusiores, comprenant la physiologie et la classification de ces animaux et la manière de les estudier à l'aide du microscope. *In* Suites à Buffon. Paris.

DUTTON, H. J. 1941. The chromatographic adsorption of plant pigments as a limnological method. *In* A Symposium on Hydrobiology. Madison.

DUTTON, H. J., and MANNING, W. M. 1941. Evidence for carotenoid-sensitized photosynthesis in the diatom *Nitzschia Closterium*. Amer. Jour. Bot., 28; 516–526.

EDDY, SAMUEL. 1927.* The plankton of Lake Michigan. Ill. Nat. Hist. Surv., 17:

203–232. 1930.† The fresh-water armored or thecate Dinoflagellates. Trans. Amer. Microsc. Soc., 49: 277–321; Pls. 28–35.

EDMONDSON, C. H. 1906. The Protozoa of Iowa. Proc. Davenport Acad. Sci., 11: 1–124; Pls. 1–30.

EGGLETON, F. E. 1939. Rôle of the bottom fauna in the productivity of lakes. In Problems of lake biology. Amer. Assoc. Adv. Sci., Publ. No. 10: 123–131. 1939a. Freshwater communities. Amer. Midl. Nat., 21: 56–74.

EHRENBERG, C. G. 1832. Die geographische Verbreitung der Infusionthierchen in Nord-Afrika und West Asien. Abh. d. Phys. Kl. Königl. Akad. Wiss. z. Berlin, 1829: 1–20. 1832a. Beiträge zur Kenntniss der Organisation der Infusorien und ihre geographische Verbreitung besonders in Sibirien. Abh. d. Köngl. Akad. Wiss. z. Berlin, 1830: 1–88. 1832b. Ueber die Entwicklung und Lebensdauer der Infusionsthiere; nebst ferneren Beitragen zu einer Vergleichung ihrer organischen Systeme. Phys. Abh. Königl. Akad. Wiss. z. Berlin, 1831: 1–154. 1835. Dritter Beitrag zur Erkenntniss grosser Organisation in der Richtung des kleinsten Raumes. Abh. d. Königl. Akad. Wiss. z. Berlin, 1833: 145–336. 1837. Zusätze zur Erkenntniss grosser organischer Ausbildung in den kleinsten thierischen Organismen. Ibid., 1835: 151–180. 1838. Die Infusionsthierchen als vollkommene Organismen. Leipzig. 1849. Beobachtung zweier generisch neuer Formen der Frühlingsgewässers bei Berlin. Monatsber. Königl. Akad. Wiss. z. Berlin, 1848: 233–247.

EICHWALD, V. 1847. Erster Nachtrag zur Infusorienkunde Russlands. Bull. Soc. Imp. Nat. Moscou, 20: 285–366. 1849. Ibid., 2. Ibid., 22: 400–548. 1852. Ibid. 3. Ibid., 25: 388–536.

ELENKIN, A. A. 1909. Neue, seltene oder interessante Arten und Formen der Algen in Mittel-Russland 1908–1909 gesammelt. Bull. Jard. Imp. Bot. Pierre le Grand, 9(No. 6): 121–154. 1915. [Note sur une algue nouvelle Leptobasis caucasica mihi (nov. gen. et sp.) suivé de la révision critique de genre Microchaete Thur.] Ibid., 15(No. 1): 5–22. 1922. Calothrix Ramenskii mihi nov. sp. Not. Syst. Inst. Crypt. Horti Bot. Petropol., 1(No. 1): 6–9. 1922a. De nova specie Aulosirae notula. Ibid., 1(No. 8): 127–128. 1923. De Chroococcacearum classificatione notula. Ibid., 2(No. 4): 49–62. 1923a. Schema Chroococcacearum classificationis. Ibid., 2(No. 5): 65–69. 1923b. De gen. Anabaenopsis (Wołoszyńska) Miller notula. Ibid., 2(No. 5): 73–78. 1924. De spec. duabus gen. Microcystis Kütz. notula. Ibid., 3(No. 1): 12–15. 1924a. Descriptio specierum formarumque novarum e gen. Characium A. Braun et Characiopsis Borzi cum Crustaceis symbioticis. Ibid., 3(No. 3): 33–36. 1924b. De Euglenarum sine flagello sectione nova. I–II. Ibid., 3(No. 9/10): 129–160.

ELENKIN, A. A., and HOLLERBACH, M. M. 1923. De Coelosphaerio Naegeliano Unger nonnullisque speciebus hujus generis et de Gomphosphaeria Kuetz. notula. Not. Syst. Inst. Crypt. Horti Bot. Petropol., 2(No. 10): 145–155. 1923a. Schema specierum gen. Gomphosphaeriae Kuetz. et Coelosphaerii (Naeg.) nob. emend. Ibid., 2(No. 10): 155–157.

ELENKIN, A. A., and OHL, LYDIA. 1926. Die Fortschutte der floristischen algologie in USSR wahrend der letzten 25 Jahre. Ver. Inter. Vereinig. f. Theoret. u. Angew. Limnol., 3: 166–177.

ELENKIN, A. A., and STARK, N. V. 1923. De Asterocyti ramosa (Thwait) Gobi caeterisque speciebus hujus generis notula. Not. Syst. Inst. Crypt. Horti Bot. Petropol., 2(No. 8): 117–128.

EL-NAYAL, A. A. 1935. Egyptian freshwater algae. Egyptian Univ. Bull. Fac. Sci., No. 4: 1–106; Figs. 1–143. 1939. On some new freshwater algae from Egypt. Rev. Algol., 8: 311–319.

ENTZ, G. 1909. Ueber die Organisationsverhältnisse Peridineen. Math.-Natur. Berichte aus Ungarn, 25(1907): 246–274. 1926. Beiträge zur Kenntnis der Peridineen. I. Zur Morphologie und Biologie von *Peridinium Borgei* Lemmermann. Arch. f. Protist., 56: 397–416. 1927. Beiträge zur Kenntnis der Peridineen. II. resp. VII. Studien an Süsswasser-Ceratien. *Ibid.*, 58: 344–440.

ERNST, A. 1902. Siphoneen-Studien. 1. *Dichotomosiphon tuberosus* (A. Br.) Ernst, eine neue oogame Süsswasser-Siphonee. Beih. Bot. Centralbl., 13: 115–148; Pls. 6–10. 1904. Siphoneen-Studien. III. Zur Morphologie und Physiologie der Fortpflanzungszellen der Gattung *Vaucheria* DC. *Ibid.*, 16: 367–382; Pl. 20. 1908. Beiträge zur Morphologie und Physiologie von *Pithophora*. Ann. Jard. Bot. Buitenzorg, 22: 18–55; Pls. 1–4.

ESMARCH, FERDINAND. 1914. Untersuchungen über die Verbreitung der Cyanophyceen auf und in verschiedenen Böden. Hedwigia, 55: 224–273.

FARLOW, W. G. 1877. Remarks on some algae found in the water supplies of the city of Boston. Bull. Bussey Inst., 2: 75–80. 1883. Relations of certain forms of algae to disagreeable tastes and odors. Science, 2: 333–334.

FASSETT, N. C. 1930. The plants of some northeastern Wisconsin lakes. Trans. Wis. Acad. Sci., Arts, and Letters, 25: 157–168.

FITCH, C. P., BISHOP, LUCILLE M., et al. 1934. "Water bloom" as a cause of poisoning in domestic animals. Cornell Veterinarian, 24: 31–40.

FJERDINGSTAD, E. 1945. Planktonstudien. I. Zur Ausbreitung der *Microcystis aeruginosa* Kütz. emend. W. L., *Microcystis flos-aquae* (Wittr.) Kirchner emend. W.-L. und *Microcystis viridis* (A. Br.) Lemmermann. II. Das phytoplankton im Vejle So im Sommer 1943 nebst einigen systematischen und biologischen Bemerkungen. Dansk. Bot. Ark., 12(No. 1): 1–21.

FLAHAULT, CH. 1887. Note sur les Nostocacées hétérocystées de la flore Belge. Bull. Soc. Roy. Bot. Belgique, 26(Pt. II): 171–179.

FLANIGON, THOMAS H. 1943. Limnological observations on three lakes in eastern Vilas County, Wisconsin. Trans. Wis. Acad. Sci., Arts and Letters, 34: 167–175.

FLING, EVA M. 1939. One hundred algae of West Virginia. Castanea, 4: 11–25.

FLINT, L. H. 1947. Studies of freshwater red algae. Amer. Jour. Bot., 34(No. 3): 125–131; Figs. 1–31. 1948. *Ibid.*, 35(No. 7): 428–433; Figs. 1–40.

FLOTOW, J. VON. 1844. Beobachtungen über *Haematococcus pluviatilis*. Nova Acta Acad. Caes. Leop.-Carol., 20: 413–606; Pls. 24–26.

FOGG, G. E. 1942. Studies on nitrogen fixation by blue-green algae. I. Nitrogen fixation by *Anabaena cylindricum* Lemm. Jour. Exper. Biol., 19: 78–87.

FORTI, A. 1907. Sylloge Myxophycearum. *In* G. B. DeToni, Sylloge algarum. V. Padua.

FRANZÉ, R. H. 1892. Beiträge zur Morphologie des *Scenedesmus*. Természtrajzi Füzetek kiadja a Magyar Nemzeti Muzeum, 15: 144–165. 1892a. Zur Systematik einiger Chlamydomonaden. *Ibid.*, 15: 273–286. 1893. Ueber einige Algenformen. Oesterr. Bot. Zeit., 43: 202–205, 247–252, 282–286, 346–350, 381–386.

FREEMAN, E. M. 1899. Observations on *Chlorochytrium*. Minn. Bot. Studies, 2(No. 16): 195–204.

FRÉMY, P. 1922. Algues de l'Afrique centrale équatoriale. Bull. Soc. Bot. Linn. Normandie, 5: 25–26. 1924. Contribution à la flore algologique de l'Afrique équatoriale française. Rev. Algol., 1: 28–49. 1927. Les Scytonémacées de la France. *In* Flore algologique de France, Cyanophycées. Fasc. 1. Paris and Saint-Lô. (*Ibid.* 1925. Rev. Algol., 2: 258–279. 1926. *Ibid.*, 3: 55–98.) 1927a. Species des Stigonemacées de Normandie: *Fischerella, Stigonema, Capsosira, Nostochopsis*. Bull. Soc. Linn. Bot. Normandie, 9: 41–44. 1930.†

Les Myxophycées de l'Afrique équatoriale française. 507 pp.; Figs. 1–362. Thesis. Caen. 1930a. Algues provenant des récoltes de M. Henri Gadeau de Kerville dans le canton de Bagnères-de-Luchon (Haut-Garonne). Bull. Soc. Amis Sci. Nat. Rouen, 1928–1929: 159–227; Figs. 1–139. 1936. Une nouvelle Cyanophycée précipitant de l'oxyde de fer. *Microcoleus ferrugineus* Frémy n. sp. Acta Inst. Bot. Univ. Zagreb., 11: 58–62; Figs. 1–7. 1936a. Les Lyngbyées de la Normandie. Soc. d'Archeol. et d'Hist. Nat. Dept. de la Manche, 47: 116–188; Figs. 1–13. 1938. Algues d'eau douce & subaériennes des anciennes antilles danoises. D'après les récoltes de M. le Dr. Boergesen. Mém. Soc. Nation. Sci. Nat. et Math. Cherbourg, 43: 37–62; Figs. 1–6.

FRESENIUS, G. 1851. Ueber *Sphaeroplea annulina*. Bot. Zeit., 9: 241–248; Pl. 6. 1858. Beiträge zur Kenntniss mikroskopischer Organismen. Abh. Senck. Nat. Ges., Frankfurt A.M., 2: 211–242.

FRIES, E. M. 1825. Systema orbis vegetabilis. Plantae homonemeae. 374 pp.

FRITSCH, F. E. 1902. Algological notes. I. Observations on species of *Aphano-chaete*. II. The germination of zoospores in *Oedogonium*. Ann. Bot., 16: 403–417; Figs. 1–7, 23. 1902a. Algological notes.—III. Preliminary report on the phytoplankton of the Thames. *Ibid.*, 16: 576–584. 1903. Further observations on the phytoplankton of the River Thames. *Ibid.*, 17: 631–647. 1905. Algological notes. VI. The plankton of some English rivers. *Ibid.*, 19: 163–167. 1907. A general consideration of the subaërial and fresh-water algal flora of Ceylon, Part I. Subaërial algae and algae of the inland fresh-waters. Proc. Roy. Soc. London (B), 79: 197–254 .1907a. The subaërial and freshwater algal flora of the tropics. Ann. Bot., 21: 235–275. 1914. Notes on British flagellates. I–IV. New Phytol., 13: 341–351. 1916. The algal ancestry of the higher plants. *Ibid.*, 15: 233–250; Figs. 1, 2. 1918. A contribution to our knowledge of the fresh-water algae of Africa. Ann. S. African Mus., 9: 483–611. 1929. The encrusting algal communities of certain fast-flowing streams. New Phytol., 28: 165–196. 1929a. Evolutionary sequence and affinities among protophyta. Biol. Rev. and Biol. Proc. Cambridge Philos. Soc., 4: 103–151; Figs. 1–7. 1929b. The genus *Sphaeroplea*. Ann. Bot., 43; 1–26; Figs. 1–8. 1931. Some aspects of the ecology of fresh-water algae. Jour. Ecol., 19: 233–272. 1935.† The structure and reproduction of the algae. I. 791 pp.; Figs. 1–245. New York. 1942. The interrelations and classification of the Myxophyceae (Cyanophyceae). New Phytol., 41: 134–148; Figs. 1–5. 1945.† The structure and reproduction of the algae. II. 939 pp.; Figs. 1–335. New York.

FRITSCH, F. E., and DE, P. K. 1938. Nitrogen fixation by blue-green algae. Nature, 142: 878.

FRITSCH, F. E., and JOHN, R. P. 1942. An ecological and taxonomic study of the algae of British soils. II. Consideration of the species observed. Ann. Bot., 6(n.s.): 371–395; Figs. 1–8.

FRITSCH, F. E., and RICH, FLORENCE. 1913. Studies on the occurrence and reproduction of British freshwater algae in nature. 3. A four year's observation of a freshwater pond. Ann. Biol. Lacustre, 6: 33–115. 1930. Contributions to our knowledge of the freshwater algae of Africa. 7. Freshwater algae (exclusive of diatoms) from Griqualand West. Trans. Roy. Soc. S. Africa, 18(1929): 1–92; Figs. 1–32. 1937. Contributions to our knowledge of the freshwater algae of Africa. 12. Algae from the Belfast Pan, Transvaal. *Ibid*, 25(Pt. II): 153–228; Figs. 1–31.

FRITSCH, F. E., and STEPHENS, EDITH L. 1921. Contributions to our knowledge of the freshwater algae of Africa. 2. Fresh-water algae (exclusive of diatoms), mainly from the Transkei Territories, Cape Colony. Trans. Roy. Soc. S. Africa, 9(Pt. 1): 1–72; Figs. 1–29.

FRITSCH, F. E., and TAKEDA, H. 1916. On a species of *Chlamydomonas* (*C. sphagnicola* F. E. Fritsch and Takeda—*Isococcus sphagnicolus,* F. E. Fritsch). Ann Bot., 30: 373–377; Figs. 1–12.

GAIDUKOV, N. 1903. Ueber die Kulturen und die *Uronema*-Zustand der *Ulothrix flaccida.* Ber. d. Deutsch. Bot. Ges., 21: 522–524.

GARBINI, A. 1899. Intorno al plankton dei laghi di Mantova. Atti e Mem. Accad. Verona, 74(Ser. 3) Fasc. 3: 255–314. 1901. Intorno plankton del Lago Maggiore. *Ibid.,* 76(Ser. 3), Fasc. 2: 67–80.

GARD, M. 1920. Division chez *Euglena limosa* Gard. Comp. Rend. Acad. Sci. Paris, 170: 291–292. 1922. Recherches sur une nouvelle espèce d'Euglène (*Euglena limosa* nov. spec.). Bull. Soc. Bot. France, 69: 306–313.

GARDNER, N. L. 1927. New Myxophyceae from Porto Rico. Mem. N. Y. Bot. Gard., 7: 1–144.

GATES, F. C. 1912.* The vegetation of the beach area in northeastern Illinois and southeastern Wisconsin. Bull. Ill. State Lab. Nat. Hist., 9: 255–372.

GAY, F. 1888. Sur les *Ulothrix* aériens. Bull. Soc. Bot. France, 35: 65–75. 1891. Recherches sur le développement et la classification de quelques algues vertes. 116 pp.; Pls. 1–15. Paris. 1891a. Le genre *Rhizoclonium.* Jour. Bot. 5: 53–58.

GEITLER, L. 1921. Versuch einer Lösung des Heterocysten-Problems. Sitz. K. K. Akad. Wiss. Wien, Math.-Nat. Kl., 130: 223–245. 1921a. Kleine Mitteilungen über Blaualgen. Oesterr. Bot. Zeit., 70: 158–167; Figs. 1–7. 1923. Studien über das Hämatochrom und die Chromatophoren in *Trentepohlia. Ibid.,* 72: 76–83; Figs. 1–5. 1923a. Der Zellbau von *Glaucocystis Nostochinearum* und *Gloeochaete Wittrockiana* und die Chromatophoren-Symbiostheorie von Mereschkowsky. Arch. f. Protist., 47: 1–24; Pl. 1. 1924. Die Entwicklungsgeschichte von *Sorastrum spinulosmum* und die Phylogenie der Protococcales. *Ibid.,* 47: 440–447; Pl. 22. 1925. Beiträge zur Kenntnis der Flora ostholsteinischer Seen. *Ibid.,* 52: 603–611. 1925a. Cyanophyceae. *In* A. Pascher, die Süsswasserflora Deutschlands, Oesterreichs und der Schweiz. Heft 12: 1–450; Figs. 1–560. 1925b. Ueber neue oder wenig bekannte interessante Cyanophyceen aus der Gruppe der Chamaesiphoneae. Arch. f. Protist., 51: 321–360; Pls. 12, 13. 1928. Neue Blaualgen aus Lunz. *Ibid.,* 60: 440–448. 1928a. Zwei neue Dinophyceenarten. *Ibid.,* 61: 1–8. 1928b. Neue Gattungen und Arten von Dinophyceen, Heterokonten und Chrysophyceen. *Ibid.,* 63: 67–83; Pl. 7. 1930. Ueber die Kernteilung von Spirogyra. *Ibid.,* 71: 79–100. 1930–1931.† Cyanophyceae. *In* L. Rabenhorst, Kryptogamen-Flora von Deutschland, Oesterreich und der Schweiz. 14, Lf. 1(1930): 1–288; Lf. 2(1931): 289–464; Figs. 1–131. Leipzig. 1931a. Untersuchungen über das sexuelle Verhalten von *Tetraspora lubrica.* Biol. Centralbl., 51: 173–187; Figs. 1–5.

GELLIS, S. S., and CLARKE, G. L. 1935. Organic matter in dissolved and in colloidal form as food for *Daphnia magna.* Physiol. Zool., 8: 127–137.

GEMEINHARDT, K. 1938–1939.† Oedogoniales. *In* L. Rabenhorst, Kryptogamen-Flora von Deutschland, Oesterreich und der Schweiz. 12, Abt. 4: 1–453; Figs. 1–539. Leipzig.

GERLOFF, J. 1940. Beiträge zur Kenntnis der Variabilität und Systematik der Gattung *Chlamydomonas.* Arch. f. Protist., 94: 311–502; Figs. 1–48.

GERNECK, R. 1907. Zur Kenntnis niederen Chlorophyceen. Beih. Bot Centralbl. 21(Abt. 2): 221–290; Pls. 11, 12.

GICKLHORN, J. 1921. Ueber den Blauglanz zweier neuer Oscillatorien. Oesterr. Bot. Zeit., 70: 1–11.

GIMESI, N. 1930. Die Geburt von *Trachelomonas volvocina* Ehrb. Arch. f. Protist., 72: 190–197; Pl. 14.

GMELIN, C. G. 1826. Flora Badensis Alsatica. IV: 643–647. Carlsruhe. (Not seen.)

GOBI, C. 1879. Kurzer Bericht üeber die im Sommer 1878 ausgeführte algologische Excursion (rossice). St. Petersb. Ges. d. Naturf., 10: 93–97. 1886–1887. *Peroniella Hyalothecae,* eine neue Süsswasseralge. Script. Bot. Hort. Petropol., 1(Fasc. 2): 233–250; 1 pl.

GÖTZ, H. 1897. Zur Systematik der Gattung *Vaucheria* DC. speciell der Arten der Umgebung Basels. Flora, 83: 88–134; Figs. 1–55.

GOJDICS, MARY. 1934. The cell morphology and division of *Euglena deses* Ehrbg. Trans. Amer. Microsc. Soc., 53: 299–310; Pls. 21–23. 1939. Some observations on *Euglena sanguinea* Ehrbg. *Ibid.,* 58: 241–248; 1 pl.

GOLENKIN, M. 1899. Algologische Mitteilungen. Ueber die Befruchtung bei *Sphaeroplea annulina* und über die Struktur bei einigen grunen Algen. Bull. Soc. Imp. Nat. Moscou, 13: 343–361.

GOMONT, M. 1885. Sur deux algues nouvelles des environs de Paris. Bull. Soc. Bot. France, 32: 208–212. 1890. Essai de classification des Nostocacées homocystées. Jour. Bot., 4: 349–357. 1892. Monographie des Oscillariées (Nostocacées homocystées). Part 1. Ann. Sci. Nat. Bot., 15(Sér. 7): 263–368; Pls. 6–14. 1892a.† Monographie des Oscillariées. Part 2. *Ibid.,* 16(Sér 7): 91–264; Pls. 1–7. 1893.† Monographie des Oscillariées (Nostocacées homocystées). Paris. 1895. Note sur le *Scytonema ambiguum* Kütz. Jour. Bot., 9: 49–53. 1895a. Note sur un *Calothrix* sporifere (*Calothrix stagnalis* sp. n.). *Ibid.,* 9: 197–202.

GOROSCHANKIN, J. 1891. Beiträge zur Kenntnis der Morphologie und Systematik der Chlamydomonaden. I. *Chlamydomonas Braunii.* Bull. Soc. Imp. Nat. Moscou, 1890 (No. 3): 498–520; Pls. 14, 15. 1891. Beiträge zur Kenntniss der Morphologie und Systematik der Chlamydomonaden. II. *Chlamydomonas Reinhardii* (Dangeard) und seine Verwandten. Pls. 1–3. Moskau.

GRECER, J. 1915. Beitrag zur Kenntnis der Entwicklung und Fortpflanzung der Gattung *Microthamnion* Naeg. Hedwigia, 56: 374–380.

GREVILLE, R. K. 1824. Flora Edinensis. Edinburgh. 1830. Algae britannicae. Edinburgh.

GRIFFITHS, B. M. 1912. The algae of Stanklin Pool, Worcestershire; an account of their distribution and periodicity. Proc. Birmingham Nat. Hist. and Phil. Soc., 12: 1–23. 1915. On *Glaucocystis Nostochinearum,* Itzigsohn. Ann. Bot., 29: 423–432; Pl. 19.

GROVES, J., and BULLOCK-WEBSTER, G. R. 1920-1924.† The British Charophyta. I, 1920; II, 1924. Ray Society, London.

GRUNOW, A. 1858. Die Desmidiaceen und Pediastreen einiger Oesterreichischen Moore, nebst einigen Bemerkungen über beide Familien im Allgemeinen. Ver. K. K. Zool.-Bot. Ges. Wien, 8: 489–502. 1867. Algen. Leipzig.

GÜNTHER, F. 1928. Ueber der Bau und die Lebensweise der Euglenen, besonders der Arten E. *terricola, geniculata, proxima, sanguinea* und *lucens* nov. spec. Arch. f. Protist., 60: 511–590; Pls. 13–15; Figs: 1–5.

GUGLIELMETTI, G. 1910. Contribuzioni alla flora algologica Italiana. I. Protococcaceae raccolte nel Padovano. Nuova Notarisia, 21: 28–39.

GUSTAFSON, A. H. 1942.* Notes on the algal flora of Michigan. Pap. Mich. Acad. Sci., Arts and Letters, 27(1941): 27–36. 1942a. Notes on some freshwater algae from New England. Rhodora, 44: 64–69.

GUTWIŃSKI, R. 1890. Zur Wahrung der Priorität. Vor laüfige Mittheilungen über einige neue Algen-Species und Varietäten aus der Umgebung von Lemberg. Bot. Centralbl., 43: 65–73. 1893. Glony stawów na Zbruczu. Akad. Umiej. w Krakowie Spraw. Komisyi Fizyogr., 29: 23–28. 1894. Flora glonów okolic Tarnapola. *Ibid.*, 30: 45–173. 1894a. Glony stawów na Zbruczu (Ueber die in den Teichen des Zbrucz-Flusses gesammelten Algen). *Ibid.*, 29: 23–38. 1896. De nonnulis algis novis vel minus cognitis. Akad. Umiej. w Krakowie, Rozpr. Wydz. Mat.-Przyr. 33: 32–63. 1897. Materyaly do flory Glonow Galicyi. Res ad floram algarum Galiciae congestae. Pars IV. A. Algae a Prof. Arsenio Dorozynski in Mizun ad Dolina anno 1896 collectae. B. Algae a Prof. Francisco Tondera in Knihynin ad Stanislowów anno 1894 collectae. Nuova Notarisia, 8: 125–136. 1900. Additamenta ad floram algarum Indiae Batavorum cognoscendam. Algae a cl. Dre. M. Raciborski in montibus vulcanis: Kraktau et Slamat anno 1897 collectae. Diss. Mat.-Physic. Acad. Litter. Cracoviens, 39: 287–307; Anz. Akad. Wiss. Krakau, 1900. 400–402. 1902. De algis a Dre. M. Raciborski anno 1899. in insula Java collectis. Bull. Inter. Acad. Sci. Cracovie, Cl. Sci. Math. et Nat., 1902: 575–617; Pls. 36–40. 1909. Flora algarum montium Tatrensium. *Ibid.*, 4: 415–560. 1913. Ueber die Algenflora und das Plankton des Tatra-Sees 'Morskie Oko'. Kosmos, 1923: 1426–1437 (reprint).

HAASE, G. 1910. Studien über *Euglena sanguinea.* Arch. f. Protist., 20: 47–59; Pls. 4–6.

HALE, FRANK E. 1930. Control of microscopic organisms in public water supplies, with particular reference to New York City. New Eng. Water Works Assoc., 44: 361–385.

HALLAS, E. D. 1905. Nye Arter af *Oedogonium* fra Danmark. Bot. Tids., 26: 397–410.

HAMEL, G. 1925. Floridées de France. III. Rev. Algol., 2: 39–67, 280–309.

HAMILTON, J. M. 1948. Sexual reproduction in the genus *Basicladia* (Thallophyta) Chlorophyceae. Trans. Amer. Microsc. Soc. 67: 201–205; Figs. 1–9.

HANSGIRG, A. 1883. Beiträge zur Kenntniss der Flora von Böhmen. I, II. Sitz. d. Königl. Böhm. Ges. d. Wiss. Math.-Nat. Kl. Prag, 1882: 280–289. 1883a. Neue Beiträge zur Algenkunde Böhmens. *Ibid.*, 1883: 203–211; Neue Beiträge zur Kenntniss böhmischer Algen. *Ibid.*, 1883: 263–273; Neue Beiträge zur Kenntniss der böhmischen Algenflora. *Ibid.*, 1883: 360–371. 1885. Anhang zu meiner Abhandlung "Ueber Polymorphismus der Algen." Bot. Centralbl., 23: 229–233. 1885a. Ueber den Polymorphismus der Algen. *Ibid.*, 23: 385–406. 1886.† Prodromus der Algenflora von Böhmen. Erster Theil enthaltend die Rhodophyceen, Phaeophyceen und einen Theil der Chlorophyceen. Heft 1. Archiv f. Natur. Landes von Böhm., 5(Bot. Abth.): 3–96; Figs. 1–126. 1887. Ueber *Trentepohlia* (*Chroolepus*) artige Moosvorkeimbildungen. Flora, 70: 81–85. 1887a. Algarum aquae dulcis species novae. Oesterr. Bot. Zeit., 37: 121–122. 1888.† Prodromus der Algenflora von Böhmen. Erster Theil enthaltend die Rhodophyceen, Phaeophyceen und Chlorophyceen. Heft 2. Archiv f. Natur. Landes von Böhm., 6(No. 5): 3–290. 1888a. Ueber die Süsswasser-gattungen *Trochiscia* Ktz. (*Astericium* Corda, *Polyedrium* Näg., *Cerasterias* Reinsch). Hedwigia, 27: 126–132. 1888b. Synopsis generum subgenerumque Myxophycearum (Cyanophycearum) hucusque cognitorum, cum descriptione generis nov. "*Dactylococcopsis.*" Notarisia, 3: 584–590. 1888c. Beitrag zur Kenntniss der Algengattungen *Entocladia* Reinke, etc. Flora, 71: 499–507; Pl. 12. 1888d. De *Spirogyra insigni* (Hass.) Ktz. nov. var. *fallaci, Zygnemate chlabeospermo* nov. sp. et

Z. *rhynconemate* nov. sp., adjecto conspectu subgenerum. sectionum, subsectionumque generis *Spirogyrae* Link et *Zygnematis* (Ag.) DeBy. Hedwigia, 27: 253–258; Pl. 10. 1888e. Algae novae aquae dulcis. Notarisia, 3(No. 9): 398–400. 1888f. Ueber die Gattungen *Herpostiron* Näg. und *Aphanochaete* Berth. non A. Br., etc. Flora, 71: 211–223. 1889. Nachträge zu den in Hedwigia 1888, No. 5 und 6, No. 9 und 10 veröffentlichten Abhandlungen. Hedwigia, 28: 17–19. 1889a. Resultate der vom Verfasser im J. 1888 ausgeführten Durchforschung, der Süsswasseralgen und der saprophytischen Bacterien Böhmens. Sitz. d. Konigl. Böhm. Ges. d. Wiss. Math.-Nat. Kl. Prag, 1889: 121–164. 1890. Uber neue Süsswasser- und Meeres-Algen und Bacterien, mit Bemerkungen zur Systematik dieser Phycophyten und über den Einfluss des Lichtes auf die Ortsbewegungen des *Bacillus Pfefferi*, nob. *Ibid.*, 1890: 1–34. 1890a. Physiologische und algologische Mittheilungen. *Ibid.*, 1890: 83–140. 1891. Algologische und bacteriologische Mittheilungen. *Ibid.*, 1891: 300–365. 1892[1893]. Prodromus der Algenflora von Böhmen. Zweiter Theil welcher die blaugrünen Algen (Myxophyceen, Cyanophyceen), nebst Nachträgen zum ersten Theile und einer systematischen Bearbeitung der in Böhmen verbreiteten saprophytischen Bacterien und Eugleenen enthält. Archiv f. Natur. Landes von Böhm., 8(Bot. Abth.): 1–268; Figs. 1–67. 1892a. Beiträge zur Kenntnis der Süsswasser-Algen und Bacterien-Flora von Tirol und Böhmen. Sitz. d. Königl. Böhm. Ges. d. Wiss. Prag, 1892: 105–156. 1893. Mein letztes Wort über *Chaetosphaeridium Pringsheimii* Kleb. und *Aphanochaete globose* (Nordst.) Wolle. Bot. Centralbl., 56: 321–326. 1905. Grundzüge der Algenflora von Niederösterreich. Beih. Bot. Centralbl., 18: 417–522.

HARIOT, P. 1889–1890. Notes sur le genre *Trentepohlia* Martius. Jour. Bot., 3(1889): 345–350, 366–375, 378–388, 393–405. *Ibid.*, 4(1890): 50–53, 85–92, 178–189, 192–197; Figs. 1–24. 1891. Le genre *Polycoccus* Kuetzing. *Ibid.*, 5: 29–32. 1895. Algues du Golfe de California. *Ibid.*, 9: 167–170.

HARPER, R. A. 1908.* Organization of certain coenobic plants. Bull. Univ. Wis. No. 207(Sci. Ser., 3): 279–334; Pls. 1–4. 1916. On the nature of types in *Pediastrum*. Mem. N. Y. Bot. Gard., 6: 91–104; Figs. 1, 2. 1918. Organisation, reproduction, and inheritance in *Pediastrum*. Proc. Amer. Philos. Soc., 57: 375–439; Pls. 5–6. 1918a. The evolution of cell types and contact and pressure responses in *Pediastrum*. Mem. Torr. Bot. Club, 17: 210–240; Figs. 1–27.

HARVEY, F. L. 1888. The freshwater algae of Maine. I. Bull. Torr. Bot. Club, 15: 155–161. 1889. *Ibid.* II. *Ibid.*, 16: 181–188. 1892. *Ibid.* III. *Ibid.*, 19: 118–125.

HARVEY, H. W. 1926. Nitrates in the sea. Jour. Mar. Biol. Assoc., 14: 71–88.

HARVEY, W. H. 1833. Algae Gloiocladeae. *In* Hooker's British Flora, 5: 385–400. London. 1855–1859. *In* J. D. Hooker, The botany of the antarctic voyage. Part III. Flora Tasmania. 1858. Nereis Boreali-Americana. III. Chlorospermeae. Smiths. Contrib. Knowledge, 10(No. 2): 1–140; Pls. 37–50.

HASSALL, A. H. 1842. Observations on the genera *Zygnema*, *Tyndaridea* and *Mougeotia*, with descriptions of new species. Ann. and Mag. Nat. Hist., 10(Ser. 1): 34–47. 1843. Descriptions of British freshwater Confervae, mostly new, with observations on some of the genera. *Ibid.*, 11(Ser. 1): 428–437. 1843a. Observations on some points in the anatomy and physiology of the freshwater algae. *Ibid.*, 12(Ser. 1): 20–30; 1 pl. 1843b. Observations on the genus *Mougeotia*, on two new genera of fresh water algae, and on *Tyndaridea*, with descriptions of species. *Ibid.*, 12(Ser. 1): 180–188; 1 pl. 1843c. Observations on the growth, reproduction, and species of the branched fresh-water Confervae. *Ibid.*, 11(Ser. 1): 359–364. 1845. A history of fresh-water algae. 462 pp.; Pls. 1–103. London. 1852. A history of the freshwater algae, including descriptions of Desmidiaceae and Diatomaceae. 2 vols. 462 pp.; Pls. I–CIII. London.

HASSLOW, O. J. 1939. Einige Characeenbestimmungen. Bot. Notiser, 1939: 295–301, 817–818.

HAUCK, F. 1885. Die Meeresalgen Deutschlands und Oesterreichs. *In* Rabenhorst's Kryptogamenflora. II. Leipzig.

HAYDEN, ADA. 1910. The algal flora of the Missouri Botanical Garden. 21st Ann. Rep. Missouri Bot. Gard., 1910: 25–48; Pls. 1–5.

HAZEN, TRACY E. 1899. The life history of *Sphaerella lacustris* (*Haematococcus pluvialis*). Mem. Torr. Bot. Club, 6: 211–224; Pls. 86–87. 1902. The Ulothricaceae and Chaetophoraceae of the United States. *Ibid.*, 11: 135–250; Pls. 20–42.

HEERING, W. 1906. Die Süsswasseralgen Schleswig-Holstein, etc. Jahrb. Hamburg. Wiss. Anstal., 23(1905): 61–150. 1914.† Ulotrichales, Microsporales, Oedogoniales. *In* A. Pascher, Die Süsswasserflora Deutschlands, Oesterreichs und der Schweiz. Heft 6. Chlorophyceae 3: 1–250; Figs. 1–384. Jena. 1921.† Siphonocladiales, Siphonales. *Ibid.* Heft 7. Chlorophyceae 4: 1–103; Figs. 1–94. Jena.

HEERING, W., and HOMFELD, H. 1905. Die Algen des Eppendorfer Moores bei Hamburg. Ver. Natur. Ver. in Hamburg, 12(1904): 77–97.

HEINRICHER, E. 1883. Zur Kenntniss der Algengattung *Sphaeroplea*. Ber. d. Deutsch. Bot. Ges., 1: 433–450; Pl. 12.

HENFREY, A. 1859. On *Chlorosphaera*, a new genus of uni-cellular fresh-water algae. Trans. Microsc. Soc. London, 7(n.s.): 25–29; Pl. 3.

HENRICI, A. T. 1938. Studies of freshwater bacteria. IV. Seasonal fluctuations of lake bacteria in relation to plankton production. Jour. Bact., 35: 129–139. 1939. The distribution of bacteria in lakes. *In* Problems of lake biology. Amer. Assoc. Adv. Sci., Publ. No. 10: 39–64.

HENRICI, A. T., and McCOY, ELIZABETH. 1938. The distribution of heterotrophic bacteria in the bottom deposits of some lakes. Trans. Wis. Acad. Sci., Arts, and Letters, 31: 323–361.

HERMANN, J. 1863. Ueber die bei Neudamm aufgefundenen Arten der Genus *Characium*. Leipzig.

HIERONYMUS, G. 1887. Ueber einige Algen des Riesengebirges. Jahr. Schles. Ges. Vater. Kul., 1887: 293–297. 1892. Ueber *Dicranochaete reniformis* Hieron., eine neue Protococcacea des Süsswassers. Beitr. Biol. Pflanzen., 5: 351–372; Pls. 11, 12. 1892a. Beiträge zur Morphologie und Biologie der Algen. I. *Glaucocystis Nostochinearum* Itzigsohn. *Ibid.*, 5: 461–495. 1895. Bemerkungen über einige Arten der Gattung *Stigonema* Ag. Hedwigia, 34: 154–172.

HIGINBOTHAM, NOE. 1942. *Cephalomonas*, a new genus of the Volvocales. Bull. Torr. Bot. Club, 69: 661–668; Figs. 1–43.

HIRN, KARL E. 1895. Verzeichnis finländischer Oedogoniacéen. Acta Soc. Fauna et Flora Fenn., 11(No. 6): 1–24. 1895a. Die Finnländischen Zygnemaceen. *Ibid.*, 11(No. 10): 1–15. 1900.† Monographie und iconographie der Oedogoniaceen. Acta Soc. Sci. Fenn., 27: 1–395; Pls. 1–64; Figs. 1–27. 1900a. Finnländische Vaucheriaceen. Medd. Soc. Fauna et Flora Fenn., 26(1900): 1–6 (reprint).

HODGETTS, W. J. 1918. *Uronema elongatum*, a new fresh water member of the Ulotrichaceae. New Phytol., 17: 159–166; Figs. 1–11. 1921. A study of some of the factors controlling the periodicity of fresh-water algae in nature. *Ibid.*, 20: 150–164, 195–227. 1922. *Ibid.*, 21: 15–33; Figs. 1–11.

HOFFMAN, W. E., and TILDEN, JOSEPHINE. 1930. *Basicladia,* a new genus of Cladophoraceae. Bot. Gaz., 89: 374–384; Figs. 1–22.

HOLMAN, R. M., and REED, E. 1918.* Notes on the phytoplankton and other algae of Douglas Lake and vicinity. Ann. Rep. Mich. Acad. Sci., 20: 153–154.

HOOKER, J. D. 1855–1859. The botany of the antarctic voyage. Part III. Flora Tasmaniae.

HOOKER, W. J. 1833. The English flora. 5. Part 1. 432 pp. London.

HOPPAUGH, KATHERINE. 1930.† A taxonomic study of species of the genus *Vaucheria* collected in California. Amer. Jour. Bot., 17: 329–347; Pls. 24–27.

HUBER, J. 1892. Contributions à la connaissance des Chaetophorées épiphytes et endophytes et de leurs affinités. Ann. Sci. Nat. Bot., 16(Sér. 7): 265–359; Pls. 8–18. 1894. Sur l'*Aphanochaete repens* A. Braun et sa reproduction sexuée. Bull. Soc. Bot. France, 41(Sér. 3): XCIV–CII.

HUBER-PESTALOZZI, G. 1919. Morphologie und Entwicklungsgeschichte von *Gloeotaenium Loitelsbergerianum* Hansgirg. Zeit. f. Bot., 11: 401–472. 1924. Notiz über *Gloeotaenium Loitelsbergerianum* Hansgirg. *Ibid.,* 16: 624–626. 1925. Zur Morphologie und Entwicklungsgeschichte von *Asterothrix (Cerasterias) raphidioides* (Reinsch) Printz. Hedwigia, 65: 169–178; Figs. 1–5. 1929. Das Phytoplankton naturlicher und künstlicher Seebecken Südafrikas. Ver. Inter. Vereining. f. Theor. u. Angew. Limnol., 4: 343–390. 1930. Algen aus dem Knysnawalde in Südafrika. Zeit. f. Bot., 23: 443–480. 1938.† Das Phytoplanktons des Süsswassers. Systematik und Biologie. 1 Teil. Stuttgart. 342 pp.; Pls. 3–66. 1941. *Ibid.* 2 Teil. Stuttgart.

HUBER-PESTALOZZI, G., and NAUMANN, E. 1929. *Phormidium mucicola* Naumann et Huber, ein Epibiont in der Gallerte pflanzlicher und tierischer Planktonorganismen. Ber. d. Deutsch. Bot. Ges., 47: 67–76.

HUEBNER, E. 1886. Euglenaceen-Flora von Stralsund. Progr. d. Realgymnasiums zu Stralsund. Ostern.

HUFF, N. L. 1923. Observations on the relation of algae to certain animals of Vadnais Lake. Univ. Minn. Biol. Sci., 4: 185–197.

HUGHES, E. O. 1948. New fresh-water Chlorophyceae from Nova Scotia. Amer. Jour. Bot., 35(No. 7); 424–427; Figs. 1–6.

HUITFELDT-KAAS, H. 1900. Die limnetischen Peridineen in norwegischen Binnenseen. Vidensk. Skrifter, Mat.-Nat. Kl. Christiania, 1900(No. 2): 1–7.

HUTCHINSON, G. EVELYN. 1944. Limnological studies in Connecticut. VII. A critical examination of the supposed relationship between phytoplankton periodicity and chemical changes in lake waters. Ecology, 25: 3–26.

HYLANDER, C. J. 1928. The algae of Connecticut. Bull. Conn. Geol. and Nat. Hist. Surv., 42: 1–245; Pls. 1–28.

HY, T. C. 1913–1914. Les Characées de France. Bull. Soc. Bot. France, 60(1913. Mém. 26): 1–47. Note additionelle. *Ibid.,* 61(1914): 235–241.

IMHOF, O. E. 1887. Studien über die Fauna hochalpiner Seen, insbesondere des Cantons Graubünden. Jahrb. d. Naturf. Ges. Graubündens, 30: 45–164. 1890. Das Flagellatengenus *Dinobryon.* Zool. Anz., 13: 483–488.

ISRAELSSON, GUNNAR. 1938. Ueber die Süsswasserphaeophyceen Schwedens. Bot. Notiser, 1938, 113–128.

ITZIGSOHN, H. 1850. Charologisches. Bot. Zeit., 8: 337–340. 1855. Skizzen zu einer Lebensgeschichte des *Hapalosiphon Braunii.* Acta Acad. Caes. Leop.-Carol., 25: 249–298.

IWANOFF, L. A. 1898. Zur Entwicklungsgeschichte von *Botrydium granulatum* Woronin et Rostaf. Trav. Soc. Imp. Nat. St. Pétersb. Comp. Rend., 29(No. 4): 155–156. (Not seen.) 1898a. Zur Entwicklungsgeschichte von *Botrydium*

granulatum Woronin et Rostaf. Arb. d. Kais. St. Petersb. Ges. d. Naturf., 29:
   1–10. 1900. Ueber neue Arten von Algen und Flagellaten (*Stigeoclonium,
   Vaucheria, Spirogyra, Gonyostomum*), welche an der biologischen Station
   zu Bologoje gefunden worden sind. Bull. Soc. Imp. Nat. Moscou, 1899(No.
   4): 423–449. 1900a. Beitrag zur Kenntnis der Morphologie und Systematik
   der Chrysomonadinen. Bull. Acad. Imp. Sci. St. Pétersb. 11: 247–262; 1 pl.;
   Figs. A, B.

IYENGAR, M. O. P. 1923. Notes on some attached forms of Zygnemaceae. Jour.
   Indian Bot. Soc., 2: 1–9. 1925. Note on two species of *Botrydium* from India.
   Ibid., 4: 193–201. 1925a. *Hydrodictyon indicum,* a new species from Madras.
   Ibid., 4: 315–317. 1933. Contributions to our knowledge of the colonial
   Volvocales of South India. Jour. Linn. Soc. Bot., 49: 323–373.

IYENGAR, M. O. P., and IYENGAR, M. O. T. 1932 On a *Characium* growing on
   Anopheles larvae. New Phytol., 31: 66–69.

JAHN, T. L. 1946. The euglenoid flagellates. Quart. Rev. Biol., 21: 246–274;
   Figs. 1–6.

JANET, C. 1912. Le *Volvox*. Limoges. 1918. *Botrydium granulatum*. Limoges.
   1922. Le *Volvox*. Deuxième mémoire. Paris. 1923. Le *Volvox*. Troisième
   mémoire. 179 pp.; Pls. 5–21. Paris.

JAO, C. C. 1934. New Oedogonia collected in China. Pap. Mich. Acad. Sci.,
   Arts, and Letters, 19(1933): 83–92; Pls. 5–7. 1934a. *Oedogonium* in the
   vicinity of Woods Hole, Massachusetts. Rhodora, 36: 197–214; Pls. 286–
   288. 1935. New Oedogonia collected in China. II. Pap. Mich. Acad. Sci.,
   Arts, and Letters, 20(1934): 57–63; Pls. X, XI. 1935a. New Zygnemataceae
   from Woods Hole. Trans. Amer. Microsc. Soc., 54: 1–7; Pl. 1. 1936. Notes
   on *Oedogonium* and *Bulbochaete* in the vicinity of Woods Hole, Massachusetts. Rhodora, 38: 67–73; Pl. 407. 1936a. New Zygnemataceae collected
   in China. Amer. Jour. Bot., 23: 53–60.

JÖRGENSEN, E. 1911. De Ceratien. Eine kurze Monographie der Gattung
   Ceratium Schrank. Inter. Rev. d. Ges. Hydrobiol. u. Hydrogr., 4(Suppl.),
   Pt. 1: 1–124.

JOHNSON, L. N. 1894.* Some new and rare desmids of the U. S. I. Bull. Torr.
   Bot. Club, 21: 285–291. 1895.* *Ibid.* II. *Ibid.*, 22: 289–298.

JOHNSON, L. P. 1944.† Euglenae of Iowa. Trans. Amer. Microsc. Soc., 63:
   97–135; Pls. 1–6.

JOLLOS, V. 1910. Dinoflagellatenstudien. Arch. f. Protist., 19: 178–206; Pls. 7–10.

JOST, L. 1895. Beiträge zur Kenntniss der Coleochaeteen. Ber. d. Deutsch. Bot.
   Ges., 13: 433–452; Pl. 34.

JUDAY, C. 1914. The inland lakes of Wisconsin. The hydrography and morphometry of the lakes. Bull. Wis. Geol. and Nat. Hist. Surv., 27 (Sci. Ser.
   No. 9): 1–137. 1934.* The depth distribution of some aquatic plants.
   Ecology, 15: 325. 1942. The summer standing crop of plants and animals
   in four Wisconsin lakes. Trans. Wis. Acad. Sci., Arts, and Letters, 34:
   103–135; Figs. 1–4.

JUDAY, C., and BIRGE, E. A. 1931. A second report on the phosphorus content
   of Wisconsin lake waters. Trans. Wis. Acad. Sci., Arts, and Letters, 26:
   353–382. 1941. Hydrography and morphometry of some northeastern Wisconsin lakes. *Ibid.*, 33: 21–72.

JUDAY, C., BIRGE, E. A., KEMMERER, G. I., and ROBINSON, R. J. 1927. Phosphorus content of lake waters of northeastern Wisconsin. Trans. Wis. Acad.
   Sci., Arts, and Letters, 23: 233–248.

JUDAY, C., BIRGE, E. A., and MELOCHE, V. W. 1935. The carbon dioxide and
   hydrogen ion content of the lake waters of northeastern Wisconsin. Trans.

Wis. Acad. Sci., Arts, and Letters, 29: 1–82. 1938. Mineral content of the lake waters of northeastern Wisconsin. *Ibid.*, 31: 223–276.

JUDAY, C., and SCHOMER, H. A. 1935.° The utilization of solar radiation by algae at different depths in lakes. Biol. Bull., 69: 75–81.

JÜRGENS, G. H. B. 1822. Algae aquaticae. Dec. XV.

JUST, L. 1822. *Phyllosiphon Arisari.* Bot. Zeit., 40: 1–8, 17–26, 33–47, 49–57; Pl. 1.

KAMMERER, G. 1938. Volvocalen und Protococcalen aus dem unteren Amazonasgebiet. Sitz. K. K. Akad. Wiss. Wien. Math.-Nat. Kl., 147(Abt. 1): 183–228.

KARSTEN, G. 1891. Untersuchungen ueber die Familie der Chroolepideen. Ann. Jard. Bot. Buitenzorg, 10: 1–66; Pls. 1–6.

KASANOWSKY, V., and SMIRNOFF, S. 1913. *Spirogyra borysthenica* n. sp. Oest. Bot. Zeit., 63: 137–141.

KATER, J. M. 1929. Morphology and division of *Chlamydomonas* with reference to the phylogeny of the flagellate neuro-motor system. Univ. Calif. Publ. Zool., 33: 125–168; Pls. 11–16; Figs. 1–7.

KEEFE, A. M. 1926. A preserving fluid for green plants. Science, 64(n.s.): 331–332. 1927. A new species of *Aphanocapsa*. Rhodora, 29: 39–41.

KEISSLER, K. VON. 1911. Untersuchungen über die Periodizität des Phytoplanktons des Leopoldsteiner-Sees in Steiermark, in Verbindung mit einer eingehenderen limnologischen Erforschung dieses Seebeckens. Arch. f. Hydrobiol. u. Planktonk., 6: 480–485.

KEMMERER, G., BOVARD, J. F., and BOORMAN, W. R. 1924. Northwestern lakes of the United States. Bull. U. S. Bur. Fish., 39: 51–140.

KENT, S. 1880–1882. (See Seville-Kent, W.)

KIENER, W. 1944. Notes on distribution and bio-ecology of Characeae in Nebraska. Butler Univ. Studies Bot., 6: 131–148.

KINDLE, E. M. 1915. Limestone solution on the bottom of Lake Ontario. Amer. Jour. Sci., 189: 651–656; Figs. 1–3.

KIRCHNER, O. 1878. Algen. *In* F. Cohn, Kryptogamen-Flora von Schlesien Breslau. 1900. Schizophyceae. *In* A. Engler and K. Prantl, Die Natürlichen Pflanzenfamilien. 1 Teil, Abt. 1a; 45–92. Leipzig.

KISSELEW, J. A. 1927. Zur Kenntnis der Algen des Aralsees. Bul. Bur. Appl Ichth., 5: 274–305. 1931. Zur Morphologie einiger neuer und seltener Vertreter des pflanzlichen Microplanktons. Arch. f. Protist., 73: 235–250.

KJELLMAN, F. R. 1898. Zur Organographie und Systematik der Aegagropilen. Nova Acta Reg. Soc. Sc. Upsala, 17(Ser. 3); No. 7: 1–26.

KLEBAHN, H. 1892. *Chaetosphaeridium Pringsheimii,* novum genus et nova species algarum chlorophycearum aquae dulcis. Pringsh. Jahrb. f. Wiss. Bot., 24: 268–282; Pl. 4. 1893. Zur Kritik einiger Algengattungen. *Ibid.* 25: 278–321; Pl. 14. 1895. Gasvacuolen, ein Bestandtheil der Zellen der wasserblüthebildenden Phycochromaceen. Flora, 80: 241–282; Pl. 4. 1896. Ueber wasserblüthebildende Algen, insbesondere des Plöner Seengebiets, und über das Vorkommen von Gasvacuolen bei den Phycochromaceen. Forsch. Biol. Stat. z. Plön, 4: 189–206. 1899. Die Befruchtung von *Sphaeroplea annulina* Ag. Festschr. f. Schwendener, 1899: 81–103; Pl. 5.

KLEBAHN, H., and LEMMERMANN, E. 1895. Vorarbeiten zu einer Flora des Plöner Seengebietes. I. Forsch. Biol. Stat. z. Plön, 3: 1–17.

KLEBS, G. 1881. Beiträge zur Kenntniss niederer Algenformen. Bot. Zeit., 39: 249–257, 265–272, 281–290, 297–308, 313–319, 329–336; Pls. 3, 4. 1883. Ueber die Organisation einiger Flagellatengruppen und ihre Beziehungen zu Algen und Infusorien. Untersuch. a. d. Bot. Inst. z. Tübingen, 1: 233–362;

Pls. 2, 3. 1892. Zur Physiologie der Fortpflanzung von *Vaucheria sessilis*. Ver. d. Naturf. Ges. z. Basel, 10(Heft 1): 45–72. 1893. Flagellatenstudien. I–II. Zeit. Wiss. Zool., 55: 265–351, 353–445; Pls. 17, 18. 1896. Die Bedingungen der Fortpflanzung bei einigen Algen und Pilzen. Jena. 1912. Ueber Flagellaten- und Algen- ähnliche Peridineen. Ver. Naturh. med. Vereins Heidelberg, 11(Heft 4): 367–451; Pl. 10; Figs. 1–15. 1928. Die Bedingungen der Fortpflanzung bei einigen Algen und Pilzen. Jena.

KLERCHER, J. 1896. Ueber zwei Wasserformen von *Stichococcus*. Flora, 82: 90–106.

KLYVER, F. D. 1929. Notes on the life history of *Tetraspora gelatinosa* (Vauch.) Desv. Arch. f. Protist., 66: 290–296; Pl. 8.

KOFOID, C. A. 1896, A report upon the Protozoa observed in Lake Michigan and the inland lakes in the neighborhood of Charlevoix, during the summer of 1894. Appendix II. In: Michigan Fish Comm. Bull. 6: 3-93. On *Pleodorina illinoisensis*, a new species from the plankton of the Illinois River. Bull. Ill. State Lab. Nat. Hist., 5: 273-293; Pls. 36, 37. 1899. Plankton studies. III. On *Platydorina*, a new genus of the family Volvocoidae, from the plankton of the Illinois River. *Ibid.*, 5: 419-440; Pl. 38. 1910. Plankton studies. V. The plankton of the Illinois River 1894-1899. Part. II. Constituent organisms and their seasonal distribution. *Ibid.*, 8: 1-361; Pls. 1-5. 1914. *Phytomorula regularis,* a symmetrical protophyte related to *Coelastrum*. Univ. Calif. Publ. Bot., 6: 35-40; Pl. 7.

KOFOID, C. A., and MICHENER, J. R. 1911. New genera and species of Dinoflagellates. Bull. Mus. Comp. Zool. (Harvard College), 54: 267–302.

KOFOID, C. A., and SWEZY, OLIVE. 1921. The free-living or unarmored Dinoflagellata. Mem. Univ. Calif., 5: 1–562; Pls. 1–12; Figs. A–VV.

KOLKWITZ, R., and KRIEGER, W. 1941. Zygnemales. *In* L. Rabenhorst, Kryptogamen-Flora von Deutschland, Oesterreich und der Schweiz. 13, Abt. 2, Lief. 1/2. Leipzig.

KOPPE, FRITZ. 1924. Die Schlammflora der ostholsteinischen Seen und des Bodensees. Arch. f. Hydrobiol., 14: 619–719.

KORSCHIKOV, A. A. 1917. Contribution à l'étude des algues de la Russie. Trav. Stat. Biol. Borodinskaja, 4: 219–267; Pl. 2. 1923. Zur Morphologie des geschlechtlichen Prozesses bei den Volvocales. (Russian with German summary.) Arch. Russ. Protist. 2: 179–194. 1924. Zur Morphologie und Systematik der Volvocales. (Russian with German summary.) *Ibid.*, 3: 45–56; Pl. 2. 1924a. Protistologische Beobachtungen. (Russian with German summary.) *Ibid.*, 3: 57–74. 1925. Beiträge zur Morphologie und Systematik der Volvocales. I. (Russian with German summary.) *Ibid.*, 4: 153–197; Pls. 7–9. 1925a. Contribution à l'étude des algues de la Russie. Rech. algol. aux environs de la station Biol. Borodinskaja pendant l'été 1925. 1927. On the validity of the genus *Schizomeris* Kütz. (Russian with English summary.) Arch. Russ. Protist., 6: 71–82; Pls. 5, 6. 1928. On two new Spondylomoraceae: *Pascheriella tetras* n. gen. et sp. and *Chlamydobotrys squarrosa* n. sp. Arch. f. Protist., 61: 233–238; Pl. 9; Figs. 1–5. 1928a. Notes on some new flagellates. (Russian and English.) *Ibid.*, 7: 151–158. 1937. On the sexual reproduction (oögamy) in the Micractineae. Kharkov A. Gorky State Univ. Book No. 10(1937): 109–126. 1941. On some new or little known flagellates. Arch. f. Protist., 95: 22–44.

KORSCHIKOV, A. A., and ANACHIN, I. K. 1928. [Contribution to the study of the validity of *Chlamydobotrys gracilis* Korsch.]. (Russian with English summary.) Arch. Russ. Protist., 7: 145–150.

KOSSINSKAJA, C. 1940. Die Algen des Neva Beckens. Akad. nauk S.S.R.R., Leningrad. Bot. Inst. Trudy, Ser. 2, Plantae Crypt. (Acta Inst. Bot. Acad.

Sci. URSS), 4(1938): 83–106. 1940a. [Algae from the environments of Jukki]. (Russian with English summary.) *Ibid.*, 4(1938): 107–130.

Kozminski, Z. 1938. Amount and distribution of the chlorophyll in some lakes of northeastern Wisconsin. Trans. Wis. Acad. Sci., Arts and Letters, 31: 411–438.

Krieger, W. 1932. Untersuchungen über Plankton-Chrysomonaden. Die Gattungen *Mallomonas* und *Dinobryon* in monographischer Bearbeitung. Bot. Arch., 29: 257–329.

Krogh, August. 1931. Dissolved substances as food of aquatic organisms. Biol. Rev. and Biol. Proc. Cambridge Phil. Soc., 6: 412–442.

Kuehn, J. 1878. Ueber eine neue parasitische Alge, *Phyllosiphon Arisari*. Sitz. Natur. Ges. Halle, 1878: 24–26.

Kuehne, Paul E. 1941 The phytoplankton of southern and central Saskatchewan. Part II. Can. Jour. Res., 19 (Sec. C): 313–322; Figs. 1–3.

Kuetzing, F. T. 1833. Algologische Mittheilungen. I. Ueber *Gloionema* Agh. II. Ueber eine neue Gattung der Confervaceen. Flora, 16: 513–528. 1833a. Beitrag zur Kenntniss über die Entstehung und Metamorphose der niedern vegetabilischen Organismen, etc. Linnaea, 8: 335–382. 1833b. Synopsis Diatomacearum oder Versuch einer systematischen Zusammenstellung der Diatomeen. *Ibid.*, 8: 529–620. 1833–1835. Algarum dulcis germanicarum. Dec. I–XVI. Halis Saxorum. 1835. Description de quelques nouvelles espéces de *Chara*. Ann. Sci. Nat. Bot., 3(Sér. 2): 64. 1839. Ueber ein neues *Botrydium*. Nova Acta Acad. Caes. Leop.-Carol., 19: 385. 1843.† Phycologia generalis, oder Anatomie, Physiologie und Systemkunde der Tange. 458 pp.; Pls. 1–80. Leipzig. 1843a. Ueber die Systematische Eintheilung der Algen. Linnaea, 17: 75–107. 1845. Phycologia germanica, d. i. Deutschlands Algen in bündigen Beschreibungen. 340 pp. Nordhausen. 1847. Diagnosen und Bemerkungen zu neuen oder kritischen Algen. Bot. Zeit., 5: 164–167. 1846–1871. Tabulae phycologicae oder Abbildungen der Tange. I–XIX; Pls. 1–1900. Nordhausen. 1849. Species algarum. 922 pp. Leipzig.

Kufferath, H. 1913. Contribution à la physiologie d'une Protococcacée nouvelle *Chlorella luteo-viridis* Chodat, nov. spec. var. *lutescens* Chodat, nov. var. Rec. Inst. Léo Errera, 9: 114–319; Figs. 1–28. 1914–1915. Contributions à la flore du Luxembourg meridional. II. Chlorophycées (exclus. Desmidiacées), Flagellates et Cyanophycées. Ann. Biol. Lacustre, 7: 231–271.

Kurssanow, L. J., and Schemakhanova, N. M. 1927. Sur la succession des phases nucléaire chez les algues vertes. I. Le cycle de développement du *Chlorochytrium Lemnae* Cohn. Arch. Russ. Protist., 6: 131–146; Pls. 9, 10; Figs. 1, 2.

Kylin, H. 1912. Studien über die schwedischen Arten der Gattungen *Batrachospermum* Roth und *Sirodotia* nov. gen. Nova Acta. Reg. Soc. Sci. Upsala, 3(Ser. 4), No. 3: 1–40. 1917. Ueber die Entwicklungsgeschichte von *Batrachospermum moniliforme*. Ber. d. Deutsch. Bot. Ges., 35: 155–170.

Lackey, James B. 1936. Some fresh water protozoa with blue chromatophores. Biol. Bull., 71: 492–497. 1939. Notes on plankton flagellates from the Scioto River. Lloydia, 2: 128–143. 1940. Limitations of Euglenidae as polluted water indicators. U. S. Publ. Health Rep., 55(No. 7): 268–280; Figs. 1–6. 1944.* Quality and quantity of plankton in the south end of Lake Michigan in 1942. Jour. Amer. Water Works Assoc., 36: 669–674; Figs. 1–7.

Lagerheim, G. 1882. Bidrag till kännedomen om Stockholmstraktens Pediastéer, Protococcacéer och Palmellacéer. Oefv. Kongl. Sv. Vet.-Akad. Förhandl., 39(No. 2): 47–81; Pls. 2, 3. 1883. Bidrag till Sveriges algflora. *Ibid.*,

40(No. 2): 37–78; Pl. 1. 1884. Ueber *Phaeothamnion,* eine neue Gattung unter den Süsswasseralgen. Bih. Kongl. Sv. Vet.-Akad. Handl., 9(No. 19): 3–14; 1 pl. 1886. Algologiska bidrag. I. Contributions algologiques à la flora de la Suède. Bot. Notiser, 1886: 44–50. 1887. Note sur l'*Uronema,* nouveau genre des algues d'eau douce de l'ordre des Chlorozoosporacées. Malpighia, 1: 517–523; Pl. 12. 1887a. Zur Entwickelungsgeschichte einiger Confervacéen. Ber. d. Deutsch. Bot. Ges., 5: 409–417. 1887b. Ueber einige Algen aus Cuba, Jamaica und Puerto-Rico. Bot. Notiser, 1887: 193–199. 1888. Sopra alcune alghe d'acqua dolce nuovo o rimarchevoli. Notarisia, 1888: 590–595. 1889. Studien über die Gattung *Conferva* und *Microspora.* Flora, 72: 179–210; Pls. 5, 6. 1890. Contribuciones a la flora algológica del Ecuador. I–II. Anal. Univ. Central de Quito, Ecuador, 4(1890–1891): 79–88. 1892. Die Schneeflora des Pichincha. Ber. d. Deutsch. Bot. Ges., 10: 517–534; Pl. 28. 1893. Chlorophyceen aus Abessinien und Kordofan. Nuova Notarisia, 4: 153–160. 1895. Studien über die arktische Cryptogamen. 1. Ueber die Entwickelung von *Tetraëdron* Kütz. und *Euastropsis* Lagerh., eine neue Gattung der Hydrodictyaceen. Tromsö Mus. Aarschefter, 17(1894): 1–24. 1900. Vegetabilisches Süsswasser-Plankton aus der Bareninseln (Beeren-Eiland). Bih. Kongl. Sv. Vet.-Akad. Handl., 26, Afd. 3, No. 11: 1–25.

LAGLER, KARL. 1940. A turtle loss? Amer. Wildlife, 29: 41–44. 1943. Food habits and economic relations of the turtles of Michigan with special reference to fish management. Amer. Midl. Nat., 29: 257–312.

LAMBERT, F. D. 1909. Two new species of *Characium.* Rhodora, 11: 65–74.

LAPHAM, I. A. 1850.* Plants of Wisconsin. Proc. Amer. Assoc. Adv. Sci., 1849: 19–59.

LARSEN, E. 1904. The fresh water algae of East Greenland. Medd. om Grönland, 30(B): 75–100.

LAUTERBORN, R. 1896. Diagnosen neuer Protozoen aus dem Gebiete des Oberrheins. Zool. Anz., 19: 14–18. 1899. Protozoenstudien. Flagellaten aus dem Gebiete des Oberrheins. Zeit. Wiss. Zool., 65: 365–391; Pls. 17, 18. 1913. Zur Kenntnis einiger sapropelischer Schizomyceten. Allg. Bot. Zeitschr., 19: 97–100. 1913a. Süsswasserfauna. Handwört. Naturwiss., 9: 861–920. 1914–1917. Die Sapropelische Lebewelt. Ver. Natur. mediz. Ver. Heidelberg, 13: 395–481.

LEAKE, DOROTHY V. 1938. Preliminary note on the production of motile cells in *Basicladia.* Proc. Okla. Acad. Sci., 19: 109–110.

LEBOUR, MARIE V. 1925. The dinoflagellates of northern seas. Plymouth, Eng.

LEFÈVRE, M. 1925. Contribution à la flore des algues d'eau douce du nord de la France. Bull. Soc. Bot. France, 72 (Vol. 1, Ser. 5): 689–699. 1932. Monographie des espèces d'eau douce du genre *Peridinium.* Arch. d. Bot., 2(1928, Mém. 5): 1–210. 1932a. Sur la structure de la membrane des Euglènes du groupe, *Spirogyra.* Comp. Rend. Acad. Sci. Paris, 195: 1308–1309.

LEFÈVRE, M., and BOURRELLY, P. 1939. Sur la stabilité de l'ornamentation chez les espèces du genre *Pediastrum* Meyen. Comp. Rend. Acad. Sci. Paris, 208: 368–370.

LEMMERMANN, E. 1895. Verzeichnis der in der Umgegend von Ploen gesammelten Algen. Forsch. Biol. Stat. z. Plön, 3: 18–67. 1896. Zweiter Beitrag zur Algenflora des Plöner Seengebietes. *Ibid.,* 4: 134–188. 1896a. Zur Algenflora des Riesengebirges. *Ibid.,* 4: 88–133. 1897. Die Planktonalgen des Müggelsees bei Berlin. II. Zeit. f. Fisch., 1897: 177–188. 1897a. Resultate einer biologischen Untersuchungen von Forellenteichen. Forsch. Biol. Stat. z. Plön, 5: 67–114. 1898. Der grosse Waternerstorfer Binnensee. Eine biologische Studie. *Ibid.,* 6: 166–204. 1898a. Beitrag zur Algenflora von

Schlesien. Abh. Natur. Ver. Bremen, 14(1897): 241–263; Pl. 1. 1898b. Algologische Beiträge. IV–V. *Ibid.*, 14: 501–512; Pl. 5. 1898c. Beiträge zur Kenntniss der Planktonalgen. I. *Golenkinia* Chodat, *Richteriella* Lemm., *Franceia* nov. gen., *Phythelios* Frenzel, *Lagerheimia* Chodat, *Chodatella* nov. gen., *Schroederia* nov. gen. Hedwigia, 37: 303–312; Pl. 10. 1898d. Beiträge zur Kenntniss der Planktonalgen. II. Beschreibung neuer Formen. Bot. Centralbl., 76: 150–156. 1899.† Das Genus *Ophiocytium* Naegeli. Hedwigia, 38: 20–38; Pls. 3, 4; Figs. 15–18. 1899a. Das Phytoplankton sächsischer Teiche. Forsch. Biol. Stat. z. Plön, 7: 96–140; Pls. 1, 2. 1900. Ergebnisse einer Reise nach dem Pacific (H. Schauinsland 1896–1897) Planktonalgen. Abh. Natur. Ver. Bremen, 16(1899): 313–398. 1900a. Beiträge zur Kenntniss der Planktonalgen. III. Neue Schwebalgen aus der umgegend von Berlin. Ber. d. Deutsch. Bot. Ges., 18: 24–32. 1900b. Beiträge zur Kenntniss der Planktonalgen. IV. Die Coloniebildung von *Richteriella botryoides* (Schmidle) Lemm. *Ibid.*, 18: 90–91; Pl. 3. 1900c. Beiträge zur Kenntniss der Planktonalgen. VIII. Peridiniales aquae dulcis et submarinae, Hedwigia, 39: [115–121]. 1900d. Beiträge zur Kenntniss der Planktonalgen. VI. Das Phytoplankton brackischer Gewasser Ber.d.Deutsch.Bot.Ges.,18:90–94. IX. *Lagerheimia Marssonii* nov. spec., *Centratractus belonophora* (Schmidle) nov. gen. et sp., *Synedra limnetica* nov. spec., *Marssoniella elegans* nov. gen. et sp. Ber. d. Deutsch. Bot. Ges., 18: 272–275. 1900e. Beiträge zur Kenntniss der Planktonalgen. XI. Die Gattung *Dinobryon* Ehrenb. *Ibid.*, 18: 500–524; Pls. 18, 19. 1901. Beiträge zur Kenntniss der Planktonalgen. XII. Notizen über einige Schwebalgen. *Ibid.*, 19: 85–92. 1901a. Beiträge zur Kenntniss der Planktonalgen. XIII. Das Phytoplankton des Ryck und des Greifswalder Boddens. *Ibid.*, 19: 92–95. 1901b. Beiträge zur Kenntniss der Planktonalgen. XIV. Neue Flagellaten aus Italien. *Ibid.*, 19: 340–348. 1901c. Zur Kenntnis der Algenflora des Saaler Boddens. Forsch. Biol. Stat. z. Plön, 8: 74–85. 1901d. Algenflora eines Moortümpels bei Plön. *Ibid.*, 8: 64–73. 1902. Bericht der Commission für die Flora von Deutschland. VI. Algen des Süsswassers. Ber. d. Deutsch. Bot. Ges., 20: [243–253, 257–263]. 1903. Beiträge zur Kenntnis der Planktonalgen. XV. Das Phytoplankton einiger Plöner Seen. Forsch. Biol. Stat. z. Plön, 10: 116–176. 1903a. Brandenburgische Algen. Hedwigia, 42: [168–169]. 1903b. Brandenburgische Algen. II. Das Phytoplankton des Müggelsees und einer benachbarter Gewässer. Zeit. f. Fisch., 11(Heft 2): 73–123. 1903c. Beiträge zur Kenntnis der Planktonalgen. XVI. Phytoplankton voh Sandhem (Schweden). Bot. Notiser, 1903: 65–69. 1903d. Das Phytoplankton des Meeres. II. Beitrag. Abh. Natur. Ver. Bremen, 17: 341–418. 1904. Das Plankton schwedischer Gewasser. Arkiv f. Bot., 2, No. 2(1903–1904): 1–209; Pls. 1, 2. 1904a. Beiträge zur Kenntnis der Planktonalgen. XIX. Das Phytoplankton der Ausgrabenseen bei Plön. Forsch. Biol. Stat. z. Plön, 11: 289–311; Figs. 1–17. 1904b. Beiträge zur Kenntnis der Planktonalgen. XVIII. Ueber die Entstehung neuer Planktonformen. Ber. d. Deutsch. Bot. Ges., 22: 17–22. 1905. Brandenburgishe Algen. III. Neue Formen. Forsch. Biol. Stat. z. Plön, 12: 145–153. 1905a. Beiträge zur Kenntnis der Planktonalgen. XX. Phytoplankton aus Schlesien. *Ibid.*, 12: 154–163. 1905b. Beiträge zur Kenntnis der Planktonalgen. XXI. Das Phytoplankton sächsischer Teiche. Zweiter Beitrag. *Ibid.*, 12: 164–168. 1905c. Die Algenflora der Sandwich-Inseln. Ergebnisse einer Reise nach dem Pacific. H. Shauinsland 1896/97. Engler. Bot. Jahrb., 34: 607–663; Pls. 7, 8. 1906. Ueber die von Herrn Dr. Walter Volz auf seiner Weltreise gesammelten Süsswasseralgen. Abh. Natur. Ver. Bremen, 18 (1905–1906): 143–174; Pl. 11. 1906a. Das Phytoplankton des Meeres. Beih Bot. Centralbl.,

19(Heft 2): 1–74. 1906b. Beiträge zur Kenntnis der Planktonalgen. Ber. d. Deutsch. Bot. Ges., 24: 535–538. 1906c. Uber das Vorkommen von Süsswasserformen in Phytoplankton des Meeres. Arch. f. Hydrobiol. u. Planktonk., 1: 409–427. 1907. Das Plankton der Weser bei Bremen. *Ibid.*, 2: 393–447. 1907a. Das plankton des Jang-tse-Kiang (China). *Ibid.*, 2: 534–544. 1907b. Brandenburgische Algen. IV. *Gonyaulax palustris,* eine neue Süsswasser-Peridinee. Beih. Bot. Centralbl., 21: 296–300. 1907–1910.† Kryptogamenflora der Mark Brandenburg. Algen. I. Leipzig. 1908. Algologische Beiträge. VI. Algen aus der Biviera von Lentini (Sizilien). VII. Ueber Scheidenbildung bei *Oscillatoria Agardhii* Gomont. VII. Zur Algenflora des Anapo. IX. Neue Schizophyceen. X. Die Micrasterias-Formen des Königreichs Sachsen. XI. *Oedogonium cardiacum* var. *minor* Lemm. nov. var. Arch. f. Hydrobiol. u. Planktonk., 4: 165–192; Pl. 5. 1908a. Beiträge zur Kenntnis der Planktonalgen. XXIII. Das Phytoplankton des Lago di Varano und des Lago di Monate (Italien). *Ibid.*, 3: 349–386; Figs. 1–25. 1908b. Beiträge zur Kenntnis der Planktonalgen. XXIV. Plankton aus Schlesien. 2 Beitrag. *Ibid.*, 3: 386–404; Figs. 26–35. 1908c. Beiträge zur Kenntnis der Planktonalgen. XXV. Die Algen Stralsunder Rohwassers. *Ibid.*, 3: 404–410; Figs. 36–40. 1908d. Das Phytoplankton des Menam. Hedwigia, 48: 126–139. 1910 (1907–1910). Kryptogamenflora der Mark Brandenburg. Algen. I. Leipzig. 1913.† Euglenineae. Flagellatae II. *In* A. Pascher, Die Süsswasserflora Deutschlands, Oesterreichs und der Schweiz. Heft 2. Flagellatae 2: 115–174; Figs. 181–377. Jena. 1914. Algologische Beiträge. XII. Die Gattung *Characiopsis* Borzi. Abh. Natur. Ver. Bremen, 23: 249–261; Figs. 1–14. 1915.† Tetrasporales. *In* A. Pascher, Die Süsswasserflora Deutschlands. Oesterreichs und der Schweiz. Heft 5. Chlorophyceae 2: 21–51; Figs. 1–33. Jena.

LEONHARDI, H. VON. 1863. Die böhmischen Characeen. Lotos, 13: 55–80, 110–111.

LEVANDER, K. M. 1900. Der Kenntniss der Lebens in den stehenden Kleinigewässern auf den Skäreninseln. Acta Soc. Fauna et Flora Fenn., 18(No. 6): 1–107. 1901. Beiträge zur Fauna und Algenflora der sussen Gewässer an der Murmanküste. *Ibid.*, 20(No. 8): 1–35.

LEVERETT, FRANK. 1911. Surface geology of the Northern Peninsula of Michigan. Mich. Geol. and Biol. Surv. Publ. No. 5: 1–86. 1917. Surface geology and agricultural conditions of Michigan. *Ibid.*, No. 25(Geol. Ser. 21): 1–223.

LEWIS, I. F. 1913.* *Chlorochromonas minuta,* a new flagellate from Wisconsin. Arch. f. Protist., 32: 249–256; Pl. 12. 1925. A new conjugate from Woods Hole. Amer. Jour. Bot., 12: 351–357; Pls. 36, 37.

LEWIS, I. F., ZIRKLE, C., and PATRICK, RUTH. 1933. Algae of Charlottesville and vicinity. Jour. Elisha Mitchell Sci. Soc., 48: 207–222.

LEY, S. H. 1947. Heleoplanktonic algae of North Kwangtung. Bot. Bull. Acad. Sinica, 1: 270–282; Figs. 1a–1h.

LI, L. C. 1933. New species and varieties of freshwater algae from China. Ohio Jour. Sci., 33: 151–154.

LIEBMANN, F. 1841. Bemärkninger og Tilläg til den danske Algeflora. Kröyers Tidsk., 1841. Kjobenhavn. 1841a. Algologisk Bidrag. Kjobbenhavn. (Not seen.)

LILLEY, GENE. 1903. *Nitella batrachosperma* in Minnesota. Minn. Bot. Studies, 3: 79–82; Pl. 18.

LILLICK, LOIS C. 1935. A new species of *Spirulina.* Amer. Midl. Nat., 16: 210–211; Figs. 1A–1D.

LINDEMAN, RAYMOND L. 1941. Seasonal food cycle dynamics in a senescent lake. Amer. Midl. Nat., 26: 636–673. 1942. The trophic-dynamic aspect of ecology. Ecology, 23: 399–418.

LINDEMANN, E. 1925. Ueber finnische Peridineen. Arch. f. Hydrobiol. u. Plankt-tonk., 15: 1–4. 1928. Vorläufige Mitteilung. Arch. f. Protist., 63: 259–260. 1928a. Peridineae (Dinoflagellatae). *In* A. Engler and K. Prantl, Die Natürlichen Pflanzenfamilien. 2: 1–104; Figs. 1–92. 2nd. ed. Leipzig.

LINK, H. F. 1809. Nova plantarum genera e classe Lichenum, Algarum, Fungorum. Schrader's Neue Journal f. die Botanik, 3(Stück 1): 1–19. 1820. Epistola de Algis aquaticis in genera disponendis. *In* C. G. H. Nees von Esenbeck, Horae physicae berolinenses, pp. 1–8. 1833. Handbuch zur Erkennung der nutzbarsten und am häufigsten vorkommenden Gewachse, Dritter Teil. Berlin.

LINNAEUS, CARL VON. 1737. Genera plantarum. Leiden. 1753. Species plantarum. Stockholm., 1754. Genera plantarum. 5th ed. 1758. Systema naturae. Regnum animale. Vol. I. 10th ed. Leipzig.

LOBIK, A. I. 1915. Catalogue des algues d'eau douce recueillies au Caucase par A. A. Elenkin et V. P. Savicz dans la région Czernomorsk pendant l'été 1912. Bull. Jard. Imp. Bot. Pierre le Grand, 15(No. 1): 23–47.

LOHMAN, H. 1911. Ueber das Nannoplankton und die Zentrifugierung kleinster Wasserproben zur Gewinnung desselben in lebenden Zustande. Inter. Rev. Ges. Hydrobiol. u. Hydrogr., 4(Pt. 1/2): 1–38.

LOISELEUR-DESLONGCHAMPS, J. L. A. 1810. Notice sur les plantes à ajouter à la flore de France, pp. 135–139. Paris.

LOWE, C. W. 1927. Some freshwater algae of southern Quebec. Trans. Roy. Soc. Canada, 5: 291–316.

LUCKS, R. 1907. Zur Kenntnis der westpreussischen Pediastrumarten. Jahrb. d. Westpr. Lehrevereins f. Naturk., 1906–1907: 31–49.

LUND, J. W. G. 1947. Observations on soil algae. III. Species of *Chlamydomonas* Ehr. in relation to variability within the genus. New Phytol., 46(2): 185–194; Figs. 1–3.

LYMAN, F. E. 1936.* Plankton of inland waters. Mich. State College Agric. Appl. Sci. Eng., Exper. Sta., Bull. No. 66: 20–24.

LYNGBYE, H. CH. 1819. Tentamen Hydrophytologiae Danicae. Kjobenhavn.

MACMILLAN, CONWAY. 1894. *Sphaeroplea annulina* in Minnesota. Bot. Gaz., 19: 246.

MAGNUS, P. 1883. Das Auftreten von *Aphanizomenon flos-aquae* (L.) Ralfs in Eise bei Berlin. Ber. d. Deutsch. Bot. Ges., 1: 129–132.

MAINX, F. 1926. Einige neue Vertreter der Gattung *Euglena* Ehr. Arch. f. Protist., 54: 150–182. 1928. Beiträge zur Morphologie und Physiologie der Eugleninen. I. *Ibid.*, 60: 305–414; Pl. 10.

MANGIN, L. 1911. Modifications de la curiasse chez quelques Péridiniens. Inter. Rev. Ges. f. Hydrobiol. u. Hydrogr., 4: 44–54; Pls. 7, 8.

MANNING, W. M., and JUDAY, C. 1941. The chlorophyll content and productivity of some lakes in northeastern Wisconsin. Trans. Wis. Acad. Sci., Arts and Letters, 33: 363–393.

MANNING, W. M., JUDAY, C., and WOLF, MICHAEL. 1938. Photosynthesis of aquatic plants at different depths in Trout Lake, Wisconsin. Trans. Wis. Acad. Sci., Arts and Letters, 31: 377–410.

MARSH, C. D: 1903.* The plankton of Lake Winnebago and Green Lake. Bull. Wis. Geol. and Nat. Hist. Surv., 12, Sci. Ser., No. 3: 1–94.

MARSHALL, F. T., and HAGUE, S. M. 1938. *Basicladia* in Illinois. Trans. Ill. Acad. Sci., 31: 111–112.

MARTIUS, C. F. P. VON. 1817. Flora cryptogamica Erlangensis. Nuremberg.

MASKELL, W. M. 1887. On the fresh-water infusoria of the Wellington district. Trans. N. Z. Inst., 20: 3–19.

[639]

MASSEE, G. 1891. Life-history of a stipitate freshwater alga. Jour. Linn. Soc. Bot., 27: 457–462.

MENEGHINI, G. 1837. Conspectus algologiae euganeae. 37 pp. Patavia. 1840. Synopsis Desmidiacearum hucusque cognitarum. Linnaea, 14: 201–240. 1842. Monographia Nostochinearum italicarum. Aug. Taurinorum. (Not seen.)

MESSIKOMMER, ED. 1927. Biologische Studien im Torfmoor von Robenhausen unter besondere Berücksichtigung der Algenvegetation. Mitt. Bot. Mus. Univ. Zürich, 122: 1–171.

MEUNIER, A. 1919. Microplankton de la Mer Flamande. Part III. Les Péridiniens. Mém. Mus. Roy. Hist. Nat. Belgique, 8(No 1): 1–116.

MEYEN, F. J. F. 1829. Beobachtungen über einige niedere Algenformen. Nova Acta Acad. Caes. Leop.-Carol., 14: 768–778. 1838. Neues System Pflanzen-Physiologie. Bd. 2. Berlin. 1839. Jahresberichte über die Resultate der Arbeiten im Felde der physiologischen Botanik von dem Jahre 1838. Arch. f. Naturg., 2: 1–153.

MEYER, A. 1895. Ueber den Bau von *Volvox aureus* Ehrenb. und *Volvox globator* Ehrenb. Bot. Centralbl., 63: 225–233; Figs. 1–4. 1896. Die Plasmaverbindungen und die Membranen von *Volvox globator, aurens* und *tertius* mit Rücksicht auf die thierischen Zellen. Bot. Zeit., 54: 187–217; Pl. 8; Figs. 1–7.

MEYER, C. I. 1922. Algae nonnullae novae baicalenses. Not. Syst. Inst. Crypt. Horti Bot. Petropol., 1(No. 1): 13–15. 1930. Einige neue Algenformen des Baikalsees. Arch. f. Protist., 72: 158–172.

MEYER, K. I. (See Meyer, C. I.)

MIGULA, W. 1907. In Thome, Kryptogamen-Flora Deutschland, Deutsch-Oesterreich und der Schweiz, 6, Kryptogamen 2, Algen 1. Gera.

MILLER, V. V. 1923. Zur Systematik der Gattung *Anabaena* Bory. Arch. Russ. Protist., 2: 116–126; Figs. 1–5.

MOEBIUS, M. 1888. Beitrag zur Kenntniss der Algengattung *Chaetopeltis* Berthold. Ber. d. Deutsch. Bot. Ges., 6: 242–248; Pl. 12. 1888a. Ueber einige in Portorico gesammelte Süsswasser- und Luft-Algen. Hedwigia, 27: 221–249. 1889. Bearbeitung der von H. Schenck in Brasilien gesammelten Algen. *Ibid.*, 28: 309–347. 1892. Australische Süsswasseralgen. Flora, 75: 421–450. 1894. Australische Süsswasseralgen. II. Abh. Senck. Natur. Ges. Frankfurt A. M., 18: 309–350. 1895. Beitrag zur Kenntniss der Algengattung *Pithophora*. Ber. d. Deutsch. Bot. Ges., 13: 356–361.

MOEWUS, FRANZ. 1935. Ueber einige Volvocalen aus dem Geogenfelder Moor (Erzgebirge). Sitz. Abh. Naturwis. Ges. Isis in Dresden, 1933–1934: 45–51; Figs. 1–6. 1936. Neue Volvocalen aus der Umgebung von Coimbra (Portugal). Bol. Soc. Broteriana, 10: 1–14; Figs. 1–6 (reprint).

MOLISCH, H. 1896. Die Ernährung der Algen (Süsswasseralgen II. Abhandlung). Sitz. Kais. Akad. Wiss. in Wien, Math.-Nat. Kl., 105(Abt. 1): 633–648.

MOORE, G. T. 1897. Notes on *Uroglena americana*. Bot. Gaz., 23: 105–112; Pl. 10. 1900. New or little known unicellular algae. I. (*Chlorocystis Cohnii*). *Ibid.*, 30: 100–112. 1901. *Ibid.* II. (*Eremosphaera viridis, Excêntrosphaera*). *Ibid.*, 32: 309–325. 1917. *Chlorochytrium gloeophilum* Bohlin. Ann. Missouri Bot. Gard., 4: 271–278; Pl. 18.

MOORE, G. T., and CARTER, NELLIE. 1923. Algae from lakes in the northeastern part of North Dakota. Ann. Missouri Bot. Gard., 10: 393–422; Pl. 21.

MOORE, G. T., and KELLERMANN, K. F. 1904. A method of destroying or preventing the growth of algae and certain pathogenic bacteria in water supplies. U. S. Dept. Agric., Bur. Plant Indust., Bull. 64. Washington. 1905. Copper as an algacide and disinfectant in water supplies. *Ibid.*, Bull. 76. Washington.

MOROSOWA-WODJANITZKAJA, N. W. 1925. Dichomologischen Reihen als Grundlage zur Klassification der Gattung *Pediastrum* Meyen. Russkii Ark. Protot., 4(No. 1/2): 5–31.

MORREN, CH. 1830. Mémoire sur un végétal microscopique d'un nouveau genre, proposé sous le nomme *Microsoter*, ou conservateur des petites choses. Ann. Sci. Nat. Bot., 20(Sér. 1): 404–426. 1838. Recherches physiologiques sur les hydrophytes de la Belgique. Premier Mémoire. Histoire d'un genre nouveau de la tribu Confervées, nommé par l'auteur, Aphanizomène. Mém. Acad. Roy. Belgique, 11: 5–20 (in unnumbered memoirs in vol.), 1 pl.

MUELLER, O. F. 1773. Vermium terrestrium et fluviatilium. Hauniae, Faber. 1776. Zoologiae Danicae prodromus, seu animalium Daniae et Norvegiae indigenarum characteres, nomina et synonyma imprimis populorium. Havnia, Hallogeriis. 1786. Animalicula infusoria, fluviatilia et marina. Hafniae et Lipsiae.

MURRAY, GEORGE. 1892–1895.* Calcareous pebbles formed by algae. Phycol. Mem., Part II(No. 13): 74–77.

NAEGELI, C. W. 1847. Die neuern Algensysteme und Versuch zur Begründung eines eignen Systems der Algen und Florideen. Zurich. 1849.† Gattungen einzelligen Algen, physiologische und systematische bearbeitet. 137 pp.; Pls. 1–8. Zurich.

NAMYSLOWSKI, B. 1921. Studja Hydrobiologiczne. III. Prace Koniisji Matew.-Przyrod. Tow. Pizyinc. Nauk. w. Pozanaiu. Ser. B. 1, z. 1(1921). Poznaɔ. (Not seen.)

NAYAL. *See* El-Nayal.

NEEDHAM, J. G., and LLOYD, J. T. 1916. The life of inland waters. Ithaca, N. Y.

NEEDHAM, J. G., and NEEDHAM, P. R. 1938. A guide to the study of freshwater biology with special reference to aquatic insects and other invertebrate animals and phytoplankton. 4th ed. Ithaca, N. Y.

NEEL, J. K. 1948.* A limnological investigation of the psammon in Douglas Lake, Michigan, with especial reference to shoal and shoreline dynamics. Trans. Amer. Microsc. Soc., 67: 1–53.

NICHOLS, G. E., and ACKLEY, ALMA B. 1932.* The desmids of Michigan with particular reference to the Douglas Lake region. Pap. Mich. Acad. Sci., Arts, and Letters, 15(1931): 113–140.

NISHIMURA, M. 1923. The theory of the spherical thallus formation of *Aegagropila Sauteri* (Nees) Kuetz. Bot. Mag. Tokyo, 37: 62.

NORDSTEDT, [C. F.] O. 1876. *In* C. F. O. Nordstedt & V. Wittrock. 1876. I Desmidieae (Kütz.) De Bar. Oef. Kongl. Sv. Vet-Akad. Förhandl., 33 (No. 6): 25–44. 1877. Bohusläns Oedogonieer. *Ibid.*, 34(No. 4) 21–33. 1878. De Algis aquae dulcis et de Characeis ex insulis sandvicencibus a Sv. Berggren 1875 reportatis. Minnesskr. Fys. Sallsk. Lund, 7: 1–24; Pls. 1, 2. 1879. Algologiska smäsaker, II. *Vaucheria*-studier. 1879. Bot. Notiser, 1879: 177–190. 1888. Freshwater algae collected by Dr. S. Berggren in New Zealand and Australia. Bih. Kongl. Sv. Vet.-Akad. Handl., 22(No. 8): 1–98. 1891. On the value of original specimens (translated from Botaniska Notiser, 1891: 76–82). Nuova Notarisia, 1891: 449–454.

NORDSTEDT, C. F. O., and WITTROCK, V. 1876. Desmidieae et Oedogonieae ab O. Nordstedt in Italia et Tyrolia collectae, quas determinaverunt. Oef. Kongl. Sv. Vet.-Akad. Förhandl., 33(No. 6): 25–56; Pls. 12, 13.

NOWAKOWSKI, L. 1877. Beitrag zur Kenntnis der Chytridiaceen. Beitr. Biol. Pflanzen, 2(No. 1): 73–100.

[641]

Nygaard, G. 1932. Contributions to our knowledge of the freshwater algae and phytoplankton from the Transvaal. Trans. Roy. Soc. S. Africa, 20: 101–148. 1949. Hydrobiological studies on some Danish ponds and lakes. Kongl. Danske Vid. Selsk. Biol. Skrift., 7(No. 1): 1–293; 126 figs.

Oersted, A. S. de. 1842. Beretning om en Excursion til Trindelen, en alluvialdannelse i Odensefjord. Kjobenhavn.

Ohashi, H. 1926. Oedogonium nebraskensis (sic), sp. nov. Bot. Gaz., 82: 207–214; Figs. 1–20.

Olive, Edgar W. 1905.* Notes on the occurrence of Oscillatoria prolifica (Greville) Gomont in the ice of Pine Lake, Waukesha County. Trans. Wis. Acad. Sci., Arts and Letters, 15(Pt. 1): 124–134.

Oltmanns, F. 1922.† Morphologie und Biologie der Algen. Vol. 1: 1–459; Figs. 1–287; Vol. 2: 1–439; Figs. 288–612; Vol. 3: 1–558; Figs. 613–797. 2nd ed. Jena.

Osorio Tafall, B. F. 1941. Materiales para el estudio del microplankton del Lago de Patzcuaro (México). I. General idades y fitoplankton. Anal. Escuela Nac. Cien. Biol. (México), 2: 331–382.

Ostenfeld, C. H. 1907. Beiträge zur Kenntnis der Algenflora des Kosogol-Beckens in der nordwestlichen Mongolei, mit spezieller Berüchsichtigung des Phytoplanktons. Hedwigia, 46: 365–420. 1909. Notes on the phytoplankton of Victoria Nyanza, East Africa. Bull. Mus. Comp. Zool. (Harvard College), 52(No. 10): 171–181.

Ostenfeld, C. H., and Nygaard, G. 1925. On the phytoplankton of the Gatun Lake, Panama Canal. Dansk Bot. Arch., 4: 1–16; Figs. 1–20.

Oye, P. van. 1924. Note sur l'Euglena acus Ehrenberg. Bull. Soc. Bot. Belgique, 56, Fasc. 2(1921–1923): 124–132.

Palla, E. 1894. Ueber eine neue, pyrenoidlose Art und Gattung der Conjugaten. Ber. d. Deutsch. Bot. Ges., 12: 228–236; Pl. 18.

Palmer, C. Mervin. 1941. A study of Lemanea with notes on its distribution in North America. Butler Univ. Studies, 5: 1–26; Figs. 1–4.

Palmer, T. C. 1905. Delaware valley forms of Trachelomonas. Proc. Acad. Nat. Sci. Phila., 57: 665–675. 1925. Trachelomonas: New or notable species and varieties. Ibid., 77: 15–22.

Papenfuss, G. F. 1946. Proposed names for the phyla of algae. Bull. Torr. Bot. Club, 73(3): 217–218.

Pascher, A. 1909. Einige neue Chrysomonaden. Ber. d. Deutsch. Bot. Ges., 27: 247–254. 1910.' Neue Chrysomonaden aus den Gattungen Chrysococcus, Chromulina, Uroglenopsis. Oesterr. Bot. Zeit., 60: 1–5. 1912. Eine farblose, rhizopodiale Chrysomonade. Ber. d. Deutsch. Bot. Ges., 30: 152–158; Pl. 6. 1912a. Ueber Rhizopoden-und Palmellastadien bei Flagellaten (Chrysomonaden), nebst einer Übersicht über die braunen Flagellaten. Arch. f. Protist., 25: 153–200; Pl. 9; Figs. 1–7. 1912b. Zur Kenntnis zweier Volvokalen. Hedwigia, 52: 274–287. 1913.† Chrysomonadineae, Cryptomonadineae. In A. Pascher, Die Süsswasserflora Deutschlands, Oesterreichs und der Schweiz. Heft 2. Flagellatae 2: 7–95; Figs. 1–150. Jena. 1913a. Die Heterokontengattung Pseudotetraëdron. Hedwigia, 53(1912): 1–5; Figs. 1–6. 1913b. Zur Gliederung der Heterokonten. Ibid. 53(1912): 6–22. 1914. Ueber Symbiosen von Spaltpilzen und Flagellaten mit Blaualgen. Ber. d. Deutsch. Bot. Ges., 32: 339–352. 1914a. Ueber Flagellaten und Algen. Ibid., 32: 136–160. 1921. Ueber die Ubereinstimmungen zwischen den Diatomeen, Heterokonten und Chrysomonaden. Ibid., 39: 236–248; Figs. 1–6. 1925. Heterokontae, Phaeophyta. In A. Pascher, Die Süsswasserflora Deutschlands, Oesterreichs und der Schweiz. Heterokontae, Phaeophyta, Rhodophyta, Charophyta. Heft 11:

1–118; Figs. 1–96. 1925a. Neue oder wenig bekannte Protisten. XV. Arch. f. Protist., 50: 486–510. 1925b. Die braune Algenreiche der Chrysophyceen. *Ibid.*, 52: 489–564. 1927. Volvocales-Phytomonadinae. *In* A. Pascher, Die Süsswasserflora Deutschlands, Oesterreichs und der Schweiz. Heft 4: 1–506; Figs. 1–45. Jena. 1927a. Neue oder wenig bekannte Protisten. XX. Arch. f. Protist., 58: 577–598. 1927b. Die braune Algenreiche aus der Verwandtschaft der Dinoflagellaten (Dinophyceen). *Ibid.*, 58: 1–54; Figs. 1–38. 1930. Zur Kenntnis der heterokonten Algen. *Ibid.*, 69: 401–454; Pl. 21; Figs. 1–45. 1930a. Berichtigung zum Aufsatze: Zur Kenntnis der heterokonten Algen. *Ibid.*, 69: 666. 1930b. Ein grüner *Sphagnum*-Epiphyt und seine Beziehung zu freilebenden Verwandten (*Desmatractum, Calyptobactron, Bernardinella*). *Ibid.*, 69: 637–658. 1932. Einige neue oder Kritische Heterokonten. *Ibid.*, 77(No. 2): 305–359. 1932a. Zur Kenntnis mariner Planktonalgen. I. *Meringosphaera* und ihre Verwandten. *Ibid.*, 77(No. 2): 195–218. 1932b. Ueber eine in ihrer Jurgend rhizopodial und animalisch lebende epiphytische Alge (*Perone*). Beih. Bot. Centralbl., 49(Abt. 1): 675–685; Figs. 1–7. 1937–1939. Heterokonten. *In* L. Rabenhorst, Kryptogamen-Flora von Deutschland, Oesterreich und der Schweiz. XI: 1–1092; Figs. 1–912. Leipzig. 1940. Zur Kenntnis der Süsswassertetrasporalen I. Beih. Bot. Centralbl., 60A: 135–156; Pl. 4; Figs. 1–22.

PASCHER, A., and LEMMERMANN. E. 1913. (See Pascher, 1913.)

PASCHER, A., and SCHILLER, J. 1925. (See Pascher, 1925.)

PAVILLARD, J. 1923. A propos de la systématique des Péridiniens. Bull. Soc. Bot. France, 70: 876–882.

PEARSALL, W. H. 1924. Phytoplankton and environment in the English lake district. Rev. Algol., 1: 53–67.

PEEBLES, F. 1909. The life history of *Sphaerella lacustris* (*Haematococcus pluvialis*) with especial reference to the nature and behaviour of the zoospores. Centralbl. Bakt., 24: 18–22, 511–521.

PENARD, C. 1891. Les Péridiniacées du Lac Leman. Bull. Trav. Soc. Bot. Genève, 6: 1–63.

PENHALLOW, D. P. 1896.* Note on calcareous algae from Michigan. Bot. Gaz., 21: 215–217.

PENNAK, ROBERT W. 1939. The microscopic fauna of the sandy beaches. *In* Problems of Lake Biology. Amer. Assoc. Adv. Sci., Publ. No. 10: 94–106.

PERTY, M. 1849. Ueber verticale Verbreitung mikroskopischer Lebensformen. Natur. Ges. in Bern Mitt., 1849: 17–45. 1852. Zur Kenntniss kleinster Lebensformen nach Bau, Funktionen, Systematik, mit Specialverzeichnis der in der Schweiz beobachteten. Bern.

PETERSEN, C. G. JOH., and PETERSEN, P. BOYSEN. 1911. Valuation of the sea. I. Animal life of the sea bottom, its food and quantity. Rep. Danish Biol. Sta. to Bd. Agric., 20: 1–76.

PETIT, P. 1880. *Spirogyra* des environs de Paris. Paris.

PETKOFF, ST. 1914. Les Characées de Bulgarie. Nuova Notarisia, 25: 35–56.

PHILSON, P. J. 1939. Freshwater algae of North and South Carolina. Part I. Cyanophyceae. Jour. Elisha Mitchell Sci. Soc., 55: 83–116.

PHINNEY, HARRY K. 1943.* The filamentous algae of northern Michigan. M. A. thesis. Albion College. 1945. Notes on *Cladophora*. Amer. Midl. Nat., 34: 445. 1946.* A peculiar lake sediment of algal origin. *Ibid.*, 35: 453–459.

PIETERS, A. J. 1894.* Plants of Lake St. Clair. Bull. Mich. Fish. Comm., No. 2: 1–11.

PLAYFAIR, G. I. 1915. Freshwater algae of the Lismore district with an appendix on the algal fungi and Schizomycetes. Proc. Linn. Soc. N. S. Wales, 40: 310–362; Pls. 41–46. 1916. The genus *Trachelomonas*. *Ibid.*, 40(1915):

1–41. 1916a. *Oocystis* and *Eremosphaera*. *Ibid.*, 41: 107–147; Pls. 7–9; Figs. 1–28. 1917. Australian freshwater phytoplankton. *Ibid.*, 41: 823–852; Pls. 56–59. 1918. New and rare freshwater algae. *Ibid.*, 43: 497–543; Pls. 54–58; Figs. 1–11. 1920. Peridineae of New South Wales. *Ibid.*, 44(1919): 793–818; Pls. 41–43; Figs. 1–18. 1921. Australian freshwater flagellates. *Ibid.*, 46: 99–146; Pls. 1–9; Figs. 1, 2. 1923. Notes on freshwater algae. *Ibid.*, 48: 206–228; Figs. 1–30.

POCHMAN, A. 1942. Synopsis der Gattung *Phacus*. Arch. f. Protist., 95(No. 2): 81–252; Figs. 1–170.

POCOCK, MARY A. 1933. *Volvox* and associated algae from Kimberly. Ann. S. African Mus., 16: 473–521. 1933a. *Volvox* in South Africa. *Ibid.*, 16: 523–646.

POLJANSKY, G. I. 1923. De nova Euglenarum specie. Not. Syst. Inst. Crypt. Horti Bot. Petropol., 1(1922): 177–183.

POLLOCK, J. E. 1942.* Blue-green algae as agents in the deposition of marl in Michigan lakes. Ann. Rep. Mich. Acad. Sci., 20: 247–260; Pls. 16. 17.

POTZGER, J. E. 1942.* Study on the rooted aquatic vegetation of Weber Lake, Vilas County, Wisconsin. Trans. Wis. Acad. Sci., Arts, and Letters, 34: 149–166; Figs. 1–3.

POULTON, E. 1926.† Etude sur les Heterokontées. Thesis, Univ. Genève, Class. Sci. Ser. 10, Fasc. 11: 96 pp.; Figs. 1–13.

POWERS, E. B., SHIELDS, A. R., and HICKMAN, M. E. 1939. The mortality of fishes in Norris Lake. Jour. Tenn. Acad. Sci., 14: 239–260.

POWERS, J. H. 1905. New forms of *Volvox*. Trans. Amer. Microsc. Soc., 27: 123–149; Pls. 11–14.

PRESCOTT, G. W. 1927. The motile algae of Iowa. Univ. Iowa Studies Nat. Hist., 12: 1–40; Pls. 1–10. 1931. Iowa algae. *Ibid.*, 13: 1–235; Pls. 1–39. 1931a. Iowa lake survey. A report to the Iowa State Fish and Game Commission. Mimeographed. 1936. Notes on the algae of Gatun Lake, Panama Canal. Trans. Amer. Microsc. Soc., 55: 501–509; Pls. LXIV–LXV. 1937.* Preliminary notes on the desmids of Isle Royale, Michigan. Pap. Mich. Acad. Sci., Arts, and Letters, 22: 201–212; Pl. 19. 1938.* A new species and a new variety of the algal genus *Vaucheria* De Candolle with notes on the genus. Trans. Amer. Microsc. Soc., 57: 1–10; Pls. 1, 2. 1938a. Objectionable algae and their control in lakes and reservoirs. Municipal Rev., 1(No. 2/3) [reprint; pages not numbered]. 1938b.* Further notes on the desmids of Isle Royale, Michigan. The genus *Cosmarium*. Pap. Mich. Acad. Sci., Arts, and Letters, 23: 203–214. 1939.* Some relationships of phytoplankton to limnology and aquatic biology. *In* Problems of lake biology. Amer. Assoc. Adv. Sci., Publ. No. 10: 65–78; Figs. 2–4. 1940.* Desmids of Isle Royale, Michigan. The genera *Staurastrum, Micrasterias, Xanthidium*, and *Euastrum*, with a note on *Spinoclosterium*. Pap. Mich. Acad. Sci., Arts, and Letters, 25(1939): 89–100. 1941.* A concluding list of desmids from Isle Royale, Michigan. *Ibid.*, 26(1940): 23–29; Pls. 1, 2. 1942. The fresh-water algae of southern United States. II. Trans. Amer. Microsc. Soc., 61: 109–119. 1944.* New species and varieties of Wisconsin algae. Farlowia, 1: 347–385. 1948. Objectionable algae with reference to the killing of fish and other animals. Hydrobiologia, 1(No. 1): 1–13.

PRESCOTT, G. W., and CROASDALE, HANNAH T. 1937. New or noteworthy fresh water algae of Massachusetts. Trans. Amer. Microsc. Soc., 56: 269–282; Pls. 1–3. 1942. The algae of New England. II. Amer. Midl. Nat., 27: 662–676; Pls. 1–5.

PRESCOTT, G. W., and MAGNOTTA, ANGELINA. 1935.* Notes on Michigan desmids with descriptions of some species new to science. Pap. Mich. Acad. Sci., Arts, and Letters, 20: 157–170.

PRESCOTT, G. W., SILVA, H., and WADE, W. E. 1949.* New or otherwise interesting fresh-water algae from North America. Hydrobiologia, 2(No. 1): 84–91; Pls. 1–2.

PRINGSHEIM, E. G. 1942. Contributions to our knowledge of saprophytic algae and flagellata. III. *Astasia, Distigma, Menoidium* and *Rhabdomonas*. New Phytol., 41: 171–205.

PRINGSHEIM, N. 1856. Untersuchungen ueber Befruchtung und Generationswechsel der Algen. Monatsber. d. Königl. Akad. d. Wiss. z. Berlin, 1856: 225–237; 1 pl. Figs. 1–10. 1858. Beiträge zur Morphologie und Systematik der Algen. Pringsh. Jahrb. Wiss. Bot., 1: 1–81; Pls. 1–6. 1860. Beiträge zur Morphologie und Systematik der Algen. III. Die Coleochaeteen. *Ibid.*, 2. 1–38; Pls. 1–6.

PRINTZ, H. 1913. Eine systematische Uebersicht der Gattung *Oocystis* Nägeli. Nyt Mag. f. Natur., 51: 165–203; Pls. 4–6. 1914. Kristianiatraktens Protococcoideer. Skr. Vidensk. i Kristiania. Mat.-Nat. Kl., 1913(No. 6): 1–123; Pls. 1–7. 1915. Beiträge zur Kenntnis der Chlorophyceen und ihrer verbreitung in Norwegen. Det. Kgl. Norske Vidensk. Selskabs Skrifter, 1915 (No. 2): 1–76. 1915a. Die Chlorophyceen des südlichen Sibiriens und des Uriankailandes. *Ibid.*, 1915 (No. 4): 1–52; Pls. 1–7. 1927.† Chlorophyceae. *In* A. Engler and K. Prantl, Die Natürlichen Pflanzenfamilien. 3: 1–463; Figs. 1–366. Leipzig. 1940.† Vorarbeiten zu einer Monographie der Trentepohliaceen. Nyt Mag. f. Natur., 80: 137–210.

PRITCHARD, A. 1841. A history of infusoria, living and fossil. London. 1861. A history of infusoria, including the Desmidiaceae and Diatomaceae, British and foreign. 4th ed. London.

PÜTTER, A. 1909. Die Ernahrung der Wassertiere und der Stoffhaushalt der Gewässer. Jena.

RABENHORST, L. 1847. Deutschlands Kryptogamen-Flora, oder Handbuch zur Bestimmung der kryptogamischen Gewächse Deutschlands, der Schweiz, des Lombardisch-Venetianischen Königreichs und Istriens. II, No. 2. Algen. Leipzig. 1849–1860. Die Algen Sachsen's. 1863. Kryptogamen-Flora von Sachsen, der Ober-Lausitz, Thüringen und Nordböhmen, mit Berücksichtigung der benachbarten Länder. Erste Abtheilung. Leipzig. 1864–1868. Florae Europaea algarum aquae dulcis et submarinae. 3 Vols. Leipzig.

RACIBORSKI, M. 1889. Przeglad Gatunków Rodzaju *Pediastrum*. Rozpr. i Sprawozd. Wydz. III., Akad. Umiej.'w. Krakowie, 20: 1–37.

RALFS, J. 1844. On the British Desmidieae. Ann. and Mag. Nat. Hist., 14(Ser. 1): 187–194, 256–261, 391–396, 465–471. 1848. The British Desmidieae. 266 pp.; Pls. 1–35. London. 1850. On the Nostochineae. Ann. and Mag. Nat. Hist., 5(Ser. 2): 321–343.

RANDHAWA, M. S. 1936. Contributions to our knowledge of the freshwater algae of northern India. I. Oedogoniales. Proc. Indian Acad. Sci., 4: 97–107; Pls. 6–8. 1937. Genus *Zygnemopsis* in northern India. *Ibid.*, 5: 297–314; Figs. 1–8. 1938. Observations on some Zygnemales from northern India. Parts I–II. *Ibid.*, 8: 109–150, 336–366; Figs. 1–58. 1939. Genus *Vaucheria* in northern India. Arch. f. Protist., 92: 537–542.

RAO, C. B. 1936. The Myxophyceae of the United Provinces, India.—II. Proc. Indian Acad. Sci., 3: 165–174; Figs. 1–3. 1937. The Zygnemoideae of the United Provinces, India. I. Jour. Indian Bot. Soc., 16: 269–288. 1937a. The Myxophyceae of the United Provinces, India.—III. Proc. Indian Acad. Sci., 6: 339–375. 1938. The Zygnemoideae of the Central Provinces, India.—I. Jour. Indian Bot. Soc., 17: 341–353.

RAWSON, D. S. 1930. The bottom fauna of Lake Simcoe and its rôle in the ecology of the lake. Univ. Toronto Studies, Publ. Ontario Fish Res. Lab., No. 40. 1939. Some physical and chemical factors in the metabolism of lakes. *In* Problems of Lake Biology. Amer. Assoc. Adv. Sci., Publ. No. 10: 9–26.

RAYMOND, M. R. 1937.* A limnological study of the plankton of a concretion-forming marl lake. Trans. Amer. Microsc. Soc., 56: 405–430.

RAYSS, TSCHARNA. 1915. Le *Coelastrum proboscideum* Bohl. Etude de planctologie expérimentale suivi d'une revision des *Coelastrum* de la Suisse. Matér. pour la Flore Crypt. Suisse, 5: 1–65; Pls. 1–20. 1930. *Microthamnion Kuetzingianum* Naeg. Bull. Soc. Bot. Genève, 21(Sér. 2): 143–160; Figs. 1–9.

REIF, C. B. 1939. The effect of stream conditions on lake plankton. Trans. Amer. Micros. Soc. 58: 398–403.

REINBOLD, D. T. 1890. Die Chlorophyceen (Grüntange) der Kieler Föhrde. Schrif. des naturw. Vereins f. Schleswig-Holstein, 8(Heft 1): 109–144.

REINHARD, E. G. 1931.* The plankton ecology of the upper Mississippi, Minneapolis to Winona. Ecol. Monogr., 1: 395–464; Figs. 1–11. 1941. Notes on *Aphanizomenon* with a description of a new species. Amer. Jour. Bot., 28: 326–329.

REINHARDT, L. 1876. Entwickelungsgeschichte der Characien (rossice). Protoc. de Seckt der 5. Versamml. russ. Naturf. und Aerzte in Warschau. Warsaw.

REINKE, J. 1879. Zwei parasitische Algen. Bot. Zeit., 37: 473–478.

REINSCH, P. F. 1867. Die Algenflora des mittleren Theiles von Franken, enthaltend die vom Autor bis jetzt in diesen Gebieten beobachteten Süsswasseralgen, etc. Abh. Naturh. Ges. Nürnberg, 3(1866): 1–238; Pls. 1–3. (Also printed separately, Nürnberg, 1867.) 1875. Contributiones ad algologeam et fungologeam. Leipzig. 1878. Contributiones ad floram algarum aquae dulcis Promontorii Bonae Spei. Jour. Linn. Soc. Bot., 16: 232–248. 1879. Eine neues Genus der Chroolepideae. Bot. Zeit., 37: 361–366. 1887. Eine neue *Vaucheria* der Corniculatae, sowie über gynandrische Bildung bei *Vaucheria*. Ber. d. Deutsch Bot. Ges., 5: 189–192. 1888. Familiae Polyedriearum monographia. Notarisia, 3: 493–516; Pls. 4–8.

RENDLE, A. B., and WEST, W. 1899. A new British freshwater alga. Jour. Bot., 37: 289–291.

RICH, FLORENCE. 1932. Contributions to our knowledge of the freshwater algae of Africa. 10. Phytoplankton from South Africa Pans and Vleis. Trans. Roy. Soc. S. Africa, 20(Pt. 2): 149–188. 1935. Contributions to our knowledge of the freshwater algae of Africa. 11. Algae from a Pan in Southern Rhodesia. *Ibid.*, 23(Pt. 2): 107–160; Figs. 1–24.

RICH, FLORENCE, and POCOCK, MARY A. 1933. Observations on the genus *Volvox* in Africa. Ann. S. African Mus., 16: 427–471.

RICHTER, P. 1884. In Literaturöfversigt. Algae aquae dulcis exsiccatae praecipue scandinavicae quas adjectis chlorophyllaceis et phychromaceis distribuerunt Veit Wittrock et Otto Nordstedt. Bot. Notiser, 1884: 121–128. 1894. *Gloiotrichia echinulata* P. Richt., eine Wässerblute des Grossen und Kleinen Plöner Sees. Forsch. Biol. Stat. z. Plön, 2: 31–47. 1896. *Scenedesmus Opoliensis* P. Richt. nov. sp. Zeit. f. Angw. Mikro., 1: 3–7. 1897. Süsswasseralgen aus dem Umanakdistrikt. Bibl. Bot., 8(Heft 42): 1–12.

RICKETT, H. W. 1921.* A quantitative study of the larger aquatic plants of Lake Mendota. Trans. Wis. Acad. Sci., Arts, and Letters, 20: 501–527. 1924.* A quantitative study of the larger aquatic plants of Green Lake, Wisconsin. *Ibid.*, 21: 381–414; Figs. 1–7.

RILEY, GORDON A. 1939. Correlations in aquatic ecology, with an example of their applications to problems of plankton productivity. Jour Marine Res. 2: 56–73; Figs. 14–16.

RIPART, J. 1876. Notice sur quelques espèces rares ou nouvelles de la flore cryptogamique de la France. Bull. Soc. Bot. France, 25: 158–168.

ROBINSON, CHAS. BUDD. 1906.† The Chareae of North America. Doctoral thesis, Columbia University. New York,

ROLL, J. 1925. Les nouvelles espèces des algues trouvées aux environs de la station biologique du Donetz du Nord. (Russian with French summary.) Arch. Russ. Protist., 4(No. 3/4): 137–152. 1926. Untersuchungen am Phytoplankton der Binnengewässer in Ukaja. Ibid., 5: 1–44.

ROSE, EARL T. 1934. Notes on the life history of Aphanizomenon flos-aquae. Univ. Iowa Studies Nat. Hist., 16: 129–136.

ROSENBERG, MARIE. 1939. A discussion of freshwater biology and its applications. III. Algal physiology and organic production. Ann. Appl. Biol., 26: 172–174.

ROSTAFINSKI, J. 1875. Quelques mots sur l'Haematococcus lacustris et sur les bases d'une classification naturelle des algues Chlorosporées. Mém. Soc. Nat. Cherbourg, 19: 137-154.

ROSTAFINSKI, J., and WORONIN, M. 1877. Ueber Botrydium granulatum. Leipzig. Bot. Zeit., 35: 649–671; Pls. 7–11.

ROTH, A. W. 1797. Bemerkungen über das Studium der kryptogamischen Wassergewächse. Hannover. 1797–1806. Catalecta botanica, 1–3. Leipzig. 1800. Tentamen florae germanicae. Vol. 3. Leipzig.

ROUSSELET, C. F. 1914. Remarks on two species of African Volvox. Jour. Quekett Microsc. Soc., 12(Ser. 2): 393–394.

SANDOR, LANGER. 1934. A Spirogyrák. A Spirogyrák monografikus Feldologozása, Kulönös Tekintettel Nagymagyaroszágra. Folia Crypt., 1: 1253–1304.

SAUNDERS, DE ALTON. 1894. Protophyta-Phycophyta. Flora of Nebraska. Vol. L. Lincoln.

SAWYER, C. N., LACKEY, J. B., and LENZ, A. T. 1943.* Investigation of the odor nuisance occurring in the Madison Lakes particularly Lakes Monona, Waubesa and Kegonsa from July 1942 to July 1943. A mimeographed report to the Hon. S. Goodland, Acting Governor of Wisconsin.

SCHAARSCHMIDT-ISTVANFFI, J. 1881. Specimen Phycologiae aequatoriensis. Magyar Növenytanu Lapok, 5: 17–24.

SCHERFFEL, A. 1899. Phaeocystis globosa n. sp. Ber. d. Deusch. Bot. Ges., 17: 317–318. 1908. Asterococcus n. g. superbus (Cienk.) Scherffel und dessen angebliche Beziehungen zu Eremosphaera. Ibid., 26A: 762–771. 1908a. Einiges zur Kenntnis von Schizochlamys gelatinosa A. Br. Ibid., 783–795. 1911. Beitrag zur Kenntnis der Chrysomonadineen. Arch. f. Protist., 22: 299–344.

SCHEWIAKOFF, W. 1893. Ueber die geographische Verbreitung der Süsswasser-Protozoën. Mém. Acad. Imper. Sci. St. Pétersb., 41(Ser. 7): 1–201.

SCHILLER, J. 1933–1937.† Dinoflagellatae. In L. Rabenhorst, Kryptogamen-Flora von Deutschland, Oesterreich und der Schweiz. 10(1933), Teil 1: 1–617; Teil 2, Lf. 1(1935): 1–160; Lf. 2(1935): 161–320; Lf. 3(1937): 321–480; Lf. 4(1937): 481–590. Leipzig.

SCHILLING, A. J. 1891. Die Süsswasser-Peridineen. Flora Allgm. Bot. Zeit., 74: 220–299. 1913. Dinoflagellatae (Peridineae). In A. Pascher, Die Süsswasserflora Deutschlands, Oesterreichs und der Schweiz. Heft 3: 1–66; Figs. 1–69. Jena.

SCHKORBATOW, L. 1925. Myxophycearum in provincia Charkoviensi (Ukraïnae) inventarum novae species et varietates. Not. Syst. Inst. Crypt. Horti Bot. Petropol., 2(No. 6): 87–89.

SCHMARDA, L. K. 1850. Neue Formen von Infusorien. Denschr. Kais. Akad. Wiss. Wien, 1(Abt. 2): 9–14; Pls. 3, 4. 1854. Zur Naturgeschichte Aegyptens. Ibid., 7(Abt. 2): 1–28.

SCHMIDLE, W. 1893. Beiträge zur Algenflora des Schwarzwaldes und der Rheinebene. Ber. d. Natur. Ges. Freiburg, 7: 1–45 (68–112, double paging)

1894. Aus der Chlorophyceen-Flora der Torfstiche zu Virnheim. Flora, 78: 42–66; Pl. 7. 1895. Weitere Beiträge zur Algenflora der Rheinebene und des Schwarzwaldes. Hedwigia, 34: 66–83. 1895a. Einige Algen aus Sumatra. *Ibid.*, 34: 293–307; Pl. 4. 1897. Algen aus den Hochseen des Kaukasus. Rep. Bot. Gard. Tiflis, 2: 267–276. 1897a. Beiträge zur Algenflora des Schwarzwaldes und des Oberrheins. VI. Hedwigia, 36: 1–25. 1897b. Algologishen Notizen. II. *Conferva Sandvichense* Ag. Allg. Bot. Zeitschr., 3: 3–4. 1897c. Algologische Notizen. V–VII. *Ibid.*, 3: 107–108. 1898. Ueber einige von Prof. Lagerheim in Ecuador und Jamaika gesammelte Blattalgen. Hedwigia, 37: 61–75. 1898a. Ueber einige von Knut Bohlin in Pite Lappmark und Vesterbotten gesammelte Süsswasseralgen. Bih. Kongl. Sv. Vet.-Akad. Handl., 24, Afd. 3, No. 8: 1–71. 1899. Vier neue Süsswasseralgen. Oesterr. Bot. Zeit., 1899(No. 1): 1–4. 1899a. Einige Algen aus preussischen Hochmooren. Hedwigia, 38: 156–176. 1900. Algologische Notizen. VIII–IX. Allgm. Bot. Zeitschr., 5(1899): 2–4. 1900a. Algologische Notizen. X–XIII. *Ibid.*, 5: 17–20. 1900b. Ueber einige von Professor Hansgirg in Istindien gesammelte Süsswasseralgen. Hedwigia, 39: 160–190. 1900c. Einige von Dr. Holderer in Centralasien gesammelte Algen. *Ibid.*, 39: [141–143]. 1900d. Ueber Planktonalgen und Flagellaten aus dem Nyassasee. Engler's Bot. Jahrb., 27: 229–237; Pls. 1–3. 1900e. Beiträge zur Kenntniss der Planktonalgen. Ber. d. Deutsch. Bot. Ges., 18: 144–158. 1900f. Drei interessante tropische Algen. Bot. Centralbl., 81: 417–418. 1900g. Algen des Süsswassers. Ber. d. Deutsch. Bot. Ges., 18: [107–117]. 1901. Algologische Notizen. XV. Allg. Bot. Zeitschr., 6: 233–235. 1901a. Ueber drei Algengenera. Ber. d. Deutsch. Bot. Ges., 19: 10–24. 1901b. *In* Beiträge zur Flora von Afrika XXII. Schizophyceae, Conjugate, Chlorophyceae. Engler's Bot. Jahrb., 30: 239–445. 1902. Notizen zu einigen Süsswasseralgen. Hedwigia, 41: 150–163. 1902a. *In* Hans Simmer, Vierter Bericht über die Kryptogamenflora der Kreuzeckgruppe in Karnten. Allg. Bot. Zeitschr., 7(1901): 41–43, 83–86. 1903. Algen, insbesondere solche des Plankton, aus dem Nyassa-See und seiner Umgebung gesammelt von Dr. Fülleborn. Engler's Bot. Jahrb., 32(1902): 56–88; Pls. 1–3. 1903a. Bemerkungen zu einigen Süsswasseralgen. Ber. d. Deutsch. Bot. Ges., 21: 346–355.

SCHMIDT, J. 1899. Danmarks blaagrönne Alger (Cyanophyceae Daniae). Bot. Tidsskr., 22: 283–419.

SCHOMER, H. A., and JUDAY, C. 1935.* Photosynthesis of algae at different depths in some lakes of northeastern Wisconsin. I. Observations of 1933. Trans. Wis. Acad. Sci., Arts, and Letters, 29: 173–193.

SCHRAMM, J. R. 1914. A contribution to our knowledge of the relation of certain species of grass-green algae to elementary nitrogen. Ann. Missouri Bot. Gard., 1: 157–184.

SCHRANK, F. VON PAULA. 1783. Botanische Rhapsodien. Der Naturforscher, 19: 116–128. 1793. Mikroskopische Wahrnehmungen. *Ibid.*, 27: 26–37.

SCHROEDER, B. 1897. Ueber das Plankton der Oder. Ber. d. Deutsch. Bot. Ges., 15: 482–492. 1897a. Die Algen der Versuchsteiche des Schles. Fischereivereins zu Trachenberg. Forsch. Biol. Stat. z. Plön, 5: 29–66. 1898. Neue Beiträge zur Kenntnis der Algen des Riesengebirges. *Ibid.*, 6: 9–47; Pls. 1, 2. 1898a. Planktologische Mittheilungen. Biol. Centralbl., 18: 525–535. 1899. Das Plankton des Oderstromes. B. Das pflanzliche Plankton der Oder. Forsch. Biol. Stat. z. Plön, 7: 15–24. 1902. Untersuchungen über Gallertbildung der Algen. Ver. Naturh. med. Vereins Heidelberg, 7: 139–196. Pls. 1, 2. 1920. Schwebepflanzen aus dem Saarbor-Seen und aus den grösseren Seen bei Liegnitz. Ber. d. Deutsch. Bot. Ges., 38: 122–135.

SCHUETTE, H. A. 1918.* A biochemical study of the plankton of Lake Mendota. Trans. Wis. Acad. Sci., Arts, and Letters, 19(Pt. 1): 594–613.

SCHUETTE, H. A., and ALDER, H. 1929.* A note on the chemical composition of *Chara* from Green Lake, Wisconsin. Trans. Wis. Acad. Sci., Arts, and Letters, 24: 141–145.

SCHUETTE, H. A., and HOFFMAN, ALICE E. 1921.* Notes on the chemical composition of some of the larger aquatic plants of Lake Mendota. I. *Cladophora* and *Myriophyllum*. Trans. Wis. Acad. Sci., Arts, and Letters, 20: 529–531.

SCHULZE, B. 1927. Zur Kenntnis einiger Volvocales. Arch. f. Protist., 58: 508–576.

SCHUTT, F. 1896. Peridiniales. *In* A. Engler and K. Prantl, Die natürlichen Pflanzenfamilien. Teil 1, Abt. 1. Leipzig.

SECKT, H. 1922. Estudios hidrobiológicos en la Argentina—Flagellatae. Bol. Acad. Nac. Cienc. Córdoba, 25: 430–490. 1938. Contribución al conocimiento de las algas aerofilas en la Argentina. *Ibid.*, 34: 108–141.

SELIGO, A. 1887. Untersuchungen über Flagellaten. Beitr. Biol. Pflanzen, 4: 145–180; Pl.8.

SENN, G. 1899. Ueber einige coloniebildende einzellige Algen. Bot. Zeitg., 57: 39–104; Pls. 2–3. 1900. Flagellata. *In* A. Engler and K. Prantl, Die Natürlichen Pflanzenfamilien. Teil 1, Abt. 2: 93–192; Figs. 63–140. Leipzig.

SETCHELL, WM. A. 1895. Notes on some Cyanophyceae of New England. Bull. Torr. Bot. Club, 22: 424–431. 1896. Notes on Cyanophyceae. I. Erythea, 4: 87–89. 1896a.* Notes on Cyanophyceae. II. *Ibid.*, 4: 189–194.

SETCHELL, WM. A., and GARDNER, N. L. 1903.† Algae of Northwestern America. Univ. Calif. Publ. Bot., 1: 165–418; Pls. 17–27.

SEVILLE-KENT, W. 1880-1882. A manual of the Infusoria. London.

SHAW, W. R. 1894. *Pleodorina,* a new genus of the Volvocineae. Bot. Gaz., 19: 279–283; Pl. 27.

SIMMER, HANS. 1898. Erster Bericht über die Kryptogamenflora der Kreuzeokgruppe in Kärnthen. Allg. Bot. Zeitschr., 4: 74–78; 99–100; 118–120; 141–144; 158–159. 1901. Vierter Bericht über die Kryptogamen-flora der Kreuzeckgruppe in Kärnten. *Ibid.*, 7: 41–43, 83–86.

SINGH, R. N. 1938. The Oedogoniales of the United Provinces, India. Proc. Indian Acad. Sci., 8: 373–395.

SIRODOT, S. 1884.† Les Batrachospermes. Organisation, fonctions, développement, classification. Paris.

SKUJA, H. 1926. Zwei neue Zygnemaceen mit blauem Mesospor. Acta Horti Bot. Univ. Latviensis, 1: 109–114; 1 pl. 1926a. Vorarbeiten zu einer Algenflora von Lettland. I. *Ibid.*, 1: 33–54. 1926b. Vorarbeiten zu einer Algenflora von Lettland. II. *Ibid.*, 1: 149–178. 1927. Vorarbeiten zu einer Algenflora von Lettland. III. *Ibid.*, 2: 51–116. 1928. Vorarbeiten zu einer Algenflora von Lettland. IV. *Ibid.*, 3: 103–218; Pls. 1–4. 1930. Süsswasseralgen von den westestnische Inseln Saaremaa und Hiiumaa. *Ibid.*, 4(1929): 1–74. 1931. Untersuchungen über die Rhodophyceen des Süsswassers. Arch. f. Protist., 74: 297–308. 1934. Beitrag zur Algenflora Lettlands I. Acta Horti Bot. Univ. Latviensis, 7(1932): 25–86. 1935. Die Flechte *Coenogonium nigrum* (Huds.) Zahlbr. und ihre Gonidie. *Ibid.*, 8: 21–44. 1937. Süsswasseralgen aus Griechenland und Kleinasien gesammelt von Prof. C. Regel. Hedwigia, 77: 15–70; Pls. 1–3. 1938. Die Süsswasserrhodophyceen der Deutschen Limnologischen Sunda-Expedition. Arch. f. Hydrobiol. (Suppl.) 15: 603–637; Pls. 29–35. 1939. Beitrag zur Algenflora Lettlands. II. Acta Horti Bot. Univ. Latviensis, 11/12: 41–169. 1939a. Versuch einer systematischen Einteilung der Bangioideen oder Protoflorideen. *Ibid.*, 11/12: 23–40.

[649]

1948. Taxonomie des Phytoplanktons einiger Seen in Uppland, Schweden. Symbol. Bot. Upsal., 9(No. 3): 1–399; Pls. 1–39.

Skvortzow, B. W. 1917. Ueber Flagellata aus Mandschurei. Zhurnal Mikrobiol. (Petrograd), 4(No. 1/2): 55–77. 1919. Notes on the agriculture, botany and the zoology of China. XXXI. On new flagellata from Manchuria. Jour. N. China Branch Roy. Asiatic Soc., 50: 96–104. 1922. On the winter phytoplankton of the fishponds of Foochow. *Ibid.*, 53: 190–195. 1925. Die Euglenaceengattung *Trachelomonas* Ehrenberg. Eine systematische Uebersicht. Sungari Station zu Harbin der Ges. z. erforschung der Mandschurei, 1(No. 2): 1–101; Pls. 1–8. 1925a. Ueber einige Süsswasseralgen Umgegend von Peking (China). Arch. f. Hydrobiol. u. Planktonk., 16: 337–340. 1925b. Zur Kenntnis der Mandschurischen Flagellaten. Beih. Bot. Centralbl., 41 (Abt. 2): 311–315. 1925c. Ueber neue und wenig bekannte Formen der Euglenaceengattung *Trachelomonas* Ehrenberg. Ber. d. Deutsch. Bot. Ges., 43: 306–315. 1926. Ueber einige Süsswasseralgen aus der Nord-Mandschurei, im Jahre 1916 gesammelt. Arch. f. Hydrobiol. u. Planktonk., 16(Heft 3): 421–436; Figs. 1–8. 1927. Ueber neue und wenig bekannte Formen der Euglenaceengattung *Trachelomonas* Ehrenb. II. Ber. d. Deutsch. Bot. Ges., 44: 603–621. 1928. Die Euglenaceengattung *Phacus* Dujardin. *Ibid.*, 46: 105–125; Pl. 2. 1929. Einige neue und wenig bekannte Chlamydomonadaceae aus Manchuria. Arch. f. Protist., 66: 160–163.

Smith, Gilbert M. 1913.° *Tetradesmus*, a new four-celled coenobic alga. Bull. Torr. Bot. Club, 40: 75–87; Pl. 1. 1914.° The organization of the colony of certain four-celled coenobic algae. Trans. Wis. Acad. Sci., Arts, and Letters, 17 (Pt. II): 1165–1220; Pls. 85–91. 1916.° New or interesting algae from the lakes of Wisconsin. Bull. Torr. Bot. Club, 43: 471–483; Pls. 24–26. 1916a.°† A monograph of the algal genus *Scenedesmus*, based upon pure culture studies. Trans. Wis. Acad. Sci., Arts, and Letters, 18: 422–539; Pls. 25–33. 1916b.° A preliminary list of the algae found in Wisconsin lakes. *Ibid.*, 18(Pt. II): 531–565. 1917.° The vertical distribution of *Volvox* in the plankton of Lake Monona. Amer. Jour. Bot., 5: 178–185. 1918.° A second list of algae found in Wisconsin lakes. Trans. Wis. Acad. Sci., Arts, and Letters, 19: 614–654; Pls. 10–15. 1920.°† Phytoplankton of the inland lakes of Wisconsin. Part. 1. Wis. Geol. and Nat. Hist. Surv., Bull. 57: 1–243; Pls. 1–51. 1922. The phytoplankton of the Muskoka region, Ontario, Canada. Trans. Wis. Acad. Sci., Arts, and Letters, 20: 323–364; Pls. 8–13. 1922a. The phytoplankton of some artificial pools near Stockholm. Arkiv f. Bot., 17(No. 13): 1–8; Figs. 1–28. 1924. Ecology of the plankton algae in Palisades Interstate Park, including the relation of control methods to fish culture. Roosevelt Wild Life Bull., 2: 95–195; Pls. 3–24. 1924a.°† Phytoplankton of the inland lakes of Wisconsin. II. Wis. Geol. and Nat. Hist. Surv., Bull. 57: 1–227; Pls. 52–88. Madison. 1926. The plankton algae of the Okoboji region. Trans. Amer. Microsc. Soc., 45: 156–233; Pls. 1–20. 1930. Notes on the Volvocales. I–IV. Bull. Torr. Bot. Club, 57: 359–370; Pls. 17, 18. 1931. A consideration of the species of *Eudorina*. *Ibid.*, 57: 359–364; Pl. 17. 1933.°† Freshwater algae of the United States. 716 pp.; Figs. 1–449. New York. 1937. Cryptogamic Botany. Vol. I. 545 pp.; Figs. 1–292. New York. 1944.° A Comparative study of the species of *Volvox*. Trans. Amer. Microsc. Soc., 63: 265–310; Figs. 1–46.

Smith, Gilbert M., and Klyver, F. D. 1929. *Draparnaldiopsis*, a new member of the algal family Chaetophoraceae, Trans. Amer. Microsc. Soc., 48: 196–203; Pl. 25; Fig. 1.

Smith, J. E. 1790. English Botany, or coloured figures of British plants. London.

Smith, L. L. 1941.° A limnological investigation of a permanently stratified lake in the Huron Mountain region of Michigan. Pap. Mich. Acad. Sci., Arts, and Letters, 26 (1940): 281–296.

SNOW, JULIA. 1899.* Ulvella Americana. Bot. Gaz., 27: 309–314; Pl. 7. 1899a.* *Pseudopleurococcus*, nov. gen. Ann. Bot., 13: 189–195; Pl. 11. 1903. The plankton algae of Lake Erie, with special reference to the Chlorophyceae. Bull. U. S. Fish. Comm., 1902: 369–394. 1911. Two epiphytic algae. Bot. Gaz., 51: 360–368; Pl. 18.

SOMMERFELDT, S. G. 1824. Physisk-Oeconomisk Beskrivelse over Saltdalen i Nordlandene. Det. Kgl. Norske Vid. Selsk-Skr. i det., 19th Aarh, 2: 1–148.

STEIN, F. R. VON. 1862. Der Organismus der Infusionsthiere. II, Abteilung; Naturgeschichte der heterotrichen Infusorien. Leipzig. 1878. Der Organismus der Flagellaten nach einigen Forschungen in systematischer Reinenfolge bearbeitet. Der Organismus der Infusionstiere. III Abteilung. I Häfte. Die Naturgeschichte der Flagellaten oder Geisselinfusorien. Den noch nicht abgeschlossenen allgemeinen Teil nebst Erklärung der sömtlichen Abbildungen enthaltend. 154 pp. Leipzig. 1883. Der Organismus der Infusionsthiere nach eigenen Forschungen in systematischer Reinenfolge bearbeitet. III Abteilung. II Hälfte. Die Naturgeschichte der Arthrodelen Flagellaten. 30 pp. Leipzig.

STICKNEY, M. E. 1909.* Notes on *Spondylomorum quaternarium* Ehrenb. Bull. Sci. Lab. Denison Univ., 14: 233–238; Pl. 6.

STIZENBERGER, ERNST. 1852. *Spirulina* und *Arthrospira* nov. gen. Hedwigia, 1: 32–34.

STOCKMAYER, S. 1890. Ueber die Algengattung *Rhizoclonium*. Ver. K. K. Zool.-Bot. Ges. Wien, 40: 571–586.

STOKES, A. C. 1885. Notes on some apparently undescribed forms of fresh-water infusoria. No. 2. Amer. Jour. Sci., 29(Ser. 3): 313–328; Pl. 3. 1885a. Notices of new fresh-water infusoria. IV. Amer. Monthly Microsc. Jour., 6: 183–190. 1886. Notes on *Peridinium* and other infusoria. Jour. Trenton Nat. Hist. Soc., 1(No. 1): 18–22. 1886a. Notices of new fresh-water infusoria. Proc. Amer. Philos. Soc., 23: 562–568; 1 pl. 1886b. Notices of new fresh-water infusoria. V. Amer. Monthly Microsc. Jour., 7: 81–86; Figs. 1–18. 1887. Notices of new fresh-water infusoria. VI. *Ibid.*, 8: 141–147. 1888. A preliminary contribution toward a history of the freshwater infusoria of the United States. Jour. Trenton Nat. Hist. Soc., 1(No. 3): 71–319; Pls. 1–13. 1890. Notices of new fresh-water infusoria. Proc. Amer. Philos. Soc., 28: 74–80; 1 pl. 1894. Notices of presumably undescribed infusoria. *Ibid.*, 33: 338–344.

STRASBURGER, E. 1884. Das botanische Practicum. Jena.

STRICKLAND, J. C. 1940. The Oscillatoriaceae of Virginia. Amer. Jour. Bot., 27: 628–633; Fig. 1.

STRÖM, K. MUNSTER. 1921. The phytoplankton of some Norwegian Lakes. Videns. Skrift. I. Mat.-Nat. Kl., 1921(No. 4): 1–51; Pls. 1–3. 1926. Norwegian mountain algae. Det. Norske Vid.-Akad. Oslo. I. Mat.-Nat. Kl., 1926 (No. 6): 1–263; 25 pls. 1928. Production biology of temperate lakes. Inter. Rev. Ges. Hydrobiol. u. Hydrogr., 19: 329–348.

SURBER, EUGENE W. 1929. The utilization of sloughs in the Upper Mississippi Wild Life and Fish Refuge as fish ponds. Trans. Amer. Fish. Soc., 59: 106–113.

SWINGLE, W. T. 1894.* *Cephaleuros mycoidea* and *Phyllosiphon*, two species of parasitic algae new to North America. Proc. Amer. Assoc. Adv. Sci., 42: 260.

SWIRENKO, D. O. 1914. Zur Kenntnis der russischen Algenflora. I. Die Euglenaceengattung *Trachelomonas*. Arch. f. Hydrobiol. u. Planktonk., 9: 630–

647. 1915. Materialy k florie vodoroslei Rossii. Niepotoryia dannyia k sistematikie i geografii Euglenaceae. Obschchestvo Ispytatelei Prirody, Khar'kov. Trudy, 48(No. 1): 67–148. 1915a. Zur Kenntnis der russischen Algenflora. II. Euglenaceae (excl. *Trachelomonas*). Arch. f. Hydrobiol. u. Planktonk., 10: 321–339. 1928. Contributions à l'étude algologique de l'Ingoule. (Russian with French summary.) Arch. Russ. Protist., 7: 75–130.

TAFT, C. E. 1935. The Oedogoniaceae of Oklahoma including new species and varieties. Bull. Torr. Bot. Club, 62: 281–290; Pls. 15, 16. 1937. A new species of *Vaucheria*. *Ibid.*, 64: 557; 1 fig. 1939.* Additions to the algae of Michigan. *Ibid.*, 66: 77–85; Figs. 1–12. 1942. Additions to the algae of the west end of Lake Erie. Ohio Jour. Sci., 42: 251–256; Pls. 1, 2. 1946. Some Oedogoniaceae and Zygnemataceae from Texas and Louisiana. Trans. Amer. Microsc. Soc., 65: 18–26; 1 pl. 1949.* New, rare, or otherwise interesting algae. Trans. Amer. Microsc. Soc., 68: 208–216, Pls. 1, 2.

TANNER-FULLMAN, M. 1906. Sur un nouvel organisme du plancton du Schoenenbodensee le *Raphidium Chodati* Tanner. Bull. Herb. Boiss., 6(Ser. 2): 156–158.

TAYLOR, WM. RANDOLPH. 1922. Notes on some algae from British Columbia. Rhodora, 24: 101–111. 1924. Further notes on British Columbia algae. *Ibid.*, 26: 160–166. 1928. Alpine algal flora of the mountains of British Columbia. Ecology, 9: 343–348. 1932. Notes on the genus *Anabaenopsis*. Amer. Jour. Bot., 19: 454–463; Pls. 39, 40. 1933. Methods for collection and study of fresh-water algae. Jour. Mich. Schoolmasters Club, 1933: 114–125. 1935. Alpine algae from the Santa Marta Mountains, Colombia. Amer. Jour. Bot., 22: 763–781; Pls. 1–3. 1935a.* Phytoplankton of Isle Royale. Trans. Amer. Microsc. Soc., 54: 83–97; Pls. 14–17. 1937.† Marine algae of the northeastern coast of North America. 427 pp.; Pls. 1–60. Ann Arbor.

TAYLOR, WM. RANDOLPH, and COLTON, H. S. 1928. The phytoplankton of some Arizona pools and lakes. Amer. Jour. Bot., 15: 596–614; Pls. 46, 47.

TEILING, E. 1912. Schwedische Planktonalgen. I. . Phytoplankton aus dem Rástasjön bei Stockholm. Svensk Bot. Tidskr., 6: 266–281. 1916. *Ibid.*, II. *Tetrallantos*, eine neue Gattung der Protococcoideen. *Ibid.*, 10: 59–66; Figs. 1–15. 1941. *Aeruginosa* oder *flos-aquae*, eine kleine *Microcystis*-studie. *Ibid.*, 35(No. 4): 337–349; Figs. 1–12. 1946. Zur Phytoplanktonflora Schwedens. Bot. Notiser, 1946: 61–88; Figs. 1–22.

TEMPERLY, B. N. 1936. The boghead controversy and the morphology of the boghead algae. Trans. Roy. Soc. Edinburgh, 58(Pt. 3): 855–868.

TEODORESCO, E. C. 1907. Matériaux pour la flore algologique de la Roumaine. Beih. Bot. Centralbl., 21(No. 2): 103–219.

THIENEMANN, AUGUST. 1935. Die Bedeutung der Limnologie für die Kultur der Gegenwart. Stuttgart.

THOMPSON, H. D. 1896.*` Report on the plants. Appendix I. *In* A biological examination of Lake Michigan in the Traverse Bay region. Bull. Mich. Fish. Comm., 6: 3–93; Pls. 1–3.

THOMPSON, R. H. 1938. A preliminary survey of the freshwater algae of eastern Kansas. Univ. Kansas Sci. Bull., 25: 5–83; Pls. 1–12. 1938a. *Coronastrum*, a new genus of algae in the family Scenedesmaceae. Amer. Jour. Bot., 25: 692–694; Figs. 1–10. 1947. Fresh-water Dinoflagellates of Maryland. State Md. Bd. Nat. Resources, Publ. No. 67: 3–24; Pls. 1–4. 1949. Immobile Dinophyceae. I. New records and a new species. Amer. Jour. Bot., 36 (No. 3): 301–308; Figs. 1–34.

THUNMARK, S. 1945. Die Abwasserfrage der Växjöseen in hydrobiologische Beleuchtung. Medd. f. Lunds Univ. Limnol. Inst., No. 4: 1–239; Figs. 1–46.

THURET, G. 1850. Recherches sur les zoospores des algues et les anthéridies des cryptogames. Ann. Sci. Nat. Bot., 14(Sér. 3): 214–260; Pls. 16–31. 1875. Essai de classification des Nostochinées. *Ibid.*, 1(Sér. 6): 372–382. 1885. *In* Hauck, F. 1885. Des Meeresalgen Deutschlands und Oesterreichs. Rabenhorst's Kryptogamen-Flora. 2. Leipzig. 1887. *In* E. Bornet and Ch. Flahault, Revision des Nostocacées. Ann. Sci. Nat. Bot., 5(Sér. 7): 51–129.

THURET, G., and BORNET, E. 1878. Etudes phycologiques. Paris.

TIFFANY, L. H. 1921. New forms of *Oedogonium*. Ohio Jour. Sci., 21: 272–274. 1921a. Algal food of the young gizzard shad. *Ibid.*, 21: 113–122. 1924. Some new forms of *Spirogyra* and *Oedogonium*. *Ibid.*, 24: 180–190; Pls. 1–3. 1926. The filamentous algae of northwestern Iowa, with special reference to the Oedogoniaceae. Trans. Amer. Microsc. Soc., 45: 69–132; Pls. 1–16. 1926a. The algal collection of a single fish. Pap. Mich. Acad. Sci., Arts, and Letters, 6: 303–306. 1927. New species and varieties of Chlorophyceae. Bot. Gaz., 83: 202–206; Pl. 9. 1928. The algal genus *Bulbochaete*. Trans. Amer. Microsc. Soc., 47: 121–177; Pls. 14–23. 1929. A key to the species, varieties, and forms of the algal genus *Oedogonium*. Ohio Jour. Sci., 29: 62–80. 1930.†* The Oedogoniaceae, a monograph. 188 pp.; 64 pls. Columbus, Ohio. 1934.†* The Oedogoniaceae. Supplementary paper number one. Ohio Jour. Sci., 34: 323–326. 1934a. The plankton algae of the west end of Lake Erie. Ohio State Univ., Franz Theodore Stone Lab., Contrib. No. 6. 112 pp.; Figs. 1–374. 1936. Wille's collection of Puerto Rican fresh-water algae. Brittonia, 2: 165–176; Pls. 1–3. 1936a. New species of *Oedogonium*. Trans. Amer. Microsc. Soc., 55: 1–5; Pl. 1. 1937.† Oedogoniales. Oedogoniaceae. N. Amer. Flora, 11, Part 1. 102 pp. New York Bot. Gard. 1937a. The filamentous algae of the west end of Lake Erie. Amer. Midl. Nat., 18: 911–951; Pls. 1–9. 1937b. Brazilian Oedogoniales. Rev. Sudamer. Bot., Montevideo, 4: 5–14; Figs. 1–6. 1938. Algae: the grass of many waters. Springfield, Ill.

TIFFANY, L. H., and AHLSTROM, E. H. 1931. New and interesting plankton algae from Lake Erie. Ohio Jour. Sci., 31: 455–467; Pls. 1–3.

TIFFANY, L. H., and BRITTON, M. E. 1944. Freshwater Chlorophyceae and Xanthophyceae from Puerto Rico. Ohio Jour. Sci., 44: 39–50.

TIFFANY, L. H., and TRANSEAU, E. N. 1927. Oedogonium periodicity in the north central states. Trans. Amer. Microsc. Soc., 46: 166–174; Figs. 1–3.

TILDEN, JOSEPHINE E. 1895. List of freshwater algae collected in Minnesota during 1884. Minn. Bot. Studies, 1(No. 20): 228–237. 1898. List of freshwater algae collected in Minnesota during 1896 and 1897. *Ibid.*, 2(No. 3): 25–29. 1910.* Minnesota algae. I. 328 pp.; Pls. 1–20. Minneapolis. 1935. The algae and their life relations. 550 pp.; Figs. 1–257. Minneapolis.

TIMBERLAKE, H. G. 1902.* Development and structure of the swarmspores of *Hydrodictyon*. Trans. Wis. Acad. Sci., Arts, and Letters, 13: 486–522.

TRANSEAU, E. N. 1913. The periodicity of algae in Illinois. Trans. Amer. Microsc. Soc., 32: 31–40; Figs. 1–8. 1913a. Annotated list of algae of eastern Illinois. Trans. Ill. Acad. Sci., 6: 69–89. 1913b. The life history of *Gloeotaenium*. Bot. Gaz., 55: 66–73; Pl. 3. 1914. New species of green algae. Amer. Jour. Bot., 1: 289–301; Pls. 25–29. 1915.* Notes on the Zygnemales. Ohio Jour. Sci., 16: 17–31. 1916. The periodicity of freshwater algae. Amer. Jour. Bot., 3: 121–133; Figs. 1–3. 1917.* The algae of Michigan. Ohio Jour. Sci., 17: 217–232. 1925.†* The genus *Debarya*. *Ibid.*, 25: 193–199; Pls. 1, 2. 1926.†* The genus *Mougeotia*. *Ibid.*, 26: 311–351; Pls. 1–7. 1933.†* The genus *Zygogonium*. *Ibid.*, 33: 156–162; Pls. 1, 2. 1934.†* The genera of the Zygnemataceae. Trans. Amer. Microsc. Soc., 53: 201–207. 1934a. Notes on the Zygnemataceae. Ohio Jour. Sci., 34: 420. 1938. Notes on Zygnemataceae. Amer. Jour. Bot., 25(7): 524–528; Figs. 1–19. 1943. Two new Ulotrichales.

Ohio Jour. Sci., 43: 212–213. 1944. Notes on Zygnemataceae. *Ibid.*, 44: 243–244.

TRANSEAU, E. N., and TIFFANY, L. H. 1919. New Oedogoniaceae. Ohio Jour. Sci., 19: 240–243.

TRANSEAU, E. N., TIFFANY, L. H., TAFT, C. E., and LI, L. C. 1934.* New species of Zygnemataceae. Trans. Amer. Microsc. Soc., 53: 208–230; Pls. 17–21.

TRELEASE, W. 1889.* The "working" of the Madison Lakes. Trans. Wis. Acad. Sci., Arts, and Letters, 7: 121–129.

TRESSLER, W. L. 1939. The zooplankton in relation to the metabolism of lakes. *In* Problems of Lake Biology. Amer. Assoc. Adv. Sci., Publ. No. 10: 79–93.

TRESSLER, W. L., and DOMOGALLA, B. P. 1931.* Limnological studies of Lake Wingra. Trans. Wis. Acad. Sci., Arts, and Letters, 26: 331–351.

TRESSLER, W. L., TIFFANY, L. H., and SPENCER, W. P. 1940. Limnological studies of Buckeye Lake, Ohio. Ohio Jour. Sci., 40: 261–290.

TROÏTZKAJA, O. V. 1922. De Carteriis nonnullis minus cognitis notulae. Not. Syst. Inst. Crypt. Horti Bot. Petropol., 1(No. 8): 114–119. 1922a. De varietate nova *Anabaena Scheremetievi* Elenk. *Ibid.*, 1(No. 5): 77–78. 1923. *Chlamydomonas sphaerica* Troïtzk. nov. sp. *Ibid.*, 2(No. 6): 81–82. 1923a. De affinitate inter *Coelosphaerium* Näg. et *Gomphosphaerium* Kütz. *Ibid.*, 2(No. 5): 69–73.

TURNER, W. B. 1893. Algae aquae dulcis Indiae orientalis. Kongl. Sv.-Vet. Handl., 25(No. 5): 1–187; Pls. 1–23.

TURPIN, P. J. 1827. Dictionnaire des Sciences Naturelles. Vol. 50. ed. F. G. Levrault. 1828. Aperçu organographique sur le nombre deux. Mém. Mus. d'Hist. Nat. par les Prof. de cet establissement, 16: 296–344.

UNGER, FRANZ. 1854. Beiträge zur Kenntniss der niedersten Algenformen, nebst Versuchen ihre Entstehung betreffend. Denskr. Akad. Wiss. Wien, 7: 185–196.

UNGER, W. B. 1941. A new variety of *Trachelomonas urceolata* (Protozoa, Mastigophora). Bull. Mt. Desert Isl. Biol. Lab., 1941: 15–17. 1941a. A preliminary survey of the protozoa of Beaver Lake near Salsbury Cove, Maine. *Ibid.*, 1941: 17–18.

VAUCHER, J. P. 1803. Histoire des confervés d'eau douce. Geneva.

VELASQUEZ, GREGORIA T. 1939. On the viability of algae obtained from the digestive tract of the gizzard shad, *Dorosoma cepedianum* (Le Sueur). Amer. Midl. Nat., 22: 376–412; Pls. 1–7. 1940.* A list of the filamentous Myxophyceae from Michigan. *Ibid.*, 23: 178–181.

VIRIEUX, J. 1916. Recherches sur le plancton des lacs du Jura central. Ann. Biol. Lacustre, 8: 5–192; Figs. 1–46.

VISCHER, W. 1920. Sur le polymorphisme de L'*Ankistrodesmus Braunii* (Naegeli) Collins. Zeit. f. Hydrol., 1: 5–50.

WAERN, M. 1938. Om *Cladophora aegagropila*, *Nostoc pruniforme* och andra alger i Lilla Ullevifjärden, Mälaren. Bot. Notiser, 1938: 128–142.

WAHLSTEDT, L. J. 1875. Monografi öfver Sveriges och Norges Characeer. Christiania.

WAILES, C. H. 1928. Dinoflagellates and Protozoa from British Columbia with descriptions of new species. Mus. and Art Notes (Vancouver, B. C.), 3: 1–8. 1929. Alpine Rhizopoda and Peridiniidae from British Columbia. Ann. Protist., Paris, 2: 179–183.

WAKSMAN, SELMAN A. 1941. Aquatic bacteria in relation to the cycle of organic matter in lakes. *In* A Symposium on Hydrobiology. Madison.

WALLICH, G. C. 1877. Observations on the Coccosphere. Ann. and Mag. Nat. Hist., 19(Ser. 4): 342–349.

WALLROTH, F. W. 1815. Annus botanicus, sive supplementum tertium ad Curtii Sprengelii floram Halensem. Halle. 1833. Flora cryptogamica germanicae. Pars posterior. Nürnberg. 1833a. Compendium florae germanicae. IV. Nürnberg.

WALTON, L. B. 1915.† A review of the described species of the order Euglenoidina Bloch. Ohio State Univ. Bull., 19: 343–459; Pls. 12–26; Fig. 1. 1930. Studies concerning organisms occurring in water supplies with particular reference to those found in Ohio. Part. I. Ohio Biol. Surv. Bull. 5(No. 24): 1–86.

WALZ, J. 1866.† Beitrag zur Morphologie und Systematik der Gattung *Vaucheria* DC. Jahrb. Wiss. Bot., 5: 127–160; Pls. 12–14.

WARD, H. B., and WHIPPLE, G. C. 1918. Freshwater biology. 1111 pp.; Figs. 1–1547. New York.

WARMING, E. 1876. Om en Fircellet *Gonium* (Dujardins *Tetramonas socialis*). Bot. Tids., 9(Ser. 3): 69–83.

WARTMANN, B., and SCHENK, B. 1862. Schweizerische Kryptogamen. Exsiccate. Fasc. I. St. Gallen.

WATSON, J. B., and TILDEN, JOSEPHINE E. 1930. The algal genus *Schizomeris* and the occurrence of *Schizomeris Leibleinii* Kützing in Minnesota. Trans. Amer. Microsc. Soc., 49: 160–167.

WEBER, ROLAND. 1933. Beiträge zur Kenntnis der Gattung *Calothrix*. Arch. f. Protist., 79: 391–415.

WELCH, PAUL S. 1935. Limnology. New York. 1936.* Limnological investigation of a strongly basic bog lake surrounded by an extensive acid-forming bog mat. Pap. Mich. Acad. Sci., Arts, and Letters, 21: 727–751. 1936a.* A limnological study of a small *Sphagnum*–leather leaf–black spruce bog lake with special reference to its plankton. Trans. Amer. Microsc. Soc., 55: 300–312. 1938.† A limnological study of a bog lake which has never developed a marginal mat. *Ibid.*, 57: 344–357. 1941. Dissolved oxygen in relation to lake types. *In* A Symposium on Hydrobiology. Madison.

WESENBURG-LUND, G. 1908. Plankton investigations of the Danish lakes. General Part. The Baltic fresh-water plankton, its origin and variation. Copenhagen.

WEST, G. S. 1899. The alga-flora of Cambridgeshire. Jour. Bot., 37: 49–58, 106–116, 216–225, 262–268, 291–299. 1902. On some algae from hot springs. *Ibid.*, 40: 241–248; Pl. 439. 1904. A treatise on the British freshwater algae. 372 pp.; Figs. 1–166. Cambridge. 1904a. West Indian freshwater algae. Jour. Bot., 42: 281–294; Pl. 464. 1905. A comparative study of the dominant phanerogamic and higher cryptogamic flora of aquatic habit in three lake areas of Scotland. Proc. Roy. Soc. Edinburgh, 25(No. 11): 976–1023. 1907. Report on the freshwater algae, including phytoplankton, of the Third Tanganyika Expedition conducted by Dr. W. A. Cunnington, 1904–1905. Jour. Linn. Soc. Bot., 38: 81–197; Pls. 1–8. 1908. Some critical green algae. *Ibid.*, 38: 279–289; Pls. 20, 21. 1909. A biological investigation of the Peridineae of Sutton Park, Warwickshire. New Phytol., 8: 181–196. 1909a. The algae of the Yan Yean Reservoir, Victoria; a biological and ecological study. Jour. Linn. Soc. Bot., 39: 1–88; Pls. 1–6; Figs. 1–10. 1912. Algological notes.—X–XIII. Jour. Bot., 50: 321–331. 1914. A contribution to our knowledge of the freshwater algae of Columbia. Mém. Soc. Neuchat. Sci. Nat., 5: 1013–1051. 1915. Algological Notes XIV–XVII. Jour. Bot., 53: 73–84. 1916.† Algae. Vol. I. Myxophyceae, Peridineae, Bacillariaceae, Chlorophyceae, together with a brief summary of the occurrence and distribution of freshwater algae. 475 pp.; Figs. 1–271. Cambridge.

WEST, G. S., and FRITSCH, F. E. 1927.† A treatise on the British fresh-water algae. 534 pp.; Figs. 1–207. Cambridge.

WEST, W. 1891. Notes on Danish algae. Nuova Notarisia, 1891: 418–425. 1892. Algae of the English lake district. Jour. Roy. Microsc. Soc. London, 1892: 713–748; Pls. 9–10.

WEST, W., and WEST, G. S. 1894. New British freshwater algae. Jour. Roy. Microsc. Soc. London, 1894: 1–17. 1895. A contribution to our knowledge of the freshwater algae of Madagascar. Trans. Linn. Soc. Bot., 5(Ser. 2): 41–90. 1895a. New American algae. Jour. Bot., 33: 52. 1895b. On some freshwater algae from the West Indies. Jour. Linn. Soc. Bot., 30(1893–1895): 264–280. 1896. On some new and interesting fresh-water algae. Jour. Roy. Microsc. Soc. London, 1896: 149–165. 1896a. Algae from Central Africa. Jour. Bot., 34: 377–384. 1897. Welwitch's African freshwater algae. Ibid., 35: 1–7, 33–42, 77–89, 113–122, 172–183, 235–243, 264–272, 297–304. 1897a. A contribution to the freshwater algae of the south of England. Jour. Roy. Microsc. Soc. London, 1897: 467–511. 1898. Notes on freshwater algae of the West Indies. Jour. Linn. Soc. Bot., 34: 279–295. 1900. Notes on freshwater algae. II. Jour. Bot., 38: 289–299. 1900–1901. The alga-flora of Yorkshire; a complete account of the known fresh-water algae of the county. Bot. Trans. York. Nat. Union, 5, Pt. 22: 5–22; Pt. 23: 53–100; Pt. 25(1901): 101–164; Pt. 27(1901): 165–239. 1901. Fresh-water Cyanophyceae. In J. Schmidt, Flora of Koh Chang, Part 4. Bot. Tids., 24: 157–186. 1902. A contribution to the freshwater algae of the north of Ireland. Trans. Roy. Irish Acad., 32(B): 1–100. 1902a. A contribution to the freshwater algae of Ceylon. Trans. Linn. Soc. Bot., 6(Ser. 2): 123–215. 1903. Notes on freshwater algae. III. Jour. Bot., 41: 33–41, 74–82; Pls. 446–448. 1903a. Scottish fresh-water plankton—No. 1. Jour. Linn. Soc. Bot., 35: 519–556; Pls. 14–18. 1905. Freshwater algae from the Orkneys and Shetlands. Trans. Bot. Soc. Edinburgh, 23: 3–41. 1905a. A further contribution to the freshwater plankton of the Scottish Lochs. Trans. Roy. Soc. Edinburgh, 41, Pt. 3: 477–518; Pls. 1–7. 1906. A comparative study of the plankton of some Irish lakes. Trans. Roy. Irish Acad., 33(B): 77–116; Pls. 6–11. 1907. Freshwater algae from Burma, including a few from Bengal and Madras. Ann. Roy. Bot. Gard. Calcutta, 6(Pt. 2): 175–260; Pls. 10–16. 1909. The phytoplankton of the English lake district. Naturalist, 1909: 115–193, 260–321; Pls. 5–7. 1912. On the periodicity of the phytoplankton of some British lakes. Jour Linn. Soc. Bot., 40: 395–432; Pl. 19; Figs. 1–4.

WHELDEN, R. M. 1939. Notes on New England algae I: Cyclonexis and Actidesmium. Rhodora, 41: 133–136; Figs. 1–7. 1941. Some observations on freshwater algae of Florida. Jour. Elisha Mitchell Sci. Soc., 57: 261–271; Pls. 5, 6. 1942. Notes on New England algae. II. Some interesting New Hampshire algae. Rhodora, 44: 175–187; Figs. 1–6. 1943. Notes on New England algae. III. Some interesting algae from Maine. Farlowia, 1: 9–23; Figs. 1–18.

WHIPPLE, GEO. C. 1927. The microscopy of drinking water. 586 pp.; Pls. 1–19. 4th ed. New York.

WHIPPLE, GEO. C., and PARKER, H. N. 1902. On the amount of oxygen and carbon dioxide in neutral waters and the effect of these gases upon the occurrence of microscopic organisms. Trans. Amer. Microsc. Soc., 23: 103–144.

WHITFORD, L. A. 1936. New and little known algae from North Carolina. Jour. Elisha Mitchell Sci. Soc., 52: 93–98; Pl. 12. 1938. A new green alga: Oedocladium Lewisii. Bull. Torr. Bot. Club, 65: 23–26; Pl. 2. 1943. The fresh-water algae of North Carolina. Jour. Elisha Mitchell Sci. Soc., 50: 131–170.

WHITNEY, L. W. 1937. Microstratification of the waters of inland lakes in summer. Science, 85: 224–225.

WHITSON, A. R., DUNNEWALD, T. J., and THOMPSON, CARL. 1921. Soil survey of northern Wisconsin. Wis. Geol. and Nat. Hist. Surv. Bull. 55(Soil Ser., No. 27). Madison.

WHITSON, A. R., GEIB, W. J., and TOSTERUD, M. O. 1921. Soil survey of Waupaca County, Wisconsin. Wis. Geol. and Nat. Hist. Surv. Bull. 54–C (Soil Ser., No. 25). Madison.

WIEBE, A. H. 1930. Investigations on plankton production in fish ponds. Bull. U. S. Bur. Fish., 46: 137–176. 1930a. Notes on the exposure of young fish to varying concentrations of arsenic. Trans. Amer. Fish. Soc., 60: 270–280.

WIEBE, A. H., RADCLIFFE, R., and WARD, FERN. 1929. The effects of various fertilizers on plankton production. Trans. Amer. Fish. Soc., 59: 94–105.

WILLE, N. 1879. Ferskvandsalger fra Novaja Semla samlede af Dr. F. Kjellman paa Nordenskiölds Expedition. Oefv. Kongl. Sv. Vet.-Akad. Förhandl., 36 (No. 5): 13–74. 1881. Om Hvileceller hos Conferva (L) Wille. Ibid., 38(No. 8): 3–26; Pls. 1, 2. 1884. Bidrag til Sydamerikas Algflora I–III. Bih. Kongl. Sv. Vet.-Akad. Handl., 8(No. 18): 1–64; Pls. 1–3. 1887. Algologische Mittheilung. I. Ueber die Schwärmzellen und deren Copulation bei Trentepohlia Mart. Jahrb. Wiss. Bot., 18: 426–434; Pl. 16; Figs. 1–11. 1887a. Ibid., IV. Ueber die Zelltheilung bei Oedogonium. Ibid., 18: 443–454; Pls. 16, 17. 1887b. Ibid., VIII. Ueber die Gattung Gongrosira Kütz. Ibid., 18: 484–491; 1 pl. 1897. Chlorophyceae. In A. Engler and K. Prantl, Die Natürlichen Pflanzenfamilien. Teil 1, Abt. 2. Leipzig. 1898. Beschreibung einiger Planktonalgen aus norwegischen Süsswasserseen. Biol. Centralbl., 18: 302. 1899. New forms of green algae. Rhodora, 1: 149–150. 1900. Asterocytis ramosa (Thw.) Gobi. Nyt Mag. f. Natur., 38: 7–10; Pl. 1. 1900a. Algologische Notizen. I–VI. Nyt Mag. f. Natur., 38: 1–27. 1901. Studien über Chlorophyceen. I–VII. Videns. Skrift. i Christiania, I. Mat.-Nat. Kl., 1900(No. 6): 1–46. 1901a. Algologische Notizen. VII–VIII. Nyt Mag. f. Natur., 39: 1–22. 1902. In F. S. Collins, I. Holden, and W. A. Setchell. Phycotheca boreali-americana. 1908. Zur Entwicklungsgeschichte der Gattung Oocystis. Ber. d. Deutsch. Bot. Ges., 26A: 812–822; Pl. 15. 1909. Ueber Wittrockiella nov. gen. Nyt Mag. f. Natur., 47: 5–21; Pls. 1–4. 1910. Algologische Notizen. XVI–XXI. Ibid., 48: 281–306; Pls. 1, 2. 1911.† Conjugatae, Chlorophyceae, Characeae. In A. Engler and K. Prantl, Die Natürlichen Pflanzenfamilien. Teil 1, Abt. 2: 1–136; Figs. 1–70. Leipzig. 1912. Algologische Notizen. XXII–XXIV. Ueber eine neue epiphytische Art von Lyngbya. Nyt Mag. f. Natur., 51: 1–26. 1914. Botanische und zoologische ergebnisse einer Wissenschaftlichen Forschungsreise nach den Samoainseln, dem Nauguinea-Archipel und den Salomonsinseln von März bis Dezember 1905. Denks. d. Mat.-Nat. Kl. d. Kaiser. Akad. Wiss., 91: 1–22; Pls. 1–3 (reprint). 1918. Algologische Notizen XXV–XXIX. Nyt Mag. f. Natur., 56: 1–60; Pls. 1, 2. 1925. Vorarbeiten zu einer Monographie der Chroococcaceen. Ibid., 62: 170–209.

WILLIAMSON, BEN L., GREENBANK, JOHN, MILLER, E. P., et al. 1938–1939* Investigation of the pollution of the Fox and East Rivers and of Green Bay in the vicinity of the City of Green Bay. Mimeogr. by Wisconsin State Committee on Water Pollution, the State Board of Health and Green Bay Metropolitan Sewerage District.

WILSON, IRA T., and OPDYKE, DAVID F. 1941. The distribution of the chemical constituents in the accumulated sediment of Tippecanoe Lake. Investigation Indiana Lakes and Streams, 2: 16–43. Indianapolis.

WILSON, L. R. 1937. A quantitative and ecological study of the larger aquatic plants of Sweeney Lake, Oneida County, Wisconsin. Bull. Torr. Bot. Club, 64: 199–208. 1941.* The larger aquatic vegetation of Trout Lake, Vilas County, Wisconsin. Trans. Wis. Acad. Sci., Arts and Letters, 33: 135–146.

WIMMER, E. J. 1929.* A study of two limestone quarry pools, Trans. Wis. Acad. Sci., Arts, and Letters, 24: 363–399.

WISLOUCH, S. M. 1911. Ueber eine durch *Oscillaria Agardhii* hervorgerfene wasserblüte, sowie über *Spirulina flavovirens* (nova sp.) mihi. Bull. Jard. Imp. Bot. Pierre le Grand, 11(No. 6): 155–161. 1914. Sur les Chrysomonadines des environs de Petrograd. Jour. Microbiol. Petrograd, 1: 251–278.

WITTROCK, V. B. 1867. Algologiska Studier, I–II. Upsala. 1868. Bidrag till kannedomen om Sveriges Zygnemacéer och Mesocarpacéer. Bot. Notiser, 1868: 187–190. 1871. Dispositio Oedogoniacearum suecicarum. Oefv. Kongl. Sv. Vet.-Akad. Förhandl., 27, No. 3(1870): 119–144. 1871a. Beitrag zur Kenntnis der Zygnemaceen und Mesocarpeen. Hedwigia, 10: 88. 1872. Om Gotlands och Oelands Sötvattens-alger. Bih. Kongl. Sv. Vet.-Akad. Handl., 1(No. 1): 1–72. 1872a. Oedogoniaceae novae, in Suecia lectae, quas descripsit. Bot. Notiser, 1872: 1–8. 1875. Prodromus monographiae Oedogoniearum. Nova Acta Soc. Sci. Upsala, 9(1874): 1–64; Pl. 1. 1876. *In* C. F. O. Nordstedt and V. Wittrock. 1876. II. Oedogonieae De Bar., Pringsh. Oefv. Kongl. Sv. Vet.-Akad. Förhandl., 33(No. 6): 44–56. 1877. On the development and systematik arrangement of the Pithophoraceae, a new order of algae. *Ibid.*, Vol. Extra Ordine, Editum, 1877: 1–80; Pls. 1–6. 1878. Oedogonieae Americanae, hucusque cognitae, quas enumeravit. Bot. Notiser, 1878: 133–145. 1878a. On the spore-formation of the Mesocarpeae and especially of the new genus *Gonatonema*. Bih. Kongl. Sv. Vet.-Akad. Handl., 5(No. 5): 1–18; Pl. 1. 1880. Points-fortekning öfver Skandinaviens vaxter, Part 4. Lund. 1882. *In* V. B. Wittrock and C. F. Nordstedt, Algae aquae dulcis exsiccatae. Bot. Notiser, 1882: 51–61. 1886. Om *Binuclearia*, ett nytt confervace-slägte. Bih. Kongl. Sv. Vet.-Akad. Handl., 12, Afd. 3, No. 1: 3–10; 1 pl.

WITTROCK, V. B., and CLEVE, P. T. 1875. *In* V. B. Wittrock, Prodromus monographiae Oedogoniearum. Nova. Acta Soc. Sci. Upsala, 9(1874): 1–64; Pl. 1.

WITTROCK, V. B., and LUNDELL, P. M. 1871. *In* V. B. Wittrock, Dispositio Oedogoniacearum suecicarum. Oefv. Kongl. Sv. Vet.-Akad. Förhandl., 27 (1870): 119–144.

WITTROCK, V. B., and NORDSTEDT, C. F. O. 1877–1903. Algae aquae dulcis exsiccatae (Nos. 1–1612). 1877. Algae aquae dulcis exsiccatae (Fasc. 1 and 2, Nos. 1–100). Bot. Notiser, 1877: 21–26. 1878. Algae aquae dulcis exsiccatae, etc. (Fasc. 3, Nos. 101–150; Fasc. 4, Nos. 151–200). *Ibid.*, 1878: 67–73. 1879. Algae aquae dulcis exsiccatae (Nos. 201–298). *Ibid.*, 1879: 20–27. 1882. Algae exsiccatae (Nos. 401–500). *Ibid.*, 1882: 51–61. 1884. Algae exsiccatae (Nos. 601–698). *Ibid.*, 1884: 121–128. 1886. Algae exsiccatae (Nos. 701–850). *Ibid.*, 1886: 130–139. 1893. Algae exsiccatae (Nos. 1001–1200). *Ibid.*, 1893: 185–200.

WOLLE, FRANCIS. 1887.* Freshwater algae of the United States. 364 pp. Pls. 1–210. 2 vols. Bethlehem, Pa.

WOŁOSZYŃSKA, J. 1914. *In* B. Schroeder, Zellpflanzen Oestafricas, gesammelt auf der Akademischen Studienfahrt 1910. V. Studien über das Phytoplankton des Viktoriasees. Hedwigia, 55: 184–223; Pls. 2–8. 1916. Polonische Süsswasser-peridineen. Bull. Inter. Acad. Sci. Cracovie, Math. et Nat. Cl., Reihe B: Biol. Wissen., No. 8–10(1915): 260–285; Pls. 10–14. 1918. Neue Peridineen-Arten, nebst Bemerkungen über den Bau der Hülle bei *Gymno-* und *Glenodinium. Ibid.*, No. 4–6(1917): 114–122; Pls. 11–13. 1917a.

Beitrag zur Kenntnis der Algenflora Litauens. *Ibid.*, No. 4–6(1917): 123–130. 1919. Die Algen der Tatraseen und Tümpel. I. *Ibid.* (1918): 196–200. 1925. Beiträge zur Kenntnis der Süsswasser-Dinoflagellaten Polens. Polskie Towarzystwo botaniczne (Acta Soc. Bot. Poloniae), 3: 46–69; Figs. 1–7. 1930. Beiträge zur Kenntnis des Phytoplanktons Tropischer Seen. Arch. d'Hydrobiol. u. d'Ichty., 5: 159–160; Figs. 1–6. 1936. Die Algen der Tatraseen und Tümpel. III. Peridineen im Winterplankton einiger Tatraseen. *Ibid.*, 10: 188–196; Pl. 9.

WOOD, H. C. 1867. On *Oedogonium Huntii*. Proc. Amer. Philos. Soc., 10: 333–335. 1869.* Prodromus of a study of the fresh water algae of eastern North America. *Ibid.*, 11: 119–145. 1874.* A contribution to the history of the fresh-water algae of North America. Smiths. Contrib. Knowledge, 19 (No. 241): 1–262; Pls. 1–21.

WOOD, R. D. 1947. Characeae of the Put-in-Bay region of Lake Erie (Ohio). Ohio Jour. Sci., 47: 240–258; Pls. 1–3. 1949. The Characeae of the Woods Hole region, Massachusetts. Biol. Bull., 96(No. 2): 179–203; Pls. 1–4.

WOODS, A. F. 1894. Coleochaetaceae, Characeae. Flora of Nebraska, Part II. Lincoln, Nebr.

WORONICHIN, N. N. 1923. Algae nonnullae novae e Caucaso. I. Not. Syst. Inst. Crypt. Horti Bot. Petropol., 2(No. 7): 97–100. 1923a. *Ibid.* II. *Ibid.*, 2, (No. 8): 113–116. *Ibid.* III. *Ibid.*, 2(No. 9): 140–142. 1923b. *Ibid.* IV. *Ibid.*, 2(No. 12): 192. 1924 *Ibid.* V. *Ibid.*, 3(No. 6): 84–88. 1924a. *Ibid.* VI. *Ibid.*, 3(No. 7): 102–106. 1924b. Matériaux pour la flore algologique des eaux douces du Caucase. V. Chlorophyceae. Zeit. Russ. Bot. Ges., 8 (1923): 78–86. 1925. Materialien zur Flora des Süsswasseralgen des Kaukasus. Trav. Stat. Biol. du Caucas. du Nord, 1(1925): 1–7. 1925a. Beiträge zur Kenntnis der Süsswasseralgen des Kaukasus, II, III. Arch. Russ. Protist., 4, No. 3/4: 199–216. 1930. [Algen des Polar- und des Nord-Urals]. Trav. Soc. Nat. Leningrad Soc. Bot., 60(No. 3): 3–80.

WORONIN, M. 1869. Beitrag zur Kenntniss der Vaucherien. Bot. Zeit., 27: 137–144, 153–162; Pls. 1, 2.

WORTHINGTON, E. B. 1939. Freshwater biology and its applications: Introduction. Ann. Appl. Biol., 26: 165–167.

YAMANOUCHI, S. 1913. *Hydrodictyon africanum*, a new species. Bot. Gaz., 55: 74–79; Figs. 1–6.

YOUNG, O. W. 1945.* A limnological investigation of periphyton in Douglas Lake, Michigan. Trans. Amer. Microsc. Soc., 64: 1–20.

ZACHARIAS, OTTO. 1897. Biologische Beobachtungen an den Versuchsteichen des Schles. Fischereivereins zu Trachenberg. Forsch. Biol. Stat. z. Plön, 5: 10–28. 1898. Untersuchungen über das Plankton der Teichgewässer. *Ibid.*, 6: 89–193; Pl. 4. 1899. Zur Kenntnis der Plankton sächsischer Fischteiche. *Ibid.*, 7: 78–95. 1903. Zur Kenntnis der niedern Flora und Fauna holsteinischer Moorsümpfe. *Ibid.*, 10: 223–289. 1903a. Drei neue Pflanzenflagellaten des Süsswassers. *Ibid.*, 10: 290–303. 1907. Planktonalgen als Molluskennahrung. Arch. f. Hydrobiol. u. Planktonk., 2: 358–361. 1911. Das Süsswasser-Plankton. Einführung in die freischwebende Organismenwelt unserer teiche, Flüsse und Seebecken. Leipzig.

ZALESSKY, M. D. 1926. Sur les nouvelles algues découvertes dans le sapropélogène du Lac Beloe et sur une algue sapropélogène *Botryococcus Braunii* Kützing. Rev. Gen. Bot., 38: 31–42.

ZANARDINI, G. 1858. Plantarum in mari rubro hucusque collectarum enumeratio. Mem. Ist. Veneto, 7: 209–309; Pls. 3–14.

ZANEVELD, J. S. 1939. *Nitella madagascarensis*, nov. spec., with notes on the Charophyta of Madagascar. Blumea, 3: 372–387.

[659]

Zederbauer, E. 1904. Geschlechtliche und ungeschlechtliche Fortpflanzung von *Ceratium hirundinella*. Ber. d. Deutsch. Bot. Ges., 22: 1–8.

Zeller, G. H. von. 1873. Algae collected by Mrs. S. Kurz in Arracan and British Burma. Jour. Asiatic Soc. Bengal, 42: 175–193.

Zimmer, Carl. 1899. Das Plankton des Oderstromes. A. Das tierische Plankton der Oder. Forsch. Biol. Stat. z. Plön, 7: 1–14.

Zimmermann, W. 1927. Ueber Algenbestände aus der Tiefenzone des Bodensees. Zur Oekologie und Soziologie der Tiefseepflanzen. Zeitsch. f. Bot., 20: 1–35; Pls. 1, 2; Figs. 1–5.

Zobell, Claude E. 1940. Some factors which influence oxygen consumption by bacteria in lake water. Biol. Bull., 78: 388–402.

Zukal, H. 1894. Neue Beobachtungen über einige Cyanophyceen. Ber. d. Deutsch. Bot. Ges., 12: 256–266.

References for Desmids and Diatoms

Fritsch, F. E. 1935. Structure and Reproduction of the Algae. Vol. I. 791 pp. Cambridge.

Hustedt, F. 1929. Die Kieselalgen. In: Rabenhorst, L. Kryptogamen-Flora Deutschlands, Osterreich, und der Schweiz. Bd. VII.

Irénée-Marie, Fr. 1939. Flore Desmidiale de la Region de Montréal. 547 pp. Laprairie, Canada.

Krieger, W. 1937. Die Desmidiaceen Europas mit Berucksichtigung der ausser-europäischen Arten. In: Rabenhorst, L. Kryptogamen-Flora Deutschlands, Osterreich und der Schweiz. Bd. XIII.

Prescott, G. W. 1964. How to Know the Fresh-Water Algae. 272 pp. Wm. C. Brown Co.

Smith, G. M. 1924. Phytoplankton of the Inland Lakes of Wisconsin. Part II. Desmidiaceae. Wisconsin Geol. & Nat. Hist. Surv., Bull. 57 (II). 227 pp. Madison.

Van Heurck, Henri. 1896. A Treatise on the Diatomaceae. 558 pp. William Wesly & Son, London.

West, W. and West, G. S. 1904-1912. A Monograph of the British Desmidiaceae. Vols. I-IV. and Carter, Nellie. 1924. *Ibid.* Vol. V. Ray Society, London.

PLATES

PLATE 1

Figs. 1, 2.   *Pyramimonas tetrarhynchus* Schmarda, × 750 (after Smith)

Fig. 3.   *Chlamydomonas angulosa* Dill, × 750

Fig. 4.   *Chlamydomonas Cienkowskii* Schmidle, × 750

Fig. 5.   *Chlamydomonas Dinobryoni* G. M. Smith, × 1000 (redrawn from Smith)

Figs. 6, 7.   *Chlamydomonas epiphytica* G. M. Smith, × 750 (redrawn from Smith)

Figs. 8, 9.   *Chlamydomonas globosa* Snow, × 1000 (8 after Smith)

Figs. 10, 11.   *Chlamydomonas polypyrenoideum* Prescott, × 1000

Fig. 12.   *Chlamydomonas pseudopertyi* Pascher, × 500

Figs. 13, 14.   *Chlamydomonas Snowii* Printz, × 1000 (redrawn from Smith)

Figs. 15, 16.   *Chlamydomonas sphagnicola* Fritsch & Takeda, × 1000

Figs. 17–19.   *Carteria Klebsii* (Dang.) Dill, × 1000 (redrawn from Smith

Fig. 20.   *Carteria cordiformis* (Carter) Diesing, × 1000 (redrawn from Smith)

Fig. 21.   *Gonium pectorale* Mueller, × 500

Fig. 22.   *Gonium sociale* (Duj.) Warming, × 750

Fig. 23.   *Pandorina morum* (Muell.) Bory, × 500

Figs. 24–26.   *Eudorina elegans* Ehrenberg: 24 and 25, × 440; 26, formation of daughter colonies, × 440

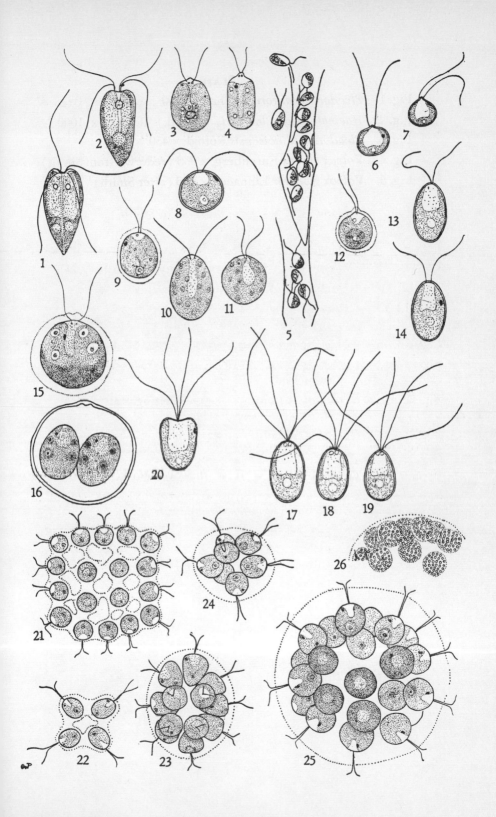

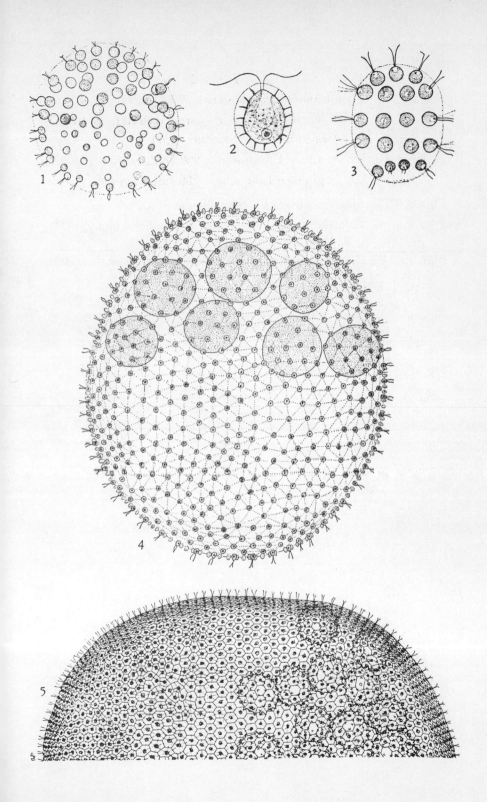

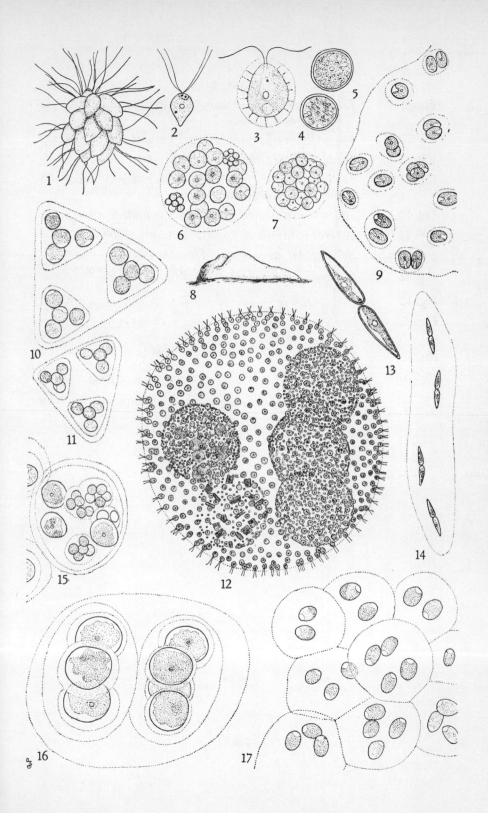

PLATE 4

Figs. 1, 2.   *Elakatothrix viridis* (Snow) Printz: 1, × about 620 (redrawn from Smith); 2, × 440

Figs. 3, 4.   *Palmodictyon varium* (Naeg.) Lemmermann, × 500

Figs. 5, 6.   *Palmodictyon viride* Kuetzing, × 500

Figs. 7–9.   *Stylosphaeridium stipitatum* (Bachm.) Geitler & Gimesi: 7, × 500; 8 and 9, single cells, × 1000

Fig. 10.   *Asterococcus superbus* (Cienk.) Scherffel, × 440

Fig. 11.   *Asterococcus limneticus* G. M. Smith, × 500

Figs. 12–14.   *Schizochlamys compacta* Prescott, × 500

Fig. 15.   *Schizochlamys gelatinosa* A. Braun, × 500

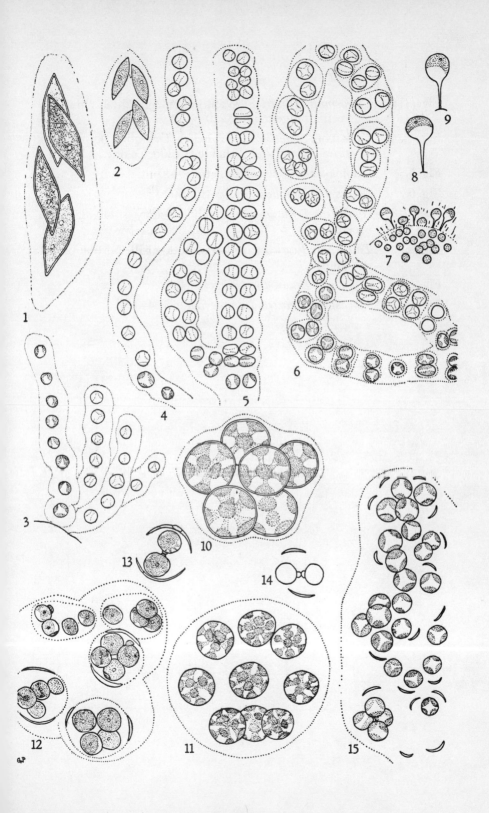

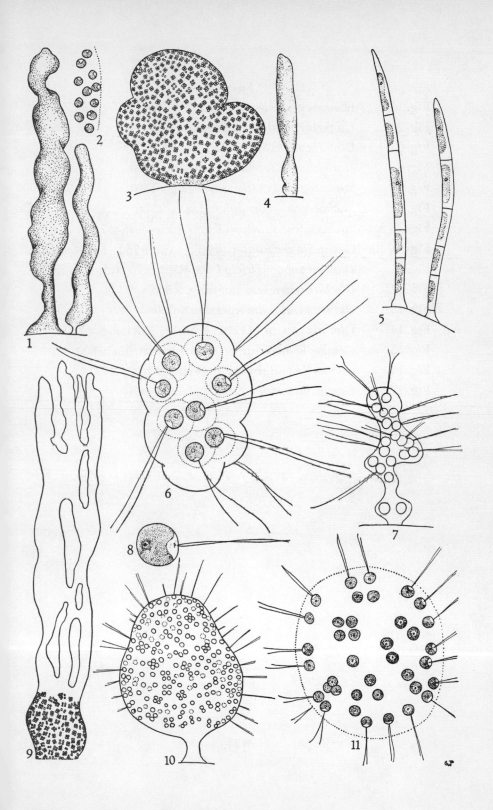

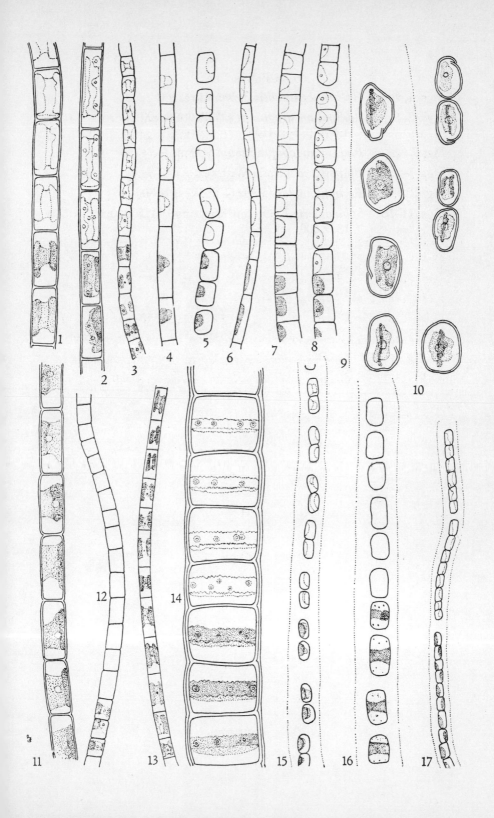

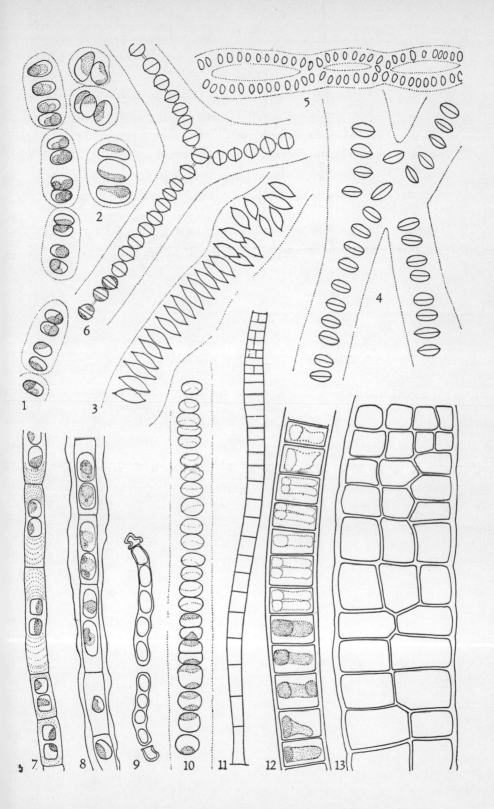

1   2   3   4   5   6

7   8   9   10   11   12   13

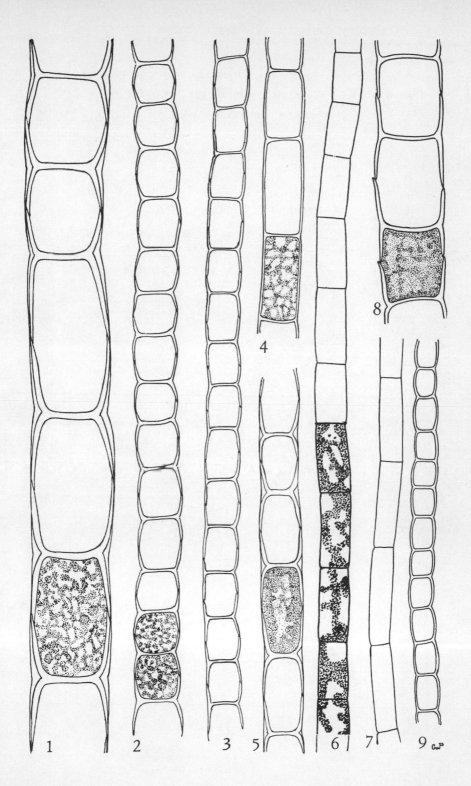

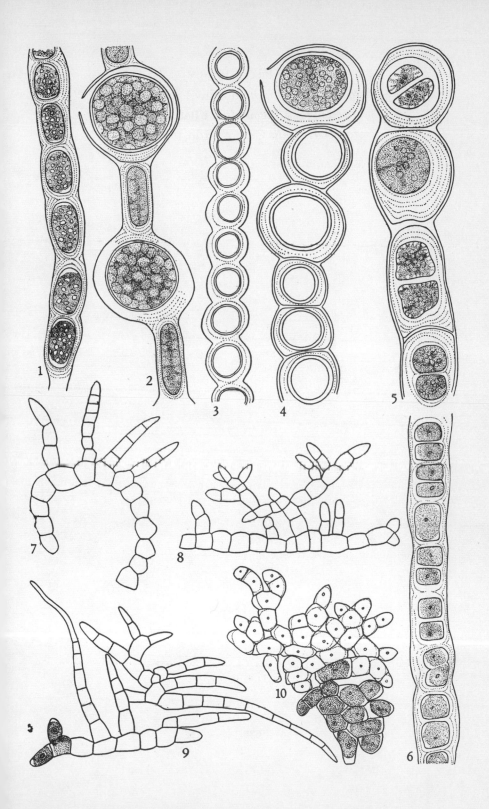

Plate 10

Figs. 1, 2. *Stigeoclonium lubricum* (Dillw.) Kuetzing, × 440

Figs. 3, 4. *Stigeoclonium subsecundum* Kuetzing: 3, × 500; 4, × 440

Figs. 5–7. *Protococcus viridis* C. A. Agardh, × 1000

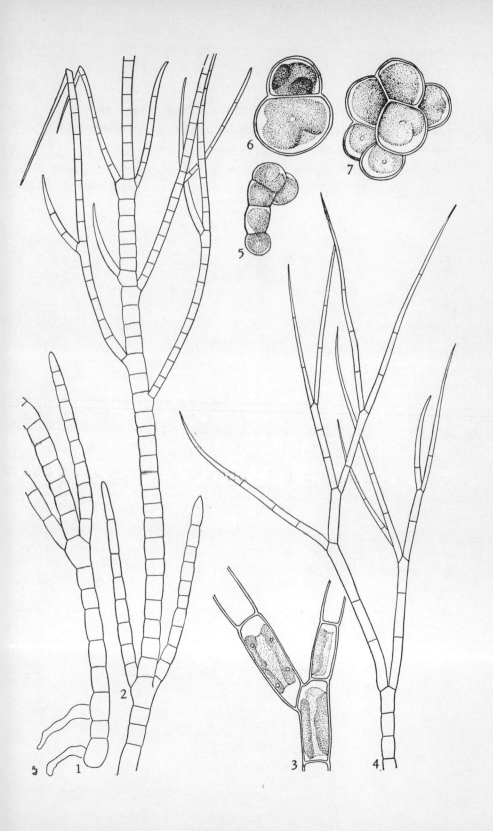

PLATE 11

Figs. 1, 2.   *Stigeoclonium flagelliferum* Kuetzing, × 440

Fig. 3.   *Stigeoclonium stagnatile* (Hazen) Collins, × 440

Fig. 4.   *Microthamnion Kuetzingianum* Naegeli, × 440

Figs. 5, 6.   *Microthamnion strictissimum* Rabenhorst: 5, × 1000; 6, base of plant, × 1000

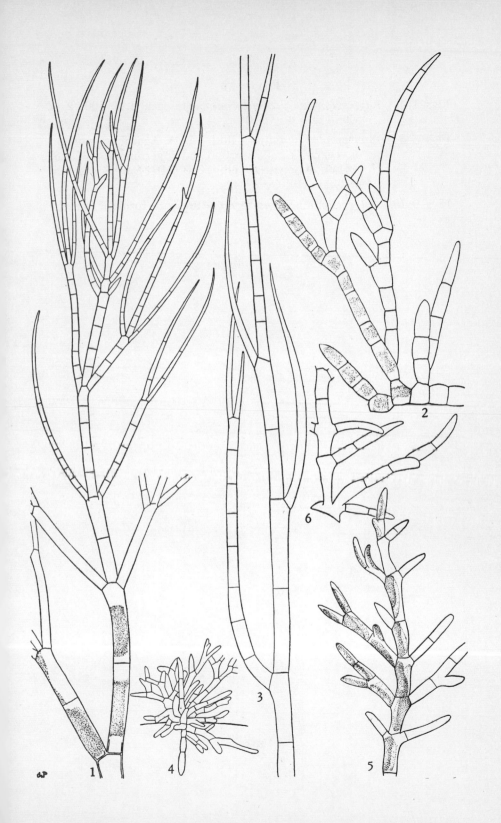

1   4   3   2   6   5

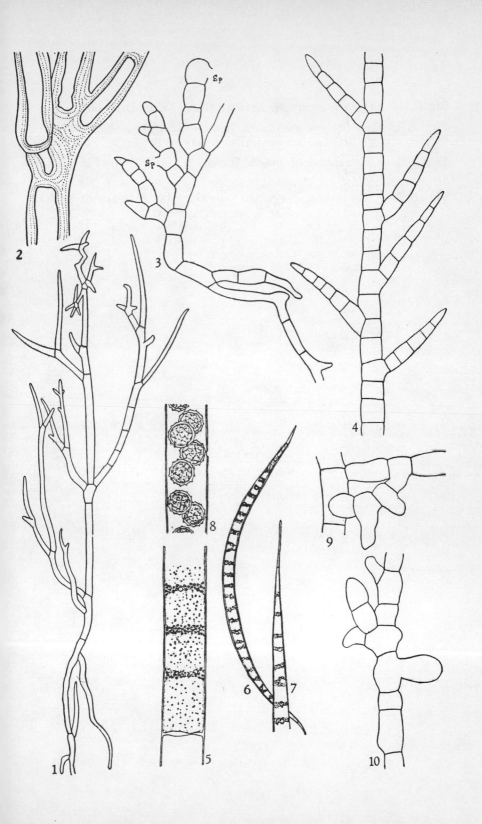

PLATE 13

Fig. 1.   *Stigeoclonium attenuatum* (Hazen) Collins, × 750

Figs. 2, 3.   *Chaetophora pisiformis* (Roth) C. A. Agardh: 2, habit, × 2; 3, portion of thallus, × 500

Figs. 4, 5.   *Chaetophora attenuata* Hazen: 4, × 440; 5, tip of branch, × 750

Figs. 6, 7.   *Chaetonema irregulare* Nowakowski: 6, filament with oogonium, × 500; 7, sporangia, × 500

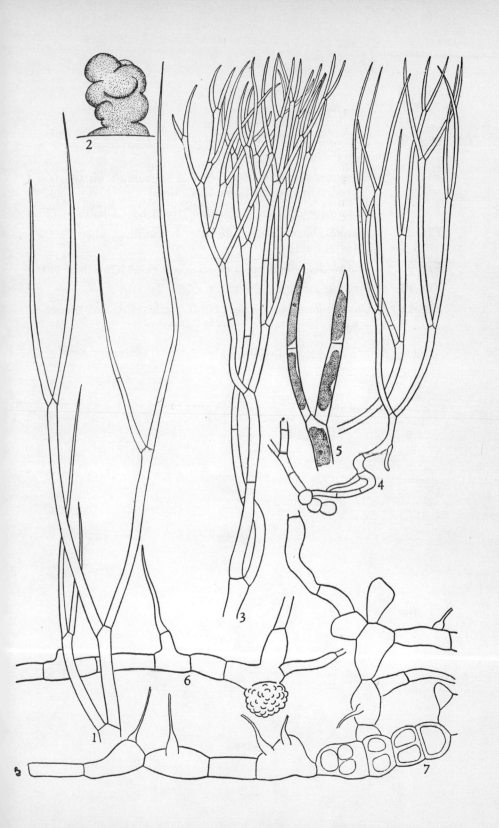

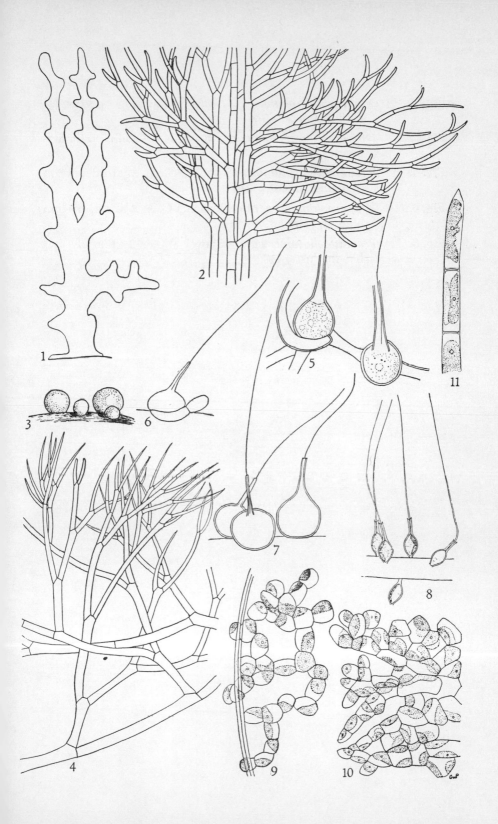

PLATE 15

Fig. 1   *Draparnaldia acuta* (C. A. Ag.) Kuetzing: portion of main filament, × 75

Figs. 2, 3.   *Draparnaldia platyzonata* Hazen: 2, portion of main filament, × 150; 3, × 350

Fig. 4.   *Draparnaldia plumosa* (Vauch.) C. A. Agardh: portion of main filament, × 165

Fig. 5.   *Draparnaldia glomerata* (Vauch.) C. A. Agardh: portion of main filament, × 150

Fig. 6.   *Pseudulvella americana* (Snow) Wille: portion of disc-like thallus, × 440

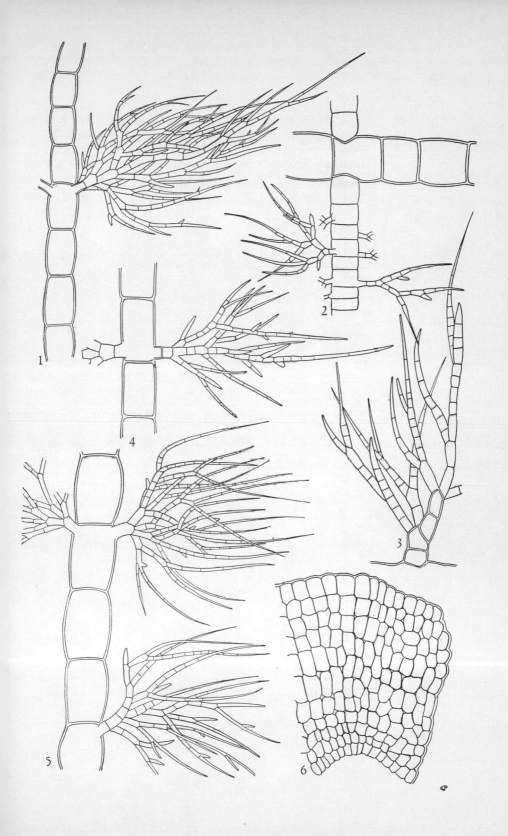

1

2

4

3

5

6

PLATE 16

Figs. 1–5.   *Draparnaldia Judayi* Prescott: 1, portion of main axis showing sparsely branched fascicles; 2–4, forms of setae, some of which replace lateral branches of main filament; 5, whorled arrangement of fascicles; all × 500

Fig. 6.   *Chaetopeltis orbicularis* Berthold: habit on filamentous alga, × 440

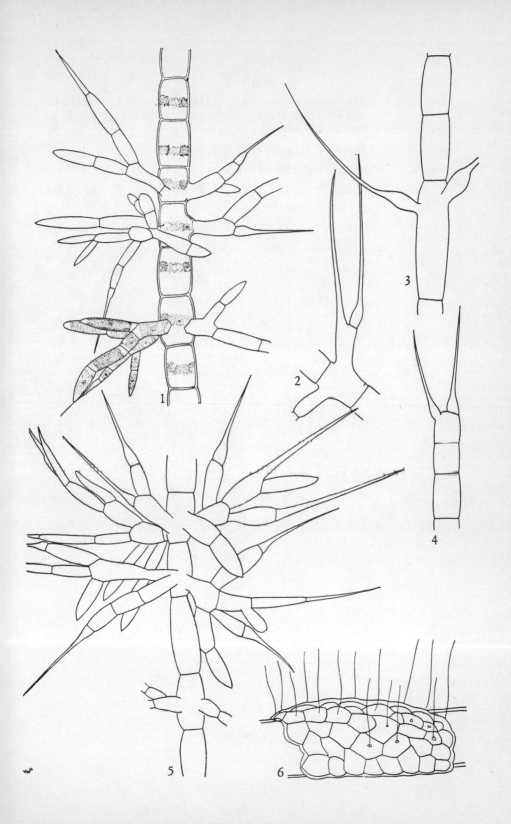

Fig. 1.   *Aphanochaete polychaete* (Hansg.) Fritsch, × 500 (redrawn from West and Fritsch, courtesy of the Macmillan Publishing Company)

Figs. 2, 3.   *Aphanochaete repens* A. Braun, × 440

Fig. 4.   *Aphanochaete vermiculoides* Wolle, × 750

Figs. 5–7.   *Coleochaete divergens* Pringsheim: 5 and 6, antheridia, × 150; 7, oogonium, × 220

Figs. 8, 9.   *Coleochaete irregularis* Pringsheim: 8, antheridia, × 440; 9, oogonium, × 220

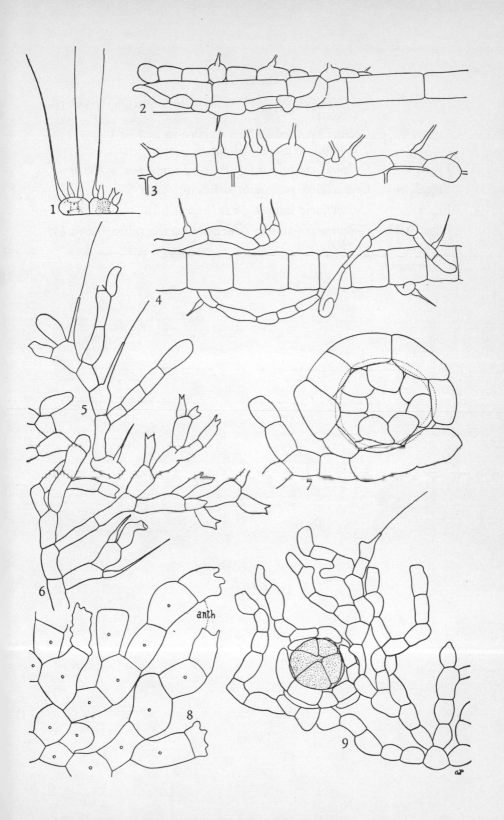

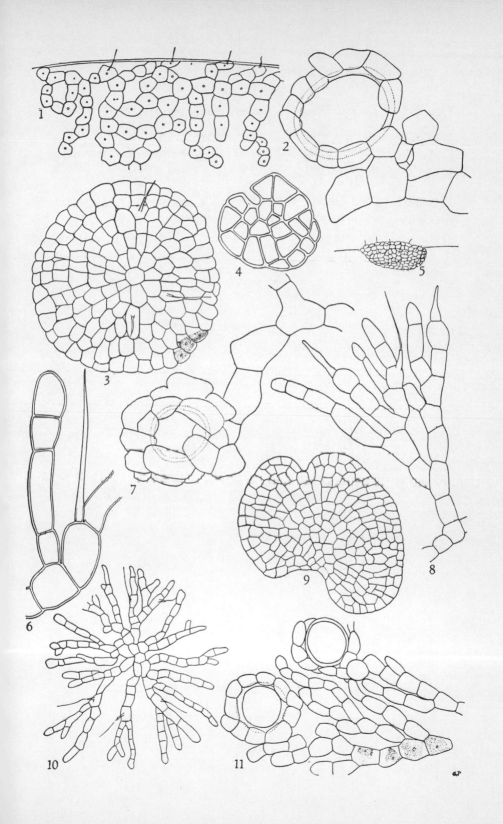

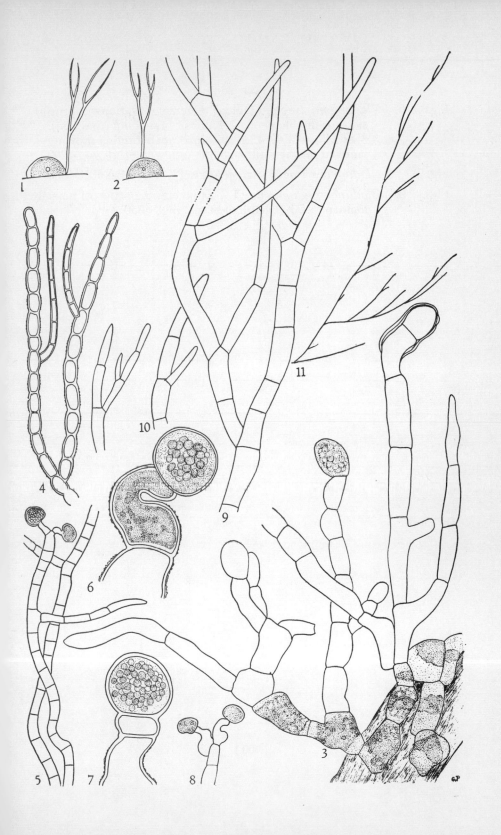

PLATE 20

Figs. 1–6.   *Cladophora fracta* (Dillw.) Kuetzing: various expressions of the filaments; 1, habit of branching (diagram); 2 and 3, × 200; 4, × 100; 5, branch origin, showing lamellations of wall, × 250; 6, old, 'winter' stage, × 200

Fig. 7.   *Cladophora fracta* var. *lacustris* (Kuetz.) Brand, × 500

Figs. 8, 9.   *Cladophora glomerata* (L.) Kuetzing: 8, portion of main filament, × 75; 9, habit of branching, × 350

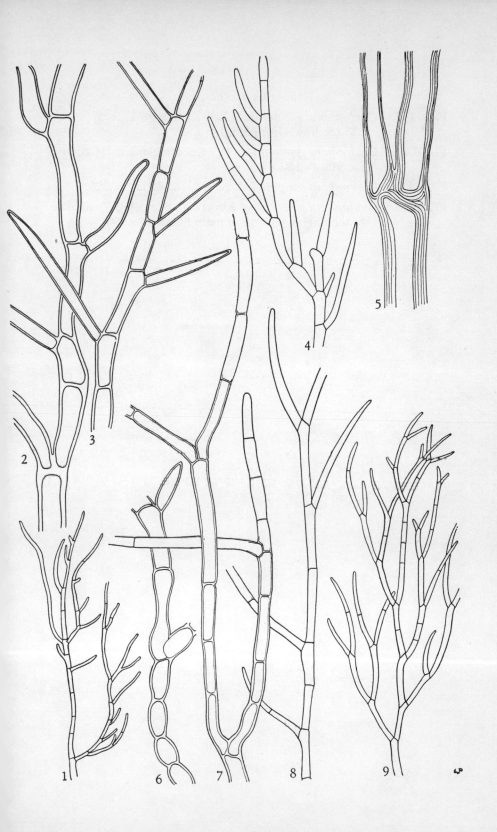

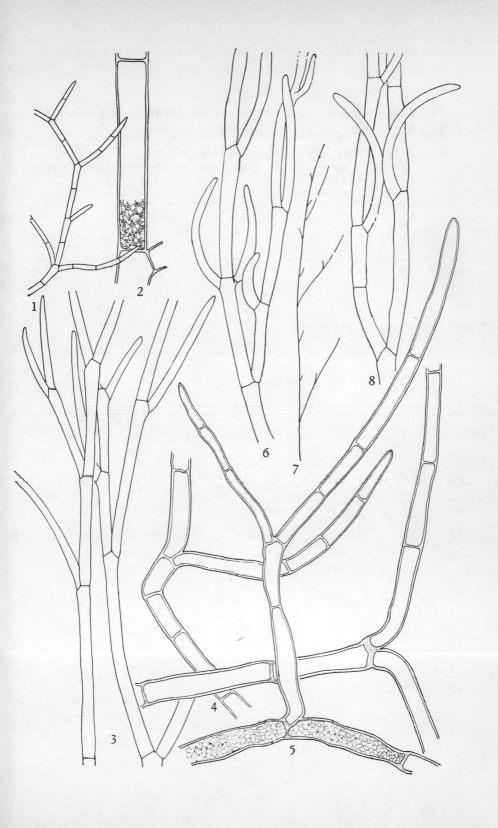

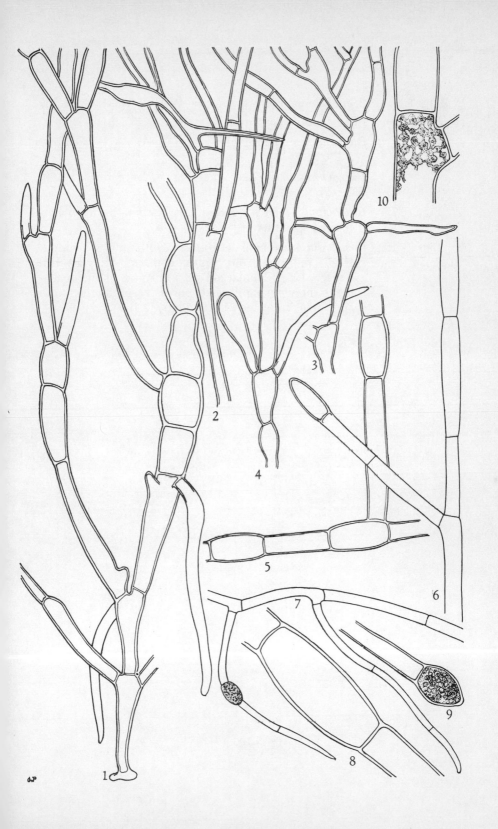

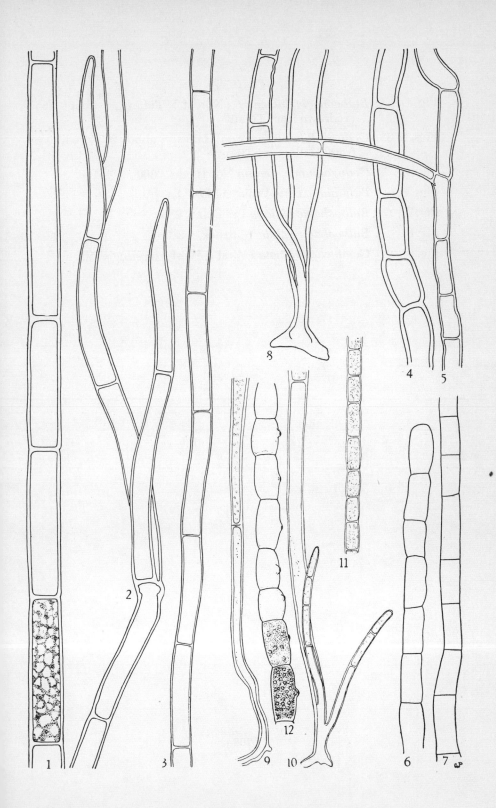

1   2   3   4   5   6   7
              8   9   10   11   12

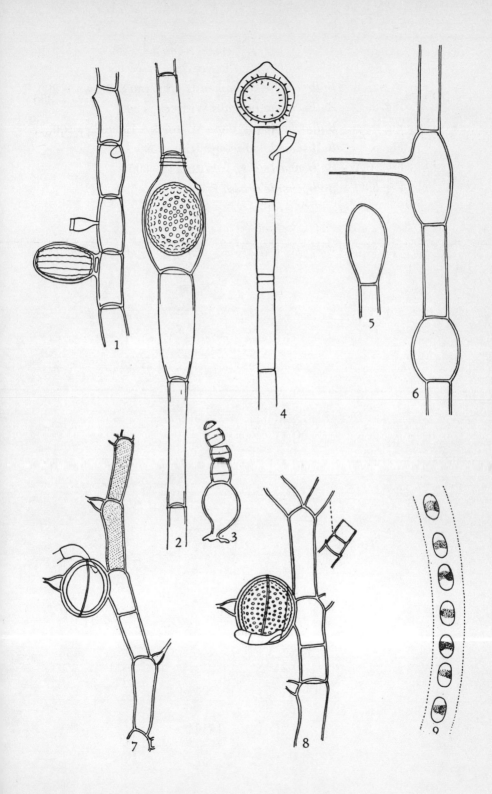

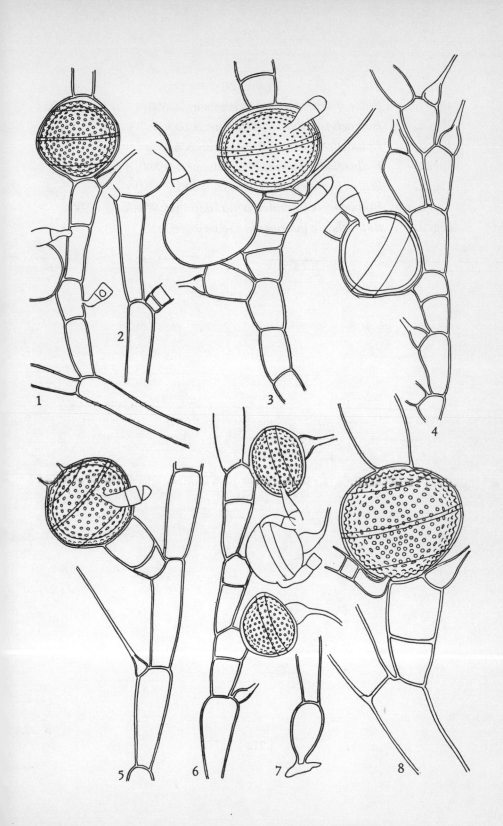

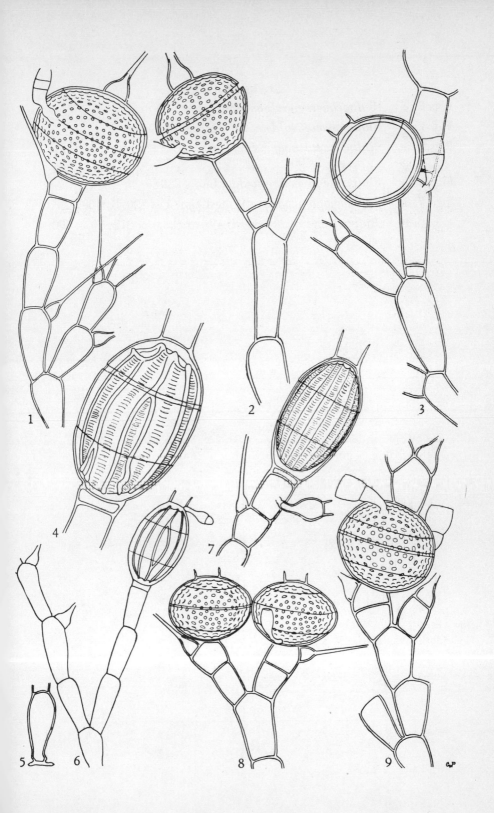

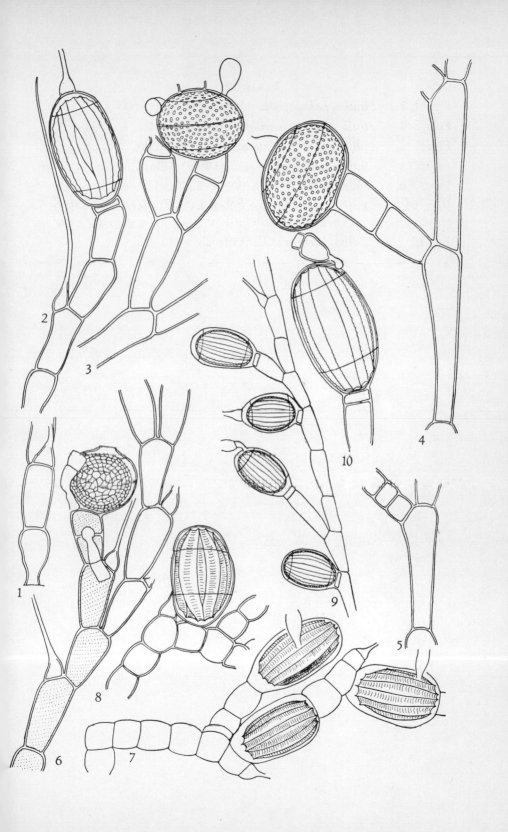

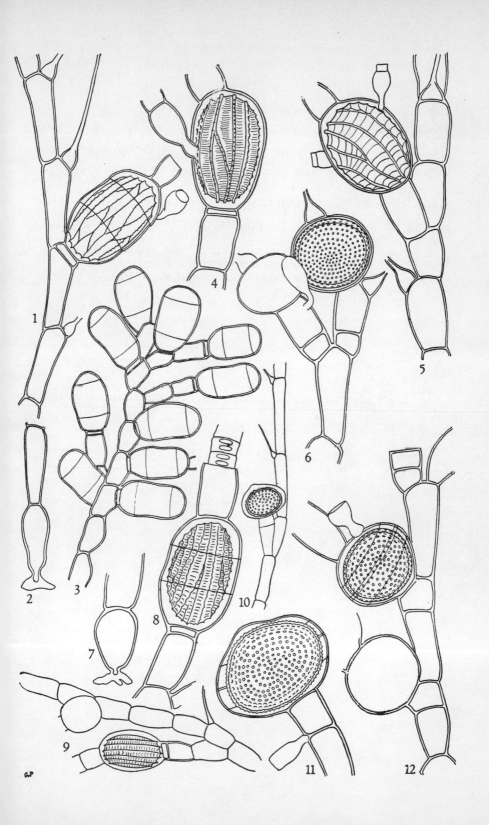

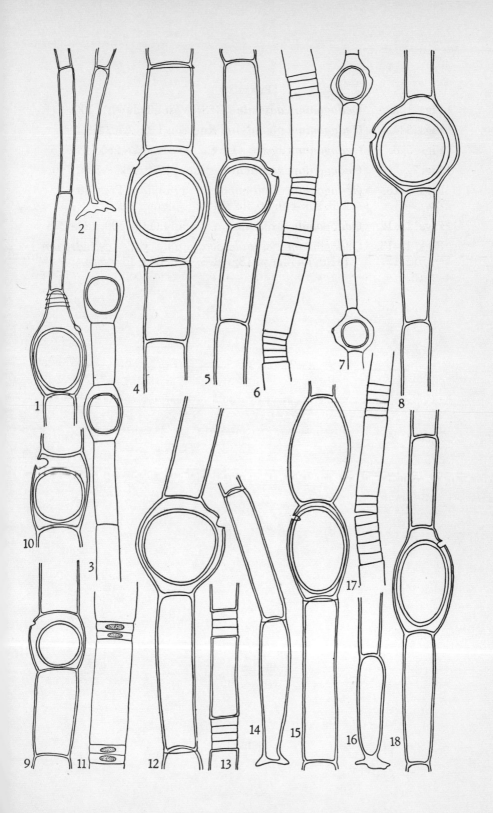

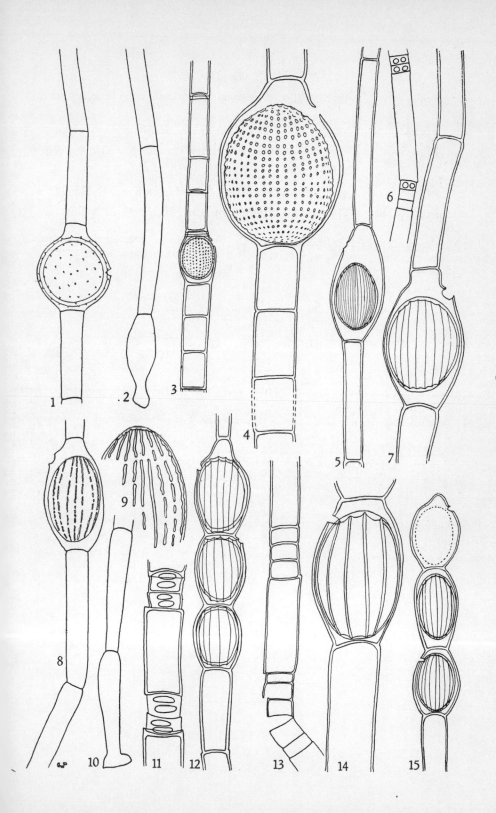

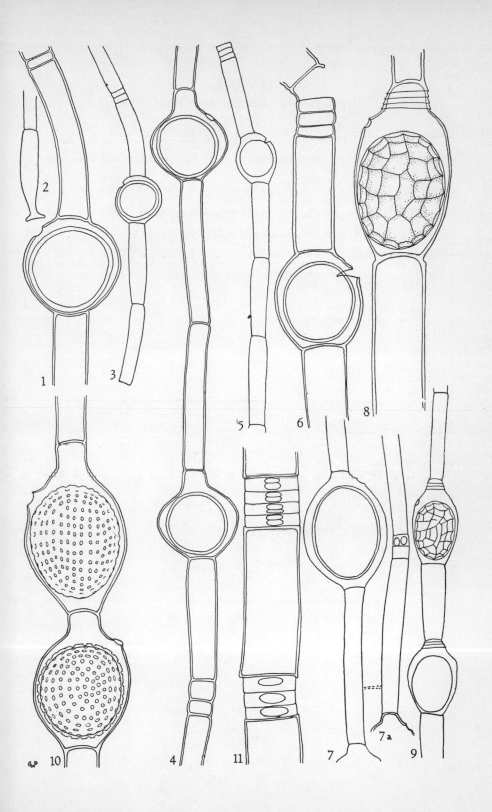

PLATE 32

Figs. 1, 2.   *Oedogonium Landsboroughii* (Hass.) Wittrock: 1, × 275; 2, × 150

Figs. 3, 4.   *Oedogonium plagiostomum* Wittrock: 3, × 600; 4, × 300

Figs. 5, 6.   *Oedogonium rivulare* (Le Cl.) A. Braun: 5, × 250; 6, × 125

Figs. 7–9.   *Oedogonium sociale* Wittrock: 7 and 8, × 275; 9, × 590

Fig. 10.   *Oedogonium varians* Wittrock & Lundell, × 600

Fig. 11.   *Oedogonium tyrolicum* Wittrock, × 500

Fig. 12.   *Oedogonium fennicum* (Tiff.) Tiffany, × 500

Fig. 13.   *Oedogonium fragile* Wittrock, × 590

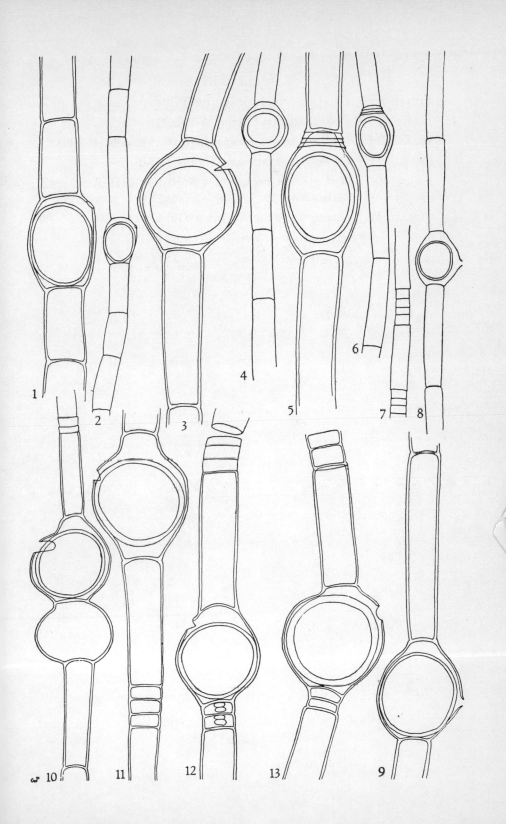

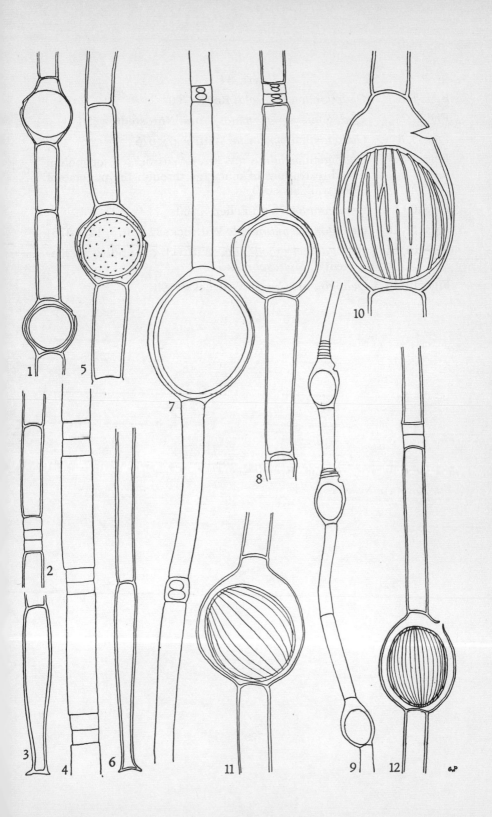

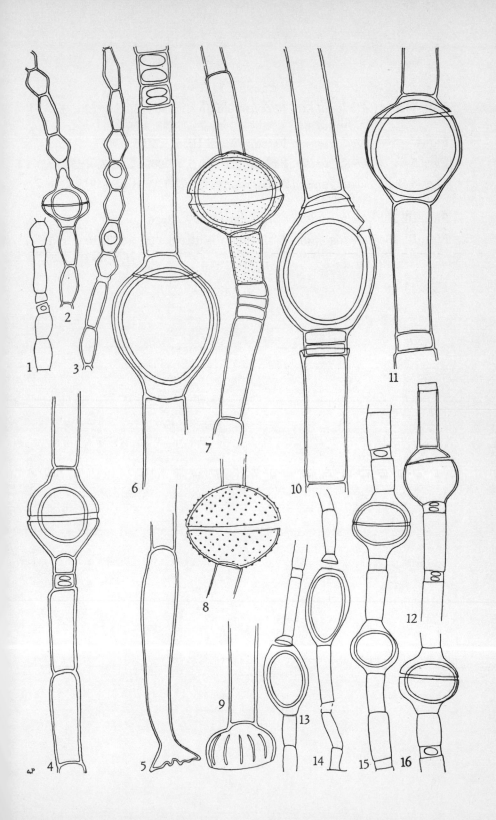

1   2   3   6   7   10   11

4   5   8   9   13   14   15   16   12

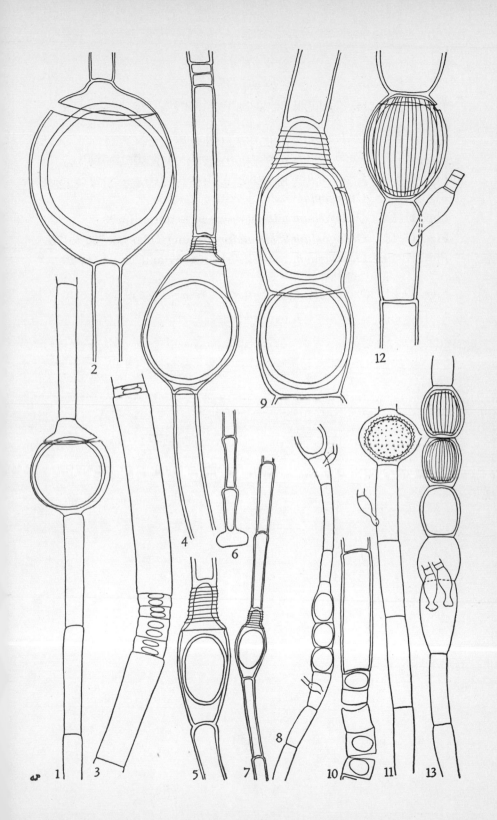

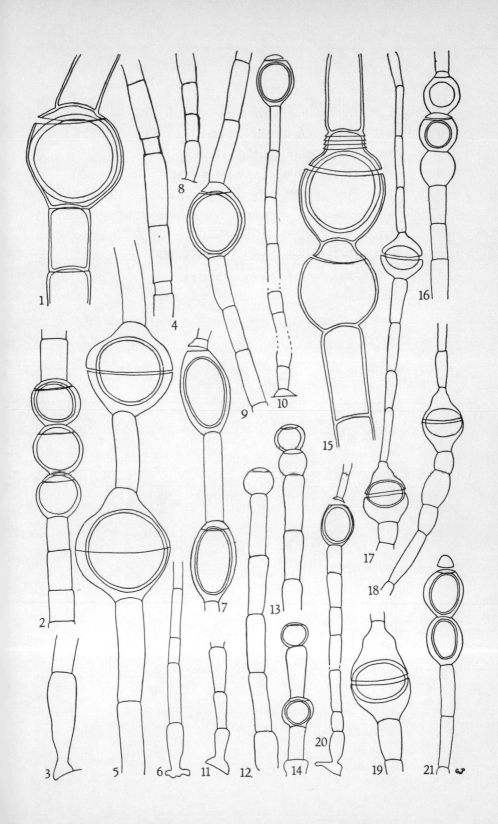

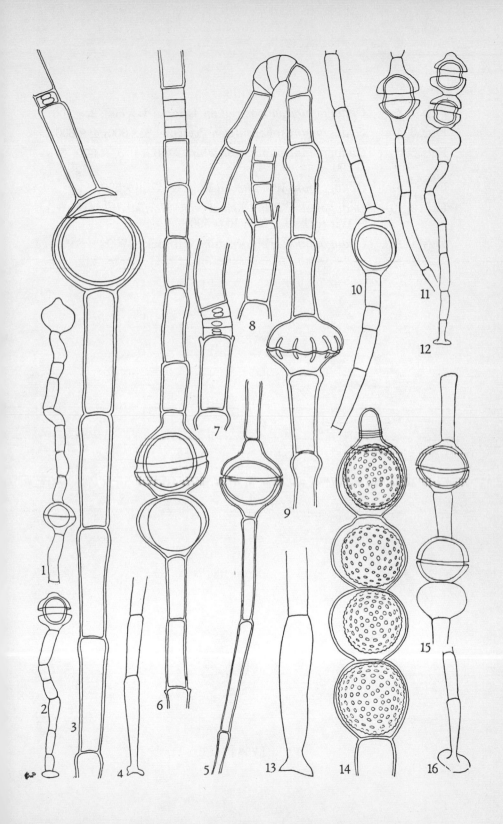

1   2   3   4   5   6   7   8   9   10   11   12   13   14   15   16

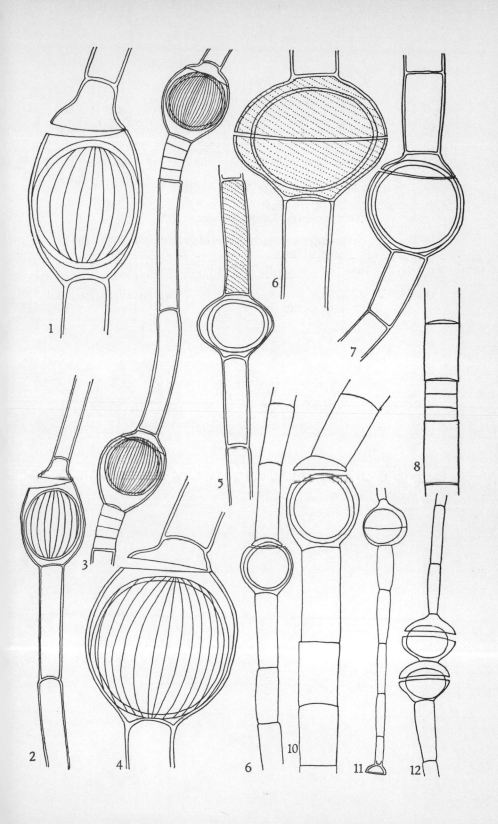

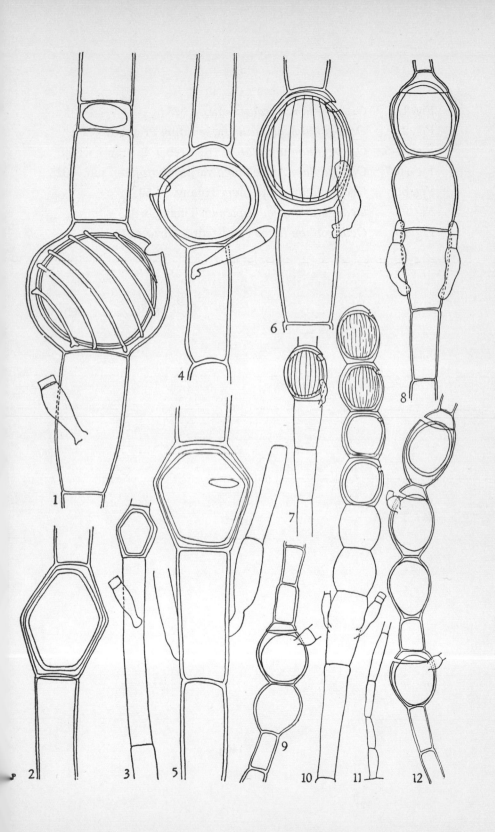

1   4   6   8

7   2   3   5   9   10   11   12

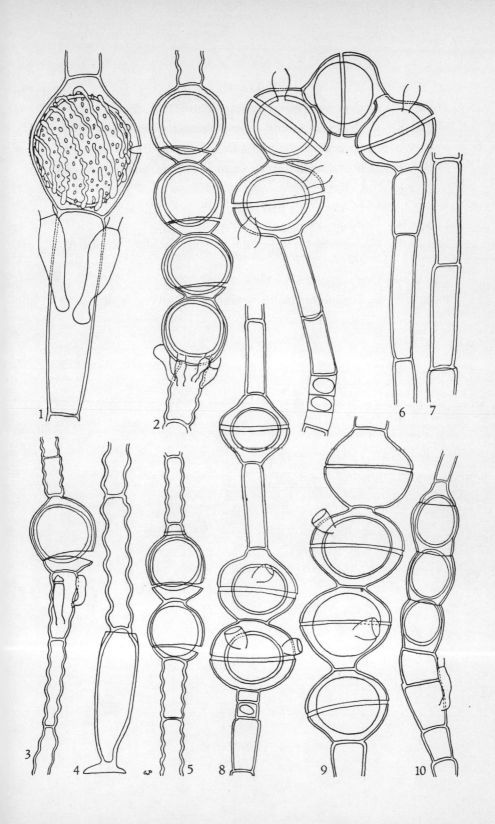

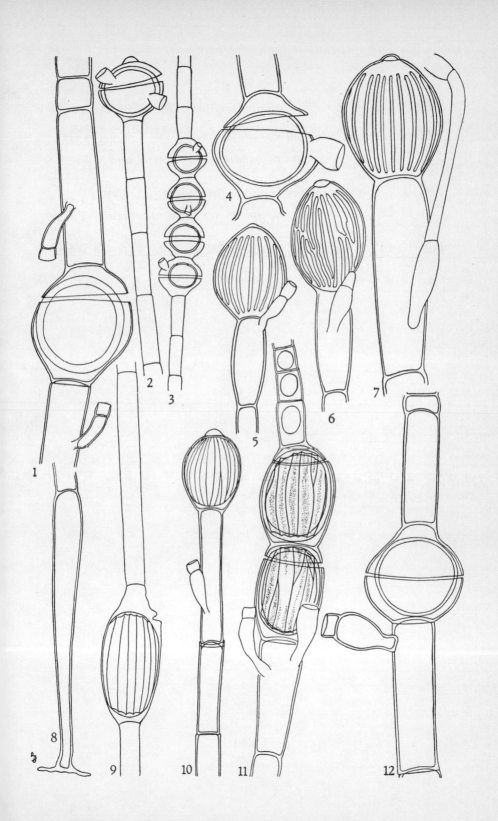

1   2   3   4   5   6   7   8   9   10   11   12

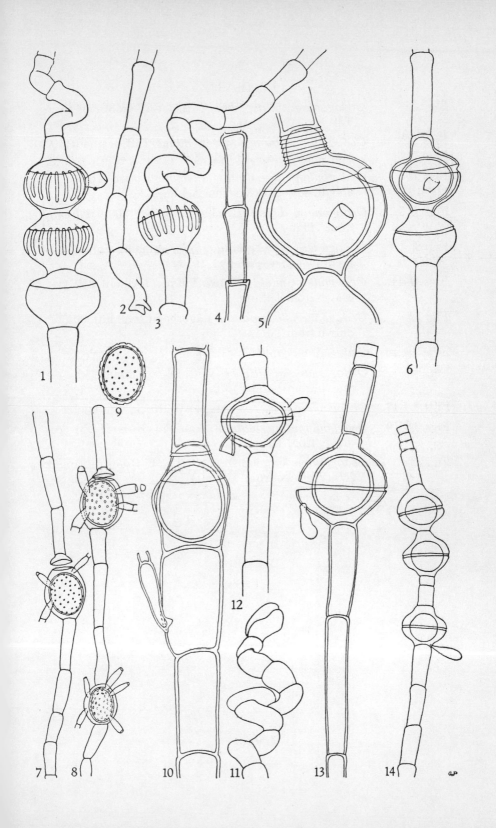

PLATE 43

Fig. 1.   *Oedogonium minisporum* Taft, × 365 (redrawn from Taft)

Figs. 2, 3.   *Oedogonium oblongum* var. *minus* Taft, × about 500 (redrawn from Taft)

Figs. 4, 5.   *Oedogonium argenteum* fa. *michiganense* Tiffany, × about 240 (redrawn from Ackley)

Figs. 6, 7.   *Oedogonium Tiffanyi* Ackley, × about 200 (redrawn from Tiffany)

Fig. 8.   *Oedogonium Richterianum* Lemmermann, × about 225 (redrawn from Tiffany)

Figs. 9–11.   *Oedogonium michiganense* Tiffany, × about 250 (redrawn from Tiffany)

Fig. 12.   *Oedogonium Sodiroanum* Lagerheim, × about 300 (redrawn from Tiffany)

Figs. 13, 14.   *Oedogonium capillare* (L.) Kuetzing, × about 280

Fig. 15.   *Oedogonium upsaliense* Wittrock, × about 250 (redrawn from Tiffany)

Figs. 16, 17.   *Oedogonium princeps* (Hass.) Wittrock, × about 185

Figs. 18, 19.   *Oedogonium americanum* Transeau, × about 200 (redrawn from Tiffany)

Fig. 20.   *Oedogonium Vaucherii* (Le Cl.) A. Braun, × about 260 (redrawn from Tiffany)

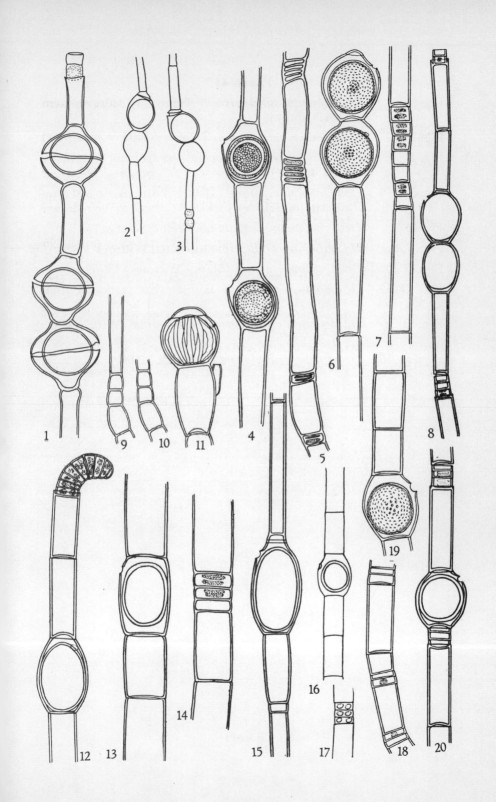

1 2 3 4 5 6 7 8 9 10 11 12 13 14 15 16 17 18 19 20

PLATE 44

Figs. 1, 2.   *Oedogonium spirostriatum* Tiffany, × 340 (redrawn from Tiffany)

Fig. 3.   *Oedogonium latiusculum* Tiffany, × 440

Fig. 4.   *Oedogonium undulatum* fa. *senegalense* (Nordst.) Hirn, × 500

Fig. 5.   *Oedogonium crispum* (Hass.) Wittrock, × 300 (redrawn from Tiffany)

Fig. 6.   *Oedogonium angustissimum* West & West, × 775

Figs. 7, 8.   *Oedogonium capilliforme* Kuetzing; Wittrock, × 425

Figs. 9, 10.   *Oedogonium crassum* (Hass.) Wittrock, × 275

Figs. 11, 12.   *Oedogonium mitratum* Hirn, × 300 (redrawn from Tiffany)

Fig. 13.   *Oedogonium cyathigerum* fa. *ornatum* (Wittr.) Hirn, × 375

Figs. 14, 15.   *Oedogonium rugulosum* Nordstedt, × 590

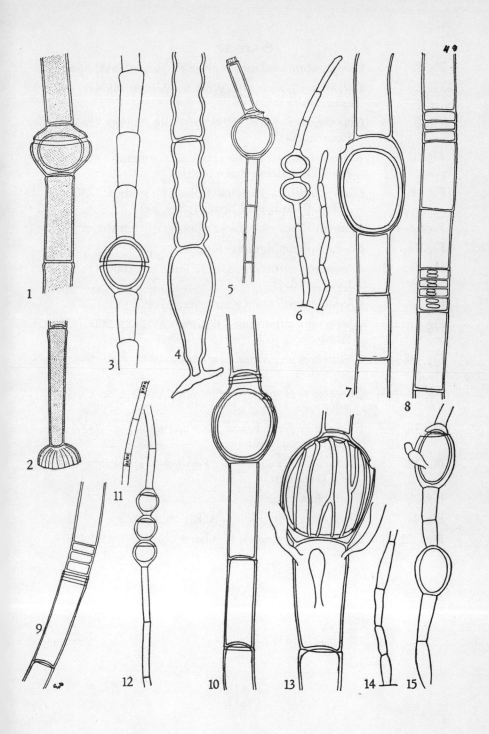

PLATE 45

Fig. 1.   *Chlorococcum humicola* (Naeg.) Rabenhorst, × 500

Fig. 2.   *Golenkinia paucispina* West & West, × 750 (redrawn from Smith)

Fig. 3.   *Golenkinia radiata* (Chod.) Wille, × 750 (redrawn from Smith)

Figs. 4, 5.   *Acanthosphaera Zachariasi* Lemmermann: 4, × 1000; 5, × 750 (redrawn from Smith)

Figs. 6, 7.   *Chlorochytrium Lemnae* Cohn: 6, × about 250 (redrawn from Bristol-Roach); 7, × 250

Figs. 8–10.   *Kentrosphaera gloeophila* (Bohlin) Brunnthaler, × 625

Fig. 11.   *Characium ambiguum* Hermann, × 500

Figs. 12, 13.   *Characium curvatum* G. M. Smith, × 2000 (redrawn from Smith)

Fig. 14.   *Characium falcatum* Schroeder, × 700

Fig. 15.   *Characium stipitatum* (Bachm.) Wille, × 2000 (after Smith)

Fig. 16.   *Characium gracilipes* Lambert, × 1000 (redrawn from Smith)

Fig. 17.   *Characium Hookeri* (Reinsch) Hansgirg, on *Cyclops*, × 500

Fig. 18.   *Characium limneticum* Lemmermann, × 1000 (redrawn from Smith)

Fig. 19.   *Characiopsis cylindrica* (Lambert) Lemmermann, × 500 (redrawn from Smith)

Fig. 20.   *Characium obtusum* A. Braun, × 1650

Fig. 21.   *Characium Pringsheimii* A. Braun, × 800

Figs. 22, 23.   *Characium rostratum* Reinhard: 22, × 500; 23, × 750

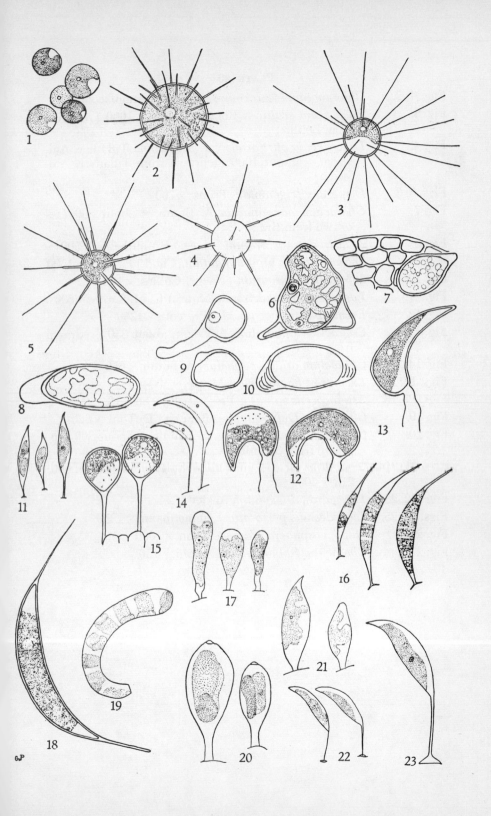

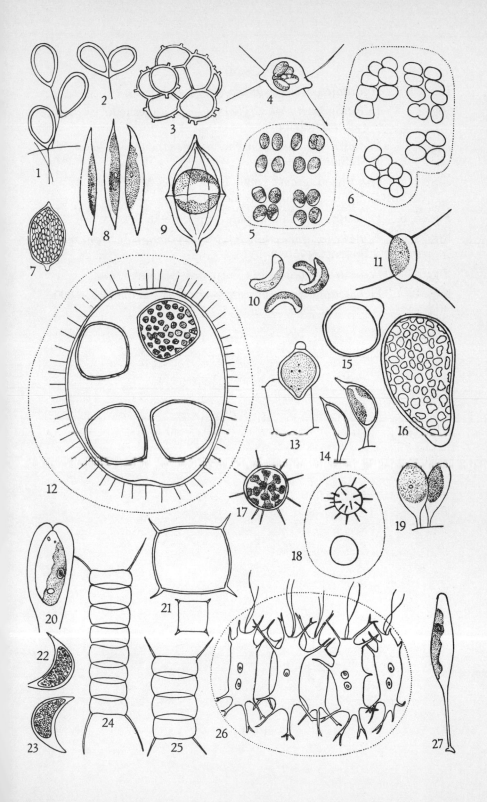

PLATE 47

Fig. 1.   *Hydrodictyon reticulatum* (L.) Lagerheim, × 75

Fig. 2.   *Euastropsis Richteri* (Schmidle) Lagerheim, × 1000 (after Smith)

Fig. 3.   *Pediastrum araneosum* var. *rugulosum* (G. S. West) G. M. Smith, × 590

Fig. 4.   *Pediastrum araneosum* (Racib.) G. M. Smith, x 590 (Reticulations on walls not shown.)

Figs. 5, 6. *Pediastrum biradiatum* Meyen: 5, × 600; 6, × 300

Figs. 7, 8. *Pediastrum biradiatum* var. *emarginatum* fa. *convexum* Prescott, × 750

Fig. 9.   *Pediastrum boryanum* (Turp.) Meneghini, × 750

Fig. 10.   *Pediastrum boryanum* var. *longicorne* Raciborski, × 590

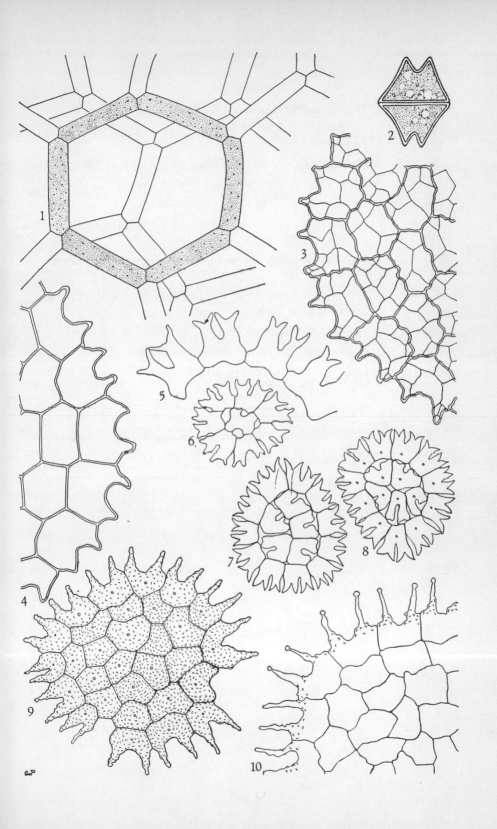

PLATE 48

Fig. 1.   *Pediastrum Boryanum* (Turp.) Meneghini, × 330 (redrawn from Smith)

Fig. 2.   *Pediastrum Boryanum* var. *undulatum* Wille, × 500

Fig. 3.   *Pediastrum Boryanum* (Turp.) Meneghini, × 500

Fig. 4.   *Pediastrum duplex* Meyen, × 500 (redrawn from Smith)

Fig. 5.   *Pediastrum Braunii* Wartmann, × 750

Fig. 6.   *Pediastrum duplex* var. *clathratum* (A. Braun) Lagerheim, × 500

Fig. 7.   *Pediastrum integrum* var. *priva* Printz, × 666 (redrawn from Smith)

Fig. 8.   *Pediastrum duplex* var. *rotundatum* Lucks, × 333 (redrawn from Smith)

Figs. 9, 10. *Pediastrum integrum* Naegeli: 9, × 330; 10, × 500

Fig. 11.   *Pediastrum duplex* var. *cohaerens* Bohlin, × 500

Fig. 12.   *Pediastrum duplex* var. *gracilimum* West & West, × 333 (after Smith)

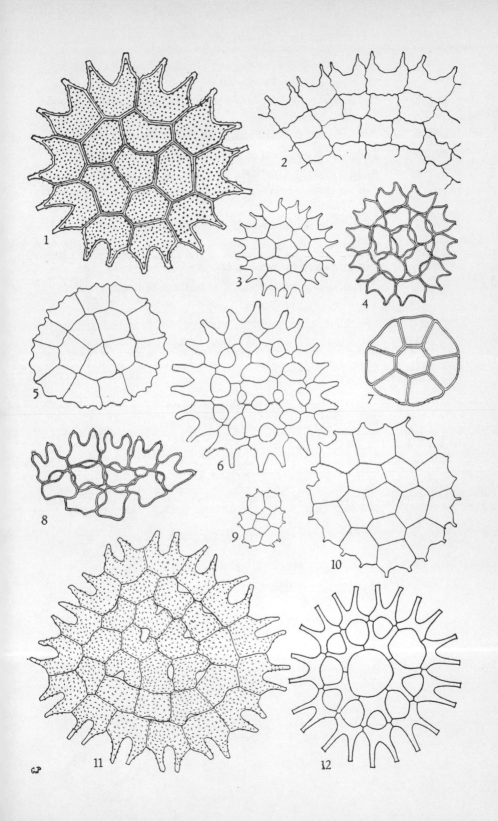

PLATE 49

Fig. 1.   *Pediastrum duplex* var. *reticulatum* Lagerheim, × 333
            (after Smith)

Fig. 2.   *Pediastrum integrum* var. *scutum* Raciborski, × 625

Fig. 3.   *Pediastrum duplex* var. *rugulosum* Raciborski, × 750

Fig. 4.   *Pediastrum glanduliferum* Bennett, × 1000 (redrawn
            from Bisley, *ex* West and Fritsch, courtesy Macmillan
            Publishing Co.)

Fig. 5.   *Pediastrum sculptatum* G. M. Smith, × 333 (after Smith)

Figs. 6, 7. *Pediastrum obtusum* Lucks, × 590

Fig. 8.   *Pediastrum muticum* Kuetzing, × 750

Fig. 9.   *Pediastrum muticum* var. *crenulatum* Prescott, × 750

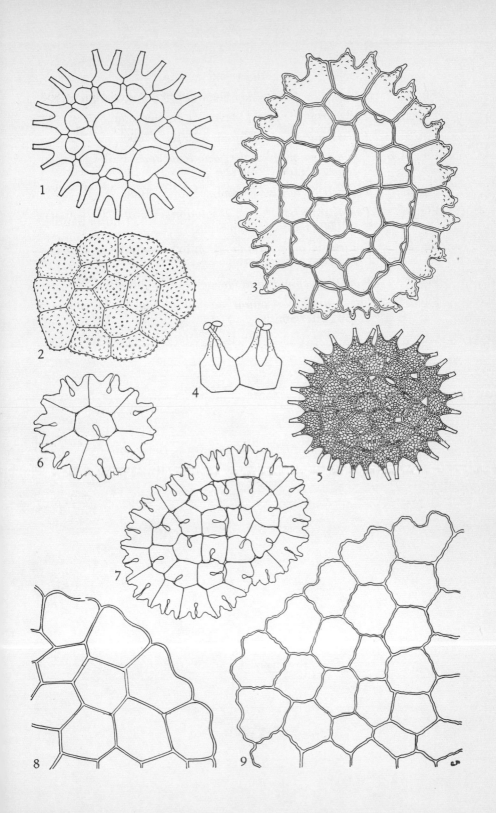

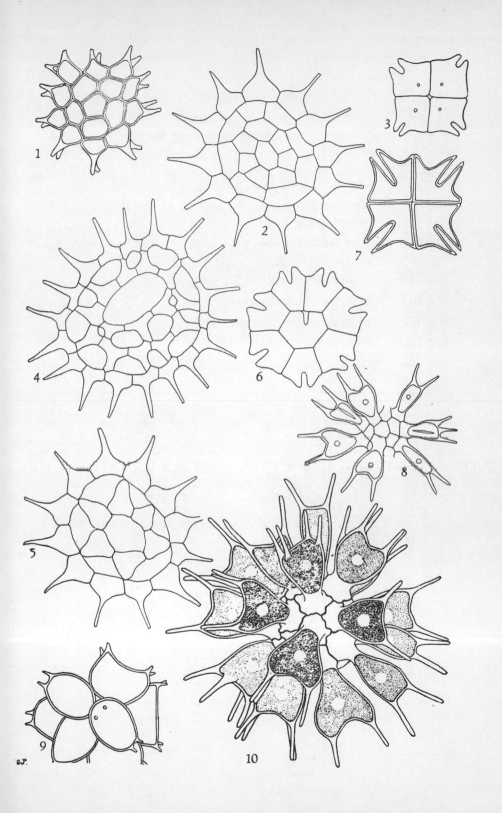

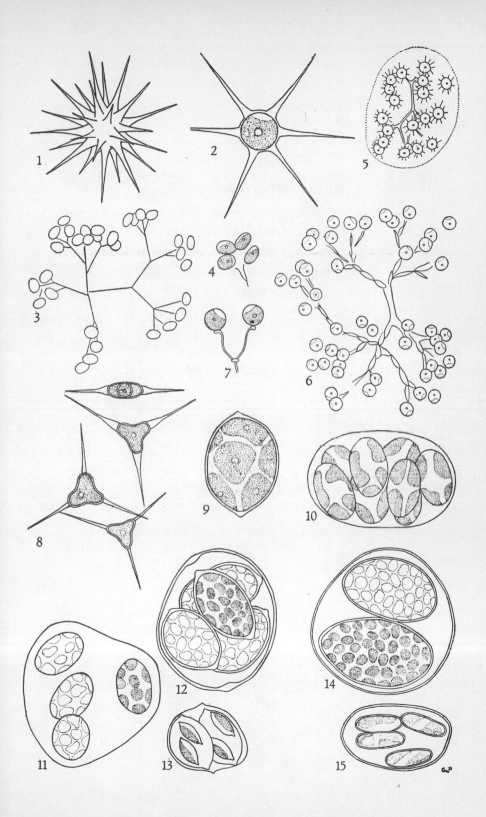

PLATE 52

Figs. 1, 2. *Botryococcus Braunii* Kuetzing, × 375 (redrawn from Blackburn)

Fig. 3. *Botryococcus sudeticus* Lemmermann, × 600 (redrawn from Smith)

Figs. 4, 5. *Botryococcus protuberans* var. *minor* G. M. Smith: 4, × 750; 5, × 1500 (redrawn from Smith)

Figs. 6, 7. *Tetraëdron enorme* (Ralfs) Hansgirg fa., × 885

Fig. 8. *Trochiscia obtusa* (Reinsch) Hansgirg, × 750

Figs. 9, 10. *Gloeocystis major* Gerneck: 9, × 750; 10, × 560

Fig. 11. *Botryococcus Braunii* Kuetzing, × 600 (after Smith)

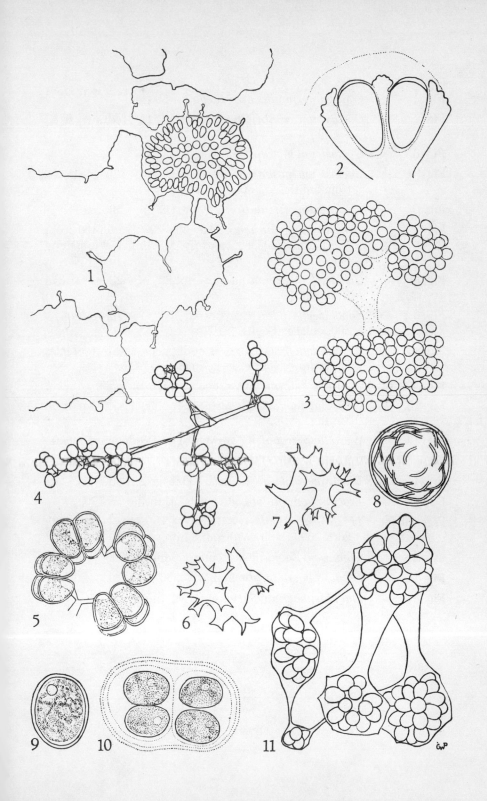

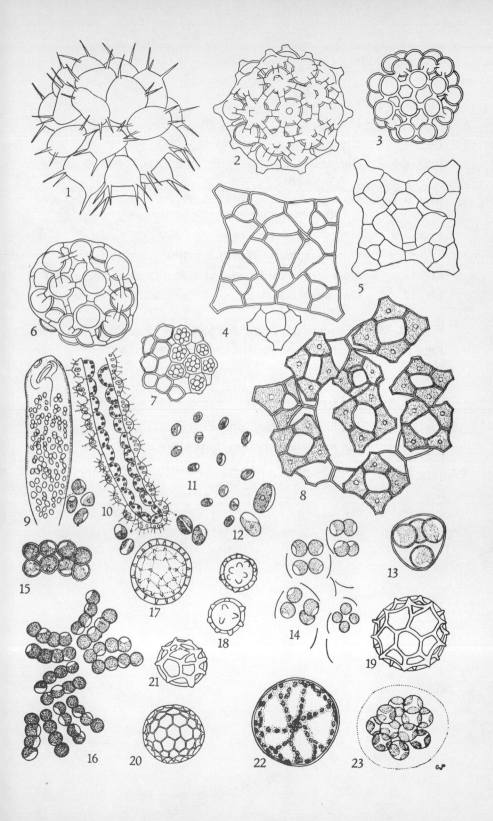

PLATE 54

Fig. 1.   *Oocystis lacustris* Chodat, × 1750

Fig. 2.   *Oocystis natans* var. *major* G. M. Smith, × 1000

Fig. 3.   *Oocystis parva* West & West, × 750

Figs. 4, 5.   *Oocystis pusilla* Hansgirg: 4, colony, × 800; 5, single
               cell, × 1350

Figs. 6, 7.   *Oocystis nodulosa* West & West: 6, × 250; 7, × 400
               (adapted from West, *ex* Brunnthaler)

Figs. 8, 9.   *Oocystis pyriformis* Prescott, × 590

Fig. 10.   *Oocystis solitaria* Wittrock, × 1000

Fig. 11.   *Oocystis panduriformis* var. *minor* G. M. Smith, × 1000

Fig. 12.   *Oocystis submarina* Lagerheim, × 1000 (redrawn from
               Smith)

Figs. 13, 14. *Gloeotaenium Loitelsbergerianum* Hansgirg, × 440

Figs. 15, 16. *Nephrocytium Agardhianum* Naegeli, × 500

Fig. 17.   *Nephrocytium ecdysiscepanum* W. West, × 500

Fig. 18.   *Nephrocytium limneticum* (G. M. Smith) G. M. Smith,
               × 500

Fig. 19.   *Nephrocytium lunatum* W. West, × 750

Fig. 20.   *Nephrocytium obesum* West & West, × 590

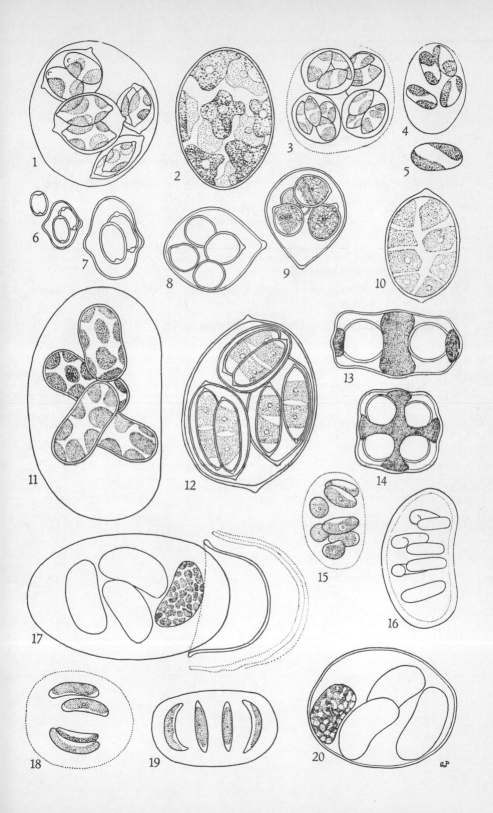

PLATE 55

Fig. 1. *Lagerheimia ciliata* (Lag.) Chodat, × 100 (redrawn from Smith)

Fig. 2. *Lagerheimia ciliata* var. *minor* (G. M. Smith) G. M. Smith, × 1000 (redrawn from Smith)

Fig. 3. *Ankistrodesmus convolutus* Corda, × 1000

Fig. 4. *Lagerheimia citriformis* (Snow) G. M. Smith, × 1000 (redrawn from Smith)

Fig. 5. *Lagerheimia longiseta* (Lemm.) Printz, × 1000 (redrawn from Smith)

Fig. 6. *Lagerheimia longiseta* var. *major* G. M. Smith, × 1000 (redrawn from Smith)

Fig. 7. *Lagerheimia subsalsa* Lemmermann, × 1000 (redrawn from Smith)

Fig. 8. *Dimorphococcus lunatus* A. Braun, × 750

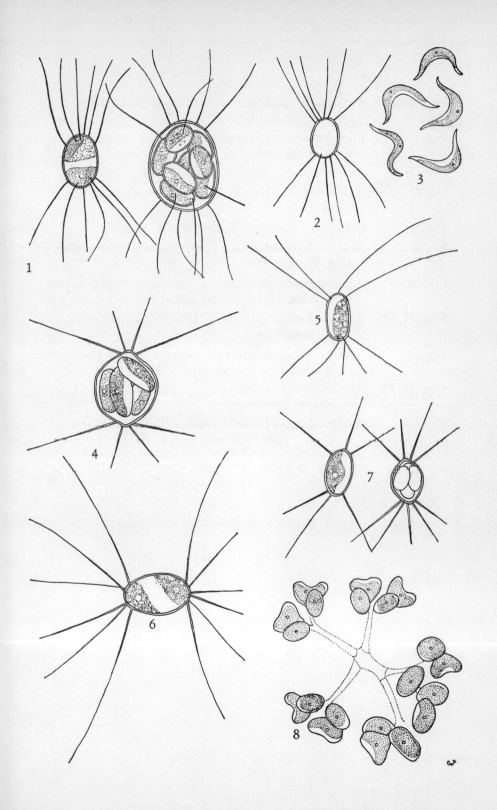

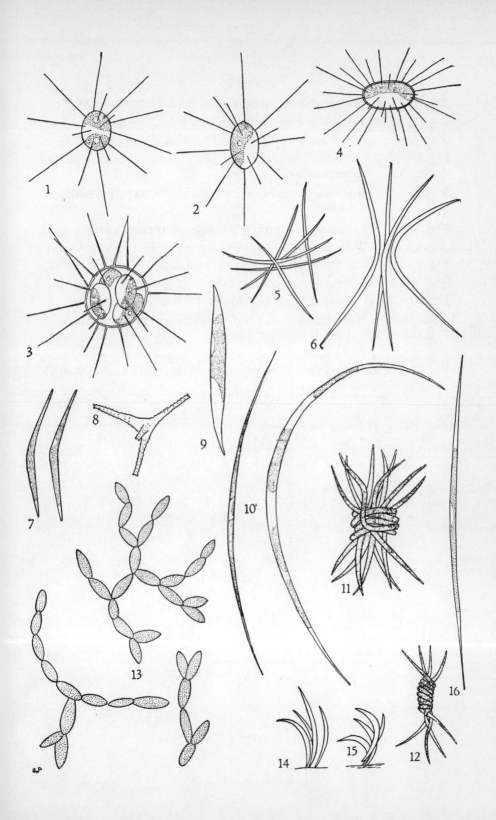

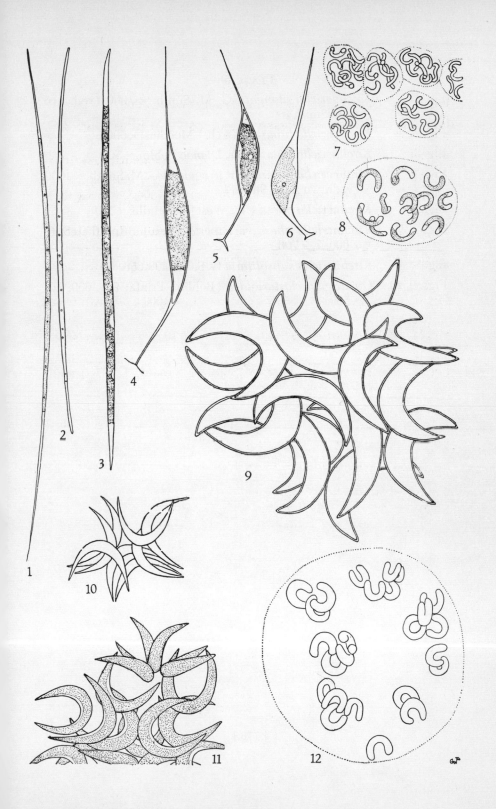

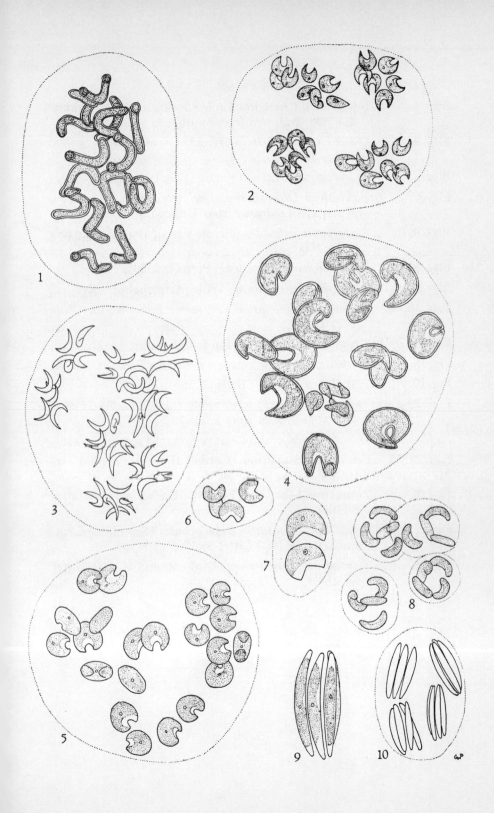

PLATE 59

Figs. 1–3.   *Quadrigula Chodatii* (Tanner-Fullman) G. M. Smith:
            1, × 500 (redrawn from Smith); 2, × 590; 3, × 500

Figs. 4, 5. *Quadrigula lacustris* (Chod.) G. M. Smith, × 500
            (after Smith)

Figs. 6, 7. *Tetraëdron armatum* (Reinsch) DeToni, × 400

Fig. 8.   *Tetraëdron arthrodesmiforme* (W. West) Wołoszyń-
            ska, × 175 (redrawn from Tiffany)

Figs. 9, 10. *Tetraëdron arthrodesmiforme* var. *contorta* Wołoszyń-
            ska, × 1000

Figs. 11–13. *Tetraëdron asymmetricum* Prescott, × 500

Fig. 14.   *Tetraëdron bifurcatum* (Wille) Lagerheim, × 500

Figs. 15, 16. *Tetraëdron bifurcatum* var. *minor* Prescott: 15, × 500;
            16, × 750

Fig. 17.   *Tetraëdron caudatum* (Corda) Hansgirg, × 200

Fig. 18.   *Tetraëdron enorme* var. *pentaedricum* Prescott, × 650

Fig. 19.   *Tetraëdron enorme* (Ralfs) Hansgirg, × 650

Figs. 20–22. *Tetraëdron caudatum* var. *longispinum* Lemmermann,
            × 1000 (redrawn from Smith)

Fig. 23.   *Tetraëdron cruciatum* var. *reductum* Prescott, × 600

Figs. 24, 25. *Tetraëdron caudatum* (Corda) Hansgirg, × 1000 (af-
            ter Smith)

Fig. 26.   *Tetraëdron hastatum* (Reinsch) Hansgirg, × 100 (after
            Smith)

Fig. 27.   *Tetraëdron hastatum* var. *palatinum* (Schmidle) Lem-
            mermann, × 1000 (after Smith)

Fig. 28.   *Tetraëdron constrictum* G. M. Smith, × 1000 (after
            Smith)

PLATE 60

Fig. 1.   *Tetraëdron gracile* (Reinsch) Hansgirg, × 1000 (after Smith)

Figs. 2–4.   *Tetraëdron limneticum* Borge: 2–3, × 590; 4, × 1000

Fig. 5.   *Tetraëdron limneticum* var. *gracile* Prescott, × 590

Figs. 6, 7.   *Tetraëdron lobulatum* (Naeg.) Hansgirg, × 1000 (after Smith)

Fig. 8.   *Tetraëdron lobulatum* var. *crassum* Prescott, × 1000

Figs. 9, 10.   *Tetraëdron lunula* (Reinsch) Wille, × 1000

Fig. 11.   *Tetraëdron lobulatum* var. *polyfurcatum* G. M. Smith, × 1000 (after Smith)

Figs. 12–15. *Tetraëdron minimum* (A. Braun) Hansgirg, × 1000 (14 and 15, after Smith)

Figs. 16, 17. *Tetraëdron muticum* (A. Braun) Hansgirg: 16, × 1000; 17, × 590

Fig. 18.   *Tetraëdron muticum* fa. *punctulatum* (Reinsch) De-Toni, × 1000 (after Smith)

Figs. 19, 20. *Tetraëdron obesum* (West & West) Wille: 19, × 600; 20, × 650

Figs. 21–23. *Tetraëdron pentaedricum* West & West, × 1000 (23, after Smith)

Figs. 24–26. *Tetraëdron regulare* Kuetzing, × 1000 (26, after Smith)

Figs. 27, 28. *Tetraëdron planctonicum* G. M. Smith, × 1500

Fig. 29.   *Tetraëdron pusillum* (Wallich) West & West, × 1750 (redrawn from Turner, *ex* Brunnthaler)

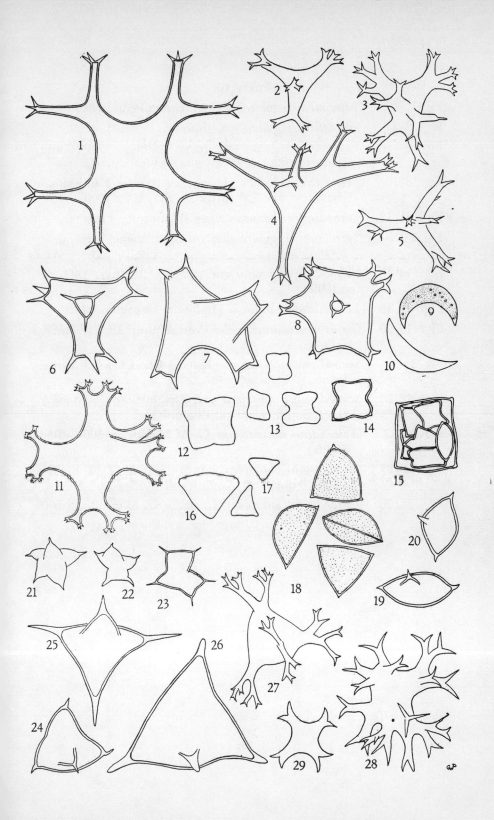

PLATE 61

Fig. 1.   *Tetraëdron regulare* var. *bifurcatum* Wille, × 500

Figs. 2, 3.   *Tetraëdron regulare* var. *granulata* Prescott, × 500

Figs. 4–7.   *Tetraëdron regulare* var. *incus* Teiling, × 500 (6 and 7, after Smith)

Figs. 8–10.   *Tetraëdron regulare* var. *torsum* (Turner) Brunnthaler: 8 and 9, × 500 (after Smith); 10, × 1000

Figs. 11, 12.   *Tetraëdron trigonum* (Naeg.) Hansgirg, × 500

Fig. 13.   *Tetraëdron regulare* var. *incus* fa. *major* Prescott, × 2500

Figs. 14–16.   *Tetraëdron trigonum* var. *gracile* (Reinsch) DeToni, × 1000

Figs. 17, 18.   *Tetraëdron tumidulum* (Reinsch) Hansgirg, × 1000

Figs. 19, 20.   *Cerasterias staurastroides* West & West: 19, × 2500; 20, × 4000

Fig. 21.   *Scenedesmus abundans* (Kirch.) Chodat, × 500 (after Smith)

Figs. 22, 23.   *Scenedesmus abundans* var. *asymmetrica* (Schroed.) G. M. Smith, × 500 (after Smith)

Figs. 24, 25.   *Tetraëdron verrucosum* G. M. Smith, × 500 (after Smith)

Figs. 26, 27.   *Scenedesmus abundans* var. *brevicauda* G. M. Smith, × 500 (redrawn from Smith)

Figs. 28, 29.   *Tetraëdron Victorieae* var. *major* G. M. Smith, × 500 (after Smith)

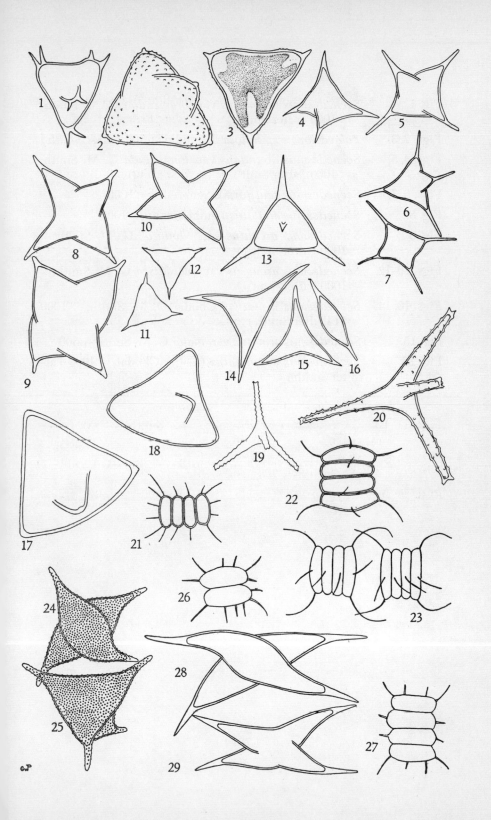

PLATE 62

Fig. 1.   *Scenedesmus abundans* var. *brevicauda* G. M. Smith, × 1000 (after Smith)

Figs. 2, 3.   *Polyedriopsis spinulosa* Schmidle, × 500 (after Smith)

Figs. 4, 5.   *Scenedesmus abundans* var. *longicauda* G. M. Smith, × 1000 (after Smith)

Figs. 6, 7.   *Scenedesmus acutiformis* Schroeder, × 1000

Fig. 8.   *Scenedesmus arcuatus* Lemmermann, × 1000

Fig. 9.   *Scenedesmus arcuatus* var. *capitatus* G. M. Smith, × 1000 (after Smith)

Figs. 10–12.   *Scenedesmus arcuatus* var. *platydisca* G. M. Smith, × 1000 (after Smith)

Figs. 13, 14.   *Scenedesmus armatus* (Chod.) G. M. Smith, × 1000 (14, after Smith)

Fig. 15.   *Scenedesmus armatus* var. *major* G. M. Smith, × 500

Fig. 16.   *Scenedesmus acuminatus* (Lag.) Chodat, × 1000 (after Smith)

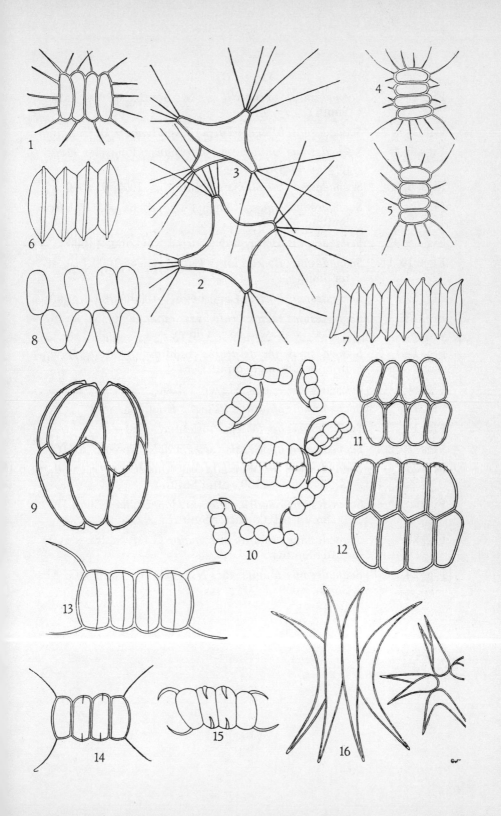

PLATE 63

Fig. 1.   *Scenedesmus Bernardii* G. M. Smith, × 1000 (after Smith)

Fig. 2.   *Scenedesmus bijuga* (Turp.) Lagerheim, × 1000

Figs. 3, 4.   *Scenedesmus bijuga* var. *alternans* (Reinsch) Hansgirg: 3, × 1000; 4 × 750

Figs. 5, 6.   *Scenedesmus brasiliensis* Bohlin: 5, × 1000; 6, × 500

Fig. 7.   *Scenedesmus bijuga* (Turp.) Lagerheim, × 750 (after Smith)

Figs. 8, 9.   *Scenedesmus dimorphus* (Turp.) Kuetzing, × 1000

Figs. 10, 11. *Scenedesmus denticulatus* Lagerheim, × 1000 (10, after Smith)

Fig. 12.   *Scenedesmus hystrix* Lagerheim, × 1000 (after Smith)

Fig. 13.   *Scenedesmus incrassatulus* var. *mononae* G. M. Smith, × 1000 (redrawn from Tiffany)

Fig. 14.   *Scenedesmus incrassatulus* Bohlin, × 750 (redrawn from Bohlin, *ex* Brunnthaler)

Figs. 15, 16. *Scenedesmus longus* Meyen, × 1000

Fig. 17.   *Scenedesmus obliquus* (Turp.) Kuetzing, × 750

Fig. 18.   *Scenedesmus opoliensis* P. Richter, × 750

Figs. 19, 20. *Scenedesmus opoliensis* var. *contacta* Prescott, × 750

Fig. 21.   *Scenedesmus quadricauda* var. *quadrispina* (Chod.) G. M. Smith, × 750 (after Smith)

Fig. 22.   *Scenedesmus quadricauda* var. *longispina* (Chod.) G. M. Smith, × 1000 (after Smith)

Fig. 23.   *Scenedesmus armatus* var. *major* G. M. Smith, × 1000 (after Smith)

Fig. 24.   *Scenedesmus longus* var. *Naegelii* (de Bréb.) G. M. Smith, × 500

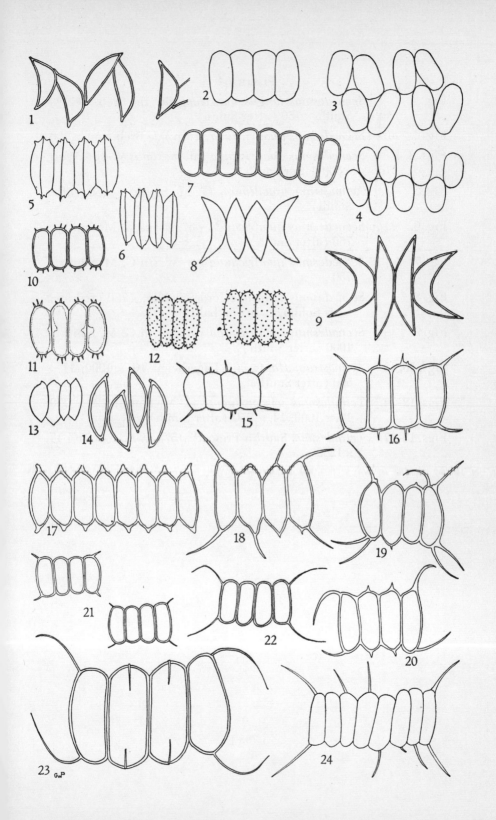

PLATE 64

Fig. 1.   *Scenedesmus longus* var. *Naegelii* (de Bréb.) G. M. Smith, × 750 (after Smith)

Fig. 2.   *Scenedesmus quadricauda* (Turp.) de Brébisson, × 750

Figs. 3, 4.   *Scenedesmus quadricauda* var. *maximus* West & West, × 500 (after Smith)

Fig. 5.   *Actinastrum gracilimum* G. M. Smith, × 750 (after Smith)

Fig. 6.   *Scenedesmus quadricauda* var. *parvus* G. M. Smith, × 750 (after Smith)

Fig. 7.   *Scenedesmus quadricauda* var. *Westii* G. M. Smith, × 750

Fig. 8.   *Scenedesmus serratus* (Corda) Bohlin, × 750 (redrawn from Bohlin, *ex* Brunnthaler)

Fig. 9.   *Scenedesmus quadricauda* var. *Westii* G. M. Smith, × 1000 (after Smith)

Figs. 10, 11. *Actinastrum Hantzschii* Lagerheim: 10, × 1000; 11, × 500 (after Smith)

Figs. 12–14. *Tetradesmus wisconsinense* G. M. Smith: 12, × 750; 13, × 1000; 14, × 750 (after Smith)

Figs. 15–17. *Tetradesmus Smithii* Prescott: 15, × 500; 16, × 750; 17, × 1250

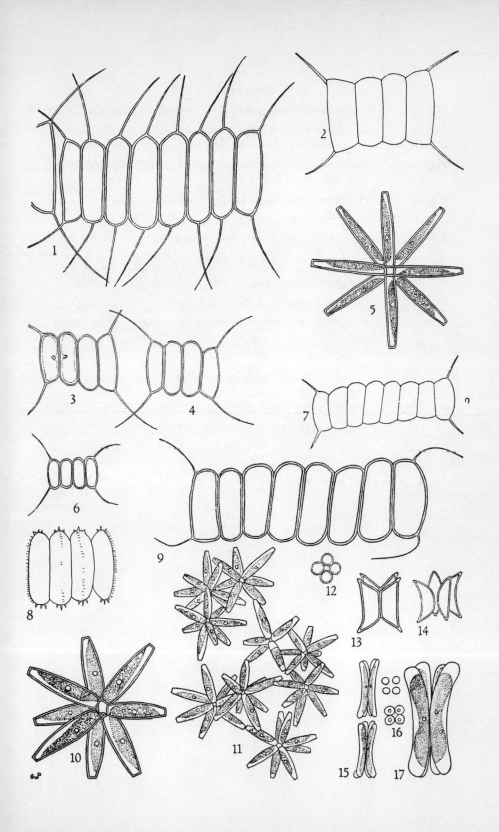

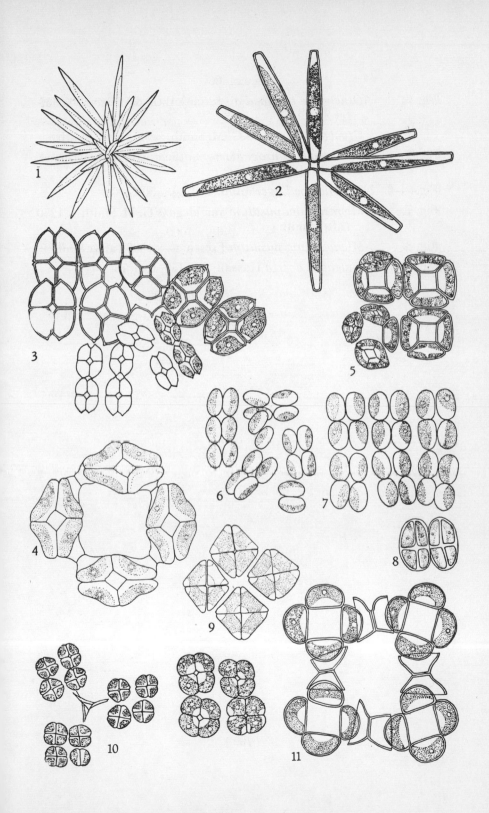

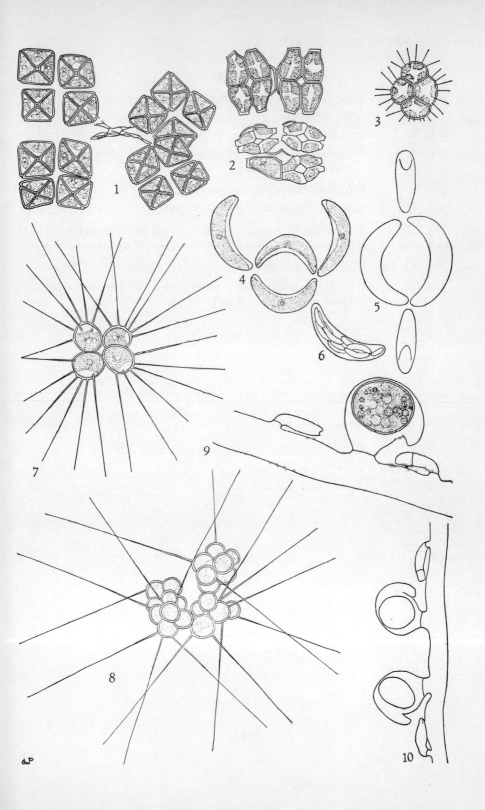

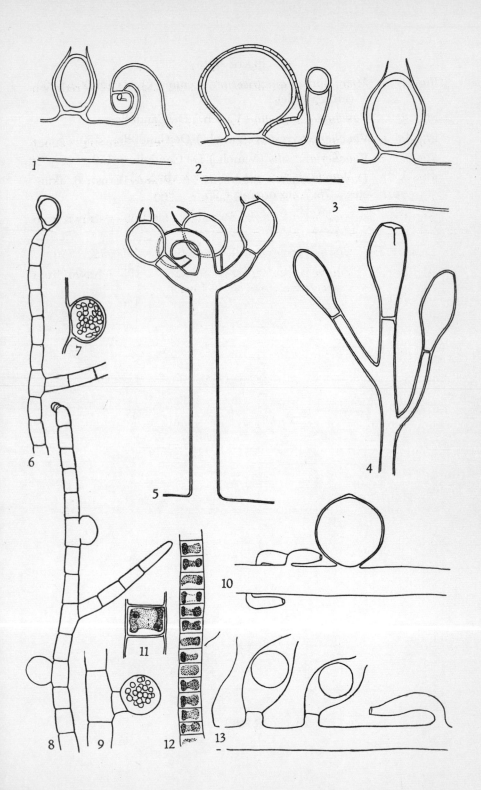

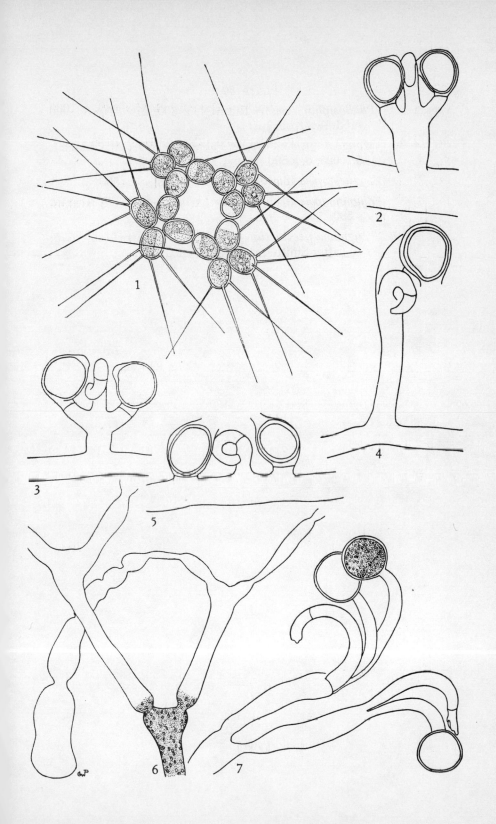

PLATE 69

Figs. 1–3.   *Phyllosiphon Arisari* Kühn: 1, × 300; 2, × 100; 3, × 60 (redrawn from Just)

Figs. 4–6.   *Mougeotiopsis calospora* Palla: 4, × 590 (after Skuja); 5, × 625; 6, × 590

Fig. 7.   *Zygnemopsis spiralis* (Fritsch) Transeau, × 590

Fig. 8.   *Zygnemopsis desmidioides* (West & West) Transeau, × 590

Figs. 9, 10.   *Zygnema pectinatum* (Vauch.) C. A. Agardh: 9, × 375; 10 (after Smith), × 400

PLATE 70

Figs. 1, 2.   *Mougeotia laevis* (Kuetz.) Archer: 1, × 212; 2, × about 425 (redrawn from West & Fritsch, courtesy Macmillan Publishing Co.)

Figs. 3, 4.   *Mougeotia abnormis* Kisselew:3, × 250; 4, × 750

Figs. 5, 6.   *Mougeotia capucina* (Bory) C. A. Agardh, × 275

Figs. 7, 8.   *Mougeotia elegantula* Wittrock: 7, × 1750; 8, × 750

Figs. 9, 10.   *Mougeotia genuflexa* (Dillw.) C. A. Agardh, × 175

Figs. 11–14.   *Mougeotia laetevirens* (A. Braun) Wittrock: 11, × 750; 12–14, × 125

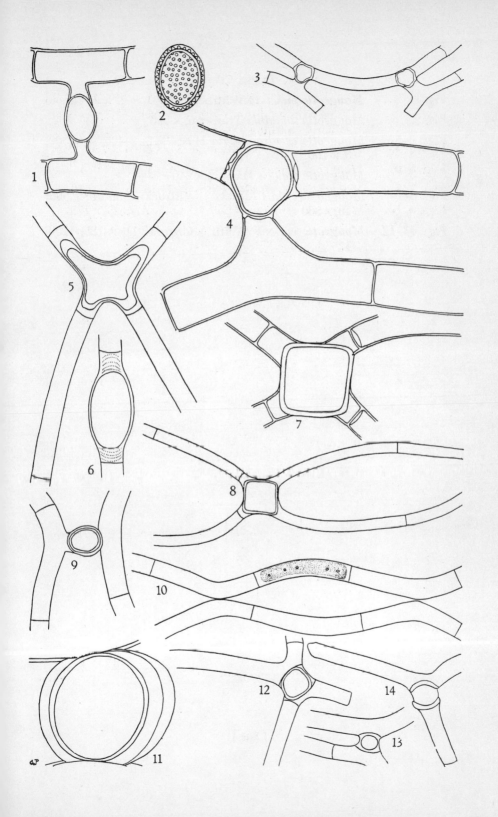

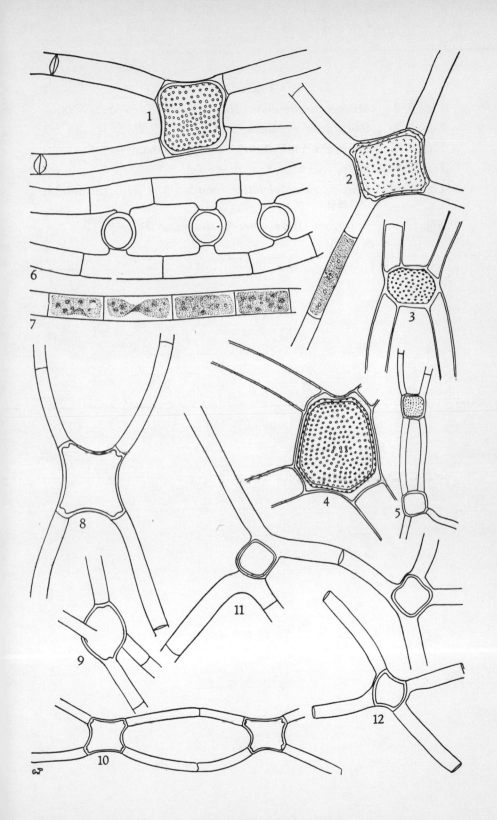

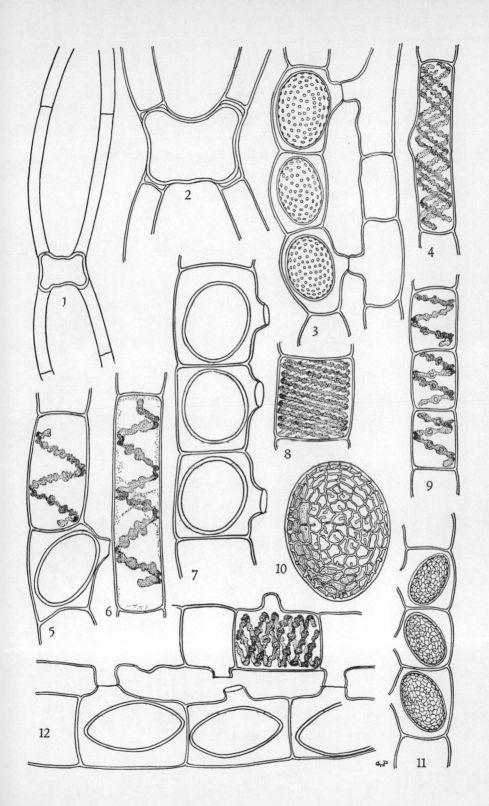

PLATE 73

Figs. 1–3.   *Spirogyra subsalsa* Kuetzing: 1, × 100; 2 and 3, × 500

Figs. 4, 5.   *Spirogyra fluviatilis* Hilse, × 230

Fig. 6.   *Spirogyra Fuellebornei* Schmidle, × 200

Figs. 7, 8.   *Spirogyra Juergensii* Kuetzing: 7, × 325; 8, × 500

Fig. 9.   *Spirogyra micropunctata* Transeau, × 240

Fig. 10.   *Spirogyra nitida* (Dillw.) Link, × 137

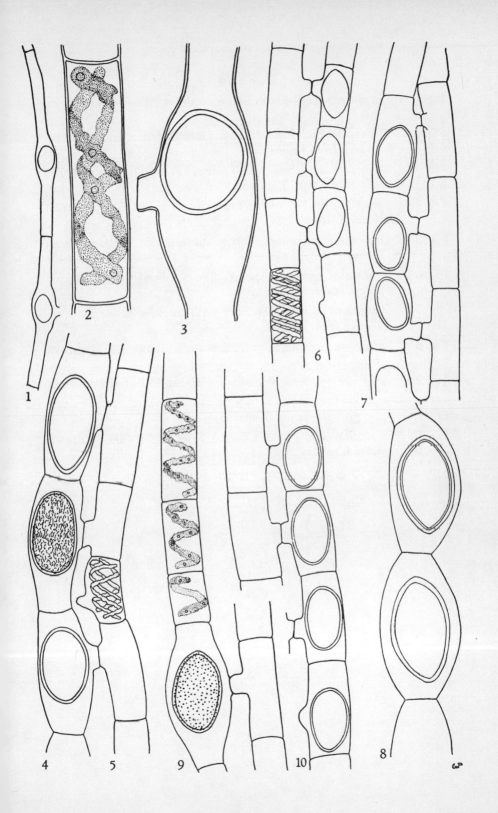

PLATE 74

Fig. 1.   *Zygnema synadelphum* Skuja, × about 290 (redrawn from Skuja)

Fig. 2.   *Zygnema chlalybeospermum* Hansgirg, × about 175 (redrawn from Kniep)

Fig. 3.   *Zygnemopsis decussata* (Trans.) Transeau, × about 180 (redrawn from Transeau)

Fig. 4.   *Zygnemopsis Tiffaniana* Transeau, × about 500 (redrawn from Transeau)

Fig. 5.   *Mougeotia micropora* Taft, × about 325 (redrawn from Taft)

Fig. 6.   *Mougeotia sphaerocarpa* Wolle, × about 190 (redrawn from Transeau)

Fig. 7.   *Mougeotia robusta* (DeBary) Wittrock, × about 215 (redrawn from Transeau)

Fig. 8.   *Spirogyra circumlineata* Transeau, × about 144 (redrawn from Transeau)

Fig. 9.   *Spirogyra gratiana* Transeau, × about 150 (redrawn from Transeau)

Fig. 10.   *Spirogyra majuscula* Kuetzing, × 125

Fig. 11.   *Spirogyra Grevilleana* (Hass.) Kuetzing, × 300 (redrawn from Czurda)

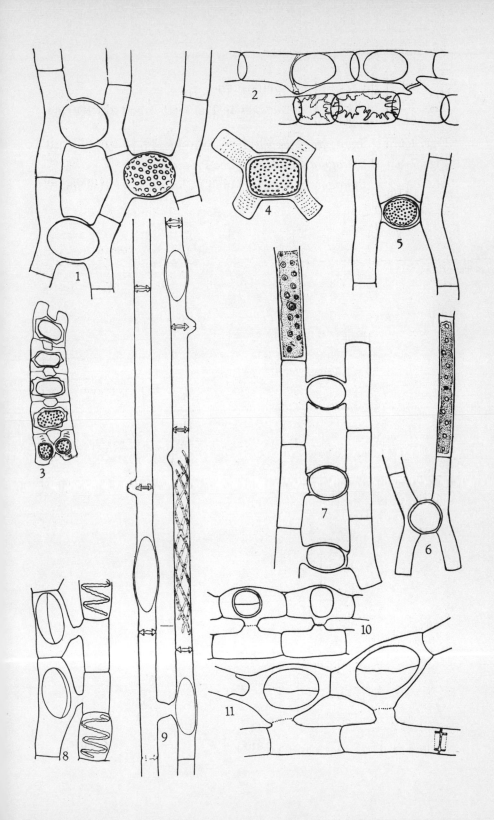

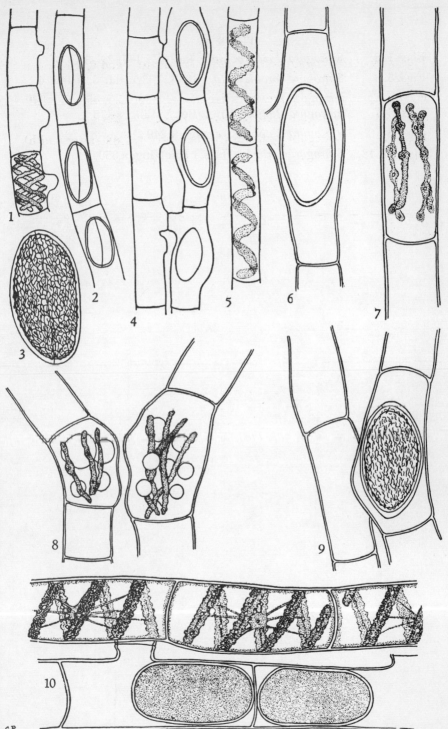

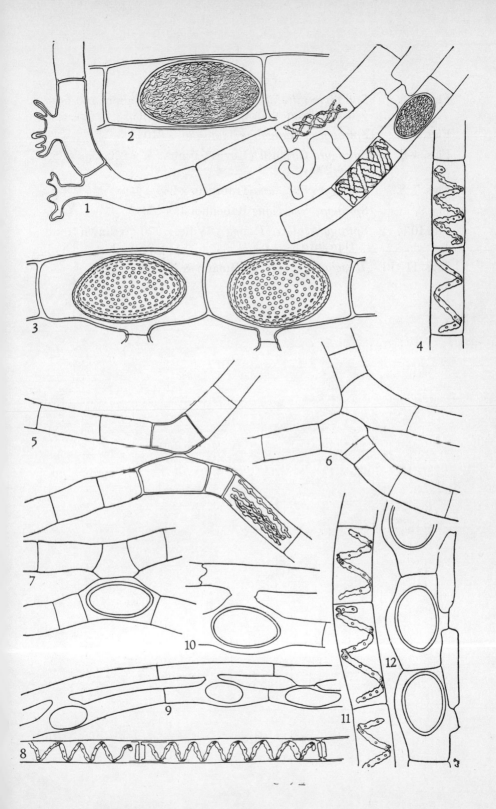

[814]

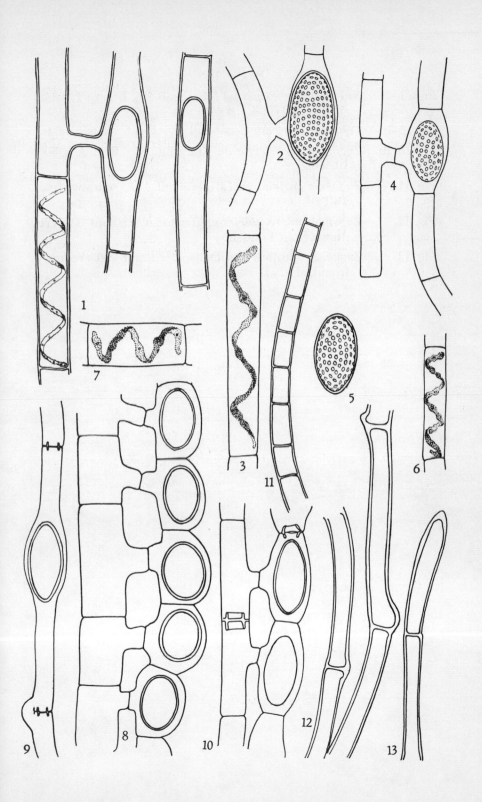

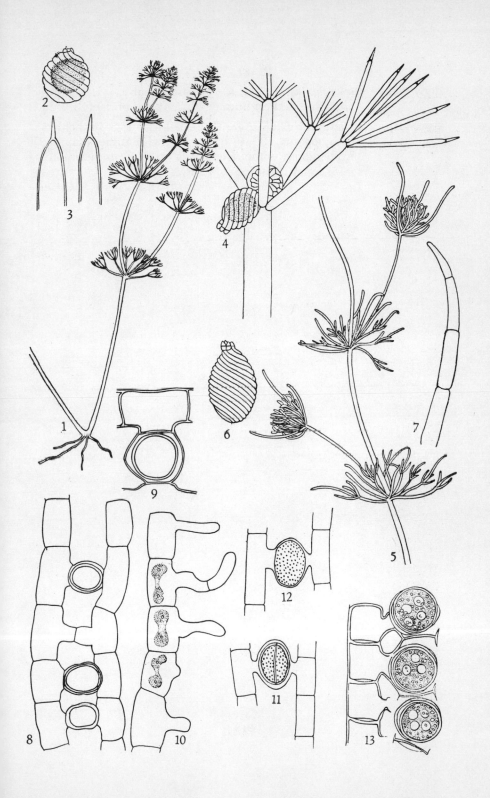

PLATE 79

Figs. 1–3. *Nitella flexilis* (L.) C. A. Agardh: 1, habit, × 1; 2, oogonium and antheridium, × 40; 3, apices of dactyls, × 30

Figs. 4–10 *Nitella opaca* C. A. Agardh: 4, habit, × 1; 5, branchlets
with oogonia, × 5; 6, branchlets with antheridia, × 5;
7, oogonium without coronula, × 25; 8, antheridium,
× 15; 9 and 10, apices of dactyls, × 40.

G.P.   1   2   3   4   5   6   7   8   9   10

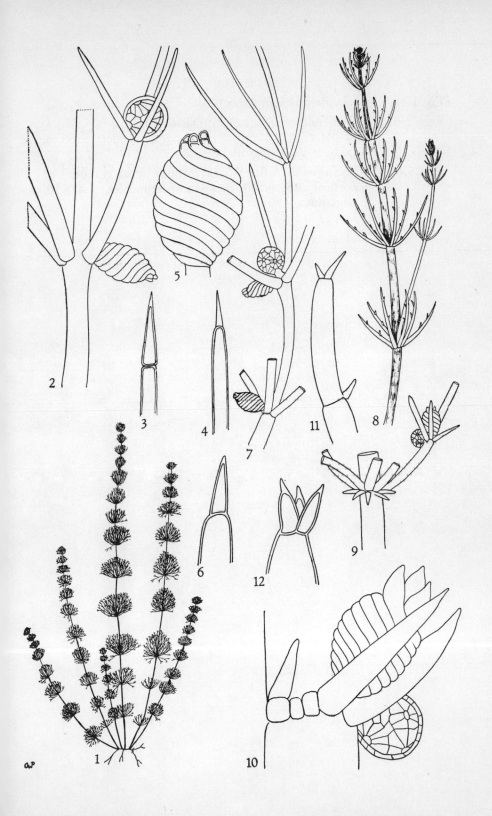

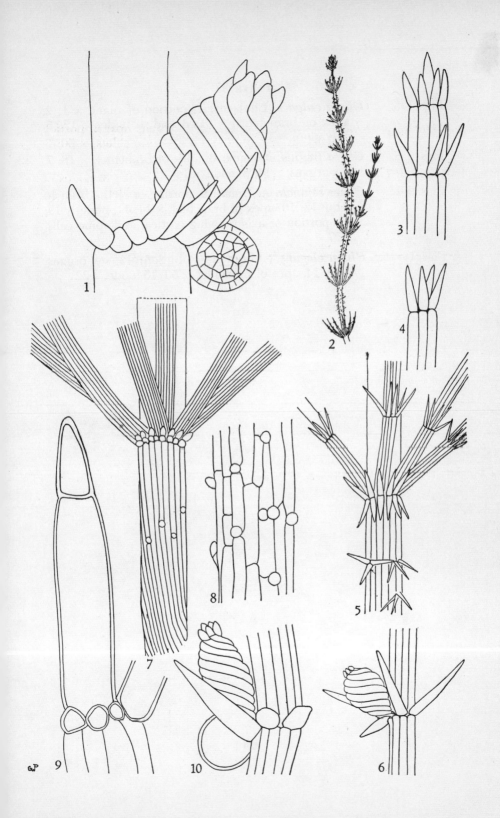

PLATE 82

Figs. 1–5.   *Chara vulgaris* Linnaeus: 1, portion of plant, × 1; 2, apex of branchlets, × 31; 3 and 4. node, × 12; 5, oogonium, × 16

Figs. 6–8.   *Chara fragilis* Desvaux: 6, apex of branchlet, × 18; 7, sex organs, × 14; 8, node, × 14

Figs. 9–12.   *Chara sejuncta* A. Braun: 9, portion of fertile branchlet, × 13; 10, apex of branchlet, × 14; 11, node, × 19; 12, portion of axis showing cortical and spine cells, × 27

Figs. 13–15.   *Chara elegans* (A. Braun) Robinson: 13, sex organs, × 50; 14, apex of branchlet, × 50; 15, node, × 22

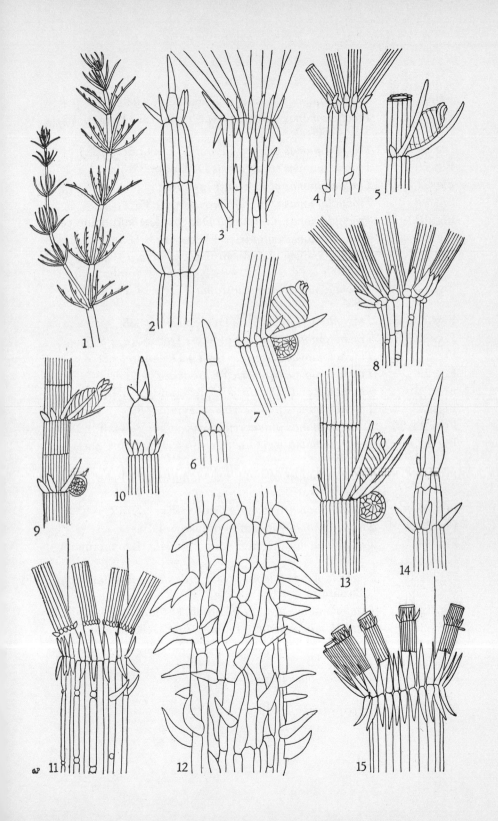

PLATE 83

Fig. 1. *Trachelomonas volvocina* Ehrenberg, × 938

Figs. 2, 3. *Trachelomonas volvocina* var. *compressa* Drezepolski: 2, × 1500; 3, × 1125

Figs. 4, 5. *Trachelomonas varians* (Lemm.) Deflandre, × 885

Fig. 6. *Trachelomonas triangularis* Deflandre, × 1500

Figs. 7, 8. *Trachelomonas volvocina* Ehrenberg fa., × 750

Fig. 9. *Trachelomonas rotunda* Swirenko, × 885

Fig. 10. *Trachelomonas intermedia* Dangeard, × 885

Fig. 11. *Trachelomonas cylindrica* Ehrenberg, × 885

Fig. 12. *Trachelomonas volvocina* var. *punctata* Playfair, × 1500

Fig. 13. *Trachelomonas acanthostoma* (Stokes) Deflandre, × 885

Figs. 14, 15. *Trachelomonas lacustris* Drezepolski, × 938

Figs. 16, 17. *Trachelomonas Kelloggii* (Skv.) Deflandre, × 885

Figs. 18, 19. *Trachelomonas abrupta* (Swir.) Deflandre, × 885

Fig. 20. *Trachelomonas cylindrica* Ehrenberg, × 885

Fig. 21. *Trachelomonas Dybowskii* Drezepolski, × 1500

Figs. 22, 23. *Trachelomonas pulcherrima* Playfair, × 885

Figs. 24, 25. *Trachelomonas pulcherrima* var. *minor* Playfair, × 1050

Fig. 26. *Trachelomonas armata* var. *Steinii* Lemmermann, × 1125

Fig. 27. *Trachelomonas armata* var. *longispina* (Playf.) Deflandre, × 975

Fig. 28. *Trachelomonas pulchella* Drezepolski, × 975

Fig. 29. *Trachelomonas robusta* Swirenko, × 1125

Fig. 30. *Trachelomonas hispida* var. *coronata* Lemmermann, × 885

Fig. 31. *Trachelomonas hispida* var. *crenulatocollis* fa. *recta* Deflandre, × 900

Fig. 32. *Trachelomonas armata* (Ehrenb.) Stein, × 1125

Fig. 33. *Trachelomonas armata* fa. *inevoluta* Deflandre, × 900

Fig. 34. *Trachelomonas superba* var. *Swirenkiana* Deflandre, × 900

Fig. 35. *Trachelomonas hispida* (Perty) Stein, × 885

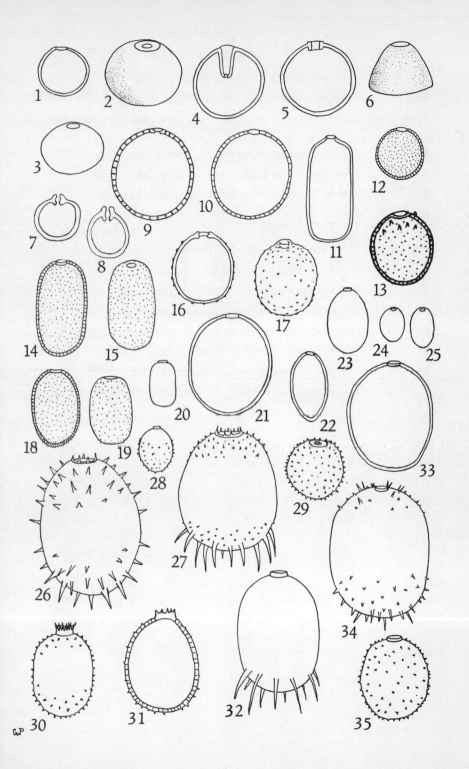

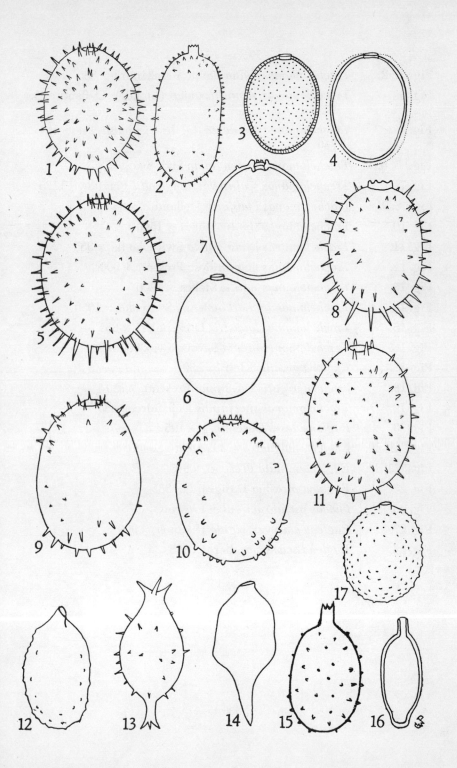

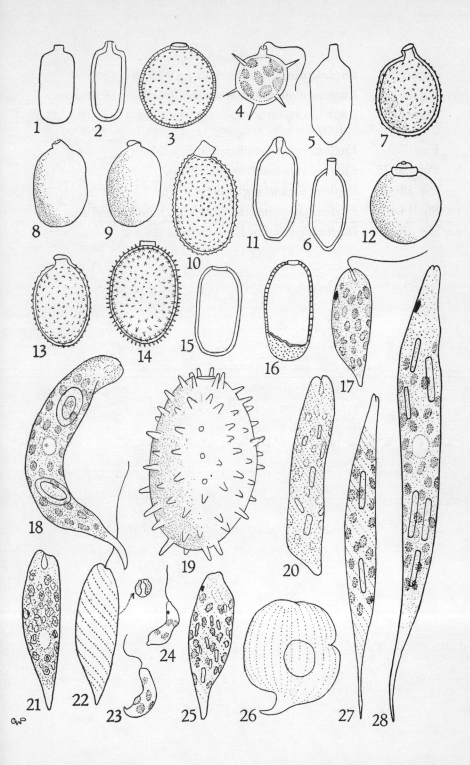

PLATE 86

Figs. 1, 2.   *Euglena sanguinea* Ehrenberg, × 750

Fig. 3.   *Euglena elongata* Schewiakoff, × 1200

Figs. 4–6.   *Euglena tripteris* (Duj.) Klebs: 4 and 5, × 885; 6, × 1200

Figs. 7–9.   *Euglena convoluta* Korshikov, × 885

Figs. 10–12.   *Euglena elastica* Prescott, × 975

Fig. 13.   *Euglena Ehrenbergii* Klebs, × 375

Fig. 14.   *Euglena convoluta* Korshikov, paramylon bodies

Fig. 15.   *Euglena Spirogyra* Ehrenberg, × 885

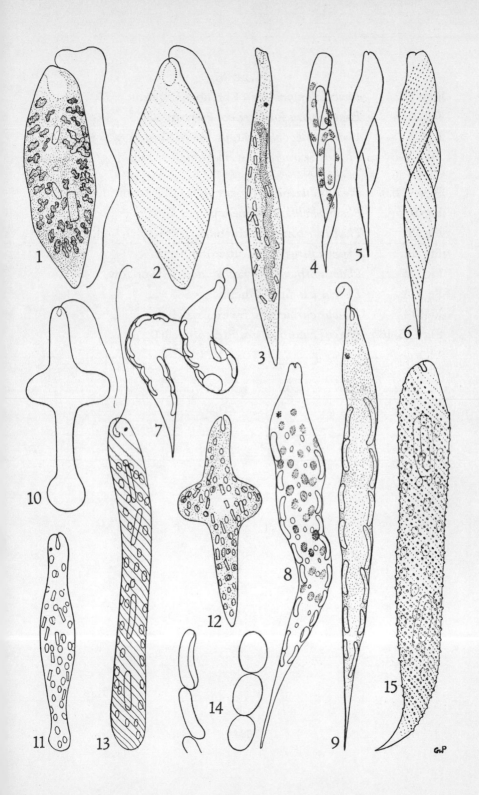

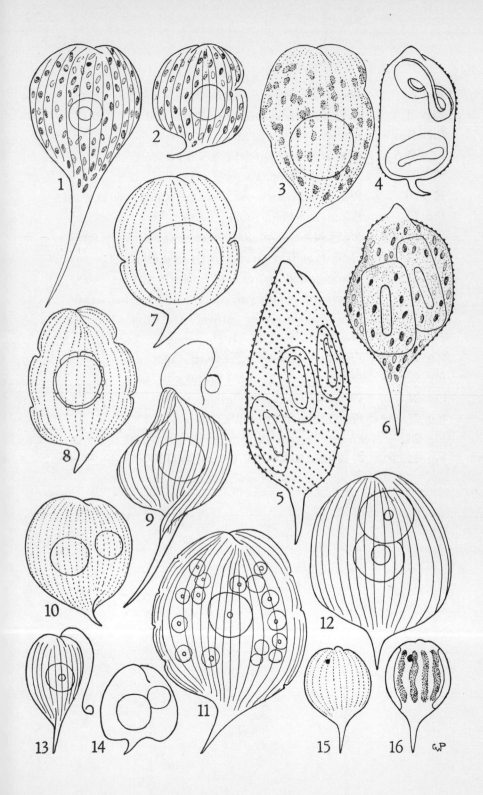

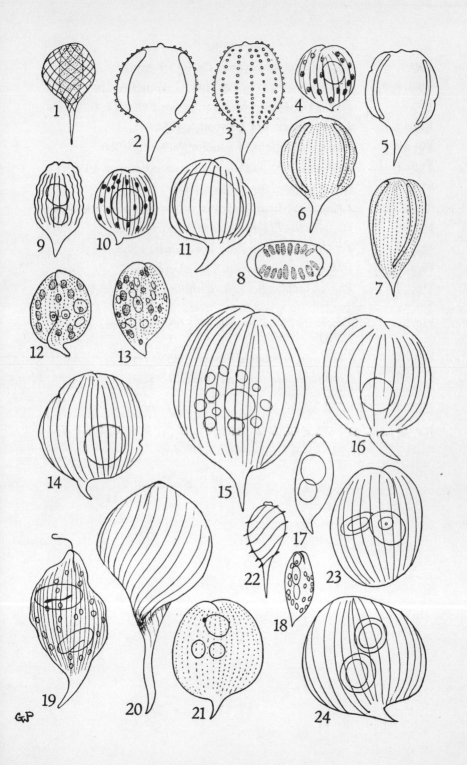

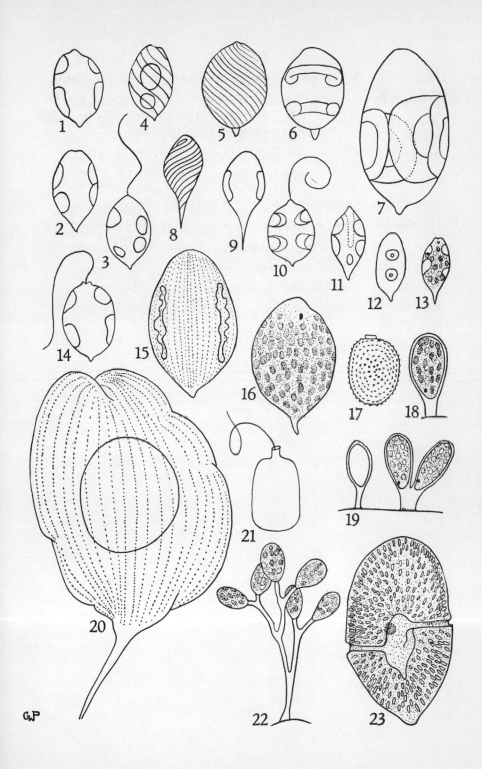

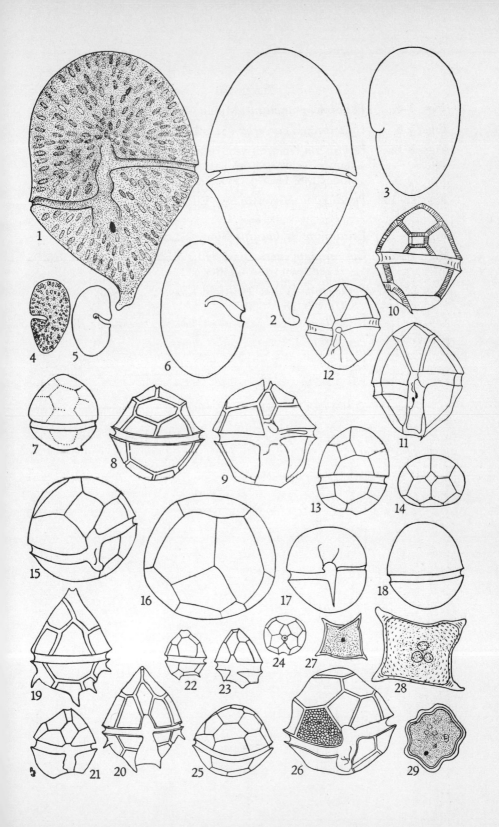

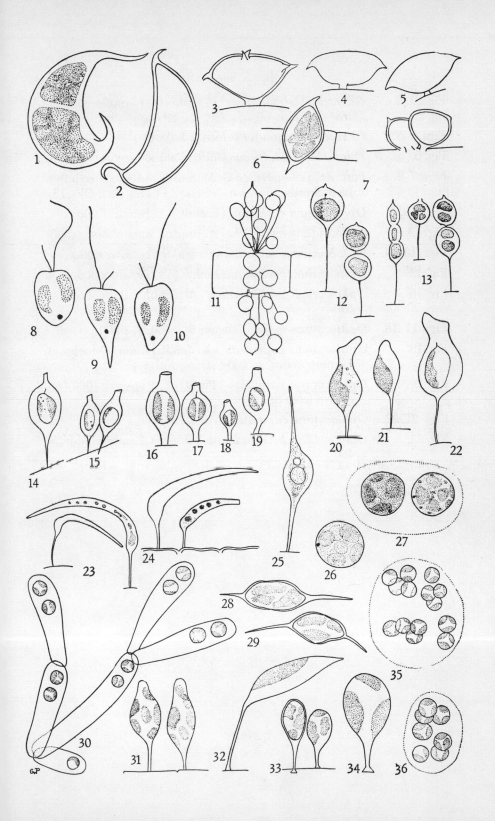

PLATE 94

Figs. 1, 2.   *Characiopsis cylindrica* (Lambert) Lemmermann, × 590

Figs. 3–5.   *Characiopsis spinifer* Printz, × 590

Fig. 6.   *Peroniella Hyalothecae* Gobi, × 590

Figs. 7–9.   *Peroniella planctonica* G. M. Smith, × 1000 (9, redrawn from Smith)

Figs. 10, 11.   *Ophiocytium cochleare* (Eichw.) A. Braun, × 590

Fig. 12.   *Ophiocytium arbuscula* (A. Braun) Rabenhorst, × 590

Figs. 13, 14.   *Ophiocytium elongatum* var. *major* Prescott, × 590

Fig. 15.   *Ophiocytium cochleare* (Eichw.) A. Braun, × 600

Fig. 16.   *Ophiocytium mucronatum* (A. Braun) Rabenhorst, × 590

Figs. 17, 18.   *Ophiocytium majus* Naegeli: 6, × 400; 7, × 590

Fig. 19.   *Ophiocytium capitatum* var. *longispinum* (Moebius) Lemmermann, × 1000 (after Smith)

Fig. 20.   *Ophiocytium parvulum* (Perty) A. Braun, × 1000 (redrawn from Smith)

Figs. 21, 22.   *Ophiocytium capitatum* Wolle, × 590

Fig. 23.   *Ophiocytium bicuspidatum* (Borge) Lemmermann, × 400

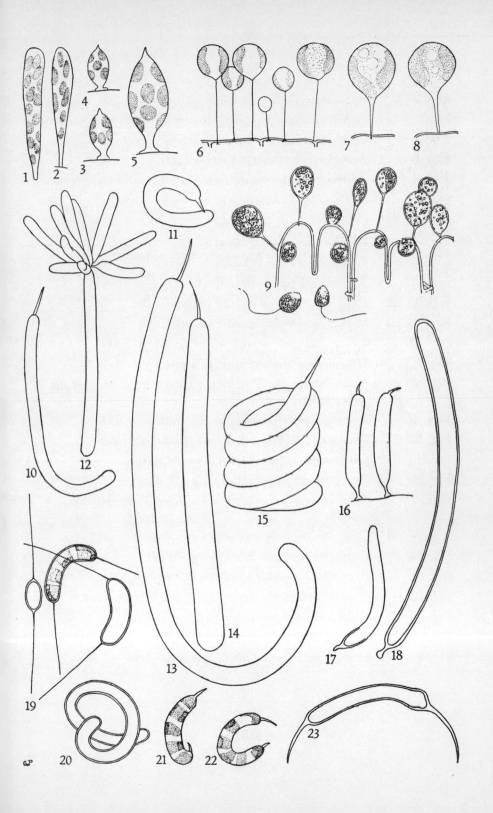

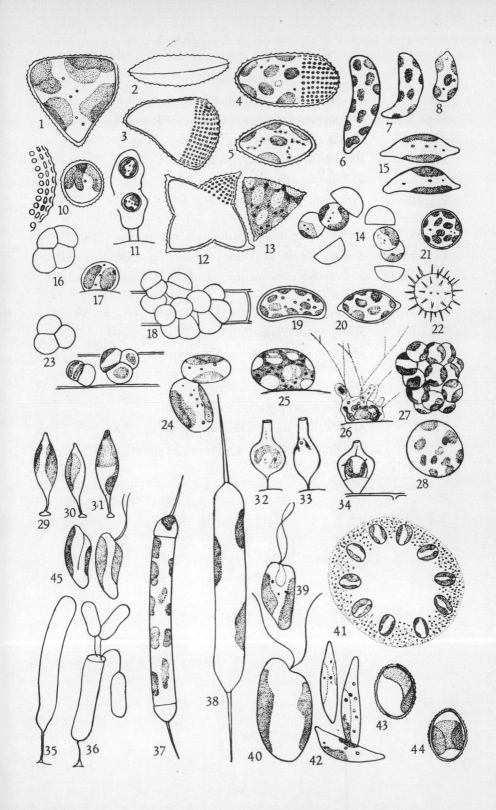

PLATE 96

Fig. 1.   *Phaeothamnion confervicola* Lagerheim, × 590

Figs. 2, 3.   *Ophiocytium desertum* var. *minor* Prescott, × 590

Figs. 4, 5.   *Ophiocytium parvulum* (Perty) A. Braun, × 590

Fig. 6.   *Bumilleria sicula* Borzi, × 590

Figs. 7–9.   *Tribonema affine* G. S. West, × 500

Fig. 10.   *Tribonema bombycinum* (C. A. Ag.) Derbés & Solier, × 600

Fig. 11.   *Tribonema bombycinum* var. *tenue* Hazen, × 750

Figs. 12, 13.   *Tribonema minus* (Wille) Hazen: 12, × 590; 13, × 1000

Figs. 14–16.   *Tribonema utriculosum* (Kuetz.) Hazen: 14 and 15, × 590; 16, × 800

Figs. 17, 18.   *Botrydium granulatum* (L.) Greville: 17, × 18; 18, × 4

Fig. 19.   *Mallomonas alpina* Pascher & Ruttner, × 500

Fig. 20.   *Mallomonas acaroides* var. *Moskovensis* (Wermel) Krieger, × 590

Fig. 21.   *Derepyxis amphora* Stokes, × 700

Fig. 22.   *Mallomonas acaroides* Perty, × 750

Fig. 23.   *Mallomonas pseudocoronata* Prescott, × 500

Fig. 24.   *Mallomonas elliptica* (Kisselew) Conrad, × 500

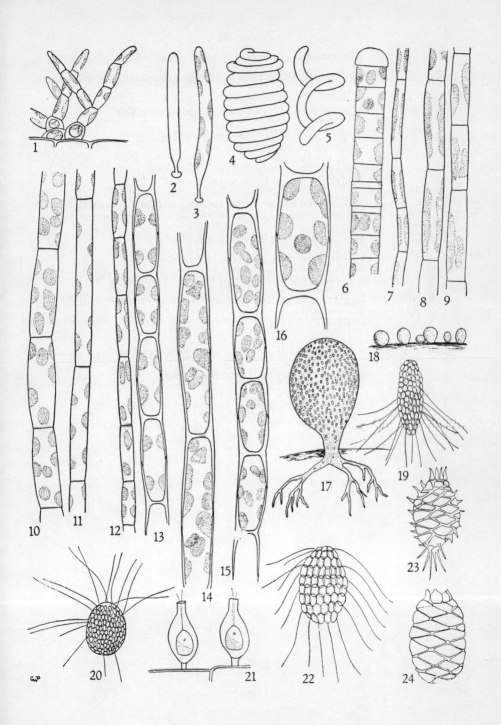

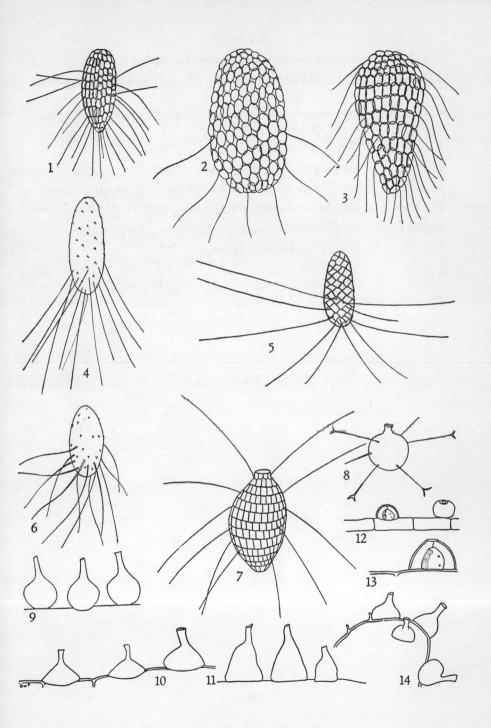

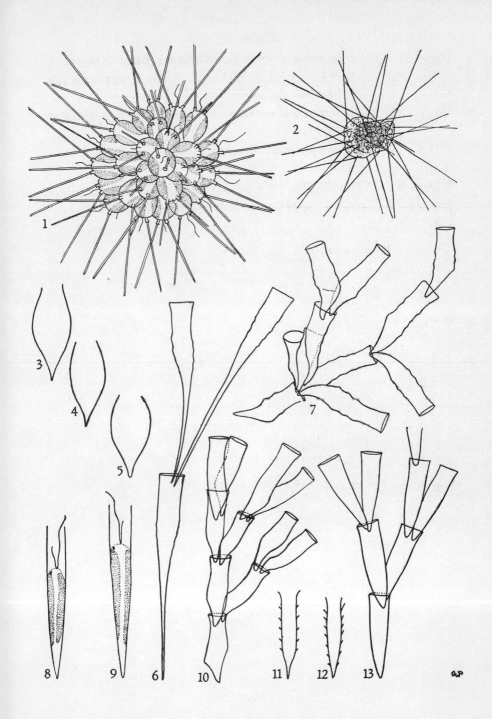

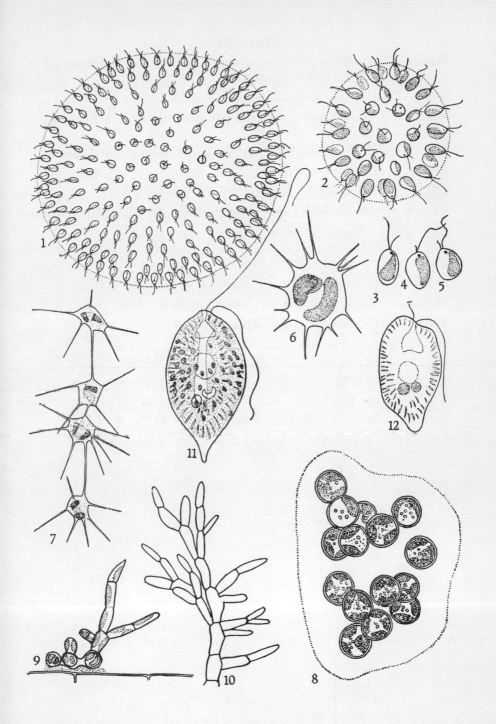

PLATE 100

Figs. 1–3.   *Chroococcus dispersus* var. *minor* G. M. Smith, × 825 (redrawn from Smith)

Figs. 4, 5.   *Chroococcus limneticus* Lemmermann, × 500

Fig. 6.   *Chroococcus limneticus* var. *carneus* (Chod.) Lemmermann, × 310

Fig. 7.   *Chroococcus dispersus* (Keissl.) Lemmermann, × 825

Fig. 8.   *Chroococcus limneticus* var. *distans* G. M. Smith, × 750

Fig. 9.   *Chroococcus minutus* (Kuetz.) Naegeli, × 600

Fig. 10.   *Chroococcus limneticus* var. *subsalsus* Lemmermann, × 825 (redrawn from Smith)

Fig. 11.   *Chroococcus limneticus* var. *elegans* G. M. Smith, × 825 (redrawn from Smith)

Fig. 12.   *Chroococcus minor* (Kuetz.) Naegeli, × 590

Fig. 13.   *Chroococcus Prescottii* Drouet & Daily, × 600

Fig. 14.   *Chroococcus pallidus* Naegeli, × 590

Fig. 15.   *Chroococcus varius* A. Braun, × 1000

Fig. 16.   *Chroococcus giganteus* W. West, × 825 (redrawn from Smith)

Fig. 17.   *Merismopedia tenuissima* Lemmermann, × 1250

Fig. 18.   *Merismopedia elegans* var. *major* G. M. Smith, × 500

Fig. 19.   *Chroococcus turgidus* (Kuetz.) Naegeli, × 590

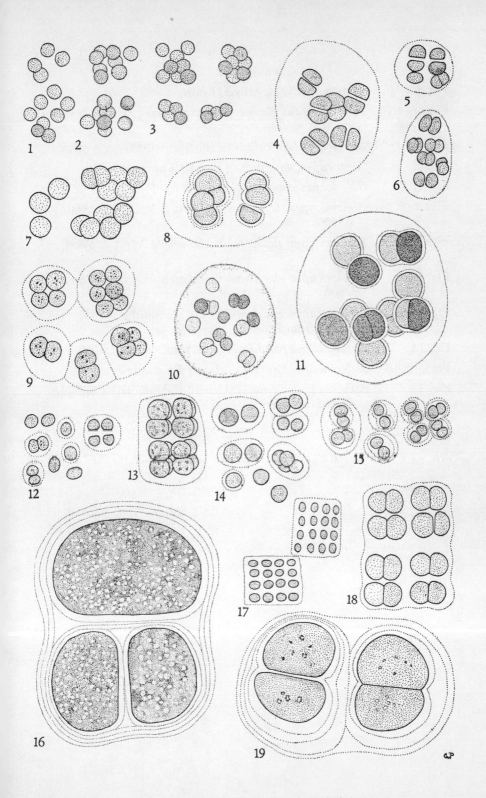

PLATE 101

Fig. 1.   *Merismopedia elegans* A. Braun, × 500

Figs. 2–4.   *Merismopedia glauca* (Ehrenb.) Naegeli: 2, × 590; 3, × 600; 4, × 590

Fig. 5.   *Merismopedia Trolleri* Bachmann, × 1000

Fig. 6.   *Gloeocapsa aeruginosa* (Carm.) Kuetzing, × 750

Fig. 7.   *Gloeocapsa punctata* Naegeli, × 750

Figs. 8, 9.   *Aphanocapsa delicatissima* West & West: 8, × 900; 9, × 1000

Figs. 10, 11.   *Aphanocapsa elachista* var. *conferta* West & West, × 750

Fig. 12.   *Aphanocapsa elachista* var. *planctonica* G. M. Smith, × 500

Fig. 13.   *Aphanocapsa endophytica* G. M. Smith, × 1000 (redrawn from Smith)

Fig. 14.   *Aphanocapsa pulchra* (Kuetz.) Rabenhorst, × 500

Figs. 15, 16.   *Aphanocapsa Grevillei* (Hass.) Rabenhorst, × 500

Fig. 17.   *Aphanocapsa rivularis* (Carm.) Rabenhorst, × 825 (redrawn from Smith)

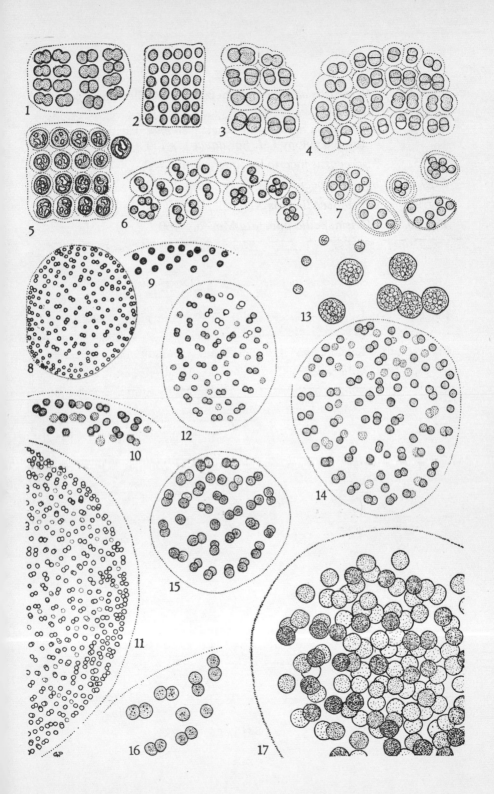

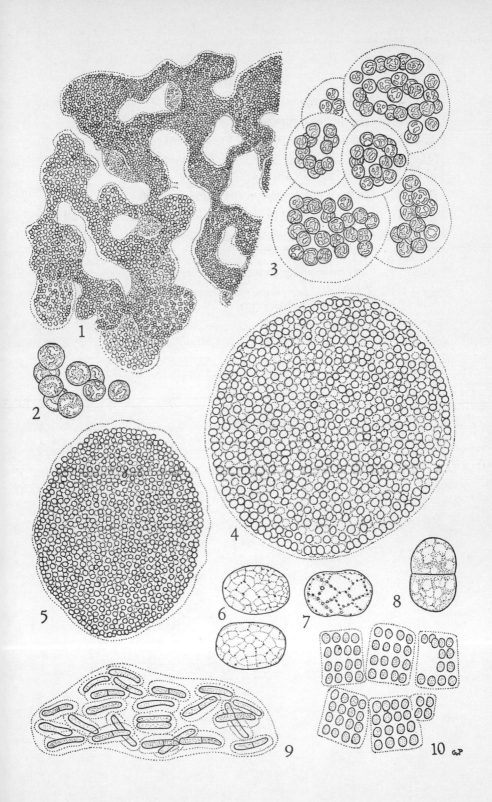

PLATE 103

Fig. 1.   *Gloeothece linearis* var. *composita* G. M. Smith, × 750

Figs. 2, 3.   *Gloeothece rupestris* (Lyngb.) Bornet, × 750

Fig. 4.   *Rhabdoderma Gorskii* Wołoszyńska, × 750

Figs. 5, 6.   *Rhabdoderma sigmoidea* fa. *minor* Moore & Carter: 5, × 750; 5, × 1875

Figs. 7, 8.   *Cyanarcus hamiformis* Pascher, × 3000

Figs. 9, 10.   *Rhabdoderma irregulare* (Naumann) Geitler, × 750

Figs. 11, 12. *Rhabdoderma lineare* Schmidle & Lauterborn: 11, × 750; 12, × 1500

Fig. 13.   *Merismopedia convoluta* de Brébisson, × 600

Figs. 14–16.   *Aphanothece stagnina* (Spreng.) A. Braun: 14 and 16, habit, × 1; 15, × 750

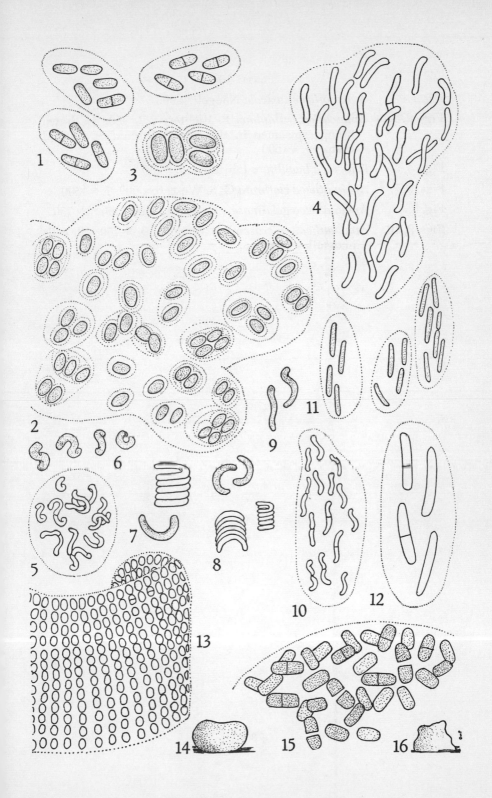

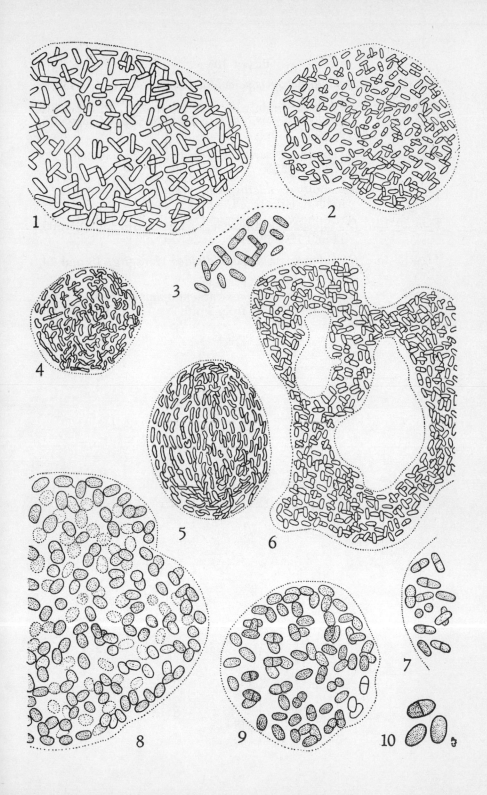

Plate 105

Figs. 1, 2.   *Dactylococcopsis acicularis* Lemmermann: 1, × 750; 2,
               × 1125

Figs. 3, 4.   *Dactylococcopsis Smithii* Chodat & Chodat: 3, × 975;
               4, × 490

Figs. 5, 6.   *Aphanothece Castagnei* (de Bréb.) Rabenhorst: 5, ×
               1875; 6, × 1500

Figs. 7–9.   *Aphanothece microspora* (Menegh.) Rabenhorst: 7,
               habit of colony, × 1; 8 and 9, × 900

Figs. 10–12.   *Dactylococcopsis fascicularis* Lemmermann: 10, × 500;
               11 and 12, × 750

Figs. 13–15.   *Dactylococcopsis rhaphidioides* Hansgirg: 13 and 14,
               × 750; 15, × 375

Fig. 16.   *Aphanothece nidulans* var. *endophytica* West & West,
               × 1500 (redrawn from Smith)

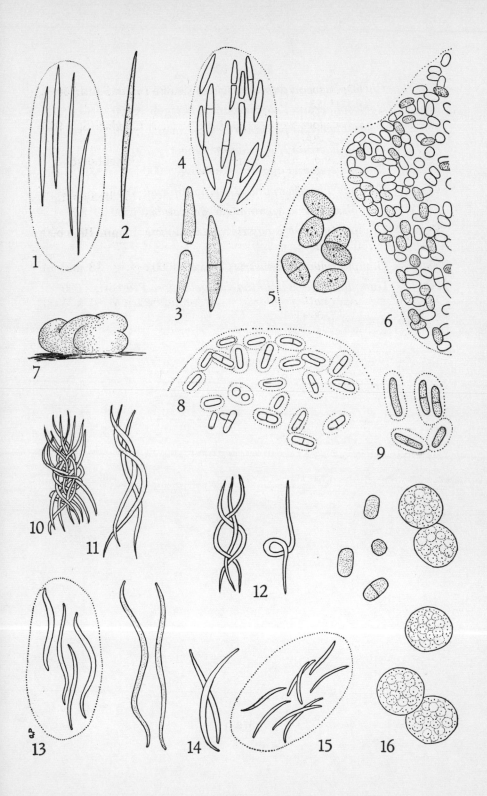

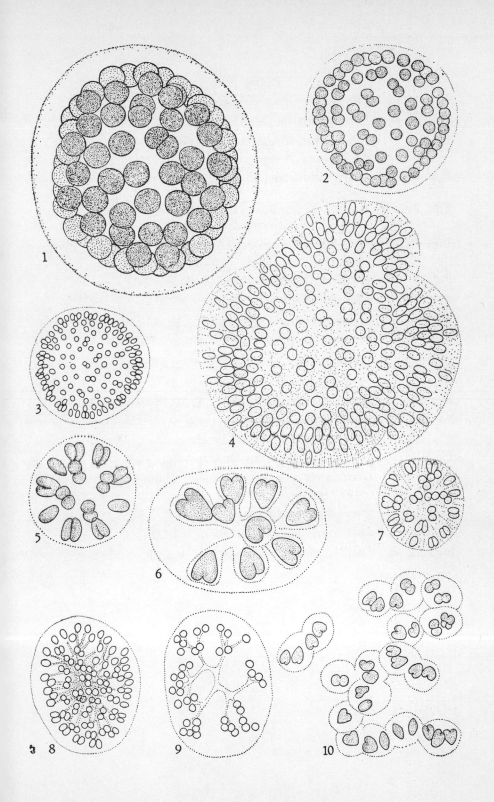

PLATE 107

Fig. 1.　　　　*Dinobryon cylindricum* Imhof, × 400

Fig. 2.　　　　*Tetradinium simplex* Prescott, × 400

Fig. 3.　　　　*Gymnodinium palustre* Schilling, × 500 (redrawn from Höll)

Figs. 4–6.　　*Phacus triqueter* (Ehrenb.) Dujardin, × 600 (redrawn from Skuja)

Figs. 7–9.　　*Peridinium pusillum* (Penard) Lemmermann, × about 1000 (redrawn from Schilling)

Figs. 10, 11.　*Holopedium irregulare* Lagerheim, × 500 (drawn from material collected in Louisiana)

Fig. 12.　　　*Marssoniella elegans* Lemmermann, × 500

Fig. 13.　　　*Gloeocapsa rupestris* Kuetzing, × 250

Fig. 14.　　　*Dinobryon Vanhoeffenii* (Krieg.) Bachmann, × 500

Fig. 15.　　　*Phormidium inundatum* Kuetzing, × 1000

Fig. 16.　　　*Phormidium subfuscum* Kuetzing, × 625

Fig. 17.　　　*Spirulina laxissima* G. S. West, × 2000

Fig. 18.　　　*Phormidium uncinatum* (C. A. Ag.) Gomont, × 625

Figs. 19, 20.　*Phormidium autumnale* (C. A. Ag.) Gomont: 19, × 925; 10, × 800

Fig. 21.　　　*Oscillatoria rubescens* De Candolle, × 625

Fig. 22.　　　*Oscillatoria articulata* Gardner, × about 1400 (redrawn from Gardner)

Fig. 23.　　　*Oscillatoria subbrevis* Schmidle, × 580

Fig. 24.　　　*Oscillatoria minima* Gicklhorn, × 1000

Figs. 25, 26.　*Oscillatoria terebriformis* C. A. Agardh, × 625

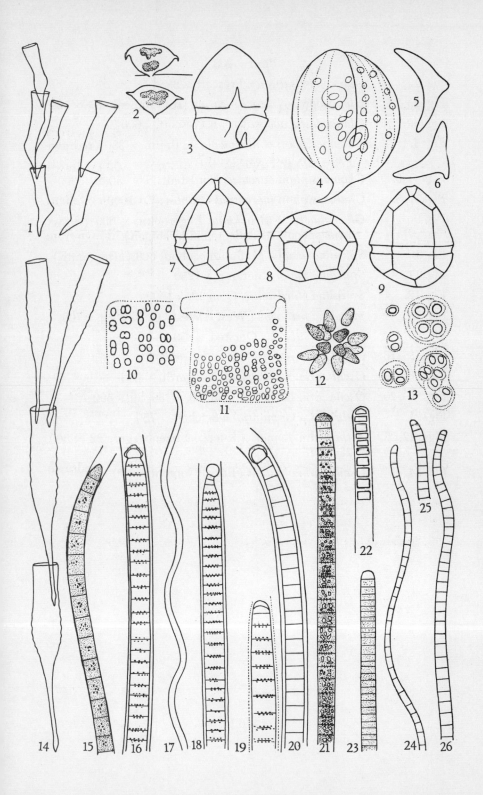

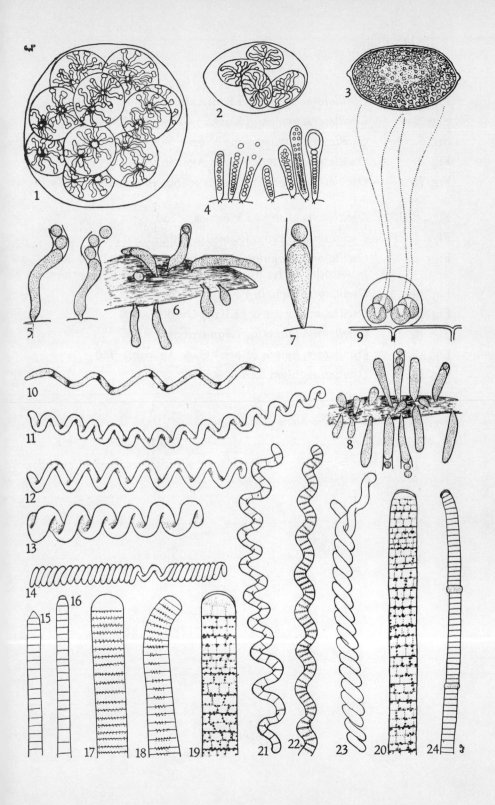

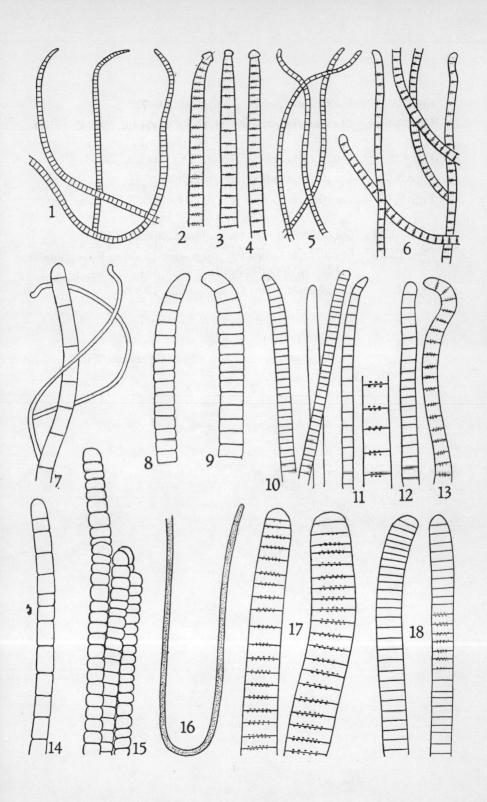

PLATE 110

Fig. 1.   *Oscillatoria princeps* Vaucher, × 660

Figs. 2, 3.   *Oscillatoria prolifica* (Grev.) Gomont, × 1240 (after Smith)

Fig. 4.   *Oscillatoria sancta* (Kuetz.) Gomont, × 750

Figs. 5–7.   *Oscillatoria splendida* Greville, × 1050

Figs. 8, 9.   *Oscillatoria tenuis* C. A. Agardh: 8, × 1240 (after Smith); 9, × 750

Figs. 10, 11.   *Oscillatoria tenuis* var. *natans* Gomont, × 750

Figs. 12, 13.   *Oscillatoria tenuis* var. *tergestina* (Kuetz.) Rabenhorst: 12, × 1240 (after Smith); 13, × 750

Fig. 14.   *Oscillatoria tenuis* C. A. Agardh, × 750

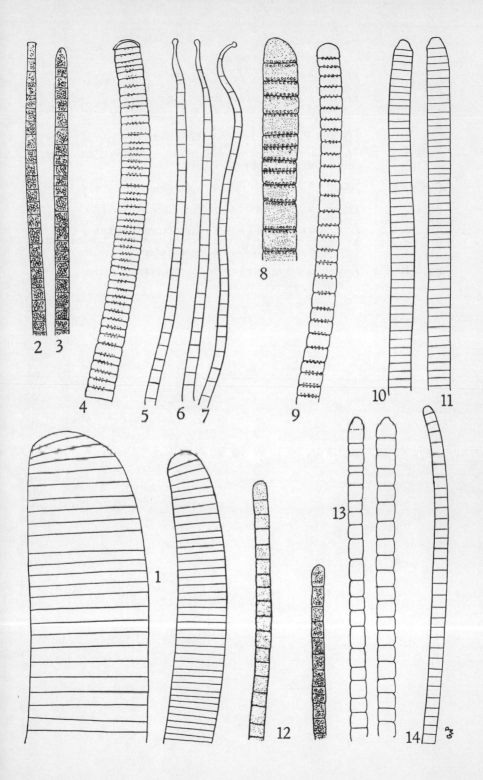

Plate 111

Fig. 1.   *Phormidium ambiguum* Gomont, × 750

Fig. 2.   *Phormidium favosum* (Bory) Gomont, × 485 (redrawn
               from Frémy)

Fig. 3.   *Phormidium inundatum* Kuetzing, × 750

Figs. 4, 5.   *Phormidium mucicola* Naumann & Huber-Pestalozzi:
               4, × 3200; 5, × 750

Fig. 6.   *Phormidium Retzii* (C. A. Ag.) Gomont, × 380

Fig. 7.   *Phormidium tenue* (Menegh.) Gomont, × 1125

Fig. 8.   *Lyngbya aestuarii* (Mert.) Liebmann, × 1050

Fig. 9.   *Lyngbya Birgei* G. M. Smith, × 750

Figs. 10, 11. *Lyngbya aerugineo-caerulea* (Kuetz.) Gomont: 10, ×
               900; 11, × 450

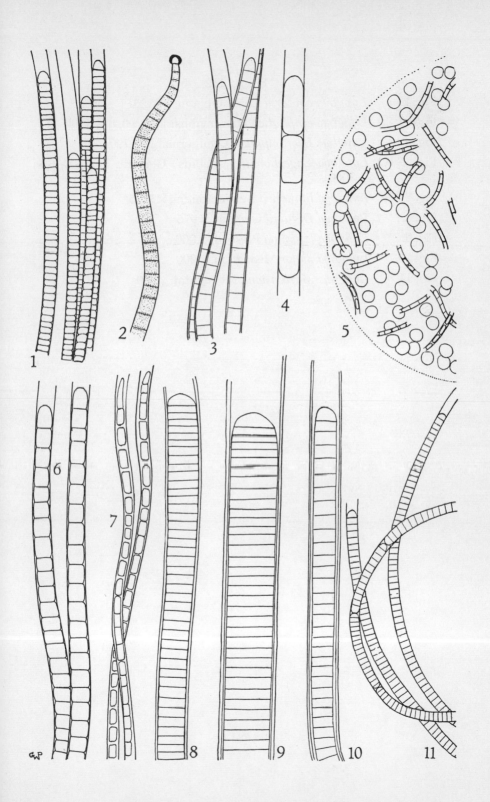

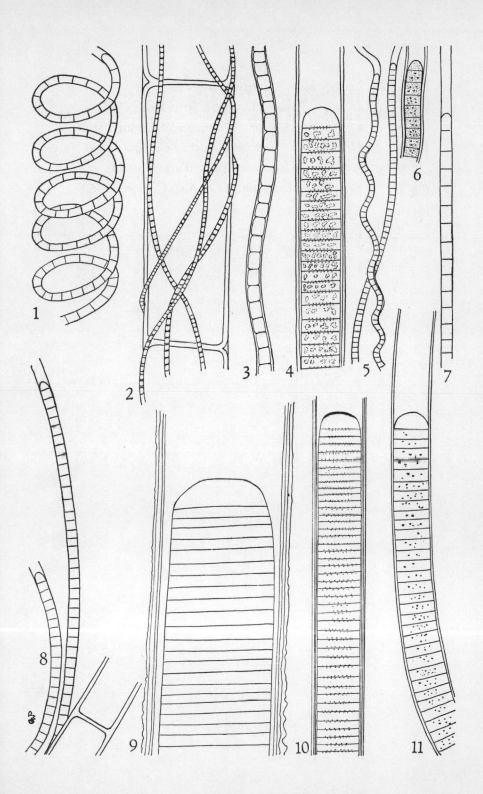

1
2
3
4
5
6
7
8
9
10
11

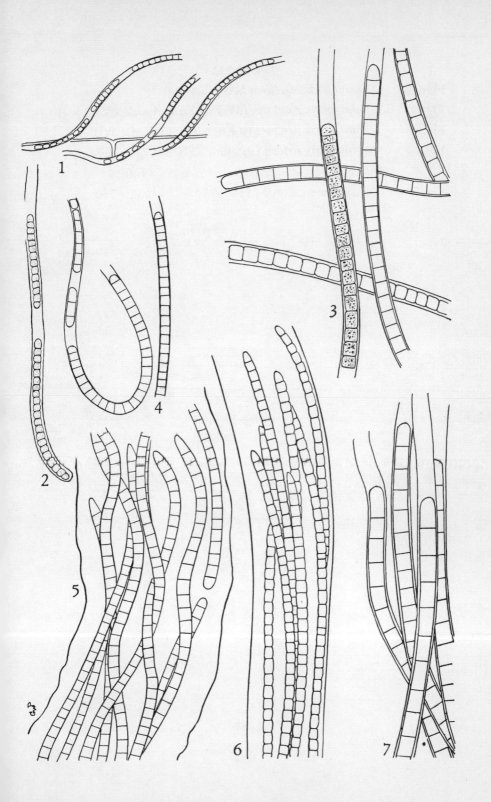

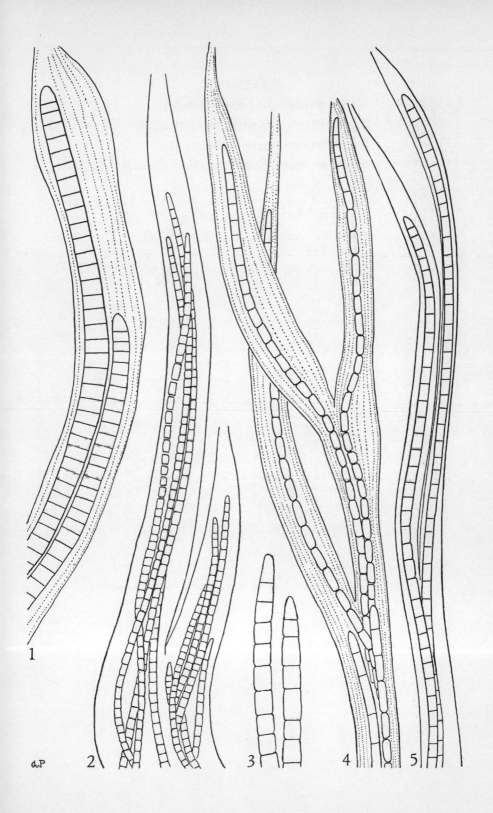

G.P.   1   2   3   4   5

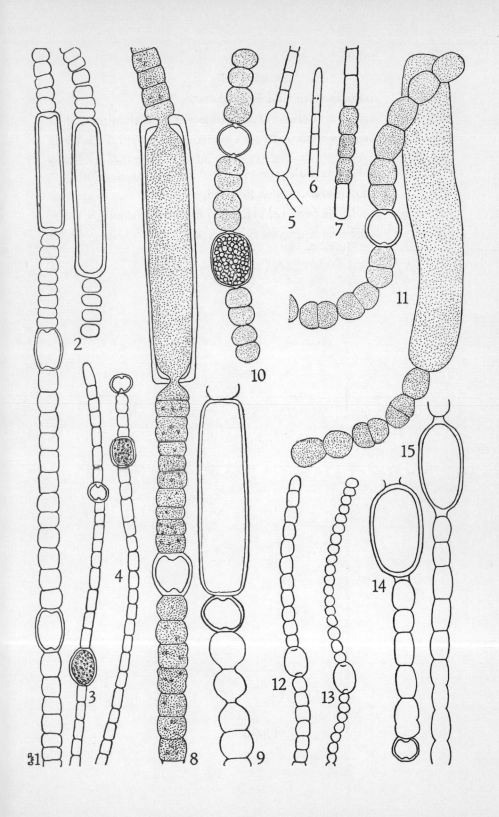

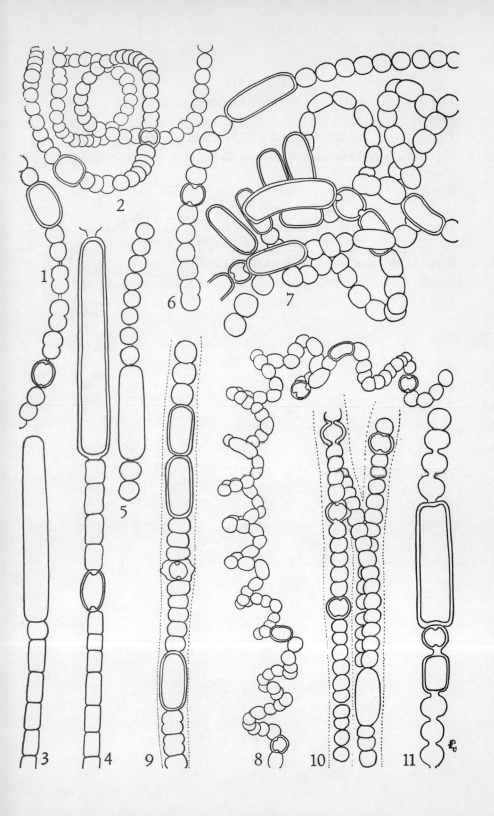

1   2   6   7

3   4   5   9   8   10   11

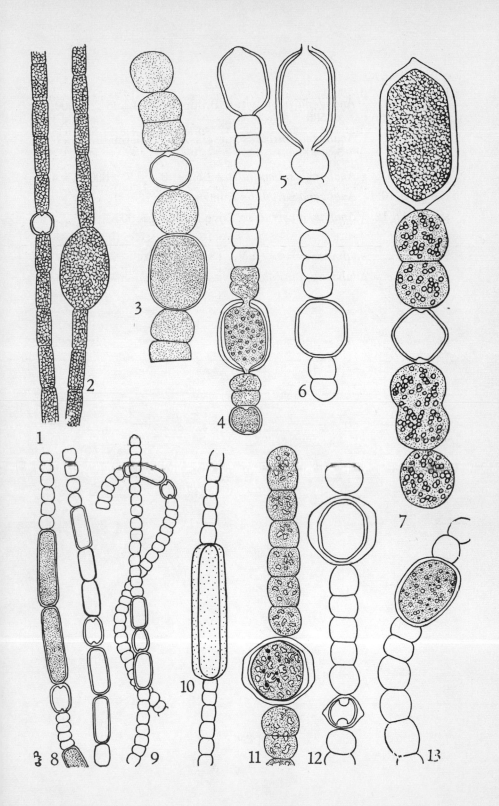

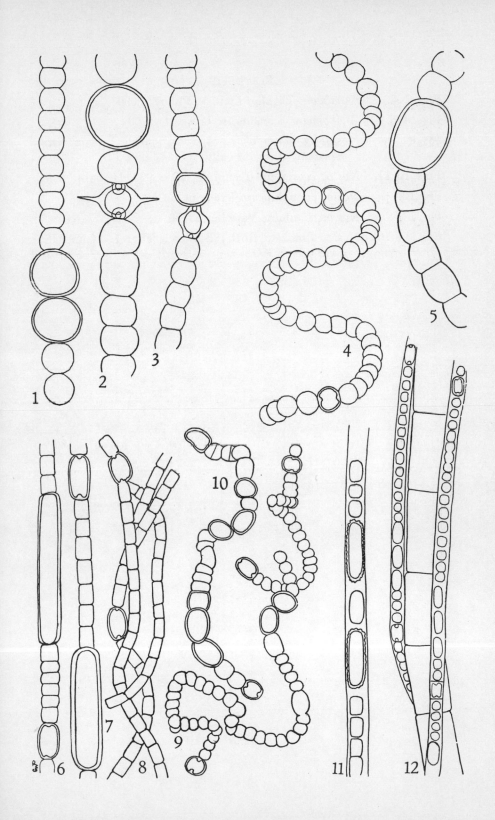

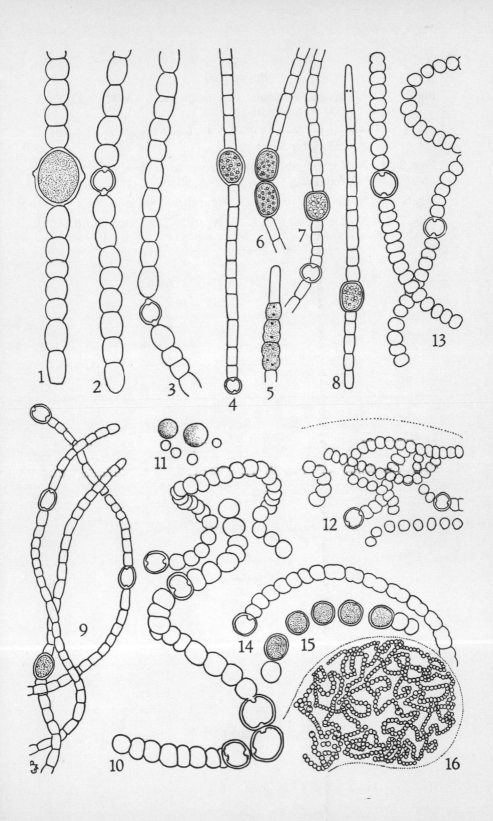

PLATE 120

Fig. 1.   ?*Anabaena circinalis* var. *macrospora* (Wittr.) DeToni, × 600 (after Smith)

Fig. 2. '   *Anabaena flos-aquae* var. *Treleasii* Bornet & Flahault, × 1225 (after Smith)

Figs. 3–5.   *Nostoc microscopicum* Carmichael: 3, × 400; 4 and 5, habit, × 2½

Fig. 6.   *Nostoc muscorum* C. A. Agardh, × 540 (after Frémy)

Figs. 7, 8.   *Nostoc pruniforme* C. A. Agardh: 7, × 750: 8, habit, × 2½

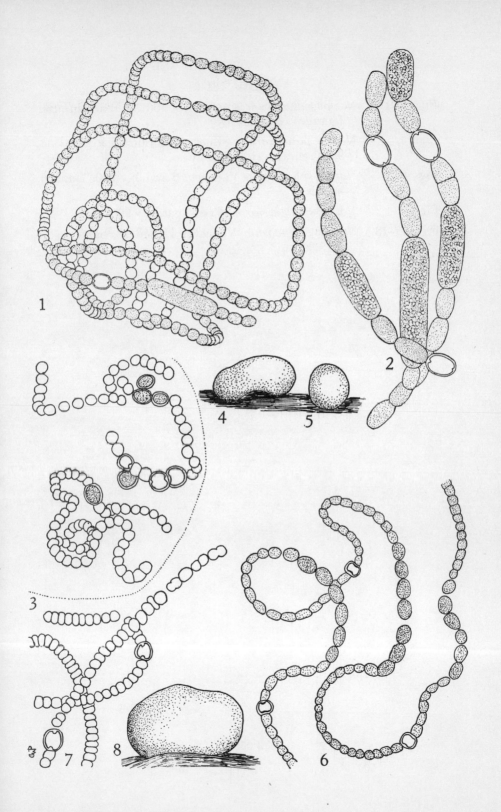

PLATE 121

Figs. 1–3. *Nostoc paludosum* Kuetzing, × 750 (3, redrawn after Janczewski, *ex* Frémy)

Figs. 4, 5. *Nostoc punctiforme* (Kuetz.) Hariot: 4, × 280; 5, × 900 (redrawn from Frémy)

Figs. 6–9. *Nostoc sphaericum* Vaucher: 6 and 9, × 900; 7 and 8, habit, × ¾

Fig. 10. *Nostoc spongiaeforme* C. A. Agardh, × 900

Figs. 11–13. *Nostoc verrucosum* Vaucher: 11 and 12, habit, × ¾; 13, × 900

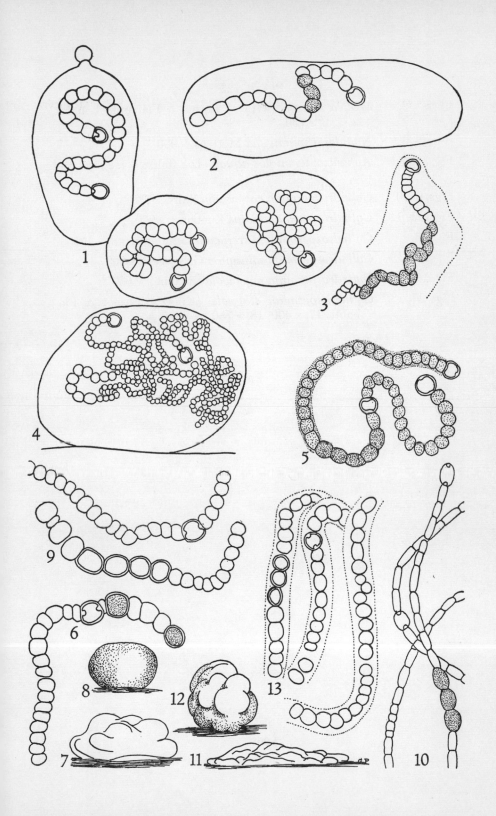

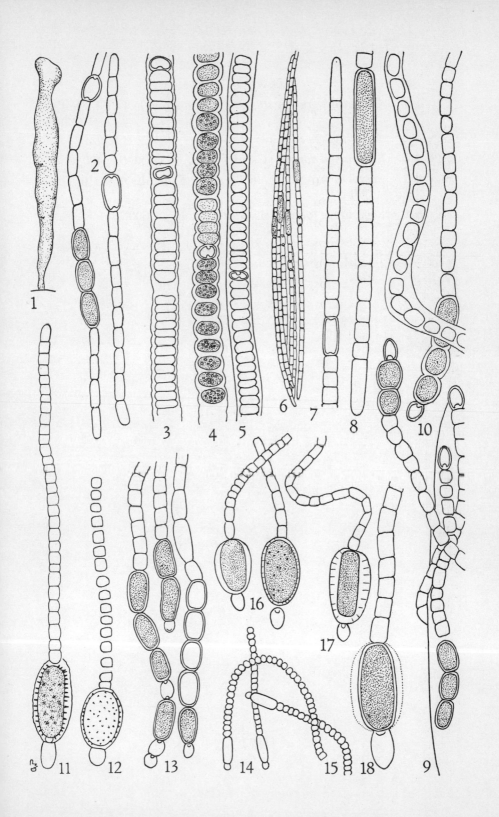

1   2   3   4   5   6   7   8   10   11   12   13   14   15   16   17   18   9

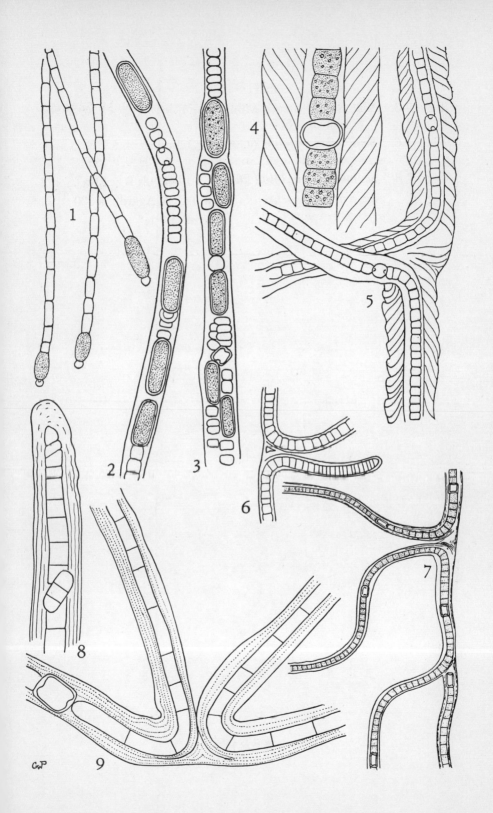

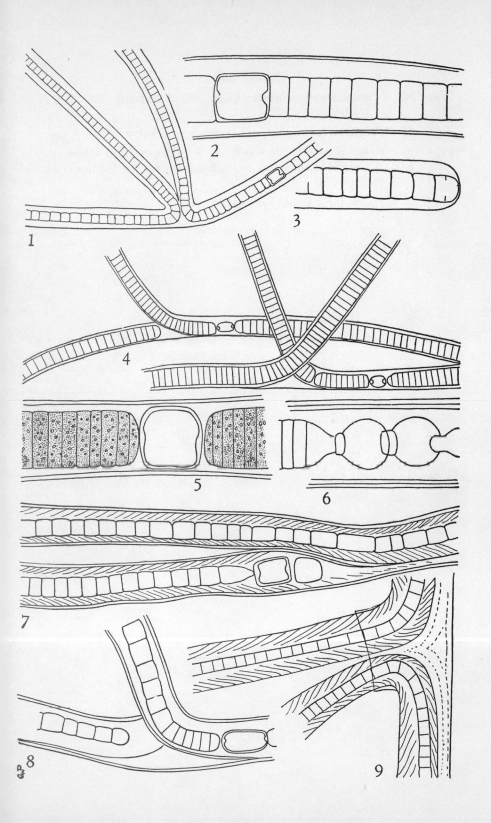

PLATE 125

Figs. 1, 2. *Scytonema myochrous* (Dillw.) C. A. Agardh: 1, × 285; 2, × 640

Figs. 3, 4. *Tolypothrix conglutinata* Borzi: 3, × 900; 4, × 1050

Figs. 5, 6. *Tolypothrix distorta* Kuetzing: 5 (redrawn from Tilden), × about 560; 6 (redrawn from Frémy, *ex* Geitler), × about 280

Fig. 7. *Tolypothrix lanata* Wartmann, × 900

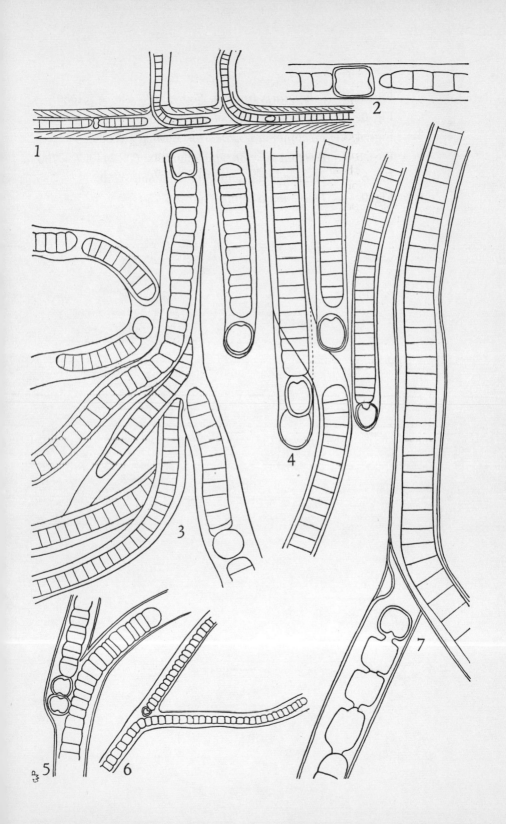

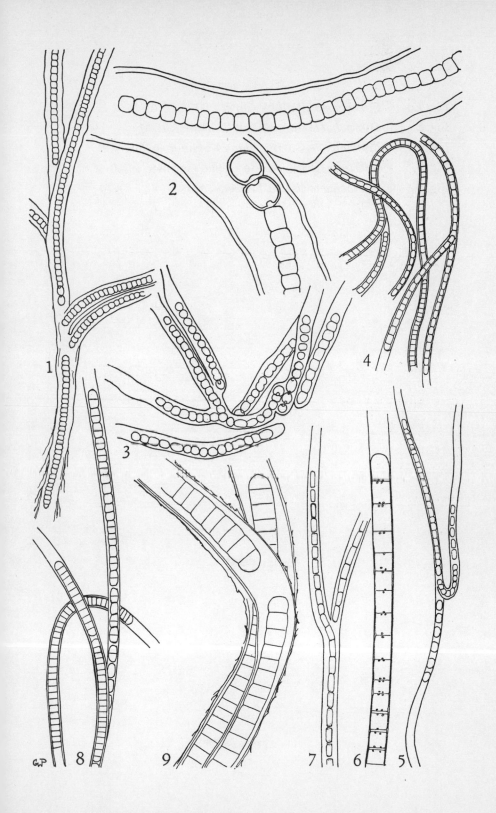

PLATE 127

Fig. 1.   *Plectonema Wollei* Farlow, × 265
Fig. 2.   *Microchaete diplosiphon* Gomont, × 1200
Figs. 3, 4.   *Microchaete Goeppertiana* Kirchner, × 750
Fig. 5.   *Microchaete robusta* Setchell & Gardner, × 750
Fig. 6.   *Microchaete tenera* Thuret, × 900

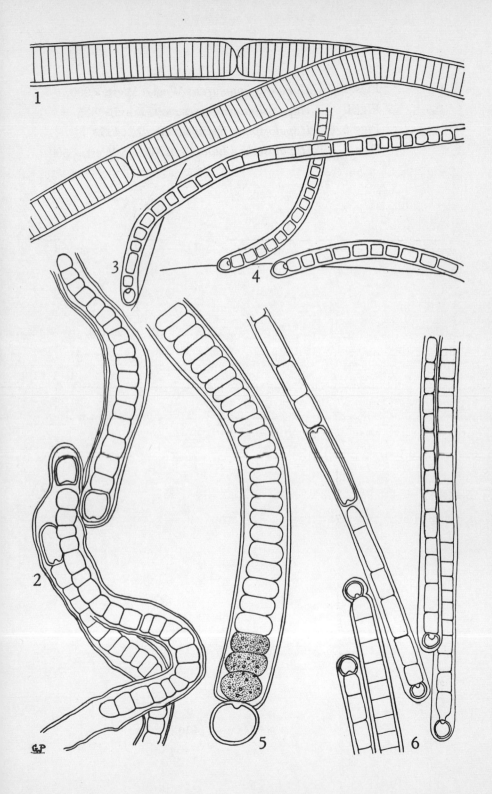

1

3

4

2

5

6

G.P

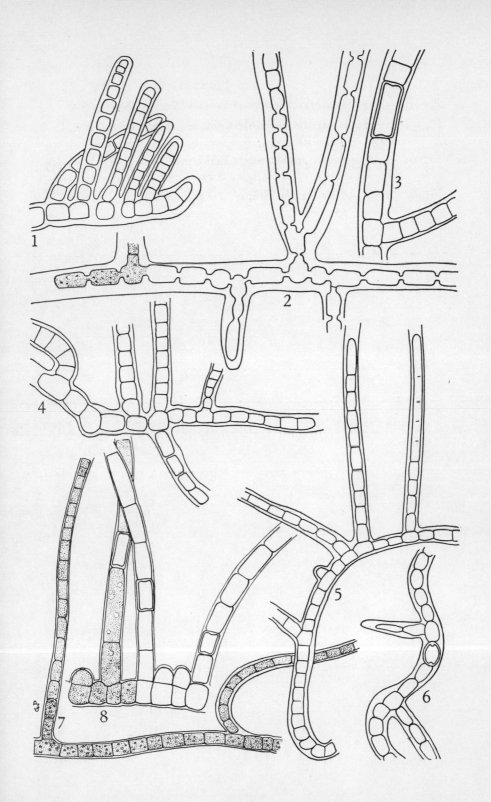

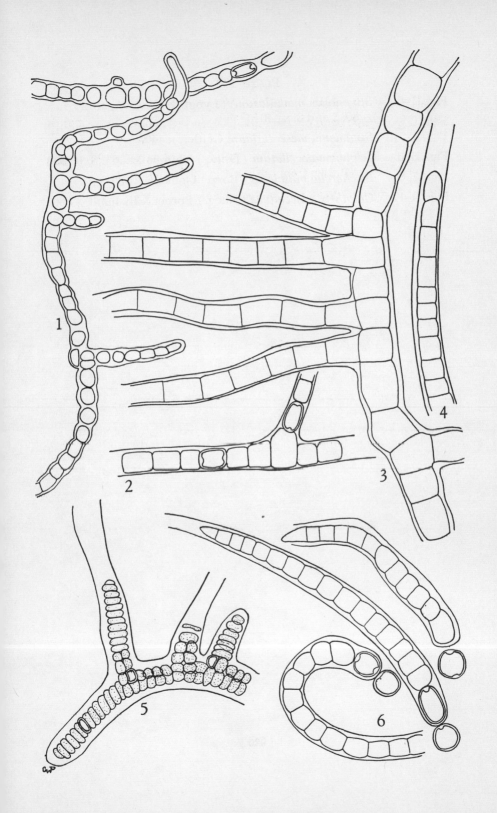

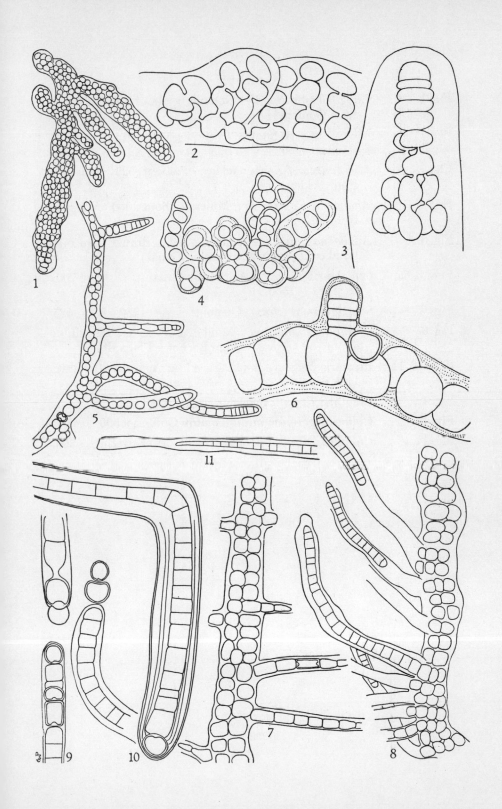

PLATE 131

Fig. 1. *Lyngbya spirulinoides* Gomont, × about 260 (redrawn from Gomont)

Fig. 2. *Microcoleus vaginatus* (Vauch.) Gomont: portion of thallus, × 500

Fig. 3. *Microchaete spiralis* Ackley, × about 325 (redrawn from Ackley)

Fig. 4. *Anabaenopsis Elenkinii* Miller, × about 1000 (redrawn from Miller)

Fig. 5. *Anabaena unispora* Gardner, × 700 (drawn from material collected in the Panama Canal)

Figs. 6, 6a. *Schizothrix lacustris* A. Braun: 6, habit, × about 700; 6a, apex, × 1500

Figs. 7, 8. *Schizothrix tinctoria* Gomont: 7, × 1250; 8, × 625

Fig. 9. *Amphithrix janthina* (Mont.) Bornet & Flahault, × about 750 (redrawn from Bornet & Flahault)

Figs. 10, 11. *Rivularia haematites* (D. C.) C. A. Agardh: 10, habit; 11, × 625

Fig. 12. *Calothrix Braunii* Bornet & Flahault, × 500

Fig. 13. *Cylindrospermum minutissimum* Collins, × 500

Fig. 14. *Cylindrospermum licheniforme* (Bory) Kuetzing, × 500

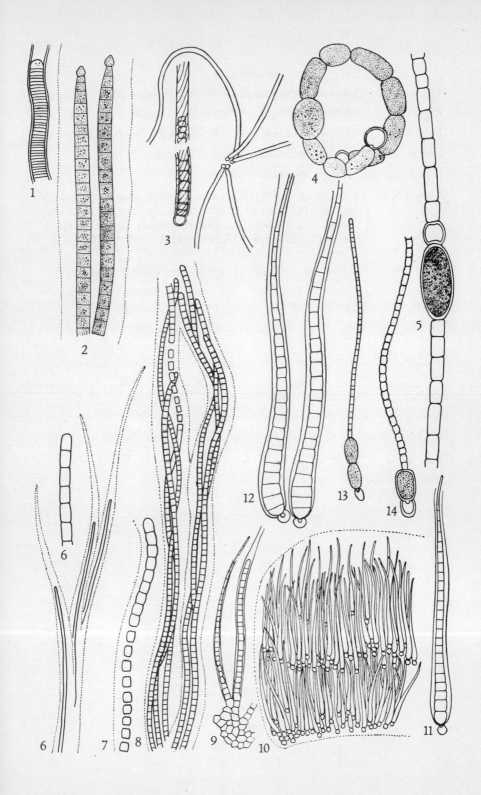

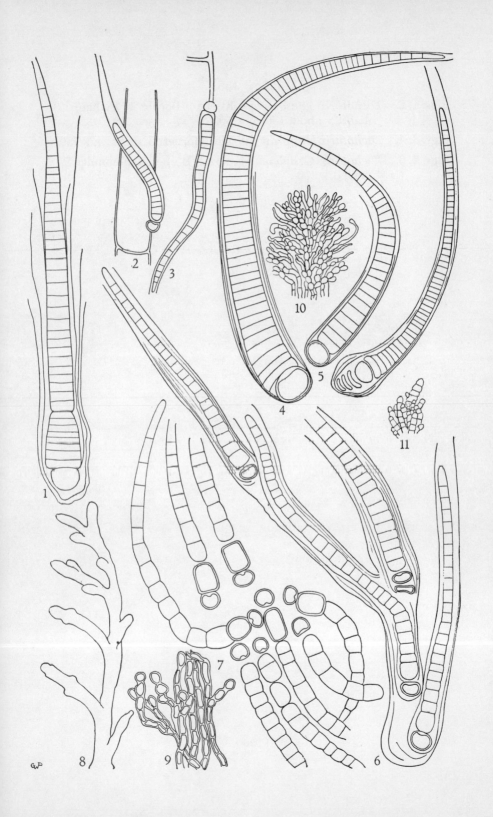

1   2   3   4   5   6   7   8   9   10   11

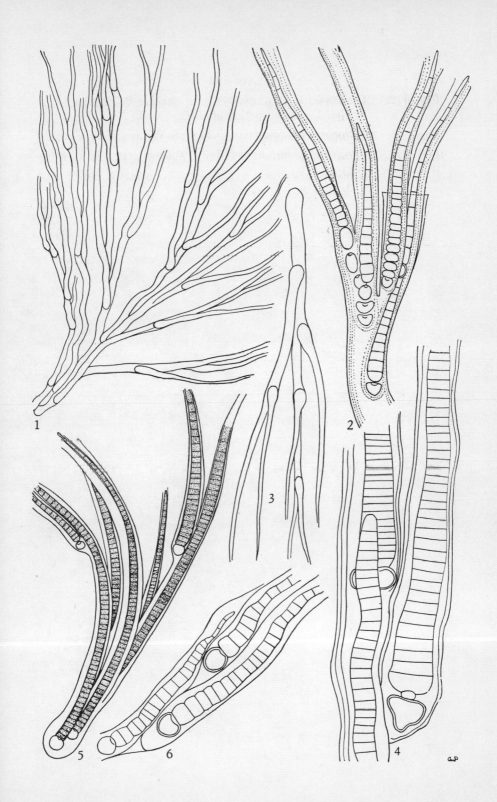

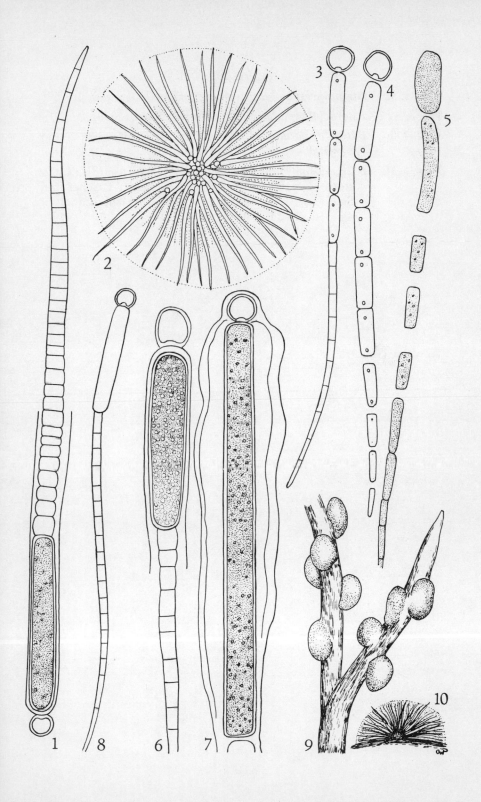

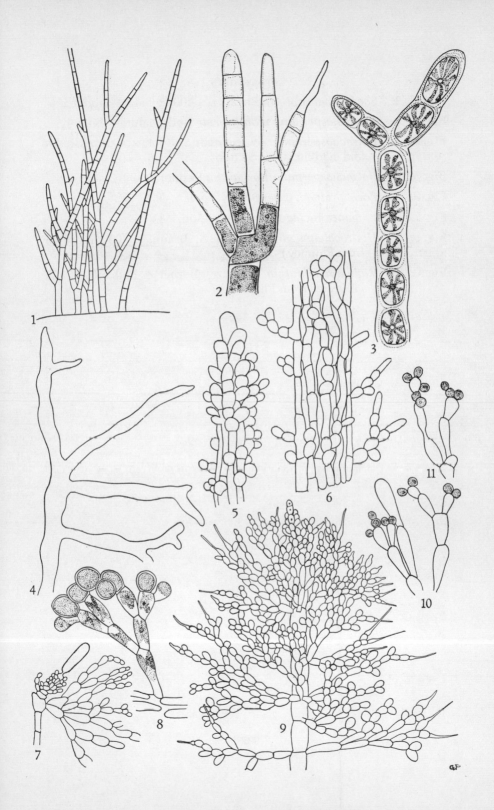

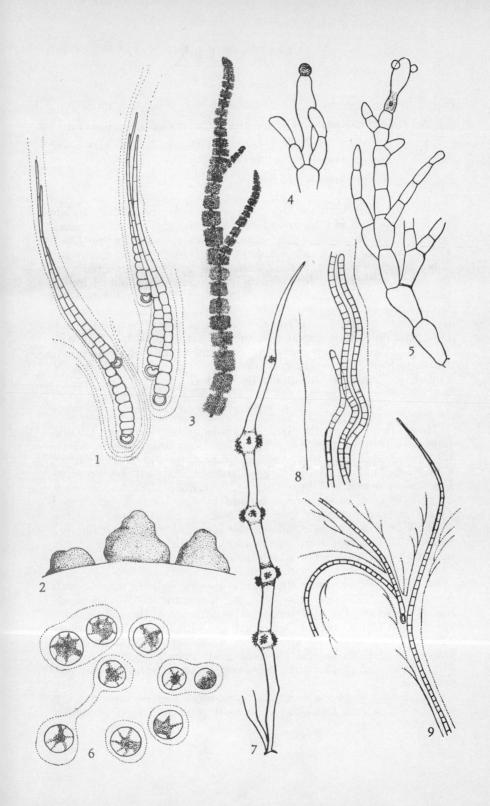

1

2

3

4

5

6

7

8

9

APPENDIX

An Illustrated Key to the Common Genera of Desmids and
Freshwater Diatoms

INTRODUCTION

The following keys are designed to give the beginning student
of the algae an aid in identifying Desmid and Diatom genera.
Those which are included here are known to occur in the Great
Lakes area, or may be expected. Like most other freshwater
algal genera Desmids and Diatoms are widely distributed over
the world, although a few genera have some geographical limitations. It is well-recognized that an ideal, facile and functional
key is not easy to prepare. This is especially true for those genera
in which there is a host of species, many of which have intergrading variations. It is hoped that the following keys, together with
the illustrations will prove useful. Some of the illustrations are
redrawn from previously published works by C. J. Elmore, N.
Foged, J. Frenguelli, M. Bourrelly, and G. W. Prescott.

I. *DESMIDS*

Three families of the Order Zygnematales (Phylum Chlorophyta) constitute the "Desmids," the Gonatozygonaceae, Mesotaeniaceae and the Desmidiaceae. Characteristic of the Order,
these plants have relatively large, ornate chloroplasts, few in number within a cell and bearing large pyrenoids. Reproduction is
by cell division, by aplanospores, and by zygotes that are formed
by a conjugation type of gametic union.

The Gonatozygonaceae (sometimes included in the next family)
includes *Genicularia* and *Gonatozygon*, cylindrical cells commonly
occurring in filaments but which may be solitary. They are found
in the same habitats as true Desmids.

In the Mesotaeniaceae the plants are one-celled; have a wall
constructed of a single piece, and are not constricted in the midregion (as in the Desmidiaceae). The contents of the cells usually
are divided in two symmetrical portions, with the nucleus median.
The wall is smooth and contains no mucilage pores. These are
known as the Saccoderm Desmids and include such genera as
Mesotaenium, Cylindrocystis, Netrium, Roya, Spirotaenia and *An-
cylonema.*

The remainder of the Desmids, 24 or more genera, comprise the
true or Placoderm Desmids. The wall is in two sections which

adjoin at the midregion where there is a constriction or sinus (in most forms). There is an isthmus, therefore, between the two cell halves (semicells). The walls are often ornamented with spines, teeth, granules, verrucae, scrobiculations, etc. and in many forms there are mucilage pores.

In studying and in differentiating Desmid genera (and especially species), it is often necessary to view the cell from the top or from the side as well as from the 'front', the position in which the cell most commonly lies. It is found to be desirable to use a weak glycerine solution (3%), dilute agar, or some other such medium which will permit the cell to remain in a given position to which it may be manipulated by the observer.

Desmids occur principally in soft water or acid habitats. *Sphagnum* bogs are especially suitable, but standing water which is rich in organic acids and low in calcium may contain an abundance of these plants. Some forms are subaerial, growing on soil and among mosses, especially in high altitudes. One genus (*Oocardium*) is found only in limey concretions. It is noteworthy that the greatest number of genera, the greatest number of individuals, and the largest cells occur in highly acid habitats. See: G. M. Smith, Freshwater Algae of the United States, McGraw-Hill Co. and G. W. Prescott, *Desmids* in Botanical Review, 14(10): 644-676, 1948 for information on this group of the algae.

A Key to the Common Genera of Desmids

1. Cells joined side by side or end to end to form filaments 2
1. Cells solitary, or inclosed in a common mucilaginous
   sheath to form a colony, but not occurring as filaments 11
2. Cells adjoined only by the interlocking of short, straight or hooked
   spines or horn-like processes (prong-like extension) at the polar walls .. 3
2. Cells adjoined by their end walls, either along the entire apical margin, or by the adjoining of blunt arms projecting from the ends of the cells (the arms being extensions of the cell, not merely outgrowths from the wall mentiond in 2 above) 5
3. Interlocking processes simple, slender, hornlike and straight *Onychonema*
   Pl. 1, Fig. 5, 6
3. Interlocking processes curved hooks, or stubby, wart-like or tuberculate processes 4
4. Interlocking processes curved hooks which are sometimes forked (filaments incidentally formed and not true filaments .... *Micrasterias foliacea*
   Pl. 4, Fig. 5
4. Interlocking processes short and stubby, tuberculate outgrowths on the wall .... *Sphaerozosma*
   Pl. 1, Fig. 14

[936]

25. Cells narrowly elongate, with one chloroplast in the cell which extends throughout its length; with a row of from four to six pyrenoids; lateral margins nearly parallel (cells often slightly curved)............*Roya*
Pl. 2, Fig. 8

25. Cells stout, fusiform, the lateral margins convex; cells with two chloroplasts, one in each half of the cell, bearing longitudinal, radiating plates; nucleus located medianly between the two chloroplasts ....*Netrium*
Pl. 2, Fig. 13

26. Cells inclosed, several together, within a colonial mucilage, interjoined by fine, almost indiscernible fibrils ....*Cosmocladium*
Pl. 4, Fig. 13

26. Cells not inclosed in a colonial mucilage............27

27. Cells flat, nearly circular in outline, star-shaped in front view, or disc-like; median incision very deep; semicells deeply lobed or incised, these lobes often with secondary lobes and lobules.......*Micrasterias*
Pl. 4, Fig. 1, 2, 4, 5, 8, 9

27. Cells not flat and disc-like in 'front' view; without star-like, radiating lobes and lobules 28

28. Cells with a shallow and broad, or a deep and narrow notch in the apices ....*Euastrum*
Pl. 3, Fig. 4, 5, 6, 9

28. Cells without a notch or depression in the apex of the semicell (if slightly retuse at the apex, then without a prominent facial swelling in the midregion of the semicell which may be seen easily in vertical or side view if not in face view).........29

29. Apex of the cell extended into three or more arms or lobes, the arms usually extended radiately so that the cell appears star-shaped or triangular when seen in vertical or end view.........*Staurastrum*
Pl. 3, Fig. 8, 11, 13, 14

29. Apex of semicells not extended into lobes or arms, or if with arms then not radiate in three or more planes, the arms in one plane............30

30. With extended arms at the apical angles; arms in one plane...*Staurastrum*
Pl. 3, Fig. 10

30. Without extended arms at the apical angles.........31

31. Margin of cells without spines although often furnished with granules or conical warts or horn-like thickenings 32

31. Margin of cells with definite spines at the angles, sometimes spines divided (bi- or trifurcate).........33

32. Face of semicell with one, two or three protuberances or swellings as seen in front view; the protuberances usually with granules .. *Euastrum*
Pl. 3, Fig. 9

32. Face of semicell without prominent protuberances (although in some species there may be a low swelling).........*Cosmarium*
Pl. 3, Fig. 1, 2, 3

33. Face of semicell smooth.........*Arthrodesmus*
Pl. 4, Fig. 6, 7, 10, 11, 12

33. Face of semicell with a protuberance or with granular decorations; not smooth 34

34. Face of semicell with granular decorations but without a protuberance or swelling; spines at the angles horizontally extended and
usually divided (see *Xanthidium armatum*, however); cells narrowly
oval in side view..*Spinocosmarium*
Pl. 4 Fig. 3
34. Face of semicell with a swelling; cell appears broadly oval in side
view; with simple spines (but divided in *Xanthidium
armatum*) ....*Xanthidium*
Pl. 3, Fig. 7, 12; Pl. 4, Fig. 14

II. *DIATOMS*

The Diatoms (Bacillariophyceae) belong to the division (phylum) of the plant kingdom known as the Chrysophyta. The
chromatophores contain a predominating brown pigment, diatomin
in addition to an abundance of xanthophyll and carotene, and
chlorophyll. Hence healthy Diatoms are golden-brown or yellowish-green in color. Stored food accumulates as oil (in globules)
and the iodine test for starch is negative. The wall is siliceous
(glassy) and brittle and ordinarily is etched with lines, rows of dots
or puncta. One of the pecularities of the Diatoms is the gliding or
jerky movement often exhibited as a result of currents of water
and mucilage through canals in the wall and through pores to
the exterior.

The cell, usually referred to as a frustule when the shell or wall
is under consideration, is varied in shape, as is also the pattern of
ornamentation. The wall is composed of two sections, one of
which is slightly larger, the epivalve. This overlies and overlaps
the edges of the smaller, hypovalve much as a lid fits over a box.
The parts are known as valves.

There are two groups of Diatoms, although precise limitations
break down in some instances and some diatomists have come to
disregard the two groupings. The two Orders, however, provide
convenient assignment of two principal types of Diatoms. 1. The
Centrales have cells which in the main are radially symmetrical,
often round when seen from the top or valve view; wall ornamenta-
tions are radially disposed. 2. The Pennales, on the other hand,
are elongate, cigar-shaped, boat-shaped, rectangular, or wedge-
shaped, and the wall decorations are bilaterally symmetrical. The
cells are often rectangular when seen from the side, or in girdle
view.

In the Pennales many of the genera have a distinct median or
marginal canal in the wall of one or both valves, extending parallel
with the long axis. Within the canal there is a raphe which shows
as a straight or curved line, usually seen in valve view. Sometimes
a narrow, clear area appears in the midline of the valve where
there are no wall markings. This region which appears as a line

is called the pseudoraphe and may be present in one or both valves. In some forms there are cross partitions or longitudinal partitions called septa.

To identify Diatoms it is usually necessary to observe empty frustules or cleared cells. The wall markings, costae and puncta, the septa and the raphe must be discerned. A number of genera may be identified in the living or 'filled' condition, but it is advisable to follow a technique for clearing the frustule so that taxonomic characters become apparent. Special terms are used to describe and differentiate Diatom genera and species. Some of these appear in the following simple glossary.

Diatoms are found in a variety of habitats, both acid and basic waters; on and in soil. Although some genera occur commonly in acid habitats, the majority are found in basic water and often occur in profusion with blue-green algae. They are macroscopically visible as brownish films on submerged objects, sand, and leaves of aquatic plants. Whereas most genera occur as solitary cells, many are filamentous and some are arranged in tufts and in attached, gelatinous colonies. (See reference, p. 660).

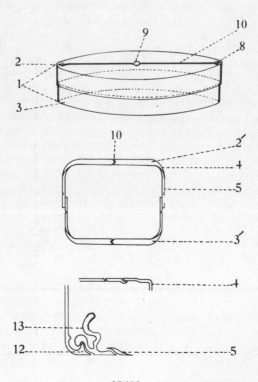

PREPARATION OF DIATOMS FOR STUDY

The preparation of diatoms for study involves: 1) Washing sand or mud, or macerating and flushing materials (water weeds, mosses, etc.); 2) separating diatoms from debris; 3) boiling in acid and potassium dichromate; 4) washing; 5) drying and mounting in Hyrax. Various and modified techniques may be used.

A simple procedure that is suitable for general purposes or for casual study is to make a thin smear of diatomaceous material on a microscope slide in copious water. This is held over a flame and 'cooked' until dry and charred. The smear can then be stirred in a drop of water or water and glycerine and remounted under a cover glass

The essentials of a more involved technique are as follows: 1. Shake sand or other material vigorously. Allow the coarse material to settle for a few seconds, and then the top water is poured off while it is still swirling. Repeat several times. 2. Use small aliquots of the washed material and wash these again, collecting in a clean evaporating dish or small jar. 3. Dry the washed material in an evaporating dish. 4. After drying pour on nitric acid and boil (carefully) until the acid ceases to fume. 5. Add 2 or 3 crystals of potassium dichromate. 6. Boil this mixture again and *cool*. 7. Pour off acid into a waste acid jar (not water), saving the material in the bottom, and cover with sulphuric acid. 8. Boil for several minutes and again add two crystals of potassium dichromate. In this boiling process it may be desirable to repeat or to add a little fresh acid a time or two. 9. Cool and then pour off acid into a waste jar. 10. Rinse the sediment in several waters, stirring it and allowing it to settle. 11. Swirl vigorously and pour off the top water so as to eliminate as much remaining sand as possible. 12. Collect several aliquots treated as above in a jar and repeat the swirling-rinsing-pouring until acid has been removed. 13. Place the washed material in an evaporating dish of water and bring to a boil. Then add a small piece of sodium hydroxide (a lump about 1/2-inch long is sufficient). 14. Continue to boil for *not more* than 3 minutes. 15. Rinse and rewash two or three times to remove all the hydroxide. 16. The material can then be rewashed and poured into watch glasses or preserving vials, or spread on slides where a smear is allowed to dry. A drop of Hyrax or other mounting medium can now be added to the smear and a cover glass put in place.

Terms Referring to the Structures of Diatom Frustules

(Numbers refer to the illustrations; plan of diagrams (p. 940) borrowed from Fritsch.)

1. Frustule: the Diatom cell; the shell.
2. Epitheca: the older, larger portion of the shell fitting over the smaller. 2', Epivalve.
3. Hypotheca: the younger, smaller portion of the shell; 3', Hypovalve.
4. Connecting Band: the rim of the hypotheca or epitheca; rim of the valves.
5. Girdle: the section composed of the connecting bands which lock the two portions of the wall together.
6. Valve View: view of the frustule as seen from top or bottom.
7. Girdle View: view of the frustule as seen from the side so that the girdle area is in view and when the overlapping of the two valves is visible.
8. Polar nodule: internal wall thickening of the valve near the poles.
9. Central nodule: internal wall thickening of the valves at the center.
10. Raphe: a well-marked line formed by a canal which runs through the top or bottom walls of the valve, connecting the polar and central nodule.
11. Pseudoraphe: a narrow, linear area in the mid-line of the valve which is smooth, i. e. contains no wall markings and superficially appears as a raphe.
12. Intercalary Bands: hoop-like, secondary connecting bands which are the incurved edges of the valve and which are attached to the connecting bands.
13. Septa: incomplete partitions running parallel with the valves and which result from internal extention of the intercalary bands.
14. Valve Markings:
    a. Striae-linear markings, sometimes actually composed of closely spaced puncta (points).
    b. Puncta: minute points or pits in the wall, usually occurring in rows.
    c. Costae: conspicuous ribs, double lines, actually tubular structures in the wall.

A Key to the Common Genera of Freshwater Diatoms

1. Frustules elongate, rod-shaped, boat-shaped, rectangular or wedge-shaped, two or more times longer than wide 14
1. Frustules isodiametric or nearly so; round, triangular, or oval, but less than twice the diameter in length 2
2. Frustules, rectangular in side or girdle view, joined in chains by interlocking of long, slender, spine-like horns which arise from the corners of the valve; frustules without raphe; horns hollow or solid ....*Chaetoceros*

Pl. 5, Fig. 1

2. Frustules without spine-like horns 3
3. Frustules triangular in valve view; seldom seen lying in girdle view; raphe and pseudoraphe lacking .... *Hydrosera*

Pl. 5, Fig. 3

3. Frustules some other shape 4

13. Frustules with transverse septa which show as bands across the cell in valve view; raphe in a canal within a marginal keel, the canal with pores ....*Denticula*
Pl. 5, Fig. 11
13. Frustules without transverse septa; raphe in a central axis of the valve; a prominent central nodule which extends both directions on either side of the raphe, the valve with costae ....*Diploneis*
Pl. 5, Fig. 13
14(1). Frustules bilaterally undulate in valve view, the poles capitate; in girdle view rectangular, the septa showing as inward projecting processes extending to the intercalary bands ....*Terpsinoe*
Pl. 5, Fig. 10
14. Frustules shaped otherwise, without septa, or, if present, not so arranged 15
15. Frustules with one or two spine-like extensions at the poles 16
15. Frustules without spines at the poles 18
16. Frustules with many intercalary bands; cells solitary 17
16. Frustules without intercalary bands; cells arranged in filaments *Melosira*
Pl. 6, Fig. 4
17. Frustules rectangular in girdle view, with two spines at each pole *Attheya*
Pl. 6, Fig. 2
17. Frustules extended into a single spine at each pole; wall markings usually lacking ....*Rhizosolenia*
Pl. 5, Fig. 6
18. Frustules cylindrical in girdle view (quinine capsule-shaped), attached end to end in filaments; polar margins often with denticulations ....*Melosira*
Pl. 6, Fig. 4
18. Frustules not cylindrical, not attached in filaments 19
19. Frustules triangularly divided (3-parted) with a pseudoraphe in each valve; frustules non-septate ....*Centronella*
Pl. 7, Fig. 16
(According to some students this is a questionable genus of Diatoms)
19. Frustules not triangularly divided 20
20. Frustules without a raphe in valves; pseudoraphe showing in both valves 21
20. Frustules with a raphe in at least one valve 30
21. Frustules in girdle view elongate-rectangular, forming a circular colony in which the cells radiate from a common center like spokes of a wheel, in valve view slightly enlarged at the poles ....*Asterionella*
Pl. 6, Fig. 6
21. Frustules shaped and arranged otherwise 22
22. Frustules wedge-shaped in girdle view, adjoined side by side to form flat, circular, semicircular or fan-shaped colonies (sometimes spiral bands or ribbons) ....*Meridion*
Pl. 6, Fig. 3
22. Frustules other shapes, or without fan-like arrangement 23
23. Frustules slightly arcuate or bent in the longitudinal axis 24
23. Frustules not arcuate 25

24. Central smooth area present, extending to ventral (concave) margin as seen in valve view, the ventral margin with a slight swelling in the midregion ....*Ceratoneis*
Pl. 6, Fig. 7

24. Central smooth area lacking; pseudoraphe narrow throughout length of valve, margins showing sharply pointed undulations in valve view ....*Amphicampa*
Pl. 6, Fig. 5

25. Frustules attached in zig-zag chains (sometimes semi-stellate or radiate); longitudinal septa present, straight; rows of transverse puncta visible in valve view; frustules not showing transverse costae ....*Tabellaria*
Fig. 1, p. 949; Pl. 6, Fig. 11

25. Frustules not arranged in zig-zag chains, or if so, with curved septa .. 26

26. Frustules with curved septa; costae present, appearing as septa; frustules arranged in bands (sometimes in zig-zag chains) ....*Tetracyclus*
Pl. 6, Fig. 10

26. Frustules without septa 27

27. Frustules with prominent costae in the valves 28

27. Frustules without prominent costae 29

28. Valve view symmetrical, usually elliptic or subcylindric, often with subcapitate poles; in valve view with a faint pseudoraphe; girdle view rectangular ....*Diatoma*
Pl. 6, Fig. 8

28. Valve view symmetrical, egg-shaped; asymmetrical and wedge-shaped in girdle view; transverse costae conspicuous .... *Opephora*
Pl. 6, Fig. 15

29. Frustules quadrate or rectangular in girdle view, attached side by side to form ribbons (rarely in chains); valve view fusiform, the poles narrowed from an enlarged central region ....*Fragilaria*
Fig. 2, p. 949; Pl. 6, Fig. 14

29. Frustules elongate and straight (rarely slightly curved), needle-shaped in both views, or with slightly capitate poles; pseudoraphe between transverse striae; frustules solitary or in radiating colonies, attached to substrate, singly or in clumps, at one end by short gelatinous stalks ....*Synedra*
Pl. 6, Fig. 9

30. Frustules lunate or slightly curved in valve view; rectangular or boat-shaped in girdle view 31

30. Frustules some other shape in valve view 34

31. Curvature slight (frustules often nearly straight); frustules bearing a keel near the margin of a valve in which the raphe is inclosed, the location of the keel marked by a row of dots; frustule quadrangular in cross section ....*Hantzschia*
Pl. 7, Fig. 1

31. Curvature decidedly evident; frustules not bearing a keel on the valve; asymmetrical in longitudinal axis; the raphe usually lying much closer to the ventral (concave) margin 32

32. Arcuate valve view showing prominent transverse lines of the septa of the frustules (appearing as costae); raphe along the ventral margin and in the midregion bent inwardly to form a 'V' as seen in valve view; frustules epiphytic on filamentous algae and aquatic plants .... *Epithemia*
Pl. 7, Fig. 19

32. Frustules without transverse septa (costae) showing in the valve view 33

33. Axial field expanded in the midregion, forming a clear area in the valve ornamentation which extends to the ventral margin of the curved frustule; cells usually with concave margin against a substrate .... *Amphora*
Pl. 7, Fig. 15

33. Axial field central and small, not expanded as above; frustules forming linear colonies in gelatinous tubes, or attached singly at the end of a gelatinous stalk (often found floating free); lunate, with a slight swelling in the midregion of the ventral margin ....*Cymbella*
Pl. 7, Fig. 7

34. Frustules 'S'-shaped or sigmoid; wall ornamented with transverse and longitudinal striae which make a pattern of intersections .... *Gyrosigma*
Pl. 7, Fig. 14

34. Frustules not sigmoid 35

35. Frustules broadly elliptic, slipper-shaped or boat-shaped in valve view, the margins showing prominent, often short costae; surface of valve undulate; in girdle view elongate but with the sides undulate; pseudoraphe often indistinct ....*Cymatopleura*
Pl. 5, Fig. 9

35. Frustules without such costae; not undulate, not showing marginal undulations in girdle view 36

36. Raphe along both margins of the valve, located within a keel 37

36. Raphe not marginal; keel present or absent 38

37. Valve sharply bent to form a saddle; raphe in a marginal keel ....*Campylodiscus*
Pl. 6, Fig. 1

37. Valve arched or twisted, sometimes flat, prominent costae extending from the valve margin toward the smooth, pseudoraphe area ...... *Surirella*
Pl. 5, Fig. 14

38. Frustule in valve view curved and 'bone'-shaped, one pole distinctly larger than the other; transverse rows of puncta in valve view....*Actinella*
Pl. 6, Fig. 13

38. Frustules some other shape 39

39. Valve with 'wings', furnished with a sigmoid keel vertical to the face of the valve; boat-shaped in valve view, '8'-shaped or hour glass-shaped in girdle view .... *Amphiprora*
Pl. 6, Fig. 12

39. Valves without a sigmoid keel, some other shape than above in girdle view 40

40. Pseudoraphe on one valve; true raphe on the other 41

40. Raphe in both valves 43

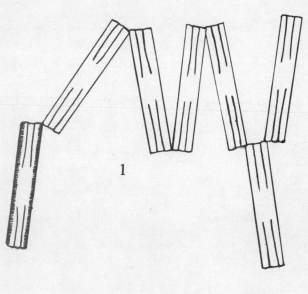

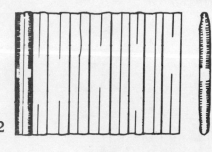

Plate 1

Fig. 1. *Phymatodocis*

Fig. 2. *Spondylosium*

Fig. 3. *Desmidium*

Fig. 4. *Desmidium*

Fig. 5. *Onychonema*

Fig. 6. *Onychonema*

Fig. 7. *Bambusina*

Fig. 8. *Bambusina*

Fig. 9. *Hyalotheca*

Fig. 10. *Hyalotheca*

Fig. 11. *Desmidium*

Fig. 12. *Spondylosium*

Fig. 13. *Spondylosium*

Fig. 14. *Sphaerozosma*

Fig. 15. *Spinoclosterium*

Fig. 16. *Cylindrocystis*

Fig. 17. *Mesotaenium*

Fig. 18. *Spondylosium*

Fig. 19. *Spondylosium*

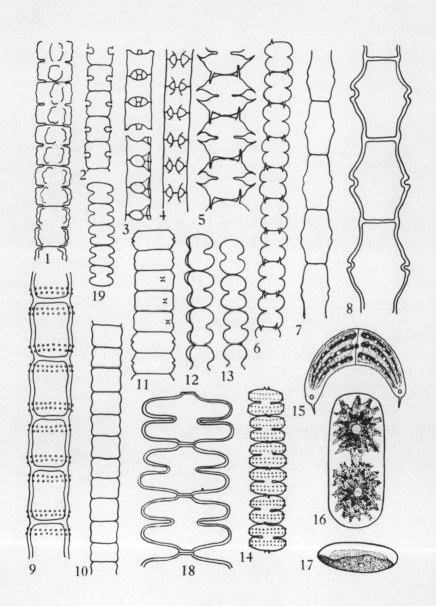

Plate 2

Fig. 1. *Gonatozygon*

Fig. 2. *Gonatozygon*

Fig. 3. *Spirotaenia*

Fig. 4. *Tetmemorus*

Fig. 5. *Triploceras*

Fig. 6. *Pleurotaenium*

Fig. 7. *Pleurotaenium*

Fig. 8. *Roya*

Fig. 9. *Closterium*

Fig. 10. *Closterium*

Fig. 11. *Docidium*

Fig. 12. *Closterium*

Fig. 13. *Netrium*

Fig. 14. *Penium*

Fig. 15. *Genicularia*

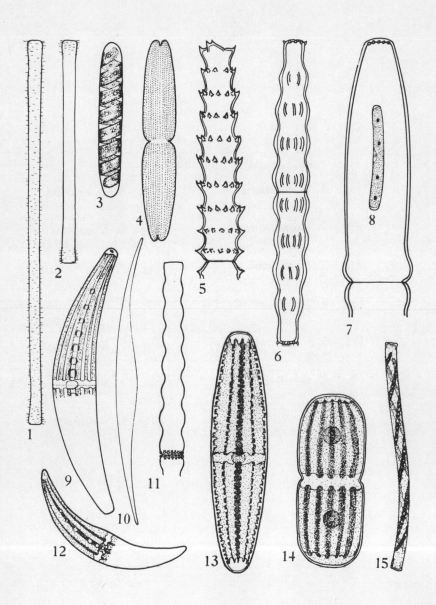

Plate 3

Fig. 1. *Cosmarium*

Fig. 2. *Cosmarium*

Fig. 3. *Cosmarium*

Fig. 4. *Euastrum*

Fig. 5. *Euastrum*

Fig. 6. *Euastrum*

Fig. 7. *Xanthidium*

Fig. 8. *Staurastrum*

Fig. 9. *Euastrum*

Fig. 10. *Staurastrum*

Fig. 11. *Staurastrum*

Fig. 12. *Xanthidium*

Fig. 13. *Staurastrum*

Fig. 14. *Staurastrum*

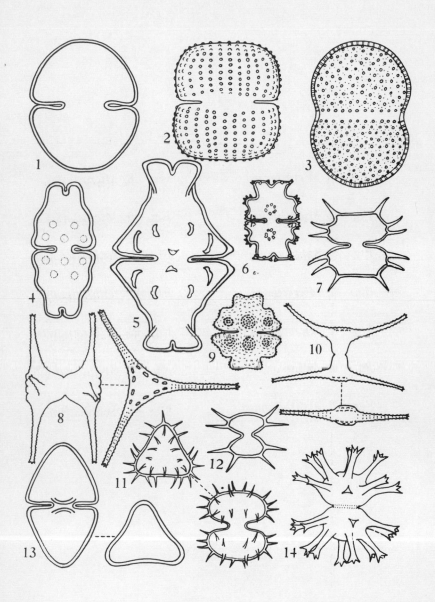

Plate 4

Fig. 1. *Micrasterias*

Fig. 2. *Micrasterias*

Fig. 3. *Spinocosmarium*

Fig. 4. *Micrasterias*

Fig. 5. *Micrasterias foliacea*

Fig. 6. *Arthrodesmus*

Fig. 7. *Arthrodesmus*

Fig. 8. *Micrasterias*

Fig. 9. *Micrasterias*

Fig. 10. *Arthrodesmus*

Fig. 11. *Arthrodesmus*

Fig. 12. *Arthrodesmus*

Fig. 13. *Cosmocladium*

Fig. 14. *Xanthidium*

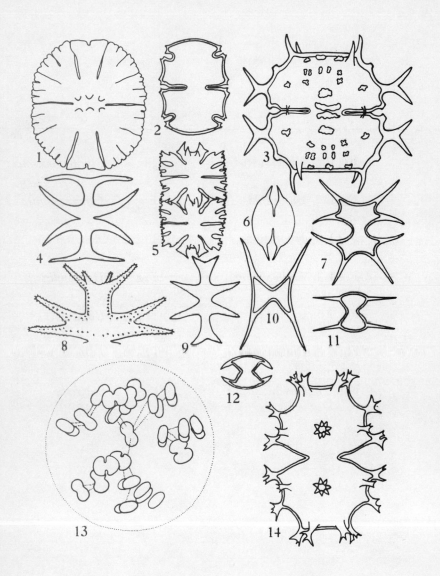

Plate 5

Fig. 1. *Chaetoceros*

Fig. 2. *Biddulphia*

Fig. 3. *Hydrosera*

Fig. 4. *Actinocyclus*

Fig. 5. *Cyclotella*

Fig. 6. *Rhizosolenia*

Fig. 7. *Coscinodiscus*

Fig. 8. *Stephanodiscus*

Fig. 9. *Cymatopleura*

Fig. 10. *Terpsinoe*

Fig. 11. *Denticula*

Fig. 12. *Cocconeis*

Fig. 13. *Diploneis*

Fig. 14. *Surirella*

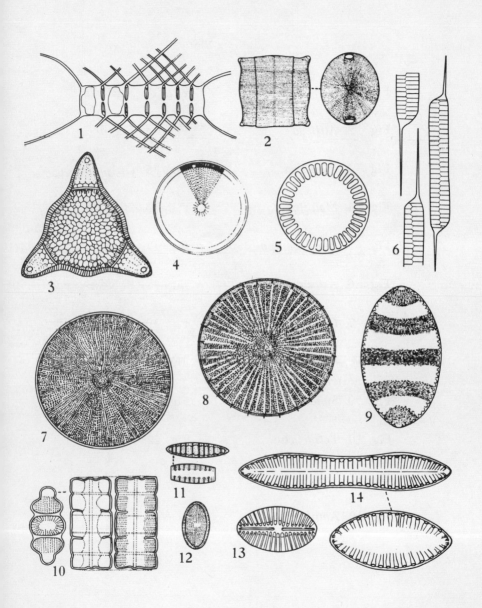

Plate 6

Fig. 1. *Campylodiscus* Fig. 13. *Actinella*

Fig. 2. *Attheya* Fig. 14. *Fragilaria*

Fig. 3. *Meridion* Fig. 15. *Opephora*

Fig. 4. *Melosira* Fig. 16. *Stauroneis*

Fig. 5. *Amphicampa* Fig. 17. *Denticula*

Fig. 6. *Asterionella* Fig. 18. *Rhoicosphenia*

Fig. 7. *Ceratoneis* Fig. 19. *Achnanthes*

Fig. 8. *Diatoma* Fig. 20. *Rhopalodia*

Fig. 9. *Synedra* Fig. 21. *Gomphonema*

Fig. 10. *Tetracyclus* Fig. 22. *Eunotia*

Fig. 11. *Tabellaria* Fig. 23. *Amphipleura*

Fig. 12. *Amphiprora*

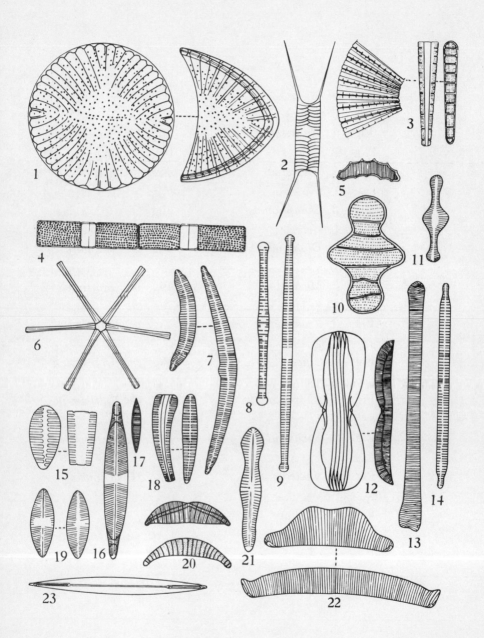

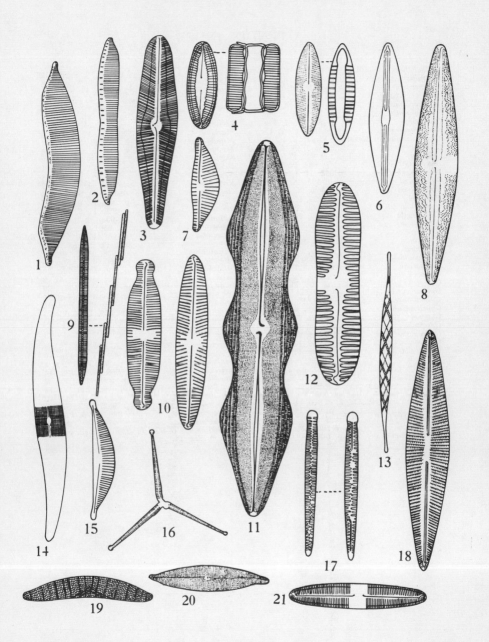

APPENDIX INDEX

INDEX

(See Appendix Index to Genera p. 977)

Page numbers in italics after scientific names indicate that there is a reference to the organism, but no description. The highest page numbers following the genus name refer to the genus key at the end of the text.

Jack-in-the-pulpit. *See* Arisaema

Kentrosphaera, 214, also 580
  gloeophila, 214; Pl. 45
Kirchneriella, 257, also 234, 256, 575
  contorta, 258, also 257; Pl. 57
  elongata, 258, also 257; Pl. 58
  lunaris, 258, also 257; Pl. 58
    var. Dianae, 258; Pl. 58
    var. irregularis, 258; Pl. 58
  obesa, 259, also 257; Pl. 58
    var. aperta, 259; Pl. 58
    var. major, 259; Pl. 57
  subsolitaria, 259, also 257; Pl. 58
Lagenidium, *295*
Lagerheimia, 249, also 234, 251, 578
  ciliata, 250; Pl. 55
    var. minor, 250; Pl. 55
  citriformis, 250, also 249; Pl. 55
    var. paucispina, 250; Pl. 46
  longiseta, 250; Pl. 55
    var. major, 251; Pl. 55
  quadriseta, 251, also 250; Pl. 46
  subsalsa, 251, also 250; Pl. 55
Lagynion, 382, also 345, 374, 381, 589
  ampullaceum, 383; Pl. 97
  macrotrachelum, 383; Pl. 97
  reductum, 383; Pl. 97
  Scherffelii, 384, also 383; Pl. 97
  triangularis, 384, also 383
    var. pyramidatum, 384; Pl. 97
Lakes
  Acid, acid bog, 14, 25
  Alkaline, 14, 28
  Area (Michigan), 4; (Wisconsin), 4
  Bog, 13, 25
  Basic. *See* Lakes, hard water
  Drainage, 14, 19
  Eutrophic, 7, 17, 43
  Glacial. *See* Lakes, origin
  Hard water, 6, 12, 14, 15, 19, 31, 43
  Oligotrophic, 23, 24, 43
  Origin, 5, 14
  Seepage, 14, 19, 22, 23, 26, 27
  Soft water, 6, 7, 12, 14,. 19, 23, 26, 27, 32, 33, 41
  Sphagnum bog. *See* Lakes, bog
  Types, 13, 48
Lemaneaceae, 568
Lemanea, 569, also 565, 586
  fucina, 569; Pl. 136
Lepocinclis, 404, also 389, 585
  acuta, 405; Pl. 89
  costata, *406*
  fusiformis, 406, also 405; Pl. 89
    var. major, 406, also 405; Pl. 89
  glabra, 406, also 405; Pl. 89
    fa. minor, 406; Pl. 89
  ovum, 407, also 405; Pl. 89
  Playfairiana, 407, also 405; Pl. 89
  sphagnophila, 407, also 405; Pl. 89
  Steinii, *406*
Leucosin, 342, 369, 370, 377, 385
Light, 40
Lyngbya, 497, also 478, 509, 535, 540, 541, 592, 593
  aerugineo-caerulea, 498; Pl. 111
  aestuarii, 499, also 497, 498; Pl. 111
  Birgei, 499, also 11, 471, 497, 501; Pl. 111
  contorta, 500, also 497; Pl. 112
  Diguetii, 500, also 498; Pl. 112
  epiphytica Hieronymus, 500, also 497; Pl. 112
  epiphytica Wille, *500*
  gigantea, *502*
  Hieronymusii, 501, also 498; Pl. 112
  Hummelii, *502*
  Lagerheimii, 501, also 497; Pl. 112
  latissima, 501, also 497, 501; Pl. 112

limnetica, 502, also 498; Pl. 112
  major, 502, also 498, 501, 503; Pl. 112
  Martensiana, 502, also 498; Pl. 112
  Nordgaardii, 503, also 498, 500; Pl. 113
  purpurea, 503, also 498
  putealis, *503*
  spirulinoides, 503, also 497, 498; Pl. 131
  Taylorii, 503, also 498; Pl. 113
  versicolor, 504, also 498; Pl. 113

Mallomonadaceae, 370
Mallomonas, 370, also 589
  acaroides, 371, also 370; Pl. 96
    var. Moskovensis, 371; Pl. 96
  alpina, 371; Pl. 96
  apochromatica, 371, also 370; Pl. 97
  caudata, 372, also 370; Pl. 97
  elliptica, 372, also 370; Pl. 96
  fastigata var. macrolepis, 372, also 370; Pl. 97
  producta, 372, also 371; Pl. 97
    var. Marchica, 373; Pl. 97
  pseudocoronata, 373, also 370; Pl. 96
  tonsurata, 373, also 371; Pl. 97
  urnaformis, 373, also 370; Pl. 97
Marl, 7, 8, 341
Marssoniella, 471, also 445, 591
  elegans, 471; Pl. 107
Melosira, *11*, 499
Meringosphaera, 352, also 349, 587
  brevispina, *352*
  spinosa, 352; Pl. 95
Merismopedia, 457, also 445, 592
  aeruginea. *See* Merismopedia glauca
  chondroidea, 458
  convoluta, 458; Pl. 103
  elegans, 459, also 458; Pl. 101
    var. major, 459; Pl. 100
  glauca, 459, also 458; Pl. 101
  Marssonii. *See* Merismopedia Trolleri
  punctata, 459, also 458; Pl. 102
  tenuissima, 459, also 458; Pl. 100
  Trolleri, 460, also 458; Pl. 101
Mesogerron fluitans. *See* Mougeotiopsis calospora
Micractinium, 287, also 272, 576
  pusillum, 287; Pl. 66
    var. elegans, 288; Pl. 66
  quadrisetum, 288, also 287; Pl. 68
Microchaetaceae, *541*
Microchaete, 541, also 533, 594
  diplosiphon, 541; Pl. 127
  Goeppertiana, 542, also 541; Pl. 127
  robusta, 542, also 541; Pl. 127
  spiralis, 542, also 541; Pl. 131
  tenera, 542, also 541; Pl. 127
Microcoleus, 505, also 497, 593
  lacustris, 505; Pl. 113
  paludosus, 505; Pl. 113
  vaginatus, 506, also 505; Pl. 131
Microcystis, 455, also 445, 468, 493, 495, 592
  aeruginosa, 456, also 11, 41, 43, 453, 471, 495, 497, 499, 514, 515, 528, 558; Pl. 102
    fa. major, *456*
    var. major. *See* Microcystis aeruginosa
    fa. minor, *456*
  flos-aquae. *See* Microcystis aeruginosa
  glauca, *457*
  ichthyoblabe. *See* Microcystis aeruginosa
  incerta, 457; Pl. 102
  pulverea. *See* Microcystis incerta
Microspora, 106, also 28, 366, 383, 540, 582
  amoena, 107, also 106; Pl. 8
  crassior, 107, also 106; Pl. 8
  elegans, 107
  floccosa, 107, also 106; Pl. 8
  Loefgrenii, 107; Pl. 8
  pachyderma, 108, also 106, 107; Pl. 8

fennicum, 177, also 160, 178; Pl. 32
fragile, 178, also 159; Pl. 32
gallicum, 195, also 158; Pl. 39
giganteum, 170, also 162; Pl. 30
globosum, 178, also 160; Pl. 31
gracilius, 170, also 161; Pl. 29
gracilimum, 190, also 164; Pl. 34
grande, 170, also 162; Pl. 29
  var. aequatoriale, 170; Pl. 29
Gunnii, 190, also 164; Pl. 34
hians, 205, also 159; Pls. 40, 42
Hirnii, 178, also 160; Pl. 31
hispidum, 198, also 158; Pl. 24
Howardii, 183, also 163
Howei, 185
hystricinum, 195, also 158
idioandrosporum, 195, also 157
inclusum, 183, 191, also 164, 165; Pl. 35
inconspicuum, 183, also 163, 188; Pl. 37
intermedium, 178, also 160; Pl. 31
iowense, 184, also 164; Pl. 35
irregulare, 196, also 157
Itzigsohnii, 191, also 164
Kjellmanii, 171, also 163
  var. granulosa, 171; Pl. 30
Kozminskii, 201, also 158; Pl. 42
Kurzii, 179, also 160; Pl. 34
laeve, 179, also 160
Landsboroughii, 171, also 162; Pl. 32
latiusculum, 184, also 163; Pl. 44
latviense, 198
lautumniarum, 172, also 161
longiarticulatum, 172, also 162
longatum, 201, also 159, 202
macrandrium, 202, 206, also 159; Pl. 41
macrospermum, 208, also 159; Pl. 41
magnum, 196, also 157, 158
Magnusii, 172, also 161
majus, 172, also 162
margaritiferum, 175, 171
martinicense, 172
megaporum, 202, also 159
mexicanum, 172, also 162
michiganense, 206, also 159; Pl. 43
microgonium, 184, also 163; Pl. 36
minisporum, 191, also 164; Pl. 43
minus, 191, also 164; Pl. 34
mirandrium, 201
mitratum, 185, also 163; Pl. 44
monile, 206, also 159
moniliforme, 173, also 162
multisporum, 196, 198, also 157
nanum, 185, also 164; Pl. 36
nodulosum, 192, also 164
oblongum, 192, also 165
  var. majus, 192
  var. minus, 192; Pl. 43
oelandicum, 206, also 158
  var. contortum, 207; Pl. 42
orientale, 173, also 162; Pl. 41
oviforme, 179, also 161; Pl. 31
  fa. gracile, 179; Pl. 33
pachydermum, 192, also 165
paludosum, 179, also 160
patulum, 180, also 160; Pl. 33
paucocostatum, 185
paucostriatum, 185, also 163; Pl. 38
perfectum, 196, also 158; Pl. 39
pisanum, 186, also 164; Pl. 36
plagiostomum, 173, also 161; Pl. 32
plusiosporum, 180, also 160; Pl. 33
poecilosporum, 186, 192, also 163, 164
polyandrium, 202, also 159; Pl. 42
porrectum, 186, also 164; Pl. 36
pratense, 186, also 163; Pl. 36
princeps, 173, also 162; Pl. 43
Pringsheimii, 187, also 164; Pl. 36
  var. Nordstedtii, 187; Pl. 38
psaegmatosporum, 192, also 164; Pls. 34, 37

pseudo-Boscii, 180, also 160; Pl. 35
pseudoplenum, 202, also 159; Pl. 40
punctatostriatum, 187, also 163, 194; Pl. 38
pusillum, 187, also 163, 164, 193; Pl. 37
pyriforme, 193, also 165; Pl. 34
Reinschii, 193, also 164; Pl. 34
Richterianum, 180, also 160, 161; Pl. 43
rivulare, 174, also 161; Pl. 32
rufescens, 174, also 161
rugulosum, 207, also 159; Pl. 44
  var. rotundatum, 207; Pl. 39
Sancti-Thomae, 187, also 164
Sawyerii, 198, also 158; Pl. 39
sexangulare, 198, also 157, 158; Pl. 39
sinuatum, 203, also 158
  fa. seriatum, 203; Pl. 40
Smithii, 188, also 163; Pl. 36
sociale, 174, also 161; Pl. 32
Sodiroanum, 181, also 160; Pl. 43
spheroideum, 194, also 164; Pl. 38
spiralidens, 200, also 158; Pl. 40
spiripennatum, 198
spirostriatum, 194, also 165; Pl. 44
spurium, 188, 194, also 163, 164; Pl. 37
stellatum, 198, also 158
striatum, 200, also 158; Pl. 39
subplenum, 209, also 159; Pl. 40
subsexangulare, 199, also 159; Pl. 39
suecicum, 174, also 161, 167; Pl. 33
tapeinosporum, 188, also 163, 184; Pl. 38
taphrosporum, 175, also 162
Tiffanyi, 175, also 162; Pl. 43
trioicum, 189, also 163, 165, 194; Pl. 37
tyrolicum, 181, also 160; Pl. 32
undulatum, 209, also 158, 203; Pl. 40
  fa. senegalense, 209; Pl. 44
upsaliense, 181, also 160; Pl. 43
urceolatum, 175, 162; Pl. 33
varians, 181, also 160; Pl. 32
Vaucherii, 182, also 160; Pl. 43
verrucosum, 176, also 162; Pl. 24
vulgare, 182, also 160
Welwitschii, 189, also 164; Pl. 38
Westii, 197, also 157; Pl. 39
Wolleanum, 200, also 158; Pl. 35
Wyliei, 176, also 162; Pl. 37
Oligotrophic lakes. See Lakes
Oocystaceae, 233, also 211, 272, 473
Oocystis, 242, also 234, 235, 577, 580
  apiculata, 247
  Borgei, 243; Pl. 51
  crassa, 243; Pl. 51
  elliptica, 244, also 243; Pl. 51
    var. minor, 244
  Eremosphaeria, 244, also 243; Pl. 51
  gigas, 244, also 243; Pl. 51
  gloeocystiformis, 244, also 243; Pl. 51
  lacustris, 245, also 243; Pl. 54
  natans, 245, also 242, 243
    var. major, 245; Pl. 54
  nodulosa, 245, also 242; Pl. 54
  novae-semliae, 245, also 243
    var. maxima, 246
  panduriformis, 246, also 242
    var. minor, 246; Pl. 54
  parva, 246, also 243; Pl. 54
  pusilla, 246, also 243; Pls. 51, 54
  pyriformis, 246, also 242; Pl. 54
  solitaria, 247, also 243; Pl. 54
    var. major, 247
  submarina, 247, also 243; Pl. 54
Ophiocytium, 362, also 347, 360, 361, 587, 588
  arbuscula, 363, also 362, 364; Pl. 94
  bicuspidatum, 363, also 362; Pl. 94
  capitatum, 363, also 362; Pl. 94
    var. longispinum, 363; Pl. 94
  cochleare, 363; Pl. 94
  desertum, 364, also 362

Bernardii, 276, also 272, 273; Pl. 63
bijuga, 276, also 273; Pl. 63
  var. alternans, 277; Pl. 63
  var. flexuosus, 277
  var. irregularis, 277
brasiliensis, 277, also 274; Pl. 63
denticulatus, 277, also 273; Pl. 63
  var. linearis, 277
dimorphus, 277, also 273; Pl. 63
hystrix, 278, also 273; Pl. 63
incrassatulus, 278, also 273; Pl. 63
  var. mononae, 278; Pl. 63
longus, 278, also 274; Pls. 63, 64
  var. brevispina, 278
  var. ellipticus, 278
  var. minutus, 279
  var. Naegelii, 279; Pls. 63, 64
obliquus, 279, also 273; Pl. 63
opoliensis, 279, also 274; Pl. 63
  var. contacta, 279; Pl. 63
perforatus, 279, also 274; Pl. 46
quadricauda, 280, also 274; Pl. 64
  var. longispina, 280; Pl. 63
  var. maximus, 280; Pl. 64
  var. parvus, 280; Pl. 64
  var. quadrispina, 280; Pl. 63
  var. Westii, 281; Pl. 64
serratus, 281, also 273; Pl. 64
Schizochlamys, 90, also 87, 574
compacta, 90; Pl. 4
delicatula, 90
gelatinosa, 90; Pl. 4
Schizogoniales, 67
Schizomeridaceae, 104
Schizomeridineae, 104
Schizomeris, 104, also 581
Leibleinii, 105; Pl. 7
Schizothrix, 506, also 479, 505, 593
fasciculata, 507
Friesii, 507, also 506; Pl. 114
fuscescens, 507, also 506; Pl. 114
lacustris, 507; Pl. 131
lardacea, 508, also 506
Muelleri, 508, also 506; Pl. 114
rivularis, 508, also 506; Pl. 114
tinctoria, 508, also 507; Pl. 131
vaginata, 509, also 507
Schroederia, 255, also 234, 578
Judayi, 256, also 255; Pl. 57
setigera, 256, also 255; Pl. 57
Scirpus, 548
Scytonema, 533, also 595
alatum, 534; Pl. 123
Archangelii, 534; Pl. 123
cincinnatum. See Scytonema crispum
coactile, 534; Pl. 124
crispum, 535, also 534; Pl. 124
figuratum. See Scytonema mirabile
mirabile, 535, also 533, 534; Pl. 124
  var. tolypothricoides. See Scytonema
    tolypothricoides
myochrous, 535, also 534; Pls. 124, 125
ocellatum, 25
tolypothrichoides, 536, also 534; Pl. 123
Scytonemataceae, 532, also 478, 543
Seepage lakes. See Lakes
Selenastrum, 256, also 235, 575
Bibraianum, 256; Pl. 57
gracile, 257, also 256; Pl. 57
minutum, 257, also 256; Pl. 46
Westii, 257, also 256; Pl. 57
Silicon, 342, 370, 375, 385
Siphonales, 266, also 67
Sirogonium, 296
Snapping turtle, 47, 143
Sodium arsenite, 45
Soft water lakes. See Lakes
Soils, 5, 8, 11
Sorastrum, 227, also 219, 577
  americanum, 228; Pl. 50

var. undulatum, 228; Pl. 50
spinulosum, 228; Pls. 50, 53
Spelaeopogon, 532
Sphaerella (See Haematococcus)
lacustris, 80; Pls. 2, 3
Sphaerellaceae, 80, also 68
Sphaerocystis, 83, also 82, 574
Schroeteri, 83, also 88, 240; Pl. 3
Sphaeroplea, 111, also 110, 581
annulina, 111; Pl. 12
Sphaeropleaceae, 111
Sphaeropleales, 110, also 66
Sphaerozosma, 359
Spirogyra, 307, also 6, 7, 295, 296, 581, 583
aequinoctialis, 310, also 311; Pl. 72
affinis, 311, also 310
Borgeana, 311, also 310; Pl. 77
borysthenica, 311, also 308
catenaeformis, 311, also 310
circumlineata, 312, also 309; Pl. 74
Collinsii, 312, also 309; Pl. 77
communis, 312, also 309
condensata, 312, also 309; Pl. 72
crassa, 312, also 28, 48, 310, 314; Pl. 72
daedalea, 321
daedaleoides, 313, also 309; Pl. 72
decimina, 313, also 28, 310
dubia, 313, also 310
ellipsospora, 313, also 310; Pl. 72
esthonica, 321
fallax, 314, also 308; Pl. 77
Farlowii, 314, also 308
flavescens, 314, also 309
floridana, 319
fluviatilis, 314, also 310; Pl. 73
Fuellebornei, 315, also 310; Pl. 73
gracilis, 315, also 309
gratiana, 315, also 308; Pl. 74
Grevilleana, 315, also 308; Pl. 74
illinoisensis, 319
inconstans, 315, also 308
inflata, 316, also 308
Juergensii, 316, also 309; Pl. 73
jugalis, 316, also 310
laxa, 316, also 308
longata, 316, also 309
majuscula, 317, also 310; Pl. 74
maxima, 317, also 310, 314
micropunctata, 317, also 309; Pl. 73
mirabilis, 317, also 309; Pl. 77
nitida, 318, also 310; Pl. 73
novae-angliae, 318, also 310; Pl. 75
orientalis, 318, also 310
porangabae, 318, also 309; Pl. 77
porticalis, 318, also 309; Pl. 75
pratensis, 319, also 309; Pl. 75
protecta, 319, also 308
pseudofloridana, 319, also 310; Pl. 75
reflexa, 319, also 309
rhizobrachialis, 320, also 310; Pl. 76
rivularis, 320, also 310
scrobiculata, 320, also 309; Pl. 76
singularis, 320, also 309
Spreeiana, 321, also 308; Pl. 77
stictica, 321, also 310; Pl. 76
subsalsa, 321, also 309; Pl. 73
suecica, 321, also 309
sulcata, 321, also 309
tenuissima, 322, also 308
Teodoresci, 322, also 310
triplicata, 322, also 310
varians, 322, also 310; Pl. 76
Weberi, 322, also 308; Pl. 76
Spirulina, 479, also 478, 481, 591, 592
laxa, 479; Pl. 108
laxissima, 480, also 479; Pl. 107
major, 480, also 479; Pl. 108
Nordstedtii, 480, also 479; Pl. 108
princeps, 480, also 479; Pl. 108
subsalsa, 480, also 479; Pl. 108

[975]